A MANUAL OF
PAPER CHROMATOGRAPHY
AND PAPER ELECTROPHORESIS

A MANUAL OF
Paper Chromatography
AND
Paper Electrophoresis

RICHARD J. BLOCK

*Boyce Thompson Institute for Plant Research, Inc.,
Yonkers, N. Y. and Department of Biochemistry,
New York Medical College, New York, N. Y.*

EMMETT L. DURRUM

*Associate Research Director, Spinco Division, Beck-
man Instruments, Inc., Palo Alto, California; Associate Clinical Professor of Medical Microbiology,
Stanford University School of Medicine, Palo Alto,
California.*

GUNTER ZWEIG

*Associate Chemist, Pesticide Residue Research
Project University of California, Davis, California.*

With the cooperation of Raymond Lestrange,
Winston H. Wingerd, and Kathryn W.
Weiss

SECOND EDITION
REVISED AND ENLARGED

1958

ACADEMIC PRESS INC · PUBLISHERS · NEW YORK

PREFACE TO PART I, SECOND EDITION

The object of the first section of this monograph is to provide a readily accessible source for some of the many uses of paper chromatography that have appeared since the publication by Consden, Gordon, and Martin approximately fifteen years ago. No attempt has been made to list all the references in which paper chromatography has been used but rather an effort has been made to write a practical manual in which tried and proved procedures, employing relatively simple equipment and available reagents, are summarized. It is hoped that sufficient detailed information is provided, in the majority of instances, so that the reader will be able to apply the technique of paper chromatography to his particular problem without recourse to an extensive search of the literature.

The authors will appreciate the corrections of any erroneous statements and hope that readers will be so kind as to call to our attention important papers which may have been omitted.

We wish to thank many workers in the field of paper chromatography who contributed numerous photographs and drawings.

RICHARD J. BLOCK
GUNTER ZWEIG

Summer, 1957

PREFACE TO PART II, SECOND EDITION

A number of changes have been incorporated in the present edition, particularly in Chapter XIX. A classified bibliography of more than 1800 articles on paper electrophoresis has been added.

The author particularly wishes to thank Dr. Henry Kunkel and Dr. Rodes Trautman for valuable suggestions relating to the treatment of mobility which appear in Chapter XV. Mr. F. G. Williams has afforded great assistance, particularly in connection with revisions of the chapter relating to quantitative considerations. I also wish to thank Miss Ernestine Hutchins and Mrs. Eve Lier for their services in connection with the organization and classification of the bibliography.

E. L. DURRUM

Stanford University School of Medicine
Palo Alto, California
August 13, 1957

Contents

Part II Paper Electrophoresis

Part I
PAPER CHROMATOGRAPHY

Chapter I

INTRODUCTION

"By chromatography is meant those processes which allow the resolution of mixtures by effecting separation of some or all their components in concentrated zones on or in phases different from those in which they are originally present, irrespective of the nature of the force or forces causing the substances to remove from one phase to another" (T. I. Williams, 1952).

Paper chromatography may have had its origin with the description by Pliny (23–79 A.D.) of the use of papyrus impregnated with an extract of gall nuts for the detection of ferrous sulfate. Or it may have had its origin with the studies of "Kapillaranalyse" by Runge, Schönbein, and Goppelsroeder[1] in the period 1850 to 1910. (See also Weil, 1950, 1951, 1953a, b.)

There is little doubt that M. S. Tswett should be given credit for discovering the principle of preferential adsorption (adsorption chromatography) of plant pigments on a large variety of adsorbents packed in a glass tube. Tswett reported his findings to the Biological Section of the Warsaw Society of Natural Sciences in 1903. (See Hesse and Weil, 1954, for a translation of Tswett's first paper on chromatography.) It is not within the scope of this book to cover the field of column chromatography.

The great popularity of the present-day paper chromatography is due, in the authors' opinion, to A. J. P. Martin of Cambridge and London and his coworkers, R. Consden, A. H. Gordon, and R. L. M. Synge. In 1938 Neuberger was interested in separating the neutral amino acids and observed that the partition coefficients of acetylated amino acids between water and an immiscible organic solvent differed for the various amino acids. This observation was extended by Martin and Synge (1941a), who built a rather complicated forty-plate apparatus for the continuous separation of acetylated amino acids. In order to simplify the equipment and to enhance the separation of substances with very similar partition coefficients by increasing the number of theoretical plates, Martin and Synge (1941b) decided to use an inert support (e.g., silica gel) to hold one of the phases (water) and to pass the immiscible solvent through a bed of the water-containing silica gel. The ideal conditions for this type of chromatogram employing two liquid phases were, first, that the solute is not absorbed by the supporting material and, second, that its distribution between the two liquid phases is not influenced by its concentration or by the presence of closely related solutes. These ideal conditions were approached experimentally by Mar-

[1] Cf. W. G. Brown (1939) for an adaptation of capillary analysis.

3

tin and Synge and by a number of other investigators.   The procedure was, however, difficult and tedious, and the preparation of the inert support left much to be desired.

In order to eliminate the preparation of silica gel and to reduce the quantity of materials needed, Martin *et al.* (Consden, 1944) replaced silica gel by filter paper as the inert support.   With the use of filter paper the acetylation of the amino acids was no longer necessary, and they could now be detected directly on the paper by treatment with ninhydrin (triketohydrindene hydrate).

The method of paper partition chromatography consists in applying a *small* drop of the solution containing the substances to be separated to a strip of filter paper a short distance from one end.   The drop is allowed to dry, and the end of the paper nearest to the spot is placed in the developing solution, usually a water-containing organic solvent, so that the solvent flows past the "spot" by capillary action and on down the length of the paper.

Although it was originally believed that the paper functioned solely as an inert support for the aqueous portion of the developing solvent, hence the original name paper partition chromatography, it is now generally recognized that, although paper chromatography may function in some cases purely by partition, it more commonly acts by a combination of partition, adsorption, and ion exchange.   Regardless of the mode of action, the modifications, or the extensions of the method of paper chromatography, there has seldom been a technical development so thoroughly described and so adequately presented.   In spite of hundreds of studies with this procedure, no major improvements or changes have been made since the original publication of "Qualitative Analysis of Proteins: A Partition Chromatographic Method Using Paper" by R. Consden, A. H. Gordon, and A. J. P. Martin in 1944.

The impetus given by Martin *et al.* has encouraged other investigators to apply the procedures of paper partition chromatography, capillary analysis (Goppelsroeder, 1899), and combinations of these methods to a host of substances, natural and synthetic, organic and inorganic, with striking success.   The object of this manual is to present some of the results of these numerous investigations on paper chromatography so that the student may have a sufficient idea of past studies in order to allow him to choose the method which appears to be the most promising for the solution of his particular problem.   Although experiments on both qualitative and quantitative paper chromatography are described, the quantitative aspects are stressed where possible.

Because this manual is of a practical nature, the theoretical aspects of chromatography are minimized, although it will be seen from the results presented that certain simple rules should be employed:

1. The composition of the flowing solvent should be kept constant throughout the development. This is done by keeping the chromatogram in an enclosed chamber, the space of which is saturated with the developing solvents at constant temperature.

2. The developing solvent should move at a relatively slow rate (*ca.* 2–3 cm./hr.). The rate of solvent flow is dependent on the type of paper used, on the ratio of the width of the "wick" to that of the paper chromatogram, on the composition of the solvent, and on the temperature of the chromatogram chamber.

3. The choice of a solvent should be one in which the components to be separated have a small but definite solubility. If the substances are too soluble, they will appear at or near the solvent "front" of the chromatogram. If they are too insoluble in the solvent, they will remain at the point of application. If the factors of adsorption and ion exchange are neglected, the movement of a substance in a paper chromatogram is a function of its solubility in the developing solvent. Thus, solvents for water-soluble substances are usually water-containing organic compounds, whereas solvents for substances soluble in organic solvents but insoluble in water are often aqueous solutions of organic solvents.

Chapter II

THEORY OF PAPER CHROMATOGRAPHY

The resolution of mixtures of solutes on filter paper may depend on surface adsorption, on ion exchange, or on partition between solvents. Goppelsroeder's investigations of the capillary ascent of organic and inorganic solutes into strips of paper were examples of adsorption chromatography. Substances adsorbed to filter paper were separated by passing through the paper a solvent which would preferentially elute each substance in the mixture. The separation of materials on strips of filter paper impregnated with alumina is another example of adsorption phenomena (Flood, 1949).

Ion exchange may have an effect on the separation of substances on paper. In the resolution of mixtures of ions, some exchange must occur with polar constituents of the cellulose and with impurities present in the paper.

Although adsorption and ion exchange must be present to some extent in all chromatographic work on filter paper, the predominant factor is usually that of partition between two immiscible phases. In the early work on separation of mixtures of amino acids, Consden (1944) found that excellent separations were obtained with solvents that were only partially miscible with water. After equilibration of the paper with the vapor of a solvent saturated with water, solvent development produced separations.

The movement of a solute zone was explained conveniently as follows: The cellulose fibers have a strong affinity for the water present in the solvent phase but very little for the organic liquid. The paper itself is thought of as an inert support holding a stationary aqueous phase. As solvent flows through a section of the paper containing the solute, a partition of this compound occurs between the mobile organic phase and the stationary water phase. Thus, some of the solute leaves the paper and enters the organic phase. When the mobile liquid reaches a section of the paper containing no solute, partition again occurs. This time, solute is transferred from the organic phase to the paper phase. With continuous flow of solvent, the effect of this partition between the two phases is the transfer of a solute from the point of its application to the paper to a point some distance along the paper in the direction of solvent flow.

The processes which occur during the chromatographic analysis on filter paper may be compared with the techniques of fractional distillation and continuous liquid-liquid extraction. Martin and Synge (1941a) first experimented with a stage continuous liquid-liquid extraction train for the separation of amino acids. This laborious procedure was simplified and improved by immobilizing one phase on a mechanical support known to have weak adsorptive properties, such as silica, starch, or paper.

These investigators have worked out a theory of chromatography based on its similarity to distillation with fractionating columns. This analogy gives a picture of the concentration of solute at any time and place in a chromatographic column and of the way in which the resolution of a mixture depends on the length of the column. (Martin and Synge developed this treatment of chromatography in connection with separations on columns of silica gel, but it is also applicable to partition chromatography on paper.)

The chromatographic column is regarded as being divided into successive layers of such thickness that the solution issuing from each is in equilibrium with the mean concentration of solute in the non-mobile (silica) phase throughout the layer. The thickness of such a layer is termed the H.E.T.P. (height equivalent to one theoretical plate). For the equations to be manageable, certain simplifying assumptions are made. It is assumed that diffusion from one plate to another is negligible and that the partition of solute between the two phases is independent of its concentration and of the presence of other solutes. The following symbols are used.

h = H.E.T.P.

A = Area of cross section of the column.

A_s = Area of cross section of the non-mobile phase.

A_1 = Area of cross section of the mobile phase.

A_I = Area of cross section of the inert solid; i.e., $A_s + A_1 + A_I = A$.

v = Volume of solvent used to develop the chromatogram.

α = Partition coefficient = grams solute per milliliter of non-mobile phase per gram solute per milliliter of mobile phase at equilibrium.

V = $h (A_1 + \alpha A_s)$.

R = $\dfrac{\text{Movement of position of maximum concentration of solute}}{\text{Simultaneous movement of surface of developing fluid in the empty part of the tube above the chromatographic column.}}$

r = Serial number of "plate" measured from top of column.

Q_r = Total quantity of solute in plate r.

Suppose that a unit mass of a single solute is put into the first plate and is followed by pure solvent; it is possible to calculate the amount of solute in each plate after infinitesimal volumes, δv, of the mobile phase have passed (see Table I). The quantity of solute in each plate can be expressed as a term of the binomial expansion of $[(1 - \delta v/V) + \delta v V]^n$. When n

TABLE I

Volume of solvent passed	Serial number of plate, r			
$x\delta v$	1	2	3	4
0	1	0	0	0
1	$(1-\delta v/V)$	$\delta v/V$	0	0
2	$(1-\delta v/V)^2$	$2(1-\delta v/V)\delta v/V$	$(\delta v/V)^2$	0
3	$(1-\delta v/V)^3$	$3(1-\delta v/V)^2\delta v/V$	$3(1-\delta v/V)(\delta v/V)^2$	$(\delta v/V)^3$
4	$(1-\delta v/V)^4$	$4(1-\delta v/V)^3\delta v/V$	$6(1-\delta v/V)^2(\delta v/V)^2$	$4(1-\delta v/V)(\delta v/V)^3$

successive volumes of solvent δv have passed,

$$Q_{r+1} = \frac{n!(1 - \delta v/V)^{n-r}(\delta v/V)^r}{r!(n - r)!} . \tag{1}$$

When n is large, this becomes

$$Q_{r+1} = \frac{1}{r!}\left(\frac{n\,\delta v}{V}\right)^r e^{-n\delta v/V}. \tag{2}$$

But $n\,\delta v = v =$ volume of solvent used to develop the chromatogram. Therefore,

$$\frac{Q_{r+1}}{z} = \frac{1}{r!}\left(\frac{v}{V}\right)^r e^{-v/V}. \tag{3}$$

By Stirling's approximation this becomes, when r is large,

$$Q_{r+1} = \frac{1}{(2\pi r)^{1/2}}\left(\frac{v}{Vr}\right)^r e^{r-v/V}. \tag{4}$$

When $v/rV = 1$, Q_{r+1} is a maximum and has the value $(2\pi r)^{-1/2}$. If r is the number of the plate containing the maximum concentration of solute, its distance from the top of the column is rh. But

$$rh = \frac{hv}{V}, \tag{5}$$

i.e., the position of maximum concentration has moved a distance hv/V directly proportional to the volume of solvent used to develop the chromatogram. If

$$R = \frac{\text{Movement of zone}}{\text{Movement of surface of liquid}}, \tag{6}$$

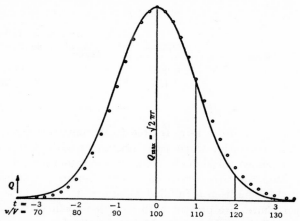

FIG. 1. The points represent the relation between Q and v/V for $r = 100$. The full line is the normal curve of error with abscissa t, $i.e.$, $Q/Q_{max} = \exp(-\frac{1}{2}t^2)$.

then

$$R = \frac{vh/V}{v/A} = \frac{Ah}{V} = \frac{A}{A_1 + \alpha A_s} \tag{7}$$

Therefore,

$$\alpha = \frac{A}{RA_s} - \frac{A_1}{A_s}. \tag{8}$$

If the concentration of solute in plate $(r + 1)$ is plotted against v/V using equation 4, the curve shown in Fig. 1 is obtained. This curve is plotted for $r = 100$. When r becomes infinite, this curve becomes identical with the normal curve of error and can be expressed in the form

$$\frac{Q}{Q_{max}} = e^{-\frac{1}{2}t^2}. \tag{9}$$

v/V and t are related by the equation

$$\frac{v}{V} = r + t(r)^{\frac{1}{2}} + \frac{t^2}{3}. \tag{10}$$

Similarly, the area under the curve can be expressed as

$$\frac{v}{V} = r + t(r)^{\frac{1}{2}} + \frac{t^2}{4}. \tag{11}$$

The values of Q/Q_{max} for various values of t are shown in Table II.

For a given solute the position of maximum concentration is determined

TABLE II

t	Q/Q_{max}	Area under tail of curve as % of whole area under curve
1	0.606	15.9
2	0.135	2.27
3	0.011	0.13

by v/V. But V contains a term related to the partition coefficient of the solute, and consequently, when two substances with different partition coefficients are passed through the column, separation occurs. Separation is complete when the two curves no longer overlap. The figures shown indicate that this condition is fulfilled when $t = 3$.

Now if two solutes are present with partition coefficients α and β, then complete separation will be obtained when $t = 3$; then

$$\frac{A_1 + \alpha A_s}{A_1 + \beta A_s} = \frac{r - 3(r)^{1/2} + 2.25}{r + 3(r)^{1/2} + 2.25}, \tag{12}$$

since less than 0.2 % of the solute with partition coefficient β has passed the $(r + 1)$th plate and more than 99.8 % of the solute with partition coefficient α is passed the same plate.

In practice, the whole of the solute will not be initially concentrated in the first plate but will be spread over a number of plates. The effect of this will be for a number of chromatograms to be successively started, and the concentration in any plate at a given time will be the sum of the concentrations due to each chromatogram. Thus the region of maximum concentration will be broadened, and the total width of the band will be greater than that shown in Fig. 1 approximately by the initial width of the band before development by solvent was begun. The number of plates required for resolution will be correspondingly increased.

The separations obtainable in practice are less than the theory predicts for two principal reasons. First, the partition coefficient is seldom a constant, usually decreasing as the solution becomes stronger. This results in the front of the band becoming sharper and the rear more diffuse and wider, since the concentrated part moves faster than the more dilute part.

An increase in separation over the theoretical may be produced by interaction between two solutes. The more strongly adsorbed solute may displace the weakly adsorbed one and form a sharp boundary between the two.

The conclusion that R and α are related was checked by Martin and Synge in an actual experiment. They passed a solution of 2 mg. each of

TABLE III

Acid	R	From band rate	Direct measurement
Acetylproline	0.37	9.4	9.5
Acetylphenylalanine	1.07	1.4	1.3

acetyl-L-proline hydrate and acetyl-DL-phenylalanine through a silica gel column 1 × 20 cm. The chromatogram was developed with chloroform containing 1 % by volume of n-butyl alcohol until the two zones were well separated. The R values were measured from the movement of each band and the movement of the solvent, and the partition coefficients were calculated using equation 8. These values were compared with partition coefficients obtained by direct measurement. The column contained 5 g. of dry silica, 3.5 ml. of water, and 10 ml. of chloroform phase. Taking the density of silica as 2.3 g./ml., $A_I = 0.11$ cm.^{2}, $A_s = 0.175$ cm.^{2}, and $A_1 = 0.5$ cm.^{2}, they found the values shown in Table III. The agreement is seen to be excellent.

Consden (1944) showed that the theory developed for a chromatographic column could be applied to partition chromatography on filter paper. From equation 8,

$$R = \frac{A}{A_1 + \alpha A_s} \,. \tag{13}$$

However, R is not conveniently measurable in paper chromatograms, so a new symbol, R_f, was introduced.[1]

$$R_f = \frac{\text{Movement of band}}{\text{Movement of advancing front of liquid}} \,. \tag{14}$$

Therefore,

$$R_f = \frac{RA_1}{A} = \frac{A_1}{A_1 + \alpha A_s} \tag{15}$$

[1] Although R_f values are given in numerous places in this monograph, the following points are worth remembering: The R_f values depend on (1) composition of development phase, (2) kind of paper, (3) direction of paper fibers, (4) manner of development (descending, ascending, ascending-descending, radial), (5) length of paper used for development, (6) distance of starting line from solvent, (7) concentration of solute, (8) presence of other substances, and (9) temperature of development (Zimmermann, 1953a). Although the rate of flow of the solvent in descending paper chromatography is practically constant, the rate of flow of solvent in radial or ascending chromatography falls off rapidly from the point of solvent contact with the paper (Wood, 1954).

or

$$\alpha = \frac{A_1}{R_f A_s} - \frac{A_1}{A_s} = \frac{A_1}{A_s}\left(\frac{1}{R_f} - 1\right). \tag{16}$$

A_1/A_s is equal to the ratio of the volumes of solvent and water phase in the chromatogram. Assuming a given water content of the paper, A_1/A_s may be deduced from the ratio of weight of dry paper to that of the developed chromatogram.

The water content of the paper is apt to vary from experiment to experiment and is difficult to measure in the presence of n-butanol or other solvents. Table IV shows the partition coefficients of a number of amino acids calculated from the R_f and A_1/A_s values for four separate runs under slightly different conditions. The water content has been so chosen that the partition coefficient for glycine is equal to that given by England (1935). The last column gives the direct measurements of England.

Table IV shows the validity of equation 16, relating R_f values to the partition coefficients. Of course, the deviations from the direct measurement indicate to what extent this equation is a simplification of the true chromatographic process. Interaction between amino acids, heterogeneity of the paper, degree of saturation of the paper with water, and many other factors would tend to prevent exactly similar values being obtained for the partition coefficients. Unlike the chromatogram in a tube, the ratio of solvent to stationary phase varies at different levels in a strip of filter paper. This ratio becomes progressively greater, the shorter the distance from the trough. As a result of the distribution of solvent, the greater distance between the trough and the starting point of the amino acid, the smaller are the R_f values. Finally, the aqueous phase present in the cellulose cannot have the same properties as the water phase used in obtaining values for partition coefficients by direct measurement.

The relationship between the partition coefficient of a solute and its

TABLE IV

Number of run	1	2	3	4	
Water in paper, %	28.7	18.0	22.6	17.7	Direct
A_1/A_s	3.25	4.56	3.70	2.93	measurements
PARTITION COEFFICIENTS					
Glycine	70.4	70.4	70.4	70.4	70.4
Alanine	35.9	39.9	43.7	36.6	42.3
Valine	12.2	14.1	14.8	12.5	13.8
Norvaline	8.7	10.8	10.5	9.2	9.5
Leucine	4.5	5.4	5.6	6.0	5.5
Norleucine	3.5	4.2	4.4	4.6	3.2

chemical structure has been predicted by Martin (1949). For ideal solutions,

$$\mu - \mu_A^S = \mu_A^{S_0} + RT \ln N_A^S , \qquad (17)$$

where μ_A^S is the chemical potential of the substance A, $\mu_A^{S_0}$ is the chemical potential in some defined standard state, and N_A^S is the mole fraction of A in the phase S.

If two phases S and M are in equilibrium, the chemical potential of all components is the same in each. Thus,

$$\mu_A^M - \mu_A^S = 0 = \mu_A^{M_0} - \mu_A^{S_0} + RT \ln N_A^M - RT \ln N_A^S , \qquad (18)$$

or, if

$$\mu_A^{S_0} - \mu_A^{M_0} = \Delta\mu_A , \qquad (19)$$

$$\Delta\mu_A = RT \ln \frac{N_A^M}{N_A^S} . \qquad (20)$$

N_A^M/N_A^S is the partition coefficient, α, expressed in terms of mole fractions. Therefore,

$$\ln \alpha = \frac{\Delta\mu_A}{RT} , \qquad (21)$$

and $\Delta\mu_A$ is equal to the free energy required to transport 1 mole of A from phase S to phase M.

Now to a first approximation, $\Delta\mu_A$ may be regarded as made up of

$$d \, \Delta\mu_{CH_2} + e \, \Delta\mu_{COO^-} + f \, \Delta\mu_{NH_3^+} + g \, \Delta\mu_{OH} + \ldots , \text{ etc.},$$

the sum of the potential differences of the various groups of which molecule A is composed. That is to say, as a first approximation the free energy required to transport a given group, e.g., CH_2, from one solvent to another is independent of the rest of the molecule.

Now, if we consider the partition coefficients α_A and α_B of two substances A and B which differ in that B contains, in addition to those contained in A, a group X, we have,

$$\ln \alpha_A = \frac{\Delta\mu_A}{RT} , \qquad \ln \alpha_B = \frac{\Delta\mu_B}{RT} + \frac{\Delta\mu_X}{RT} , \qquad \ln \frac{\alpha_B}{\alpha_A} = \frac{\Delta\mu_X}{RT} . \qquad (22)$$

Thus, the addition of a group X changes the partition coefficient by a given factor, depending on the nature of the group and on the pair of phases employed, but not on the rest of the molecule.

Since A_l/A_s is assumed to be a constant for a given temperature, α is directly proportional to $(1/R_f) - 1$ (equation 16), and the relationship deduced by Martin mentioned above may be written:

$$\ln \frac{(1/R_{f_B}) - 1}{(1/R_{f_A}) - 1} = \frac{\Delta\mu_x}{RT} .\qquad(23)$$

Calling $R_M = \log_{10}(1/R_f - 1)$,

$$\frac{R_{M_B}}{R_{M_A}} = \frac{\Delta\mu_X}{RT} .\qquad(24)$$

Therefore, if R_M is plotted against the number of similar groups in a homologous series, a straight line should result.

Bate-Smith (1950) has tested Martin's deduction on hydroxyl and glucosidic groups in a large number of complex phenols and found it to be fairly accurate. Bremner (1951) and Serchi (1953) found that when the R_M values in various solvents of two homologous series of amines are plotted against the number of methylene ($-CH_2-$) groups a series of approximately parallel straight lines is obtained. The mobility of an amino acid is increased by decarboxylation or substitution by a phenyl group of a hydrogen atom and decreased by replacement of a hydrogen atom by a hydroxyl group.

Pardee (1951) has tested a relationship between the R_f values on paper chromatograms of peptides and the amino acids of which they are composed. From Martin's theory, $\Delta F^\circ = RT \ln \alpha = RT \ln (A_1/A_s)(1/R_f - 1)$, ($\Delta F^\circ = \Delta\mu$), and ΔF° can be divided into the work required to transfer separate parts of solute molecules from the water phase to the solvent phase. Thus the total work, ΔF°_P, for a peptide containing n amino acid residues is divided into the work required to transfer n residues, $\sum \Delta F^\circ_{RP}$; $n-1$ peptide bonds, $(n-1)\Delta F^\circ_{CONH}$; and the terminal amino and carboxyl groups, $ZF^\circ_{PCOO-} + \Delta F^\circ_{PNH_3^+}$. Therefore:

$$\Delta F^\circ_P = RT \ln \frac{A_1}{A_s}\left(\frac{1}{R_f} - 1\right)_P \qquad(25)$$

$$= (n-1)\Delta F^\circ_{CONH} + \Delta F^\circ_{PCOO-} + \Delta F^\circ_{PNH_3^+} + \sum \Delta F^\circ_{RP} .\qquad(26)$$

Similarly, the work required to transfer n free amino acids which make up the peptide is:

$$\Delta F^\circ_{AA} = \sum RT \ln \frac{A_1}{A_s}\left(\frac{1}{R_f} - 1\right)_{AA} \qquad(27)$$

$$= n\Delta F^\circ_{AACOO-} + n\Delta F^\circ_{AANH_3^+} + \sum \Delta F^\circ_{RAA} ,\qquad(28)$$

where the subscript AA refers to an amino acid. The ΔF° terms for amino and carboxyl groups of amino acids are assumed to be different from those of peptides because the dissociation constants and spatial separations are different.

If it is assumed that $\Delta F^{\circ}_{RP} = \Delta F^{\circ}_{RAA}$, the following relation can be obtained by combining constant terms:

$$RT \ln \left(\frac{1}{R_f} - 1\right)_P = (n - 1)A + B + \sum RT \ln \left(\frac{1}{R_f} - 1\right)_{AA}. \quad (29)$$

A is a constant which includes the ΔF° of the amino, carboxyl, CONH groups, and A_1/A_s, and B is a correction term for the difference between the terminal amino and carboxyl groups of a peptide and the corresponding amino acids.

According to equation 29, a plot of $RT \ln (1/R_f - 1)_P - \sum RT \ln (1/R_f - 1)_{AA}$ against the number of peptide bonds should yield a straight line of slope A and intercept B. Pardee obtained fairly good results for two solvents. Equation 29 was also tested by comparing R_f values calculated by this equation with those measured experimentally. Constants A and B were determined experimentally for each solvent, so that the deviation between measured and calculated R_f values was a minimum. With the system phenol:water, $A = -460$ calories per mole and $B = +460$ calories per mole. From these values, the R_f value for each of 33 peptides was calculated. The average deviation was 0.05 R_f unit, and the standard deviation was 0.06 R_f unit. These deviations are only slightly higher than those existing in duplicate experiments on filter paper, so that the validity of equation 29 (in these experiments, at least) seems proved (see Brockmann, 1951).

Isherwood (1951) has discovered an empirical relationship between the movement of sugars on a paper chromatogram and the molar fraction of water (N) in the solvent. The graph of R_M against $-\log N$ is a straight line for each sugar. The relationship holds over a wide range of solvent mixtures, the only exceptions being those containing phenols as the organic solvent. The relationship is given a theoretical basis in terms of the strong association of the hydroxyl groups of the sugars with the water molecules in mixed solvents containing water. The sugars separate in the same order in all solvents, except phenols.

Isherwood (1951) has made a detailed analysis of the contribution of each hydroxyl group to the observed R_f value in the case of the aldohexoses, aldopentoses, and ketohexoses.

It follows from Martin's theoretical treatment of chemical potential as related to the number and kind of groups present in a molecule that the chemical potential for a large molecule is correspondingly large. A large enrichment ratio of one substance to another implies a large difference in the changes of chemical potential of the two substances. For similar compounds such a difference can occur only if the two phases themselves are dissimilar in composition. In general, therefore, phases should be chosen as far as possible from critical solution composition.

Factors which affect the partition coefficient are those known to chemists familiar with other laboratory techniques. Thus, in the distribution of a CH_2 group between ether and water, partition highly favors the organic phase. Benzene favors aromatic more than aliphatic substances, and in cyclohexane this is reversed. Hydrogen bonding between the solute and the solvents is of great importance in determining the partition coefficient. These bonds are much stronger than van der Waals' forces. Phenol and collidine, when saturated with water, are excellent solvents for substances capable of forming hydrogen bonds. They are of opposite character in that phenol is a proton donor, whereas collidine is a proton acceptor. Water, of course, is both a proton donor and acceptor. Thus we find that the addition of an amino group has little influence on the partition between phenol and water, but it greatly changes the partition between collidine and water, in favor of the water. The amino group is a proton acceptor. Collidine, on the other hand, can accept a proton from a hydroxyl group, and thus the addition of a hydroxyl group makes little difference to the partition between collidine and water, whereas a hydroxyl group displaces molecules from phenol to water. The carboxyl group contains both the proton-donating hydroxyl and the proton-accepting carbonyl group, with the hydroxyl character usually predominating (see Berl, 1950).

In partition chromatograms using phenol as the solvent, proline runs faster than valine. With butanol, valine is faster than proline. Here the imino group of proline is a stronger proton acceptor than the amino group of valine, and phenol is a stronger proton donator than butanol.

In the separation of inorganic substances, the addition of a complexing agent to the solvent mixture often improves the partition into the organic phase. In this case it is the partition of the complex between the two phases rather than that of the cation or its salt. The addition of a strong acid to a solvent system, e.g., butanol:water, will usually increase the resolution of cation mixtures. Increased solubility in the organic phase is the result of the strongly polar acid.

Solvents used to resolve mixtures of fatty acids usually contain a small percentage of a strong acid. Under these conditions, the ionization of the fatty acids is repressed and the partition coefficient depends only on the distribution of the free acid, not on the complicating circumstances which are present when both free acid and its base are together in the same solvent mixture. The latter situation usually leads to long diffuse bands being formed on the chromatogram. Since ionization would tend to increase partition in favor of the aqueous phase and since ionization is greater in more dilute solutions, it would be expected that the partition coefficient would be strongly concentration dependent. A concentration gradient exists throughout any chromatographic zone, so that different sections of the same zone will move at different rates, which results in spreading.

The authors hope that this review of some of the theoretical explanations of the chromatographic process has not oversimplified in the mind of the reader the intricate phenomena present. Although partition coefficients have been of value assistance in predicting R_f values, numerous exceptions occur. Adsorption[2] by the paper is always an important factor, and in some cases the dominant one (as in the separation of mixtures of dyes). Water alone can be used to separate a few amino acids on paper. In this case, there is clearly no liquid-liquid partition involved. Craig (1950) reports that the results of partition chromatography are of little use in selecting systems for countercurrent distribution.

Structural Analysis

Reichl (1954, 1956) and Schauer (1955a, 1955b; 1956) have attempted to correlate the experimental R_M values in several solvent systems and the structure of chemical compounds. To this end two constants are determined for each solvent system, *fundamental* and *group* constant. These constants are determined by the following method (example: amino acids):

$$Group\ Constant\ (CH_2\ group)\ =\ R_M(\text{alanine})\ -\ R_M(\text{glycine}) \qquad (30)$$

$$\begin{aligned} Fundamental\ Constant\ =\ 2R_M(\text{methionine}) \\ -\ R_M(\text{cystine})\ -\ 4K_{CH_2} \end{aligned} \qquad (31)$$

The *group constant* (K_{CH_2}) calculated in equation 30 is substituted in equation 31.

Similar calculation for *group constants* may be made for any other functional group. If the R_M values for an unknown amino acid are determined in three solvent systems, the following equation is set up for each solvent:
$$aX_1\ +\ bX_2\ +\ cX_3\ =\ R_M\ -\ K_{(\text{fundamental})}$$

$$\begin{aligned} X_n\ =\ &\text{number of C-atoms, carboxyl, and } \alpha\text{-amino} \\ &\text{groups} \end{aligned} \qquad (32)$$
$$a,\ b,\ c\ =\ group\ constants$$

The three equations are solved simultaneously for X_n which should reveal

[2] Adsorption of materials on paper will increase as the solubility of solutes is reduced by changes in the medium which do not appreciably affect the adsorbing surface. Thus, if the lower portion (25%) of the filter paper is treated with a mixture of M Na_2HPO_4 and $2\ M$ NaH_2PO_4, the order of R_f values of amino acids is to a certain extent reversed as compared to ordinary chromatography using n-butanol:water as the developing solvent (Hagdahl, 1952).

the structure of the unknown α-amino acid.   Similar calculations have been made for organic acids, sugars (M. F. Levy, 1954), and alkaloids (Macek, 1955).

Filter paper will enjoy its reign of popularity only until a better supporting material is found.[3]   When a more uniform material with less adsorptive capacity is developed, the concepts of countercurrent distribution and fractional distillation will undoubtedly be more closely allied with those of partition chromatography.

The reader is referred to the theoretical and practical discussions by Ackerman (1954), Balston (1952), Bergamini (1956), Boulanger (1952a, b), Brimley (1953), Burma (1955), Calvo (1955), Cramer (1953), the monograph by the Faraday Society (1949), Kirk (1954), Lederer (1957), Strain (1954), and others.   The books by Brimley and Barrett (1953), by the Lederers (1957) and by Cassidy (1957) are recommended.

Some Theoretical Factors of Horizontal Paper Chromatography

(Le Strange, 1954)

a. Factors Affecting Rate of Solvent Flow.   Studies were made using the system Bi^{+++}, Cu^{++}, Hg^{++}, and the solvent n-butanol:3 N HCl = 1:1 v/v.   (1) The increase in area developed by the solvent in unit time is proportional to tab width and time of development.   (2) An empirical relationship is established between t (time of development) and h (distance between paper and solvent surface):

$$t = 13.8h - 31.$$

(3) The zones due to the resolved substances are elliptical in shape for filter paper with and without machine direction.   The ratio of major to minor axis was found to be 1.15 $\pm$ 0.02.

b. Separation by Horizontal Filter Paper Chromatography.   (1) R_r factors (radius to point of maximum density/radius to solvent front) are constant and independent of development time.   (2) Band widths become thinner at first and then wider gradually with increasing time of development.

c. Comparison Between Descending (Strip) and Horizontal Chromatography.   The speed of separation by horizontal chromatography is at least as fast as by the descending technique, but the definition in the first is often superior.   Since the concentric zones are thinner than the spots,

---

[3] Supporting media made from cellulose acetate, "Dynel," glass fibers, polyvinylchloride and zein cellulose have been introduced by H. Reeve Angel and Co. (52 Duane St., New York 7, N. Y.).   The preparation of paper containing finely ground ion exchange resins has also been announced (Hale, 1955; *Amber Hi-Lites*, 1957, H. Reeve Angel and Co.).

the separation occurs earlier by the horizontal method. There is also less tailing in the horizontal technique. As a gross observation, the following relationship holds:

$$R_r{}^2 \text{ (disk)} = R_f \text{ (strips)}.$$

This relationship has been confirmed for other systems, e.g. amino acids and sugars (Ganguli, 1955b).

(d) *Factors Affecting* R_f. For some separations, development to a circle of diameter of 6 cm. or less is sufficient and takes about ten minutes. The rate of solvent flow is proportional to the wick diameter. This does not, however, influence the reproducibility of R_f's from one run to the next (Saifer, 1953). Other factors which apparently do not influence the R_f are: (a) equilibration of paper, (b) time of development, and (c) concentration of solutes (amino acids). These observations suggest that circular paper chromatography is a more rapid and simpler method than ascending or descending chromatography.

Chapter III

GENERAL METHODS

The majority of methods which have been devised for paper chromatography are based on the following principle: ". . . [Paper chromatography is the] separation of substances from a mixture by the passage of solvent in a definitedirection and selective fixation. . ." (Weil, 1953*a, b*). The phenomenon of the resolution of a complex mixture by paper chromatography has been likened to a schizophrenic dilemma which each component of this mixture has to face (Asimov, 1955).

The mechanics of the process of paper chromatography are simply this: A drop of a solution containing a mixture of substances is placed on a piece of filter paper near one end. Next, this end is placed in a suitable solvent within a closed container. The solvent passes the spot where the solution had been applied. Each substance in this mixture will ideally move along with the solvent at a unique rate, so that after a while all of the components of the mixture will occupy a distinct position somewhere along the path of the flow of the solvent (Fig. 1).

In practice, of course, many compounds of closely related structure will not separate in one single solvent development, and more elaborate procedures are necessary. Other difficulties are encountered when the substances to be separated are water-insoluble, and the "reversed phase chromatography" becomes the preferred technique.

The great advantages of paper chromatography lie in the relative simplicity of the operations and, in many cases, the small expense of the equipment. Even the amateur can assemble a home-made piece of equipment to demonstrate the separation of organic compounds or plant pigments (Ingalls, 1953).

The following scheme outlines the procedure generally followed in paper chromatography:

1. Choice of filter paper.
2. Preparation of sample.
3. Application of sample to paper.
4. Choice·of solvents.
5. Development of chromatogram.
6. Drying of chromatogram after development and detection of spots.
7. Quantitative estimation (Consden, 1954).

The Chromatography Laboratory

For the laboratory that is planning to do extensive work in paper chromatography, it is recommended to set aside a small room, approximately

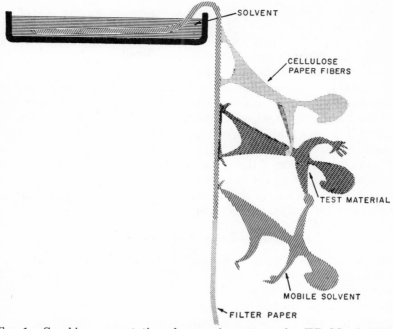

SOLVENT

CELLULOSE
PAPER FIBERS

TEST MATERIAL

MOBILE SOLVENT

FILTER PAPER

FIG. 1. Graphic representation of paper chromatography (PB, March 1956).

the size of an average photographic dark room. For very careful work the room should be air-conditioned and humidity-controlled. For most routine analyses, however, it is sufficient that the room has a minimum of window space and is located somewhere in the center of the building, protected from sudden draft and radical changes in the temperature. This room may also be equipped with a standard-size laboratory hood which should only be turned on when organic solvents are being handled (e.g., during the drying procedure following the development of the chromatogram). Many of the commonly used solvents in chromatography are highly toxic (e.g., phenol), and others have offensive odors. It is needless to say that the air-conditioning and the draft system of this "chromatography room" be independent from the rest of the laboratory. This room should also contain a laboratory shaker for the equilibration of solvent systems. All solvents used in chromatography should be stored and mixed in this room.

The draft hood in this room will be used for the "drying" of the chromatograms, the spraying of the chromatograms for the detection of spots, and the steaming of papers for certain procedures (e.g. amino acid chromatography, organic acid chromatography, see Chapters V and VII). It is desirable, therefore, to have steam and compressed-air connections in this hood.   This room should be used mainly for the solvent development of the chromatograms.

The preliminary preparation and final evaluation of chromatograms should be done outside this "chromatography room." Besides the usual equipment found in a chemical laboratory, the following items may be found useful for chromatographic work: a rotating evaporator ("Rinco"), an ordinary hair dryer, an X-ray viewing box, an ultraviolet light source (both short and long-wave), a storage cabinet for large sheets of filter paper (18 × 22"), a large table for spotting samples onto the filter paper, and a constant-temperature oven.

This brief description of the "ideal" chromatography laboratory may be altered, of course, to fit the individual's needs and means.   The reader is also referred to the end of this chapter where a list of manufacturers of chromatographic equipment may be found.

Methods of Paper Chromatography

The solvent development in paper chromatography has been the subject of a great number of variations.   The choice of the method may depend on the class of compounds being investigated, or it may be mainly one of personal preference.   It is curious that one particular method may be predominant in a certain geographical part of the world (e.g. circular chromatography in India).   Most of the methods which will be described in detail are being used widely today with the exception of method I, "Kapillaranalyse," which is mainly one of historical interest.

Method I: "Kapillaranalyse"

Around 1860, Schönbein recognized that in filter paper strips water travels faster than the solute in solution, and that in a mixture of components in solution one component travels faster than the others (Rheinboldt, 1921).   This observation was made the basis for the analysis of dyes. Schönbein's student, Goppelsroeder, named this analysis of dyes using filter paper "Kapillaranalyse."   Goppelsroeder applied this method to the separation of plant pigments, alkaloids, fats and oils, impurities in food products, etc.   The principle of the analysis was that the substances were adsorbed on the filter paper directly from their solution; the height of the substance and the solvent front were observed and correlated.   "Kapillaranalyse" differed from paper partition chromatography, which was to be developed eighty-odd years later, in that no developing solvent was used.

Goppelsroeder (1909) describes in detail a chromatographic chamber (Fig. 2) which differs little from the more elaborate chromatographic chambers of today.

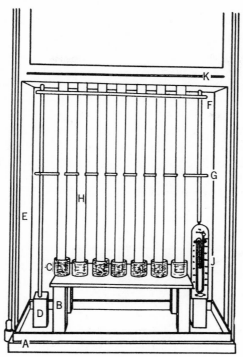

FIG. 2. Chromatograph chamber (Goppelsroeder, 1909): A, wooden floor; B stand for samples; C, beakers containing samples; D, lead support; E, glass rods; F, G, wooden connecting bars between glass rods; H, double-face glass rulers with paper strips; J, thermometer; K, glass door.

Method II: Descending Chromatography

In this technique the solvent is permitted to flow along the paper in a *downward* direction. Consden, Gordon, and Martin (1944) first reported the successful separation of a mixture of amino acids by descending paper chromatography.

The essentials of the apparatus consisted of a filter paper strip the upper end of which was immersed in a glass trough (Fig. 3) containing the solvent. The strip was hung in an air-tight chamber, a section of drain pipe. After the insertion of the paper, the chamber was sealed with a piece of glass plate (Fig. 4). The bottom of the chamber was covered with water-saturated organic solvent in order to provide a saturated atmosphere. The trough was provided with a glass bar which served as the paper support, and the paper strip passed over a glass rod to prevent capillary siphoning of the solvent down the paper.

1. SOLVENT TROUGH

The construction of a glass trough is described by Atkinson (1948), Longenecker (1948), and J. F. Thompson (1956). The ends of a 40-mm. Pyrex tube of desired length are sealed, leaving a small vent on the side of the tube. A one-inch-wide strip of adhesive tape, covering the air vent, is placed on the tube, extending the desired length of the trough. The rest of the glass tube is taped up with four additional adhesive tape strips, and the glass is cut with a two-inch Carborundum disk mounted on a flexible-shaft power take-off. A stream of water is played on the disk and glass while cutting. When the panel of glass has been cut around, it will fall off intact (Fig. 5).

A simple tray and tray support rest on a steel band fastened on the

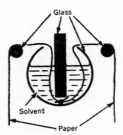

FIG. 3.   Cross section of small trough (Consden, 1944).

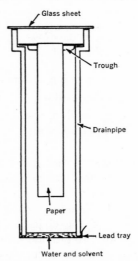

FIG. 4.   Diagram of chromatograph chamber made from drain pipe (Consden, 1944).

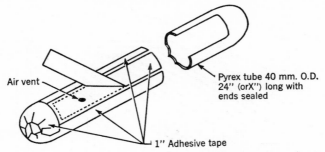

Air vent

Pyrex tube 40 mm. O.D.
24" (orX") long with
ends sealed

1" Adhesive tape

FIG. 5. Diagram of glass trough. *Left,* before cutting; *right,* completed channel (Longenecker, 1948).

inside of a glass or metal* cylinder (Porter, 1954a). Glass troughs with support rods, antisiphoning rods, and trough supports are commercially available.

Another type of glass trough, consisting of several segments, has been used to study the influence of the ionic strength of a solvent on the resolution of a mixture of amino acids (Wunderly, 1954). This procedure enables one to run replicates of mixtures on the same sheet of paper under identical conditions except with different solvents. A stainless-steel trough to accommodate ten chromatograms simultaneously is made from sheet metal shaped into a shallow trough (von Arx, 1956) (Fig. 5A). The bottom of the trough is provided with ten 3.5 mm. wide slits and is divided into ten compartments by 30 mm.-high stainless-steel dividers which are securely soldered along the slits. Four adjustable screw rods provide the support for this multitrough. The advantage of this arrangement is that as many as ten chromatograms can be handled at the same time (e.g. lifting the papers from the chromatographic cabinet into the hood for drying). However, there seems to be no provision for antisiphon rods which may spoil the chromatograms due to fast solvent flow by siphoning.

If no suitable glass-cutting or metal shop equipment is available, any glass, porcelain, stainless-steel, or polyethylene dish with a suitable support may be improvised.

2. CHROMATOGRAPH CHAMBER

Evaporation of the solvent from the paper should be kept at a minimum during a chromatographic run. For that reason, an airtight chamber must be chosen, so that the chamber atmosphere will be at all times saturated with the respective solvent. Graduated glass cylinders fitted with airtight covers may be used for one-dimensional work. Consden (1944) found stoneware drainpipes to be convenient, the tops of which were ground

* Metal troughs may be obtained from Luger Boutellette, 11 Reuthel St., Auburn, Mass.

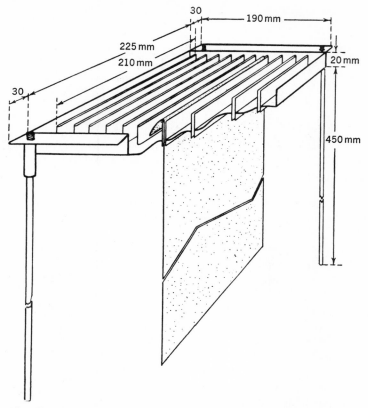

FIG. 5A. Stainless-steel "slit trough" for descending chromatography (von Arx, 1956).

flat and covered by sheets of glass (Fig. 4). The advantage of a glass-walled chamber is that the progress of the solvent front may be followed conveniently.

For the use of filter paper sheets, several models of cabinets are made commercially (see Fig. 6). For two-dimensional chromatography, it is recommended that two cabinets be used side by side, one for each solvent (see method V).

A hygienically safe chromatographic cabinet has been equipped with an iron outlet pipe on the bottom, so that the solvent vapors, which may be highly toxic, can be safely removed at the end of a run. An exhaust fan is attached to the outlet by means of a flexible pipe (Mendenhall, 1956). Another feature of this same design is a frame which holds all of the anti-siphon rods which are in use. At the termination of the development, the papers can be clipped to the rods with stainless-steel clips, and all of the

FIG. 6. RECO Chromatographic cabinet (Chromatocab).

papers can be moved to a drying cabinet at the same time. The frame consists of two parts, each one an upper and lower piece of paraffin-coated wood, drilled with eight holes, and held together by three stainless-steel clips (Fig. 7).

3. EXPERIMENTAL PROCEDURE

The directions recommended for one-dimensional chromatography using a large chromatographic cabinet of the type depicted in Fig. 6, are as

Side   End

FIG. 7. Wooden support for anti-siphon rods (one section) (Mendenhall, 1956).

follows: The solutions to be analyzed are spotted by means of a micropipette (see Section III, Experimental Techniques) on a line 3 in. distant and parallel from one edge of the filter paper sheet (18 × 22″). The spots should be spaced at 2½ in. intervals. After the spots are dry, the paper is folded sharply along a line 2 in. from the edge; the samples are, therefore, one inch from the fold. The paper is now transfered to the chromatographic cabinet, where the paper is fastened to the antisiphon rod with two stainless steel chromatographic clips. A second chromatogram may be placed on the opposite antisiphon rod, so that both papers reach into the same empty trough. The glass support rod, which is a heavy glass or stainless steel rod bent at right angles at the ends, is lowered into the trough where it holds the papers in position. The clips are now removed. After a convenient equilibration time, the solvent is added to the trough, and the development proceeds, usually overnight. At the end of the run, the papers are clipped again to the antisiphon rods, the support bar is removed, and the papers are dried to be processed further (e.g. color development, elution).

A similar procedure is recommended for paper strip chromatography, using smaller troughs and glass cylinders (18 × 6 in.). Frierson (1954) has described an exceedingly simple arrangement. A 500-ml. graduated cylinder is placed into a cylindrical glass pipette washer (18 × 6 in.), and a bacterial slide staining jar, placed on top of the graduated cylinder, serves as the solvent trough. The filter paper strip is tucked under a glass slide which is placed in the first groove of the jar.

For slow-moving substances better resolution may be achieved by permitting the solvent to drip off the serrated lower edge of the paper. It is possible to carry out solvent development for several days and to effect good separation of difficult mixtures, e.g. leucine and isoleucine; monosaccharides. For lack of a better English word, this technique is called "Durchlauf" chromatography.

Method III: Ascending Chromatography

Ascending paper chromatography (i.e. the solvent travels in an *upward* direction) is especially suitable for quick analyses of a large number of samples or for exploratory work involving the use of many different solvents. The apparatus for this technique is exceedingly simple and yields reproducible results (R. J. Williams, 1948). One must bear in mind, however, that the upward flow of solvent is eventually counteracted by gravity, resulting in a definite slow-up after the solvent front has traveled more than twenty-five centimeters. The chromatographic development should be stopped at this point. In order to achieve maximum resolution by this method, "multiple development" should be tried (method V).

1. CHROMATOGRAPH CHAMBER

The choice of the chromatographic chamber for this technique depends on the size of the filter paper one wishes to use. For paper sheets (5 × 5 in.) in a museum jar, Size #4 (internal dimensions: 15 × 9 × 15 in.) can be fitted with three wooden dowels (diameter 0.25 in.) inserted in the grooves already provided for on the two narrow sides (Rockland, 1951; Underwood, 1954). The paper sheets are mounted on the dowels with pressure adhesive tape. A soft-rubber gasket (e.g. sponge rubber weather stripping) is mounted on the underside of the glass cover to provide for a saturated chamber atmosphere.

Filter paper sheets (18 in. wide; 10 in. high) may be developed in 10-gal. glass aquaria which are fitted with glass rods running the length of the chamber (see method IV for detailed description). The sheets are fastened to the rods with stainless-steel clips.

An inexpensive all-glass chromatographic chamber may be constructed from single-weight window panes, held together with a fast-drying plastic cement (Miwa, 1955). This chamber is not completely air-tight which may be desirable in order to minimize sweating but will not be satisfactory where careful equilibration is essential.

When filter paper strips are used for rapid determination of a large number of samples, an ordinary Pyrex tube serves as a very satisfactory chromatographic chamber (Rockland, 1949b). A paper strip, narrowed down at one end, is held by a paper clip which in turn is inserted into a cork. The paper may also be shaped into the form of a trapezoid with the wider end touching the sides of the test tube so that the narrow end is immersed into the solvent.

A slightly more elaborate glass-tube chamber is made from a tube 51 mm. diameter and 380 mm. long (H. T. Gordon, 1955) (Fig. 8). The ends of the tube are fitted with Number 26 corks with 12 mm.-centered holes. The bottom is fitted through a peg on a wooden board. The upper cork is fitted with a small glass hook and a paper clip. A medical prescription glass sawed off at the 30 ml. mark rests on the bottom and serves as solvent trough. A filter paper strip folded into a loop is held at its ends by the paper clip, and a short piece of glass rod at the loop serves to separate the two parts. Two samples may be spotted about one inch above the fold and developed at the same time.

When a completely saturated atmosphere is essential, as for the fatty acids and steroids (see Chapters VII and VIII), a test-tube chamber with a sealed side arm may be advantageous (Pan, 1956). Provisions are made in this design to keep a small tube within the larger chamber, filled with one phase of the solvent. The paper strip is equilibrated for a convenient time, and the mobile development phase of the solvent is added through a side tube; in this manner the saturated atmosphere remains completely undisturbed.

A popular technique for ascending chromatography using sheets of filter paper is to shape the paper into a cylinder.   The samples are spotted in the usual manner about one inch from the bottom edge of the paper.   The vertical edges are fastened together with staples (do not use metal if solvent contains acid), cotton thread, or adhesive tape (Wolfson, 1949), or with polyethylene clips (Sommer, 1955) (Fig. 9).   In this technique the edges of the paper must not touch.

When cylinder-chromatograms are used, a large variety of chromatograph chambers are available.   In each case the paper cylinder must conform to the size and shape of the chamber.   A one-liter graduated cylinder, fitted with a rubber stopper (Ma, 1949) and a wide mouthed one-gallon screw-cap "pickle jar" (Palmer, 1955) have been used successfully.

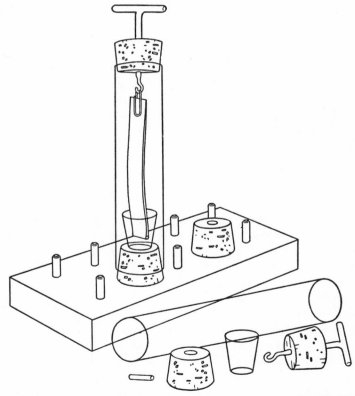

FIG. 8.   Glass tube arrangement for ascending chromatography (H. T. Gordon, 1955).

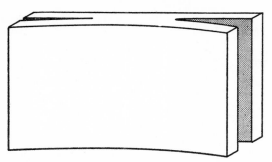

Fig. 9. Plastic clip for paper cylinders for ascending chromatography (Sommer, 1955).

2. CHROMATOGRAPH RACKS

A frame for the rigid support of up to fifty paper strips may be constructed from 4 × 4 mm. strips of cold-rolled steel (Singer, 1951). Two strips of the steel (73 cm. long) are bent into two circles with a diameter of 22.5 cm., and the ends are brazed together. The circles are brazed at 90° intervals to four strips each 50 cm. long. Friction tape is then wound around the rings, pointing toward the center. The paper strips may then be fastened on the lower and upper pins and pulled taut.

Another stainless steel holder for paper cylinders has the advantage that, with a movable coil, any size of filter paper can be shaped into a cylinder and held in place without staples or adhesive tape (Ma, 1949).

A cross-shaped aluminum holder around which the paper strips may be wound in coil form features the advantage of space-saving with a long solvent path (Schwartz, 1952). Another stainless-steel rack of compact size will hold five paper sheets, 9 × 9 in. (Hunter, 1956) (Fig. 10). The papers are clipped to the frame, and rest against crossbars A (Fig. 10), so that contact between adjacent papers is prevented, although the distance between papers is slightly more than one inch. Eight of these racks can fit into a tank of appropriate size, and forty chromatograms can be developed at one time in a comparatively small space (40 × 24 in.).

3. EXPERIMENTAL PROCEDURE

When it is convenient to work with filter paper cylinders, the following technique is recommended: Filter paper sheets, 18 × 11¼ inches, are used. Along one edge of the paper, about 2.5 cm. from the margin, are placed, at intervals of about 2 cm., drops of the samples to be analyzed. After the spots are dried, the sheet is formed into a cylinder, about 6 inches in diameter, by stapling the edges together so that the edges do not quite touch.

The paper cylinder is placed in an upright position into a Pyrex dish (10-

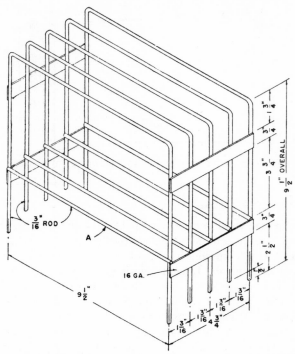

FIG. 10. Metal rack for ascending chromatography, holding four sheets (Hunter, 1956).

inch pie plate) containing the solvent mixture.   The spots comprising the samples to be analyzed are on the bottom of the cylinder, just slightly above the level of the solvent.   For good equilibration, especially of highly volatile solvents the following techniques may be adopted:

The bottom of the chromatographic tank is covered with the solvent (usually the aqueous phase for a two phase solvent combination).   Thick sheets of filter paper (Whatman No. 3 or Eaton and Dikeman 301) are pressed against the wall of the tank, and development is started when this paper is soaked with solvent.   In most cases it is necessary to add large amounts of solvent to the bottom of the tank, since both paper grades are very absorbent.

For the one-gallon "pickle jar," the atmosphere is best saturated by immersing a small roll of filter paper into the stationary phase of the solvent contained in a small vial in the center of the jar.   The small filter roll should reach almost to the top of the jar, and the paper cylinder will surround it (Palmer, 1955).

The chromatographic cabinet is covered with a glass plate during chromatography. By grinding the upper edge of the jar to a plane surface and sanding the glass cover at the area of contact, an airtight seal is made by the use of desiccator grease. The screw cover for the "pickle jar" is of metal and should be painted with paraffin. Chromatography is completed when the solvent front has traveled almost to the top of the paper cylinder.

4. MISCELLANEOUS TECHNIQUES

Two miniature chromatographic cabinets have been designed to handle strips as long as 50 cm. in a plastic "chromatobox" of overall dimensions $7 \times 7 \times 4$ cm. (Oertel, 1956b, Barrollier, 1955). In one design the paper strip is loosely wound around two glass rods and the two bottom edges of the square-shaped solvent trough. The front end of the strip reaches through a slit in the cabinet to the outside atmosphere, so that the fastest moving substance will be concentrated at the front due to evaporation of the solvent. This latter principle has been incorporated in another ascending chromatography tank (Fischbach, 1955a). Barrollier (1955) winds a 50-cm.-long strip around a spiral-shaped plastic film (e.g. Teflon) with a raised surface to minimize the wetting properties of the plastic even further.

Method IV: Ascending-Descending Chromatography

The technique of Block (1950) combines the better features of both ascending and descending chromatography. The filter paper sheet containing spots of samples to be analyzed is draped over a glass rod, and the long end is immersed into the solvent, in such a manner that the solvent climbs by capillary action up the paper past the support rod and down the other side.

1. CHROMATOGRAPH CHAMBER

Ten-gallon rectangular glass aquaria, 52 cm. long, 32 cm. high, and 26 cm. wide, are used. The lower portion of the sides and all the joints are covered by a layer of paraffin. Two glass rods running the length of the chamber are sealed with paraffin to the sides of the chamber about 5 cm. out and 2–3 cm. from the top. A third rod is sealed halfway between the other two at the same height. Glass troughs are made by sealing the ends of a 2-inch borosilicate glass tubing and cutting longitudinally down the middle. (They may also be obtained from the Yonkers Laboratory Supply Company.) The chamber is covered by a heavy glass plate and held down with a lead weight (Fig. 11).

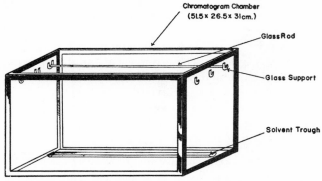

Fɪɢ. 11. Chromatograph chamber for the ascending-descending technique (Block, 1950).

2. Experimental Procedure

Three sheets of filter paper, 18 × 19 inches, are cut, and the unknown solution is applied as drops about 2.5 cm. from the bottom of the sheets and 2 cm. apart. The spots are dried with an infrared lamp or a hair dryer. The lower edge of the sheets is immersed in the solvent. The chamber is covered with the lid, and the solvent is allowed to travel 40–50 cm. beyond the point of application of the substances.

Comments. A "bridge unit" for paper chromatography of carbohydrates has been devised by Kawerau (1951) (Fig. 12). An all-glass apparatus consisting of two 500-ml. round-bottom flasks and two T-shaped connecting links makes up the chromatograph chamber. The filter paper strip is inserted by opening the "bridge" and is immersed on one end into the organic layer. The other flask contains the aqueous layer of the solvent in order to saturate the atmosphere with respect to the solvent and water.

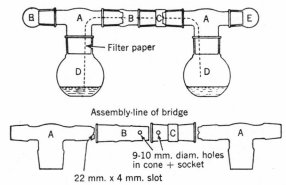

Fɪɢ. 12. Assembly of bridge unit for filter paper chromatography (Kawerau, 1951).

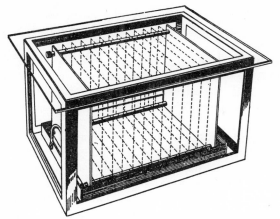

FIG. 13. "Two-way" rack for ascending two-dimensional technique, holding twelve paper sheets (Shandon Scientific Co.; Micro-Metric Instrument Co.).

Method V: Two-Dimensional Chromatography

For maximum resolution of a complex mixture, two-dimensional paper chromatography is recommended. The principle of this technique is the successive development of the chromatogram with two different solvents (e.g., a basic and an acidic solvent), whose advancing fronts are at right angles to each other.

1. FILTER PAPER RACK

A filter paper rack accommodating 12 sheets, 8 × 8 inches, for use in two-dimensional chromatography is manufactured by Shandon Scientific Co. and Micro-Metric Instrument Co. The rack (Fig. 13) is made of aluminum and consists of two square plates connected by four rods, fastened to the plates with nuts. Four holes are punched into the corners of the filter paper sheets (it is suggested that a template be made), and the sheets are placed on the rack by stacking them on the rods through the holes. The sheets are separated from each other by ¾- to 1-inch washers fitting on the rods.

2. EXPERIMENTAL PROCEDURE

The same apparatus as described for unidimensional chromatography will lend itself to two-dimensional chromatography with the difference that a single spot is applied 2.5 cm. from the lower corner of a sheet, 27 cm. square. After the first solvent has traveled almost to the top edge, the sheet is removed, dried, and re-run in a second solvent whose front is at right angles to that of the first solvent. After the development with a second solvent, the chromatogram is ready for further processing and evaluation.

When the paper cylinder technique for ascending chromatography (cf. Method III) is used, the cylinder is unfastened after the first development and re-formed into a new cylinder whose axis is perpendicular to the axis of the first cylinder. The development with the second solvent proceeds as before.

A new technique for two-dimensional descending chromatography utilizes large sheets of filter paper (18 × 22 in.), the upper edges of which are cut at 1.25 in. intervals to a depth of three inches. The tabs are folded back to serve as wicks, and the paper is shaped into a cylinder. The chromatographic cabinet is a 12 × 24 in. glass cylinder, and the solvent trough is a six-inch pie plate supported on a funnel. The funnel is inserted through a rubber stopper which is placed on a 250 ml. graduated cylinder (Yamaguchi, 1955). The two-dimensional chromatographic development proceeds as above; however, no great advantage is gained over the simpler ascending chromatography of paper cylinders.

With three different solvents and three sets of two-dimensional chromatograms, it has been possible to separate the amino acids from a protein hydrolyzate (Decker, 1951b). For example, the following different solvents may be chosen: (a) water-saturated phenol; (b) α-picoline:water; (c) isopropanol:acetic acid:water. Three sets of two-dimensional chromatograms may then be run with the following solvent combinations:

Chromatogram	Solvent, first dimension	Solvent, second dimension
I	a	b
II	a	c
III	b	c

These methods are generally applicable to any class of compounds, and a study of the R_f tables usually will suggest a suitable combination of solvents.

3. MISCELLANEOUS TECHNIQUES

A segment of a one-dimensional chromatogram is woven or sewed (with a sewing machine) into a second sheet of filter paper which is developed with another solvent (Boggs, 1952). If complete resolution has not resulted after these two operations, another development with a third solvent may be undertaken (Stockli, 1954). Further transfers are impractical since the spots become too diffuse.

After the development of a chromatogram with one solvent, segments containing still unresolved substances are cut out and attached with a stainless steel pin to a new paper strip. These substances are eluted and transferred to the new strip by an ascending chromatographic technique in a specially constructed glass flask. The paper strip is then developed with another solvent (Winteringham, 1953).

Method VI: Multiple Development

Multiple development technique is used to gain a greater effective distance of solvent front while retaining a shorter length for the paper itself. After the mixture has been separated by the solvent and the paper dried, the paper is returned to the solvent trough for a repetition of the passage of solvent. After two to four such developments, an excellent resolution of a mixture of simple sugars was effected (Jeanes, 1951). A similar technique is applied to the separation of amino acids with acetic acid : water as solvent (Csobán, 1952).

A simple formula for the multiple development of amino acids for strip- and circular chromatography may be found to be generally applicable (Chakrabortty, 1956). The rule states: The distance between two substances will increase in the second development if

$$R_{f(1)} + R_{f(2)} < 1$$

(R_f is the ratio of distance traveled by solute to the distance traveled by the solvent.)

It is sometimes desirable to use a "fast" solvent to get rid of unwanted substances or impurities. These may then be located by suitable detection methods, and the paper sheet is cut off parallel to the solvent flow just below this region. The remaining part of the sheet is fastened with a sewing machine to another piece of filter paper of the same width, and a second development (with the same or another solvent) is undertaken.

In the chromatography of P^{32}-labeled nucleotides (see Chapter IX), it is first necessary to remove phosphate ions by a preliminary short-time ascending development (Krebs, 1953). Whatman No. 1 filter paper, 20 × 60 cm., is folded for this purpose 38 cm. from one end and fastened with two paper clips. The solutions are placed 3 cm. from the fold. The fast-moving phosphate front located by a Geiger counter is cut off, and the second development takes place in the opposite direction.

Method VII: Circular or Horizontal Filter Paper Chromatography

The principle of this technique is that the substances to be analyzed are resolved into circular zones instead of spots. A "tail" is cut from a circular filter paper disk and is immersed into the developing solvent after a drop

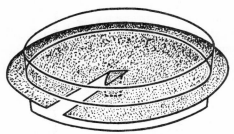

Fɪɢ. 14. Petri-dish arrangement for circular filter paper chromatography (Rutter, 1948).

of the substance to be analyzed has been deposited on the paper at the joint (Fig. 14).

Rutter (1948, 1950) is generally credited with originating this technique, which is sometimes referred to as the "Rutter technique." Weil and Williams (1953b) give the credit to Runge, whose book, "Der Bildungstrieb der Stoffe" (1855), is illustrated with numerous examples of "radial" chromatography. It seems, however, that Runge's "radial" chromatography was another variation of capillary analysis (see Goppelsroeder). The first description of horizontal paper chromatography was given by W. G. Brown in 1939, thus preceding the "classical" publication on the subject of paper chromatography by Consden, Gordon, and Martin (1944).

1. Apparatus

The apparatus consists of two upper or lower sections of a Petri dish and a filter paper disk slightly larger than the glass sections (Fig. 14). The "tail" is fashioned by making two parallel cuts, about 2 mm. apart, from the same edge up to the center of a circular filter paper, and the tail is bent at the joint perpendicular to the plane of the paper and cut down to about 1.5 cm. in length. Care must be taken that the cuts are of equal length; otherwise the development may not result in truly circular zones.

Instead of fashioning the wick from the filter paper disk itself, it may be formed from another strip of filter paper (0.5 × 4–5 cm.), which is folded in the center and inserted into a 0.5-cm.-long slit in the center of the filter paper disk. The wick may also be made from a strip of filter paper, rolled into a cylinder (2–3 mm. thick), cut at the end into the form of a brush and inserted through a small hole at the center of the disk (Giri, 1952h) or the solvent may be fed onto the paper disk by means of a glass capillary. The size of the capillary regulates the rate of feed and thus the rate of development (Lakshminarayanan, 1954). A small cone made of filter paper and placed with its apex at the center of the disk is used as an irrigating wick (Berlingozzi, 1952a).

A versatile apparatus accommodating various sizes of filter paper disks may be made simply from two glass funnels (Irreverre, 1954). A 115-mm. and an 80-mm. funnel are joined by their tubes and fastened by a Teflon ring with a setscrew. A crystallizing dish set on top of the cone of the smaller funnel serves as the solvent trough. The cone of the other funnel serves as the base. The paper disk rests on the upper edge of a paper cylinder which surrounds the glass funnels. The wick is made from a cotton thread pulled through the center of the paper disk. The entire apparatus is placed into a 6 × 18-inch glass cylinder.

The use of glass desiccators for large filter paper disks is recommended. The paper disk, having a larger diameter than the bottom half of the desiccator, is supported on the rim and held down by the desiccator top. The solvent is fed from the bottom by a cotton wick (Schwerdtfeger, 1953) or from the top by a self-regulating pipette (Brockmann, 1953). The bottom of a bulb-shaped pipette (capacity 25–50 ml.) is bent at such an angle that the opening is perpendicular to the paper disk and placed about 2–3 mm. from the surface of the paper. A stopcock at the upper end of the pipette is closed until the first drop of the developing solvent touches the paper. The stopcock is then opened, and the flow of solvent will be self-regulating.

A commercial circular chromatography apparatus (Shandon Scientific Co.) is designed so that reproducible results are obtained (Kawerau, 1956) (Fig. 14A). The solvent feed is from a glass capillary tube, and a drop of solvent placed at the center of the circular filter paper starts a run. The filter paper disks are specially machine-stamped into five triangular sectors (Whatman Papers KCT 14 and 26). This sector analysis permits the analyses of five samples per disk and also achieves better equilibration on the top and bottom of the paper. A similar apparatus utilizes the glass capillary wick and has an added feature for the equilibration of the paper with the volatile solvent phase prior to the actual development (Wolf, 1956). This is accomplished by a concentric upper capillary tubing reaching through the top of the apparatus and just touching the filter paper. The solvent flow is simply started by applying suction to the upper capillary tubing.

Another variation of the apparatus for circular paper chromatography results in excellent resolution of a complex mixture of amino acids (Krishnamurthy, 1955b) (Fig. 15). The chromatographic chamber is a glass crystallizing dish (30 cm. diameter) inverted over a glass plate. A circular glass stand with four legs (26 cm. diameter) serves as the support for the filter paper disk. The solvent is kept in a small Petri dish in the same plane as the filter paper by resting on an inverted beaker of appropriate size. This arrangement permits the saturation of the chamber atmosphere

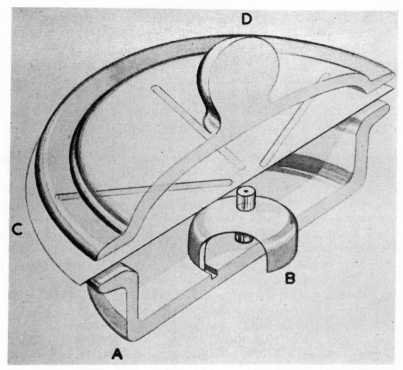

FIG. 14A. Exploded view of circular chromatography apparatus using sectored filter paper disks (Kawerau, 1956). A, bottom; B, adjustable capillary feed tube in holder; C, filter paper disk; D, top.

by keeping the aqueous solvent phase in two additional Petri dishes on the bottom of the apparatus.

2. EXPERIMENTAL PROCEDURE

The drop to be analyzed is placed on the paper disk at the joint of the wick and is air-dried. The disk is then placed between the two glass dishes, the lower containing the developing solvent. The solvent rises, by capillarity, and the rate of development may be readily controlled by the width of the tail and the distance between the liquid surface and the plane of the paper.

In most cases of chromatographic identification it is advantageous to analyze both standard and unknown solutions on the same chromatogram. This may be accomplished by applying six to eight equidistant spots on a pencil-drawn circle with a radius of 1 cm. from the center of the paper

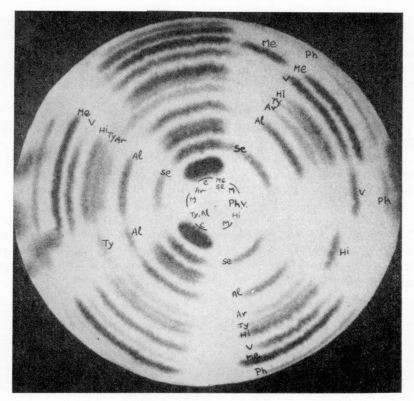

FIG. 15. Circular paper chromatogram of amino acids developed in Krishna-murthy (1955b) apparatus.

disk (Proom, 1951, 1953b; Giri, 1952a, b, c, h).   In this case a series of seg-ments, instead of concentric circles, result after an appropriate color de-velopment.

A modification of the above technique consists in the shift of the wick from the center of the paper disk to a spot near the periphery (Rao, 1953; Matthias, 1956).   Several equidistant spots are placed on an arc with a 1.5 cm. radius with the wick as center.   This technique apparently results in a better resolution of compounds, e.g., glutamic acid and glycine, using n-butanol:acetic acid:water (see Chapter V).   An improved wick may be fashioned from a "T" shaped piece of filter paper (20 × 20 mm.) the crossbar of which is rolled up and inserted through a small hole in the center of the filter paper disk (Ganguli, 1955a).

Circular paper chromatography is adaptable for two-dimensional technique (Airan, 1953).   A ring about 0.5–1 cm. wide is cut from Whatman

No. 1 filter paper. The mixture to be resolved is placed about 1 inch from one end of the strip which is bent downward just below the point of application. This serves as the wick for horizontal development with Solvent No. 1. The ring is then stitched onto a 24-cm. Whatman No. 1 paper disk which is then developed in the usual manner, with another solvent.

3. IDENTIFICATION OF ZONES

Solutions containing colored constituents give sharp separations into individual zones.

In the case of colorless chromatograms, a test sector is cut out after development and pressed between filter papers impregnated with a suitable color reagent. The chromatograms also may be sprayed with or dipped into the reagent.

After the positions have been marked on the main chromatogram using the developed test sector as a guide, the bands are cut out as circular strips. Both ends are placed into a solvent so that the substance in each band is concentrated in the center of the strip, whence it is drawn off by a capillary pipette in order to be analyzed by micromethods.

4. MISCELLANEOUS TECHNIQUES

A technique analogous to circular paper chromatography is the following (Marchal, 1951; Reindel, 1953): A strip of filter paper 8–10 cm. wide is trimmed at one end so that a tab 2 cm. wide and 4 cm. long is left attached to the main section by a section 10–15 mm. long and 2 mm. wide. The mixture is placed at the lower wide section, and the strip is developed by the ascending method. The substances separate in a series of concentric arcs. This method has been applied to the separation of amino acids.

By serrating a large sheet of filter paper (40 × 28 cm.) and shaping the ends in the same manner as in the above technique, as many as ten samples can be chromatographed at the same time (Matthias, 1954; Schwerdtfeger, 1954). It is necessary to pull a glass rod through the lower tabs in order to facilitate the transfer of the filter paper into the cabinet and the solvent trough. Similar chromatograms are obtained when rectangular sections (10 × 2 mm.) are cut out with a razor blade, and the chromatogram is developed horizontally (Ganguli, 1954a, b).

There is a certain amount of extra labor involved in the preparation of the filter paper for these miscellaneous techniques which have been described. The improved resolution which may be gained by these modifications may not warrant this additional effort.

A novel modification of circular paper chromatography has been called "Ladder Papyrography" (Ambe, 1954). Six filter paper disks can be developed at the same time, being wetted by the same wick. This is accomplished by cutting holes in the center of the paper disks of increasing diameter. The wick is of cone-shape and is pushed through the holes, with the apex immersed in the solvent. A three-hour development concludes the chromatography.

For samples of micro size it is possible to prepare well resolved chromatograms of several sugars using a filter paper square, 4 × 4 cm. The wick is a capillary of 0.005 cm. diameter which is supported by a small square piece of cardboard. The chamber is a 12 × 4 cm. flat-mouthed glass cylinder, and a 2 ml. vial serves as solvent trough. The developed bands are observed under the microscope by first mounting the chromatogram on a slide. Reproducible chromatograms have been obtained (Lakshmirayanan, 1954).

For a more detailed description of circular paper chromatography and its application to the resolution of a wide variety of compounds, the following additional papers are cited: Giri (1951, 1952, 1953a, 1953b), Rao (1952, 1953), Kariyone (1952), Luderitz (1952a, 1952b), Zimmermann (1951), and Berlingozzi (1952), Ceriotti (1955).

Method VIII: "Reversed Phase" Chromatography

When water-insoluble compounds are separated by paper chromatography, one cannot use water as the stationary phase. For this purpose the filter paper is impregnated with rubber, silicone, or Vaseline (Boldingh, 1948; Banigan, 1953; Strain, 1953; Metcalf, 1953; Markwardt, 1954; Ashley, 1955). Paraffin oil has also been used to impregnate the paper (Michalec, 1955). As an example, Boldingh (1948) has separated water-insoluble fatty acid esters by "reversed phase" chromatography. Schleicher and Schüll No. 595 filter paper strips are immersed in vulcanized rubber latex, dried in air, rinsed with alcohol and acetone, and stored in acetone. The rubber content of the paper amounts to 30 per cent. The rubber acts as stationary solvent phase or the carrier for the less polar component of the solvent mixture. Substances such as fatty acid esters are developed with methanol or methanol:acetone v/v. (see Chapter VII). Other substances like rubber itself, chloroplast pigments, parathion, and steroids have been resolved by this method (see Chapters VIII, XI, and XII).

Method IX: Preparative Paper Chromatography

1. The Chromatopile

The essential features of this apparatus, which was designed by Mitchell (1949) are depicted in Figure 16. These features are a pile of filter paper disks (7), a clamp arrangement for packing the filter paper disks tightly in order to prevent channeling (5), and a solvent distributor on top of the pile (1, 2). The principle of the operation of the "chromatopile" is a large-scale descending chromatogram using a cellulose column. The detailed instructions for its use are as follows:

Forty filter paper disks of Whatman No. 1 paper, 9 cm. in diameter are placed on top of the perforated steel plate (6). Above them are placed twenty-five paper disks which were soaked in the solution to be separated (e.g. amino acids) (4). Above these are stacked nine packages of filter paper disks. The cover plate is now put in place, and the wing nuts (8) are evenly tightened by the criss-cross "tire" method. The solvent distributor is now connected with a piece of rubber tubing to a two-liter flask containing the solvent. The distributor is filled with the solvent through the opening (1); this operation will automatically start the siphon action from the solvent reservoir. The level of the solvent should be adjustable by raising or lowering the reservoir. After a 28-hour development, the column is disassembled and the paper disks are extracted. A 92% recovery of amino acids has been achieved, containing 50 mg. of each component. Flavin dinucleotide (FDN) from pig liver has been isolated by this method (Yagi, 1950).

2. FILTER PAPER COLUMN

This column for preparative paper chromatography consists of a roll of filter paper tightly machine-wound around a central solid polyethylene rod (Hagdahl, 1954). The column itself is also of polyethylene, and both

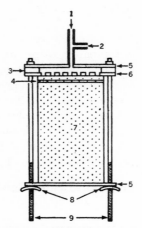

FIG. 16. Diagram of "Chromatopile" (Mitchell, 1949): 1, rubber tube connection for filling siphon; 2, connection for siphon tube; 3, rubber gasket; 4, filter paper disks containing sample; 5, stainless steel plates; 6, perforated stainless steel plate; 7, filter paper disks; 8, wing nuts; 9, bolts at four corners of steel plates.

ends consist of plastic covers which are sealed to the column with paraffin. The solvent distributor consists of an inlet tube (connected to the solvent reservoir as in the "chromatopile") and the air space between the cover and the filter paper roll. The separation of mixtures proceeds by the descending flow.

Since the filter paper is so tightly wound around the central core, the column behaves essentially like a filter paper sheet, and exploratory experiments can be conducted on strips of the same grade filter paper as is used for the roll. Solvents are limited to those that do not attack polyethylene, like dilute ethanol.

It is impossible to prepare the paper roll without special machinery, so that the column must be purchased from the manufacturers (L. K. B., Sweden) (Fig. 16 A).

FIG. 16A. Column for preparative chromatography (Hagdahl, 1954).

3. "ISOLIERPACK" (A. Fischer, 1952)

The solution to be separated is applied as a line 8 cm. from the lower edge on each of about one hundred filter paper sheets (58 cm.²). The sheets are placed on top of each other, separated by pieces of glass slightly longer than the paper. The ends of the glass sheets, thus protruding, are tied with rubber bands, and the "isolierpack" is developed as a single chromatogram by the ascending method, using one trough. At the end of the run the regions are cut out and eluted (see Experimental Technique, pp. 82–83).

A less elaborate technique is to apply the sample on any desired number of single sheets of Whatman No. 3 paper (Specify: for chromatography) and to develop each sheet individually by the ascending method (Decker, 1951) in the form of cylinders or by the descending method. As much as 0.5 ml. to 1.0 ml. of a solution may be applied as a stripe without overloading the paper.

4. "CHROMATOBLOCK" (von Arx, 1956)

A circular segment is cut out of the top edge of one hundred sheets of Whatman No. 1 filter paper, leaving 25 mm. straight edge on both sides of the segment. A desired volume of the solution to be separated is applied to each sheet on a straight line 90 mm. from the top edge. All of the papers are now tightly fastened on the top to a stainless-steel press, so that the lower parts of the papers are relatively loose. The whole apparatus is placed into a chromatographic cabinet, and solvent is fed from a reservoir until the front has reached the lower edge.

Using one sheet of Eaton and Dikeman Paper No. 320 (0.1 in. thick) and enclosing it into a glass press, it is possible to isolate milligram quantities from a mixture (Frierson, 1954). In order to prevent "creeping" of solvent along the edges of the paper, strips of platinum foil are fastened along the edges of the paper curtain. The paper may be shaped to a point, and the solvent may be allowed to flow off the end. The eluant may be further resolved on a fraction collector, obviating the elution process as in the previous methods.

Milligram quantities of sugars have been separated on a horizontal "chromatopack," consisting of five pieces of paper disks held together by two thick glass plates (¼ in. thick) (Giri, 1955a). The glass was provided with ¼ in. holes in the center for the insertion of a cylindrical paper wick. Five 0.2 ml. aliquots of the solution to be separated were applied at the center of each disk.

5. CONTINUOUS PAPER CHROMATOGRAPHY (Solms, 1955)

This ingenious apparatus, depicted in Figure 17 consists of a rotating paper cylinder (2), a stationary capillary solution applicator (1), and a circular bank of stationary collecting tubes (3). The principle of the method is that the inert carrier (cellulose) moves at right angles to the elution stream.

Operating Procedure. A filter paper cylinder is serrated at the bottom edge. The top edge is cut every centimeter and is hung into the solvent trough. The solvent starts flowing down the paper by capillarity. The cylinder and the trough are turned slowly around their common axis by a synchronous motor. The mixture to be separated is applied from a capillary tubing in a fixed position. The application is automatically interrupted at the seam of the paper cylinder. The fractionated sample is collected off the drip points into twenty-eight stationary collection tubes. About ten milligrams each of xylose and galactose were separated in a twenty-hour period. LiCl and KCl have also been separated by this method. The apparatus will become commercially available (AG. für

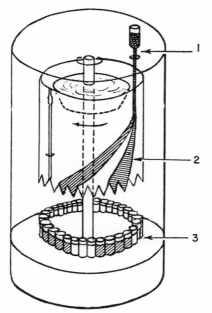

FIG. 17. Schematic drawing of continuous chromatography apparatus (Solms, 1955): 1, sample applicator (stationary); 2, rotating paper cylinder; 3, collecting tubes (stationary).

Chemie-Apparatebau, Männedorf ZH, Switzerland; U. S. Distributor: C. A. Brinkmann & Co., N. Y.).

X. Miscellaneous Methods

1. GRADIENT ELUTION ANALYSIS

Brief mention should be made of a method of chromatography employing a solvent the composition of which is varied during development of the chromatogram (Lederer, 1953b). Ascending chromatography is used, and the solvent at the bottom of the chromatographic jar is agitated with a magnetic stirrer. The chromatogram is placed in the tank, and a second solvent is added dropwise with a buret inserted through a hole in the cover. A mixture of Hg, Cd, Bi, Fe, Ni, Cu, and Co was resolved with n-butanol as the first solvent and concentrated HCl as the added solvent.

2. "REAR-PHASE CHROMATOGRAPHY"

Certain chromatographic solvent mixtures split into two phases (acid, base) during development. This may be the explanation for single components producing two spots ("multiple spots") on chromatograms—the spots may represent different ionic species of the same component. In "rear phase chromatography" the solvent is first allowed to flow a certain distance so that the phase boundary has reached the desired point (Pollard, 1955b). The sample is applied at this time, and the chromatography is continued. In this manner the solute will traverse only the slower, single phase of the solvent.

Procedure. Descending chromatography is modified by the introduction of two glass bars, one inch apart, on the same side, and one inch above the solvent trough. The paper is inserted into the solvent and is allowed to rest over the two bars. A pencil line is drawn on the paper somewhere between the two bars. The lid of the chromatographic cabinet is provided with a slit directly above this pencil line. Since the solvent will have to flow off the paper, a filter paper pad is clipped to the bottom edge of the chromatogram. The sample is applied to the paper at the pencil mark by inserting a capillary tubing through the slit. This technique has been applied to the separation of thionic acids without causing multiple spots (see Chapter XIV).

3. COMBINATION COLUMN-DISK CHROMATOGRAPHY

The difficulty of analyzing extremely dilute solutions by paper chromatography may be solved by a combination column-disk technique (Erbring, 1954). A cellulose column is inserted through a rubber stopper into the lid of a vacuum desiccator. The bottom of the chromatography tube touches the center of a filter paper disk. By a preliminary separation of plant extracts, for example, on the column, the components of the mixture have already undergone a multifold concentration. As the components are eluted off the column, they are then further separated by circular chromatography. The chromatograms can be evaluated by quantitative techniques, described in Chapter IV.

4. TEFLON BARRIERS

If two spots are very close together on a chromatogram, it may be difficult to identify the origin of fast moving spots due to lateral movement during solvent development. In order to confine the migration of each spot, solvent-proof barriers may be drawn along the length of the paper. Teflon Resin Dispersion (E. I. DuPont, Wilmington, Delaware) is applied as lines with a medicine dropper, bent at an angle of 45° and drawn out into a capillary (Usdin, 1955).

The migration of a substance may also be confined by paraffin barriers (Mori, 1954). By forcing the substance to move through a narrow passage, the resultant chromatograms produce rectangular instead of the usually round spots. The length of the rectangle has been found to be related to concentration, in the case of auramine (see Chapter XII).

5. CENTRIFUGAL CHROMATOGRAPHY

By combining two vectors, chromatography and centrifugal acceleration, it is possible to separate within a few minutes a simple mixture of dyes (McDonald, 1957). The apparatus consists of a motor-driven disk-shaped head, rotating in a horizontal plane and inclosing a circular sheet of filter paper or other suitable material. The head is made of two round pieces of stainless steel or Plexiglas in the shape of a shallow pie-plate. The paper disk is held only at the center and assumes a taut position during the operation. The sample is spotted slightly off-center on the moistened paper, and the disk is slowly set in motion. When the desired speed is attained (300–1,000 r.p.m.), the aqueous solvent is fed in a continuous jet stream through an opening of the top plate near the center. The difficulty is the even control of the solvent flow which has a tendency to cause sputtering, thus resulting in rather diffuse bands on the chromatogram. This technique, with some refinements, may make possible rapid analyses of comparatively simple mixtures of water-soluble compounds.

Experimental Technique

I. Filter Paper

"In its most elementary aspect, there is much about the physics and chemistry of paper that is either unknown to the chromatographer or ignored by him as a consequence of more urgent duties;" so writes Clegg-Müller (1952). It is also probable that many of the abnormalities occurring in paper chromatography of ionizable substances may be explained by the ion exchange of the H^+ ions of the solute with the cations of the paper (Schute, 1953a, 1953b). In many cases it may be necessary to remove metal ion impurities from the paper. This is best accomplished by washing the paper with dilute hydrochloric acid or oxalic acid, followed by water. The papers may also be washed with dilute solution of "Versene," which serves as a metal-complexer. Washing filter paper with ether seems to remove traces of vegetable oil, thus resulting in improved amino acid chromatograms (Kellner, 1954). Subsequent chapters will contain sections on filter paper applicable to specific classes of compounds.

Generally, however, it may be stated that commercial filter paper, designated by the manufacturer for "use in chromatography" will give very satisfactory results for qualitative paper chromatography. Rounder chromatographic spots are usually obtained when the first solvent development occurs in the machine direction of the paper. Some paper manufacturers indicate machine direction by an arrow on the wrapping of the filter paper sheets. Other papers can be simply inspected by holding them against a light and observing "lines" of the machine direction.

1. Choice of Filter Paper

A study of the suitability of various grades and types of filter paper for the separation of amino acids by different solvents resulted in the following classification for the filter papers (Kowkabany, 1950):

1. Degree and clarity of separation.
2. Diffuseness of spots.
3. Degree of formation of stains or streaks, presumably caused by impurities in the paper.
4. Extent of formation of "tails," i.e., zones other than amino acids giving color reactions with ninhydrin.
5. Deviation from vertical development.
6. Rate of movement of solvent front.

Rockland (1951) has tested thirteen different grades and types of paper as to their texture, uniformity, and solvent speed (Table I). These paper characteristics, however, cannot be correlated with the resolving power of each of the papers, and it is not possible to predict on the basis cf these characteristics which paper is most suitable for the separation of certain compounds. It is necessary, therefore, to try several grades of paper in preliminary experiments before undertaking a long-range chromatographic study.

TABLE I
FILTER PAPER CHARACTERISTICS (ROCKLAND, 1951)

Filter paper[a]	Texture[b]	Uniformity[c]	Solvent speed,[d] min.
S. & S. 589 Blue	B	A	260
S. & S. 507	A	A	240
S. & S. 589 Red	B	A	180
S. & S. 602 E. & D.	B	A	270
W. 1	B	B	190
S. & S. 602	B	A	280
S. & S. 576	A	A	280
Munktells O	C	B	60
S. & S. 598 YD	B	A	100
E. & D. 7	B	C	120
Munktells IF	D	B	80
E. & D. 248	D	B	240
E. & D. 613	D	A	180

[a] W.—Whatman filter paper; S. & S —Schleicher and Schüll filter paper (U.S.A.); E. & D.—Eaton and Dikeman filter paper.

[b] A, smooth; B, medium rough; C, rough; D, very rough.

[c] Based on per cent transmittance over four different areas of the paper. Mean deviation: A, 0–1%; B 1–2%; C, more than 2%.

[d] Time required at 26°C. for water:phenol solvent to ascend 120 mm.

2. MODIFIED FILTER PAPER

By modifying filter paper chemically, it may be possible for the paper to become less hydrophyllic, behave like an ion exchange resin or it may even be possible to resolve a racemic mixture of amino acids.

a. Alkylation of Filter Paper. Whatman No. 1 or Schleicher and Schuell Paper 602 ED may be partially acetylated by the following procedure (Buras, 1955): A large sheet of filter paper is rolled into a cylinder together with a glass cloth. This is inserted into a glass cylinder filled with glacial acetic acid and 5% acetic anhydride where it is allowed to stand at room temperature overnight. The solution is then replaced by 22.5% acetic anhydride:1.8% perchloric acid in acetic acid (8:2 v/v). The perchloric acid is slowly added with cooling, so that the temperature remains at 28–29°C. After two to three hours the filter papers are removed, washed with cold water, and rinsed with methanol. The papers are dried at room temperature. The acetyl content is about 26% by weight (dry).

For the chromatography of hydrophobic substances (e.g. tetraacetylated sugars; see Chapter VI), it is useful to prepare butyryl-cellulose filter paper by the following procedure (Micheel, 1954c): Whatman No. 1 paper is first kept in a solution of benzenesulfonic acid:acetic acid (20:400 v/v) for two hours, after which the papers are removed and dried at room temperature. These pretreated papers are immersed for two hours at 21°C in a solution of 250 ml. butyric anhydride, 1.09 ml. concentrated sulfuric acid, and 1.475 ml. of petroleum ether (60–90°C.). The butyric anhydride should contain some butyric acid, and this is accomplished by distilling butyric acid and acetyl chloride at 82–88°C., 14 mm./Hg. The papers are washed with petroleum ether and dried at 70°C. in a fresh air draft. They are then washed with methanol and water and dried at 110°C. for ten minutes.

b. Ion Exchange Paper. The chemical modification of filter paper, such as the introduction of carboxyl, sulfonic acid, phosphate, and amine groups has found application in the separation of dicarboxylic acids (Lautsch, 1953, Kember, 1955). The introduction of these groups converts the cellulose to cation or anion exchange material. One per cent-carboxylated paper has been used to separate the basic amino acids, using 0.05 N sodium phosphate buffer, pH 7 (Ströle, 1955).

Another type of ion exchange paper is made by impregnating filter paper with ion exchange resin (e.g. Dowex 50) (Lederer, 1956a). Whatman No. 1 is drawn through a water suspension of 500 g. of colloidal aggregate Dowex 50, previously treated with 6 N HCl. The paper is quickly blotted between two other sheets of Whatman No. 1 filter paper and dried overnight. The paper is examined for irregularities. Ion exchange paper has been useful in the separation of inorganic anions, like SeO_3^{--} and TeO_3^{--}.[1]

c. Miscellaneous Impregnated Papers. A Whatman No. 1 filter paper strip is divided alternately into buffered and untreated zones. The buffered zones range from pH 4.2 to 6.4. These buffered zones are brushed on or rolled on with glass rods, using double strength McIlvaine's buffer solutions. This technique has been helpful in the identification of alkaloids (Schmall, 1956) (see Chapter XII). By impregnating the paper with D-10-camphorsulfonic acid, it is possible to resolve a racemic mixture of an amino acid (D,L-aminophenylacetic acid) (Berlingozzi, 1951).

II. Preparation of Sample

No attempt is made in this section to give a generalized experimental procedure for the preparation of a sample prior to separation by chromatography. These procedures will be found in later chapters dealing with specific classes of compounds.

1. DESALTING OF SAMPLES

The most common interfering factor in the chromatography of sugars (Westall, 1948) and amino acids has been found to be the high inorganic

---

[1] Whatman papers have been incorporated with ion exchange resin, and the following papers may be obtained from H. Reeve Angel & Co. for experimental evaluation: IR-120, IRC-50, IRA-400, and IR-4B.

salt concentration of the sample. Common cations, e.g., $Al^{+++}Fe^{++}$, Ag^+, and Cu^{++}, abolish the ninhydrin color of alanine when the cation concentration is 10^{-6} mole per 10 mg. of alanine. The addition of Versene reverses this effect (Meyer, 1953).

Another method to reduce the cation concentration is to "desalt" the sample prior to chromatography. This may be accomplished by ion exchange treatment (see Chapter V) or by the use of an electrolytic desalter (Research Specialties Co., Oakland, California). Ninety per cent of all the inorganic salts of a water-soluble tissue fraction are removed during 10 minutes of desalting at 40–50 volts (Katz, 1954) (see Chapter V).

An improved version of the original apparatus by Consden, Gordon, and Martin (1947) operates on the principle that cations are discharged at a mercury cathode, becoming amalgamated. The amalgam decomposes when coming into contact with water. The chloride ions are discharged as chlorine gas. Whereas in the Martin and RECO apparatus the solution floats on top of the mercury cathode, in this modified desalter the mercury passes through the solution by constant dripping, thus furnishing a fresh mercury surface and also helping to cool the solution (Astrup, 1951). Further modifications of this electrolytic desalter utilize a Viscose bottle seal as semipermeable membrane. Volumes ranging from 0.5 ml. to 3.0 ml. of the solutions may be treated (Stevens, 1956).

A microdesalter has been designed by Zweig (1957) for the qualitative chromatography of amino acid mixtures having a high salt content. The essential parts are shown in the photograph (Figure 18). The novel feature of this apparatus is that the sample is first spotted on the paper and is then desalted; a treatment which only requires about two minutes per sample. After about twenty-five to fifty microliters of the sample have been spotted on the filter paper, the paper (G), while the spot is still damp, is placed underneath the anode (A), taken from a RECO desalter. A slow stream of 1 % sulfuric acid trickles through the anode during the operation. The stopcock (E) is now turned, which causes the mercury in the thistle tube (B) to spill into the plastic dish (D), while at the same time closing the circuit from a direct-current power supply. While the current is kept at a maximum of 40 ma., the voltage is slowly raised manually to 30 volts, and is kept there until the current has dropped to less than 10 ma. About 99 % of the salt has been removed in less than two minutes, as demonstrated with the use of $Na_2S^{35}O_4$. Since there results some loss of the more highly ionized amino acids (especially cysteic acid), the apparatus may only be recommended for routine qualitative chromatography of biological samples, e.g. body fluids, plant sap.

A small electrodialyzer utilizes ion exchange membranes and only causes a loss of 16 % organic material in a two-hour run while removing all of the inorganic ions (Wood, 1956).

Fig. 18. Microdesalter for qualitative paper chromatography of amino acids (parts explained in text) (Zweig, 1957).

2. Ultrafiltration

For the analysis of small organic molecules in blood plasma it is essential to remove the proteins. Chemical precipitation of the proteins with tungstate or trichloroacetic acid causes severe interference in paper chromatography. Heat-coagulation may destroy or alter some organic compounds. A method of ultrafiltration by centrifugation may be recommended as the preferred method for the preparation of protein-free plasma filtrate for chromatography (Toribara, 1953). Three milliliters of plasma are introduced into a knotted strip of Visking Nojax Casing (size $24\!\!/_{32}$). The open end is also knotted after the bag is collapsed, the two ends are fastened together with a rubber band, and the bag is carefully pushed down into the apparatus (Fig. 19). The bag rests on the sintered glass separator which protects the bag from breakage during the centrifugation. A side arm is used for flushing out the tube before it is centrifuged and for the removal of the protein-free filtrate afterwards. At least 0.5 ml. of ultra-filtrate may be collected when centrifuging for three hours at 2,000 r.p.m. The tube and adapter are available commercially (Will Corp.).

III. Application of Sample (Spotting)

Probably the most important single factor for successful paper chromatography is the proper application of the sample onto the filter paper. The original spot must be small (5 mm. diameter), and for quantitative work the spot size and the deposited volume must be absolutely uniform. It is no wonder, therefore, that with these aims in mind a variety of devices have been developed for "spotting" samples.

1. MICROPIPETTES

Self-filling micropipettes are available in sizes ranging from 1 to 10 microliters (1 μl. = 1λ = 0.001 ml.). The sample is immersed in the solution to be chromatographed, and it is filled to the mark by capillarity. The tip is then lightly touched to the mark on the paper onto which it empties with an even flow. In order to keep the spot size to a minimum diameter, the solution may be dried as it flows on the paper either with an infra-red lamp or a hair dryer. The operator can easily manipulate the pipette in one hand and the dryer in the other (Fig. 20). The filter paper may rest on a clean glass plate, and there is very little loss of material, because any solution which reaches the glass is immediately reabsorbed on the underside of the paper.

These pipettes may be cleaned with hot soap water, distilled water, and acetone, in this sequence.

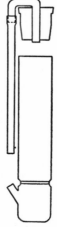

Fig. 19. Ultra filtration apparatus (Toribara, 1953).

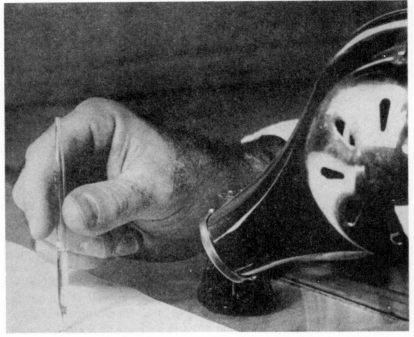

Fig. 20.   Application of sample; self-filling pipette.

In ascending chromatography, the spots are usually placed about 2–3 cm. from the lower edge of the paper, 2–2.5 cm. apart from each other. The positions are indicated by weak pencil marks.   A simple device for marking a large number of sheets is as follows:

A strip of sheet aluminum is marked with raised points, 2–2.5 cm. apart, with the point of a nail.   The lower edge ($\frac{1}{4}''$) is bent slightly back to form a small ledge.   The chromatogram is then placed between two sheets of filter paper and fitted into the aluminum template.   A quick movement of the thumb across the protective paper will thus mark the chromatogram conveniently.   It is advisable to place the initial spot as close to the solvent surface as possible, as the R_f decreases with the increase of that distance (Kowkabany, 1952).

When more than one chromatogram is run simultaneously, the filter papers are placed on clean glass plates, one over the other in echelon, each separated by a glass plate.   It is important to hold the papers flat on the glass plates.   This is accomplished by placing the covering plate about 1 cm. above the point where the spot will be applied.   Spotting platforms made from wood with removable glass plates (1 inch wide) and flush with the surface of the platform have also been used.   This technique is more convenient than the former, since between runs only the thin glass plates instead of the larger plates of glass have to be cleaned.

For best results not more than 5 μl. of solution should be applied at one time. If more than this quantity is desired, other aliquots are applied on top of the initial spot. The spots are dried after each application with an infrared lamp or the warm air blast from a hair dryer. If the applied spot is too large, initially, the shape of the spots on the developed chromatogram becomes diffuse and indefinite.

When applying as much as 25 to 50 microliters of a solution, it is recommended to use Kirk transfer-type pipettes. The flow of liquid from this pipette is controlled with a micro syringe equipped with a screw control (Fig. 21). By a careful turn of the thumbscrew as little as 1 μl. of solution can be delivered by this method.

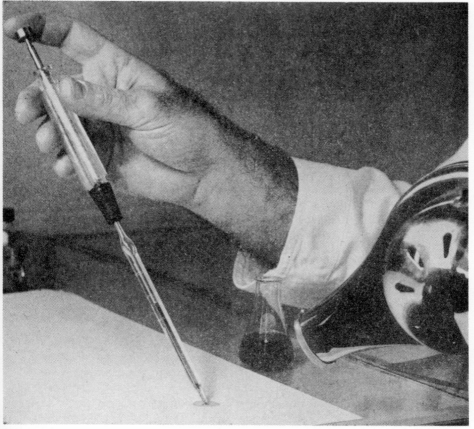

Fig. 21. Application of sample; Kirk-transfer type pipette.

2. Miscellaneous Techniques

Livingston (1953) states that a principal factor in obtaining reproducible results in paper chromatography from day to day and by different operators is the placing of the micropipette at right angles to the paper. This is not always possible as is shown by the technique depicted in Figure 21. A parallelogram arm pipette holder was developed to eliminate the personal error in paper chromatography. (Blue prints for this apparatus may be obtained from Dr. C. Livingston, Chemistry Department, Colorado State College of Agricultural and Mechanical Arts, Fort Collins, Colorado.)

The problem of applying sufficient amounts of dilute solutions has been solved in various ways:

a. The paper strips are stretched horizontally above a hot plate, and both ends of the strips are weighed down by window display hooks or clothes pins (Urbach, 1949).

b. The sample may be applied directly on the paper as a streak (Slotta, 1952) or the total sample is first absorbed on a small strip or disk of filter paper which is then fastened to a larger paper sheet (von Euler, 1952; Clark, 1954).

c. The size of the spot application may be limited by depositing a small drop of a mixture of 52.5 % hexachloroethane and 47.5 % naphthalene with a fire-polished end of a glass tube. The sample is spotted, and the ring of hexachloroethane-naphthalene is removed by sublimation at 50°C. (Ultee, 1952). Similarly, the spot size may be confined by a one cm.² paraffin boundary which is formed by touching the paper with the edge of a hot microscope slide dipped into paraffin. As large a volume as 500 microliters may be deposited within this area. Prior to solvent development longitudinal razor blade cuts are made through the paraffin dikes to permit the free flow of solvent (Wiegand, 1956).

d. A glass device has been made by which warm air is circulated on the top and bottom of the paper near the point of application while using a conventional micropipette for spotting (van Gulick, 1956).

e. An automatic pipetter has been designed, which utilizes a synchronous motor (2 r.p.m.) whose shaft is connected to the piston of a micrometer head which in turn actuates a small syringe (Figure 22) (Levenbook, 1957). The pipetter may be adjusted to deliver a definite volume of liquid by means of a simple disengaging mechanism (D, E, F, G, Fig. 22).

f. Modified paper electrophoresis has been applied to the problem of spotting a very dilute solution of one metal cation in the presence of much higher concentrations of another metal ion (de Vries, 1955). This is accomplished by immersing the lower end of a paper strip near the point of application in the solution to be analyzed. This solution also serves as the anode, using a platinum electrode. Another platinum wire is inserted through the paper at the point of application and serves as the cathode. By applying about one hundred volts dc for several minutes, a compact circular area containing both ions will form around the cathode by electrophoretic migration.

IV. Solvent Development

1. CHOICE OF SOLVENT

As has been discussed previously, most developing solvents in partition chromatography are two-phase systems or mixtures of miscible organic solvents. The chemical nature of the solutes to be chromatographed usually suggests the class of solvents or mixtures to be used. (In each subsequent chapter a list of solvents and their preparation are given.)

The choice of a suitable developing solvent may be governed partly by the observation that slower moving solvents produce rounder and less

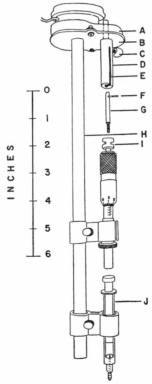

FIG. 22. Diagram of automatic pipette (Levenbook, 1957): A, synchronous motor; B, brass plate; C, thumb screw; D, brass sleeve; E, slot; F, pin; G, shaft; H, brass support rod; I, micrometer ratchet stop; J, syringe.

TABLE II
Choice of Filter Paper for a Given Solvent

Solvent	Filter paper[a] (Arranged in descending order of excellence)
Collidine	W. 3, S. & S. 595, W. 4, W. 1
Phenol	W. 3, S. &. S. 595, W. 1, W. 4
1-Butanol	S. & S. 589 Black Ribbon, 595, 598, W. 3
2-Butanol:formic acid	W. 3, 1, 2, S. & S. 602
2-Butanol:ammonia	S. & S. 589, Blue, Red, White Ribbon, W. 1

[a] W.—Whatman filter paper; S. & S.—Schleicher and Schüll filter paper; E. & D.—Eaton and Dikeman filter paper.

diffuse spots (Kowkabany, 1952). The rate of movement of the solvent is governed, among other properties, by its viscosity, surface tension, and density. It is also observed that the R_f increases by raising the water content of a miscible pair of solvents, e.g., collidine:lutidine. This R_f increase is also true for the component, which is most soluble in the mobile phase. The choice of solvent may also be governed by the grade of filter paper used for chromatography (see Table II).

2. Effects of Temperature and Saturation

It is preferable to run a chromatographic separation at constant temperatures. Elaborate thermal control does not improve the resolution, and it is sufficient, for example, to wrap an electric blanket with thermostatic control around the chromatograph chamber if higher temperatures are desired. It is preferable in reporting R_f values to specify the temperature at which the experiments have been conducted. A change in temperature from one run to another will change the R_f value inasmuch as the partition coefficient in the system is changed.

The atmosphere of the chamber must be saturated with respect to the solvent or solvent mixtures. It is usually sufficient to place a small vessel containing the solvent to be used at the bottom of the chamber 24 hours prior to the experiment. Another technique to saturate the atmosphere is to line the walls of the chamber with filter paper extending the height of the chamber and to immerse this paper into solvent covering the bottom of the chamber (McFarren, 1951b).

In most reports, the paper actually is not truly saturated with respect to the volatile portion of the solvent (Müller, 1952). By chromatographing standard and unknown solutions on the same sheet or in the same tank, however, any variations of temperature and saturation are canceled out. To minimize the formation of an uneven solvent front, the following rules have been suggested by Münz (1954): a) Use Whatman papers. b) Use solvent-saturated papers on the walls of the cabinet. *c*) Use a well-insulated tank. *d*) Control temperature closely. *e*) Keep chromatographic cabinets on an unheated floor in a room with a minimum of window space. Rule (*a*) certainly seems too exclusive, although there seems to be less disagreement on the other points.

3. EFFECT OF CHAMBER SIZE

A study has been made to show how the chamber size affects the R_f values of amino acids (Clayton, 1956). Some of these observations may be just as well applicable to other classes of compounds. A critical solvent volume has been found which is dependent on the size of the chromatographic cabinet. For example, a 37 liter cabinet had a critical solvent volume of 375 ml. Above the critical solvent volume the R_f values are at a minimum, even when the solvent volume is increased. Below the critical solvent volume the R_f values are at a maximum. It is, therefore recommended to stay above the critical solvent volume for constant R_f values. No significant change in R_f values was noted with or without pre-equilibration time with the solvent system that was used in this study, *n*-butanol, acetic acid, and water.

An explanation has been advanced for these observations. Below the maximum critical solvent volume unequal vaporization occurs, the solvent becomes richer in water, and, hence, the R_f values of the water-soluble amino acids, tend to increase.

V. Detection of Spots

The procedure for detecting the spots on the chromatogram after solvent development is as important as the actual chromatography. The simplest method is the detection by a suitable color reaction. If no such color reaction is applicable, the spots may be revealed by fluorescence or absorption in the ultraviolet range. It is also possible to detect radioactive or "tagged" compounds by autoradiography and biologically active compounds by bioautographic methods.

1. DRYING OF CHROMATOGRAM

It is necessary that the chromatogram is dried thoroughly to remove all of the solvent prior to color development. When phenol is used as a solvent, it is recommended to dry the chromatogram at room temperature in order to prevent decomposition of some compounds, like glutathione, for example. For the detection of organic acids by indicator dyes, the chromatograms are usually treated with steam to remove any acid component of the solvent by steam-distillation (see Chapt. VII, Section II). Drying the chromatograms at elevated temperatures may be accomplished

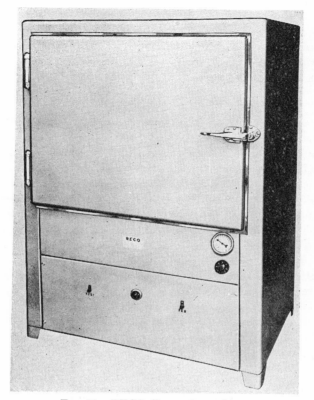

Fig. 23. RECO Chromatographic oven.

in a hood with the aid of a fan-type electric heater. For faster solvent evaporation an electric, forced-air oven is recommended. Several commercial chromatographic ovens (Research Specialties Co. and Scientific Fabrications Co.) with explosion-proof safety devices are available. These ovens are large enough to handle up to 10 paper sheets, $18\frac{1}{4} \times 22\frac{1}{2}$ inches (Figs. 23 and 24).

A simple home-made oven from a cookie tin box is described as follows (Proom, 1951): The box (9-inch cube) is fitted with a 60-watt electric lamp inside the box. The filter paper is suspended from a rod, and the solvent vapors are removed by attaching an outlet to a water aspirator.

2. Color Development on Chromatogram

The choice of color reactions is given in subsequent chapters for each class of compounds. If the research worker is confronted with a compound or class of compounds not heretofore investigated by paper chro-

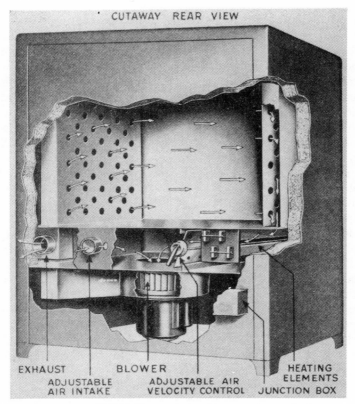

CUTAWAY REAR VIEW

EXHAUST | BLOWER | HEATING ELEMENTS
ADJUSTABLE AIR INTAKE | ADJUSTABLE AIR VELOCITY CONTROL | JUNCTION BOX

FIG. 24.   RECO Chromatographic oven (rear view).

matography, he may use Feigl's "Spot Tests" (1956).   Many of the spot tests can be easily adapted to spraying or dipping techniques.

   a. Dipping.   Dipping of chromatograms is recommended for smaller size sheets and disks.   It is necessary, of course, to choose a solvent for the color reagent in which the substances to be detected are insoluble. Several advantages for the dipping of amino acid chromatograms in an acetone solution instead of spraying are as follows (I. Smith, 1953):

   1. Amino acids are insoluble in acetone and do not spread.
   2. There is no offensive smell (e.g., *n*-butanol).
   3. It is economical.
   4. It conserves space.

A tray for dipping chromatograms consists of a free-rolling glass rod fitted loosely into glass sleeves which are sealed to the ends of a glass trough. The dried chromatogram is slipped under the roller tube and is drawn quickly through the reagent solution (Morris, 1956).

A multiple dipping procedure for the amino acids utilizes three to four successive color reagents: ninhydrin or isatin, Ehrlich reagent (dimethylaminobenzaldehyde), Sakaguchi or diazo reagents (Jepson, 1956) (see Chapters IV and V for details). The spots should be marked in pencil after each reagent. In this manner most of the amino acids may be identified on the same chromatogram by their position and characteristic color reactions.

A polychromic dipping reagent (isatin, zinc acetate) has been used for the quantitative analysis of amino acids (Barrollier, 1956). Different colored spots are produced for various concentration levels of a single amino acid. The spots are compared with a color chart, and good semiquantitative estimations may be made by simple inspection (details in Chapters IV and V).

b. Spraying. For the spraying of chromatograms, a glass atomizer may be made with only moderate skill in glass blowing (Wingo, 1953) (Fig. 25). A bulb, *A*, is blown on one end of a piece of 3-mm. borosilicate glass tubing. The tubing is cut 1.5 inches below the bulb, and the end is fire-polished. The bulb is sealed into a piece of 9-mm. tubing and a bulge, *C*, is blown in the larger tube just below the ring seal. While the tube is still plastic, the tubing is manipulated so that the inner and outer tubings are concentric; the assembly is allowed to cool, and the outer tube is constricted, *D*, leaving a clearance of about 1 mm. between the inner and outer tubes. A side arm for the air hose, *E*, of 7-mm. tubing is now at-

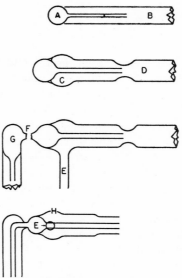

FIG. 25. Diagram for the construction of an all-glass atomizer (Wingo, 1953).

tached, and a 5-mm. hole is blown in the bulb, *F*. The liquid feed tube *G*, is prepared from 2-mm. capillary tubing, and sealed to *F* as shown. Finally a control hole, *H*, 5 mm. in diameter, is blown in the top of the bulge; the outer tube is cut off and polished to be flush with the inner tube. The atomizer is attached by fixing the fluid feed tube in a two-hole rubber stopper so that the tube reaches nearly to the bottom of a 250-ml. Erlenmyer Flask. An all-glass atomizer may be easily constructed from a 250 ml. reagent bottle (Ortegren, 1954). De Vilbiss atomizers are satisfactory if the spray solution is not metal-corrosive (e.g. some spray reagents contain perchloric acid). Commercial all-glass spray bottles of various sizes are available; the 250 ml. RECO indicator spray bottle is recommended for most spraying. A ninhydrin-aerosol spray for amino acid chromatograms has also been developed. This atomizer does not require a source of compressed air and may be useful for portable applications (Zweig, 1956).

Chromatograms are sprayed in a chemical hood by hanging the papers on a suitable rack by means of chromatographic stainless-steel clips. The atomizer is held at a distance twelve to fifteen inches from the paper and is moved in a slow but even, left-to-right movement, starting at the top of the paper and working downwards. Care must be exercised not to overload the paper with spraying reagent since the spots tend to diffuse and migrate, especially when aqueous reagents are employed.

A spray box has been made from a metal box fitted to an exhaust fan with an adjustable diaphragm (von Arx, 1956; see Fig. 25A). On the

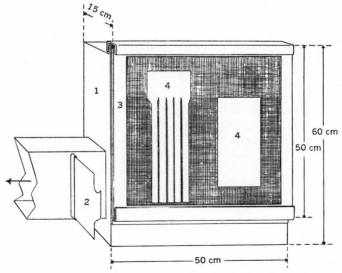

FIG. 25A. Spraying chamber (von Arx, 1956); 1, metal cabinet; 2, adjustable diaphragm; 3, frame with wire screen; 4, chromatograms.

front of the box is a removable wire screen on which the chromatogram is held by the suction of the fan. Any excess spraying reagent is removed through the exhaust. The back of the box is painted white, or it may be equipped with illuminated frosted glass.

The spots of a chromatogram may be detected by laying the dried chromatogram next to a wet sheet soaked with the color reagent (Bowden, 1954). The technique has been applied to the detection of thyroxine and related substances (see Chapter V).

A detection method of "differential charring" may have limited applications for substances for which no suitable spraying reagent is available (Caldwell, 1955). The chromatogram, which must be developed with a solvent that is completely volatile, is heated over a hot plate until the paper gradually begins to darken. Regions in which substances are present tend to darken more rapidly than the rest of the paper, so that the spots appear as brown-black on a light brown background.

3. ULTRAVIOLET ABSORPTION AND FLUORESCENCE SCREENS

A number of compounds are detected by ultraviolet absorption and fluorescence (e.g., vitamins A and E, purines, pyrimidines, flavonoids, steroids). These spots may be detected by visual observation with ultraviolet illumination, by contact photographs with the aid of selective filters, or by scanning procedures (see Section VII below). The Chromatolite (Hanovia, Ltd., Slough, Bucks, England) or G.E. Bactericidal Lamps are good ultraviolet light sources.

A method for the fluorescent visualization of barbituric acid and derivatives is described (Grieg, 1952): The chromatogram in firm contact with a fluorescent screen is placed in front of an ultraviolet light source; the paper faces the light. A low-pressure mercury lamp with a 2537-Å filter is used. Barbiturates sprayed with 0.5 N NaOH show up as black spots on the fluorescent screen.

An ultraviolet scanner camera consists of a light-tight box containing a 15-watt ultraviolet germicidal lamp with an adjustable shutter (Fig. 26) (Drake, 1956). A transmission filter (Corning 9863) is placed on top of the shutter, and the chromatogram is placed on top of the filter. Next comes a fluorescent screen which is made by depositing DuPont zinc silicate phosphor 609 on a plate of glass with polyvinyl alcohol (DuPont Elvanol 71-24).

Operating Procedure. The chromatogram is placed on top of the filter in a darkened room, and any ultraviolet-absorbing substances appear as dark spots on a fluorescent screen. For a photographic record, the fluorescent screen is replaced by Kodagraph contact paper, and the exposure time is two to four seconds. The spots appear as white on black back-

FIG. 26. Labline Fluoroscopic Papergram Scanner (Drake, 1956).

ground in the print. This camera is commercially available (Labline, Inc., Chicago 22, Illinois).

An alternate fluorescent screen is made from zinc orthosilicate (Westinghouse Electric Co., Lamp Division) (Feigelson, 1956). The phosphor is spread as a thin layer on a sheet of filter paper, and the screen may be preserved by enclosing it with a polyethylene envelope.

Comments. Attempts to use infrared spectrophotometry to detect substances directly on paper have not been found suitable, because the quantities necessary for successful detection by this method have been of the order of milligrams (Kalkwarf, 1956). However, when an unknown ninhydrin-positive spot was eluted off the paper, and a potassium bromide pellet was pressed, a satisfactory infrared spectrum could be obtained and tentative identification was made (Toribara, 1954).

4. HIGH-FREQUENCY AND CONDUCTOMETRIC PAPYROGRAPHY

The chromatogram is scanned between the plates of a condenser in a tuned-grid-type high-frequency circuit. Large changes in the grid current due to resolved cations are observed and recorded (Hashimoto, 1953a, Oehme, 1956). It is important that the developing solvent be completely removed prior to scanning. It is also necessary that filter paper with a small background noise be used. This method has been applied to the detection of Pb^{++} and Ag^+ after chromatography.

The air-dried chromatogram is passed between two steel rolls at a potential difference of from 4 to 80 volts. The changes in resistance are read on a galvanometer (coil resistance, 450 ohms). De Vries (1954) has used this procedure to identify Na^+, K^+ and Li^+ after separation of the chlorides with amyl alcohol:methanol = 3:7 v/v.

An impedance method for zone localization has been developed by Blake (1955, 1956a, 1956b). The principle of this method is the measurement of the variation of rectified radio-frequency, caused by changes in solution concentration. The method uses electrodes which come in direct contact with the paper which is sufficiently hydroscopic to be conductive. The electrodes are separated from the solid conductive substance (paper) by a piece of glass or other dielectric through which displacement currents operate. The separation of 1 M solutions of KCl and $CuCl_2$ could be followed by this technique.

If these detection techniques can be refined so that they become sufficiently sensitive to detect ionized and unionized substances of chromatographic concentrations, they will answer a great need for a "universal detector."

5. POLAROGRAPHIC SCANNING (Langer, 1956)

Substances which can be analyzed polarographically have been detected on chromatograms by a new technique. A strip chromatogram of metal cations is supported on a porous porcelain tube which is rotated by a synchronous motor at slow speeds. As the porous tube rotates, it is moistened with potassium chloride solution from a saturated calomel half-cell. The paper strip is slowly passed under an amalgamated gold wire which serves as the polarizable electrode. The whole unit is enclosed in a plastic container which can be flushed out with nitrogen. The polarizing potential of the wire electrode is -1.6 to -1.8 V, and the voltage is recorded on a Sargent XXI recording polarograph.

6. MICROBIOLOGICAL AND ENZYMATIC METHODS

Antibiotics separated by paper chromatography may be detected by zones of inhibition of growth produced when the paper strip is laid on a suitable assay plate (see Chapter XIII). When dealing with proteolytic enzymes, an exposed photographic film may be substituted for the assay plate (see Chapter V).

VI. Radioisotope Techniques

1. AUTORADIOGRAPHY

The technique of autoradiography (or radio-autography; for semantics see Tauxe, 1954; Joftes, 1956) has been widely used since radioactive tracers became generally available. With the aid of C^{14}, autoradiography has advanced greatly the fields of photosynthesis and intermediate metabolism. Space does not permit the description of the many experimental details involved in the handling of radioisotopic materials but is confined merely to the description of the detection of radioactive "tagged" compounds after their separation by paper chromatography. (See Aronoff, 1956, for a detailed description of radioisotopic techniques.) The first experiments involving autoradiography were reported by Fink (1949) and Calvin (1949). An alcohol extract and protein hydrolyzates of the alga *Chlorella*, which had been photosynthesizing in the presence of $C^{14}O_2$, were analyzed by paper chromatography. The resolved substances were detected by exposing the chromatogram to X-ray film, and the resultant picture was called autoradiogram.

Experimental Procedure. The developed and dried chromatogram, containing "tagged" substances is first marked with a stamped number, containing some radioactivity. A few drops of a weak beta-emitter (e.g. $H_2S^{35}O_4$), containing several microcuries, are added to the stamp pad and spread thoroughly over a marked area. This number serves as an identification of a particular chromatogram as well as a marker when the autoradiogram is superimposed on the color-developed chromatogram.

The chromatogram is loaded in the dark room equipped with a safe light (yellow filter) by placing it face-down against an X-ray film keeping both film and paper in the protective cover furnished with each film. It is recommended to use Ansco No-Screen film or DuPont Type 507, single-side emulsion. The latter film economizes the fixing bath, but care must be taken to place the chromatogram against the emulsion side (concave). The film and chromatogram are next placed inside a cardboard X-ray holder. These holders may be stored by distributing an even weight on top. A special press has been found helpful when two or three holders have to be stored for long periods of time (Lotz, 1952) (Fig. 27).

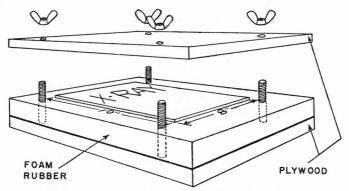

FIG. 27. Press for autoradiography (Lotz, 1952).

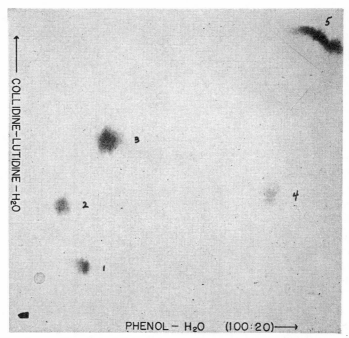

Fɪɢ. 28.   Autoradiogram of S^{35} water-soluble compounds of *Chlorella p.* (Zweig, 1954).

The press consists of two ¾-inch pieces of plywood, padded with foam rubber 1 inch thick, and is tightened with four bolts and wing nuts passing through the wood and the rubber (Fig. 27) at the corners.   After an exposure of 1–7 days (depending on the activity of the sample), the film is developed with X-ray developer, using standard darkroom procedures. Darkened spots on the film indicate the presence of "tagged" compounds (Fig. 28).   For short exposure times or low radioactivity the optical density of the autoradiographic spots may be enhanced about five-fold by using DuPont X-Ray Film Intensifier.   The black spots on the film appear now as dark blue spots and may be viewed to the best advantage on an illuminated surface with a red filter.   Caution should be exercised in the interpretation of the results, as some spots may be of chemographic origin.

In order to identify the spots corresponding to the blackened areas on the autoradiogram, the following procedures may be tried (Katz, 1954): Spots on the chromatogram are cut out, eluted with suitable solvents, and rechromatographed unidimensionally in several solvents in the presence of added carrier (nonradioactive compound).   Coincidence of area of radioactivity on the radiogram and the area detected by color reagents may be considered as proof of identity. By a similar technique, "tagged" reference compounds may be substituted for the added carrier. A greater blackening of the areas on the autoradiogram is taken as tentative identification.

2. RADIOACTIVE SCANNING TECHNIQUES

One-dimensional strips containing radioactive compounds may be scanned with a Geiger tube using various designs of movable stages, some of which are described below. By attaching a recorder to the rate meter, "distance-versus-counting rate" curves may be obtained, which can be compared directly with the chromatogram.

A simple strip scanner has been described by Frierson (1951): The chromatogram is attached to the strip chart of a recording Brown potentiometer. As the chart feeds, the chromatogram is brought under a slit arrangement (from the mechanical stage of a microscope) and a Geiger counter. The pulses from the counter are fed to a counting rate meter in which the rate meter is replaced by a 10-ohm resistor. The potential drop across the resistor is proportional to the counting rate and is recorded by the Brown instrument. A similar arrangement may be made by attaching a Geiger-Müller tube to an automatic densitometer (Hofmann-Credner, 1953).

Another scanning device has been adapted from the paper strip drive of a commercial densitometer (Photovolt) (Cohn, 1955). The Plexiglass channel of the paper drive is set into the absorber or sample-slide slot of a Tracerlab G.-M. lead shield (Figs. 29 and 30). The paper is pulled through the channel by a rubber wheel attached to a synchronous clock

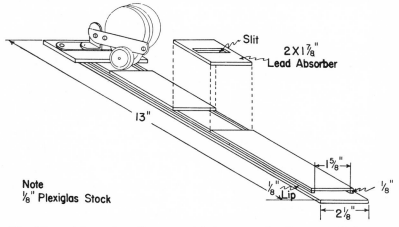

FIG. 29. Channel for automatic paper strip scanner of radiograms (Cohn, 1955).

Fig. 30.   Automatic paper strip scanner for radiograms (Cohn, 1955).

motor (Haydon Co., Torrington, Connecticut).   By selecting the appropriate size wheel, one may synchronize the scanning speed with the recorder chart speed.   An adjustable opening through a lead shield is provided on the top surface of the channel (Fig. 29).   For continuous scanning, the strip chromatograms are spliced together with Scotch tape, and each chromatogram may be indexed by spotting a radioactive dye spot ahead of each solvent front.   A paper-feed reel and a weight-powered take-up reel may be used to wind up the consecutive strips (see Fig. 30).

For greater sensitivity, especially for scanning weak beta emitters, the end window of the counting tube may be constructed of DuPont Mylar (0.25 mil. thickness) (Fuller, 1956).   A mixture of 90% argon and 10% methane is kept flowing through the tube as quenching gas.   Other gas-flow counters have been designed by Demorest (1954), Roberts (1956), and Bangham (1956).   The last design is a collimated windowless counter (Fig. 31).   An effective gas seal is achieved by the paper strip itself resting on a sponge rubber pad.   A commercial gas-flow chromatograph scanner features an exchangeable window in case of contamination (Forro Scientific Co.) (see Fig. 31 A).

Several attempts to scan two-dimensional radiograms suffer from the necessarily cumbersome arrangement of scanning the paper from left to right, counting each square centimeter for one minute (Piper, 1956; Wingo, 1954).   Thus one chromatogram takes twenty-seven hours to be scanned, a time period long enough for autoradiography.   Wingo's arrangement consists of a cylinder around which the chromatogram is wound.   The

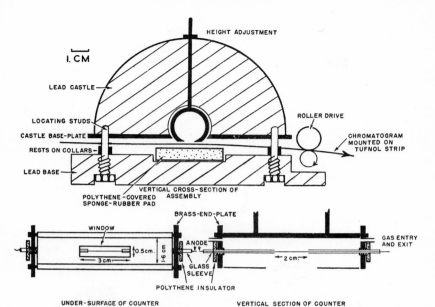

HEIGHT ADJUSTMENT

1. CM

LEAD CASTLE

LOCATING STUDS

CASTLE BASE-PLATE

RESTS ON COLLARS

LEAD BASE

ROLLER DRIVE

CHROMATOGRAM
MOUNTED ON
TUFNOL STRIP

VERTICAL CROSS-SECTION OF
POLYTHENE-COVERED   ASSEMBLY
SPONGE-RUBBER PAD

BRASS-END-PLATE

WINDOW

0.5 cm.

3 cm.

1·6 cm

ANODE

2 cm.

GAS ENTRY
AND EXIT

GLASS
SLEEVE

POLYTHENE INSULATOR

UNDER-SURFACE OF COUNTER   VERTICAL SECTION OF COUNTER

FIG. 31. Windowless Geiger counter for scanning chromatograms (Bangham, 1956).

cylinder rotates slowly and moves in a linear direction by a threading mechanism past the Geiger tube. A recording pen translates the signal from the detector into a pattern which resembles an autoradiogram.

3. ISOTOPE INDICATORS

Amino acids after chromatography may be treated on the paper with p-I^{131}-phenylsulfonylchloride, thus forming I^{131} derivatives ("pipsyl derivatives") which can be located by the methods described above (Keston, 1947). The amino acid chromatogram may also be exposed to CH_3I^{131}, resulting in the liberation of I_2^{131} in the amino acid zones owing to methylation (Winteringham, 1952b, 1952c).

Detection of trace metals by the use of H_2S^{35} is performed in the following manner (van Erkelens, 1953): After chromatography, the dried papers are exposed to ammonia for $\frac{1}{2}$ hour. They are then placed in a glass bell jar, containing 2 ml. of concentrated NH_4OH, 0.2 ml. of hydrazine hydrate, and 3 mg. of ZnS^{35}. The jar is flushed out with nitrogen. Two-tenths ml. of water and 0.2 ml. of concentrated H_2SO_4 are added to the ZnS^{35}, and the apparatus is placed in the dark. After 10 minutes the excess H_2S^{35} is removed by flushing the jar with a stream of nitrogen and passing the vapors through zinc acetate. After the radioactive areas are located, the spots are cut out, and washed with 0.1 N HCl, 1 % Na citrate

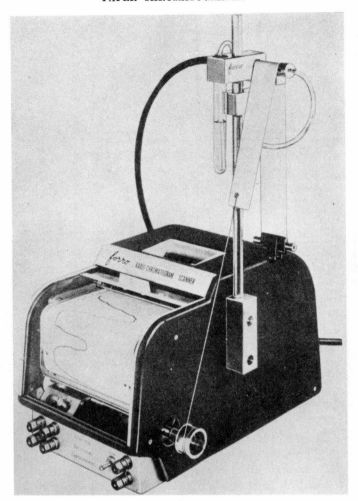

Fig. 31A. Automatic radiochromatogram scanner (Forro Scientific Co.).

and water. The paper is then ashed at 400°C., and the residue is counted in the usual manner. Mo, Zn, Mn, Cu, and Fe may be analyzed by this method. A similar principle is employed for the quantitative determination of sugars by the use of Ag^{110} (Jaarma, 1954). The chromatograms of reducing sugars are dipped into $Ag^{110}NO_3$-acetone solution (Trevelyan, 1950). The papers are dried at room temperature and are sprayed with alcoholic 0.5 N NaOH. After a definite "development time," the strip is immersed in 6 N NH$_4$OH, washed in running water, air-dried and the elemental Ag^{110} is counted.

4. NEUTRON ACTIVATION

The finished chromatogram is placed in an atomic pile where it undergoes neutron bombardment. The carbon, hydrogen, and oxygen of the paper itself do not possess significant neutron activation and, therefore, do not cause a serious background problem. This method has been successfully applied to bromine analogues of DDT derivatives where the reaction is Br^{81} (n, γ) Br^{82} (Winteringham, 1952c). Nucleic acid derivatives have been detected by this method, scanning the chromatogram one week after irradiation and using an aluminum screen in front of the Geiger tube. This eliminated any stray counts from Na^{24}, K^{42}, and S^{35} (Cl^{35} (n, p) S^{35}) thus counting P^{32} exclusively (Winteringham, 1955).

VII. Photoelectric Instrumentation

1. DENSITOMETERS

A useful tool for the quantitative estimation of colored spots on a paper chromatogram is the photoelectric densitometer (see also Chapter IV). The densitometer may be operated manually or may be equipped with automatic scanning and recording devices. This latter refinement is only applicable to paper strips or sheets cut up into strips. Other scanners have been adapted to the detection of colorless substances possessing other properties, such as ultraviolet absorption, fluorescence, and radioactivity.

A densitometer designed by Block (1950) (see also Fosdick, 1949) consists of a barrier layer photocell, a suitable light source, and a sensitive galvanometer (Rubicon Spotlight No. 3402-HH or Pfaltz and Bauer Multiple Mirror Galvanometer No. 1810). When used on one-dimensional chromatograms, the filter paper strip may be pulled slowly across the beam of light, and the amount of transmittance is recorded on the galvanometer via the photocell. Figure 32 shows the light box in greater detail. The a-c line current (115 volts) is passed through a voltage regulator, adjusted by a coarse and fine variable resistance, and is reduced to 6 volts by a stepdown transformer. The line is then connected to the light source, an automobile headlight, whose beam is adjusted by a focusing device to pass through the circular opening. (A light source sold by the Photovolt Corporation may be substituted.) Commercial photoelectric transmission densitometers are manufactured by W. M. Welch Mfg. Co., The Photovolt Corp., and other firms (see Figs. 33 and 34).

Any electric recorder that has full-scale excursion for 200 microamperes or less and an input resistance of not more than 2500 ohms can be attached to the densitometer.[2] (See Part II for automatic scanner for paper elec-

[2] The Photovolt Corporation has introduced a variable response recorder for use with their densitometer. It is claimed that this instrument can be adjusted to draw ordinates that are precisely proportional to concentration (Fig. 34).

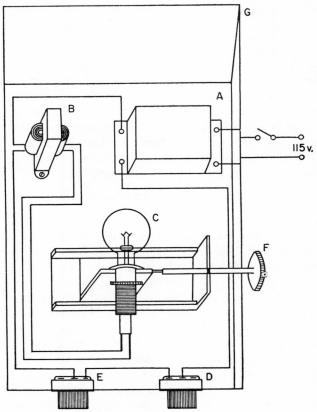

FIG. 32. Diagram of light source of photoelectric densitometer (Block, 1950): A, voltage stabilizer, output 115 volts; B, stepdown transformer, 115–6 volts; C, light source; D, light intensity control (coarse); E, light intensity control (fine); F, control to position light source; G, housing for assembly.

trophoresis patterns.) The self-recording galvanometer of the Heyrovsky polarograph, whose response is logarithmic, has been used (Miettinen, 1953).

Planimetry. The areas underneath the curves obtained by photoelectric scanning may be measured with a manual planimeter or by the method of Sendroy (1952): The modified head of an enlarger is mounted on top of a light-proof cabinet with a base. An aperture, designed to hold a sample base plate, is cut into the top of the cabinet. A focusing lens and a photoelectric cell are located on the bottom. The photocurrent is measured by a galvanometer. In the operation of this planimeter, the unknown area is cut out from an opaque material, and the photocurrent

Fig. 33. Welch Densichron densitometer.

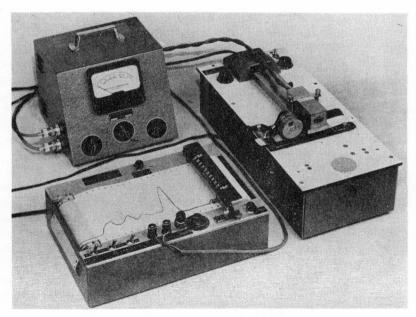

Fig. 34. Photovolt photoelectric densitometer.

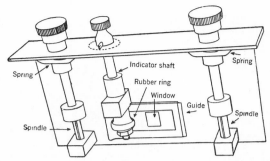

FIG. 35. Manual paper strip scanner for Beckman DU Spectrophotometer (Tennent, 1951).

is measured with the sample placed in the path of the phototube. A blank is set at 100 % transmission reading.

2. ADAPTERS FOR SPECTROPHOTOMETERS

For the scanning of chromatogram strips of ultraviolet absorbing compounds, several automatic attachments have been designed for use in the Cary or Beckman Spectrophotometers (Parke, 1952; J. A. Brown, 1953b; Ehrmantrout, 1954; Silver, 1956). An adapter for the Beckman Spectrophotometer, Model DU, is depicted in Figure 35 (Tennent, 1951).

Construction. (The adapter may be obtained from K. Kniazuk, 614 Franklin St., Elizabeth, New Jersey.) The apparatus consists of a metal frame which supports two splitshaft spindles on which the paper strip is wound. In passing from one spindle to the other the paper runs behind a guide which holds it close to a window, 9 × 7 mm. in the supporting frame. A third shaft has near its lower end a rubber ring that is in contact with the paper. As the strip is wound from one spindle to the other the idling shaft turns, indicating the distance the strip has moved. Free rotation of the spindles is prevented by springs attached to the frame.

Directions for Use. The paper strip is wound on one of the spindles, with the end, to which the spot was applied, innermost. The other end is run behind the guide to the other spindle, and the strip is wound from the first to the second spindle until the solvent front has nearly reached the window. At this point the paper in front of the window has not been touched by the solvent. This position is used for the zero setting of the spectrophotometer.

The apparatus is put into the spectrophotometer with the window on the side next to the photocell. The wavelength dial is set at the absorption maximum of the compound being investigated. The density knob is set at zero (100 % transmission) and the selector switch at the 0.1 position. The dark current is adjusted to null in the usual manner, the shutter is opened, and the instrument is brought to balance by adjusting the slit width and the sensitivity knob. If the instrument cannot be brought to balance, the adjustment of the focusing mirrors in the spectrophotometer should be checked.

When the zero setting has been made, the paper is advanced an arbitrary amount (5–10 mm. or $\frac{1}{8}$ to $\frac{1}{4}$ turn of the indicator shaft) by turning the proper spindle, the spectrophotometer is brought to balance with the density knob, and the reading is recorded. Another movement of the paper is then made, the spectrophotometer is brought to balance again, and the second reading is recorded. This process is continued for the length of the strip.

The absorbance readings are plotted against the distance along the strip, measured in turns of the indicator shaft and the R_f values of the different components can be calculated in the usual manner. A semiquantitative evaluation can be made by measuring the areas under the curve. Fully automatic attachments for the Beckman Spectrophotometers, Models DU and B are commercially available. Both attachments fit into the sample compartment, and the paper strips are moved past the light source by a motor drive (Fig. 36).

3. FLUORESCENCE SCANNERS

For the detection and quantitative estimation of fluorescent compounds on chromatograms several methods have been developed (Nanninga, 1951; Kühn, 1955; Mavrodineanu, 1955). A transmission densitometer (see VII, 1) with an ultraviolet light source is used. For gentisic acid, for example, an additional filter at 3655Å is used for optimum results. The ultraviolet light must be further filtered before reaching the photo cell (e.g. Schott-Jena U.G.) so that the galvanometer readings are a true measure of the emitted fluorescence. Galvanometer deviations are plotted against concentration of standards.

4. MISCELLANEOUS TECHNIQUES

A sensitive measurement of ultraviolet absorbing compounds on chromatograms employs a fluoroscopic screen (Price, 1954; 1955b). The fluoroscope is made from calcium chlorofluorophosphate deposited on a polyethylene sheet. A densitometer with a Mineralight and a yellow filter are used. As a secondary detector either a Se phototube or a modified Geiger tube (photon counter) is placed above the fluoroscope (see Fig. 37 for sequence). By comparing the fluorescence through a blank piece of paper (F_0) and through a light absorbing compound on the chromatogram (F), a quantitative relationship may be established. Compounds absorb-

Fig. 36.   Automatic scanning attachment for Beckman Model B Spectrophotometer.

ing in the 240 to 290 mμ region can be analyzed (purines, pyrimidines). The greatly enhanced sensitivity of this method over others described previously (V, 3; VII, 2) is due to hyperchromic absorption by a compound in dry filter paper (Price, 1955a).

A Perkin-Elmer flame photometer has been modified for sensitive transmittance spectrophotometry (Fink, 1956).

Reflectance photometry has been found to be an accurate method for well resolved chromatographic spots of low R_f values (Vaeck, 1953). The standard reflectance attachment of the Beckman spectrophotometer, Model DU, is used for the quantitative estimation of nickel in alloys (see Chapter XIV). The requirements for this technique are: (1) the spot to be measured must be larger than the circular opening of the reflectance

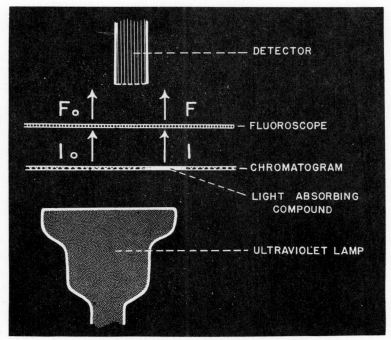

FIG. 37. Detection by hyperchromic absorption (schematic drawing) (Price, 1954).

attachment; and (2) the color of the spot must be uniform over the entire surface; this is usually achieved by the high acidity of the test solution and by spots having a smaller R_f than 0.1. This latter requirement naturally limits the method severely.

VIII. Evaluation of Chromatograms

1. Measurement of R_f

The R_f value is defined as follows:

$$R_f = \frac{\text{distance traveled by substance}}{\text{distance traveled by solvent front}}$$

It is not recommended to use R_f values as constitutive properties of compounds unless conditions are rigorously controlled. It is much simpler to run standards, if possible, on the same chromatogram, so that any experimental variations will cancel out automatically. Still, it is convenient to calculate R_f values when dealing with a large number of compounds in order to present the data in tabular form. Sometimes it seems more convenient and reproducible to calculate R_x values, where the ratio is as follows:

$$R_x = \frac{\text{distance traveled by substance}}{\text{distance traveled by Reference Compound } X}$$

Since the solvent front has run off the paper during "Durchlauf-chromatography," it is not possible to calculate R_f values, and R_x must be used. H. T. Gordon (1957) has proposed the convention $R\%$ units which is defined as $100 \times R_f$. The size of a spot may be described by the $R\%$ of the forward front and the rear of the spot. Extensive use of this convention has been made by Lacourt (see Chapter XIV).

Several devices for the rapid measurement of R_f values have been designed (Phillips, 1948; Rockland, 1950; Nettleton, 1952). A graphic R_f-chart (Chromatogrid) may be obtained from the California Research Foundation.

A simple device for the rapid measurement of R_f values is made as follows (Glazko, 1953): A right triangle is cut from the transparent material, e.g., 0.1-inch Lucite or Plexiglas (see Fig. 38). The R_f scale is placed on the hypotenuse, and parallel lines are drawn one inch apart. All lines are inscribed with a razor blade and filled in with India ink. A movable pivot arm with an index line down the middle is fastened at the apex.

To read off the R_f values, the paper strip is placed parallel to the hypotenuse with the origin at the left-hand arm and the solvent front at the right. The movable arm is shifted until it intersects the spot, and the R_f value is read directly.

2. ELUTION TECHNIQUES

It is sometimes convenient to elute spots, separated by chromatography, in order to carry out *in vitro* microanalyses or to rechromatograph the spot, if incomplete resolution was achieved at first.

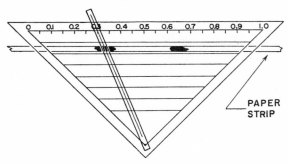

FIG. 38.   Device for measurement of R_f values (Glazko, 1953).

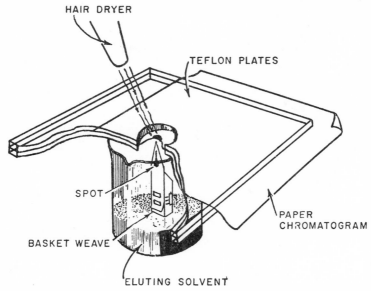

HAIR DRYER

TEFLON PLATES

SPOT

BASKET WEAVE

PAPER
CHROMATOGRAM

ELUTING SOLVENT

Fig. 39. Method of transferring substance onto another chromatogram by ascending elution (Gregory, 1955).

A widely used technique consists of the simultaneous development of a test strip that is cut off and treated with a color reagent at the end of the run. The test strip with the colored spots is placed alongside the rest of the chromatogram, the regions are marked by pencil, and the paper areas are eluted in a small beaker. This technique, however, is not suitable for rechromatography, as the volume of the eluate becomes too large to be handled conveniently. Alternate methods have been suggested by Winteringham (1953), Work (1949), and Lewis (1956).

A simple method by Moore (1953) has been found to be satisfactory: The paper containing the spot to be eluted is cut into a strip with a pointed end. The strip is placed between two glass slides, with the point just touching a new paper strip. By downward chromatography the spot is transferred to the new paper strip at such a rate that the size of the spot remains fairly small. This is facilitated by directing a stream of air from a hair dryer against the underside of the new paper. Identical results are achieved by ascending elution (Gregory, 1955) (see Fig. 39). An apparatus is described by Giri (1955d) by which bands on filter paper disks are successively eluted, using a fraction collector. A miniature extractor, using the Soxhlet principle, can handle small paper cut-outs and has a high extraction efficiency without increasing the volume of the final solution appreciably (Zimmermann, 1955).

3. CHROMATOGRAM RECORDS

Since many color reactions tend to fade with time (e.g., ninhydrin color of amino acids), it is necessary to keep a permanent record of the chromatogram. Contact prints of fresh chromatograms with the Contoura (F. G. Ludwig Associates) are recommended. For best results the chromatogram is placed on top of the photographic paper, with the exposure varying from 5–15 seconds, depending on the color intensity of the spots.

Chapter IV

QUANTITATIVE METHODS

The use of paper chromatography as a quick, convenient, and accurate means of qualitative analysis immediately raised the question of the possibility of quantitative paper chromatography. This chapter will give an account of the general methods employed in quantitative and semiquantitative analyses based on paper chromatography. The results of such experiments will be illustrated largely from the amino acid literature as these were the compounds first studied by Martin *et al.* and because the authors have had the greatest experience with them. Details of the methods to be employed for both qualitative and quantitative analyses of the many other groups of substances amenable to paper chromatography will be described in later chapters. However, one or another of the principles described in this chapter are generally applicable to any group of substances.

Method I: Visual Comparison

Casual inspection of a finished paper chromatogram reveals that both the intensity of color and the size of the spot varies with the quantity of the substance chromatographed. Thus, a reasonably accurate estimation of the quantity of a substance of unknown concentration may be obtained by developing on the *same chromatogram* a series of dilutions of the unknown and a series of dilutions of known concentrations. Then, where a spot of unknown concentration matches a spot of known concentration with respect to area and density of color, it may be assumed that the quantity of material in the "unknown" is equal to that of the standard. It is important that the *same volumes of solution* (both standard and unknown) be used throughout. If volumes of varying size are applied, then the areas of the spots will vary irrespective of the concentration of the substance under test. In practice, volumes of 0.001–0.010 ml. are the most satisfactory.

The general principle of quantitative analysis by visual comparison has been modified by placing on the paper a series of drops which contain known concentrations of the substances to be chromatographed. Then a series of dilutions of the "unknown" are superimposed on the same spots and on blank spaces of the paper. The volumes of solutions applied must be equal throughout the experiment. After development of the chromatogram, the spots derived from the unknown are matched with those containing the unknown plus an added quantity of standard. Thus the concentration of the unknown is readily estimated.

A further modification of the visual dilution procedure is to estimate the minimum detectable quantity of each substance in the "unknown" compared with the minimal quantity that can be seen when the standard is applied. In the authors' experience this latter procedure is the poorest of the three visual methods because the estimation of color and area of a spot at the lowest visual levels is subject to very large errors due to background coloration, light intensity, thickness of paper, etc.

These procedures may be subject to large errors in judgment and require a great many replicate analyses at various dilutions to give reasonably satisfactory results, i.e., ±10%. They, however, have been successfully used for the analyses of a number of proteins by Polson (1948), Berry (1949), Hôjô (1950), and others.

a. Application of Sample (Berry and Cain, 1949). The long edge of a sheet of Whatman No. 1 filter paper (28 × 45 cm.) is marked with a series of small dots 2 cm. apart and 2.5 cm. from the edge to be inserted into the solvent. Beginning at the left bottom edge, the unknown solution is added to the penciled dots as shown in Table I. The solution is applied

TABLE I

VISUAL COMPARISON TECHNIQUE

No.	Unknown, μl.	Amino acid standard,[a] mM
1	5	1.25
2	2 × 5	1.25
3	5	
4	2 × 5	
5	5	2.5
6	2 × 5	2.5
7	5	
8	2 × 5	
9	5	5.0
10	2 × 5	5.0
11	5	
12	2 × 5	
13	5	10.0
14	2 × 5	10.0
15	5	
16	2 × 5	
17	5	10.0
18	3 × 5	10.0
19	5	
20	3 × 5	

[a] 5 μl. of each dilution.

with a 2.5 or 5.0-μl. capillary pipette. For quantities larger than 5 μl., a second application is made after the first spot is thoroughly dried, and so on until the desired volume has been added. This procedure permits the size of each spot to remain small and uniform.

b. *Matching of Colors.* The developed chromatograms are cut into strips so that spots of equal intensity may be most readily matched by placing two strips alongside each other over a uniform source of light such as supplied by an X-ray viewer. If an amino acid spot in position 1 (5 μl. of unknown plus 5 μl. of 1.25 mM. standard) is equal in color density and area to the same spot in position 4 (10 μl. of unknown), then 5 μl. of unknown contains 1.25 mM. of the amino acid.

Comment. This procedure is tedious and suffers from all the subjective errors of visual colorimetry. Berry (1949) claims 10–15% accuracy, although the recovery of added amino acids varied over the range 63–160%. However, the equipment required is that available in the simplest laboratory and consequently is useful where only a few casual quantitative comparisons are to be made. By sufficient replication the method is capable of considerable accuracy where the substances are well separated in tight spots on the chromatogram and where the colors formed are readily seen (see Auclair, 1952; Takeda, 1951).

Method II: Elution

The most widely used and probably the most generally accurate quantitative procedure is based on the simple expedient of cutting out the section of the developed chromatogram which contains a single substance, removing the substance from the paper, and determining its amount in the elutriate by an appropriate method. In many instances, where the substances are clearly separated, the accuracy of this procedure is better than $\pm 5\%$, and in highly special cases, where the compounds contain two radioisotopes, it is possible to obtain accurate analyses even though distinct separations are not achieved.

Several examples of procedures which have been successfully employed for the quantitative determinations of amino acids after elution of the chromatograms will be described. Other methods are given in later chapters.

Details of preparation of a two-dimensional chromatogram will be described, although essentially the same technique is used for one-dimensional chromatography provided that distinct separations of the spots may be achieved for the materials in question.

a. *Preparation of Paper* (Fowden, 1951a, Boissonnas, 1950, Block, 1950). A sheet of Whatman No. 1 filter paper 18.5 × 21 inches is marked with a line drawn 2.5 cm. from the edge of the lesser length of the paper and parallel to it, and a mark is made 2.5 cm. from one edge along this line.   The mark indicates the point of application of the substances.

The papers are then placed on clean glass plates one over the other in echelon; each paper is separated by a glass plate.   The papers must lie flat.   This is accomplished by placing the covering plate approximately 1 cm. above the point to which the solution is to be applied and placing glass strips on the lower portion of the paper.

In order to increase the rate of drying of the solution, an infrared lamp is held over the paper.   The solution is applied by means of a micropipette. The tip of the micropipette is gently touched to the paper at the designated point so that the solution is slowly sucked from the pipette by the paper. For best results, only 5-μl. aliquots should be applied at one time.   If more solution is desired, the paper is thoroughly dried by the infrared lamp (or a blast of warm air), and then a second aliquot is applied.   In this way, 60 μl. or more of solution containing from 2 to 24 μg. of *each* amino acid may be applied without increasing the area of the spot at the point of application.

b. Neutralization and Hydration.   After the spots are dry, the lower edges of the sheets containing the applied amino acid hydrochlorides are placed over a trough that contains 4 N NH$_4$OH for 4 minutes.   This treatment with NH$_3$ vapor effectually neutralizes the HCl bound to the amino acid group and any free HCl in the solution.   The papers are then hung in a hood and subjected to steam for 10–15 minutes.   This hydration of the paper results in more uniform chromatograms and very compact spots.   The hydration, but not the neutralization, is also carried out before the sheets are placed in the lutidine solvent.

c. Development of the Chromatogram.   The filter paper sheets are then placed in the phenol tank (rectangular glass aquarium, see Chapter III) and developed with aqueous phenol in the presence of approximately 50 mg. of NaCN in 5 ml. of water.   The solution of NaCN is placed in a 50-ml. beaker.

At the end of the development (36 hours at 23°C.), the papers are removed and the phenol is evaporated in the hood by a strong current of air. It is important to continue this operation until the sheets no longer smell of phenol.   This is usually accomplished in 2–3 hours.

The paper is then cut at a distance of 2–3 cm. below the solvent front in order to remove a large part of the phenol decomposition products.   The portion of the paper below the point of application is also removed.   The chromatograms are then steamed as described above and placed in a chamber which contains the second solvent (55 ml. of 2,6-lutidine, 20 ml. of absolute ethanol, and 25 ml. of water plus 1 ml. of diethylamine).

d. Locating the Spots.   PROCEDURE A.   After the chromatograms have been dried in the hood to remove the greater part of the solvent, the paper is sprayed with a 0.01 % solution of ninhydrin in 99 % isopropanol. The sheets are then dried and placed in an oven at 60–70°C. for 15 minutes. The locations of the amino acids are thus revealed. The areas are marked with pencil.

PROCEDURE B. After the chromatograms have been dried in the hood to remove the greater part of the solvent, the sheets are washed with ether or equal parts of ether and acetone in order to remove all traces of solvent. Then, the sheets are dried in air and placed in an 100°C. oven for 15 minutes. When these thoroughly dried chromatograms are viewed with ultraviolet light, the amino acids will appear as fluorescent spots and are outlined with pencil. If all traces of solvent, especially phenol, are not removed, the heating at 100°C. will cause considerable destruction of amino acids.

e. Removal of Ammonia. It is then advisable to remove traces of ammonia and other volatile nitrogenous substances from the paper by spraying with 1 % KOH in methanol. The papers are then dried in air and the amino acid spots, previously outlined in pencil, are cut out. The cuts are placed in individual test tubes and put in a vacuum desiccator over sulfuric acid.

f. Amino Acid Determination. NINHYDRIN REAGENT. Four grams of ninhydrin[1] and 80 mg. of hydrindantin are dissolved in 100 ml. of peroxide-free methyl cellosolve. One hundred and sixty milligrams of $SnCl_2 \cdot 2H_2O$ are then dissolved in 100 ml. of 0.2 M sodium citrate buffer of pH 5. This solution is then added to the ninhydrin, and the precipitate which forms after a few hours standing is removed. The reagent is stored in the refrigerator. Other ninhydrin reagents are described in Chapter V.

DEVELOPMENT OF COLOR. To each tube is added 1.5 ml. of the ninhydrin reagent, and the tubes are mechanically shaken for 10 minutes. They are then covered with aluminum caps and placed in a boiling water bath for 25 minutes. The tubes are cooled, and 10 ml. of water is added to each. The contents, after brief shaking, are transferred to 25-ml. stoppered graduated cylinders. Care is taken to leave the filter paper in the test tubes. A second extraction is made with 10 ml. of acetone, and the solutions are diluted to 25 ml. with water. The colored solutions are read in a Klett-Summerson or similar colorimeter using a 550-mμ filter (Fitzpatrick, 1949) for all amino acids except proline and hydroxyproline where a 440-mμ filter is employed.

Comment. Naftalin (1948), Awapara (1949), Pereira (1951), Porath (1951), J. F. Thompson (1951*a*), Ansell (1954), Bode[2] (1955), Clarkson

---

[1] The ninhydrin may be recrystallized from hot 2 N HCl (Hamilton, 1950).

[2] Bode (1955) used the following procedure: Spray with a solution of 500 mg. of ninhydrin, 90 ml. of acetone, 5 ml. of H_2O and 5 ml. of glacial acetic acid. Dry and spray with a mixture of 1 ml. of saturated $Cu(NO_3)_2$, 0.02 ml. of 65% HNO_3 and 99 ml. of acetone. Elute the color with methanol.

(1956), Gerok (1955), Gorbach (1956), N. R. Jones (1955), Kay (1956) Krishnamurthy (1955), Lacourt[3] (1956), Montreuil[4] (1954), Rogina (1955), Spoerl (1954), and others have described similar procedures for the quantitative determination of amino acids after their elution from the chromatograms. Martin (1948), T. S. G. Jones (1948), Woiwod (1949a), Blackburn (1950), and Kuroda (1951) have described methods for determining the quantities of amino acids extracted from paper chromatograms based on the use of the Pope and Stevens (cf. Block, 1951c) copper phosphate method. Because of the small quantities of copper which must be determined, colorimetric, polarographic or radiometric (Cu[64]) methods must be employed instead of the usual iodometric titration of the copper. Udenfriend (1950) has described an accurate method based on the use of amino acid derivatives containing two radioactive isotopes.

The many other substances which may be determined more or less accurately after elution of paper chromatograms will be described in subsequent chapters[5]. The obvious prerequisites for this type of quantitative paper chromatography are, first, a clear-cut separation of one substance from all the others if a non-specific method of determination is to be employed and, second, accurate micromethods for the determination of the eluted materials.

The disadvantages of the elution type of procedure are the requirements of absolute separation of each substance from the others except in the few cases where the material can be doubly labeled with radioactive isotopes (see Keston, 1949), the time-consuming nature of the experimental manipulations, and the need for absolute avoidance of contaminants. The latter requirement is especially difficult in the case of the ninhydrin method for amino acids because of the ubiquity of ammonia, but it is not nearly so serious when sugars, nucleic acids, inorganic ions, etc., are to be determined.

Method III: Area of Spot[6]

Fisher et al. (1948, 1949) have described an excellent procedure for the quantitative estimation of substances on one-dimensional paper chromatograms. They found that, when volumes of solution of constant size are applied to the paper, the areas of the resultant spots are proportional to the logarithm of the concentration of material in each spot.

[3] A review.

[4] Spray with ninhydrin, cut out each colored spot and add 0.5 ml. of 0.1% cadmium chloride in 60% v/v methanol. Dilute to 5 ml. with 60% methanol, read color after 10 minutes.

[5] Kofranyi (1955) believes that because of "tailing" the prospects for developing an accurate quantitative method for amino acids is not hopeful.

[6] Recommended where applicable.

In practice, 5 μl. of solutions containing 1.25, 2.5, 5.0, and 10.0 mM. of the amino acids, which may be readily separated by one-dimensional chromatography or which are revealed by specific tests, are placed on the paper 2 cm. apart. At the completion of the chromatogram, the circumferences of the spots are carefully marked in pencil, and the areas derived from the standards are plotted on semilogarithmic paper against the concentrations, a straight-line relationship is obtained.

Fisher (1949) has described the following method of calculating this type of experiment:

The procedure of assay is to develop four spots in parallel containing amounts S_1, S_2, U_1 and U_2 of the component to be assayed, where the s's are known and the u's are unknown, and where $s_1/s_2 = u_1/u_2 = k$. If the corresponding areas of spots on the developed chromatogram are S_1, S_2, U_1 and U_2, then the logarithmic relation gives

$$\log \frac{u_1}{s_1} = \frac{(U_1 + U_2) - (S_1 + S_2)}{(U_1 - U_2) + (S_1 - S_2)} \log k.$$

Comment. Accuracies of $\pm 5\%$ are readily obtained by this method when the spot has distinct edges. If there is an overlapping or if the spot is distorted by any reason whatsoever, this method should not be used. The chief disadvantage of this method is the tediousness of the area determinations.

In case the circumference of the spot is fuzzy, a more successful outline can often be obtained by reproducing the developed chromatogram on photographic paper by means of the usual equipment for copying documents (such as Contoura, F. P. Ludwig Associates).

This procedure has been used successfully by Block (1950, 1951b), Fromageot (1949, 1950), Ohtsu (1952), and others for the estimation of amino acids. Its use for other substances separated on paper chromatograms will be described elsewhere.

Fowler (1951) has reported that the logarithm of the spot content is a constant function of the logarithm of the spot length on 5-mm. paper strips over the range 4–450 μg. of sucrose, i.e.,

$$\frac{\log c}{\log l} = K.$$

This simple procedure is suitable only where a few components are clearly separated and where the boundaries are distinct.

Miyaki (1952) has used the spot length to measure the concentration of material in the spot by the following formula $\log L = a \log C + b$, where L is length of spot, C is concentration, and a and b are constants (see Mori, 1954).

Method IV: Total Color of Spot

It appeared from the inspection of paper chromatograms that, if the total color of the spot could be quantitatively determined, and if Beer's law held for the reaction employed, then a relatively simple method would be available for estimating the concentration of the material on the chromatograms. Block (1948) and Bull (1949) independently were able to prove this hypothesis as follows:

1. TOTAL COLOR DENSITY ACCORDING TO BLOCK (1948), BULL (1949), AND REDFIELD (1952)

One-dimensional chromatograms are carried out in the manner previously described. Five or ten microliters of solutions containing known and unknown quantities of the substances under investigation are developed alternatively on the chromatogram. After the color has developed, the sheet is cut into strips parallel to the direction of solvent flow and each strip is scanned at 5-mm. intervals along the length of the chromatogram using a transmission densitometer of the type described in Chapter III. Five to ten strips of blank paper from the chromatogram are also scanned to obtain 100 % transmission readings along the entire length of the chromatogram.

The average color densities obtained from ten or more colored strips as well as the average absorption by the blank paper are plotted on graph paper (Fig. 1) (semilogarithmic paper is used when the densitometer reads in per cent transmission), and the areas representative of each amino acid are determined (Fig. 2).

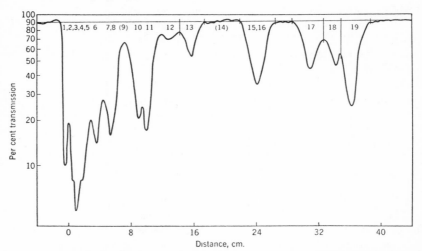

FIG. 1. Typical calibration curves of several amino acids (Redfield, 1952).

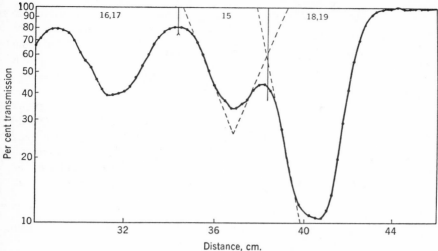

Fig. 2. Calculation of area (Redfield, 1952).

Redfield (1952) has employed the following method for calculating the concentration of amino acids by the total color density method.

"The transmission curves were plotted on semilogarithmic paper with per cent transmission along the log scale versus distance in centimeters. The best apparent base line was drawn, and the areas of the bands were determined with the aid of a planimeter. In the bands that show a slight overlap, the correct dividing line was approximately that drawn from the lowest point of the valley between the peaks of the bands perpendicular to the base line. Where the overlapping of the bands was greater, a more reliable indicator for drawing the dividing line was based on the observation that the bands of the chromatograms are essentially symmetrical and of a triangular nature (Block, 1950). A line drawn along the limb of the band away from the overlap was taken as one side of the triangle. The high point of the peak indicated the position of the vertex. The other side of the triangle was drawn from the vertex to the base line so as to form an isosceles triangle. A triangle could similarly be drawn for the other overlapping band. A line dividing the areas included between the dotted lines, curve, and base line approximately equally and drawn vertical to the base line was then taken as the dividing line (Fig. 2). This method was found to give results of an accuracy within the precision of this method of assay. However, where the overlap was so marked as to encroach upon the peaks of the bands, as could be determined by inspection of the curves with the aid of the drawn triangles, the error became larger. These chromatograms were discarded."

"The standard areas (sq. in.) were then plotted on Cartesian coordinate paper versus area (sq. in.)/concentration (μM.) to provide a standard curve for each amino acid, and the unknown concentrations were calculated from these curves (Block, 1948). To assure maximum accuracy, it was found necessary to run no fewer than four standards of different concentrations. The standard curves should not be extrapolated."

Grassmann[7] (1951a) and others increase the transparency of the paper by dipping it into a mixture of mineral oil and bromonaphthalene (80:20 v/v). Rosenberg (1952) rendered the papers translucent by applying Krylon Clarifier (Krylon, Inc., 2601 N. Broad St., Philadelphia, Pennsylvania) with a cloth to one side of the paper, then coating both sides of the paper with Krylon Plastic Spray. This technique is unnecessary if an adequate densitometer is used (pp. 75–78).

2. Total Color Density According to Rockland (1951; 1956) and Polson (1951)

This procedure is basically similar to that described above except that the *entire* spot is read with a densitometer or an adapted colorimeter. The important points in this method are that the spots must be clearly separated and very small. The latter is accomplished by the placing of very small quantities of solution (0.1 μl.) on the paper and developing for relatively short distances (5–10 cm.). The finished chromatogram is then placed in a suitable sample holder that masks all transmitted light except what passes through the colored spot. This requires a series of masks that will just accommodate spots over the expected range of concentrations. The color density, thus determined, indicates the concentration of substance in the spot when read from appropriately prepared standard curves.

Comment. The scanning methods described above, which were introduced by Block (1948) and Bull (1949), will give accurate analyses ($\pm 5\%$) if carefully conducted (see Brüggemann, 1952; Grassmann, 1953a, b; Hiller, 1952, 1953; Irvin, 1953; Sulser, 1953). If hand scanning is used, it becomes an exceedingly tedious procedure. However, if responses from the photocell are recorded on an automatic recording galvanometer with a

---

[7] Grassmann (1955) first separates the amino acids in a hydrolyzate by means of continuous electrophoresis at pH 3.0 into 4 or 5 fractions (basic amino acids, neutral amino acids, glutamic acid, aspartic acid and sometimes cysteic acid). Subsequent electrophoresis of the neutral fraction separated glycine and alanine from the others.

Separation of the mixtures was effected on one-dimensional paper chromatograms. After staining with ninhydrin, the quantities of each amino acid was determined with an error of approximately 3% by scanning the paper strips with an automatic recording densitometer.

logarithmic output, a simple, efficient procedure is available (see Sober, 1950; Sendroy, 1953; Miettinen, 1953).[8]

When several amino acids are incompletely separated from each other, the following formula has proved useful (Block, 1951c): If A_1, A_2, A_3, etc., are the quantities of amino acid indicated by the first, second, third, etc., peaks, and H_1, H_2, H_3, etc., are the heights of each peak as determined by the color density, and T is the total area under the peaks (corrected for the blank), then:

$$A_1 = \frac{H_1 T}{H_1 + H_2 + H_3 \text{, etc.}},$$

$$A_2 = \frac{H_2 T}{H_1 + H_2 + H_3 \text{, etc.}},$$

$$A_3 = \frac{H_3 T}{H_1 + H_2 + H_3 \text{, etc.}}.$$

It is important to remember that only good chromatograms with sharp peaks and a minimum amount of "tailing" should be read. If the run has not been satisfactory because of imperfections in the paper, overloading, high salt concentration, etc., the chromatogram should be discarded.

Tennent (1951) has described a simple adapter which permits the Beckman spectrophotometer to be used as a photoelectric densitometer (see Chapter III).

Method V: Maximum Color Density[9]

During the investigations on amino acids and amines by Method IV, it was observed that, because of the symmetrical nature of the color density curves, accurate results could be obtained by reading the concentration of the unknown material directly from calibration curves prepared from the maximum color densities of the standard solutions. The maximum density method is particularly well adapted to two-dimensional paper chromatography for which mechanical scanning has not yet been developed.

1. MAXIMUM COLOR DENSITY ON TWO-DIMENSIONAL PAPER CHROMATOGRAMS (AFTER BLOCK, 1950)

a. *Apparatus.* The chromatograms are developed in two 10-gallon glass aquaria on two-way racks each holding 12 squares of paper similar to that described by Datta (1950). These racks may be obtained from the Micro-Metric Instrument Co. and from the Shandon Scientific Co.

---

[8] The reliability of the total color density method has been recently confirmed by Frank (1955) for compounds which give colors with Pauly's reagent.

[9] Recommended method.

MICROPIPETTES. The self-fiiling transfer type, capacity 1 μl., 2 μl., and 2.5 μl., No. 282-A or 282-B, supplied by the Microchemical Specialties Co. has proved to be very satisfactory, although it is probably not as accurate as the Gilmont ultramicroburet (E. Greiner Co.).

b. Paper. Whatman No. 1 filter paper cut in 205-mm. squares is most suitable for amino acid determinations. It is inadvisable to apply more than 2.5 μl. of solution to the paper at one time for quantitative results. If greater amounts are needed, the drops should be put on in succession after the preceding drop has dried.

c. Preparation of Standard Amino Acid Solutions. A mixture containing aspartic acid, glutamic acid, cystine, serine, glycine, threonine, alanine, arginine, lysine, tyrosine, phenylalanine, valine, leucine, isoleucine, methionine, proline, hydroxyproline, and histidine is dissolved in 10 % isopropanol containing a little 6 N HCl so that the final concentration of each amino acid will be 8.0 mM. More dilute standards are prepared from the original at concentrations of 4.0, 2.0, and 1.0 mM.

d. Solvents. Aqueous *phenol* is prepared by warming a mixture of 80 ml. of Mallinckrodt Gilt Label liquid phenol "for chromatography" with 20 ml. of metal-free water. This will be sufficient solvent for eighteen chromatograms. A beaker containing 50–100 mg. of NaCN in 4–6 ml. of water is also placed in the chamber to reduce the decomposition of the phenol. The leading edge of the phenol cannot be cut off these small chromatograms (*cf.* Method IV) so that there tends to be more distortion near the phenylalanine area.

Aqueous *lutidine* is prepared by mixing 55 volumes of 2,6-lutidine (Matheson, Coleman & Bell Co., East Rutherford, New Jersey), 25 volumes of 95 % ethanol, and 20 volumes of water. To every 100 ml. of this mixture 1–2 ml. of diethylamine are added.

e. Neutralization of Acid. After the solutions have been applied to the paper, the excess acid is neutralized by placing the corner of the squares which contain the amino acids, over a trough containing 4 N NH₄OH for 4 minutes.

f. Hydration of the Paper. The squares are placed on the chromatogram racks, and then the paper is hydrated in the hood by exposure to steam for 10–15 minutes. The excess moisture is wiped from the metal end plates, and the racks are quickly placed in the appropriate solvents. This hydration is carried out before the development with phenol and with lutidine.

g. Time of Development. The development with phenol requires approximately 7 hours at 23°C. for Whatman No. 1 paper. The phenol should not be allowed to run past a line drawn 1 cm. below the top of the paper. The development with lutidine is conveniently carried out overnight.

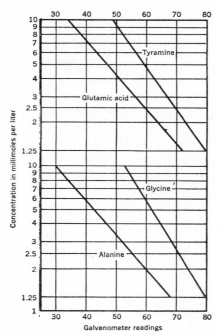

FIG. 3. Typical calibration curves of several amino acids by the maximum density method (Block, 1950).

h. Removal of Solvents. The rack is taken from the phenol tank at the end of the development and placed before an electric fan in the hood. The phenol is removed at room temperature within 2 hours. The lutidine is similarly removed in 30 minutes.

i. Development of Color. The squares of paper still on the racks are dipped into the ninhydrin reagent (0.25% of ninhydrin in acetone), and the color is developed by heating in the oven at 76°C.[10] for 10 minutes. The chromatograms are stored in the dark until the next day.

j. Measurement of Color Density. The maximum color density of each of the twelve amino acids on the chromatograms is then determined using a piece of blank paper as 100% transmission with one of the densitometers described in Chapter III. The average of the replicate analyses at each concentration of standard is plotted on semilogarithmic paper. The standard curves thus obtained allow the estimation of amino acids in mixtures of unknown concentration, provided that their concentrations fall within the range 1.0–10.0 mM (Fig. 3).

[10] The oven should be saturated with moisture by placing a tray of water in it. The air in the oven is circulated.

We have found that twelve amino acids may be read on 24 sheets in a total of 60–75 minutes. Amino acids and amines may be estimated with an accuracy of 10–15% using twelve replicate analyses. The error is smaller with certain acids (serine, glycine, alanine) and larger with others (tyrosine, phenylalanine, arginine, lysine). The error may be reduced by increasing the number of replicates.

If one does not have a rough idea of the amino acid composition of the proteins which are being analyzed, it is advisable to run two-dimensional chromatograms using the 8 × 8-inch racks described above (also Chapter III). By the use of this apparatus, twenty-four chromatograms can be carried out in two aquaria in one day. The following scheme is useful.

Standards	No. of replicates
2μM.	4
4μM.	4
8μM.	4

Unknown	No. of replicates
2.5 mg. of protein/ml.	3
5.0 mg./ml.	3
10.0 mg./ml.	3
20.0 mg./ml.	3

The sheets containing the standards are alternated with those containing the hydrolyzate of unknown composition.

When aqueous phenol (in the presence of NaCN) is the first solvent and lutidine:collidine:water (plus $(C_2H_5)_2NH$) is the second solvent, cystine, cysteic acid, aspartic acid, glutamic acid, serine, glycine, threonine, alanine, lysine, arginine, hydroxyproline, histidine, proline, tyrosine, phenylalanine, leucine plus isoleucine, valine, methionine, methionine sulfoxide, and methionine sulfone may be estimated with an average error of approximately ±15%.

When n-butanol:acetic acid:water is used as the first solvent (develop three times) and lutidine:collidine:water:diethylamine is the second solvent; cystine, cysteic acid, lysine, arginine, histidine, serine, glycine, aspartic acid, glutamic acid, threonine, alanine, valine, methionine, tyrosine, phenylalanine, and the leucines may be estimated with an average error of approximately ±10%.

2. MAXIMUM COLOR DENSITY ON ONE-DIMENSIONAL PAPER CHROMATOGRAMS (Block, 1950, 1954)[11]

The quantitative estimation of colored substances directly on the paper after one-dimensional paper chromatography is more accurate than on

---

[11] Recommended method.

two-dimensional chromatograms, as both the standards and unknowns are placed on the same sheet. A detailed description of the procedure for amino acids in use in our laboratories is given below.

a. *Preparation of Sample.* This has been discussed extensively by Block and Bolling (1951c).

b. *Acid Hydrolysis for All Amino Acids Except Tryptophan.* Unless the sample is limited in quantity, protein containing 32.0 mg. of nitrogen (equivalent to 200 mg. of "protein") is hydrolyzed with 20 ml. of 6 N HCl under reflux for 18–24 hours. At the end of the hydrolysis period, the contents of the hydrolyzing flask are transferred to an evaporating dish and the excess HCl is removed by repeated concentration to dryness on the steam bath. The hydrolyzate is then dissolved in 25 ml. of water and filtered, and, after thorough washing of the precipitate, the solution is decolorized with a little Darco G-60. After removal of the carbon, the hydrolyzate is again evaporated to dryness on the steam bath and the residue is dissolved in exactly 5.0 ml. of 10 % aqueous isopropanol. The hydrolyzate then contains the equivalent of 40 mg. of protein per milliliter. It may be kept without harm for at least a year at room temperature. Subdilutions containing 20, 10, 5, and 2.5 mg. of protein per milliliter are prepared. Other methods of hydrolysis as described by Block and Bolling (1951c) and in Chapter V may also be used.

c. *Alkaline Hydrolysis for Tryptophan.* This is described in Chapter V, except that 32.0 mg. of nitrogen, rather than 1.60 mg. of nitrogen, is preferred in food and feed analyses.

d. *Preparation of Standards.* Dissolve all amino acids except tryptophan in dilute HCl, add sufficient water and isopropanol so that the final concentration is 10 μM./ml. and isopropanol is 10 %. Prepare subdilutions (from 10 μM. of standard with 10 % isopropanol) of 8, 6, 4, 2, and 1 μM./ml. Tryptophan standards in 10 % isopropanol should be prepared separately.

e. *Chromatographic Equipment.* Although a number of commercial chromatogram chambers are available at prices ranging from $100 to $300, we have used ordinary 10-gallon stainless steel fish aquaria which cost $8 to $10 for both one- and two-dimensional chromatography (see Chapter III). The bottom, lower portion of the sides and all joints are covered with paraffin. Horizontal rods are fastened by paraffin to each end of the box to act as supports for three glass rods which are to be held 2–3 cm. from the top of the box. The two outside rods are 5 cm. from the sides of the box with the third rod equidistant from the other two. By using these easily removable rods, the same aquaria may be used for either one- or two-dimensional chromatograms. A description of the troughs and glass covers, etc., are given in Chapter III and Block and Bolling (1951).

f. Application of Spots. The method of application and the description of the types of pipettes used are given in Chapter III.

g. Paper Chromatography.

GROUP A. Paper: Whatman No. 1. Size: 18 × 11 inches (long).

Solvent: $C_6H_5OH:H_2O$ = 100 ml. of 88% liquid phenol plus 20 ml. of H_2O. A small quantity of 8-hydroxyquinoline is added to the phenol before the addition of the water. Beakers containing 10 ml. of 1% NaCN and 25 ml. of 0.3% NH_4OH are placed in box. Treat hydrolyzate spots with 1:4 NH_4OH for 4 minutes.

Pipette: 2.5 λ (if necessary 1λ).

Length of Run: 23 cm.

Color Reagent: 0.25% ninhydrin in acetone.

Standards: 2, 4, and 8 $\mu M./ml.$ (if necessary 1 $\mu M.$).

Unknown To Contain at Lowest Level (also apply two times and if necessary four times):

Aspartic acid	R_f	0.25	0.20–0.60 mg./ml.
Glutamic acid	R_f	0.33	0.20–0.50 mg./ml.
Serine	R_f	0.43	0.20–0.45 mg./ml.
Glycine	R_f	0.48	0.12–0.30 mg./ml.
Threonine	R_f	0.55	0.20–0.50 mg./ml.

GROUP B. Paper: Whatman No. 1. Size: 18 × 11 inches (long).

Solvent: *n*-Butanol:acetic acid:water = 450:50:125 v/v.

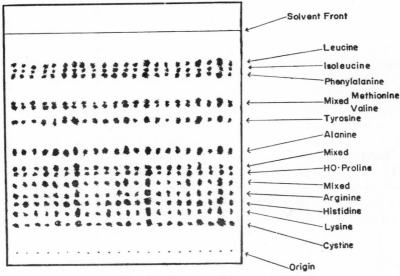

FIG. 4. Chromatogram of group B.

Pipette: 1 λ (if necessary 2.5 λ).

Length of Run: 23 cm., dry, and re-run three times for 23 cm. (See Fig. 4.)

Color Reagent: Ninhydrin.

Standards: 2, 4, and 8 μM./ml. (if necessary 1 μM.).

Unknown To Contain at Lowest Level:

Cystine	R_f	0.12	0.20–0.50 mg./ml.
Lysine	R_f	0.18	0.25–0.60 mg./ml.
Histidine	R_f	0.22	0.25–0.60 mg./ml.
Arginine	R_f	0.26	0.25–0.70 mg./ml.
Alanine	R_f	0.45	0.14–0.40 mg./ml.
Tyrosine	R_f	0.60	0.25–0.65 mg./ml.
Phenylalanine	R_f	0.80	0.30–0.70 mg./ml.
Isoleucine	R_f	0.82	0.30–0.55 mg./ml.
Leucine	R_f	0.85	0.30–0.55 mg./ml.

GROUP B₂. Iso-Amyl alcohol:pyridine:water:diethylamine = 50:50: 35:2 v/v in the presence of NaCN and aqueous phenol may be used for valine, methionine, tyrosine, isoleucine, leucine, and phenylalanine.

Length of Run: 23 cm., dry, and re-run twice for 23 cm.

GROUP C. Paper: S. & S. 598. Size: 18 × 11 inches (long).

Solvent: n-Butanol:acetic acid:water = 450:50:125 v/v.

Pipette: 5 λ (if necessary 2.5 λ).

Length of Run: 25 cm.

Color Reagent: Diazotized sulfanilamide (see Chapter V).

Standards: 2, 4, and 8 μM./ml.

Unknown To Contain at Lowest Level:

Histidine	R_f	0.17	0.30–0.70 mg./ml.
Tyrosine	R_f	0.40	0.20–0.70 mg./ml.

GROUP D. Paper: Whatman No. 1. Size: 18 × 11 inches (long).

Solvent: Lutidine:collidine:water = 1:1:1. Solvent contains 1% $(C_2H_5)_2NH$ by volume. Beakers containing 5 ml. of 1% NaCN and 5 ml. of aqueous phenol are placed in box. Treat hydrolyzate spots with 1:4 NH_4OH for 4 minutes.

Pipette: 2.5 λ (if necessary 1 λ).

Length of Run: 25 cm.

Color Reagent: Ninhydrin.

Standards: 1, 2, and 4 μM./ml.

Unknown To Contain at Lowest Level:

Valine	R_f	0.36	0.15–0.50 mg./ml.

GROUP E. Paper: S. & S. 598   Size: 18″ x 11″ (long).
Solvent: n-Butanol:acetic acid:water = 450:50:125 v/v.
Pipette: 5 λ (if necessary 2.5 λ).
Length of Run: 25 cm.
Color Reagent: Platinic iodide in acetone.
Standards: 1, 2 and 4 μM./ml. (if necessary 8μM./ml.).
Unknown to contain at Lowest Level: Methionine R_f .50
   0.15–0.60 mg./ml.

GROUP F. Paper: Whatman No. 1.   Size: 18 × 11 inches (long) or
18 × 20 inches (long).
Solvent: n-Butanol:acetic acid:water = 450:50:125 v/v.
Pipette: 5 λ.
Length of Run: 25 cm. for proline only; 46 cm. for proline
and hydroxyproline.
Color Reagent: 0.2% isatin in acetone. After spraying,
air dry, put sheets in oven at 70–76°C. for 10 minutes.
Oven to be saturated with H_2O vapors. For hydroxypro-
line counter spray with color reagent G.
Standards: 1, 2, and 4 μM./ml.
Unknown To Contain at Lowest Level:

Hydroxyproline	R_f	0.20	0.25–0.60 mg./ml.
Proline	R_f	0.30	0.10–0.30 mg./ml.

GROUP G. Paper: Whatman No. 1.   Size: 18 × 11 inches (long).
Solvent: 2-Butanol:3.3 % NH_3 = 150:50 v/v.
Pipette: 2.5 λ or 5 λ.
Length of Run: 25 cm.
Color Reagent: p-Dimethylaminobenzaldehyde (1 g.) in a
mixture of 10 ml. of concentrated HCl and 90 ml. of
acetone. Prepare fresh just before use.
Standards: 2, 4, and 8 μM./ml.
Unknown To Contain at Lowest Level:

Tryptophan	R_f	0.60	0.25–0.80 mg./ml.

GROUP H. Paper: Whatman No. 3.   Size 18 × 22 inches (long).
Solvent: 2-Butanol:3.3% NH_3 = 150:60 v/v (3.3% NH_3
is prepared by diluting 60 ml. of 14.5–15.0 N NH_4OH to
500 ml. with water). A marker of bromocresol purple
placed at the starting line permits one to follow the development as the solvent is allowed to drip off the paper
(Mandl, unpublished). Bromocresol purple moves
slightly ahead of phenylalanine.
Pipette: 1.0 λ or 2.5 λ.

Length of Run: The bromocresol purple should travel 45 cm.
beyond the origin.

Color Reagent: Ninhydrin.

Standards: 1, 2, 4, 6, 8 μM/ml.

Unknown to Contain at Lowest Level:

Lysine	0.25–0.60 mg./ml.
Arginine	0.25–0.75 mg./ml.
Tyrosine	0.25–0.65 mg./ml.
Valine	0.20–0.50 mg./ml.
Methionine	0.30–0.90 mg./ml.
Isoleucine	0.30–0.60 mg./ml.
Leucine	0.30–0.60 mg./ml.
Phenylalanine	0.30–0.75 mg./ml.

h. Replication. We usually employ five or six replicate spots for each
level of standard and for both levels of the unknown. Each sheet should
have at least one application of each level of standard. The results are
then averaged, and the concentration of the unknown is read from the
standard curve or calculated by the method of least squares. When the
spots are applied 2 cm. apart, then 22 applications may be made on a
single sheet 18 inches wide or 66 applications on 3 sheets fitting in a single
aquarium. It is advisable to use the same pipette for the application of
standards and unknowns.

When six or more proteins are analyzed simultaneously, it is advisable
to stagger the applications of standards and unknowns over the sheet in
order to avoid having the same material always located near either end of
the sheet.

i. Method of Reading. All amino acids are roughly outlined in pencil
using transmitted light (X-ray viewer). This facilitates centering each
spot on the densitometer for the determination of the maximum color
density.

j. Time for Determination. After the hydrolyzates have been prepared
and when six or more proteins are run simultaneously, it takes 15–20
minutes of bench time per amino acid per sample.

k. Calculations. The average densitometric readings of the standard
solutions may be used to prepare standard curves (see Fig. 3), or the results may be calculated as follows: Assuming that a logarithmic relationship holds between a standard (amino acid, sugar, etc.) at a single (s)
and a double level $(2s)$ and an unknown at a single (u) and a double level
$(2u)$, a general equation has been derived which permits rapid calculation
of the quantity of unknown, given the average densitometric readings for
both standards and unknowns. This method of computation compares

very well with the commonly used standard curve procedure and involves the derivation of nine sums which are then substituted in the appropriate equation to solve for the antilog of the lowest unknown level.

DERIVATION OF THE SUMS AND SOLUTION OF THE EQUATION. Using the average chromatogram readings (as per cent transmission) for standard (s and $2s$), and similar levels (u and $2u$) for the unknown, the following nine sums are calculated:

$$s + u, \tag{1}$$
$$(\log s)\,(s + u), \tag{2}$$
$$2s + 2u, \tag{3}$$
$$(\log 2s)(2s + 2u), \tag{4}$$
$$s + 2s = Ys, \tag{5}$$
$$u + 2u = Yu, \tag{6}$$
$$\frac{Ys - Yu}{2} = C \tag{7}$$
$$Ys + Yu = B, \tag{8}$$
$$\log s\,(s + u) + \log 2s(2s + 2u) = A. \tag{9}$$

The values A, B, and C are then substituted in the equation given below:

$$\text{Answer} = \text{Antilog}\ \frac{0.0906C}{(0.1505 + \log s)B - A}.$$

The resulting answer will be related to the weight of the standard (i.e., milligrams, etc.).

Example. In the determination of lysine by paper chromatography, the following data were obtained:

Standard $= s = 2$ mM.
Unknown $= u = 5$ mg. protein/ml.
Average % transmission values (from densitometer):
Reading of lower standard $= S\ \ = 69.4$
Reading of higher standard $= 2S = 56.8$
Reading of lower unknown $= U\ \ = 60.1$
Reading of higher unknown $= 2U = 45.3$

From the above figures, the following sums were calculated:

$$S + U = 69.4 + 60.1 = 129.5, \tag{1}$$
$$\log s(S + U) = 0.301 \times 129.5 = 38.98, \tag{2}$$
$$2S + 2U = 56.8 + 45.3 = 102.1, \tag{3}$$
$$(\log 2s)(2S + 2U) = 0.602 \times 102.1 = 61.46, \tag{4}$$
$$S + 2S = 69.4 + 56.8 = 126.2 = Ys, \tag{5}$$
$$U + 2U = 60.1 + 45.3 = 105.4 = Yu, \tag{6}$$
$$\frac{Ys - Yu}{2} = \frac{126.2 - 105.4}{2} = +10.4 = C, \tag{7}$$
$$Ys + Yu = 231.6 = B, \tag{8}$$
$$(\log s)(S + U) + (\log 2s)(2S + 2U) = 38.97 + 61.46 = 100.4 = A. \tag{9}$$

The values A, B, and C are substituted in the appropriate equation which is then solved, and the resulting quantity is used in the calculation of the per cent lysine in the protein.

   a. Since the lower level of the standard is 2 mM., the appropriate equation is:

$$\text{Antilog} \frac{0.0906C}{(0.1505 + \log s)B - A} = \text{Antilog} \frac{0.0906C}{(0.1505 + 0.301)B - A}$$

$$= \text{Antilog} \frac{0.0906C}{0.4515B - A} \cdot$$

   b. Substitute values A, B, and C:

$$\text{Antilog} \frac{0.0906 \times 10.4}{0.4515 \times 231.6 - 100.4} = \text{Antilog} \frac{0.9422}{4.17}$$

$$= \text{Antilog } 0.2259 = 1.68 \text{ mM.}$$

   c. Total millimoles $= 2 \times 1.68 = 3.36$.

   d. To calculate the per cent lysine in the protein:

$$\% \text{ lysine} = \frac{\text{Total millimoles} \times \text{M.W. lysine}}{\text{Mg. protein/ml. (lower level)}} = \frac{3.36 \times 146.19}{5} = 9.82.$$

Comment. McFarren (1951a), using unidimensional chromatography and and the maximum color density method with the Photovolt Densitometer (filter 570 mμ), has carried out a complete amino acid analysis of β-lactoglobulin which compares very favorably with microbiological and starch column analyses of the same preparation. The same group (McFarren, 1951b) have reported that the error of the maximum color density method as applied to sugars is from 1 to 5%. Patton (1951), Salander (1953), Gassner (1952), Polson (1951), and Kosikowsky (1954) have also reported that accurate analyses of amino acids separated on unidimensional chromatograms are obtained by the maximum color density method. In fact, Miettinen (1953) has reported a reproducibility of ±0.5% for amino acids determined by this method. He pointed out that the most important limiting factor is without doubt the variation in the chromatograms.

   Roland (1954) has used the maximum color density method on unidimensional chromatograms. Lysine, arginine, alanine, proline, tyrosine, valine, methionine, isoleucine, leucine, and phenylalanine were separated after 48 hours on Whatman No. 1 paper with peroxide-free 2-butanol:3% ammonia = 3:1 v/v. Three per cent NH_4OH is prepared by diluting 55 ml. of 15 N NH_4OH with water to 500 ml. Histidine was separated with 2-butanol:acetic acid:water = 120:15:25 v/v. The other amino acids were separated with aqueous phenol. The colors were developed with 0.2% ninhydrin in acetone to which 1% acetic acid was added just before use.

All amino acids except lysine, glutamic acid, and glycine were determined within confidence limits of $P = 0.95$. Roland states: "The procedures ... provide a less tedious, more rapid, and reasonably accurate approach to the analysis of protein hydrolyzates than has previously been available."

Winslow (1949) has shown that transmittance densitometry is superior to reflection densitometry when applied to colored materials on filter paper. However, Goodban (1953) and Vaeck (1954) found that reflectance maximum density of amino acids or inorganic ions gave a straight line when the logarithm of the concentration was plotted against the maximum density (see Kubelka, 1931).

Polson (1951) used the following procedure for the photometric estimation of amino acids: The galvanometer deflection (560-mμ filter) for each spot is divided by the average of the two galvanometer deflections of the clean paper on either side of the spot. The values so obtained as % transmission are plotted as ordinates versus the dilution factors as abscissas for the standard and unknown spots. The concentration of the unknown is that which has the same galvanometer reading as the standard.

Colorless substances may be scanned with infrared light by means of the maximum optical density method with an error of $\pm 10\%$; error may be reduced to approximately $\pm 5\%$ by plotting the weight of material against the product of the maximum optical density and the band width at half-optical density (see Method VI) (Goulden, 1954).

It appears that the maximum color density method should be applicable to all types of substances that are separated on one- or two-dimensional paper chromatograms and are colored or give colored derivatives. The most accurate results are obtained when the colored spots are small and either round or slightly elliptical. In order to achieve this it is important that the solution be applied as a round spot of approximately 5 mm. diameter or less. When one-dimensional chromatograms are used, the strip of paper must be wide enough to allow a margin of at least 2 cm. from the edge of the paper to the nearest point on the circumference of the developed spot (*cf.* Roberts, 1957; error < 3 %).

The maximum density of color in a spot, if the spot spreads by diffusion, should be proportional to the amount of substance originally put on the chromatogram (Brimley, 1953). Even if this proposition does not hold under practical conditions, quite accurate estimations have been made from calibration curves which may not agree with any theory. Among the possible causes of departure from theory are the difficulty of determining the maximum density at a point, *i.e.*, not over a finite area, the variability of the color (especially in the case of ninhydrin), and the possibility of incomplete reaction.

Table II illustrates a comparison of the amino acid values of β-lacto-

TABLE II

APPROXIMATE AMINO ACID COMPOSITION OF CRYSTALLINE β-LACTOGLOBULIN

(Calculated in grams of amino acid per 16.0 g. of nitrogen)

Arginine	3.1	2.6	3.0	3.0	3.0	3.1
Histidine	2.1	1.0	1.7	1.6	1.7	1.7
Lysine	12.1	11.5	11.5	11.7	12.9	12.1
Tyrosine	3.9	4.0	4.0	3.9	3.7	3.9
Tryptophan	2.5	1.9	—	2.0	—	2.7
Phenylalanine	4.3	3.5	3.7	3.6	3.9	3.8
Cystine	3.5	3.2	—	3.5	—	2.6
Methionine	3.6	3.0	3.2	3.3	3.3	3.7
Serine	4.7	3.4	3.9	5.1	4.0	5.3
Threonine	5.8	4.7	5.3	5.9	5.0	4.9
Leucine	16.0	11.0	15.6	16.0	15.9	16.1
Isoleucine	8.3	5.2	7.5	8.6	6.0	9.3
Valine	5.8	4.6	6.3	5.9	5.8	5.8
Glycine	1.5	1.4	1.4	1.4	1.4	1.7
Alanine	7.0	6.5	6.0	7.3	7.3	7.0
Glutamic acid	17.8	20.2	18.9	20.0	19.5	20.8
Aspartic acid	14.0	11.4	11.6	11.7	11.8	11.5
Proline	5.0	5.0	5.1	5.4	5.3	5.9
Hydroxyproline	0.0	0.0	—	0.0	—	—
NH_3-N	8.5					
N_2 accounted for	100%			99%	100%	103%
Method	Maximum color density		Microbiological and/or chemical		Column chromatography	

globulin estimated by paper chromatography (maximum density method), chemical, microbiological, and column chromatographic methods (from Block, 1955). It is apparent that the four procedures give approximately the same results, although for certain amino acids one method may be superior to the others.

Table III illustrates the per cent deviation from the mean of amino acid values on two separate determinations of β-lactoglobulin (Block, 1955). Here again the error is of the same order of magnitude as that found by the other widely used methods of amino acid analyses (Block and Bolling, 1951; Block, 1955).

Method VI: Area × Density Method

It was found that if the volume of solution applied to the paper is not constant, the concentration of material in the spots can be determined by a combination of Methods III and V, *i.e.*,

$$\frac{\text{Concentration in mg.}}{\text{Area of spot} \times \text{maximum color density}} = K,$$

where K is a constant (Block, 1948; Bolling, 1949; Souchon, 1952).

TABLE III

PER CENT DEVIATION FROM MEAN OF AMINO ACID VALUES ON TWO
SEPARATE DETERMINATIONS OF β-LACTOGLOBULIN AMINO ACIDS

(Calculated in grams per 16.0 g. of nitrogen)

Amino acid	A	B	Deviation, %
Arginine	3.2	3.0	3
Histidine	2.1	2.1	0
Lysine	11.5	12.6	5
Tyrosine	3.9	3.9	0
Phenylalanine	4.2	4.3	1
Cystine	3.2	3.8	9
Methionine	3.6	3.6	0
Serine	4.7	4.7	0
Threonine	5.4	6.2	7
Leucine	16.0	—	—
Isoleucine	8.3	8.5	1
Valine	6.0	5.5	5
Glycine	1.5	1.5	0
Alanine	6.8	7.1	2
Glutamic acid	17.8	17.8	0
Aspartic acid	—	14.0	—
Proline	4.8	5.2	4
AVERAGE DEVIATION			3

This procedure, although of possible value, offers no real advantage over the area or the maximum color density methods and requires double the labor.

Method VII: Retention Analysis

If a developed chromatogram is dipped into a new developing agent which contains a substance which will react chemically with the substances on the paper, Wieland (1951b) has found that the flow of the reagent in the second developer is retarded in proportion to the quantity of material in the spot. For example, amino acids on a developed chromatogram may be determined by a second development at right angles to the first, using 1% cupric acetate in aqueous tetrahydrofurane (5:95 v/v) (sufficient acetic acid is added to dissolve any precipitate). After the Cu-containing solvent has passed beyond all the amino acids, the sheets are dried and sprayed with 1% rubeanic (dithiooxamide) acid. The colorless gaps in the gray-green background are proportional to the amount of amino acid in the spot of the original chromatogram. Other substances may be similarly estimated.

The size of the gaps, within experimental error, are directly proportional to the concentration of substances in the spots.   The spots may also be cut out and analyzed individually.

All α-amino acids, β-alanine, and β-amino butyric acid react with copper in a ratio of 2 mole : 1 mole copper.   It is, therefore, possible to determine the molecular weight of an unknown amino acid retentiometrically.

Alanine, valine, threonine, and glycylglycine : copper complexes are slightly soluble in tetrahydrofurane, but may be evaluated as described.

The Cu complexes of leucine, isoleucine, and phenylalanine are quite soluble in tetrahydrofuran; therefore, up to 80 % of isopropanol must be added to the solvent.

The method is unsuitable in the presence of PO_4^{---}, SO_4^{--}, Cl^- (at more than 1 %), malonate, tartrate, citrate, and other ions.

Quantitative Evaluation.   A 3 % aqueous solution of alanine, glycine proline, hydroxyproline, serine, threonine, and valine is applied to filter paper in the usual manner.   The chromatogram is developed with water-saturated phenol.   After drying in air the residual phenol is removed by washing with acetone.   A test strip is then identified with ninhydrin.   The main portion of the chromatogram is cut perpendicular to the direction of the solvent flow underneath the *lowest* spot.   This paper is then immersed in tetrahydrofurane : copper acetate : H_2O.   The areas of the gaps are measured and calculated, using the one produced by hydroxyproline as the standard.   The areas are directly proportional to the amounts of amino acids.

Example	Serine plus glycine	Threonine plus alanine	Hydroxy-proline	Valine	Proline
Measured areas	260	228	85	98	99
Weighed amounts	255	223	85	95	97

Chapter V

AMINO ACIDS, AMINES, AND PROTEINS

Section I: Amino Acids and Peptides

As we have mentioned earlier in this manual, present-day paper chromatography may be considered to have started with the report of Martin *et al.* (Consden, 1944) on the separation of amino acids from protein hydrolyzates. It is hoped to summarize in this chapter some of the many experiments on the separation and determination of amino acids and peptides which have been published since 1944.[1]

General Directions

1. QUANTITIES OF AMINO ACIDS USED

The quantities of amino acids required to give a visible spot on the chromatogram are dependent on a number of factors, the most important of which is the color reagent.   Other factors are the size of the spot initially applied, the length of the development, the type of paper, the solvents employed, and the type of chromatogram (*i.e.*, one- or two-dimensional). Table I lists the minimum quantities of amino acids necessary for visualization on large (*ca.* 18 × 20-inch) sheets of Whatman No. 1 filter paper after two-dimensional chromatography using aqueous phenol and collidine:lutidine as the solvents with ninhydrin as the color reagent.

For quantitative estimation on 200 × 200-mm. sheets of Whatman No. 1 paper by transmission densitometry (see Chapter IV) we have found that 2.5 μl. of solutions of amino acids over the range 1–10 mM concentration is most satisfactory.   If the large sheets are used, then 5 μl. of the above-mentioned concentrations should be employed (Block, 1950).   The quantities of amino acids can be further reduced for one-dimensional strips, if very small aliquots are applied (*ca.* 0.2 μl.).

2. PAPER[2]

Whatman No. 1 and No. 4 filter papers ("for chromatography") have been the most widely employed since their introduction by Consden (1944). Our experience, after testing all the samples of filter paper generally available on the American market, has confirmed the finding that Whatman No. 1 filter paper is the most suitable for the separation and determination

---

[1] Reviews covering the topics presented in this chapter have been published by Duggan (1956), I. Smith (1955), Strain (1956), and R. J. P. Williams (1954).

[2] Chemically modified papers have been employed by Micheel (1956) and Ströle 1955).

TABLE I

DETECTABLE QUANTITIES OF SOME AMINO ACIDS AND PEPTIDES BY NINHYDRIN ON LARGE TWO-DIMENSIONAL CHROMATOGRAMS WITH AQUEOUS PHENOL AND WITH COLLIDINE:LUTIDINE

Compound	Dent (1948) μg.	Pratt (1948) μg.	Auclair (1952) μg.	Compound	Dent (1948) μg.	Pratt (1948) μg.	Auclair (1952) μg.
α-Alanine	2	0.2	0.06	Valine	3	0.2	0.15
β-Alanine	5	0.2	0.22	Glutathione	10	10	
Allothreonine	6			Glycine	1	0.1	0.05
α-Amino-n-butyric acid	4	0.2	0.12	Histidine	20	25	7.5
α-Aminoisobutyric acid	4			Homocysteic acid			
γ-Aminobutyric acid	5			Homocystine			
ε-Aminohexanoic acid	5	0.5		Hydroxylysine	15	4	
α-Amino-ε-hydroxycaproic acid	10			Hydroxyproline	15	1	1.0
α-Aminoöctanoic acid	6			Lanthionine	6		
δ-Aminopentanoic acid	5			Leucine	10	0.5	0.25
α-Aminophenylacetic acid	8			Isoleucine	10	0.5	0.25
Arginine	15	4	4.0	Lysine	15	3	1.5
Asparagine	5	1	0.8	Methionine	10	1	
Aspartic acid	5	0.4	0.2	Methionine sulfone	10	5	
Carnosine	15			Methionine sulfoxide	5	1	0.5
Citrulline	5	0.5		α-Methyl-α-amino-n-butyric acid	10		
Cystathionine	8			Methylhistidine	20		
Cysteic acid	1	8	0.2	Monoiodotyrosine	30		
Cystine	Lost			Norleucine	10	0.4	
Diiodotyrosine	40			Norvaline	5	0.5	
β,β-Dimethylcysteine	Lost			Ornithine	10	3	
Djenkolic acid	5			Phenylalanine	10	5	1.25
Ethanolamine	5			Proline	8	1	1.5
Ethanolamine phosphate	10			Serine	2	0.3	0.08
Glutamic acid	3	0.1		Serine phosphate	10		
Glutamine	5	2	0.4	Taurine	3	1	0.2
Tryptophan	20	3	2.0	Threonine	10	2	0.2
Tyrosine	15	3	1.0	Thyroxine	60		

of the majority of α-amino acids which occur in proteins (confirmed by Burma, 1952). However, when the reagent used to reveal the substances on the chromatogram is prepared in aqueous solution a more absorbent paper such as Schleicher and Schuell No. 598 is superior.

Bull (1949) and Redfield (1952) prefer S. and S. No. 507 for quantitative chromatography; but Kowkabany (1950), after investigating twenty-two types of filter paper on collidine and three n-butanol-containing solvents, prefers Whatman No. 3 and S. and S. No. 589 Blue or Black Ribbon papers for qualitative chromatography. Toennies (1951) uses S. and S. No. 589 Green Ribbon for the detection of methionine after development with aqueous phenol (see Chapter III). Other papers are mentioned during the description of specific methods.

Where larger amounts of amino acids or peptides are to be separated for subsequent elution, it is advantageous to use a thicker paper.[3] We have found (Block, 1951b,c) that Whatman No. 3 is very satisfactory. However, Mueller (1950) uses an extremely heavy filter paper (S and S No. 470-A) for this purpose. The thickness of this paper results in very fast movement of the solvent with poor separation. Mueller, therefore, uses the simple expedient of attaching a strip of Whatman No. 1 paper to one edge of the thick sheet, overlapping 1–2 cm. The two papers are fastened with a double row of stitches by means of a sewing machine. The material to be separated is applied just above the "seam" on the 470-A paper. The No. 1 paper, approximately 9 cm. wide, acts as a valve to control the rate at which the solvent is fed into the thick paper.

When buffered solvents are employed for chromatography, it is customary to buffer the paper also. Thus McFarren (1951a) dips Whatman No. 1 paper in pH 12.0 phosphate buffer (50 ml. of M Na$_2$HPO$_4$ plus 50 ml. of 0.067 M NaOH) before developing with buffered aqueous phenol. The paper is dried at low temperature[4] before use. Other buffers for paper will be mentioned along with the solvents employed.

3. SOLVENTS

Although a great many solvents have been employed for the separation of amino acids and peptides, only three of the most useful will be described

---

[3] Kellner (1954) has suggested the following method for increasing the concentration of small amounts of amino acids. The amino acids are applied as a band along the whole length of the paper and the chromatogram is developed as usual. Then the paper is turned at right angles and the amino acids are concentrated at one edge by developing with water or dilute acid or dilute ammonia.

[4] Vaidyanathan (1955) has shown that if the amino acids, after applying to the paper, are heated to 90–100° there is considerable loss. Furthermore, if oxo acids are present there is not only a loss of amino acids but also the formation of other amino acids by transamination.

in detail here. The others are mentioned in an appendix to this section of this chapter.

a. Phenol. One hundred milliliters of metal-free water is dissolved in 400 ml. of Mallinckrodt Gilt Label liquid phenol by gentle warming. Add 25 to 50 mg. of 8-hydroxyquinoline. The solvent is stored in a dark bottle in the refrigerator where the cold causes separation into two layers. When this solvent is to be used, the bottle is vigorously shaken and the desired quantity of the emulsion is removed and gently warmed to effect solution.

A beaker containing 100 mg. of NaCN in 4–6 ml. of water is commonly placed in the chamber. The liberated HCN retards the decomposition of the phenol. If the use of NaCN is undesirable, the addition of 0.04% 8-quinolinol (8-hydroxyquinoline) (Block, 1950) or 0.1% cupron (α-benzoinoxime) (Fromageot, 1950) to the phenol will serve the same purpose.

The relative distance (R_f) traveled by the more basic amino acids (arginine, lysine, ornithine, hydroxylysine) in phenol is influenced by the pH of the developing medium. Thus, if a beaker containing 0.3% NH_3 is placed in the chamber, these amino acids will travel farther in the solvent than in its absence. Because the spots, under these conditions, are larger and more elongated, they are not as suitable for quantitative estimation on two-dimensional chromatograms.

b. Lutidine:Ethanol. A mixture of 55 ml. of 2,6-lutidine (Matheson), 25 ml. of ethanol, 20 ml. of water, and 2 ml. of diethylamine (Sharples Chemical Co., Philadelphia, Pennsylvania) is made. This solvent is completely miscible and is not subject to change in composition over rather large variations in temperature.

c. Lutidine:Collidine. A mixture of 2,6-lutidine, 2,4,6-collidine, water, and diethylamine (100:100:100:3 v/v) is equivalent to the lutidine: ethanol solvent given above (Dent, 1947a, 1948; Block, 1951c).

d. Butanol:Acetic Acid.[5] To 500 ml. of a freshly shaken mixture of equal volumes of water and *n*-butanol is added 60 ml. of glacial acetic acid. After the layers separate, the upper layer is used as the moving phase. An aliquot of the lower layer (25–100 ml.) is placed in the chromatogram chamber (Woiwod, 1949).

Comment. All α-amino acids which normally occur in protein hydrolyzates and in most biological fluids can be separated on one- and two-di-

---

[5] Heyns (1952) has pointed out that glutamic acid hydrochloride may give three spots with butanol:acetic acid. These are glutamic acid, the γ-butyl ester of glutamic acid, and the cellulose ester. The latter does not move from the start. Beck (1954) and Hackman (1955) have pointed out that it is necessary to have each amino acid present as one ionic species only and that at high concentration of amino acids there is danger of interaction between amino acids which may produce new spots. The phenomenon of a single substance giving multiple spots has also been commented upon by Hassall (1954b).

mensional paper chromatograms by the three types of solvents given above (see Chapter IV and Figures 1–5). The use of special solvents for a separation of specific amino acids or groups of amino acids will be mentioned under the individual compounds. In general, we may say that, because the amino acids are soluble in water and much less soluble in organic solvents, the R_f value in any solvent generally increases with water content of the organic phase. The R_f value is also dependent on the type of paper and on the temperature at which the chromatogram is developed (*i.e.*, it is important to keep the temperature as constant as possible throughout the development). In the case of solvents which are not completely miscible with the aqueous phase, the primary effect of temperature is that of the solubility of water in the solvent. However, R_f values in solvents that are completely miscible with water also change with variations in temperature (Burma, 1951). Thus, the R_f value of an amino acid

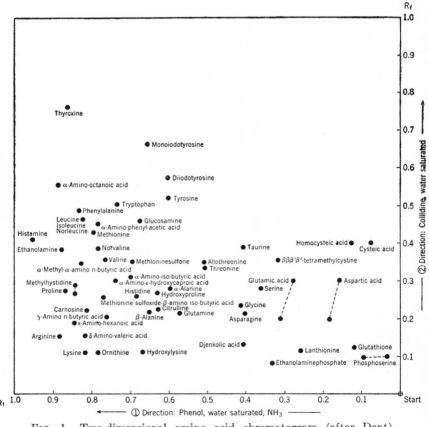

Fig. 1. Two-dimensional amino acid chromatogram (after Dent).

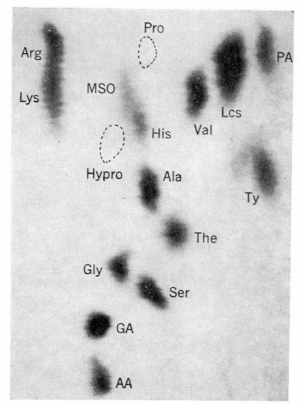

FIG. 2. Two-dimensional chromatogram with phenol and lutidine.

is dependent on other factors besides simple distribution between water and solvent. Generally, solvents of a homologous series give similar R_f patterns which decrease with increasing molecular weight and boiling point of the solvent (Shibatani, 1951).

These various effects have been summarized by Burma (1953a) as follows:

PHASE I. CELLULOSE. Filter paper contains 22% of moisture of which 5.9% is directly bound to the cellulose and has little or no solvent power.

PHASE II. SOLVENT WATER. This is solvent water, i.e., $22 - 6 = 16\%$ of weight of paper. Certain organic solvents may replace a part of the solvent water; e.g., methanol reduces the solubility of the solute in the aqueous phase.

PHASE III. ORGANIC SOLVENT. Organic solvent containing water is the moving phase. As soon as the molecules to be separated come into contact with the developing liquid (moving phase), they distribute themselves between Phases II and III in proportion to their respective solu-

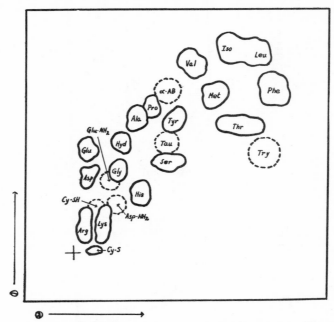

Fig. 3.   Two-dimensional chromatogram: 1, methanol:water:pyridine = 80:20:4; 2, *tert*-butanol:methyl ethyl ketone:water:diethylamine = 440:40:20:4 [after Redfield, *Biochim. et Biophys. Acta* **10**, 344 (1953)].

bilities (*i.e.*, partition chromatography; see Chapter II).   However, as the solvent moves along the paper, it becomes gradually impoverished in its water content; therefore, the partition coefficient, *i.e.*, the R_f value, will change as the organic solvent moves further from the point of origin Paper chromatography, at least of amino acids, therefore consists of two processes: (a) distribution between Phases II and III is pure partition; (b) distribution between Phases I and II is primarily adsorption.

4. TECHNIQUE

The application of the amino acid solutions and the apparatus used for the chromatograms have been discussed in Chapters III and IV.   Many obvious minor variations of these techniques have been devised for specific problems and need not be described in a general laboratory manual.

5. PREPARATION OF SAMPLES

a. Hydrolysis of Proteins and Preparation of Hydrolyzate.   WITH HYDROCHLORIC ACID.   A sample of protein containing 1.60 mg. of nitrogen is hydrolyzed under reflux with 10 ml. of 6 *N* HCl for 20 hours.   The excess

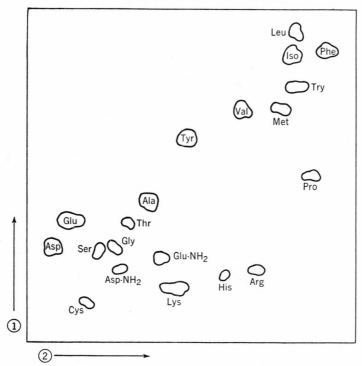

Fig. 4. Two-dimensional chromatogram: 1, butanol:acetic acid:water = 4:1:5; 2, 1:1 *m*-cresol:phenol, pH 9.3, borate buffer [after Levy and Chung, *Anal. Chem.* **25**, 396 (1953)].

HCl is removed by evaporation to dryness *in vacuo* at 35°C. or on the steam bath, and the resulting thin film of amino acid hydrochlorides is placed in a vaccum desiccator over soda lime for 24 hours or longer. The hydrolyzate is then taken up in warm water, filtered, again evaporated to dryness, and finally taken up in exactly 1 ml. of 10 % 2-propanol. This solvent is used because it is an effective preservative and yet does not cause esterification under these conditions (Block, 1951*c*).

The excess HCl may be removed by extracting the diluted hydrolyzate with a 5 % solution of di-2-ethylhexylamine [bis(2-ethylhexyl)amine] (Carbide and Carbon Chemicals Corp.) until the aqueous layer is neutral (Smith, 1948). The excess amine is then removed by repeated extraction with chloroform, and the aqueous layer is evaporated to dryness. The neutral amino acids are dissolved in 10 % 2-propanol as described above.

WITH HYDROCHLORIC FORMIC ACID. It has been previously shown that cystine is decomposed when a hydrolyzate is allowed to stand (Block,

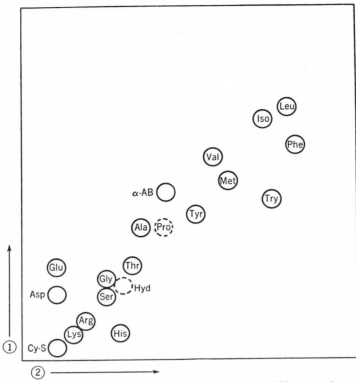

FIG. 5. Two-dimensional chromatogram: 1, 2-butanol:3% ammonia = 150:60
2, 2-butanol:formic acid:water = 150:30:20 [after Hausmann, *J. Am. Chem. Soc.*
74, 3181 (1952)].

1951).   Therefore, fresh hydrolyzates are prepared by the above described
procedure or preferably with a 1:1 mixture of 6 *N* HCl and 90% formic
acid (by volume).

WITH SULFURIC ACID.   Approximately 10 mg. of protein is hydrolyzed
by boiling under reflux with 10 ml. of 8 *N* H_2SO_4 for 20–24 hours.   Hot
saturated barium hydroxide is added to the hydrolyzate until pH 11 or
higher is reached.   Ammonia is removed by distillation *in vacuo*.   The
barium ion is then precipitated by the addition of a slight excess of 1 *N*
H_2SO_4, and the precipitated barium sulfate is removed by centrifugation
and thoroughly washed with hot water.   The filtrate and washings are
concentrated to dryness and taken up in 10% isopropyl alcohol.

WITH TRIFLUOROACETIC ACID.   The several proteins (casein, lactalbumin,
and wheat gluten) that have been tested are satisfactorily hydrolyzed by
boiling under reflux with 80% trifluoroacetic acid for 48 hours.   At the
end of this period, the excess organic acid is removed by extraction with

ether. The aqueous layer is evaporated to dryness and taken up in 10 % aqueous isopropyl alcohol as described above.

A micromodification (see Levy, 1953) of the above method is as follows: Approximately 1 mg. of protein is placed in a 2-inch length of soft glass tubing (6 mm. o.d.) sealed at one end. One hundred microliters of 6 N HCl (glass distilled) is added, and the tube is evacuated and sealed. The protein is hydrolyzed in the oven at 110°C. for 18–24 hours. After the tube is opened, the excess HCl is removed by evaporation in a vacuum desiccator over NaOH pellets. The evaporation is speeded up by the use of an infrared lamp. The residue is taken up in 100 μl. of 10 % isopropanol.

WITH BARIUM HYDROXIDE. A sample of protein containing 1.60 mg. of nitrogen is boiled with 10 ml. of 14 % barium hydroxide in an oil bath at 125°C. under reflux for 18–20 hours. The barium is removed with a slight excess of 1 N H_2SO_4, and the barium sulfate precipitate is thoroughly washed with hot water containing a drop of acetic acid. The filtrate is concentrated to a small volume *in vacuo* and then evaporated to dryness in a desiccator over calcium chloride. The residue is taken up in 1 ml. of 10 % isopropyl alcohol.

The excess $Ba(OH)_2$ may also be removed from the diluted hydrolyzate by CO_2 (dry ice). The slight quantity of Ba^{++} remaining in the hydrolyzate does not interfere with the chromatogram.

b. Separation of Free Amino Acids and Peptides in Tissues. Where an investigation of the free amino acids and peptides in plant or animal tissues is to be made, as many of the other constituents as possible must be removed. Dialysis or precipitation with trichloroacetic acid, perfluorooctanoic acid (Nordby, 1956), tungstic acid, ferric hydroxide, zinc sulfate: barium hydroxide at pH 7.2–7.6, perchloric acid, acetone, and ethanol have been used (see Ågren, 1949; de Verdier, 1948; McFarren, 1951a; Roberts, 1950; Block, 1934, and many others).

One method is to grind the tissues with sufficient absolute ethanol in a Waring blendor so that the final concentration of alcohol is 80 % by volume. The insoluble material is removed by filtration and washed with 80 % ethanol. Then, 3 volumes of chloroform is added to each volume of the ethanol extract. After thorough shaking the resulting aqueous layer (upper) is removed and concentrated to the desired volume (Awapara, 1948).

Another procedure is to precipitate the protein with a slight excess of $HClO_4$ (1 or 2 M). The excess $HClO_4$ is then removed by the addition of the minimum quantity of potassium acetate (Neuberg, 1944), which results in the formation of the insoluble $KClO_4$.

c. Desalting of Amino Acid Solutions. A large excess of inorganic ions[6] will interfere with the preparation of "good" chromatograms, especially

[6] Frame (1952) has described a procedure for separating the amino acids in urine.

with those amino acids of low R_f values in phenol. Several procedures have been proposed for their removal, but no one of these methods is entirely satisfactory. Some of the available desalting procedures will be described.

ION EXCHANGE METHODS. All the cations in the solution, which include all amino acids except the strongly acidic taurine, are adsorbed on a cation exchange resin (Duolite C-3 (H+); Amberlite IR-120 (H+), etc.). The column is washed with water until all anions and non-ionic material (carbohydrates, etc.) have been removed. The amino acids and the weaker cations are then eluted with N or 2 N NH$_4$OH using the ninhydrin test to indicate complete elution (see Redfield, 1953). After removal of the excess ammonia by concentration *in vacuo*, the residue is dissolved in water and passed through a column of an anion exchange resin (Amberlite IRA-410 (CO$_3^{--}$), etc.). Because the amino acids are ampholytes, they will be adsorbed on the anion resin whereas the cations will pass through. Arginine and sometimes lysine because of their basicity are, however, usually incompletely adsorbed on the anion resin. The amino acids are eluted with N HCl (Block and Bolling, 1951; Carsten, 1952), or with concentrated NH$_4$OH (Clarkson, 1956).

A column of Permutit 50 (H+), 16 mm. in diameter and 20–30 cm. high, is washed with 500–1000 ml. of 2 N HCl. The excess HCl is then removed by washing with 3–6 liters of water. The capacity of the column is ascertained by saturating it with N NH$_4$OH. The amino acid solution, containing salts, is dissolved in 1 % HCl and passed through the column at 10–20 drops per minute. The column is washed with 200–300 ml. of water, and the amino acids are eluted with N NH$_4$OH (Boulanger, 1951). Acidic polypeptides which pass through Permutit 50 in the water wash may be adsorbed on a column of Deacidite (regenerated with 0.25 N sodium acetate).

ELECTROLYTIC DESALTING. Since Consden (1947) first described an electrolytic desalting apparatus for use with amino acids, various modifications have been proposed (see Block and Bolling, 1951). Because the modification of Astrup *et al.* (1951) appears to be one of the best available, it is described in detail (Fig. 6). *cf.* pp 52–54.

Sulfuric acid (0.1 M) is passed continuously through the anode compartment during the electrolysis in order to remove the heat evolved by passage of the current. The acid may be cooled first by passing through a glass coil placed in an ice bath, but this is not always necessary. The anode compartment is constructed in a manner which allows the sulfuric acid to flow immediately over the dialysis membrane (a piece of Visking casing, size 36/32, which is renewed at least once a day), before it enters an inner tube containing the anode. The anode is a coil of platinum wire reaching to about 1 cm. from the end of the inner glass tube.   In this manner the flowing H_2SO_4 will carry away all the ions passing through the dialysis membrane into the anode compartment.   It will at the same time remove all chlorine produced at the electrode, thus avoiding any back-diffusion of dissolved uncharged chlorine molecules into the compartment containing the amino acid mixture.   It is possible to remove ions, such as phosphate and acetate, from the solutions.   The sulfuric acid on its flow from the anode passes a small thermometer pocket for controlling its temperature.   From there the acid runs to the sink.

The mercury is circulated through the cathode vessel by means of the water-lifting pump introduced for this purpose by Consden.   It is, however, not passed directly into the cathode vessel but is introduced through an inner glass tube, which protrudes up into the amino acid solution.   The tip of the glass tube is narrowed and bent so that mercury leaves it tangentially to the wall of the vessel and appears as a jet introduced into the solution.   In this way the amino acid solution undergoing desalting is given a rotational movement, which helps to mix it, and at the same time is efficiently cooled by the cold, washed mercury.   The stream of mercury falls down on the mercury surface and thus continuously furnishes a fresh

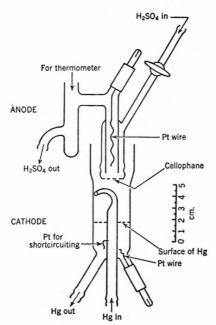

FIG. 6.   Construction of electrode compartments of Astrup (1951) desalting apparatus.

electrode surface to the solution.   In this manner the ions taken up by the Hg during electrolysis are rapidly removed.   In order to form an electrical connection between the Hg in the bottom of the cathode vessel and the Hg introduced into the inner tube, a platinum wire is inserted through the walls of the latter.   In this manner the Hg system is short-circuited and the appearance of sparks during or at the beginning of the desalting process is avoided.   The capacity of the cathode vessel depends on the amount of Hg present.   When the vessel is filled with amino acid solution to about 3 cm. above the tip of the inner tube, it contains 10–20 ml. of solution.   By increasing the amount of the mercury in the bottom, smaller volumes may be handled.   From the cathode vessel the mercury passes in the usual manner to the water-lifting pump, from which it flows to a wide vertical glass tube where it settles after being washed by the water from the pump, and finally into the cathode vessel again.   The mercury can be removed from the system by means of a side tube at the lowest point of the connection between the vertical settling tube and the inner tube of the cathode vessel.   This system contains a much smaller amount of Hg than the apparatus described by Consden (1947) and may need renewal more often. The water appearing from the settling tube passes through a sedimenting flask in the usual manner in order to prevent Hg escaping from the settling tube into the sink.   In order to avoid breakage of the tip of the inner tube and the platinum wires, the fluid is emptied and the vessel washed out by means of a pipette provided with a short rubber tubing (5 cm.) on its tip.

Solutions of 0.9 % NaCl (10 ml.) are desalted in 15–20 minutes starting with a current of about 0.7 ampere and ending with about 0.1 ampere. Such a desalted solution gives practically no reaction with silver nitrate. Because the time used for carrying out the desalting is only a fraction of that needed in the original apparatus it is convenient to have a buzzer to indicate the end point.   It can be regulated to indicate this end point at any strength of current wanted.   The use of an automatic current breaker is not recommended, as the back-diffusion will set in as soon as the electrical potential is removed.

A considerable proportion (20–25 %) of the arginine is converted to ornithine and other substances even in an 11-minute operation (Astrup, 1951; Stein, 1951).   Stevens (1954) reports that cooling, in contrast to the statement of Stein (1951), is very effective in reducing losses of arginine during electrolytic desalting.   Other changes which occur during desalting are: reduction of $R \cdot CH{=}CHCOOH$ to $R \cdot CH_2CH_2COOH$, conversion of indoxyl sulfate to indigo, and the deiodination of diiodotyrosine, thyroxine, etc. (Jepson, 1956).

DESALTING IN SPECIAL SOLVENTS.   The amino acid solution is adjusted to pH 4–5 with NH_4OH, filtered, concentrated to dryness, and ground to a fine powder.   The powder is then suspended in 0.2 N dl-camphorsulfonic acid in acetone using 50 ml. of solution per gram of amino acid.   After being stirred for at least 1 hour, the residue is removed by filtration and tested for undissolved amino acids with ninhydrin.   If positive, it should be extracted with more reagent.   The amino acid camphorsulfonates are decomposed with dry NH_3 gas, and the insoluble ammonium camphorsulfonate is removed (McCollum, 1952).

Alternative procedures are to extract the dried, defatted tissues or body fluids with acetone containing 1 % v/v concentrated HCl (prepare fresh) (Boulanger, 1951; S. Gordon, 1954) or with 0.18 % w/v HCl in ethanol (Balinga, 1955) or with 1 % v/v NH_4OH in methanol (Block, 1956).

6. Detection of Substances on the Chromatogram

After the chromatogram has been developed, it is necessary to detect the amino acids and peptides.   This is based on the reaction of the amino acid directly on the paper to produce a colored spot, or the amino acid spot is cut out of the chromatograms and the reaction is carried out *in vitro*.   When the amino acids are to be visualized on the paper, the developed chromatogram is either sprayed with or dipped into the reagent. In the discussion below, the terms sprayed or dipped are used interchangeably and without prejudice.   The particular operation employed depends on the convenience of the experimenter.

Group Tests—Ninhydrin[7]

The use of ninhydrin (triketohydrindene hydrate) for the detection of amino acids has been the subject of numerous minor modifications some of the more important of which will be described.[8]

METHOD 1 (*recommended*).   0.25 % w/v ninhydrin in acetone (Toennies, 1951).

METHOD 2 (*recommended*).   0.3 % ninhydrin in 95 % ethanol (Patton, 1951; Salander, 1953).   The color is developed at room temperature in the dark for 18 hours.

METHOD 3 (*recommended*).   Two grams of ninhydrin is dissolved by warming in 50 ml. of water.   To this solution 80 mg. of stannous chloride in 50 ml. of water is added.   The mixture is allowed to stand in the dark

---

[7] The purification of ninhydrin is readily achieved as follows: 100 g. of ninhydrin is dissolved in 500 ml. of hot 2 N HCl, any insoluble material is removed by filtration if necessary, then 10 g. of neutral Norit is added.   The solution is boiled for 10 minutes and filtered while hot.   The crystals are allowed to form slowly at room temperature, then at 40°C.   The ninhydrin is filtered off, washed three times with 50-ml. portions of ice-cold 1 N HCl, and dried over KOH *in vacuo*.   Store in the dark (Hamilton, 1950).

[8] 1,2-Diacetylbenzene has been used to identify amino acids (Riemschneider, 1955).

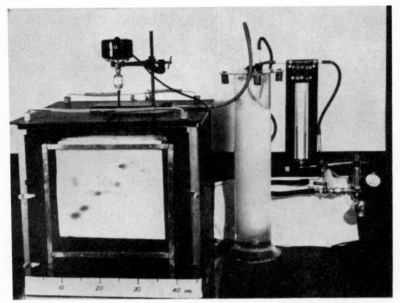

FIG. 7. The effect of relative humidity on the reaction of ninhydrin with amino acids on paper chromatograms [E. F. Wellington, *Can. J. Chem.* **31,** 486 (1953)].

for 24 hours or longer, after which the precipitate is removed by filtration. This stock solution of 2 % ninhydrin will remain useful for many months if kept in the refrigerator.   Twenty-five milliliters of stock ninhydrin solution is diluted to 50 ml. with water; then 450 ml. of isopropanol is added. The chromatograms are either dipped into or sprayed (DeVilbiss spray gun) with this 0.1 % ninhydrin solution (Block, 1950).   The chromatograms are dried, placed in a warm chamber (35°C.) for 60–90 minutes, and kept in the dark for 24 hours or longer.

METHOD 4.   A 0.1 or 0.2 % solution of ninhydrin in water-saturated *n*-butanol is prepared (Consden, 1944).   The chromatograms are sprayed with the reagent, and the color is developed at room temperature for 24–36 hours (Dent, 1948; Roberts, 1950).

METHOD 5. . When alkaline salts have been used to buffer the paper (see Solvents, above) or where the material to be chromatogrammed contains a considerable quantity of alkali, this alkali must be neutralized by the incorporation of acetic acid into the ninhydrin solution (Consden, 1948).   If the buffer has a pH of 6–8.5, then 2 % acetic acid is used.   If the pH of the buffer is 8.5–12, the ninhydrin solution should contain 4 % of acetic acid.   McFarren (1952) suggests 0.4 % of ninhydrin in water-saturated

n-butanol as the color reagent. The color is developed by placing the chromatogram in a mechanical convection oven at 60°C. for exactly 15 minutes.

METHOD 6. 4% ninhydrin in pyridine (Rockland, 1951).

METHOD 7. 0.4% ninhydrin in n-butanol containing 10% phenol (Bull, 1949). The chromatograms should be steamed after spraying.

METHOD 8. 0.1 or 0.2% ninhydrin is incorporated directly into the developing solvent (Nicholson, 1949).

METHOD 9. 0.1% ninhydrin in ethanol containing 5% v/v collidine; use after developing with acidic solvent. After basic solvent development use 0.1% ninhydrin in 50 ml. of ethanol plus 2 ml. of collidine and 15 ml. of acetic acid. When dry, spray with 1% $Cu(NO_3)_2$ in ethanol. The amino acids show pink spots on a green background (Levy, 1953).

METHOD 10. 0.5% ninhydrin in water-saturated butanol. Dry at 80°C. for 30 minutes. Spray both sides with water, then with a reagent composed of 1 ml. of saturated $Cu(NO_3)_2$, 0.2 ml. of 10% HNO_3, add 95% ethanol to 100 ml. (Bode, 1952).

METHOD 11. 0.2% ninhydrin in 10% v/v acetic acid (Jepson, 1953b).

METHOD 12. 0.4% ninhydrin in 10% isopropanol to which 5% v/v collidine is added just before using. Heat in moist atmosphere at 80°C. (Lewis, 1952).

METHOD 13. 0.4% ninhydrin plus 0.2% $CoCl_2$ in isopropanol. Heat for 10 minutes at 100°C. (Wiggins, 1952).

METHOD 14. The chromatograms are equilibrated at 20 ± 1°C. to 40 ± 3% humidity and sprayed with 2% ninhydrin in ethanol. The color is developed at this temperature and humidity in a special chamber for 30 hours (Wellington, 1952, 1953) (Fig. 7).

Other methods employing ninhydrin will be described along with the specific directions for the quantitative determination of amino acids.

CONSERVATION OF AMINO ACID CHROMATOGRAMS. The paper chromatograms developed with ninhydrin may be photographed (Contoura, F. G. Ludwig Associates) or preserved in the following manner: The traces of solvent are removed by washing with acetone:ether (v/v) or petroleum ether. The air-dried chromatograms are then treated with any of the above-mentioned ninhydrin reagents as long as $SnCl_2$ is not used in the reagent. After the ninhydrin color has developed at room temperature, the sheet is sprayed with or dipped into dilute copper nitrate (1 ml. of saturated aqueous $Cu(NO_3)_2$ + 0.2 ml. of 10% v/v HNO_3 diluted to 100 ml. with ethanol). The excess HNO_3 is neutralized by quick exposure to ammonia vapor. Then the chromatogram is dipped into a saturated solution of methyl methacrylate polymer (Perspex) in chloroform (Kawerau, 1951).

A simple procedure is to keep the chromatograms in a desiccator under N_2 in the dark (Krishnamurthy, 1952).   Other methods have been described by Adams (1951), Khabas (1955), and Pokrovskiĭ (1954).

Zweig (1956) advises the following procedure: the ninhydrin-treated chromatogram is dipped into dilute copper nitrate (1 ml. of saturated aqueous $Cu(NO_3)_2$ + 0.2 ml. of 10 % v/v HNO_3 diluted to 100 ml. with ethanol).   The papers are quickly neutralized with NH_3 vapors, air dried and sprayed with Krylon crystal clear acrylic spray (Krylon, Inc., Philadelphia 40, Pa.).

Group Tests—Nonspecific Reagents

A number of reagents have been proposed for detecting amino acids, peptides, and other substances on paper chromatograms.   These are sometimes useful in revealing the location of the amino aicds for subsequent elution.

ALLOXAN.   Spray the chromatogram with 0.25 % alloxan in acetone (Saifer, 1956), dry in air and heat for 10 minutes at 100°.

IODINE.   If the finished chromatogram is hung in a chamber that contains iodine, the vapors will color the entire paper brown.   However, if the chromatogram is then placed in the hood, the background color will disappear faster than that of the amino acids and other nitrogenous compounds (choline, betaine, etc.).   The chromatogram may be dipped into an alcoholic solution of iodine instead of being exposed to the vapors (Brante, 1949).   After the iodine has disappeared, the paper may be treated with ninhydrin or other more specific reagents. 1 % w/v iodine in 95 % ethanol can also be used (Cowgill, 1955b).   The reagent is stable for several days.

INDICATOR DYES.   Advantage may be taken of the buffering capacity of acidic, basic, or amphoteric substances by treating the chromatogram with a dilute solution of an indicator dye.

a. The chromatogram is sprayed with 0.1 % tropeolin 00 and then exposed to HCl vapors.   Owing to the buffering action of the ampholyte, the color of the spot is different from that of the surrounding area (Sluyterman, 1949).

b. The chromatogram is treated with a 0.1 % solution of the sodium salt of bromothymol blue.   After drying, the sheet is dipped into 0.2 % acetic acid.   The sheet turns yellow except for the blue amino acid or protein spots (Papastamatis, 1951).

c. The paper is sprayed with 0.04 % bromocresol green in ethanol (R. J. Williams, 1950).

d. To 20 ml. of 0.15 % w/v bromothymol blue in 95 % ethanol is added 3 ml. of formalin and 0.1 ml. of 60 % aqueous KOH.   This indicator is best used after development with neutral solvents (*i.e.*, aqueous propanol) (Kemble, 1952).

PERMANGANATE. The chromatogram is sprayed with a dilute solution of acidified $KMnO_4$ (0.03–0.15 N $KMnO_4$ acidified with 0.06 to 0.3 N H_2SO_4) (Procházka, 1950).

ORCINOL. Orcinol, which is generally used as a sugar reagent (see Chapter VI), may be employed to detect amino acids in the following manner: The dried chromatogram is sprayed with 0.1 % orcinol in ethanol made 0.004 N with sulfuric acid. The paper is dried and then heated for 30 minutes in the oven at 110–120°C. The amino acids appear as white spots against a red-violet background. The edges are more easily seen when viewed under ultraviolet light (Porath, 1951). The spots may be cut out and treated with ninhydrin, etc.

FOLIN REAGENT. Characteristic colors for amino acids are obtained by spraying with 0.02 % Na 1,2-naphthoquinone-4-sulfonate in 5 % aqueous Na_2CO_3. The chromatograms are dried at room temperature (Müting, 1952). Barrollier (1956) prepares the Folin reagent as follows: dissolve 500 mg. Zn acetate and 125 mg. of recrystallized Na 1,2-naphthoquinone-4-sulfonate in 10 ml. of water, then add 125 mg. of quinoline and 90 ml. of 1-butanol. Allow to stand 5 minutes and filter. Spray chromatogram, air dry at room temperature for 1 hour, then wash out excess reagent with 20 % Zn acetate in 95 % ethanol.

STARCH:IODINE. The developing solvent is very thoroughly removed at 60°C. The chromatogram is then exposed to Cl_2 gas for 10 minutes. The excess Cl_2 is removed in the hood. The paper is then sprayed with a 1 % soluble starch:1 % KI solution (Rydon, 1952).

STARCH:IODINE. Spray the developed chromatogram lightly with saturated aqueous solution of potassium metaperiodate, heat at 50 to 60°C. for 20 to 30 minutes. Then spray with 5 % w/v NaI in saturated $NaHCO_3$ followed by spraying with 0.1 % w/v soluble strach (Cifonelli, 1955).

STARCH:IODINE. Spray the chromatogram with 5 % w/v NaI in saturated $NaHCO_3$, then with 0.1 % w/v aqueous starch. After drying in air, spray lightly with saturated KIO_4 (Cifonelli, 1955).

BENZIDINE-BLUE. The solvent is completely removed from the chromatogram by dipping into ether:acetone = 1:1, containing 10 drops of acetic acid per 100 ml. The chromatogram is then placed on a clean piece of filter paper of the same size, and they are placed in a chromatogram chamber containing Cl_2 and ClO_2 fumes ($KClO_4$ + HCl) until the paper turns yellow. The chromatogram is then dipped into 1 % benzidine in 10 % acetic acid until the maximum color appears (Reindel, 1953). The excess reagent is removed by dipping into three changes of 95 % ethanol, and the paper is dried in air. Blue spots appear. Although the spots fade after a few hours, this test may be used after ninhydrin. It is useful for peptides and acylated amino acids but not for cysteine, cystine, methionine, and tyrosine. The reaction appears to be

$$-CO-NH- \xrightarrow{Cl_2} -CO-NCl- \xrightarrow{KI} -CO-NH- + KCl + \tfrac{1}{2}I_2$$

BENZIDINE-BLUE. Spray the chromatogram with saturated aqueous KIO_4, stand 1 to 2 minutes and then spray with 0.1 M benzidine in ethanol:0.8 N HCl = 1:1 v/v. Respraying with the benzidine reagent and/or with potassium periodate intensifies the color (Cifonelli, 1955).

BENZIDINE-BLUE. Spray with saturated KIO_4, after 1 to 2 minutes, counterstain with the following reagent: mix 10 volumes of 0.1 M benzidine in 50 % ethanol with 1 volume of 0.2 N HCl and add 2 to 3 volumes of acetone to dissolve the benzidine-HCl precipitate (Cifonelli, 1955).

COPPER SALTS. The copper salts of amino acids may be chromatogrammed with aqueous pyridine or lutidine. The chromatogram is then sprayed with 30 % acetic acid followed by a mixture of 0.4 % w/v o-toluidine and 1.0 % NH_4SCN in acetone (Miura, 1950–1951).

o-TOLUIDINE. The air dried chromatogram is washed with ethanol: acetone = 1:1 v/v and dried. The paper is then exposed to Cl_2 vapors (from 10 ml. of 0.1 N $KMnO_4$ + 10 ml. of 10 % HCl) for 5 minutes. It is then dipped immediately into an equal mixture of 0.05 M KI and a saturated solution of o-toluidine in 2 % v/v acetic acid. After 1–2 minutes, the chromatogram is washed with 2 % acetic acid and dried. The sensitivity of this reaction is 0.001 M of amino acid (Reindel, 1954).

SALICYLIC ALDEHYDE. Amino acids form yellow and blue spots under ultraviolet light after spraying with salicylic aldehyde. After the spots are marked, the Schiff bases are decomposed by exposure to air (Milletti, 1953).

Specific Reagents

Numerous tests previously used in solution for the specific groups of some of the amino acids, may be satisfactorily applied to these substances on paper chromatograms.

ARGININE[9]

α-Naphthol:hypochlorite reagent (Sakaguchi Reaction). The chromatograms are sprayed with a 0.1 % solution of α-naphthol in 1 N NaOH. After drying, the paper is sprayed with NaClO solution prepared from an equal mixture of ethanol and commercial NaClO (Clorox). Arginine appears as a red spot; 10 μg. or more must be used (R. J. Williams, 1950; see Block and Bolling, 1951c). (See Table II).

---

[9] Bonetti (1953) has used the diacetyl reaction for the quantitative estimation of arginine and other guanido compounds.

TABLE II

R_f Values × 100 of Guanidine Compounds (Smith, 1954)

Compound	Solvent[a]								Reagents[b]	
	BA	Ph	Ph Am	PhEt Am	EtAm	Bu MEK	MeAq Py	BP	Sakaguchi	F/N
Aminoguanidine·H_2SO_4	26	97	97	91	11		30	42	+	+
Agmatine·H_2SO_4 (guanidobutylamine)	32		97	97	14	9	10	12	+	+
Arcaine·H_2SO_4 (l-4-diguanidobutane)	11		97	95	0	2	10	16	+	+
Canavanine·H_2SO_4	17	51	59	37	2		16	16	+	+
Arginine	29		86	68	6	4	16	20	+	+
Creatine					16	9	55	40	–	+ wk
Creatine phosphate					11				–	+ wk
Creatinine	41		92	87	37	30	61	57	+	+
Guanidine·HCl	30		89	78	37	18	66	44	+	+
Methylguanidine	47		95	92	46	17	72	55	–	+ wk
N,N-Dimethylguanidine	53	95	97	97	51	18	78	57	–	+ wk
N,N′-Dimethylguanidine	54	97	95	95	65		80	70	–	+ wk
N,N′-Diethylguanidine	78		97				90	86	–	+ wk
N,N′-Dibutylguanidine	90			91					+	+ wk
Guanidoacetic Acid	30		71	47	10	11	40	31	+	+
γ-Guanidobutyric Acid	53	75	91	74	16	11	51	40	+	+
γ-Guanidoalanine	37	84	75	61	17			42	+	+
γ-Guanidohistidine·H_2SO_4	21	92	84	70	24			60	–	+
γ-Guanidohistidine picrate			92	77	20			57	–	+ wk
Octopine	15		47	47	2		40	22	+	+
Taurocyamine	19		61	40	16	20	52	48	+	+

[a] Solvents:

BA: 1-Butanol:acetic acid:water = 60:15:25.

Ph: Phenol:water = 80:20. Stable indefinitely.

PhAm: Add 1 ml. of 0.880 NH_4OH to 200 ml. of Ph solvent just before use.

PhEtAm: Phenol:ethanol:water = 120:40:40 plus NH_3 as above. This solvent is usually prepared by adding to the Ph (150 ml.), water (10 ml.), and ethanol (40 ml.). It is stable.

EtAm: Ethanol:water: 0.880 NH_4OH = 90:5:5.

BuMEK: tert-Butanol:methyl ethyl ketone:water = 2:2:1. To 200 ml. add 8 ml. of diethylamine.

MeAqP: Methanol:water = 80:20. To 200 ml. add 8 ml. of pyridine.

BP: n-Butanol:Pyridine:water = 1:1:1.

[b] Sakaguchi: + = red or orange. F/N: Ferricyanide nitroprusside reagent spray. + = red or orange.

Dissolve 0.01 % α-naphthol in ethanol containing 5 % urea.   Add KOH to 5 % just before spraying.   Air-dry a few minutes, and spray lightly with 0.7 ml. of Br_2 in 100 ml. of 5 % KOH (Acher, 1952).   This test is sensitive to 0.2 μg. of arginine.

8-Hydroxyquinoline.   A modified method consists in dipping the chromatogram into 0.1 % 8-hydroxyquinoline in acetone.   After the chromatogram has dried, it is dipped into a solution of 0.2 ml. of Br_2 in 100 ml. of 0.5 N NaOH.   Arginine and other guanines give orange-red spots (Jepson, 1953b).

Ferricyanide:*nitroprusside reagent.*   Mix 1 volume of 10 % $K_3Fe(CN)_6$ plus 1 volume of 10 % $Na_2Fe(CN)_5NO \cdot 2H_2O$ plus 1 volume of 10 % NaOH. After 30 minutes add 9 volumes of water and 12 volumes of acetone (I. Smith, private communication).

CITRULLINE

Ehrlich's reagent.   This amino acid is near glutamine on two-dimensional chromatograms and is best detected by spraying with a 1 % solution of *p*-dimethylaminobenzaldehyde[10] in 1 N HCl.   It gives a yellow spot (Fowden, 1951; Dalgliesh, 1952).

Diacetylmonoxime.   Miettinen (1952) advises the following method for citrulline after elution from the paper: 1000 mg. of diacetylmonoxime and 5 ml. of glacial acetic acid are diluted to 100 ml. with water (reagent A). Ten grams of arsenic acid is diluted to 100 ml. with 36 % HCl (reagent B). *Method: X* ml. (0–2 ml.) of sample plus 2 ml. of reagent A plus 2 ml. of reagent B plus $(2 - X)$ ml. of H_2O are mixed and held at 100°C. for 15 minutes.   The mixture is cooled for 2 minutes, diluted to 6 ml. with water, and read at 500 mμ.   Range, 1–150 μg. of citrulline.

CYSTINE[11]

(*cf.* Methionine).   *Phospho-18-tungstic acid.*   The paper is dipped into 1 % of Na_2SO_3 and partly dried in air.   Then the damp chromatogram is treated with Folin's phospho-18-tungstic acid reagent made alkaline with $NaHCO_3$ (Block, 1951c).   Cysteine and other reducing substances give a deep blue color without sulfite treatment (*cf.* Histidine, Ergothionine, etc.).

CYSTEINE AND HOMOCYSTEINE.   The hydrolyzate containing sulfhydryl compounds is adjusted to pH 5 and treated with an excess of HCHO for 24 hours at room temperature.   Cystine, cysteine, homocystine, homo-

[10] Addition of $10^{-3} M$ phenylhydrazine hydrochloride improves the reaction (Elodi, 1954).

[11] Toennies (1956) has shown that cysteine is oxidized after application to the filter paper after several days. The various oxidation products were separated with phenol:2-propanol:H_2O.

cysteine, and methionine are separated using 1-butanol:formic acid:water = 77:10:13 v/v (Strack, 1956).

Mercuric iodide. The chromatogram is dipped into a 5 % solution of mercuric nitrate, the excess $Hg(NO_3)_2$ is washed away with distilled water, and the sheet is dried at room temperature or at 100°C. The paper is then treated with 5 % $Hg(NO_3)_2$ followed by 0.112 N KI. The cystine area is colorless at low concentrations and yellow at higher concentrations. The background is red due to HgI_2 (Dent, 1949).

Mercuric nitrate:ninhydrin. Pasieka (1955) has reported a specific test for homocysteine. The chromatogram is sprayed with ninhydrin, dried and heated. Then it is sprayed with dilute aqueous mercuric nitrate. The reaction is catalyzed by Cl^-, $PO_4{}^{3-}$; $HCO_3{}^-$.

Feigl's sodium azide:iodine reaction. The dry chromatograms are sprayed with 0.05 N iodine in 50 % ethanol containing 1.5 % of sodium azide. The spots are best seen under ultraviolet light (K. T. Williams, 1951). Sjöquist (1953) uses a freshly prepared solution of 0.01 M I_2 in 0.5 M KI plus 0.5 M NaN_3 v/v. The sensitivity of this reagent is 0.5 μg. of methionine.

Sodium nitroprusside. The successful application of this well-known method to paper chromatograms is given by Toennies (1951) as follows: *Reagent 1:* Sodium nitroprusside (1.5 g.) is dissolved in 5 ml. of 2 N H_2SO_4 . Then 95 ml. of methanol and 10 ml. of 28 % ammonia are added. The solution is filtered and stored in the refrigerator. *Reagent 2:* Two grams of NaCN is dissolved in 5 ml. of water and diluted to 100 ml. with methanol. *Tests:* For cysteine use reagent 1; for cystine dip into reagent 1, dry slightly, and, while still damp, dip into reagent 2; for both cysteine and cystine prepare reagents at double strength and treat with equal mixture of 1 and 2.

Platinic iodide (recommended). Toennies (1951) has improved the $PtI_6{}^{--}$ reagent (Winegard, 1948; Block, 1951c) as follows: Add in the following order 4 ml. of 0.002 M $PtCl_6{}^{--}$, 0.25 ml. of 1 N KI, 0.4 ml. of 2 N HCl, and 76 ml. of acetone.[12] The dried chromatograms are dipped into this reagent. Cystine, cysteine, methionine, and some other reducing substances give a white spot on a red-purple background.

The reagent may be used after development with butanol-acetic acid and other alcoholic solvents without extra precautions. If phenol, lutidine, etc. are the developing solvents, all traces must be removed with ether-acetone (v/v), petroleum ether, etc. Palladous chloride in 0.1 N HCl may be used in place of chloroplatinic acid (Toennies, 1951).

Bromine. A 10 % solution of NaCN is added to H_2O saturated with Br_2

[12] The acetone must be purified by refluxing over and distilling from $KMnO_4$ and K_2CO_3 .

until the color disappears.   —SS— and —SH groups bring back the color (Matsukawa, 1953).

N-Ethylmaleimide.   The air-dried chromatogram is dipped into 0.05 M N-ethylmaleimide in absolute 2-propanol.   After drying in air the color is developed by dipping the chromatogram into 0.25 M KOH in 2-propanol (Benesch, 1956).   Compounds which contain —SH groups give pink to red spots.

OXIDATION AND COUPLING OF SULFUR AMINO ACIDS.   Cystine may be converted to cysteic acid, and methionine into methionine sulfoxide and sulfone, by oxidation with H_2O_2 (Dent, 1948).   The sample is applied to the paper, and the spot is dried.   Then an aliquot (equal to that of the amino acid solution) of 30 % of H_2O_2 followed by two or three times that quantity of 0.02 % of ammonium molybdate is added in the usual manner. Cysteic acid, methionine sulfoxide, and methionine sulfone are more readily identified on phenol:lutidine two-dimensional chromatograms than are the parent amino acids.   However, van Halteren (1951) cautions that oxidation by both bromine:water and H_2O_2 of cystine and cystine produce, in the presence of other amino acids, spots other than cysteic acid; and Matsuo (1953) has found that H_2O_2 oxidation of methionine (100°C. for 12 hours) yields methionine sulfoxide, methionine sulfone, α-aminobutyric acid, alanine, aspartic acid, cysteic acid, homoserine (?), and several unknown spots. Although the conditions used by Matsuo are considerably more drastic than are usually employed, the results indicate that considerable caution must be employed in the interpretation of chromatograms following the use of oxidizing reagents.[13]

In order to avoid destruction of cysteine, reduced glutathione, etc., on paper chromatograms, Hanes (1950) has coupled the —SH compounds with N-ethylmaleimide by dissolving the neutralized mixture of amino acids in aqueous $M/7.5$ reagent.   The S-substituted compounds may then be determined by the ninhydrin reaction and confirmed by the use of some of the sulfur tests.

HISTIDINE

ERGOTHIONINE, ETC.   Imidazoles are readily detected on paper chromatograms by means of Pauly's reaction.

Sulfanilamide (Block, 1951c; Bolling, 1949).   1 % sulfanilamide in 10 % v/v HCl; 5 % $NaNO_2$; half-saturated Na_2CO_3 .   Place 5 ml. of sulfanilamide and 5 ml. of $NaNO_2$ in a 50-ml. stoppered graduated cylinder.   Mix for 1 minute.   Then add n-butanol to the 50-ml. mark.   Shake for 1 minute, and let stand for 4 minutes.   Decant the butanol layer, and spray or

---

[13] Concentrated or dilute peracetic acid has given more consistent and better results in our hands than hydrogen peroxide or performic acid (unpublished).

dip the chromatogram. Dry the sheet in a current of air for 5 minutes and then spray with Na_2CO_3 solution. Imidazoles give a deep cherry red color.

p-Anisidine (Sanger, 1951). 1 % w/v *p*-anisidine in ethanolic 0.11 *N* HCl; 10 % w/v amyl nitrite in ethanol. Mix equal volumes of *p*-anisidine and amyl nitrite, let stand 3–5 minutes, and spray paper. Dry the sheets at room temperature, and develop the color either with NH_3 vapors or by spraying with 1 % KOH in ethanol.

p-Bromaniline. This reagent may be substituted for sulfanilamide. It is especially valuable for histidine and other imidazoles as it gives a relatively weak reaction with tyrosine and other phenolic derivatives (Block, 1951c).

Sulfanilic acid. Prepare fresh a mixture of 2 volumes of sulfanilic acid (9 g. of sulfanilic acid in 90 ml. of concentrated HCl per liter of water) plus 1 volume of 5 % w/v $NaNO_2$. Then add 1 volume of 20 % w/v NaOH. Ergothionine is bright red, thiolhistidine is light orange, and histidine is bright yellow with a red margin (Mann, 1953).

Sulfanilic acid. To 1.5 ml. of a solution containing 9 g. of sulfanilic acid in 90 ml. of concentrated HCl per liter add 1.5 ml. of 5 % $NaNO_2$. Let stand for 5 minutes, and then add 6 ml. of $NaNO_2$ solution. Let stand for 5 minutes, and dilute to 50 ml. This solution will keep for several days in the refrigerator (Albright, 1953).

Sulfanilic acid. Mix sulfanilic acid:HCl solution (1 g. of sulfanilic acid, 8 ml. of concentrated HCl, 100 ml. of H_2O) with an equal volume of 0.69 % $NaNO_2$. Spray, dry the chromatograms, and spray with 10 % Na_2CO (Karler, 1952; Baldridge, 1953).

Phosphotungstic acid. Spray the paper with a solution of equal volumes of 50 % w/v urea and 12 % w/v NaCN. A few minutes later spray with phosphomolybdotungstic acid (Folin's phenol reagent, see Block and Bolling, 1951). Ergothionine and thiolhistidine give blue spots (*cf.* cystine) (Mann, 1953).

2,6-Dichloroquinonechlorimide. Spray first with 0.125 *N* Na_2CO_3, then with 0.4 % w/v ethanolic 2,6-dichloroquinonechlorimide (Fearon, 1944; McAllister, 1951; Mann, 1953). This reagent differentiates ergothionine from uric acid.

2,6-Dichloroquinonechlorimide. Spray with 0.4 % w/v dye in ethanol. Then spray with diazotized sulfanilic acid buffered with 2 volumes of Na_2CO_3-CH_3COONa (1 g. of Na_2CO_3 plus 10 g. of CH_3COONa plus H_2O to 100 ml.) (Hunter, 1951) followed by a 2 *N* NaOH (Heath, 1953).

Dichlorophenolindophenol. Dissolve 800 mg. of the dye in 1 liter of water. Add an equal volume of ethanol just before use (Mapson, 1949; Mann, 1953).

Ferric sulfate.   Spray with 10% w/v KCNS; a few minutes later spray with aqueous $Fe_2(SO_4)_3$ (380 mg. of $Fe_2(SO_4)_3$ plus 2 ml. of 20% v/v H_2SO_4 diluted to 400 ml.) (Mann, 1953).

p-Chloraniline.   The paper is treated with freshly diazotized *p*-chloraniline and then exposed to the vapors of concentrated ammonia (Hall, 1952).

GLYCINE

Glycine, as well as histidine and tryptophan, gives a color when sprayed with Zimmerman's *o*-phthaldialdehyde reagent (Patton, 1949; see Block, 1951*c*, for preparation of reagent).

o-Phthalaldehyde.   0.2% in acetone, heat for 10 minutes at 50°C.   Colored spots with glycine, histidine, and tryptophan (Curzon, 1954).

METHIONINE

"ACTIVE METHIONINE" AND SULFUR COMPOUNDS (THIOHYDANTOINS). *Platinic iodide* (recommended).   See Cystine, above.

Na azide:iodine.   See Cystine, above. (See Table III for R_f values.)

Na nitroprusside.   Dissolve 500 mg. of Na nitroprusside in 10 ml. of water at room temperature.   Then add 500 mg. of $NH_2OH \cdot HCl$, followed by 1 g. of $NaHCO_3$.   After the evolution of gas has stopped, add 2 drops of Br_2.   Remove the excess Br_2 by aeration, filter the dark green or blackbrown solution, and dilute to 25 ml.   It is stable for 2 weeks (Grote, 1931). After 24 hours' standing, filter again, and store in dark.   Just before use, dilute Grote's reagent with an equal volume of saturated Na_2CO_3, and filter.   Spray, and expose moist chromatograms to steam for a few minutes (Kaiser, 1953).

ORNITHINE

Ornithine and glutamic acid have been reported to give three and four spots, respectively, on butanol:acid chromatograms after acid hydrolysis (Breyhan, 1953).

Vanillin.   Spray with a freshly prepared solution of 2% vanillin in *n*-propanol.   Heat at 110°C. for 10 minutes, then spray with 1% KOH. Heat at 110°C. for 10 minutes.   0.5 μg. of ornithine gives a yellow-brown color; sarcosine gives red spots (Curzon, 1953).

Vanillin.   Spray with 0.2% vanillin in acetone followed by 1% alcoholic KOH.   Heat.   Ornithine, proline, and hydroxyproline give red spots (Curzon, 1954).

PHENYLALANINE

If, after spraying with ninhydrin, the heated chromatogram is treated with dilute (0.15 to 10%) $NaHCO_3$, only the phenylalanine spot gives a stable blue color (Pasieka, 1956*a*).

TABLE III

R_f Values × 100 of Sulfur Amino Acids (Smith, I., 1954)

Compound	Solvent[a]							
	BA	Ph	PhAm	PhEt	EtAm	BuMEK	MeAq	Bp
Cystathionine	10	16	31	18	0	7	19	14
Cysteine	8	22	11s	15	2	6	18s	16s
Cysteic acid	7	6	7	5	6	19	41	26
meso-Cystine	8	12	17	15	5	5	16	14
Cystine	5	15	20s	16	4	6	18s	15
Djenkolic acid	9	22	38	18	3	50	17	17
Ethionine	58	84	84	70	45	57	61	60
Felinine	44	85	85	70	46	54	49	44
Homocysteine	18	32	40	21	3	11	30s	24
Homocystine	18	19	41	21	3	11	30s	24
Homocysteic acid	11	14	10	5	7	12	53	31
Lanthionine	6	9	23	10	2	6	10	11
β-Methylonine	9	15	38	18	3	7	24	15
Penicillamine	19	50	55	33	11	22	42	25
Penidisulfide	15	50	60s	33	12	25	40s	23
S-Benzyl penicillamine	82	95	95	89	70	90	62	71
S-Methylcysteine	33	72	78	58	35	41	41	45
S-Ethylcysteine	48	80	88	66	41	59	48	55
S-Propylcysteine	60	87	89	72	55	71	54	65
S-Butylcysteine	72	91	88	78	60	82	57	70
S-Amylcysteine	78	92	95	80	69	86	60	75
S-Benzylcysteine	70	91	92	79	54	80	50	75
Methionine	50	85	85	62	41	39	60	53s
Methionine sulfoxide	27	78	78	55	19	30	45	39
Methionine sulfone	22	60	64	45	18	17	43	31

[a] Solvent: BA: 1-Butanol:acetic acid:water = 60:15:25.

Ph: Phenol:water = 80:20. Stable indefinitely.

PhAm: Add 1 ml. of 0.880 NH₄OH to 200 ml. of Ph solvent just before use.

PhEtAm: Phenol:ethanol:water = 120:40:40 plus NH₃ as above. This solvent is usually prepred by adding to the Ph (150 ml.), water (10 ml.) and ethanol (40 ml.). It is stable.

EtAm: Ethanol:water: 0.880 NH₄OH = 90:5:5.

BuMEK: tert- Butanol:methyl ethyl ketone:water = 2:2:1. To 200 ml. add 8 ml. of diethylamine.

MeAqP: Methanol:water = 80:20. To 200 ml. add 8 ml. of pyridine.

BP: 1-Butanol:pyridine:water = 1:1:1.

PROLINE

HYDROXYPROLINE, ETC. *Isatin.* Dip into 0.4 % isatin in *n*-butanol containing 4 % v/v acetic acid. Develop in the dark for 24 hours (Acher, 1950), or steam for 30 minutes (Redfield, 1952).

Isatin (recommended). Spray with 0.2 % isatin in acetone. Heat for 10 minutes in H_2O saturated oven at 70–76°C. (I. Smith, 1953; Block, unpublished). Proline and hydroxyproline give blue colors; cystine and tyrosine often also given blue colors.   Glutamic and aspartic acids give pink spots which turn blue on standing.   The other amino acids give pink spots which fade (I. Smith, 1953; McKee, 1952).   Picolic acid (piperidine-2-carboxylic acid) also gives a blue color with isatin (Zacharius, 1952; McKee, 1952).

Isatin gives dark purplish blue with aspartic and glutamic acids; light brown with threonine, serine, and tyrosine; dark blue with β-alanine and γ-aminobutyric acid; bright blue with proline and hydroxyproline; bluish green with pipecolic acid, and pink with asparagine, glutamine, valine, leucine, glycine, and alanine (McKee, 1953).

Isatin.   A 0.2% solution of isatin in acetone containing 4% acetic acid (heat for 10 minutes at 100°C.) can be used to differentiate certain amino acids which are not separable with certain solvents (Saifer, 1954).   Thus blue, lavender, or blue-green colors are given by proline, phenylalanine, tyrosine, tryptophan, hydroxyproline, glutamic acid, lysine, arginine, methionine, histidine, aspartic acid, and cystine over a concentration range of from less than 1 μg. to 5 μg.   On the other hand, glycine, serine, alanine, threonine, leucine, isoleucine, glutamine and asparagine do not give an appreciable color with 10 μg. or less.

Two other isatin reagents have been described by Barrollier (1956): 1) Dissolve 1 g. of isatin and 1.5 g. of Zn acetate in 70–80 ml. of warm 2-propanol.   After cooling add 1 ml. of pyridine. 2) Dissolve 1 g. of isatin and 1.5 g. of Zn acetate in a warm mixture of 95 ml. of 2-propanol and 5 ml. of water.   After cooling add 1 ml. of glacial acetic acid.

The sprayed chromatograms, after drying in air, are heated at 80–85° for 30 minutes.   As the colored reaction products are insoluble in water, the excess reagent and background may be washed out.

Boyarkin (1956) recommends the following procedure: a mixture of 1.0 g. of isatin, 3 g. of Na acetate, 100 ml. of ethanol and 1 ml. of acetic acid is applied to the chromatogram.   After drying in air, the color is brought out by placing the paper in a chamber over ammonium carbonate.   The background color is removed by washing with 10% $Na_2SO_3 \cdot H_2O$:10% $MgSO_4$ = 2:8 v/v.

Isatin.   The air dried chromatograms are heated 2 to 3 minutes at 110°, then they are dipped into 0.4% isatin in butanol:acetic acid = 96.4 v/v. After drying in air, the paper is heated for 10–15 minutes at 110°, it is then dipped into N HCl and while still damp, the excess HCl is washed out with distilled water.   Only the proline spot remains (Pasieka, 1956b).

Isatin:p-dimethylaminobenzaldehyde.   After heating the isatin-treated paper, it is sprayed with a *freshly prepared* solution of 1 g. of p-dimethylaminobenzaldehyde, 90 ml. of acetone, and 10 ml. of concentrated HCl. Only hydroxyproline will give a purple-red color (Jepson, 1953b).   Sensitivity, 0.1 μg./cm.²

5-Bromo- and 5-nitroisatin. These compounds have been used in place of isatin (Noworytko, 1956).

Ninhydrin. If, after spraying with ninhydrin, the heated chromatogram is treated with 1 % NaHCO₃ and then with N HCl within 2 minutes, the hydroxyproline spot turns pink. The remaining color can be washed out with water (Pasieka, 1956*b*).

Vanillin. Proline, hydroxyproline, and pipecolinic acids give red spots after 6 hours with vanillin:KOH (*cf.* Ornithine above).

SERINE AND THREONINE

Periodate:Nessler reagent. The paper is sprayed with Nessler's reagent almost saturated with NaIO₄. Serine and threonine liberate ammonia and thus give yellow spots (Block and Bolling, 1951; *cf.* Giri, 1952).

TAURINE

o-Phthalaldehyde. Dip the chromatogram in 0.2 % *o*-phthalaldehyde plus 0.2 % urea in acetone. Heat for 10 minutes at 50°C. Dip into 1 % alcoholic KOH; heat for 10 minutes at 50°C. and for 10 minutes at 105°C. Taurine gives a red spot (Curzon, 1954).

TRYPTOPHAN

TRYPTAMINE, AND OTHER INDOLES. After removal of kynurenine on an ion exchange column, tryptophan, α-hydroxytryptophan, and 3-hydroxy-kynurenine are satisfactorily separated with water-saturated *m*-cresol (Hellmann, 1951).

Ehrlich's reagent. Prepare fresh a mixture of 1 g. of *p*-dimethylamino-benzaldehyde, 90 ml. of acetone, and 10 ml. of concentrated HCl (*recommended*) (I. Smith, 1953).

Ehrlich's reagent. 1 % *p*-Dimethylaminobenzaldehyde in N HCl (Block and Bolling, 1951) or 1 ml. of HCl plus 99 ml. of ethanol followed by exposure to HCl fumes (Tabone, 1948, 1950). Dalgliesh (1952) uses 2 % w/v reagent in 5 % w/v HCl. The color is developed at room temperature (*cf.* Citrulline, above). Reddi (1953) uses 500 mg. of *p*-dimethylamino-benzaldehyde, 1 ml. of concentrated HCl, and 100 ml. of absolute ethanol. Dissolve 10 g. of *p*-dimethylaminobenzaldehyde in 100 ml. of concentrated HCl. Just before use dilute with 4 vol. of acetone (Jepson, 1954*a*). The Ehrlich reaction may be stabilized by first spraying the chromatogram with 1 % w/v methionine, drying in air and then spraying with *p*-dimethylamino-benzaldehyde in HCl-acetone (after Nakajima, 1956).

Ekman's reagent. Treat the slightly damp chromatogram with HONO fumes (NaNO₂ + HCl) to diazotize, then spray with 0.2 % ethyl-1-naph-thylamine hydrochloride (Dalgliesh, 1952; Hellmann, 1451).

Ninhydrin. 0.2 % Ninhydrin in 10 % v/v acetic acid, heat for 2–3 minutes at 90–100°C.   Tryptamine and related compounds but not tryptophan and N,N-dimethyltryptamine give an intense blue-green color under ultraviolet light (3650 Å) (Jepson, 1953a).

Terephthalaldehyde.   Dip the chromatogram into 0.2% terephthalaldehyde plus 10% acetic acid in acetone.   Heat for 3 minutes at 105°C. Tryptophan gives a blue spot; tryptamine is yellow-green (Curzon, 1954).

Dichromate:formaldehyde.   Mix 0.1% $K_2Cr_2O_7$ (9 parts) with 37–41% HCHO (1 part).   Spray, and heat at 100–110°C. for 5 minutes.   View under ultraviolet light.   Sensitivity, 0.2 μg. of 5-hydroxytryptamine. Other indoles need higher concentrations (Shepherd, 1953).

p-Nitraniline.   Diazotized p-$NO_2 \cdot C_6H_4NH_2$ gives a red-brown spot with 5-hydroxytryptamine (Shepherd, 1953).

TYROSINE

DIIODOTYROSINE, THYROXINE, ETC.   *Pauly reagents.*   These are described above (Histidine).

Ceric sulfate:arsenious acid.   Iodine-containing compounds may be estimated as follows (Bowden, 1954; 1955; *cf.* Lissitsky, 1955): Mix equal volumes of 10% w/v $Ce(SO_4)_2 \cdot 4H_2O$ in N H_2SO_4 and 5% w/v sodium arsenite in N HS_2O_4 and evenly apply to Whatman No. 1 paper the same size as the chromatogram.   Then the dried, developed chromatogram is laid on the wet Ce $(SO_4)_2$ sheet and pressed firmly against it with a glass plate. After 30 minutes of drying of *both* papers, the I_2-containing compounds show as white areas against a yellow background.   View under ultraviolet light for greater sensitivity and for ultraviolet densitometry (Nanninga, 1951).

Dragúnová (1956) counterstained the ceric sulfate-sodium arsenite treated paper with ferroine (*o*-phenanthroline ferrous complex, G. F. Smith Co., Columbus, Ohio).   An aqueous solution of ferroine (0.01 to 0.066 M) gave red spots for iodine compounds on a blue background.   Fletcher (1955) counterstained with 1% *o*-phenylenediamine in acetone immediately after treatment with the ceric sulfate-sodium arsenite reagent.

Ceric sulfate-sodium arsenite-methylene blue reaction for iodoamino acids. Reagents: A. $Ce(HSO_4)_4$, 10% w/v in 10% H_4SO_4 v/v; *B.* $NaAsO_2$, 5% w/v in H_2O; *C.* Methylene blue, 0.05% w/v in H_2O.   All reagents must be made up in deionized distilled H_2O.

Procedure: The chromatogram is sprayed on both sides with a mixture of A and B in the proportion of 2:3 v/v.   An 18½ × 22½" sheet of Whatman No. 3 paper requires about 50 ml. of the reagent.   The paper is dried in an air stream for 5 min.   It is then sprayed on both sides with reagent C approximately 100 ml. per sheet.   The sheet is again dried for 5 minutes. It is then placed in a tank containing NH_3 vapors until the H_2SO_4 has been neutralized. This is indicated by the change in color of the background from pink to yellow. The chromatogram is then dried in air. The iodo-amino acids appear as bright blue spots on a yellow-green background. The spots are easily outlined and the concentration of each iodo-compound can be determined from the area of the spot (Mandl and Block, unpublished).

α-Nitroso-β-naphthol. Spray with 0.1 % α-nitroso-β-naphthol in 95 % ethanol. Dry in warm air. Spray with 10 % aqueous HNO_3. Heat at 100°C. for 3 minutes (Acher, 1952; *cf.* Block and Bolling, 1951). The test is given by phenols and 3- and 5-monosubstituted phenols, but not by ortho-substituted or 3,5-disubstituted phenols. Sensitivity, 1–2 μg. of tyrosine.

Oxides of nitrogen. Expose the phenol-free chromatogram to mixed nitrogen oxides made by the action of concentrated HNO_3 on Cu. Then expose to NH_3 vapor (Schwartz, 1957). Yellow spots appear for tyrosine and tyrosine derivatives. After fading, the spots will return on exposure to NH_3.

Comment. Although a number of investigators (Dent, Saifer, et al.) have employed multiple dipping techniques for revealing substances of different nature on the same paper chromatogram, special mention should be made of the careful studies of Jepson and Smith (1953, 1954a) on nitrogenous compounds and of Woodward (1954) on nitrogenous and non-nitrogenous substances. The former indicate that maximum information is given by sequences such as ninhdrin or isatin followed by Ehrlich reagent, followed by Sakaguchi reagent or Pauly reagent. Ninhydrin can also follow isatin. Other combinations are possible. Woodward (1954) employs the following sequences: first, ninhydrin for amino acids, amines, etc.; second, an acid-base indicator for acidic substances; and, finally, 3,5-dinitrosalicylic acid reagent for sugars (see Chapter VI).

7. "Large-Scale" Separations on Filter Paper

The separation of larger quantities[14] of amino acids, peptides, and other substances on filter paper chromatograms may be carried out by the following methods:

Method 1. The protein hydrolyzate is adjusted to contain 10–20 mg. of amino acids per milliliter. Then, thirty 0.01-ml. aliquots of this solution are applied to a 18 × 21-inch sheet of Whatman No. 3 filter paper.[15] The aliquots are placed on a line 2.5 cm. from the smaller length of the paper

---

[14] Van Gulik (1956) has described an apparatus for applying large volumes of solution in small spots. (See Chapter III.)

[15] It is preferable to wash the paper chromatographically with 0.3 N HCl, then with 0.5 N NaOH, and finally with distilled water (Bidwell, 1954).

and 2.5–3.0 cm. in from the long edge.   A mixture of known amino acids is placed on each side of the unknown.   After the chromatogram has been developed, guide strips containing the known amino acids and a small section of the unknown are cut from the paper and developed with ninhydrin.   The bands are cut from the remainder of the sheet to give suitable separations.   Bands which contain cystine, arginine, or lysine are eluted with warm dilute HCl (0.1 %); the other amino acids may be eluted with water (Block, 1951c).   This method permits the application of 3–6 mg. of hydrolyzate per sheet.   Obviously, for "large-scale" preparations a number of sheets may be employed.

Mueller (1950) recommends a very heavy filter paper (S. and S. No. 470-A) to which is attached a strip of less porous paper (Whatman No. 1) to act as a valve for slow delivery of the solvent (see section on paper, pp. 110–112).

METHOD 2.   An alternative procedure is to apply the amino acid solution in a series of twenty spots along the short side of Whatman No. 4 paper. These are applied starting 5 cm. from each short end.   The spots are kept smaller than 5 mm. in diameter by application at a very slow rate (0.01 ml. in 12 minutes) and by the use of a heat lamp (Hedén, 1950).   The chromatogram is developed with a suitable solvent (e.g., butanol:acetic acid) for such a time that the fastest moving amino acid moves to within a few centimeters of the end of the paper.   This is accomplished by allowing the solvent to drip off the paper or to attach a number of strips of blotting paper to the end of the sheet in order to absorb the surplus solvent (Miettinen, 1949).   The chromatogram is then dried and cut into strips to separate groups of amino acids.   The amino acids are then pushed to within 4–5 cm. of one end of each strip of paper by "chromatographing" with water or dilute HCl.   The strips may then be cut off and the amino acids eluted, or the amino acids may be further separated by chromatography employing different solvents for the separate strips as desired, i.e., two times one-dimensional chromatography (Block, 1950, 1951c).

8. SEPARATION OF α-AMINO ACIDS FROM OTHER AMINO ACIDS

Crumpler (1949) observed that the copper complexes of the α-amino acids are immobilized when phenol is used as the first solvent in a two-dimensional chromatogram, whereas other amino acids and amines are not.   This finding has been employed as a distinctive test as follows: The paper is lightly dusted with $CuCO_3:Cu(OH)_2$ to form a streak along the line which the amino acids would travel in phenol.   The quantity of basic copper carbonate used should be just sufficient to give the slightest visible green color.   It is important not to use ammonia or cyanide in the phenol tank.   The second development is with lutidine or lutidine:collidine without diethylamine. The α-amino acids do not move; the β- and γ-amino acids as well as the amines move in their usual positions.

9. RESOLUTION OF ISOMERS

DL-*Threonine and* DL-*Allothreonine.* Water-saturated *n*- or *sec*-butanol containing 10 % diethylamine will separate threonine and allothreonine on Whatman No. 1 paper in 114 hours development (Hardy, 1952). DL-2,3- and 2,5-Dihydroxytyrosine are separated on Whatman No. 4 paper with butanol:acetic acid:water (Dalgliesh, 1952).

Optical Isomers. DL-Tyrosine, DL-glutamic acid, and DL-tyrosine-3-sulfonic acid may be resolved into their optically pure components by *n*-butanol:acetic acid:1-methyl-2-phenylisopropylamine:water = 6:1:1:2 (Sakan, 1951) or 500:33:33:167 w/w (Nakamura, 1953; *cf.* Kotaka, 1951; Suzuki, 1951; Ogawa, 1952). Fujisawa (1954) has reported the separation of D- and L-kynurenine on paper with aqueous lutidine. The DD- and LL-isomers of alpha, epsilon-diaminopimelic acid have been separated from each other and from the other amino acids in a protein hydrolyzate using methanol:water:10 N HCl:pyridine = 80:17.5:2.5:10 v/v (Rhuland, 1955).

A preferable procedure to ascertain whether a D-amino acid is present or not is to spray the developed chromatogram, after complete removal of the solvent, with a weak solution of D-amino oxidase (Viobin Corp., Monticello, Illinois). The chromatogram is then incubated in a moist chamber for several hours, dried, and sprayed with ninhydrin. A decrease in color, compared to an untreated control chromatogram, indicates the presence and amount of D-amino acid (Proom, 1953).

10. QUANTITATIVE DETERMINATIONS OF AMINO ACIDS

Although the method recommended for the quantitative estimation of amino acids separated by paper chromatography has been given in detail in Chapter IV, it is believed that a review of some of the other procedures described in the literature will be valuable. These methods can be divided into two classes: the one involves cutting out the individual spots or bands and determining the quantity of material on the paper by conventional methods (colorimetry, etc.). This is called the *in vitro procedure.* The other method is based on the direct estimation of the amino acid on the paper and is the simpler and usually the more accurate. This is called the *direct paper method.*

In Vitro Procedures. After the amino acids, etc., have been separated by paper chromatography, their locations may be made evident by spraying with a minimum quantity of ninhydrin [0.02–0.05 %] (Naftalin, 1948; Boissonnas, 1950; Sanger, 1951) or by viewing the dried chromatogram under ultraviolet light[16] (Fowden, 1951). The appropriately marked areas are cut out of the paper (great care being taken not to touch the paper with the bare fingers), and the quantity of amino acid in the cut is developed as follows:

METHOD 1.   Each cut is placed in a test tube, and any absorbed ammonia is removed by drying *in vacuo* over sulfuric acid.   The paper is wetted with 5.0 % ninhydrin in *n*-butanol saturated with 0.1 % of phosphate buffer at pH 7.0.   After standing for 5 minutes at room temperature, the test tube is first immersed in a water bath at 55°C. for 5 minutes, then in one at 80°C. for 1–2 minutes.   The tube is cooled at room temperature for 3 minutes, and 10 ml. of 75 % aqueous acetone is added.   After 20 minutes the acetone solution is decanted, and the color is read with a 570 mμ filter (Naftalin, 1948).

METHOD 2.   Any trace of ammonia is removed from the paper by spraying with 1 % KOH in methanol and drying in a vacuum desiccator over H_2SO_4 (*cf.* Boissonnas, 1950; Fowden, 1951; and also Chapter IV).   The color is developed by any of the above-mentioned ninhydrin reagents after the paper has been buffered at any constant pH decided upon between the range pH 5.0 and 7.0.   The buffers commonly employed are 0.2 N citrate at pH 5.0 (21.008 g. of $C_6H_8O_7 \cdot H_2O$, 200 ml. of 2 N NaOH diluted to 1 liter); veronal at pH 7.0 (5.36 ml. of 0.1 M sodium veronal plus 4.64 ml. of 0.1 N HCl); or 10 % pyridine (see Moore, 1948; Awapara, 1949; Pereira, 1951; Fowden, 1951).

METHOD 2A.   Two-dimensional chromatograms [*n*-propanol:water = 7:3; water-saturated phenol (NH_4OH)] are stained with ninhydrin.   The spots are marked.   The paper is sprayed with 1 % KOH in methanol to remove ammonia.   The spots are cut out, and the individual amino acids are reacted with ninhydrin *in vitro* (Pernis, 1953).   The mean deviation of the mean is 2.4 % for the amino acids in serum albumin.

METHOD 3. The colored spots developed by ninhydrin on the chromatograms may be cut out of the sheet, and the color extracted by water, 50 % aqueous ethanol, 50 % aqueous acetone, and other solvents.   The quantity of chromogen in the spot may then be determined colorimetrically (*cf.* Chapter IV).   One of the most carefully conducted experiments of this type has been described by J. F. Thompson and co-workers (1951*a, b*) as follows:

Preparation of paper.   Whatman No. 1 filter paper (18 × 22 inches) is washed thoroughly with approximately 20 ml. of 0.3 N HCl.   Sufficient 0.5 N NaOH is put on the paper to neutralize the residual acid, and the

---

[16] In order to visualize amino acids and peptides on the dried chromatograms by ultraviolet light, it is necessary to remove every trace of phenol with ether, ether-acetone, petroleum ether, etc., before heating the paper at 100°C. for 15 minutes (Fowden, 1950, 1951).   If this is not done, considerable destruction of the amino acids may result.

sheets are washed with water until there is no test for free base. The sheets are treated with 0.1 % phosphate buffer at pH 7.0–7.5 and dried.

Two-dimensional chromatography with phenol and lutidine is carried out as described in Chapters III and IV.

Development of color. The air-dried chromatogram is sprayed with 2 % ninhydrin in 95 % ethanol which contains 2 % of a mixture of collidine and lutidine (1:3 v/v). After spraying, the sheet is placed in a jacketed chamber so designed that CO_2 will flow upward on both sides of the chromatogram. The CO_2 is passed through ethanol so that the color is developed in 30 minutes at constant temperature (60°C.) in the absence of O_2 and in the presence of CO_2 and ethanol. An internal standard should also be used (*cf.* Chapter IV).

Extraction of color. The spots are cut out of the paper and extracted for 15–30 minutes with 10 or 20 ml. of 50 % ethanol v/v. The color is read in a colorimeter or spectrophotometer with a 570-mμ filter.

METHOD 4. The color is developed with 0.5 % ninhydrin or other ninhydrin reagents in water-saturated *n*-butanol at 80°C. for 30 minutes. Then both sides of the paper are lightly sprayed with water followed by dilute $Cu(NO_3)_2$ [1 ml. of $Cu(NO_3)_2$, 0.2 ml. of 10 % HNO_3, plus ethanol to 100 ml.]. The spots are cut out and eluted with methanol. The color is read at 504 mμ. S. and S. paper No. 2043B is used (Bode, 1952; Fischer, 1953).

METHOD 5. The color is developed with 0.5 % ninhydrin in acetone. The chromatogram is air dried, then heated at 65°C. for 30 minutes. The paper is cut, and the cuts are extracted with 4 ml. of 75 % ethanol containing 0.2 mg. of $CuSO_4 \cdot 5H_2O$. The color is read at 540 mμ (Giri, 1952*h*; Airan, 1953). The small amount of Cu ions potentiate the ninhydrin color.

METHOD 6. The amino acid spots are located under ultraviolet light, cut out, and eluted with water. The eluates are concentrated to dryness, taken up in 0.1 ml. of H_2O, and the following reagents added: 0.3 ml. of 0.3 % ethylenediaminetetraacetic acid in $M/15$ citrate buffer (pH 5) and 3 mg. of ninhydrin in 3 ml. of aldehyde- and peroxide-free *n*-butanol. The solution is heated under reflux for 15 minutes, cooled, and diluted to 10 ml. with 50 % v/v ethanol. The color is read at 570 mμ (Meyer, 1953).

METHOD 7. The spots are cut out of the paper and eluted with 1 % ninhydrin in pH 7 veronal buffer (5.36 volumes of 0.1 M Na veronal plus 4.64 volumes of 0.1 N HCl). The solution is heated at 103–105°C. for 15 minutes, cooled in water for 5 minutes, and diluted to 10 ml. with water. The color is read in a colorimeter (Pereira, 1952).

METHOD 8. A very thin streak of the amino acid solution is drawn across the paper. After chromatographic development, the bands are marked under ultraviolet light (a separate strip is used as the ninhydrin control).

The bands are cut and eluted with 0.1 N HCl. The amino acids are determined by the Van Slyke method (Slotta, 1952; *cf*. Block and Bolling, 1951). Recovery experiments indicate neutral amino acids, 100 %; arginine, 80 %; lysine, 85 %; and dicarboxylic amino acids, 90 % (Slotta, 1952).

METHOD 9. The chromatogram is sprayed with buffered ninhydrin[17] (550 mg. of ninhydrin in 100 ml. of citrate buffer consisting of 21.008 g. of $C_6H_8O_7 \cdot H_2O$ in 200 ml. of water plus 200 ml. of N NaOH, diluted to 500 ml.). The colored spots are cut out, and 5 ml. of water, 1 ml. of buffer, and 1 ml. of ninhydrin in water-saturated butanol (100 mg. ninhydrin in 100 ml. of *n*-butanol) are added. After 3 minutes' heating in boiling water, 1 ml. of $SnCl_2$ solution (500 mg. of $SnCl_2$ in 250 ml. of citrate buffer, prepared fresh) is added. The solution is heated for 15 minutes, cooled, diluted with saturated NaCl to 10 ml., and 5 ml. of *n*-butanol is added. The color is extracted by shaking, and the butanol layer is read at 570 mμ (except proline, at 460 mμ) (Smith, 1951).

METHOD 10. The chromatograms are sprayed with 2 % ninhydrin in absolute ethanol. The color is developed at 20 $\pm$ 1°C. and 40 $\pm$ 3 % relative humidity for 30 hours. The spots are eluted with 5 ml. of 50 % aqueous *n*-propanol (Wellington, 1952, 1953), and the color is read at 570 mμ (except proline, at 440 mμ). The standard error as per cent of mean is 0.5–11 %. The incoming air to the chamber in which the chromatograms are developing is adjusted to 35 % saturation by bubbling it through aqueous glycerol, sp. gr. 1.234–1.235 (Wellington, 1953).

METHOD 11. The chromatogram is developed with 0.4 % w/v ninhydrin in 10 % aqueous isopropanol, to which 5 % collidine is added just before use, at 80°C. for 20–25 minutes in a moist atmosphere. The spots are cut out and placed in 3-cm.-long taped glass tubes with a sintered glass disk cemented in the tube to filter out any paper fibers. The colored compound is removed from the cut by blowing in live steam. The condensate is collected in a micro test tube containing a few crystals of sodium acetate (Lewis, 1952). The tube is weighed to determine the volume of diluent. The color is read at 606 mμ. Error, $\pm$4–6 %.

METHOD 12. One to two milliliters of solution of the amino acid is heated at 100°C. for 25 minutes with C_5H_5N, ascorbic acid, and ninhydrin (Yamagishi, 1953).

METHOD 13. The chromatogram is sprayed with 0.1 % ninhydrin and citrate buffered in methanol (Moore, 1948). The spots are cut out, wetted with 0.1 N NaOH, and heated at 100°C. for 2 minutes to remove any adsorbed NH_3 (Klatzkin, 1952). The non-ammonia N is determined by Kjeldahl. The cuts of equal size to those removed from "blank" areas of the paper showed 18–60 % as much N as in the amino acid spots.

[17] If peptides are present in the elutriate, the color yield is influenced by the nature of the N-terminal residue (Yanari, 1956).

METHOD 14. The amino acids in a hydrolyzate are separated into nine groups on circular chromatograms with 1-butanol:acetic acid. The bands are then cut, and the amino acids are rechromatogrammed with a solvent which will separate each compound of the group. Finally the separated amino acids are eluted, and the concentration is determined colorimetrically (*cf.* Method 5 above). The following groups are obtained with butanol:acetic acid: (1) lysine and histidine; (2) arginine and asparagine; (3) aspartic acid, glycine, and serine; (4) glutamic acid and threonine; (5) proline and β-alanine; (6) tyrosine and α-aminobutyric acid; (7) tryptophan and γ-aminobutyric acid; (8) methionine and valine; (9) leucine and isoleucine. The amino acids in groups 1–7 inclusive are separated by $C_5H_5N:H_2O = 80:20$; groups 8 and 9 by pyridine:isoamyl alcohol:water $= 10:10:7$ or by pyridine:amylacetate:water $= 10:5:5$ v/v (Giri, 1953 c, d).

METHOD 15. The chromatograms are run on heavier paper than is commonly recommended (Whatman No. 3MM or No. 4). After development, a marker is stained with ninhydrin. The spots (clearly separated) are then cut out and extracted overnight with 2 ml. of 0.18 M Na$_2$HPO$_4$. Two milliliters of Cu$_3$^{64} (PO$_4$)$_2$ suspension[18] is added to the amino acid solulution, and the suspension is shaken for 30 minutes. After filtering through Whatman No. 42 paper, a 1-ml. aliquot of the filtrate is dried on polyethylene and counted. The radioactivity is proportional to the amino acid composition. Error, ±2–3 % (Blackburn, 1950). This procedure requires clear-cut separation of the amino acids.

METHOD 16. The chromatograms are run on Whatman No. 3MM paper previously washed with the solvent and a small quantity of 8-hydroxyquinoline. After development with a neutral solvent such as 1-propanol:water $= 80:20$ or isobutanol:ethyl methyl ketone:water $= 70:50:30$ v/v, the amino acids are revealed by spraying with bromothymol blue (20 ml. of 0.15 % w/v bromothymol blue in 95 % ethanol plus 0.2 ml. of formalin plus 0.2 ml. of 20 % w/v KOH). The exact quantity of KOH will vary with different batches of paper. The amino acid bands or spots are marked and, after extraction from the paper, are oxidized in the Warburg with chloramine-T (Kemble, 1954). The Warburg solution consists of 0.4 ml. of pH 2.5 buffer (8.24 g. of Na$_3$ citrate plus 76.6 g. of citric acid in 250 ml. of water), 0.15 ml. of formalin (37–41 % HCHO), and amino acid solution in H$_2$O to 2.5 ml. The chloramine-T (0.5 ml. of a 12 % w/v solution) is

---

[18] To prepare the Cu$_3$^{64} (PO$_4$)$_2$ suspension, dissolve 500 mg. of Cu^{64} in a minimum quantity of HNO$_3$, add 10 ml. of 10 N HCl and concentrate to dryness. Repeat with 5 ml. of HCl. Dissolve the residue in 50 ml. of water. Run 10 ml. of Cu^{64}Cl$_2$ and 1.1 g. of Na$_2$HPO$_4$·12H$_2$O in 15 ml. of water from two burettes simultaneously into 150 ml. of water with stirring. Adjust the rate so that neither CuCl$_2$ or Na$_2$HPO$_4$ is in excess. Adjust the pH to 9 with 0.1 N NaOH, centrifuge the copper phosphate, and wash the precipitate with 2% w/v Na$_2$B$_4$O$_7$·10H$_2$O in 1.75% Na$_2$HPO$_4$·12H$_2$O. Suspend the Cu$_3$^{64}(PO$_4$)$_2$ in 200 ml. of borate:phosphate buffer, and "age" overnight.

introduced into the sidearm. The reaction is run at 30°C. for 20 minutes for all amino acids except proline and hydroxyproline, which are oxidized for 100 minutes. Since serine and glycine, as well as threonine and hydroxyproline, are not separated by either of these solvents, the amino acids may be determined before and after oxidation with periodate (see Block and Bolling, 1951). The error of the method is approximately ±4%.

METHOD 17. Dinitrophenylation (Isherwood, 1954b). After separation of the amino acids on a two dimensional paper chromatogram (washed Whatman No. 1), the dried chromatogram is sprayed with the following solution: dinitrofluorobenzene (60 mg.), ethanol 33 ml. and pH 8.4 borate buffer (0.2 M) 17 ml.[19] The reaction is completed by heating at 80° for 30 minutes. The yellow amino acid spots are cut out and eluted with a mixture of 5 ml. of 0.2 M borate buffer (pH 8.4) and 10 ml. of ethanol. Concentrate the extract to 0.5 ml., then air dry. Dissolve the residue in 1 ml. of 91% w/w H_2SO_4 and extract with 3 ml. of C_6H_6[20] by shaking for 3 minutes. Remove the benzene layer and repeat the extraction 5 times.

Dilute the acid layer with 2 g. of ice and extract the DNP-amino acids with 3 ml. of *tert*-amyl alcohol:benzene = 10:90 v/v. Repeat extraction. Back-extract solvent layer with 1 ml. of saturated $NaHCO_3$ and read color at 365 or 405 mμ. This procedure is used for all amino acids except glutamic and aspartic acids where a 1:1 mixture of toluene and benzene is used to extract the dinitrophenol.

Direct Estimations on Paper. Although several procedures for the direct estimation of amino acids (and other substances) are given in Chapter IV, it is desirable to present here several other methods which have been employed.

METHOD 1. McFarren (1952) (*cf.* Block, 1948, 1950; Block and Bolling, 1951; Patton, 1951; Salander, 1953) has used the maximum color density method (see Chapter IV) on amino acids separated by buffered solvents with good results. The amino acids are first separated into the following groups on unidimensional chromatograms: (1) Aspartic acid, glutamic acid, serine, glycine, threonine, and alanine are separated from each other and from other amino acids in protein hydrolyzates using pH 12.0 buffered phenol and paper. The alkalinity is neutralized by adding 4% acetic acid to the 0.4% ninhydrin in water-saturated butanol. (2) Tyrosine, histidine, valine, and methionine are separated with pH 8.4 buffered *m*-cresol; 2% acetic acid in ninhydrin. (3) Lysine and arginine are separated with pH 6.2 buffered lutidine; 2% acetic acid in the spray. (4) Cystine is

---

[19] The dicarboxylic amino acids are sprayed with the same mixture except pH 10 borate buffer is used.

[20] Purify the benzene over concentrated H_2SO_4, wash with H_2O, dry over Na_2SO_4, distil.

separated with pH 1.0 buffered phenol and 2 % triethylamine in the ninhydrin spray.   (5) Phenylalanine is separated with o-cresol at pH 6.2.
(6) Isoleucine and leucine are separated with n-butanol:benzyl alcohol at
pH 8.4.   (7) Tryptophan is separated with pH 9.0 buffered collidine.

Lugg (1957) has increased the accuracy of the maximum density method
as follows: after the reading of the chromatogram, as described in the previous chapter, the ninhydrin color is bleached with chlorine and the amount
of light absorbed by the paper is determined.   In this fashion, variations
in the paper are eliminated.   The standard error from triplicate chromatograms is reduced to about 8 %.

METHOD 2.   Numerous investigators have successfully employed the
technique of scanning the whole spot with a photoelectric colorimeter and
estimating the quantity of amino acid from the area under the curve obtained by a plot of the color densities (Block, 1948; Bull, 1949; Grassmann,
1951, 1953; Hiller, 1952, 1953; cf. Sulser, 1953; Sendroy, 1953; and Chapter
IV).   The German investigators usually apply paraffin oil:bromonaph-
thalene (80:20 v/v) to make the paper more translucent.   It is our experience that this added complication is quite unnecessary.   The error of
the total scanning technique was reported to be ±3 % even with rather poor
chromatograms (Hiller, 1952).   The relative molar intensities of amino
acids, read by the total scanning method after treatment with bromonaphthalene and paraffin, are tryptophan, 1.09; phenylalanine, 0.93; tyrosine,
0.79; glutamic acid, 0.84; aspartic acid, 0.89; glycine, 0.92; alanine, 1.08;
leucine, 1.00; isoleucine, 1.00; valine, 0.98; serine, 0.95; methionine, 0.85;
cystine, 1.16; proline, 0.09; hydroxyproline, 0.54 (Brüggemann, 1952).

11. APPENDIX: R_f VALUES AND SOLVENTS

The definition and use of R_f values has been given previously.   We wish
to stress the point made by Proom and Woiwod (1953): "We have not
found the R_f value of any great use in identification, and although it is often
quoted with an astonishing degree of precision, it is at the best only a rough
guide and should never be used as the sole means of identifying an unknown
substance."[21]   Table IV shows the approximate R_f values of amino acids in
certain solvents.

Although the absolute R_f values will vary with the length of flow of
solvent, the type of paper, etc., the relative order of the amino is seldom
changed.   Figures 1 and 2 show the approximate distribution of some amino

[21] Clayton (1954, 1956) showed that the R_f of an amino acid is dependent on the
relative volumes of the chromatographic chamber and the solvent.   He defines the
"critical volume" as the volume of solvent needed to saturate a specific chamber
under given conditions to give a constant R_f.   However, the order of the amino
acids is not changed.

TABLE IV
R_f Values

Compound	Solvent													
	1	5	10	11	16	18	51	65	104	82	23	96	102	105
α-Alanine	0.34	0.10	0.39		0.09	0.05	0.32	0.28	0.57	0.60	0.61	0.40	0.57	0.54
β-Alanine								0.22	0.48	0.66				
Allothreonine				0.37				0.34	0.66	0.50				
α-Amino-n-butyric acid				0.45				0.31		0.71		0.47	0.64	
β-Amino-n-butyric acid				0.50						0.74				
γ-Aminoisobutyric acid				0.48				0.32	0.59	0.77				
α-Aminobutyric acid								0.21						
α-Aminocaprylic acid				0.55										
ε-Aminohexanoic acid								0.19		0.86				
α-Amino-ε-hydroxycaproic acid								0.30		0.75				
α-Aminoöctanoic acid								0.55		0.89				
γ-Aminopentanoic acid								0.17		0.82				
α-Aminophenylacetic acid								0.44		0.80				
Anserine							0.10							
Arginine	0.34	0.02	0.19	0.19	0.05	0.01	0.16	0.17	0.22	0.89	0.30	0.20	0.43	0.31
Asparagine								0.21	0.36	0.40				
Aspartic acid	0.18	0.01	0.33		0.12	0.00	0.22	0.21	0.30	0.19	0.42	0.22	00.29	0.43
Carnosine				0.25			0.09	0.22		0.82				
Citrulline								0.23		0.63				
Cystathionine								0.14		0.31				
Cysteic acid								0.40		0.08				
Cysteine	0.16	0.02	0.17	0.07	0.01	0.00	0.14		0.24		0.11	0.17		
Cystine													0.20	
α,γ-Diaminobutyric acid				0.12				0.11						
α,ε-Diaminopimelic acid										0.30				
Dihydroxyphenylalanine				0.24										

Compound	1	2	3	4	5	6	7	8	9	10	11	12	13
Diiodotyrosine				0.70									
β,β-Dimethylcysteine													
Djenkolic acid													
Ethanolamine phosphate													
Glucosamine								0.55	0.61				
Glutamic acid	0.18	0.02	0.37		0.01	0.01	0.25	0.32	0.59	0.42	0.14	0.47	0.48
Glutamine								0.13	0.40				
Glutathione			0.17					0.38	0.89				
Glycine	0.21	0.07	0.33		0.05	0.03	0.25	0.09	0.33	0.46	0.27	0.41	0.41
Hippuric acid				0.93				0.44	0.69				
Histamine				0.22				0.20	0.31				
Histidine	0.25	0.07	0.19		0.09	0.03	0.28	0.22	0.57	0.25	0.31	0.37	0.43
Homocysteic acid								0.12	0.12				
Homoserine				0.30				0.24	0.41				
Hydroxylysine	0.35	0.10						0.41	0.95				
Hydroxyproline					0.05	0.05	0.34	0.27	0.69		0.39	0.44	0.56
Hydroxytryptophan				0.48*			0.60*	0.40	0.12				
3-Hydroxykynurenine				0.40*			0.65*	0.11	0.66				
Isoleucine	0.59	0.31	0.68	0.45	0.40	0.27	0.54	0.28	0.63	0.80	0.62	0.65	0.66
Kynurenine							0.55*	0.45	0.84				
Lanthionine								0.11	0.26				
Leucine	0.59	0.36	0.72		0.46	0.31	0.58	0.45	0.84	0.81	0.60	0.72	0.68
Lysine	0.25	0.02	0.18		0.02	0.01	0.14	0.11	0.81	0.27	0.14	0.35	0.66
Methionine	0.55	0.27	0.57		0.05	0.21	0.57	0.42	0.81	0.72	0.59	0.70	
Methionine sulfone			0.34					0.35	0.70				
Methionine sulfoxide			0.33					0.25	0.78				
α-Methyl-α-amino-n-butyric acid								0.45	0.84				
Methylhistidine								0.25	0.87				
Monoiodotyrosine								0.65	0.66				
Norleucine	0.42			0.78	0.51	0.36	0.60	0.45	0.84				

TABLE IV—*Continued*

Compound	Solvent													
	1	5	10	11	16	18	51	65	104	82	23	96	102	105
Norvaline		0.23		0.65	0.31	0.19	0.48	0.39		0.80				
Ornithine		0.02		0.15	0.03	0.00	0.13	0.11		0.79				
Phenylalanine	0.63	0.36	0.66		0.46	0.38	0.59	0.48	0.79	0.85	0.75	0.67	0.73	0.66
Proline	0.56								0.61	0.88	0.64	0.43	0.55	0.56
Serine	0.20	0.08	0.31		0.05	0.02	0.28	0.28	0.45	0.36	0.51			0.51
Serine phosphate								0.10		0.10				
Taurine			0.29					0.40		0.41				
Threonine	0.35	0.09	0.36		0.08	0.04	0.32	0.34	0.57	0.50	0.50			0.56
Thyroxine								0.76		0.86				
Trimethylalanine	0.56		0.61	0.66			0.62	0.50	0.79	0.75		0.64	0.67	0.63
Tryptophan				0.73		0.30			0.77		0.61			
Tryptamine	0.46	0.24	0.53		0.14	0.19	0.64	0.51		0.51		0.63	0.65	0.65
Tyrosine	0.50	0.18	0.56		0.22	0.15	0.45	0.36	0.71	0.78	0.75	0.55	0.70	0.65
Valine														

acids on a two-dimensional phenol and collidine chromatogram (first direction, phenol) taken from Dent (1947a). Figures 3, 4, and 5 show tracings of two-dimensional chromatograms with various solvents.

Excellent two-dimensional chromatograms have been obtained by Irreverre (1954), using *tert*-amyl alcohol:lutidine (solvent 64) followed by *tert*-butanol:formic acid (solvent 46), when a special technique which permits slow addition of the solvents to the paper is employed.

Some of the many organic solvents which have been used to separate amino acids have been given earlier in this chapter. Other useful ones are described below.

1. *Acetone:urea:water* = 60:0.5:40 v/w/v (Bentley, 1950).
2. *Acetone:chloroform:water:28% NH₄OH* = 300:50:40:2v/v (Cowgill, 1955) for imidazoles.
3. *iso-Amyl alcohol* saturated with 2 *N* NH₄OH (Roche, 1955) for iodoamino acids.
4. *iso-Amyl alcohol:1% v/v acetic acid*, saturated (Flavin, 1954) for cysteic acid peptides.
5. *tert-Amyl alcohol* saturated with water (Miettinen, 1953).
6. *tert-Amyl alcohol:2-butanol:water* = 4:4:1 (Miettinen, 1953).
7. *tert-Amyl alcohol:0.2 M phthalate buffer* (pH 5), saturated; for cysteic acid peptides (Flavin, 1954).
8. *Amyl alcohol:benzyl alcohol* = 1:1 v/v, saturated with water (Krishnamurthy, 1954).
9. *1-Butanol:acetic acid:glycerol:water* = 830:25:26:120, prepared fresh; HCN atmosphere (A. M. Smith, 1951).
10. *1-Butanol:acetic acid:water* = 250:60:250 v/v/v. Store in the presence of aqueous layer (Woiwod, 1949).
11. *1-Butanol:acetic acid:water* = 40:10:60 (Slotta, 1951).
12. *1-Butanol:acetic acid:water* = 68:5:27 (Roche, 1950).
13. *1-Butanol:acetic acid:water* = 4:1:1 (Reed, 1950).
14. *1-Butanol:2 N acetic acid* = 1:1 (Brown, 1954); for tyrosine, diiodotyrosine, etc.
15. *1-Butanol:2 N ammonia:dioxane* = 4:5:1 v/v (Brown, 1954); for tyrosine, diiodotyrosine, etc.
16. *1-Butanol* saturated with 2 *N* NH₄OH (Hird, 1948; Fromageot, 1949; Urbach, 1949; Kowkabany, 1950).
17. *1-Butanol: benzyl alcohol* = 1:1 v/v, saturated with pH 8.4 buffer (50 ml. of 0.067 *M* boric acid and KCl plus 8.55 ml. of 0.067 *M* NaOH); for leucine and isoleucine (McFarren, 1951a).
18. *1-Butanol:benzyl alcohol* = 1:1, saturated with water, in (C₂H₅)₂NH atmosphere (Block and Bolling, 1951).
19. *1-Butanol:tert-butanol: 0.1 N HCl* = 3:1:1 (Mitchell, 1949).
20. *1-Butanol:dioxane* = 4:1. The dioxane is saturated with 2 *N* NH₄OH (Gross, 1951); for thyroxine, etc.
21. *1-Butanol:dioxane* = 4:1, saturated with water (Block and Bolling, 1951).
22. *1-Butanol:ethanol:acetic acid:water* = 4:1:1:10 (Matsukawa, 1953).
23. *1-Butanol:formic acid:water* = 600:50:50. Reflux for 1 hour, then add 300 ml. of H₂O to hot solution, shake, and age for 24 hours (Wiggins, 1952). Use in place of phenol.
24. *1-Butanol*, saturated with 2 *N* HCOOH (Gross, 1951); for thyroxine, etc.

25. *1-Butanol:glycol monochlorohydrin:ammonia:water* = 50:10:5:16 (Munier, 1951).
26. *1-Butanol:1-propanol:0.1 N HCl* = 1:1:1 (Block and Bolling, 1951).
27. *1-Butanol:1-propanol: 0.1 N HCl* = 1:1:1 in 0.3% NH₃ atmosphere (Block and Bolling, 1951).
28. *1-Butanol:pyridine:water* = 4:5:1 (Miettinen, 1953).
29. *1-Butanol:pyridine:water* = 1:1:1 (Morrison, 1953); for pipecolinic acid.
30. *1-Butanol:water* = 85:15 v/v (Redfield, 1952).
31. *1-Butanol:ethylacetate:water* = 1:1:1 v/v (Cowgill, 1955) for imidazoles.
32. *1-Butanol:ethylmethylketone:water:dicyclohexylamine* = 10:10:5:2 v/v (Hardy, 1955). Hardy lists 15 other useful solvents and suggests the inclusion of cyclohexylamine or dicyclohexylamine in the solvent or applied in 95% ethanol before spraying with ninhydrin in order to produce distinctive colors with some amino acids and amines.
33. *1-Butanol:ethylmethylketone:water:diethylamine* = 20:20:10:2 v/v (Sisakyan, 1954).
34. *1-Butanol:propionic acid:H₂O* = 1246:620:974 v/v (Flavin, 1954) prepare fresh.
35. *2-Butanol:acetic acid:water* = 33:2:22 (Taurog, 1952); for thyroxine, diiodotyrosine, etc.
36. *2-Butanol:3% ammonia* = 90:40 (Hird, 1948).
37. *2-Butanol:3% ammonia* = 3:1 (Block and Bolling, 1951).
38. *2-Butanol:3% ammonia* = 150:60 (Hausmann, 1952); run twice.
39. *2-Butanol:tert-butanol:water* = 4:1:3 in 6 N HCl or 0.3% NH₃ atmosphere (Block and Bolling, 1951).
40. *2-Butanol:formic acid:water* = 150:30:20 (Hausmann, 1952).
41. *2-Butanol:acetic acid:water* = 40:10:50 v/v (Dakshinamurti, 1954).
42. *2-Butanol:3% w/v ammonia* = 150:50 v/v in the presence of a beaker containing concentrated NH₄OH:H₂O = 1:4; 1:4 or 1:2 v/v for iodoamino acids (Block and Mandl, 1957).
43. *2-Butanol:methyl acetate:0.5 N HCl:isopropyl chloride* = 50:30:16:4 v/v (Felix, 1952).
44. *tert-Butanol:ethyl methyl ketone:formic acid:water* = 160:160:1:39 v/v/v/v (Boissonnas, 1950; Block, 1952); especially useful for separating leucine and isoleucine.
45. *tert-Butanol:ethyl methyl ketone:diethylamine* = 40:40:20:4 (Redfield, 1953).
46. *tert-Butanol:formic acid:water* = 70:15:15 v/v/v (Block, 1950; Kowkabany, 1950).
47. *95% v/v tert-Butanol:pH 8.5 borate buffer* = 85:15 v/v (Hais, 1954). The buffer consists of 4.143 g. boric acid, 5.0 g. of KCl in 500 ml. of water. Then add 150 mg. of Complexon III (trisodium versenate) in 114 ml. of 0.1 N NaOH and adjust the pH to 8.5 with 0.1 N NaOH. The paper is sprayed with 0.2% ninhydrin in ethanol:acetic acid = 9:1 v/v.
48. *tert-Butyl alcohol:H₂O* = 70:30 or 70:25 v/v (Underwood, 1954).
49. *tert-Butyl alcohol:H₂O:formic acid* = 75:24.2:0.8 v/v (Underwood, 1954).
50. *Collidine* (buffered), saturated with pH 9.0 buffer (50 ml. of 0.067 M boric acid in 0.067 M KCl plus 21.30 ml. of 0.067 M NaOH) (McFarren, 1951a).
51. *Collidine:water* = 125:44 v/v. Develop in concentrated NH₄OH atmosphere (Taurog, 1950).
52. *Collidine:lutidine* = 1:1 v/v plus 35–40% H₂O (Underwood, 1954).
53. *m-Cresol* (buffered), saturated with pH 8.4 buffer (50 ml. of 0.067 M boric acid in 0.067 M KCl plus 8.55 ml. of 0.067 M NaOH) (McFarren, 1951a).
54. *m-Cresol*, saturated with water. It may be used alone, in HCN and 0.3% NH₃

(Consden, 1944; Polson, 1948), or in 0.03% NH_3 atmosphere (Sanger, 1951). Cresol is especially valuable for the smaller polypeptides.

55. *70% Ethanol* (J. M. Miller, 1952).
56. *77% Ethanol* with or without 1% diethylamine (Block and Bolling, 1951).
57. *80% Ethanol:H_2SO_4* = 1000:5 v/v (Tabone, 1951); for tryptophan, kynurenine, etc.
58. *abs-Ethanol:tert-butanol:ammonia:water* = 60:20:5:15 (Wellington, 1952).
59. *Ethanol:water:urea* ⇒ 80:20:0.5 v/v/w (Redfield, 1952); especially useful for aspartic acid and glutamic acid.
60. *Ethanol:ether:water:28% NH_4OH* = 40:50:10:1 v/v (Cowgill, 1955) for imidazoles.
61. *Ethylmethylketone:tert-butanol:H_2O:diethylamine* = 40:40:20:4 v/v (Clarkson, 1956).
62. *Ethylmethylketone:propionic acid:H_2O* = 75:25:30 v/v (Clayton, 1954).
63. *2,6-Lutidine[22]:tert-amyl alcohol:water* = 55:20:25 plus 1–2% diethylamine.
64. *2,6-Lutidine:tert-amyl alcohol* = 1:1 v/v; then saturate with water (Ågren, 1949), and add 0.1% diethylamine.
65. *2,6-Lutidine:collidine:water* = 1:1:1 (Dent, 1947; 1948). Add 1–2% diethylamine.
66. *2,4-Lutidine* (buffered), saturated with pH 6.2 buffer, 0.022 M (8 ml. of M $KHPO_4$ plus 2 ml. of M Na_2HPO_4) (McFarren, 1951a).
67. *2,4-Lutidine:collidine:water* = 1:1:2 (Auclair, 1952).
68. *2,6-Lutidine:abs-ethanol:water* = 55:20:25 v/v/v plus 1–2% diethylamine.
69. *2,4-Lutidine:methanol:urea:water* = 18:80:0.5:2 v/v/w/w (Redfield, 1952).
70. *Lutidine:H_2O:2-propanol:$(C_2H_5)_2NH$* = 55:25:20:0.6 v/v (Spoerl, 1954).
71. *Mesityl oxide:formic acid:water* = 1:1:2 (Bryant, 1951).
72. *Mesityl oxide:H_2O:88% HCOOH* = 25:50:25 v/v (Spoerl, 1954).
73. *Methanol:n-butanol:water:0.2 M citrate buffer* (pH 5.0) = 30:55:15:1 (Redfield, 1951); for methionine.
74. *Methanol:water:dimethylamine* = 80:20:0.1 v/v/v (Redfield, 1952).
75. *Methanol:ethanol:water:urea* = 45:45:10:0.5 v/v/v/w (Redfield, 1952).
76. *Methanol:pyridine:water* = 80:4:20 (Redfield, 1953).
77. *Methanol:H_2O* = 8:2 v/v (Flavin, 1954).
78. *Methanol:1-butanol:water* = 10:10:5 v/v (Hardy, 1955).
79. *Methanol:H_2O:pyridine* = 80:20:4 v/v (Clarkson, 1956).
80. *1-Pentanol:acetic acid:water* = 20:3:10 (Stanley, 1953); for thyroxine, etc.
81. *iso-Pentanol*, saturated at 20°C. with 6 N ammonia (Roche, 1953; Yagi, 1953) for diiodotyrosine, etc.
82. *Phenol[23]:water* = 100:20 v/v Mallinckrodt liquid phenol. Use in the presence of HCN (NaCN + H_2O), 0.3% NH_3, or 1:1 acetic acid (Consden, 1944).
83. *Phenol*, saturated with water, with added 0.002% 8-hydroxyquinoline (Wellington, 1951).
84. *Phenol:water:formic acid* = 79:20:1 in an atmosphere of NH_4OH plus HCN plus coal gas (A. M. Smith, 1951).

---

[22] Lutidine may be purified by refluxing over ethyl-*p*-toluenesulfonate (Cathcart, 1951) or boron fluoride (Brown, 1954).

[23] Phenol may be purified by extracting 50 g. with petroleum ether (b.p. 40–60°C.) at 50–55° with shaking. If only one phase results, add 1–2 ml. of water. Remove the aqueous layer. Crystallize the phenol from petroleum ether (Mars, 1953). Housewright (1950) purified phenol by distillation over aluminum filings (1,000:1 w/w) and $NaHCO_3$ (2,000:1 w/w).

85. *Phenol* (buffered), saturated with pH 12.0 phosphate buffer (50 ml. of 0.067 M NaH$_2$PO$_4$ plus 50 ml. of 0.067 M NaOH). Treat the paper with the same buffer before chromatography (McFarren, 1951a).

86. *Phenol* (buffered) = 100:20 buffer w/v. Buffer = 6.3% sodium citrate, 3.7% KH$_2$PO$_4$, and 0.5% ascorbic acid (Berry, 1949).

87. *Phenol:m-cresol:pH 9.3 buffer* = 25:25:7 w/w/v (Levy, 1953). Buffer is 200 ml. of 0.1 N boric acid plus 113.5 ml. of 0.1 N NaOH. This is used as the second solvent of a 2-dimensional chromatogram. The paper, except the portion where the amino acids are, is sprayed with the buffer.

88. *Phenol:ethanol:water* = 3:1:1 (Morrison, 1953) for pipecolinic acid.

89. *Phenol:H$_2$O* = 8:2 v/v (Flavin, 1954) for cysteic acid peptides.

90. *Phenol:n-butanol:acetic acid:H$_2$O* = 20:20:8:40 v/v on pH 2 paper (Krishnamurthy, 1955b).

91. *Phenol:H$_2$O* = 75:25 w/v (Underwood, 1954).

92. *Phenol:H$_2$O:concentrated NH$_4$OH* = 75:21:4 w/v/v (Underwood, 1954).

93. *Phenol:2-propanol:water* = 75:5:25 w/w in the presence of 0.1% NH$_3$ (Oreskes, 1955).

94. *alpha-Picoline:acetic acid:water* = 75:2:23 v/v (Pfennig, 1954).

95. *alpha-Picoline:pyridine:water* = 72:5:23 v/v (Pfennig, 1954).

96. *γ-Picoline:water* = 60:40 (Decker, 1950).

97. *1-Propanol:acetic acid:water* = 75:5:20 (Fincham, 1953).

98. *1-Propanol:H$_2$O* = 7:3 v/v (Flavin, 1954).

99. *1-Propanol:H$_2$O* = 80:20 v/v (Fridhandler, 1955). This solvent is especially useful in the presence of inorganic ions.

100. *1-Propanol:1% NH$_4$OH* = 2:1 v/v (Micks, 1954).

101. *1-Propanol:H$_2$O* = 70:30 v/v (Underwood, 1954).

102. *Pyridine[24]:acetic acid:water* = 50:35:15 (Decker, 1950).

103. *Pyridine:amyl alcohol:water* = 35:35:30 v/v/v (Nielsen, 1949).

104. *Pyridine:isoamyl alcohol:water:diethylamine* = 10:10:7:0.3 (Heyns, 1951; Giri, 1953; Block, unpublished).

105. *Pyridine:water* = 65:35 (Bentley, 1950).

106. *Pyridine:H$_2$O* = 8:2 v/v (Flavin, 1954) for cysteic acid peptides.

107. *Pyridine:ethanol:water* = 50:35:15 v/v (Iyer, 1954).

Section II: Amino Acid Derivatives

1. DINITROPHENYL (DNP) AMINO ACIDS

Preparation of DNP Protein

Five hundred milligrams of protein is dissolved in 0.8 M NaHCO$_3$ (pH 7.8), and 100 mg. of DNFB (dinitrofluorobenzene) in 6 ml. of ethanol added. After 3 hours of shaking at room temperature, the solution is acidified with 6 N HCl to below pH 3.0. The DNP-protein is centrifuged, washed with acetone and ether until the washings are colorless, and hydrolyzed with 6 N for 6–8 hours or longer (Sanger, 1945; Williamson, 1952). The DNP derivatives of the monoamino acids and the di-DNP derivatives

---

[24] Pyridine may be purified by heating 1 liter with 2 ml. of bromine at 50° for 30 minutes and then distilling (Dixon, 1956).

of the basic amino acids are soluble in organic solvents (ether,[25] ethylacetate, etc.).

When very small quantities of DNP derivatives are to be prepared, the following procedure is suggested (Sanger, 1953): The compound (amino acid or peptide) is dissolved in 0.1 ml. of 1 % trimethylamine; to this solution is added 0.01 ml. of DNFB in 0.2 ml. of ethanol. After 2 hours, a few drops of water and 1 % trimethylamine are added and the excess DNFB is removed by extraction with ether. The aqueous layer is evaporated to dryness, and the peptide is hydrolyzed with 3 drops of 5.7 N HCl in a capillary tube at 105° for 8 hours. The use of the amine eliminates the need for removing inorganic salts after hydrolysis.

PAPER. Whatman No. 1, No. 4, and S. and S. No. 2043 have been used. Whatman No. 4 buffered with phthalate (pH 6) is particularly useful (Blackburn, 1951).

SOLVENTS

1. *Chloroform:2-propanol:0.05 M K benzoate* = 45:49:6 (v/v) (Munier 1950).
2. *Cyclohexane:2-propanol:0.05 M K benzoate* = 60:36:4 (v/v) (Munier, 1950).
3. *Carbon tetrachloride:2-propanol:0.05 M K benzoate* = 56:40:4 (v/v) (Munier, 1950).
4. *tert-Amyl alcohol:0.1 M phthalate buffer* at pH 6.0 (Blackburn 1951). Phthalate buffer: 50 ml. of 0.1 M potassium biphthalate and 45.45 ml. of 1 N NaOH. Dilute to 100 ml.
6. *Propanol:petroleum ether* (b.p. 100–120°C.) = 30:70 (v/v), saturated with phthalate buffer of pH 6.0 (Blackburn, 1951).
7. *1-Butanol:benzyl alcohol* (v/v) plus 10% ethanol, then saturated with phthalate buffer at pH 6.0 (Blackburn, 1951).
8. *1-Butanol:ethanol:water* = 40:10:50 (v/v) (Kent, 1951).
9. *Phenol:isoamyl alcohol:water* = 1:1:1 (v/v). Place 300 ml. of 0.1% ammonia in the cabinet. After application to the paper, the spots are neutralized with NH$_3$ vapors (Biserte, 1951).
10. *Pyridine:isoamyl alcohol:1.6 N NH$_4$OH* = 6:14:20 (v/v). Place 300 ml. of 1.6 N NH$_4$OH in the cabinet (Biserte, 1951).
11. *Toluene:glycol monochlorohydrin:pyridine:0.8 N NH$_4$OH* = 5:3:1:3 (v/v). Mix toluene, pyridine, and glycol, then add 0.8 N NH$_4$OH; do *not* mix but equilibrate by standing for at least 1 hour. Carefully remove the aqueous layer, and then filter the upper layer to remove the water droplets. Place 300 ml. of 0.8 N NH$_4$OH and the aqueous layer in the chamber for 2–3 hours before starting the chromatogram. Equilibrate the paper for at least 1 hour (Biserte, 1951).
12. *1-Butanol, water-saturated* (Mellon, 1953). (See Table V).
13. *1-Butanol:n-butyl acetate:1% NH$_4$OH* = 1:2:3 (prepared 18 hours before use) (Mellon, 1953).
14. *Benzene:1% acetic acid* = 1:1 (Mellon, 1953).
15. *Isoöctane:ethylene chlorohydrin:1-propanol* = 20:1:1 (Williamson, 1952).
16. *m-Cresol*, saturated with 0.3% ammonia (Williamson, 1952).

---

[25] Ether extract should be purified by passing it through a water-based SiO$_2$ column and washed thoroughly with water-saturated ether (Mellon, 1953).

17. *Collidine*, water-saturated (Williamson, 1952).
18. *Benzyl alcohol:ethanol* = 90:10 saturated with pH 6.3 phthalate buffer (Newton, 1953).
19. *1-Butanol:acetic acid:water* = 4:1:5 is used for separating the water-soluble DNP-amino acids (ϵ-DNP-lysine, δ-DNP-ornithine, ring DNP-histidine and S-DNP-cysteine) (Newton, 1953).
20. *Sodium citrate:HCl buffer* 1 M, pH 6.2 (Rovery, 1953).

QUANTITIES USED. Usually 2–5 μg. of the diphenyl amino acid are applied to the paper[26].

DETAILED EXPERIMENT (Biserte, 1951; Williamson, 1952). The chromatograms are carried out in the dark at 20 ± 1°C. Solvent 11 divides the amino acids into seven groups: (1) DNP—aspartic acid, glutamic acid, and cysteic acid; (2) DNP—serine and hydroxyproline, (3) DNP—cystine, glycine, and threonine, (4) DNP—alanine and proline as well as dinitrophenol; (5) DNP—valine and methionine; (6) DNP—tryptophan, leucine, isoleucine, and phenylalanine, (7) DiNP—lysine.

The dinitrophenol is removed from the paper by chromatographic development with a 1:1 v/v mixture of decahydronaphthalene and acetic acid. Dinitrophenol has an R_f of 1.0 in this solvent.

DNP-valine is separated from DNP-methionine by means of cyclohexane:acetic acid = 1:1 (v/v), or the methionine spot may be oxidized with H_2O_2 and separated with solvent 11. DNP-phenylalanine is separated from the DNP-leucines with decahydronaphthalene:acetic acid (v/v). DNP-aspartic and glutamic acids are separated by means of isoamyl alcohol saturated with 5% of aqueous acetic acid. The chamber should contain the lower layer.

The quantities of the DNP-amino acids may be estimated by the methods given in Chapter IV, *i.e.*, maximum color density, area of spot, or elution.

Comment. A. R. Thompson (1951a) has pointed out that the hydrolysis of DNP-proteins and peptides with approximately 6 N HCl in the presence of tryptophan results in a considerable destruction of the DNP-amino acids. Yellow artifacts which are seen on chromatography of DNP-amino acids can often be bleached by exposure of the paper to HCl fumes (Sanger, 1953).

As an added confirmation of the identification of DNP-amino acids, the isolated DNP-amino acid should be hydrolyzed at 100°C. in a sealed tube for 2 hours with concentrated ammonia (sp. gr. 0.880) or with saturated $Ba(OH)_2$. After hydrolysis, the dinitrophenylamine or dinitrophenol is removed, and the amino acid (or acids) are identified by paper chromatography (Lowther, 1951).

If the acylamino acid (DNP, carbobenzoxycarbonyl, etc.) of a peptide is anodically oxidized, and, after hydrolysis, the amino acids are determined,

---

[26] The preparation and characterization of the individual DNP-amino acids has been described by Rao (1955).

TABLE V
R_f VALUES OF DNP DERIVATIVES (MELLON, 1953)

Compound	Solvent		
	12	13	14
DNP-amine	90	97	96
Di-DNP-tyrosine	78	90	33
DNP-leucine	74	71	70
DNP-isoleucine	73	70	70
Di-DNP-lysine	72	81	11
DNP-phenylalanine	71	70	55
DNP-tryptophan	70	68	28
DNP-valine	68	47	63
DNP-methionine	65	48	47
DNP-hydroxide	56	25	99
DNP-alanine	50	18	28
DNP-proline	48	17	44
DNP-threonine	43	12	0
DNP-glycine	36	8	7
DNP-serine	32	6	0
DNP-glutamic acid	14	0	0
DNP-aspartic acid	12	0	0
Di-DNP-histidine[a]	35	50	0
DNP-arginine[b]	37	0	0
DNP-ε-lysine[c]	32	5	0
DNP-α-lysine[c]	33	0	0

[a] Not soluble in ether layer.

[b] Preparation (Ramachandran, L. K., 1955).

[c] Folk (1956) describes methods for preparing α and ϵ-DNP-lysines.

the missing amino acid is that which was acylated (Boissonnas, 1952). Other acylamino acids are discussed under Organic Acids, Chapter VII (cf. Katz, 1954).

Acher (1953) has reported that hydrolysis of DNP-amino acids with 5.7 N HCl at 105°C. for 4–12 hours results in only a slight loss of DNP-lysine, arginine, and tyrosine, but that DNP-proline, glycine, and cystine are largely converted to the free amino acids.

Quantitative Determination of DNP-Amino Acids

Dinitrophenylation (A. L. Levy, 1954a). Dinitrophenylation is effected quantitatively by stirring an aqueous solution of the amino acids (20–30 μM. in 3 ml.) with a slight excess of 1-fluoro-2,4-dinitrobenzene (FDNB) for 80 minutes at pH 9.0 and 40°C., the pH being maintained at this value throughout this period by intermittent additions of standard alkali.[27]

[27] Koch (1956) employs a pH 9 buffer of M Na₂CO₃:M NaHCO₃ = 1:9 v/v to effect the dinitrophenylation.

Excess FDNB is then extracted with ether, the solution is acidified, and the DNP-amino acids are extracted into ether (5 × 5 ml.). The aqueous solution, which contains DNP-arginine and α-DNP-histidine, is diluted to 10 ml.

Chromatography.

PAPER. Whatman No. 1.

SOLVENTS. *Toluene:chloroethanol:pyridine:0.8 N ammonia* = 10:6:3:6 v/v; 1.5 *M phosphate* buffer, *M* NaH₂PO₄ plus 0.5 *M* Na₂HPO₄.

METHOD. A 2-ml. aliquot of the ether solution and a 1.0-ml. aliquot of the water solution are next applied to adjacent corners of an 18¼ × 22½-inch sheet of Whatman No. 1 filter paper, which is then irrigated by the ascending procedure with toluene:chloroethanol:pyridine:ammonia. The chromatogram is dried for 3–4 hours at 40°C., and the spots due to DNP-arginine and α-DNP-histidine are excised at this point. The paper is then run in the second dimension by the descending procedure with aqueous phosphate buffer. All the ether-soluble DNP-amino acids are thereby separated except DNP-leucine and isoleucine. The positions of DNP-tryptophan and di-DNP-histidine coincide, but this does not present a difficulty in practice, since the former amino acid is not normally present in acid hydrolyzates and the latter amino acid is determined as its mono-DNP derivative.

The spots are cut out and dropped into a set of labeled test tubes; three blanks are also cut from each sheet. Four milliliters of water pipetted into each of the tubes, which are then placed in a water bath at 55–60°C. for 15 minutes to allow complete elution of the color. After an additional 15 minutes to allow the solutions to cool to room temperature, they are successively decanted into a 1-cm. quartz cuvette, and the optical densities at 360 mμ (385 mμ in the case of DNP-proline) are read in the Beckman Model DU spectrophotometer against a water blank. The optical density reading of the tubes containing blank paper is 0.001–0.002 per square centimeter, and the appropriate corrections are made for each spot according to its estimated size.

CALCULATIONS. The resulting optical density ratios of the DNP-amino acids are converted to molar ratios by multiplying by the following factors, which, within the accuracy of the method (±4%), are independent of the composition of the mixture analyzed: Asp, 0.99; Glu, 0.94; CySS, 0.56; Ser, 0.97; Thr, 1.02; Gly, 1.03; Ala, 1.09; Pro, 0.93; Val, 0.99; Met, 1.21; Leu and Isoleu, 1.10; Phe, 1.03; Try, 1.54; Lys, 0.64; His, 1.62; Arg, 1.06. When the chromatograms are run in triplicate, the molar ratios are found to be reproducible to with 2–3%. Tyrosine is subject to rather wider variation.

When it is necessary to estimate the absolute amounts of the amino acids present in the mixture, two independent methods of calculation are available. The less accurate one (2–5%) involves a direct conversion of the optical density readings to micromoles by means of a set of effective millimolar extinction coefficients; they have the values $15.6/F$, where F represents the above set of factors. The greater inaccuracy of this procedure arises from differences in the absolute recovery of color from replicate chromatograms. These differences are not reflected in the molar ratios, however, since the variation seems to affect each amino acid to a comparable extent. The preferable method, therefore, combines the more accurate (2–3%) molar ratios with the total quantity of amino acids present in the mixture; the latter figure, in turn, can readily be deduced from the alkali uptake which accompanies the reaction of the amino acid mixture with FDNB. Thus, under the above-mentioned reaction conditions, the alkali uptake is found to be $77 \pm 1\%$ of the theoretical maximum (*i.e.*, 2 equivalents per NH_2 group, 1 equivalent for tyrosine-OH, and 0.25 equivalent for the imidazole ring of histidine), after due correction is made for the formation of dinitrophenol ($0.44 \mu M$. of $OH^-ml.^{-1} min.^{-1}$). The latter by-product does not interfere with the chromatography when the condensation with FDNB is carried out as described above in a solution approximately 0.01 M with respect to amino acids; for more dilute solutions, however, it is necessary to reduce the dinitrophenol concentration by sublimation (G. L. Mills, 1952) or on an alumina or silica column (Turba, 1955; Li, 1953) before application to the paper.

2. DIMETHYLAMINO ACIDS

The protein is treated with HCHO plus H_2 to give the N-dimethyl derivative (Ingram, 1953). After hydrolysis with HCl, the N-dimethylamino acids are separated as follows: (1) Wash Whatman No. 1 paper with 20% acetic acid and dry in air. (2) Develop with solvent (*1-butanol*:C_5H_5N: $H_2O = 5:2:3$; *phenol*:$H_2O = 4:1$ or *1-butanol*:*acetic acid*:*water* $= 25:6:25$). (3) Spray with either 0.04% thymol blue in 1:1 1-butanol:ethanol which is 0.01 N with respect to H_2SO_4 or with 0.1% orcinol in 1:1 n-butanol:ethanol containing 0.01 N H_2SO_4. After heating, view under ultraviolet light. N-Dimethylamino acids are definite black spots.

H. Kiessling (1954) has described the following procedure for separation and detection of the N-dimethylamino acids: *Paper.* Spray with 0.02 M sodium borate and dry. *Solvent.* tert.-Butanol:0.02 M $Na_2B_4O_7 = 87:13$ v/v. *Detection.* Expose the dried chromatogram to methyl iodide vapors in a closed container for 2 hours at 35–40°. Then heat the chromatogram at 100° for a few minutes. Dip the paper into 0.1 N $AgNO_3$ and wash with

H_2O to remove the excess $AgNO_3$. Reveal the spots with a rapid photographic developer.

$$(CH_3)_2N \cdot CHCOOH + CH_3I \rightarrow (CH_3)_3\overset{+}{N} \cdot CHCO\overset{-}{O} + \overset{+}{H} + \overset{-}{I}$$
$$\qquad | \qquad\qquad\qquad\qquad\qquad\qquad\qquad | $$
$$\qquad R \qquad\qquad\qquad\qquad\qquad\qquad\qquad R$$

3. HYDANTOINS AND THIOHYDANTOINS

The protein is treated with an excess of potassium cyanate (hot) or with phenyl isothiocyanate in pH 7.7 phosphate buffer (Jensen, 1935; Edman, 1948; Kaiser, 1953; Dautrevaux, 1955) and, after hydrolysis with 2 N HCl (Edman, 1953; Edward, 1953), or 20 % HCl at 150° for 16 hours (Aschan, 1884; A. L. Levy, 1954b). The phenylthiohydantoins are extracted with ether and separated by paper chromatography.[28]

The paper used is Whatman No. 4 previously treated with 0.05 M phosphate buffer at pH 6 (Sanger, 1945; Kaiser, 1953) or Whatman No. 1 impregnated with 0.5 % starch[29] (Sjöquist, 1953).

The following solvents have been used for the separation of the phenylthiohydantoins: (1) sec-butanol saturated with 0.05 M phosphate buffer (pH 6) (Kaiser, 1953); (2) xylene:acetic acid:pH 6 buffer = 3:2:1 (Kaiser, 1953); (3) heptane:C_5H_5N = 70:30 v/v (Sjöquits, 1953); (4) heptane:1-butanol:HCOOH = 40:20:40 v/v or 40:40:20. Use the upper layer (Sjöquist, 1953). It is important to equilibrate the paper vith the solvent atmosphere.

SPRAYS. Feigl's I_2-Na azide or Grote's nitroprusside reagent (cf. Section I, Specific Reagents) or 4 % p-dimethylaminobenzaldehyde (Phillips, 1954).

4. HYDRAZINOLYSIS OF C-TERMINAL AMINO ACID

The polypeptides are heated at 125°C. for 1 hour with an excess of anhydrous hydrazine. The excess reagent is removed over H_2SO_4 in vacuo. The residue is dissolved in water and chromatographed with pyridine:aniline:water = 9:1:4 v/v. The amino acid hydrazide is revealed by spraying with ninhydrin (red-purple) or with ammoniacal $AgNO_3$ in butanol (black spots) (Akabori, 1952; Bradbury, 1956).

[28] Drèze (1956) has used 4-dimethyl-3,5-dinitrophenylisocyanate to prepare the intensely colored DDP-amino acid hydantoins. These may be separated on Whatman No. 20 paper pretreated with 0.05 M phthalate buffer at pH 6.0 with the following solvents

    1. *Xylene:acetic acid:0.05 M phthalate*, pH 6.0 = 3:2:1 v/v
    2. *2-Butanol:0.05 M phthalate* = 7:1 v/v
    3. *Toluene:2-chloroethanol:pyridine:phthalate* = 10:6:3:6 v/v
    4. *Ligroin (B.P. > 120°):pyridine* = 7.3 v/v

[29] The starch should be washed with 2.5% 8-quinolinol in ethanol and the reagent removed by extraction with ethanol.

TABLE VI
R_f Values of Amino Alcohols (Fromageot, 1950)

	Solvent		
Compound	1	2	3
Ethanolamine	0.18	0.15	0.74
Alaninol	0.25	0.23	0.83
Serinol	0.16	0.15	0.69
Threoninol	0.17	0.31	
Valinol	0.40	0.49	1
Leucinol	0.53	0.63	1
Isoleucinol	0.50	0.63	1
Prolinol	0.28	0.26	1
Phenylalaninol	0.54	0.70	1
Tyrosinol	0.40	0.54	0.81
Aspartidiol	0.19	0.23	0.82
Glutamidiol	0.21	0.23	0.85
Lysinol	0.08	0.07	0.78
Argininol	0.08	0.07	
Histidinol	0.08	0.12	

Comment.[30] The identity of the phenylthiohydantoin is best confirmed after hydrolysis with $Ba(OH)_2$ and paper chromatography of the resulting amino acids. Evans (1954) has used the colored 4-dimethylamino-3,5-dinitrophenyl isocyanate for the qualitative and quantitative estimation of N-terminal amino acids of proteins.

5. AMINO ALCOHOLS

The free carboxyl groups of amino acids, peptides, and proteins may be reduced to the corresponding amino alcohols by lithium aluminum hydride in N-ethylmorpholine (Fromageot, 1950). The resulting alcohols, after liberation from peptide linkage by acid hydrolysis, are extracted from an alkaline solution (pH 9–10) with ether and identified on paper chromatograms.

SOLVENTS (Fromageot, 1950). (1) *1-Butanol:acetic acid:water* = 77:6:17 v/v; (2) *1-butanol* saturated with 0.1% NH_4OH; (3) *phenol* saturated with 0.1% NH_4OH.

PAPER. Whatman No. 1.

COLOR REAGENTS. Ninhydrin or specific color reagents commonly used for amino acids are employed (*cf.* Section I). The R_f values are given in Table VI.

[30] The chromatography of dithiocarbaminocarboxylic acids on paper treated with 0.05 M sodium borate has been described by Zahradnik (1956).

Comment. Lithium aluminum hydride reduction permits differentiation of the γ-COOH- and α-COOH-linked carboxyls of glutamic acid (Jollès, 1952).

Another method for ascertaining the C-terminal amino acids in peptides or proteins is that introduced by Schlack (1926). The benzoylated protein is treated with an excess of ammonium thiocyanate in acetic anhydride on the water bath in the absence of moisture. The C-terminal amino acid is then split off as the thiohydantoin.

6. Amino Acids Not Usually Present in Protein Hydrolyzates[31]

Adenosylmethionine [methyl-(5-deoxyribosyladenine)-(2-amino-butyro)thetin] separated with ethanol:acetic acid:H_2O = 80:5:15 (Cantoni, 1953) or in dilute salt solutions (Baddiley, 1953).

α-*Aminobutyric acid* is separated from other aminobutyric acids by ethanol: water = 9:1 v/v (Oshima, 1953).

γ-*Aminobutyric acid* is separated on phenol:lutidine two-dimensional chromatograms (*cf.* Fig. 2) (Dent, 1947b; Roberts, 1950; Reed, 1950).

β-*Aminoisobutyric acid* is separated with phenol followed by 2-butanol:*tert*-butanol:water = 5:1:5.6 v/v (Fink, 1952).

γ-*Amino-α-methylenebutyric acid* (*cf.* γ-methyleneglutamine; Fowden, 1953*)*.

α-*Aminopentanoic acid* is separated on phenol and butanol:acetic acid two-dimensional chromatograms (Proom, 1953).

α-*Aminopimelic acid* in green plants (Virtanen, 1954a).

Arginosuccinic acid has an R_f of 0.26 in phenol (NH_4OH) and 0.08 in 1-butanol:acetic acid (Walker, 1953).

Azetidine-2-carboxylic acid has been found in a number of plants

$$CH_2\!-\!CH\cdot COOH$$
$$CH_2\!-\!NH$$

(Fowden, 1955; 1956).

Cystathionine is separated after H_2O_2 oxidation with phenol:acetic acid followed by 1-butanol:acetic acid (Berridge, 1952).

α,ϵ-*Diamino-β-hydroxypimelic acid* below α,ϵ-diaminopimelic acid in phenol (Woolley, 1952).

α,ϵ-*diaminopimelic acid* is the slowest moving spot with 1-butanol:HCOOH = 18:2 v/v, saturated with H_2O (Gendre, 1952; *cf.* Work, 1951; Asselineau, 1950).

Felenine, presumably 4-hydroxyisoamylcysteine, is between leucine and phenylalanine on phenol:lutidine two-dimensional chromatograms (Westall, 1953).

Homoserine is between glycine and alanine on 1-butanol:water:phenol (0.5% NH_3) two-dimensional chromatograms (Miettinen, 1953).

γ-*Hydroxy-α-amino adipic acid* and its lactone have been found in green plants by Virtanen (1954b).

Lanthionine separated after H_2O_2 oxidation with phenol:acetic acid followed by 1-butanol:acetic acid (Berridge, 1952).

---

[31] Bricas (1953) has given a list of the uncommon amino acids found in naturally occurring peptides.

S-Methyl cysteine sulfoxide has been found in extracts of cabbage (Synge, 1955). *Methylhistidine, α-methyl-β-alanine, etc.* See Fig. 1, (page 114). (also Awapara, 1950; Crumpler, 1951). Methylhistidine is characterized by the fact that it gives a green spot with ninhydrin when the chromatogram is heated above 110°C.

γ-Methyleneglutamic acid (see γ-methyleneglutamine).

γ-Methyleneglutamine separated on phenol:lutidine two-dimensional chromatograms. It gives first a yellow-brown, then deep orange, and finally an orange-brown color with ninhydrin after continued heating (Done, 1952).

Piperidine-2-carboxylic acid gives a purple spot with ninhydrin after heating 1–2 minutes at 110°C. and Feigl's nitroprusside:acetaldehyde for secondary amines (Hulme, 1952). It appears between proline and phenylalanine on two-dimensional chromatograms (phenol:ethanol:water = 3:1:1; 1-butanol:C_5H_5N:water = 1:1:1) (Morrison, 1953).

Section III: Amines

The primary amines that give a color with ninhydrin have been studied most extensively. Thus, Bremner (1951) has found that, as expected, the R_f value of the primary aliphatic amines increases with increasing number of carbon atoms in various aqueous solvents, at least for the series methylamine to *n*-heptylamine. Thus $R_m = \left[\log_{10}\left(\frac{1}{R_f} - 1\right) \right]$, where m is the molecular weight. (See Table VII)

SOLVENTS. Besides the solvents commonly employed for the chromatographic separation of the amino acids (*cf.* Section I), other useful solvents are (1) *m-Cresol:acetic acid:water* = 50:2:48 v/v (Bremner, 1951); (2) *1-butanol:glycol monochlorohydrin:conc.* $NH_4OH:H_2O$ = 50:10:5:16 v/v, use the upper layer (Munier, 1951); (3) *1-butanol:acetic acid:water* = 2:1:1 (Baker, 1952); (4) methylethylketone:propionic acid:H_2O = 75:25:30 v/v (Schmidt, 1956; *cf.* Bighi, 1955; Booth, 1955; Dal Nogare, 1956; and Riley, 1954).

PAPER. The usual Whatman papers have been employed.

QUANTITIES USED. The amounts of amine which are required depend, of course, on the reagent used to develop the color, but in general from 5 to 10 μg. is needed.

COLOR REAGENTS. Besides ninhydrin and the many specific and nonspecific reagents used for the amino acids (*cf.* Section I), the following reagents are employed for the detection of amines. (*cf.* Bertetti, 1953, 1954).

1. *m-Nitraniline.* A dilute solution (2 mg./ml.) of *m*-nitraniline is sprayed on the paper, after which the dry chromatogram is exposed to amyl nitrite vapors (Burmistrov, 1946).

2. *Quinone.* Quinone (500 mg.), pyridine (10 ml.), and *n*-butanol (40 ml.) in solution has been suggested as a specific color reagent for choline (Munier, 1950). Other quaternary amines may be visualized with Dragendorff's reagent (Kariyone, 1951).

TABLE VII

R_f VALUES OF AMINES ON WHATMAN NO. 4 PAPER AT ROOM TEMPERATURE
(BREMNER, 1951)

Compound	n-Butanol (40%), acetic acid (10%), water (50%)
Methylamine	0.37
Ethylamine	0.45
n-Propylamine	0.58
n-Butylamine	0.70
n-Amylamine	0.77
n-Heptylamine	0.85
Isopropylamine	0.57
Isoamylamine	0.77
1,2-Diaminoethane	0.14
1,3-Diaminopropane	0.15
1,4-Diaminobutane (putrescine)	0.16
1,5-Diaminopentane (cadaverine)	0.17
1,6-Diaminohexane	0.20
Benzylamine	0.68
β-Phenylethylamine	0.72
β,β-Diphenylethylamine	0.72
β-Phenyl-β-hydroxyethylamine	0.65
Adrenaline	0.45
Agmatine	0.05
Allylamine	0.50
Ethanolamine	0.33
Dimethylamine	0.43
Ephedrine	0.75
Glucosamine	0.24
Histamine	0.19
Spermine	0.07
Tryptamine	0.67
Tyramine	0.62

3. *Dragendorff's $KBiI_4$ reagent.* Eight grams of bismuth subnitrate is dissolved in 20–25 ml. of 30% HNO_3 (sp. gr. 1.18). This is added slowly with stirring to a solution of 28 g. of KI and 1 ml. of 6 N HCl in approximately 5 ml. of water (Guggenheim, 1940; Bregoff, 1953). The solution is cooled in the refrigerator, filtered, and diluted to 100 ml. with water. It is stable for a few weeks in the cold and dark. The color reagent is prepared from the stock solution as follows: Mix in order 20 ml. of water, 5 ml. of 6 N HCl, 2 ml. of stock $KBiI_4$, and 5 ml. of 6 N HCl. A few drops of 6 N HCl may be added if not all the $Bi(OH)_3$ dissolves. The reagent stable for 10 days (Bregoff, 1953; *cf.* Kariyone, 1951).

4. *o-Acetoacetylphenol* (1 % in n-butanol). Spray, dry, and view under ultraviolet light (Baker, 1952). This reagent is specific for primary aliphatic amines exclusive of zwitterions.

5. *Ferric hydroxamate.* Amine esters may be revealed with the following reagents (*cf.* Chapter VII). (A) Hydroxylamine: 20 g. of $NH_2OH \cdot HCl$ in 50 ml. of water, diluted to 200 ml. with ethanol; keep cold. (B.) 50 g. of KOH in a minimum amount of water, diluted to 500 ml. with ethanol. (C) Powdered $FeCl_3 \cdot 6H_2O$ (10 g.) in 20 ml. of 10 N HCl. Shake with 300 ml. of ether until a homogeneous solution results. Mix reagents A and B (1:2 v/v), and filter off KCl. Spray paper with mixed A and B, dry briefly, spray with C (Whittaker, 1952).

6. *Chloranil: tetrachlorobenzoquinone* in epichlorohydrin gives red color with some amines, amino acids, phenols, etc. (Crippa, 1954).

PREPARATION OF SAMPLE. The majority of amines may be separated from amino acids, sugars inorganic ions, etc., by extraction from alkaline solution with a water-immiscible organic solvent. A procedure which has been found (Block, 1951c) to be very satisfactory for amines derived from the decarboxylation of the α-amino acids is as follows:

A 5-ml. aliquot of the amine-containing aqueous solution is added to 6 g. of a mixture of $K_3PO_4 : Na_2SO_4$ (1:6 w/w) dissolved in 15 ml. of hot water (Urbach, 1949; McIntire, 1947). The amines (tyramine, histamine, phenylethylamine, cadaverine, putrescine, etc.) are extracted with peroxide-free ether in a continuous liquid-liquid extractor (Scientific Glass Apparatus Co., No. J-1631) for 24 or 48 hours. In the receiving flask is placed 1 ml. of 4% aqueous phosphoric acid. At the end of the extraction period, the ether is removed from the aqueous solution in the receiver flask. The residue is diluted with water, neutralized to pH 7 with NaOH and the solution saturated with $K_3PO_4 : Na_2SO_4$ mixture. The amines are extracted from this alkaline solution with 1-butanol. The butanol extracts are dried with Na_2SO_4. A small quantity of gaseous HCl is passed into the butanol solution to neutralize the amines. The butanol is immediately concentrated *in vacuo* to a convenient volume for paper chromatography.

Comments. Racemic β-naphtholbenzylamine has been resolved with aqueous tartaric acid (Bonino, 1951).[32] Miettinen (1952) has pointed out that the R_f value of ethanolamine developed with aqueous phenol is highly sensitive to changes in pH of the solvent. Octopamine (*l-p*-hydroxyphenylethanolamine, 1-noradrenaline) may be visualized on paper with usual reagents for both amines and phenols (Erspamer, 1952).

Section IV: DNP-Amines

Dinitrofluorobenzene (0.15 μl.) in 0.2 ml. of ethanol is added to 10 μg. of amine in 0.1 ml. of H_2O plus 0.1 ml. of 0.2 N Na_2CO_3. After standing at room temperature for 15 minutes, the tube is sealed and heated at 105° for 2 hours. The excess DNFB is removed by adding 300 μg. of glycine

[32] *Threo-* and *erythro*-phenylserines have been separated by paper chromatography (Drell, 1955).

in 0.1 ml. of H_2O. After standing 2 hours at room temperature, the solution is evaporated to dryness and the residue is dissolved in 0.15 ml. of 0.2 N NaHCO$_3$. The DNP-amine is extracted into ether. After removal of the ether, the DNP-amine is dissolved in ethanol and chromatographed on Whatman No. 1 paper, previously treated with Dow-Corning silicone No. 1107, with the polar phase of methanol:chloroform:H_2O = 10:10:6 v/v. The spots are cut out, eluted with 3 ml. of ethanol and the color density is determined at 365–370 mμ (Lockhart, 1956).

Section V: Separation of Proteins

Conventional Chromatography

In contrast to the experimental results on amino acids, amines, and their derivatives, paper chromatography has not been reduced to a routine procedure for the separation of proteins. This is probably due, in part, to the successful use of paper electrophoresis which is described in detail later in this monograph and, in part, to the fact that every protein system studied may require a new system of chromatographic development. Some of the methods which have been used with reasonable success are given below.

COLOR REACTIONS. These will be given in detail under Paper Electrophoresis (cf. Papastamatis, 1951; Geschwind, 1952; Turba, 1950; Jones, 1950; Sluyterman, 1949). The Cl$_2$:ClO$_2$:benzidine reaction is also applicable to proteins (Reindel, 1953, cf. Section I). In case the proteins under consideration have enzymatic properties, a plate is made from 2% agar containing a suitable substrate for the enzyme. The moist chromatogram is placed on the agar plate at incubation temperature for some hours to permit digestion of the substrate, after which the breakdown products of the substrate are revealed by suitable tests (Reid, 1950; Giri, 1951b). Thus the starch-iodine test is used for amylase, sodium phenolphthalein phosphate for phosphatases, etc. Proteolytic enzymes are also located on chromatograms by placing the moist paper in contact with a sheet of exposed photographic film. The hydrolytic action of the enzyme on the gelatin permits localization of the enzyme (Wallenfels, 1951, Giri, 1951c, Lebez, 1954).

QUANTITIES USED. The procedures given require of the order of 20 μg. of protein at each spot.[33]

SEPARATION OF INDIVIDUAL PROTEINS. *Amylases.* These proteins are reasonably well separated by one or more of the following solvents: acetone:water = 1:1 or 3:1 or 7:3 v/v; 0.33 M NaCl; 3.0 M NaCl (Reid, 1952). The paper is Whatman No. 1. Apply very small spots and develop at 0–5°C. One per cent soluble starch in buffered (pH 4.6 or 7.0), agar is used to reveal the enzymes.

---

[33] The phenomenon of "double fronting" in the paper chromatography has been discussed by Boman (1952).

Amylases. These enzymes are separated on Whatman No. 4 paper with buffered 30–35 % ammonium sulfate (pH 6.4) (Simonart, 1951; Jones, 1950; Reid, 1950). The chromatogram is sprayed with 2 % soluble starch, incubated at 65°C. for 2 hours, and then sprayed with Lugol's solution.

Cellulases. Whatman No. 1 paper is dipped in 4 % zein in 75 % ethanol adjusted to pH 4.0 with HCl and air-dried. The chromatogram is developed at 8°C. with 0.3 M NaCl in 0.05 M sodium citrate buffer at pH 5.4 or with acetone:water = 1:1 (Reese, 1953). The enzymes are revealed after the chromatogram is cut into small sections by the production of reducing substances (*cf.* Sugars, Chapter VI) in a 0.5 % solution of carboxymethyl cellulose.

Hemoglobins. Adult and fetal hemoglobins may be wholly or partially separated on Whatman No. 1 paper by sodium acetate:veronal buffer (pH 4.3) (Kruh, 1952); by molar sucrose followed by *n*-butanol:acetic acid:water = 20:3:75 on two-dimensional chromatograms (Andersch, 1953); or by pyridine added dropwise to the point of application of the hemoglobin in the center of a filter paper disk (Sansone, 1952).

Insulin. Good paper chromatograms have been obtained with insulin using 1-butanol:H_2O:acetic acid = 12:5:2 v/v (Grodsky, 1956) or with 2-butanol:1 % acetic acid = 1:1 v/v (Light, 1956).

Miscellaneous enzymes. Various enzymes in *Aspergillus oryzae* have been separated on Whatman No. 54 paper using aqueous acetone (0–90 % acetone) buffered with 0.01 M or 0.1 M citrate phosphate at pH 4, 6, or 8; acetate at pH 5.0, pyridine-HCl at pH 5.7, and phthalate at pH 5.7 (Jermyn, 1953). The developed chromatograms were then sprayed with a reagent which would react with the specific enzyme under examination (*cf.* Rohdewald, 1951). The spray was of such a pH as to give the paper the pH optimum for the enzyme.

Peanut proteins. These have been separated with 10 % w/v NaCl under conditions which allow the solvent to evaporate (Thomson, 1952).

Peroxidase. Concentrated enzyme solution is developed on Whatman No. 54 paper with buffered aqueous acetone (acetone:water = 6:4; 8:2), buffered with 0.01 M citrate phosphate at pH 5.8 or 6.0 and sprayed with saturated aqueous guiacol containing 5 % v/v of 30 % H_2O_2 (Gillespie, 1952).

Phosphatases (*cf.* Amylases). Agar to contain Na phenolphthalein phosphate. Sodium acetate buffer (pH 5.2) is used for acid phosphatases, and glycine buffer (pH 9.2) for alkaline phosphatases (Giri, 1952*f*).

Phosphorylases (*cf.* Amylases). Agar to contain glucose-1-phosphate in pH 6.0 acetate buffer (Giri, 1952*f*).

Proteinases. These are separated on Whatman No. 4 paper with pH 6.4 buffered ammonium sulfate (30–35 %). The developed chromatogram is sprayed with 2 % casein solution, incubated at 45°C. for 12–16 hours, and then sprayed with dilute alcoholic gentian violet followed by Lugols' solution (Simonart, 1951). Papain and rennet may be separated by developing with 0.04 M Na$_2$PO$_4$ (pH 4.1) (Simonart, 1952).

Serum proteins. Serum diluted with water 1:9 is applied to Whatman No. 1 paper and developed in the first direction with pH 6.0 citrate buffer (0.75 ml. of 0.02 M sodium citrate, 9.25 ml. of 2 N HCl, and 50 g. of NaCl per liter) and 0.1 M KNa tartrate (pH 7.0) in the second direction (Tauber, 1952, 1953; Quastel, 1952). Sucrose (0.1 M) may replace KNa tartrate (*cf.* Franklin, 1950; McKerns, 1951). The protein spots are revealed by any of the methods described under Paper Electrophoresis or by the following stain: to 1.5 g. of citric acid in 1260 ml. of water is added 51 ml. of glycerol, 3000 ml. of acetone, 600 mg. of methyl orange (Eastman Kodak No. 432), and 600 mg. of eosin Y(Harleco, water- and acetone soluble). The excess dye is removed from the paper with dilute H$_2$SO$_4$ (0.5 ml. of H$_2$SO$_4$ in 8 liters of water) (Tauber, 1952, 1953).

The use of conventional filter paper chromatography as applied to serum by Franklin (1950) has been severely criticized by Hall (1951) who says, "The patterns observed in complex mixtures such as serum are so dependent on the conditions of the experiment as to be pure artifacts" (*cf.* Franklin, 1951 for rebuttal).

Serum proteins. When serum is developed with water-saturated n-butanol:water-saturated Na dodecansulfonate (shake for 30 minutes at 30°):n-butanol = 20:10:08 v/v pH 6.5–6.8, or with water-saturated n-butanol:water-saturated Na dodecansulfonate:n-propanol = 4:2:1, pH 6.8–7.0 on radial chromatograms, separation is achieved in 15 minutes on Gessner and Kreuzig paper WFI (Zimmermann, 1953b).

Viper venom. The protein solution (1 mg. per 0.01 ml.) is applied in a very thin line 1.2 cm. from the bottom of a strip of Whatman No. 1 paper 25 mm. wide and 20 cm. long by touching the paper with a glass slide on the edge of which the protein solution has been placed (Piantanida, 1953; van Os, 1952). The end of the strip is then dipped into a dilute NaCl-phosphate buffer (1.71 $\times$ 10^{-3} M NaCl, 2.00 $\times$ 10^{-4} M Na$_2$HPO$_4$; 1.00 $\times$ 10^{-3} M NaH$_2$PO$_4$), and when the solution has risen to the starting line, the strip is removed and placed in a more concentrated solution of the same mixture (3.68 $\times$ 10^{-3} M; 4.30 $\times$ 10^{-4} M; 2.15 $\times$ 10^{-3} M). This process is continued until the most concentrated solution is applied (1.71 M NaCl; 2.00 $\times$ 10^{-1} M Na$_2$HPO$_4$; 1.00 M NaH$_2$PO$_4$). The separated proteins are revealed by the usual methods (see Paper Electrophoresis).

Viruses. Plant viruses have been separated on Whatman No. 1 paper with 40–50 % aqueous ethanol (Gray, 1952).

Miscellaneous. The chromatography of proteins is discussed by Carangal (1955), Grassmann (1953a), Piantanida (1955) and Simon (1954).

QUANTITATIVE ESTIMATION. The amounts of protein in each spot may be estimated by any of the procedures given in Chapter IV. The method generally employed has been to cut out the spots, extract the dye, and determine the dye colorimetrically. If agar plates or gelatin films are employed, the area method is applicable. In any case adequate controls must be carried out (*cf.* Chapter IV).

Larger quantities of protein may be separated by employing the "chromatopile" (Mitchell, 1949). In this case, the protein solution is applied to filter paper disks near the top of a column consisting of 300–400 circles. The disks used for the application of the mixed proteins should be slightly smaller in diameter than those used in the rest of the column. The chromatopile may be also employed for fractionation with ammonium sulfate in the following manner. After application of the mixture of proteins, a solution of 20 % $(NH_4)_2SO$ at pH 7 is used as the developing solvent. As this solvent flows out of the chamber, water is added with stirring to the 20 % $(NH_4)_2SO_4$ at the same rate as solvent flows out. Thus more and more bilute $(NH_4)_2SO_4$ is used to separate the proteins (Kritsman, 1950).

Chapter VI

CARBOHYDRATES*

It has been possible, by means of one- and two-dimensional paper chromatography, to separate many common, substituted, and derived sugars. Polysaccharides may be hydrolyzed, and the hydrolyzates are treated like other simple sugar mixtures. Owing to the reducing property of many common sugars, ammoniacal silver nitrate has generally been chosen as the color reagent. Silver nitrate, however, has the disadvantage of reacting with a wide range of reducing substances other than sugars, so that more specific spraying reagents such as aniline hydrogen phthalate have come into use. The quantitative evaluation of the sugar chromatographs can be achieved by a visual or photoelectric comparison of the optical density of the colored spots of unknown and standard solutions, or by conventional microanalyses of the sugars after the spots on the chromatogram have been eluted. The reader is referred to a comprehensive review article on the paper chromatography of carbohydrates and related compounds (Kowkabany, 1954).

Section I: General Procedure

Most of the methods which were described in detail in Chapter III are being successfully applied to the paper chromatography of carbohydrates. One- and two-dimensional paper chromatography are the most popular techniques. However, circular paper chromatography has been adapted to the separation of mixtures of simple carbohydrates and their derivatives (Bersin, 1952). The advantage of this method lies in its rapid development (about 3 hours), which makes it especially applicable for less complex mixtures. The separation of C^{14}-labeled sugars and their subsequent identification has greatly advanced the progress of the research in photosynthesis (Benson, 1952; Buchanan, 1953). The separation of sugar borates by paper electrophoresis will be discussed in Part II.

Whatman No. 1 filter paper is preferred by most investigators; however, Schleicher and Schuell No. 589, White Ribbon, has also been used (McFarren, 1951b).

The critical part of many chromatographic experiments involving carbohydrates is the preparation of the sample from biological sources. For successful paper chromatography, the sample should have a low salt concentration. High salt concentration causes displacement of spots, tailing of spots, failure to produce a color, or, sometimes, even multiple spots.

* R_f tables are found at the end of each section.

The samples, similar to the amino acids, may be desalted by the electrolytic method (see Chapters III and V). Using ion exchange resins to desalt sugar solutions may result in artifact spots.

Section II: Simple Sugars and Disaccharides

1. PREPARATION OF SAMPLE

A sample containing 5–40 μg. of each sugar in a mixture is generally recommended for a successful separation and recovery by elution methods (Partridge, 1948; Jermyn, 1949). The sugars are dissolved in water, made up to a concentration of 1 % w/v of each component, and 2–5 μl. is applied with a micropipette. Much smaller quantities are detected with C^{14}-tagged sugars.

In the chromatography of the sugars, especially when isolated from urine, it is important to remove the inorganic salts by one of the following procedures:

a. Pyridine Extraction. This procedure for deionizing is based on the solubility of the sugars in dry pyridine and the insolubility of inorganic salts (Malpress, 1949). The sugar solution is dried on a steam bath, and the residue is extracted with 5.0 ml. of redistilled pyridine at 100°C for 10 minutes. The resulting mixture is cooled and filtered, and the pyridine is removed by distillation under reduced pressure at a temperature not exceeding 40°C. The residue is dissolved in 10 % isopropanol, and aliquots are applied to the filter paper. No loss of sugar was observed by Malpress (1949) when this procedure was followed. However, some epimerization of the sugars may occur by this pyridine treatment (Isherwood, 1954a).

b. Ion Exchange. Since the sugars are not ionized, they will pass through an ion exchange resin column, while the inorganic ions will be retained. A urine sample is passed through an ion exchange column, the effluent is taken to dryness, and the residue dissolved in water (Montreuil, 1953). The strong anion resin should be converted into the HCO_3^- cycle to repress the uptake of sugars on the column (Woolf, 1953). Dowex-2(OH^- cycle) and IRA-400 (OH^- cycle) also cause the formation of lactic acid and other artifacts (Hulme, 1953). The following ion exchange resins are recommended: IR-120 (H^+ cycle) and IRA-400 (CO_3^{--} cycle) or IRA-410 (acetate) for cation and anion removal, respectively (Phillips, 1953; White, 1956). A mixed resin (Bio-Deminrolit-Permutit Co.) which is saturated with CO_2 has been used in a batch process (Bickel, 1955). A centrifuge tube was filled one-quarter full with the resin, urine was added, the contents were shaken for twenty minutes and were centrifuged. The supernatant was concentrated *in vacuo* and aliquot portions were chromatographed.

Detailed procedure (Lohmann, 1956). A one-tenth milliliter sample of blood is blown into 1.5 ml. of ether-ethanol (1:3 v/v). The precipitated protein is centrifuged off and washed twice with methanol. The solution is treated with mixed resin (e.g. Dowex 1 and 50). The salt-free solution is washed twice with ethanol and evaporated to dryness. The residue, dissolved in 0.2 ml. water, is chromatographed. This procedure is useful especially for the identification of reducing sugars in blood. The quantitative values obtained by this technique are usually lower than "reducing sugar values" obtained by Fehling's method or other clinical techniques.

c. Precipitation Methods. For the analysis of sugars from urine and other biological sources it is advisable to remove proteins and other contaminants by means of basic lead acetate (Eastham, 1949) or $0.3 N$ Ba(OH)$_2$-5 % aqueous ZnSO$_4 \cdot 7$H$_2$O (Somogyi, 1945). It is important for the latter reagent that equal volumes of base neutralize exactly the zinc sulfate solution. For deproteinization two volumes of alkali are mixed with one volume of sample, followed by two volumes of the zinc sulfate solution. The mixture is vigorously shaken and filtered.

d. Hydrolysis of Disaccharides. The disaccharides may be chromatographed directly or after hydrolysis which may be performed on the filter paper in the following manner (K. T. Williams, 1951; Buchanan, 1953): 1 μl. of a disaccharide solution is applied to the filter paper, and a 5-μl. drop of an invertase solution is immediately superimposed. The reaction is permitted to proceed for 5 minutes, and the paper is developed in the usual manner.

Comments. When the pentoses rhamnose and xylose were boiled for twenty-four hours, additional spots occurred on the chromatogram. Caution should be exercised in interpreting these "artifact" spots (Soutar, 1954).

2. SOLVENTS

A detailed description of the most widely used solvents (e.g., phenol, collidine, *n*-butanol:acetic acid:water) has been given in Chapter V. Table I lists other solvents[1] which are recommended for specific applications.

The addition of 10 % malonic acid to the water:butanol solvent prevents

---

[1] The two most useful solvents are: (a) 1-Butanol:acetic acid:water = 40:10:22 v/v; (b) 1-Butanol:pyridine:water = 125:40:125 v/v. Simple sugars and lower polysaccharides are well separated on 25 cm. ascending chromatograms (Whatman No. 1 paper) when multiple development (3 or 4 times) is employed (*cf.* Chapter III).

TABLE I

Solvents for Simple Sugars and Disaccharides

Solvent composition	Solvent most suitable for	Reference
1. Ethyl acetate:pyridine:water = 2:1:2 v/v; 40:11:6	Xylose, arabinose, mannose, glucose	Jermyn, 1949; F. G. Fischer, 1954
2. Ethyl acetate:acetic acid:water = 3:1:3 v/v	Galactose	Jermyn, 1949
3. Lower layer of benzyl alcohol: acetic acid:water = 3:1:3 v/v	Ketoheptoses	Bevenue, 1951
4. n-Butanol:pyridine:water = 45:25:40 v/v	Lactose, galactose, glucose	Borkowski, 1952; Chargaff, 1948; Glegg, 1954
5. n-Butanol:ethanol:water: NH_4OH = 40:10:49:1: v/v	Glucose in urine	Bayly, 1951
6. n-Butanol:ethanol:water = 10:1:2 v/v	Melibiose, fructose, glucose	K. T. Williams, 1951
7. n-Butanol:acetone:NH_4OH: water = 40:50:3:15	Circular chromatography	Venner, 1955
8. n-Propanol:water = 3:1 v/v	Glucose + fructose in urine	Cohen, 1955
9. n-Propanol:ethyl acetate:water = 6:1:3 v/v	Glucose, lactose, sucrose	Gardner, 1955
10. n-Propanol:benzyl alcohol: water:85% formic acid = 50:72:20:20 v/v	Fructose, glucose, sucrose	Giovannozzi-Sermanni, 1956
11. i-Propanol:pyridine:acetic acid: water = 8:8:1:4 v/v	"Universal solvent" (no salt effect)	H. T. Gordon, 1956
12. Phenol:buffer = 4:1 v/v (0.05 M buffers, pH 3,4,5,5.8)	Sugars + sugar alcohols	Parikh, 1954

the appearance of spots due to impurities in the solvent and paper when silver nitrate is used as the developer. The chromatograms must be washed with ether before spraying or dipping in order to remove the malonic acid (Boggs, 1950).

For the chromatographic development of sugars, ascorbic acid, and related substances, the following solvents must be specially treated to retard the decomposition of ascorbic acid by heavy metal ions present in the paper or solvents (Chen, 1953).

a. Sixty milliliters of n-butanol is shaken with 40 ml. of water and an excess of oxalic acid. The mixture is allowed to settle in a separatory funnel, and the upper layer is used.

b. Ten grams of water is dissolved in 50 g. of phenol crystals, filtered through charcoal, and an excess of oxalic acid is added. The mixture is allowed to settle in a separatory funnel, and the lower layer is used. As a further refinement, the filter paper is washed prior to solvent development with 2 % w/v oxalic acid.

c. The presence of inorganic salts (Na_2SO_4, Na_3PO_4, but not NaCl) often produces artifacts and retardation of spots with basic solvents. However, the solvent n-propanol:ethyl acetate:water = 7:1:2 v/v yields excellent results in the chromatography of sugars isolated from urine in the presence of salts (Albon, 1952). n-Butanol:acetic acid:water = 4:1:5 v/v is also recommended (Bayly, 1951).

d. For two-dimensional separation of many simple sugars, phosphorylated sugars, organic acids, and amino acids usually encountered in photosynthetic studies, the following solvent pair is recommended (Benson, 1950):

First direction. Liquid phenol-water (100:20 v/v). This mixture is neutralized to pH 5–6 using the ion exchange resin 410 (OH^-) (Rohm and Haas).

Second direction. A: Butanol-water (1246:84 v/v). B: Propionic acid-water (620:790 v/v). Just before use, equal volumes of A and B are mixed and warmed slightly to form a single-phase solvent.

Another solvent pair for two-dimensional, ascending chromatography is:

First direction. n-Butanol:pyridine:water (3:2:1.5)

Second direction. Phenol, saturated with water (NH_3 atmosphere); small amount of 8-quinolinol is added to the solvent. Figure 1 shows a separation of ten carbohydrates with these solvents (Hamerman, 1955).

For the separation of sucrose, fructose, glucose, and sorbitol, the following two solvents have been used (Huygens, 1953):

First direction. Benzene:n-butanol:pyridine:water (1:5:3:3)

Second direction. Amyl alcohol:pyridine:water (1:1:2 v/v)

e. Using the solvent n-butanol:acetic acid:H_2O (4:1:5 v/v) and continuous descending chromatography (see Durchlauf chromatography, Chapter III) for ten days, gentiobiose could be separated from isomaltose (Bacon, 1954).

A relationship has been calculated for the rate of glucose migration using ethyl acetate-acetic acid-water of different proportions (Durso, 1956):

$$r = 7.2 + 0.11A - 3.38R$$

r = glucose movement (mm./hour)

R = molar ratio of ethyl acetate to water

A = molar content of acetic acid in per cent.

An increase in temperature causes the R_f of sugars to increase. This observation was ascribed to the change in water content of the solvent due to temperature changes (Alcock, 1956).

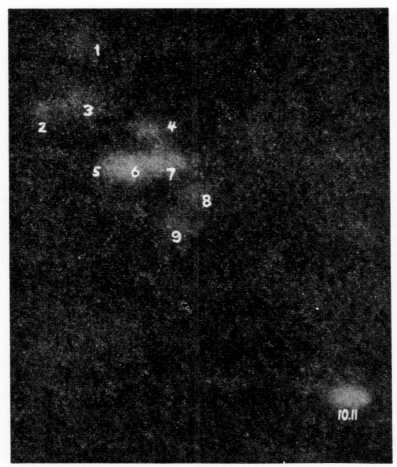

Fig. 1. Two-dimensional chromatography of carbohydrates. 1st solvent: *n*-butanol:pyridine:water = 3:2:1.5; 2nd solvent: phenol, saturated with water (Hamerman, 1955): 1, rhamnose; 2, fucose; 3, ribose; 4, xylose; 5, arabinose; 6, fructose; 7, mannose; 8, glucose; 9, galactose; 10, 11, galacturonic and glucuronic acids.

3. TECHNIQUES

a. One- and Two-Dimensional Paper Chromatography. The descending or ascending method is generally used. In order to allow the solvent to drip uniformly in the descending method, the bottom edge of the paper is serrated (Fig. 2) (Partridge, 1949).

The atmosphere of the chamber is saturated with the solvent, prior to the actual separation, by placing a dish with the solvent at the bottom of the chamber. In order to obtain a more uniform separation, the chamber

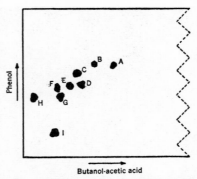

FIG. 2. Two-dimensional chromatogram, showing separation of sugars and galacturonic acid (Partridge, 1949): A, rhamnose; B, ribose; C, arabinose; D, xylose; E, mannose; F, galactose; G, glucose; H, lactose; I, galacturonic acid.

is lined with two sheets of Whatman No. 1 filter paper stapled together to form a cylinder which fits snugly against the chamber wall and is immersed in the solvent, covering the bottom of the chamber (McFarren, 1951b).

Two-dimensional chromatography of a mixture of xylose, arabinose, mannose, glucose, and galactose is carried out in a one-dimensional apparatus (Boggs, 1952). The band from a one-dimensional chromatogram is woven into a second paper sheet at right angles to the direction of flow of the first solvent, and the chromatogram is developed with another solvent.

In order to increase the solvent flow in ascending chromatography using paper cylinders (R. J. Williams, 1948), additional paper disks are placed on top of the cylinder, thus absorbing the ascending solvent as it reaches the upper edge (Radhakrishnamurthy, 1952). Good separation of lactose, maltose, sucrose, glucose, and mannose is achieved in 72 hours. This effective increase of solvent flow may also be achieved by the method of multiple development (Pazur, 1952, 1953) (see Chapter III). In the ascending technique, the solvent is permitted to rise to a predetermined height, and the paper is then dried and redeveloped with the same solvent. This process may be repeated several times (see Fig. 3).

b. *Circular Paper Chromatography.* The results achieved by circular chromatography are comparable to those obtained by unidimensional chromatography (Bersin, 1952). The method is as follows:

Filter paper disks 25 cm. in diameter are used. The edges of the disk are squeezed between two plastic rings (e.g., Plexiglas) and placed between the top and bottom of a desiccator (26 cm. in diameter). A separatory funnel, whose end is drawn out to a capillary, is inserted through the top of the desiccator. The capillary end is placed 5 mm. from the surface of the disk above its center. Three drops of a 1% sugar solution are now

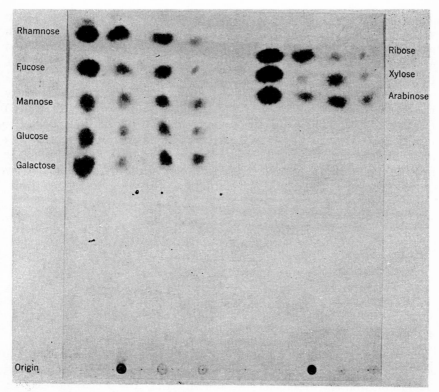

FIG. 3. Multiple ascending (3×) chromatogram of sugars (Glegg, 1954). Solvent: *n*-butanol:pyridine:water = 45:25:40 v/v. Color reagent: aniline oxalate.

applied at the center by means of a platinum loop (1.5 mm. in diameter). The solvent is next introduced at a rate of about 10 drops per minute. The development takes 3 hours. After the paper is dried, the zones are identified by suitable color reagents (see below). Table III lists the R_f values of some carbohydrates obtained by one-dimensional and circular chromatography.

Kawerau (1956) has separated a variety of sugars using the newly developed sector-analysis (see Chapter III) and a solvent composed of amyl alcohol:pyridine:water (4:3:2 v/v).

c. Paper Electrophoresis Combined with Chromatography. This technique, in effect, is two-dimensional chromatography, except that one dimension is developed by ionography instead of partition chromatography.

A sugar mixture is spotted near the edge of the paper which is saturated with borate buffer (pH 7.0–9.0). A voltage of 310 volts is then applied across the paper for 3 hours (see Part II for experimental details and design of equipment) The paper is dried and is developed unidimensionally with the solvent traveling in a direction at right angles to the migration in the electrical field. This technique has been applied to the separation of amino acids from sugars, derived by the hydrolysis of a polysaccharide (Consden, 1952).

d. *Chromatography of Radioactive Sugars.* Galactose-1-C^{14} was chromatographed with the solvent ethyl acetate:pyridine:water (2.5:1:3.5) (Roberts, 1956). The paper strips were scanned within a detector device (see Chapter III), connected to a rate meter, amplifier, and recorder. A linear relationship was established between the areas under the curves and the radioactivity, making it possible to calculate the specific activity of the C^{14}-sugar. The following equation was used:

$$X = \frac{A_s}{A_t} \frac{C}{V} \qquad (1)$$

X = specific activity of C^{14}-sugar
A_s = area of C^{14}-sugar
A_t = area of all sugars
C = total activity spotted on paper
V = volume of spotted solution

4. DETECTION OF SUGARS

Color reactions usually applied to sugar analyses have been adapted to the detection of sugars on paper chromatograms, e.g., oxidation reagents, naphthol (Molisch), resorcinol (Seliwanoff), etc. A new class of reagents, aromatic amines, is useful for carbohydrate color reactions. Most of these reagents may be applied by spraying or dipping techniques, and subsequent heating is carried out in suitable chromatographic ovens (see Chapter III).

a. *Oxidizing Agents.* (1) *Ammoniacal AgNO$_3$.* The developed chromatogram is dried to remove the solvent and is sprayed with a mixture of equal volumes of 0.1 N AgNO$_3$ and 5N NH$_4$OH. The chromatogram is placed in the oven at 105°C. for 5–10 minutes, and the reducing sugars appear as brown spots on the paper (Partridge, 1948).

This reagent may also be prepared by adding concentrated NH$_4$OH to a saturated solution of silver nitrate and diluting it to a final concentration of 0.3 M Ag(NH$_3$)$_2$$^+$ with methanol (Benson, 1952).

The brown Ag$_2$O background of developed sugar chromatograms is removed by washing the paper with water and a solution of Kodak "liquid X-ray fixer" (Benson, 1952).

Recommended method (Trevelyan, 1950; Petronici, 1953). 0.1 ml. of saturated aqueous silver nitrate is diluted to 20 ml. with acetone, and by

REACTION OF SUGARS WITH VARIOUS REAGENTS (ISHERWOOD, 1954)

Text paragraph number	Reagent	Aldohexoses	Aldopentoses	Ketohexoses	Ketopentoses	Uronic acids	Methyl pentoses	Sugar alcohols	Deoxy sugars	Glycosides	Amino sugars	Comments
a (1)	Ammoniacal AgNO₃	+	+	+	+	+	+	+		+	+	Unspecific; sensitivity: 1 μM glucose
a (2)	Alkaline permanganate	+	+	+	+	+	+	−	+	−	+	Sensitivity: 10 μM glucose; unspecific; not permanent
a (3)	Alkaline 3,5-dinitro-salicylate	+	+	+	+	+	+	−	+	+	+	Sensitivity: 10 μM glucose
a (4)	Alkaline 3,4-dinitro-benzoic acid	+	+	+	+	+	+	+	+	−	+	Ketoses react more quickly
a (5)	Triphenyltetrazolium chloride	+	+	+	+	+	+	−	−	−	+	Sensitivity: 5 μM
b (1)	Aniline phthalate	brown	red	yellow		brown	brown					
b (2)	p-Anisidine	light brown	brown			red-pink	green		light brown			
b (3)	Benzidine					+	+	+			+ −	N-acetylglucosamine + alloxan +
b (4)	m-Phenylenediamine	yellow fl.ᵃ	orange-yellow fl.	yellow fl.	yellow fl.	−						
b (6)	p-Aminohippuric acid	orange fl.	orange fl.			purple						
b (8)	2-Aminobiphenyl	green-brown	red									
c (3)	Naphthoresorcinol		blue violet	red		blue	blue violet					
c (4)	Resorcinol	pink	blue green	red								
d (1)	Anthrone			yellow	purple							Heptulose-orange

ᵃ fl. = fluorescence.

the dropwise addition of water the precipitated AgNO$_3$ is redissolved. The dried chromatogram is quickly dipped into this reagent and is dried. The paper is sprayed with 0.5 N NaOH in aqueous ethanol. Reducing sugars form black spots at room temperature. The excess Ag$_2$O background is removed by the thiosulfate technique of Benson (1952) (see above).

Similar techniques using ammoniacal or neutral silver nitrate have been successfully used for most reducing sugars and sucrose (Shamrai, 1951; Borkowski, 1952; Vavruch, 1953).

The minimum quantity of detectable carbohydrate with the ammoniacal silver nitrate reagent is 2–20 μg. (Rachinskii, 1953).

Another modification of the ammoniacal silver nitrate reaction is that ultra-violet illumination is substituted for heating of the paper (Price, 1956). This procedure detects not only reducing sugars but also cyclic amino acids, aliphatic acids, hydroxy-acids, phenolic amines, purines, pyrimidines, disulfides, and reducing steroids.

(2) *Alkaline permanganate.* The chromatogram after drying is sprayed with a 1% aqueous solution of KMnO$_4$ containing 2% Na$_2$CO$_3$. The chromatogram is heated for a few minutes at 100°C., and the sugars appear as yellow spots on a purple background; the final color changes to grey regions on a brown background. In view of this change in color, it is expedient to mark the position of the regions immediately (Pacsu, 1949).

A spray made up of four parts of 2% aqueous sodium metaperiodate and one part of 1% KMnO$_4$ in 2% Na$_2$CO$_3$ solution (pH adjusted to 7.2) reveals any reducing sugar as green spots on a red-brown background (Lemieux, 1954). If the paper is then washed with water the spots change to a permanent brown color on a white background.

(3) *Alkaline 3,5-dinitrosalicylate.* The reagent is prepared by dissolving 0.5 g. 3,5-dinitrosalicylic acid and 4.0 g. NaOH in 100 ml. of water. The reducing sugars produce permanent brown spots when the developed chromatogram is sprayed with the reagent and heated for 4–5 minutes at 100°C. (Jeanes, 1951).

(4) *Alkaline 3,4-dinitrobenzoic acid.* The chromatogram is sprayed with a 1% solution of 3,4-dinitrobenzoic acid in 2 N Na$_2$CO$_3$ and heated at 100°C. for about 5 minutes. Reducing sugars show up as blue spots owing to the formation of 2-nitro-4-carboxyl-phenylhydroxylamine (Weygand, 1950). This reagent is used for semiquantitative work by measuring the areas of the spot and plotting log area versus concentration (see Chapter IV).

(5) *Triphenyltetrazolium chloride.* This reagent (Wallenfels, 1950; Trevelyan, 1950) is made up by mixing equal volumes of a 2% aqueous solution of triphenyltetrazolium chloride and N NaOH. The dried chromatogram is sprayed with the reagent and kept in a moist atmosphere at

40°C. for 20 minutes. The excess reagent is washed out with water, and the paper is dried at 25°C. The reducing sugars give brilliant red spots owing to the formation of the colored triphenyl formazan.

A dipping reagent is composed of the following (F. G. Fischer, 1954): 1 N methanolic NaOH—4 % methanolic triphenyltetrazolium chloride (v/v). After the chromatograms are dipped, they are aerated in subdued light and heated for thirty minutes at 70°C. in a water-saturated atmosphere. This technique permits the elution of the colored spots with methanol-acetic acid (10:1 v/v) and the reading of the optical density at 482 mμ (molar extinction coefficient 16.32 $\times$ 10^3).

(6) *Ammonium molybdate-ammonium chloride* (Aronoff, 1950). Twenty milliliters of 10 % ammonium molybdate are added to 3 ml. conc. HCl with shaking, followed by 5 g. of ammonium chloride. The chromatogram is sprayed with this reagent. Phosphorylated compounds (see pp. 198 ff.) give an immediate yellow color due to ammonium phosphomolybdate. After heating the sprayed paper at 75°C. for a few minutes, reducing sugars show up as blue spots due to the reduction of molybdate to molybdenum blue. Sucrose gives a positive reaction due to hydrolysis.

b. Aromatic Amine Salts. Generally, these reagents have several advantages over the oxidation reagents, e.g., greater specificity for reducing sugars, cleaner color development, and fewer artifacts. (1) *Aniline salts*. The reagent is made by adding 930 mg. of aniline and 1.6 g. of phthalic acid to 100 ml. of water-saturated *n*-butanol. The dried paper is sprayed with this reagent and heated for 5 minutes at 105°C. Fructose and uronic acid produce fluorescent spots (Partridge, 1949). Reproduction of these chromatograms can be made on Ilford Document Paper No. 50.

Under these conditions only reducing sugars show up as colored spots. However, when the paper is heated at 115–120°C. for 10 minutes, sucrose will also react (Aso, 1951). This reaction lends itself well to the quantitative estimation of reducing sugars by visual comparison (Gibbons, 1950; Baar, 1954) or densitometry (see Chapter IV) at 480 mμ.

The reagent has been used in a modified form: 2 N aniline in *n*-butanol: 2 N H$_3$PO$_4$ = 1:2 v/v for the detection of rhamnose, xylose, arabinose, dextrose, galactose, mannose, fructose, sorbose, sucrose, maltose, lactose, and raffinose (Bryson, 1951). Another modification is as follows: 2 g. of aniline are dissolved in 100 ml. of ethyl acetate, containing 2 % trichloroacetic acid (Prepare fresh!) (McCready, 1954). The chromatograms are dipped into this reagent and heated for five minutes at 85°C. Reflection densities at 515 mμ are measured for quantitative analysis of reducing sugars.

Aniline oxalate reagent is prepared by the method of Horrocks (1949). To 100 ml. of 0.1 N oxalic acid is added 0.9 ml. of aniline. The chromatogram is sprayed with the reagent and heated at 100–105°C. for 10–20 minutes. The reducing sugars appear as brown spots. When the same chromatogram is sprayed with a 1% $KMnO_4$ solution containing 3% H_2SO_4, and heated to 100°C. for a few minutes, fructose, sucrose, and melezitose appear as grey-black spots (Malyoth, 1951). This technique distinguishes between ketoses and aldoses.

(2) *p-Anisidine HCl.* The dried chromatogram is sprayed with a 3% *p*-anisidine HCl solution in *n*-butanol and heated at 100°C. for 3–10 minutes. Aldo- and ketohexoses, as well as other sugar derivatives, produce differently colored spots with this reagent (Hough, 1950). This reagent has been used for the identification of sugars present in nectars (Wykes, 1953). An improved reagent is prepared as follows (Mukherjee, 1952): 0.5 g. of *p*-anisidine is dissolved in 2 ml. of H_3PO_4 (sp. gr. 1.75), and the solution is diluted to 50 ml. with ethanol. The precipitated anisidine phosphate is removed by filtration. The filtrate (*A*) is saved. The precipitate is dissolved in a minimum quantity of water and diluted with an equal volume of alcohol. Phosphoric acid is added to a final concentration of 2% (*B*). *A* and *B* are mixed, and the chromatogram is sprayed and heated at 95–100°C. for 3–5 minutes. Several of the sugars can be identified by the color of the spots, which remain stable for over a week (see Table II). *p*-Aminophenol may be substituted for *p*-anisidine (Vamos, 1953).

The anisidine spray reagent may be prepared as follows (Pridham, 1956): 1.0 g. *p*-anisidine-HCl is dissolved in 10 ml. of methanol and diluted to 100 ml. with *n*-butanol. 0.1 g. of $NaHSO_3$ is added, and the reagent may be stored in the refrigerator. The chromatograms are heated at 130°C. for ten minutes for full color development.

(3) *Benzidine.* Five hundred milligrams of benzidine, 200 ml. of glacial acetic acid, and 80 ml. of absolute ethanol are mixed. The chromatograms are sprayed with the reagent and heated at 100–105°C. for 15 minutes. This reagent is specific for reducing sugars (Horrocks, 1949) but produces a color reaction with a number of inorganic compounds (see Chapter XIV), so that any conclusions regarding "unknown" sugar spots must be drawn with caution (H. Miller, 1952). *N*-Acetylglucosamine, alloxan, fucose, glucuronic acid, and polyols produce colored spots with the benzidine reagent.

The following modified benzidine reagent seems to have a greater sensitivity for glucose than the above (Bacon, 1951): 0.5 g. of benzidine is added to 10 ml. of glacial acetic acid, 10 ml. of 40% w/v aqueous trichloroacetic acid, and 80 ml. of ethanol. The sprayed paper is heated at 100–120°C. for 5–10 minutes.

A combination spray of metaperiodate-$KMnO_4$ (see p. 182) followed by the benzidine spray of Bacon (1951) results in dark blue spots for the reducing sugars and hexitols. This color results from the oxidation of benzidine to "benzidine blue" by MnO_2. The sensitivity of this combination spray is 0.5 γ for mannitol, 2.4 γ for glucose, and 7.8 γ for sucrose (Wolfrom, 1956).

Dipping reagent. Five-hundred mg. of benzidine in 5 ml. of acetic acid plus 4 g. of trichloroacetic acid in 5 ml. of water plus 90 ml. of acetone. Air-dry, and then heat to 100°C. (Harris, 1954).

(4) *m-Phenylenediamine.* The dried paper is sprayed with 0.2 *M* *m*-phenylenediamine in 76% ethanol and is heated for 5 minutes at 105°C. Ten micrograms of reducing sugar produces a colored fluorescent spot. The following sugars and derivatives may be classified according to the color produced: arabinose, xylose, and ribose form an orange-yellow fluorescence; most other sugars give a yellow fluorescence (Chargaff, 1948). Galacturonic acid, glucosamine, maltose, and lactose produce a weak but discernible color.

A modified form of this reagent, 0.2% phenylenediamine and 2% oxalic acid·$2H_2O$ in 95% ethanol, is sprayed on the chromatogram which is heated to 100–110°C. for 15 minutes to bring out the fluorescent color (Chernick, 1951).

(5) *p-Dimethylaminoaniline:Zinc chloride.* A 0.3% solution of the $ZnCl_2$ double salt of *p*-dimethylaminoaniline in ethanol is a general reagent for sugars (Schneider, 1951).

(6) *p-Aminohippuric acid.* (0.3% *p*-aminohippuric acid in alcohol). The sprayed chromatogram is heated at 140°C. for 8 minutes. As little as 1 μg. of hexose or pentose produces an orange fluorescent spot under ultraviolet light (Sattler, 1952).

(7) *Diphenylamine.* The chromatogram is dipped into the following reagent: 2% w/v diphenylamine in acetone: 2% w/v aniline in acetone: 85% H_3PO_4 = 5:5:1 v/v. Prepare fresh. Air-dry, then heat at 100°C. (Harris, 1954).

(8) *2-Aminobiphenyl* (Gordon, 1956). This reagent is composed of 1.69 g. 2-aminobiphenyl, 0.9 g. of oxalic acid, 5 ml. glycerol, 10 ml. water and 84 ml. of acetone. The sprayed chromatograms are heated for five minutes at 110°C. with the following colored spots resulting: pentoses— red; hexoses—greenish brown; uronic acid—purple; sensitivity 0.01 μmols/ square cm.

(9) *N-(1-Naphthyl)-ethylenediamine HCl* (Gordon, 1956). This reagent is stored at 0°C. and is composed of the following: 1.3 g. *N*-(1-naphthyl)-ethylenediamine HCl in 2.5 ml. glycerol, 5 ml. of water, and 42 ml. of acetone. The chromatograms are heated at 110°C. for four minutes, and a red spot on tan background results for 1 μmol. of ketose (aldoses react also).

c. Phenolic Reagents. (1) *α-Naphthol.* 0.5 % w/v α-naphthol in aqueous alcohol (1:1 v/v):H_3PO_4 = 10:1 v/v (D. Gross, private communication, 1958). The sprayed chromatogram is heated at 90°C. until the spots become visible.

(2) *Orcinol reagent for ketoheptoses.* Bial's orcinol reagent is prepared by dissolving 0.5 g. of orcinol and 15 g. of trichloroacetic acid in 100 ml. of water-saturated butanol (Bevenue, 1951). The reagent should be kept cold and freshly prepared each week. The chromatograms are sprayed with the reagent and heated at 105°C. for 2–20 minutes. Ketoheptoses produce blue spots (see Table IV) (Noggle, 1952; Peeters, 1954). Spraying with 2 % orcinol in 2 N HCl and heating at 90°C. for 2–3 minutes produce orange spots for ketoses (Bidwell, 1952; Hamerman, 1955).

(3) *Naphthoresorcinol for ketoses.* This reagent is prepared by mixing equal volumes of 0.2 % w/w naphthoresorcinol in ethanol with 2 % w/w trichloroacetic acid in water. The sprayed paper is heated at 105°C. for 5 minutes. Trichloroacetic acid is advantageous because it does not attack the cellulose (Partridge, 1948; Isherwood, 1951). The chromatogram may be dipped into a freshly prepared mixture of 0.2 % w/v naphthoresorcinol in acetone:3 N H_3PO_4 = 5:1 v/v (Harris, 1954).

(4) *Miscellaneous phenols.* Two-tenths gram of phloroglucinol plus 80 ml. of 90 % ethanol plus 20 ml. of 25 % w/v trichloroacetic acid is a good reagent for pentoses with only galactose and fructose interfering (Horrocks, 1949).

A reagent composed of 1 % alcoholic phloroglucinol and 20 % trichloroacetic acid produces dark-green spots for pentoses and light-pink ones for aldohexoses (Parr, 1953).

One per cent alcoholic resorcinol:0.2 N HCl = 1:1 v/v produces different colors with the reducing sugars and sucrose (see Table III) (Rachinskii, 1953).

d. Miscellaneous Reagents (1) *Anthrone reagent.* The adaptation of Dreywood's anthrone reagent (Dreywood, 1946; Morris, 1948) to the detection of carbohydrates on paper chromatogram is as follows (Johanson, 1953): 300 mg. of anthrone is dissolved in 10 ml. of glacial acetic acid by warming, followed by the addition of 20 ml. of ethanol, 3 ml. of H_3PO_4 (sp. gr. 1.60 at 20°C.) and 1 ml. of water. The reagent is fairly stable when stored in the refrigerator. The sprayed chromatograms are heated for 5–6 minutes at 108°C.

(2) *Indicator spray* (Gardner, 1955). For quantitative analysis (see pp. 185 ff.) it is desirable to retain the unmodified sugar on the chromatogram. In this manner the sugar may be eluted without guide spots and assayed by micro-techniques. A color spray is composed of 40 mg. bromocresol purple, 100 mg. boric acid in 100 ml. methanol plus 7.5 ml. 1 % aqueous solution of borax. The sugars are revealed as yellow spots against a

blue background and the spots are marked immediately (fade!) under ultraviolet light.

(3) *β-Indolylacetic acid* (Heyrovský, 1956). *Spray solution:* 10 g. trichloroacetic acid, 2.0 ml. water, 0.2 g. β-indolylacetic acid, and 10 ml. *n*-propanol. *Dip solution:* 10 g. trichloroacetic acid, 0.3 g. β-indolylacetic acid (solution keeps only three days). Heat to 120°C. until spots are violet (ketoses)—sensitivity 2 μg. Phenol is a poor solvent for this reagent.

(4) *Modified Dische's reagent.* (Ujejski, 1955). This reagent has been used for the detection of ketoses, sedoheptulose in particular: 15 g. trichloroacetic acid, 1.5 g. cysteine-HCl dissolved in 6 ml. of water, diluted to 100 ml. with *n*-butanol plus 0.12 g. carbazole.

(5) *Color reagent for methylpentose and 2-deoxy sugars* (Waldron, 1952). The dried chromatogram is sprayed with 2.5 % aqueous sodium metaperiodate and allowed to react for 10 minutes. It is then sprayed with a fresh solution consisting of 7 % sodium nitroprusside:saturated alcoholic solution of piperazine:1 % ethylene glycol in methanol = 1:3:4 v/v. Blue spots result, owing to the formation of acetaldehyde (Rimini reaction). Threonine also forms a blue spot. The test is sensitive for quantities larger than 10 μg. of methylpentose (e.g., fucose).

(6) *Color reagents for nonreducing carbohydrates* (Greenway, 1953). The dried paper chromatogram is placed in a closed chamber containing iodine crystals. Nonreducing sugars such as sugar merceptals, alcohols, glycosides, hexonic acids, and *N*-acylamino sugars are revealed as blue-red-brown spots. The background color is cleared by placing the chromatogram in a stream of warm air. The color reaction is not suitable when the chromatogram is developed with pyridine- or collidine-containing solvents.

5. QUANTITATIVE METHODS

a. Elution and Microanalysis. In the elution technique, the sugar is not changed chemically by a spraying reagent, but the region is identified by the reaction of a parallel strip with ammoniacal silver nitrate, etc. The "indicator spray" method of detection (see 4, *d*(2)) which reveals the sugar spot without modifying it chemically, may also be employed. The area containing the sugar is cut out and extracted by refluxing with water. The sugar may then be analyzed by any of the following methods (Flood, 1948; Somogyi, 1945):

(1) *Somogyi reagent.* Twenty-eight grams of Na_2HPO_4, 40 g. of Rochelle salt, and 180 g. of Na_2SO_4 are dissolved in about 700 ml. of water, 100 ml. of 1 N NaOH is added, and with stirring 80 ml. of a 10 % solution of $CuSO_4$ is introduced. The solution is diluted to 1 liter and filtered after 1–2 days.

For the iodometric measurement of the copper, reduced by the sugars, the analysis is as follows: If the amount of glucose is not larger than 0.5 mg. per 5 ml. of solution, 5 ml. of 1 N KIO$_3$ is included in 1 liter of reagent. (It is best to prepare the reagent without the inclusion of the iodate and to add the latter in such quantities as the anticipated range of sugar concentrations requires.)   Five milliliters of the reagent and 5 ml. of the sugar solution are mixed in a 25 × 200-mm. Pyrex test tube, covered with a glass bulb, and heated by immersion in a vigorously boiling water bath. After cooling, 0.5 ml. of 2.5% KI solution is added; then 1.5 ml. of 2 N H$_2$SO$_4$ is added at once, and the liberated iodine is titrated with 0.005 N Na$_2$S$_2$O$_3$ to the starch end point.   For the quantitative analysis of lactose from mammary gland preparations, the untreated sugar spot is eluted from the paper with distilled water at 80°C. for fifteen minutes (Hayworth, 1955).   Lactose is analyzed by Somogyi's procedure.

(2) *Hypoiodite Reagent.*   Another microanalytical method for reducing sugars involves the stoichiometric titration by hypoiodite and the titration of the excess iodine by Na$_2$S$_2$O$_3$.   This method may be used for the analysis of as little as 40 μg. of sugar within ±5% (Hawthorne, 1947; Linderstrøm-Lang, 1933).

(3) *Miscellaneous Methods.*   The sugar spots are eluted with three 5–ml. portions of 80% ethanol, and 5 ml. of diphenylamine reagent is added (100 ml. of concentrated HCl, 80 ml. of glacial acetic acid, and 20 ml. of 10% alcoholic diphenylamine).   The sample is heated in boiling water for 60–90 minutes and read in a photometer at 640 mμ. (Vernon, 1952). The absorption coefficient for glucose is 0.245.

The dried chromatogram is sprayed with p-anisidine (see p. 184) and heated at 130°C. for ten minutes (Pridham, 1956).   The colored spots and paper blanks of the same size are eluted by shaking with 3 ml. of MeOH-SnCl$_2$·(10 g. SnCl$_2$ is dissolved in 5.0 ml. of water; 90 ml. of methanol is added, and the solution is filtered.)   The absorbance of the eluted solutions is measured at the following maxima: aldopentoses and hexuronic acids, 510 mμ; aldohexoses, 400 mμ; 6-deoxyaldohexoses, 385 mμ.   Standard curves are obtained by plotting concentration against absorbance.

For the quantitative determination of lactose in milk the eluted sample is reacted with alkaline potassium ferricyanide, and the resulting ferric ferrocyanide complex is measured colorimetrically (Honer, 1953).

When the sugars are chromatographed as their p-nitrophenylhydrazones (solvents: benzyl alcohol, n-butanol, or isoamyl alcohol, all saturated with water), the spots may be extracted with neutral $\frac{1}{15}$ M phosphate buffer. The color is read in a photometer (Stoll, 1952).

The eluted sugars are reacted with 40–200 mg. of phenol and 5 ml. of conc. H$_2$SO$_4$ for ten minutes (Dubois, 1956).   The resultant colors are read in the photometer at 490 mμ for hexoses and 480 mμ for pentoses and uronic acids.

b. Direct Photometry. (1) *Silver nitrate.* The ethyl acetate:pyridine: water solvent is made 0.15 N with respect to silver nitrate and is placed in the trough. Standard solutions of four different concentrations and three unknown spots are applied to the paper, and the chromatogram is allowed to develop for 10–20 hours. After the paper is air-dried, it is placed in an ammonia chamber for 1 hour and then heated for 20 minutes in the oven at 80°C. The density of the sugar spots (dark brown) is measured photometrically by means of a transmission densitometer (see Chapters III and IV), and the results of the standard solutions are plotted on semilog paper with concentration on the log scale versus optical density on the abscissa. From this standard curve and the density of the unknown spot, the concentration of the unknown may be calculated. The experimental error in this determination amounts to ±5 % (McFarren, 1951b).

(2) *Aniline.* The chromatograms, which are developed with a solvent containing phthalic acid, after drying at room temperature, are drawn through a solution of (2 %) aniline in ether and heated for 3½ minutes at 105°C. (Gustafsson, 1951). The chromatogram is photographed, and the densities of the spots on the negative are measured photometrically. A graphical method of analysis is used to determine the unknown. The experimental error of this method is 3–10 %.

Reflection densities of colored spots of reducing sugars (aniline-trichloro-acetic acid) and of ketoses (resorcinol) are measured directly on the paper with a Photovolt reflectance attachment and densitometer with filtered light at 515 mμ, (McCready, 1954). The maximum reflectance of each spot is plotted against logarithm of the concentration of standards (see Fig. 4).

(3) *Miscellaneous methods.* Sugar solutions are spotted on paper, and the color is developed with triphenyltetrazolium chloride, benzidine, and phosphomolybdic acid without prior chromatography (Wohnlich, 1956). The color density of the spots is measured directly by inserting the paper strip into the cuvette holder of a Pulfrich-Photometer. Standard curves thus obtained, follow Beer's Law; this adherence to Beer's Law is in contrast to other direct photometric methods in which the density or absorption is directly proportional to logarithm of concentration.

6. EXPERIMENTAL PROCEDURE

A resume of Partridge's classical experiments (1946, 1948) is given below. It should be pointed out that the separation of the sugars need not necessarily follow this procedure. Many modifications of this method

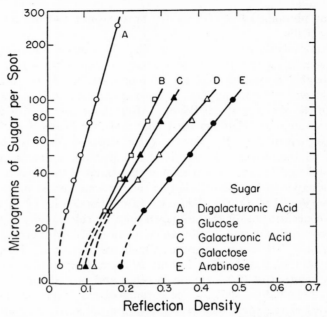

Fig. 4. Standard curves of sugars by the maximum reflectance density method (McCready, 1954).

as well as the spraying reagents, solvents, and apparatus also give good results.

Whatman No. 1 filter paper is cut into pieces 43 × 12 cm. Three to four microliters of a 1% sugar solution, containing about 30–40 μg. of each sugar, is introduced 7.5 cm. from the top of the paper strip. Several spots are placed on the same strip of paper, 1.5 cm. apart on a horizontal line. The strips are irrigated with the solvent (e.g., phenol or collidine) for 18 hours, and the solvent is dried in an oven at 100–105°C., the position of the solvent boundary being previously marked in ink. The paper is sprayed rapidly and evenly with a mixture containing equal volumes of 0.1 N AgNO₃ and 5 N NH₄OH, and the strip is replaced in the oven at 105°C. for 5–10 minutes; the sugars appear as dark-brown spots on a white or light-brown background. The apparatus used is the same as that described by Consden (1944) with one difference—the glass troughs are replaced by troughs of stainless steel.

Section III: Oligo- and Polysaccharides

The oligosaccharides can be separated by the techniques of "Durchlauf" chromatography, lasting up to 96 hours, or the "multiple ascent" development. Polysaccharides can be separated by paper electrophoresis (Rientis,

TABLE III

R_f VALUES OF SUGARS AND SUGAR DERIVATIVES AT 20°C

Compound	Solvent systems[a]				
	1	2	3	4	5
D-Glucose	0.39	0.39	0.18	0.43	0.64
D-Galactose	0.44	0.34	0.16	0.41	0.62
D-Mannose	0.45	0.46	0.20	0.46	0.69
L-Sorbose	0.42	0.40	0.20	0.46	0.68
D-Fructose	0.51	0.42	0.23	0.48	0.68
D-Xylose	0.44	0.50	0.28	0.53	0.73
D-Arabinose	0.54	0.43	0.21	0.56	0.70
D-Ribose	0.59	0.56	0.31	—	0.76
L-Rhamnose	0.59	0.59	0.37	0.58	0.82
D-Deoxyribose	0.73	0.60	—	—	—
L-Fucose	0.63	0.44	0.27	—	0.75
Lactose	0.38	0.24	0.09	0.33	0.46
Maltose	0.36	0.32	0.11	—	0.58
Sucrose	0.39	0.40	0.14	0.39	0.62
Raffinose	0.27	0.20	0.05	—	0.45
D-Galacturonic acid	0.13	0.14	0.14	0.40	0.31
D-Glucuronic acid	0.12	0.16 (.72)[b]	0.12 (.72)[b]	—	0.33 (.84)[b]
D-Glucurone	0.12	— (.72)[b]	— (.33)[b]	—	—
D-Glucosamine-HCl	0.62	0.32	0.13 (.17)[c]	—	0.38
Chondrosamine-HCl	0.65	0.28	0.12 (.16)[c]	—	—
N-Acetylglucosamine	0.69	0.50	0.26	—	0.73
L-Ascorbic acid	0.24	0.42	0.38	0.59	0.84
Dehydroascorbic acid	0.28	0.47	0.48	—	0.88
L-Inositol	0.23	0.10	0.09	—	0.31
D-Trehalose	—	—	—	—	0.52
Ca glycerate	—	—	—	—	0.59
DL-Glyceraldehyde	—	—	—	—	0.73

[a] Solvents: 1. Water-saturated phenol + 1% NH₃ (HCN atmosphere) (Partridge, 1948) (descending).
   2. Water-saturated S-collidine (descending).
   3. n-Butanol:acetic acid:water (4:1:5 v/v) (descending).
   4. n-Butanol:acetic acid:water (4:1:5 v/v) (Bersin, 1952) (horizontal).
   5. i-Propanol:pyridine:water:acetic acid (8:8:4:1 v/v) (Gordon, 1956) (ascending).

[b] Due to lactone.
[c] Due to free base.

1953) (see Part II of this book).   However, the polysaccharides are usually hydrolyzed, and the constituent monosaccharides are chromatographed by the methods described in Section II of this chapter.

1. HYDROLYSIS OF OLIGO- AND POLYSACCHARIDES

a. Polysaccharides and Hemicelluloses. A 10-mg. sample of the polysaccharide or hemicellulose is hydrolyzed with 0.5 ml. of N H₂SO₄ at 100°C. for six hours.   The hydrolyzate is carefully neutralized to Congo red paper

TABLE IV

R_f TABLE OF KETOHEPTOSES

Compound	1[a] R_f	2 (mm. from origin)
D-Glucoheptulose	0.42	103
D-Mannoheptulose	0.40	108
L-Galaheptulose	0.48	99
Sedoheptulose	0.46	125
D-Idoheptulose	0.50	147
L-Guloheptulose	0.53	138
Sedoheptulosan	0.70	153
D-Idoheptulosan	0.64	194
L-Guloheptulosan	0.65	188

[a] Solvents: 1. Water-saturated phenol (pH 5.5) (Noggle, 1952).
2. Ethyl acetate:acetic acid:water (3:1:3 v/v).

with solid $BaCO_3$ and is centrifuged. The supernatant is then spotted on the chromatogram (Flood, 1948; Forsyth, 1950; Binger, 1954). The supernatant may also be evaporated, dissolved in hot pyridine, and centrifuged. This treatment reduces the salt concentration of the sample (Whiting, 1951; Malpress, 1949). When aniline hydrogen phthalate or other acid sprays are used later for the detection of reducing sugars (see p. 183) it may not be necessary to neutralize the hydrolyzate with $BaCO_3$ for satisfactory results (Gaillard, 1953).

Quantitative estimation of the sugars is made with a reflection densitometer (Müller, 1951).

Polysaccharides from bacteria (*Leuconostoc mesenteroides*) are hydrolyzed with 2.5% H_2SO_4 at 80°C., and the hydrolyzate is developed with the following two solvents: phenol:water = 4:1 v/v and n-butanol:pyridine:water = 3:2:1.5 v/v (P. B. Smith, 1952). Other oligo- and polysaccharides from bacterial and plant sources are hydrolyzed by similar methods prior to chromatography (Zilliacus, 1951; Lüderitz, 1952; Gray, 1953).

In the study of the composition of oligosaccharides, a water extract of the sugars is spotted on filter paper. Another filter paper pad is soaked in a 20% yeast invertase solution and pressed against the appropriate area of the chromatogram containing the carbohydrate spot. The chromatogram is developed by two-dimensional technique after several minutes (Bealing, 1953).

Gum polysaccharides have been hydrolyzed by Block (unpublished data) following the method of Das, 1952. One hundred milligrams of gum per ml. of 85% formic acid is hydrolyzed for 2 hours in an oil bath of 125°C. Following the removal of the formic acid *in vacuo* in the presence of solid NaOH, the hydrolyzate is diluted to volume and its sugar content estimated chromatographically. Most of the plant gums as well as many of the synthetic gums have been identified using this procedure.

Hydrolysis of bacterial polysaccharides is carried out in sealed ampules at 100°C. for eight hours with 0.5 N H_2SO_4 (Davies, 1955). Dextran is hydrolyzed with 0.2 N H_2SO_4 at 70°C. for one hour (Wise, 1955). After neutralizing with $Ba(OH)_2$, absolute alcohol is added to a final concentration of 85 %. The precipitate is centrifuged off, the supernatant is taken to dryness *in vacuo*, and redissolved for chromatography.

b. Cellulose. One gram of wood pulp is digested at room temperature with 10 ml. of 72 % H_2SO_4 (sp. gr. 1.64) for 4 hours, after which 320 ml. of water is added, and the mixture is refluxed for 6 hours.

The hydrolyzate is passed through an anion exchange column, e.g., IR-4B or IRA-410 (Amberlite, Rohm and Haas) which is then washed with 600 ml. of distilled water. The washings are added to the hydrolyzate, and the pH of the combined solution is adjusted to 4–5 with 0.1 N H_2SO_4, whereupon the solution is evaporated to a volume of 10 ml. (Sundman, 1951). The hydrolyzate may also be deionized by the batch process with IR-4B (CO_3^{--} cycle) instead of being passed through a column (Saeman, 1953).

Another technique for the hydrolysis of carbohydrates in reticular fibers is as follows (Glegg, 1953): Permutit Q is washed with 4.4 N HCl and then with water until chloride-free. It is then air-dried. Two hundred milligrams of the carbohydrate, 2.4 g. of the washed resin, and 5 ml. of water are heated at 100°C. for 48 hours in a sealed tube. After hydrolysis, the resin is filtered and washed; the filtrates and washings are taken to dryness at 40°C. and dissolved in an appropriate volume of water to be chromatographed.

c. UltramicroHydrolysisTechniques. (Porter, 1954; K. T. Williams, 1955). One drop of a polysaccharide solution (20–30 μg.) and one drop of enzyme solution (10 mg./ml. of amylase, for example) are placed on a microscope slide. The mixture is drawn into a capillary melting point tube, centrifuged, and mixed with a fine glass rod. The tube is incubated at 30°C. for four to six hours in a moist atmosphere. The empty end of the tube is sealed, and the solution is moved to this end by centrifugation. The other end is broken off with a pair of tweezers, and the contents are applied to paper as with a micropipette. This method is claimed to be faster and more reliable than the technique of enzymatic hydrolysis on the paper.

2. SOLVENTS

Table V lists the solvents commonly employed for the chromatography of oligo- and polysaccharides. Many of these solvents are employed for

TABLE V
SOLVENTS FOR OLIGO- AND POLYSACCHARIDES

Solvent composition	Most suitable for	Reference
1. n-Butanol:ethanol:water = 10:1:2 v/v	Oligosaccharide	White, 1953
2. n-Butanol:ethanol:water = 4:1:5 v/v	Oligosaccharide	Lindberg, 1953
3. Ethyl acetate:pyridine:water = 8:2:1 v/v	Oligosaccharide	White, 1953
4. n-Butanol:pyridine:water = 6:4:3 v/v	Oligosaccharide	French, 1950, 1953; Dimler, 1952; Myrbäck, 1953
5. Fusel oil (b.p. 121–139°C.): pyridine:water = 1:1:1 v/v	Oligosaccharide	Dimler, 1952
6. 25% propanol in $M/15$ phosphate buffer (pH 6.4)	Mucopolysaccharide, Dextran sulfate	Kerby, 1953; Ricketts, 1954
7. 75% v/v isopropanol:acetic acid = 9:1 v/v	Amylose	Bird, 1954
8. n-Butanol:pyridine:water: benzene = 50:30:30:4.5 v/v	Raffinose	Brown, 1952; Serro, 1954

TABLE VI
SOLVENTS AND DEVELOPMENT TIME FOR
OLIGOSACCHARIDES (FEINGOLD, 1956)

Solvent system	Development time (descending), in hours	Degree of polymerization effectively resolved
n-Butanol:acetic acid:water = 4:1:5 v/v	72	2–5
n-Propanol:ethyl acetate:water = 7:1:2 v/v	24	2–6
n-Butanol:ethanol:water = 10:1:2 v/v	120	2–5
i-Propanol:acetic acid:water = 7:1:2 v/v	36	2–12

multiple-ascending or continuous descending techniques. The development time for the descending technique depends on the solvent and the effective resolution of oligosaccharides of different chain lengths (see Table VI). Solvents for the chromatography of dextran and mucopolysaccharides are alcohol-buffer mixtures (see Solvent No. 6, Table V). Two additional solvents for mucopolysaccharides are 0.05 M Na_2HPO_4-i-propanol (55:45 v/v) and phosphate-NaCl buffer (7 $\times$ 10^{-4} M NaH_2PO_4, 0.09 M Na_2HPO_4, and 0.07 M NaCl)-i-propanol (Hamerman, 1955). Similar difficulties as with proteins are encountered in the chromatography of these high-molecular-weight compounds, i.e., the spots remain at the point of application or they move with the solvent front. "Rear-phase" development has not been explored for the polysaccharides and may yield more satisfactory migration (see Chapter III).

3. TECHNIQUES

a. Ascending, Descending, and Horizontal Chromatography. The oligo- and polysaccharides are separated by the multiple-ascending or the continuous descending technique, due to their slow mobility. Resolution by horizontal chromatography was achieved of oligosaccharides up to four hexose units. The solvents were *n*-butanol-acetic acid-water (Parihar, 1954), *n*-butanol-pyridine-water (two developments) (Giri, 1955e; Saroja, 1955).

b. Chromatography of Oligosaccharide Derivatives. The migration rate of the oligosaccharides may be increased by chromatographing the *N*-benzyl- or *N*-(1-naphthylethylene)-glycosylamine derivatives of the sugars (Bayly, 1953; Wadman, 1954):

The sugar solution is added to an equal volume of 10 % *N*-(1-naphthyl)-ethylenediamine HCl in triethylamine-ethanol-water (5:4:1 v/v). Five μl. are applied to Whatman No. 1 filter paper, and the spots are dried at 100°C. for thirty minutes. Alternately, 2 μl. spots of the sugar solution are applied to Whatman No. 1 filter paper, 3 cm. apart. A 3-μl. spot of a 10 % solution w/v of benzylamine in methanol is superimposed on the sugar spots, and the paper is kept at 85°C. for 5 minutes. The chromatogram is developed with the solvent *n*-butanol:ethanol:water:ammonia = 40:12:20:1 v/v, and the spots are revealed with a 0.25 % alcoholic solution of ninhydrin or by their fluorescence in ultra-violet light. It is important to achieve a thorough equilibration of the chromatographic tank prior to development, by allowing the solvent to flow on a blank piece of filter paper 45 minutes before the start of development.

Table VII lists a number of R_f values for the amine derivatives and R_G values for oligosaccharides.

4. DETECTION OF SPOTS

(See pp. 178 ff. for preparation of listed reagents)

a. Modified Seliwanoff's reagent. Oligosaccharides containing ketoses are identified by a modified Seliwanoff's reagent: 0.4 ml. of 5 % alcoholic resorcinol solution dissolved in 10 ml. of an alcoholic H_2SO_4 solution (100 ml. of concentrated H_2SO_4 and 375 ml. of 95 % ethanol) (Hattori, 1951). Raffinose has been estimated with 1 % alcoholic α-naphthol:H_3PO_4 = 10:1 v/v. Heat chromatogram for 4 minutes at 90°C. (Albon, 1950; de Whalley, 1950; R. J. Brown, 1952; Serro, 1954).

b. Aniline Hydrogen Oxalate for the detection of raffinose (light pink spots) (R. J. Brown, 1952).

c. *Aniline Hydrogen Phthalate* for amyloses (Bird, 1954); the sprayed paper is heated at 100°C. for 5–15 minutes or slightly longer for dextrins containing 3–6 glucose units.

d. *Aniline Diphenylamine Phosphate* (Saroja, 1955; Schwimmer, 1956). This reagent is prepared by mixing 4 ml. of aniline in 100 ml. of acetone and 4 g. of diphenylamine in 100 ml. acetone with 20 ml. of 85 % H_3PO_4. The dried chromatograms containing oligosaccharides are sprayed or dipped and heated at 80°C. for five minutes. Oligosaccharides with a 1-4 linkage produce blue-purple spots, while those with a 1-6 linkage are slate-brown-green depending on their concentration.

e. *Somogyi's Reagent* for spraying (French, 1950): (A) 1 liter of reagent A contains 40 g. of $CuSO_4 \cdot 5H_2O$; (B) 150 gm. of molybdic acid and 75 g. of Na_2CO_3 are added to 500 ml. of water, heated, and filtered; 300 ml. of 85 % H_3PO_4 is added to the filtrate, and the solution is made up to 1 liter.

The dried chromatogram is sprayed with reagent A, heated at 105°C. for 5 minutes and then sprayed with B. Reducing polysaccharides show up as blue spots on a white background, e.g., starch degradation products (Pazur, 1955).

f. *Toluidine Blue* for the detection of mucopolysaccharides and dextran sulfate (Rientis, 1953; Kerby, 1953). The dried chromatogram is dipped into a 0.125 % w/v solution of toluidine blue or 0.05 % w/v azure A in 80 % acetone. Sulfated acid mucopolysaccharides and dextran sulfate show up as red spots on a blue background (Ricketts, 1954).

g. *Mucicarmine* for the detection of mucopolysaccharides (Hamerman, 1955). One gram of carmine, 0.5 g. of $AlCl_3$, and 2 ml. of water are heated together in a crucible for several minutes. The crucible is dropped into 100 ml. of 50 % ethanol, and after twenty-four hours the solution is filtered. For a spraying solution, 5 ml. of the stock solution are diluted to 25 ml. with 85 % ethanol.

After chromatographing the mucopolysaccharides with *i*-propanol-buffer, the papers are fixed for fifteen minutes in a solution of neutral formalin:ethanol (2:8 v/v). The papers are then sprayed with toluidine-blue (see *f.* above) or mucicarmine reagent and washed in dilute acetic acid and water. The following colored spots are observed:

	Toluidine-blue	Mucicarmine
Heparin	pink	pink
Chondroitin sulfate	purple	pink
Hyaluronate	purple	pink

(light blue background)

h. *Iodine* for the detection of starch. 1 % Alcoholic solution of iodine (Hattori, 1951) is used.

5. QUANTITATIVE ESTIMATION

For the quantitative estimation of D-glucose and its oligosaccharides the following method gives an accuracy of ±5 % (Dimler, 1952): After the development of the chromatogram, the regions containing the carbohydrates (located by the color development of a parallel strip) are eluted by descending chromatography with water as solvent (see Chapter III for elution technique). The time required for elution is 2–3 hours for D-glucose and 4–5 hours for oligosaccharides.

The eluate is mixed with an appropriate amount of freshly prepared anthrone reagent (0.2 g. of anthrone dissolved in 100 ml. of concentrated H_2SO_4). The color of the solution is read photometrically at 620 mμ and correction is made for "apparent" glucose extracted from a blank piece of filter paper.

The amine derivatives (see p. 193) are eluted with 5.0 ml. 1 % $Na_3PO_4 \cdot 12$ H_2O, and the fluorescence is determined with the fluorescence attachment of the Beckman spectrophotometer (Wadman, 1954). Fluorescence determinations may be made directly on the paper without elution. Standard curves are obtained from solutions of known concentration (Fig. 5).

6. STUDY OF POLYSACCHARIDE STRUCTURE

When a sample of dextran was hydrolyzed with 0.1 M H_2SO_4 and the hydrolyzate was chromatographed by the multiple ascent technique, the following mathematical relationship could be verified (French, 1953):

$$\log \alpha' = C_1 - nC_2 - mC_3 , \qquad (2)$$

where C_1, C_2, C_3 $\cdots$ are characteristic values for the monosaccharide unit

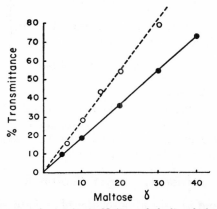

FIG. 5. Standard curves for maltose-N-(1-naphthyl) ethylenediamine derivative (Wadman, 1954). ——Fluorescence in solution after elution- - -Fluorescence on the paper.

TABLE VII

R_f VALUES OF SOME OLIGOSACCHARIDES AND DERIVATIVES

	Solvents[a]		
	1 $R_g{}^b$	2 $R_g{}^b$	3 $R_a{}^c$
Maltose	0.704	0.65	0.66
Maltotriose	0.502	0.38	0.41
Maltotetraose	0.333	0.21	0.26
Maltopentaose	0.210	0.15	0.19
Maltohexaose	0.138	0.11	0.09
Maltoheptaose	0.093	0.08	—
Isomaltose	0.545	0.45	—
Isomaltotriose	0.368	0.29	—
Isomaltotetraose	0.264	—	—
Isomaltopentaose	0.171	—	—
Isomaltohexaose	0.112	—	—
Isomaltoheptaose	0.070	—	—
Glucose	1.000	1.00	0.89

[a] Solvents: 1. n-Butanol:pyridine:water (6:4:3 v/v) descending; 20–30 hours; 22°C. (Myrbäck, 1953)

2. Ethyl acetate:pyridine:water (10:4:3 v/v) descending; 96 hours (Whistler, 1955)

3. n-Butanol:ethanol:water:NH₄OH (40:12:16:1 v/v)

[b] $R_g = R_{glucose}$ (migration relative to glucose)

[c] $R_a = R_{amine}$ (migration relative to free amine). (R_a values are of N-(1-naphthyl) ethylenediamines of sugars)

being added, and

$$\alpha' = \frac{R_f}{1 - R_f} \tag{3}$$

Equations 2 and 3 were derived in Chapter II. For multiple ascent the following equation holds:

$$(1 - R_f)^a = 1 - R_f{}^a \tag{4}$$

where a = number of ascents.

In this experiment Eaton and Dikeman No. 613 filter paper was employed and the solvent was butanol:pyridine:water = 6:4:3 v/v. A straight-line relationship was achieved when the experimental α' was plotted against "hexose units per molecule."

Section IV: Sugar Phosphates

The separation and identification of the phosphate esters of the sugars are very important in the fields of carbohydrate metabolism and in the chemistry of muscular contraction.

TABLE VIII
Solvents for Sugar Phosphates

Solvent composition	Most suitable for	Reference
1. Methanol:formic acid:water = 80:15:5 v/v	G-1-P[a] G-6-P[b]	Bandurski, 1951
2. Methanol:NH₄OH:water = 6:1:3 v/v	G-1-P G-6-P	Bandurski, 1951 Fletcher, 1953 Charalampous, 1953
3. Acetone:35% chloroacetic acid = 6:4 v/v	G-1-P F-6-P[c]	Burrows, 1952
4. Ethyl acetate:acetic acid: water = 3:3:1 v/v	F-1,6-DP[d] F-6-P	Mortimer, 1952
5. Methyl cellosolve:methyl ethyl ketone:3 N NH₄OH = 7:2:3 v/v	Glyceraldehyde-3-P 2,3-Diphosphoglyc-erate	Mortimer, 1952
6. Ethyl acetate:formamide: pyridine = 6:4:1 v/v	G-1-P F-6-P	Mortimer, 1952
7. tert-Butanol:water:picric acid = 80:20:4 v/v	G-1-P F-1,6-DP ATP[e]	Hanes, 1949 Caldwell, 1953 Loring, 1956
8. n-Propanol:NH₄OH:water = 60:30:10 v/v	F-6-P F-1,6-DP	Hanes, 1949 Caldwell, 1953
9. Methanol:ethanol:water = 9:9:2 v/v	G-1-P G-6-P	Norris, 1949
10. tert-Amyl alcohol:water: formic acid = 90:90:30 v/v; use organic phase	Miscellaneous	Hanes, 1949
11. n-Butanol:acetic acid:water = 4:1:5 v/v	Miscellaneous	Ganguli, 1953
12. i-Propyl ether:formic acid = 9:6 v/v	3-PGA[f] F-1,6-DP	Eggleston, 1952
13. n-Propanol:formic acid:water = 6:3:1 v/v	2-Ketogluconate phosphates	de Ley, 1955
14. Formic acid:water:95% ethanol = 1:29:70	2-PGA, 3-PGA G-1-P, G-6-P	Cowgill, 1955
15. Nitromethane:pyridine: water = 5:6:4 v/v	1-Glycerophosphate 2-Glycerophosphate	Dierick, 1956

[a] G-1-P: glucose-1-phosphate   [d] F-1,6-DP: fructose-1,6-diphosphate
[b] G-6-P: glucose-6-phosphate   [e] ATP: adenosine triphosphate
[c] F-6-P: fructose-6-phosphate   [f] PGA: phosphoglyceric acid

A wide variety of organic solvents has been employed in order to separate sugar phosphates which are structurally very similar, e.g., glucose-1-phosphate and glucose-6-phosphate. For the detection of these phosphate esters the reagent first developed by Hanes and Isherwood (1949) is commonly used, but several modifications have sought to overcome the disadvantage of using perchloric acid as a constituent of the reagent. Since ribose and deoxy sugars occur in the nucleic acids and their derivatives, some repetition may occur in Chapter IX.

1. PREPARATION OF SAMPLES

The phosphorylated compounds in kidney tissue may be separated into three groups by the following procedure (Gerlach, 1955): The biological sample (e.g. kidney tissue) is frozen in liquid nitrogen and is extracted with 10 % trichloroacetic acid. The mixture is centrifuged, and to the supernatant is added 25 % barium acetate. The barium-precipitated compounds are centrifuged off, and the clear solution is treated with five volumes ethanol. The three fractions are: *a. barium precipitate, dissolved in N formic acid*, 2-, and 3-phosphoglyceric acid, hexose, 1,6-diphosphate; *b. alcohol-insoluble Ba salts*, glucose-1-phosphate, fructose-6-phosphate, ribose-5-phosphate; *c. alcohol-soluble Ba salts*, 1,2-propanediol phosphate, aminoethyl phosphate.

Phosphoglyceric acid and fructose-1,6-diphosphate may be extracted from blood with 7.5 % trichloroacetic acid (Rohdewald, 1956). The excess acid is removed by ether extraction. The samples prior to chromatography are desalted by the pyridine extraction method of Malpress (1949) (see p. 173), by drying the samples over P_2O_5 and extracting them with pyridine at a temperature not exceeding 30°C. (McGeown, 1952).

2. SOLVENTS

With the aid of Tables VIII and IX, it may be possible to choose a solvent for the separation of a particular sugar phosphate mixture. Aqueous Versene solutions at a concentration of 0.002 N may replace water in any of the solvents that contain water, thus repressing the interference of cation impurities in the paper (Walker, 1951; Eggleston, 1952).

The use of any of the basic solvents may cause partial hydrolysis of the phosphate esters and interconversion of α- to β-glycerophosphate (Rousser, 1953).

For two-dimensional chromatography, the following solvents have been recommended (Fletcher, 1953): *First direction*—Methanol:NH_4OH:water = 6:1:3; *Second direction*—Methanol:acetic acid:water = 80:15:5 v/v.

TABLE IX

R_f OF SUGAR PHOSPHATES

	Solvents[a]					
	1	2	3	4	5	6
D-Glucose-1-phosphate	0.27	0.60	0.31	0.14	0.36	0.44
D-Glucose-6-phosphate	0.38	0.48	—	0.12	0.29	0.50
D-Fructose-6-phosphate	0.34	0.44	0.37	0.17	0.36	0.54
D-Fructose-1,6-diphosphate	0.40	0.24	0.37	0.08	0.08	0.13
2-Phosphoglycerate	0.46	0.18	—	0.27	0.41	0.23
3-Phosphoglycerate	0.50	0.35	—	0.23	0.22	0.28
Phosphoenolpyruvate	0.52	0.46	—	—	—	—
D-Ribose-5-phosphate	—	—	0.46	—	—	—
D-Ribose-1-phosphate	—	—	—	0.15	0.40	0.50
Glycerol-1-phosphate	—	—	—	0.26	0.39	0.54
D-Glyceraldehyde-3-phosphate	—	—	—	0.07	0.19	—
2,3-Diphosphoglycerate	—	—	—	0.11	0.07	0.15
Orthophosphate	0.63	0.28	0.67	0.33	0.21	0.50
Pyrophosphate	0.46	0.08	0.40	—	—	—

[a] Solvents: 1. Methanol:formic acid:water = 80:15:5 v/v (Bandurski, 1951)
   2. Methanol:ammonium hydroxide:water = 60:10:30 v/v (Bandurski, 1951)
   3. Acetone:35% chloroacetic acid = 60:40 v/v (Burrows, 1952)
   4. Ethyl acetate:acetic acid:water = 3:3:1 v/v (Mortimer, 1952)
   5. Methyl cellosolve:methyl ethyl ketone: 3 N NH$_4$OH = 7:2:3 v/v (Mortimer, 1952)
   6. Ethyl acetate:formamide:pyridine = 6:4:1 v/v (Mortimer, 1952)

3. TECHNIQUES

Ascending and descending one-dimensional techniques are generally employed. By two-dimensional technique, the provisional identification of glycerylphosphorylserine as a component of cerebral phospholipids has been achieved (Dawson, 1953).

By circular paper chromatography, a mixture of phosphate esters from rat liver tissue can be separated in a relatively short time without preliminary treatment of the paper or any special temperature control (Ganguli, 1953a). Multiple development with this technique improves the results.

Combination of paper electrophoresis, followed by paper chromatography has been successfully applied to the separation of a large number of sugar phosphates and other phosphates (purines, pyrimidines) (Wade, 1955).

Whatman No. 1 filter paper "for chromatography" is usually recommended, but Whatman No. 4 washed with 2 N acetic acid is also used (Caldwell, 1953). For the removal of inorganic impurities in the filter paper, the following procedure is described (Eggleston, 1952): Whatman No. 1 filter paper is soaked for 30 minutes in a 0.2 % solution of Versene neutralized to pH 8.5 with dilute NaOH.   This paper is washed with distilled water and is air-dried.

Whatman Nos. 1 and 52 have been saturated with 0.5% sodium molybdate for the separation of 2- and 3-phosphoglyceric acid using the descending technique with formic acid:water:95% ethanol (1:29:70) as solvent (Cowgill, 1955).

4. DETECTION OF SUGAR PHOSPHATES

a. Molybdic Acid Method.   The principle of this method is the hydrolysis of the phosphate esters, the formation of phosphomolybdic acid, and its subsequent reduction to "molybdenum blue."

The chromatograms are sprayed at the rate of 1 ml. per 100 cm.² with the following solution: 5 ml. of 60% w/w $HClO_4$, 10 ml. of 1 N HCl, 25 ml. of 4% w/v $(NH_4)_2MoO_4$, made up with water to a total volume of 100 ml. (Hanes and Isherwood, 1949).   The sprayed papers may be treated in one of the following ways:

(1). heated at 85°C. for seven minutes; allowed to regain moisture from the air; exposed to H_2S in a closed vessel (desiccator) for five to ten minutes;

(2) (*recommended*) illuminated with an ultraviolet light source (e.g. General Electric germicidal lamp);

(3) autoclaved for two minutes at a pressure of 8–10 pounds; exposed to ammonia;

(4) heated for ten minutes at 85°C.; sprayed with a fresh solution of 60% $HClO_4$: "metol" (1 g. of (N-methyl) p-aminophenol sulfate and 3 g. of $NaHSO_3$ in 100 ml. of water) (3:1 v/v) (Charalampous, 1953).   Dark blue spots on a pale blue background result.

The chromatogram may be dipped into the following reagent: 1 g. of ammonium molybdate in 8 ml. of water plus 3 ml. of concentrated HCl and 3 ml. of 70% perchloric acid, diluted to 100 ml. with acetone (Burrows, 1952).   Procedures (1)–(4) are applicable after the chromatogram has been dipped.

b. Enzymatic Liberation of Phosphate (Fletcher, 1953).   The dried chromatogram is sprayed with a 5% solution of $CaCl_2 \cdot 2H_2O$ in 80% ethanol. The ethanol is allowed to evaporate, and the paper is then sprayed with an alkaline phosphoesterase solution in 0.1 M glycine buffer at a pH of 9 (Schmidt, 1949).   The paper is placed between two sheets of glass and is incubated at 37°C. in a moist atmosphere for 4 hours.   The liberated phosphate reacts with the Ca^{++} impregnated in the paper.   The paper is sprayed after this time with a 5% ammonium molybdate solution in 20% HCl.   After 2 minutes the chromatogram is sprayed with a reducing solution (50 mg. of benzidine·HCl in 10 ml. of glacial acetic acid diluted with water to 100 ml.). After exposure to NH_3 vapors the phosphate esters are revealed as blue spots on a white background. This technique has the advantage over the reagents employing $HClO_4$ that the paper does not weaken appreciably and char during heating.

c. Ferric Chloride-Salicylsulfonic Acid Reagent (Wade, 1953). The dried chromatogram is sprayed with 0.1 % $FeCl_3·6H_2O$ in 80 % ethanol and is dried. It is then sprayed with 1 % salicylsulfonic acid in 80 % ethanol. Phosphates appear as white spots on a pale mauve background, provided that the pH of the paper is 1.5–2.5; i.e., this reagent can be employed only with an acidic developing solvent.

d. Acidic Naphthoresorcinol for Fructose Esters. Ten milliliters of the spraying solution is made from 4.75 ml. of 2 % w/v alcoholic naphthoresorcinol, 0.5 ml. of 60 % w/w $HClO_4$, and 4.75 ml. of 2 % aqueous CCl_3COOH. The chromatogram is sprayed with this reagent, heated for 8 minutes at 85°C., and the spots due to fructose-6-phosphate and fructose-1,6-diphosphate are cherry red (Walker, 1951).

e. Aniline Hydrogen Phthalate (Mortimer, 1952). When the dried chromatogram is sprayed with aniline hydrogen phthalate (see Simple Sugars), glucose-6-phosphate and 3-phosphoglyceric acid appear as brown spots. These esters give only a faint color with the Hanes-Isherwood molybdate reagent.

f. Picric Acid. When the sugar phosphates are chromatographed with *tert*-butanol, containing picric acid (Table VIII, 7), the air-dried chromatograms are sprayed with freshly prepared 1 N NaOH in 95 % ethanol and heated at 85°C. for seven to ten minutes. Reddish-brown spots result (Loring, 1956).

Comments. Many of the acidic color reagents used for the simple sugars (see Section II, 4) can be employed for the phosphorylated sugars, e.g. *m*-phenylenediamine, benzidine, and naphthoresorcinol (Gerlach, 1955).

g. Quantitative Determination. Untreated areas containing sugar phosphates may be cut out, ashed with a mixture of concentrated H_2SO_4-$HClO_4$ (3:2 v/v), and the resultant orthophosphate determined by the method of Berenblum and Chain (1938):

To the ashed sample the following are added: 0.5 ml. 10 N H_2SO_4, 7 ml. water, 2.5 ml. 5 % ammonium molybdate, and 10 ml. of *i*-butyl alcohol. The mixture is shaken in a separatory funnel for 1–2 minutes, and the aqueous layer is discarded. The alcoholic solution is washed twice with 5 ml. N H_2SO_4 and then shaken with 15 ml. fresh $SnCl_2$ (0.2 % in N H_2SO_4). The blue alcohol layer and several ethanol washings are diluted to 10.0 ml. and read in the colorimeter.

Section V: Polyhydric Alcohols

1. SOLVENTS (see Table XI; p. 205)

a. Phenol:water = 4:1 v/v; this solvent separates sorbitol (R_f = 0.52) from glucose (R_f = 0.41) (Pariks, 1954).

b. i-Propanol:acetic acid:water = 3:1:1 v/v; this solvent resolves inositol (R_f = 0.12), galactose (R_f = 0.28), glucose (R_f = 0.31), and glycerol (R_f = 0.56) (Böhm, 1954).

c. Solvents for separation of galactinol and inositol (Serro, 1954). Two developing solvents are employed in the same direction:

(1) Benzyl alcohol:*tert*-butanol:water = 15:5:1 v/v plus 1% of 90% formic acid. This development moves interfering organic acids with the solvent front, leaving the carbohydrates behind.

(2) Water-saturated 2,4,6-collidine:collidine = 10:1 then resolves sucrose, galactinol, and inositol.

d. Miscellaneous Solvents:

(1) *Water-saturated n-butanol.*

(2) *n-Butanol:ethanol:water* = 4:1.1:1.9 v/v.

(3) *Upper phase of n-butanol:ethanol:water* = 4:1:5, v/v (Bradfield, 1950).

(4) *Upper phase of benzene:n-butanol:pyridine:water* = 1:5:3:3 v/v.

(5) *n-Butanol:acetic acid:water* = 5:1:2 v/v; 4:1:5 v/v (Bradfield, 1950; Yoda, 1952).

(6) *n-Butanol:diethylene glycol:water* = 3:1:1 v/v for the separation of L-1-keto-*myo*-inositol (R_f = 0.25) (Magasanik, 1953).

(7) *n-Butanol:pyridine:water* = 3:2:1.5 v/v; 4:1:1 v/v (Hockenhull, 1953).

(8) *Ethyl acetate:acetic acid:water* = 3:1:3 v/v (Bradfield, 1950).

(9) *Water-saturated ether* (Bergner, 1953). 1,2- and 1,3-Propyleneglycol are well resolved by fourfold multiple development with water-saturated ether.

2. DETECTION OF POLYHYDRIC ALCOHOLS

a. Ammoniacal Silver Nitrate. Five per cent $AgNO_3$ with ammonia (sp. gr. 0.85) added in excess is used as spraying reagent, and the amounts of alcohols detectable are (Hough, 1950) 1 μg. for hexitols and glycerol and 10 μg. for ethylene glycol. The background color is reduced by dipping the sprayed chromatogram into a 4% $Na_2S_2O_3$ solution.

b. Indicator Sprays. (1) Forty milligrams of bromocresol purple is dissolved in 100 ml. of 95% ethanol containing 100 mg. of boric acid and 7.5 ml. of a 1% aqueous borax solution. Sorbitol, mannitol, dulcitol, and other sugar alcohols appear as yellow spots on a blue background; owing to a pH change by the sugar-borate complex, the color fades with time (Bradfield, 1950; Hackman, 1952; Hathway, 1956).

(2) Another indicator dye is phenol red (Hockenhull, 1953): 0.05 N sodium borate (pH 9.18): phenol red (2 mg./ml. in ethanol, made just alkaline with dilute NaOH):CH$_3$OH = 1:2:7 v/v. Sugars and sugar alcohol form yellow spots on a purple background. Prior to chromatography, the sample should be desalted by ion-exchange or other means.

(3) The following spraying reagent is recommended, since the spots do not fade on the chromatogram (Parikh, 1954): 33.3 ml. 0.1 M boric acid, 26.7 ml. 0.1 M NaOH, and 40 ml. 0.02 % methyl red in 60 % ethanol. The chromatograms are dried over a hot plate before and after spraying. Sorbitol forms a red spot immediately, which is stable for two days.

c. Oxidizing Agents (Yoda, 1952). The dried chromatogram is first sprayed with 0.5 % aqueous KIO$_4$. After 1–5 minutes the paper is sprayed with the following reagent: 15 % aqueous MnSO$_4$: saturated di-(p-dimethylaniline) methane in 2 N acetic acid = 1:1 v/v (see also Feigl, 1956). White spots on a blue background indicate the locations of α-glycols. The sensitivity of this spray is 5–50 μg.

After the periodate reagent, the dried paper may be sprayed with a solution of 35 % saturated sodium tetraborate, containing 0.8 % KI, 0.9 % boric acid, and 3 % soluble starch (Metzenberg, 1954). Since the white spots on blue background are not stable, the wet chromatogram is placed between two pieces of glass, and a contact print is made. (Phenol or buffered solvent should not be used when this reagent is employed.)

A 1 % w/v KMnO$_4$ solution in 2 % w/v Na$_2$CO$_3$ has also been used for the detection of sugar alcohols (Pacsu, 1949; Hackman, 1952).

d. Fleury's Reagent for Polyols (Fleury, 1953; Lambou, 1956). *Stock solution:* 10 g. of HgO, 10 g. of concentrated HNO$_3$, and 200 ml. of water. *Spray reagent:* dilute stock solution with water 1:1. After spraying, the chromatogram is heated for ten minutes at 90°–100°C. This is followed by a spray composed of 10 % barium acetate:glacial acetic acid = 1:10 v/v and subsequent heating for ten to thirty minutes. This latter spraying and heating may be repeated if polyols other than inositol are suspected to be present (see Table X). Sensitivity: 5–10 μg. inositol.

For greater sensitivity, the chromatogram may be sprayed next with resorcinol reagent (see p. 184) and heated for five minutes at 105°C. One microgram of inositol can be detected as a brilliant rose-orange spot.

e. p-Anisidine Phosphate. A dipping reagent is composed of the following: 0.5 g. p-anisidine in 3 ml. syrupy H$_3$PO$_4$, diluted with 100 ml. of 80 % methanol. The chromatogram, after dipping, is heated at 100°C. for ten to fifteen minutes. Sugar alcohols result in white spots on brown background while their glycosides produce brown spots (Cerbulis, 1955).

TABLE X
COLOR REACTIONS OF POLYOLS (LAMBOU, 1956)

Compound	Modified Fleury		p-Anisidine phosphate over Fleury Reagent		Sensitivity (µg.)	
	10 min.	30 min. heating	Daylight	Ultraviolet	Day-light	Ultra-violet
Inositol	orange	orange	orange	red	2	2
Adonitol	gray	black	—	lavender	—	10
Glycerol	—	gray	white	lavender	—	10
Mannitol	—	gray	dull yellow	yellow	10	5
Erythritol	gray	black	lavender	purple	10	10
Sorbitol	—	gray	tan	light brown	20	25
Dulcitol	—	gray	tan	yellow	25	20

Fleury's Reagent can be followed by p-anisidine phosphate and results in the formation of multi-colored spots when viewed in daylight and under ultra-violet illumination. These colors may help in the identification of sugars and polyols (Lambou, 1956) (see Table X).

Ethanolic solution (1 %) of vanillin: 3 % aqueous $HClO_4$ = 1:1 v/v has been used as a spraying reagent for polyols and ketoses (Godin, 1954). Sensitivity: 15 µg. hexitol; all others 20–30 µg. Inositol does not react.

3. QUANTITATIVE ESTIMATION

Inositol has been estimated in lipids after hydrolysis and chromatography using i-propanol:acetic acid:water = 3:1:1 v/v as solvent (Böhm, 1954). A marker is located with ammoniacal $AgNO_3$. The unreacted spots are eluted, oxidized with HIO_4 by the method of Hirst (1949), and the resultant iodine is titrated with standardized thiosulfate. Direct densitometry may be used with $AgNO_3$ as spraying reagent (see p. 187).

Section VI: Sugar Acids, Lactones, Anhydrides (see Table XII)

1. SUGAR ACIDS.

a. Solvents

(1) *Pyridine:amyl alcohol:water* = 7:7:6 v/v is used to resolve glucuronic, galacturonic, and mannuronic acids. Glucuronic acid gives two spots with this solvent, one being due to the lactone (Masamune, 1952).

(2) *Pyridine:ethyl acetate:acetic acid:water* = 5:5:1:3 v/v is used as developing solvent for continuous descending chromatography of a number of sugar acids (see Table XII). The cabinet is pre-saturated with a solvent system of pyridine:ethyl acetate:water (11:40:6, v/v) (F. G. Fischer,

TABLE XI
R_f Values of Polyhydric Alcohols

Compound	Solvent[a]						
	1	2	3	4	5	6	7
Inositol	0.06	0.07	0.08	—	—	0.11	—
Sorbitol	0.18	0.17	0.19	—	—	0.31	—
Dulcitol	0.16	0.17	0.18	—	—	0.31	0.48
Mannitol	0.19	0.20	0.19	—	—	0.34	0.48
Ribitol (Adonitol)	0.25	0.28	0.28	—	—	0.40	—
Arabitol	0.22	0.28	—	—	—	0.43	0.53
Xylitol	0.20	0.24	—	—	—	—	—
Erythritol	0.35	0.31	0.34	—	—	0.49	0.63
Ethylene glycol	0.64	—	—	0.47	0.08	—	0.83
Glycerol	0.48	—	—	0.18	—	0.58	0.75
1,2,4-Butanetriol	—	—	—	0.20	—	—	—
1,3-Propyleneglycol	—	—	—	0.55	0.14	—	—
1,2-Propyleneglycol	—	—	—	0.67	0.24	—	—
Diethyleneglycol	—	—	—	0.72	0.08	—	—
1,4-Butyleneglycol	—	—	—	0.74	0.26	—	—
1,3-Butyleneglycol	—	—	—	0.76	0.35	—	—
2,3-Butyleneglycol	—	—	—	0.78	0.45	—	—
Triethyleneglycol	—	—	—	0.83	0.08	—	—

[a] Solvents: 1. n-Butanol:acetic acid:water = 4:1:5 v/v (Buchanan, 1950; Hackman, 1952)
2. n-Butanol:ethanol:water = 4:1:5 v/v (Hackman, 1952)
3. Ethyl acetate:acetic acid:water = 3:1:3 v/v (Hackman, 1952)
4. Chloroform:ethanol = 3:2 v/v (Bergner, 1953)
5. Water-saturated ethyl ether (Bergner, 1953)
6. n-Propanol:ethyl acetate:water = 7:1:2 v/v (Cerbulis, 1955)
7. tert-Amyl alcohol:n-propyl alcohol:water = 4:1:1.5 v/v (Cifonelli, 1954)

1955a). In 48 hours the following acids could be resolved: D-glucuronic, D-galacturonic, and D-mannuronic acids.

(3) *Butanol:pyridine:water* = 3:2:1.5 separates uronic acid from a polysaccharide hydrolyzate derived from *Leuconostoc mesenteroides* (P. B. Smith, 1952).

(4) *Phenol:water* = 4:1 v/v and *n-Butanol:acetic acid:water* = 4:1:5 v/v as solvents in two-dimensional chromatography are employed to separate galacturonic acid (Partridge, 1949).

(5) *Sugar keto acids* have been resolved by a variety of solvents, including *n-propanol:n-butyl methyl ether:formic acid:water* = 7:3:2:5 v/v and *n-butanol:water:propionic acid* = 10:7:5 v/v (Macek, 1952). The phosphate esters of these acids can be separated with *n-propanol: 90% formic acid:water* (6:3:1 v/v) (de Ley, 1955).

(6) *Ethyl acetate:acetic acid:water* = 3:1:3 v/v is used to separate glucurone, glucuronic acid, and galacturonic acid (Rao, 1951). The same

solvent in the ratio of 10:1.3:1 has been used for the chromatography of saccharinic acids (Moilanen, 1954).

(7) *n-Butanol:acetic acid:water* = 3:1:1 v/v and *n-butanol:ethanol: water* = 5:1:4 v/v can separate D-galacturonic acid, L-galactonic acid, L-galactono-γ-lactone, and methyl-D-galacturonate (Mapson, 1956).

(8) *Acetone:water:benzene* (9:1:2 v/v) plus 4 mg. of Rhodamine B per 100 ml. of solvent is used both as chromatographic solvent and detecting reagent for the anilide derivatives of sugar acids (Green, 1954). When viewed under ultraviolet light, the anilides appear as dark spots on a light yellow background.

b. Detection of Spots. Many of the reagents listed for the detection of the simple sugars are used for the sugar acids, e.g., aniline hydrogen phthalate for galacturonic acid (Partridge, 1949) and naphthoresorcinol for uronic acid (P. B. Smith, 1952).

(1) A reagent consisting of 0.05 % *o*-phenylenediamine in 10 % aqueous trichloroacetic acid is used to detect sugar keto acids (Macek, 1952).

A similar reagent consists of 400 mg. *o*-phenylenediamine, 0.65 ml. concentrated HCl, 3 ml. water, and 16 ml. 96 % ethanol (de Ley, 1955). The chromatogram is heated for three minutes at 100°C., and 2-ketogluconate exhibits greenish fluorescence.

(2) A reagent consisting of 0.1 % naphthoresorcinol in 20 % w/v trichloroacetic acid in *n*-butanol is used for the detection of glucuronic acid (Robinson, 1955). The sprayed paper is heated for five minutes at 100°C., and blue spots will appear for the free acid or acid-labile glucuronides.

2. Ascorbic Acid (Bode, 1952; Heimann, 1953; Tegethoff, 1953)

Schleicher and Schuell No. 2043bM filter paper and *n*-butanol:acetic acid:water = 4:1:5 v/v are employed for the paper chromatography of ascorbic acid. Tegethoff (1953) recommends dissolving the standards of ascorbic acid in 4 % HPO_3 and saturating the chromatographic tank with H_2S in order to minimize oxidation during development. Dehydroascorbic acid has been chromatographed with this solvent as the 2,4-dinitrophenylhydrazone (R_f = 0.88) (Barreto, 1955).

Three color reagents are listed for the detection of ascorbic acid in the presence of interfering substances, e.g., sulfhydryl compounds, reductone, reducing sugars, etc.

a. Molybdate Reagent. The stock solution consists of 150 g. of $(NH_4)_2MoO_4$ in 1 liter of 1 % NH_4OH. For the spray reagent, the following are used: 3.0 ml. of molybdate stock solution, 2.0 ml. of HCl:citrate buffer (pH 3.8), and three drops of concentrated H_2SO_4. Ascorbic acid is revealed by blue spots (R_f 0.36) due to the reduction of Mo^{6+} to Mo^{4+}. Glucose and fructose have a much lower R_f with the butanol:acetic acid solvent and do not interfere. Sensitivity 2 μg. For quantitative estimation, unknown spots, not reacted with molybdate, are cut out, extracted, and titrated with 0.001 N dichloroindophenol.

b. Fe(NH₄)(SO₄)₂:o-Phenanthroline Reagent. Five milliliters of a 0.15 % solution of $Fe(NH_4)(SO_4)_2$ and 45 ml. of 2 % *o*-phenanthroline·HCl are shaken together. The chromatogram is sprayed with this reagent and heated at 80–100°C. for several minutes. Red spots are formed owing to the reduction of Fe^{+++} by ascorbic acid (R_f 0.36–0.40) and uric acid (R_f 0.18).

c. Cacotheline Reagent. The dried chromatogram is sprayed with a 2 % aqueous solution of cacotheline (Merck alkaloid) and heated at 100°C. for several minutes. Violet spots for ascorbic acid result. This color reaction is fairly specific for ascorbic acid but is not recommended for direct-reading densitometry.

3. Sugar Lactones

For the separation of sugar lactones, the following solvents are chosen (Abdel-Akher, 1951) (see Table XII): (1) *methyl ethyl ketone*, saturated with water; (2) *methyl ethyl ketone:petroleum ether* (100–120°C. fraction) = 9:1 v/v; use upper layer.

Detection of lactones with hydroxylamine. The sugar lactones, after development with butanol or methyl ethyl ketone solvent, are identified by spraying the paper with a freshly prepared alkaline solution of equal volumes of normal $NH_2OH·HCl$ and 1.1 N KOH, both in methanol (Abdel-Akher, 1951). The chromatogram is dried in air for 10 minutes and then sprayed with a solution of 1–2 % FeCl₃ in 1 % aqueous HCl. Blue or mauve spots are formed by the lactones.

4. Sugar Anhydrides

Fructose and glucose anhydride are separated with the solvent ethyl:acetate:water:pyridine = 25:8:7 v/v; the upper layer is used (Sattler, 1952). The anhydrides are detected by the following color reagents (see p. 178 ff. for preparation):

a. Resorcinol:H₃PO₄ reagent. The sprayed chromatogram is heated for 8 minutes at 80°C. The spots are viewed with ultraviolet light.

b. 0.1 M Aniline hydrogen oxalate.

c. α-Naphthol:H₃PO₄. The sprayed chromatogram is heated for 15 minutes at 85–90°C.

Section VII: Amino Sugars

1. Solvents

The amino sugars may be separated by conventional solvents used for the simple sugars, e.g., phenol:ammonia, collidine, and *n*-butanol:acetic

TABLE XII
R_f VALUES OF LACTONES, GLYCOSIDES, AND SUGAR ACIDS

	Solvent[a]			
Compound	1	2	3	4 R_G[b]
D-Xylono-γ-lactone			0.41	
L-Rhamnono-γ-lactone			0.50	
D-Glucono-γ-lactone		0.56	0.32	
D-Galactone-γ-lactone			0.35	
D-Mannono-γ-lactone		0.39	0.25	
D-Glucono-δ-lactone			0.22	
L-Arabono-γ-lactone		0.39, 0.59		
L-Rhamnono-γ-lactone		0.37, 0.63		
D-Glucoheptono-γ-lactone		0.23	0.13	
D-Glucose	0.42	0.39		1.00
Methyl α-D-glucoside	0.58			
Methyl β-D-glucoside	0.63			
Methyl α-D-galactoside	0.54			
Methyl β-D-galactoside	0.51			
Methyl α-D-mannoside	0.68			
Methyl α-D-mannofuranoside	0.74			
Methyl α-L-arabinoside	0.60	0.65		
Methyl β-L-arabinoside	0.68			
Methyl α-L-fucoside	0.76			
Methyl α-L-rhamnoside	0.86	0.87		
Methyl α-D-xyloside	0.75	0.76		
Methyl β-lactoside	0.33	0.25		
Methyl β-maltoside	0.37	0.33		
Galacturonic acid				0.18
Glucuronic acid				0.27
Guluronic acid				0.28
2-Ketogluconic acid				0.21
Mannuronic acid				0.35
5-Ketogluconic acid⁻				0.47
Methyl β-D-glucofuranoside			0.30	
Mannitol hexaacetate			0.85	
Arabitol pentaacetate			0.85	

[a] Solvents: 1. *tert*-Pentyl alcohol:1-propanol:water = 4:1:1.5 v/v (Cifonelli, 1954)
2. *tert*-Pentyl alcohol:1-propanol:water = 4:1:1 v/v (Cifonelli, 1954)
3. Upper phase of:1-butanol:ethanol:water = 5:1:4 (Hough, 1950a; Abdel-Akher, 1951)
4. Pyridine:ethyl acetate:acetic acid:water (5:5:1:3 v/v) (Fischer, 1955); tank saturated with pyridine: ethyl acetate:water (11:40:6 v/v)
[b] $R_G = R_f$ with respect to glucose

acid (Partridge, 1948). A number of other solvents have been employed:

a. n-Butanol acetate:pyridine:water = 5:3:1 v/v for chondrosamine and glucosamine (Yoshizawa, 1951).

b. Sodium carbonate (0.5 N) for N-acetylglucosamine (Capani, 1953).

c. Isoamyl alcohol:pyridine:NH₃ = 7:3:10 for reaction products of carbohydrates and ammonia (Raacke-Fels, 1953).

d. Pyridine:water:ethyl acetate:acetic acid = 5:3:5:1 v/v (saturate tank with pyridine:ethyl acetate:water = 11:40:6 v/v) for D-galactosamine and D-glucosamine by continuous descending chromatography (F. G. Fischer, 1955b).

e. n-Butanol:pyridine:water = 3:2:1.5 for glucosaminic acid, glucosamine, N-acetylglucosamine (Payne, 1954).

2. TECHNIQUES

a. Separation of N-(2,4-Dinitrophenyl) Derivatives (Kent, 1951). A mixture of 2 mg. of glucosamine and sugars dissolved in 1.0 ml. of 1% NaHCO₃ is shaken with 0.05 ml. of 2,4-dinitrofluorobenzene and 1.0 ml. of 95% ethanol. Two drops of the reaction mixture are spotted on Whatman No. 1 paper, and the chromatogram is developed with *n*-butanol:ethanol: water = 4:1:5 v/v. The spots are detected with the aniline hydrogen phthalate reagent. The R_f value of N-(2,4-dinitrophenyl)glucosamine is 0.1. Amino acids and other sugars do not interfere.

b. Separation of Pentoses Derived from Hexosamines (Stoffyn, 1954). The amino sugars are degraded by ninhydrin to their corresponding pentoses which are identified by paper chromatography.

After applying the hexosamine, the paper is sprayed with 2% ethanolic ninhydrin, containing 4% pyridine. The paper is kept at 80°C. for three hours in an atmosphere of 50% aqueous pyridine. The resulting pentoses are chromatographed by the descending technique (40 hours) with *n*-butanol:ethanol:water = 4:1:1 v/v. Lyxose (from galactosamine) and arabinose (from glucosamine) are detected with the AgNO₃-NaOH reagents of Trevelyan (1950) (see pp. 178–179).

3. DETECTION OF HEXOSAMINES

a. Acetylacetone-Dimethylaminobenzaldehyde Reagent (Partridge, 1949).

Preparation of color reagents. (1) Acetylacetone reagent: (*A*) 0.5 ml. of acetylacetone in 50 ml. of butanol; (*B*) 5 ml. of 50% w/v aqueous KOH and 20 ml. of ethanol; 0.5 ml. of *B* is added to 10 ml. of *A*. (2) *p*-Dimethylaminobenzaldehyde reagent: 1 g. of recrystallized *p*-dimethylaminobenzaldehyde is dissolved in 30 ml. of ethanol, and 30 ml. of concentrated HCl is added. The solution is diluted to 100 ml. with redistilled butanol. This stock solution is stable for weeks.

Development of color. The chromatograms are first sprayed with reagent (1) and heated at 105°C. for 5 minutes. They are then sprayed with reagent (2) and heated at 90°C. for another 5 minutes. Free hexosamines form cherry-red spots and N-acetylglucosamine forms purple-violet spots.

b. Ninhydrin (see Chapter V). 0.05% Ninhydrin in *n*-butanol is sprayed on the chromatogram which is heated at 105–110°C. for 10 minutes (Payne, 1954; Klenk, 1953). N-Acetylglucosamine does not react with this reagent when the spot due to galacturonic acid coincides (Solvent e).

c. *Sugar Reagents* (see pp. 178 ff.). Evidence for the presence of glucosamine and chondrosamine is the observation that reduced AgNO$_3$ spots are formed at lower temperatures than the spots due to reducing sugars (Partridge, 1948).

Other color reagents are p-anisidine-HCl-, p-aminobenzaldehyde-HCl, aniline phthalate, and orcinol (Raacke-Fels, 1953; Campani, 1953; Payne, 1954). When the color due to orcinol is eluted for quantitative analysis, it is recommended to apply 40 μl. of the 1 % test solution. This minimizes the high blank of orcinol-reacting material in the paper (Gottschalk, 1956).

Section VIII: Methyl Sugars and Glycosides (see Table XII)

1. PREPARATION OF SAMPLES

Methylated polysaccharides are mildly hydrolyzed with 4 % methanolic HCl in a sealed tube at 100°C.; this treatment hydrolyzes the methylated polysaccharides to methylated methyl glycosides. The latter are hydrolyzed with 4 % aqueous HCl at 100°C. for three hours. The resulting hydrolyzate is neutralized with Ag$_2$CO$_3$, and the excess silver is removed with H$_2$S, filtered, and passed through Amberlite IR-4B to remove interfering electrolytes. This solution is evaporated to a syrup and chromatographed (Hirst, 1949).

2. SOLVENTS

a. *Butanol :ethanol :ammonia.* The top layer of the following solvent is used to separate methylated glucose, galactose, xylose, and rhamnose: Water-saturated n-butanol:ethanol:water:ammonia = 40:10:49:1 v/v (Hirst, 1949).

Excellent separation of methylated sugars is also achieved by using water-saturated n-butanol as solvent and developing the chromatogram at 37°C. for 6 hours (Hough, 1950).

b. *Methyl ethyl ketone.* Methyl ethyl ketone, saturated with water, plus 1 % (v/v) NH$_4$OH, gives better results than the butanol solvent (Boggs, 1950; Schaefer, 1956).

c. *Methyl ethyl ketone:petroleum ether.* The upper layer of methyl ethyl ketone:petroleum ether (100–120°C) = 9:1 v/v is also employed in the separation of methylated sugars (Boggs, 1951).

d. *2,4,6-Collidine:ethyl acetate:water* = 2:5:5 v/v; upper layer; four times multiple development separates 2-O, 3-O, and 6-O-methyl-D-glucose (Fig. 6) (Lenz, 1956).

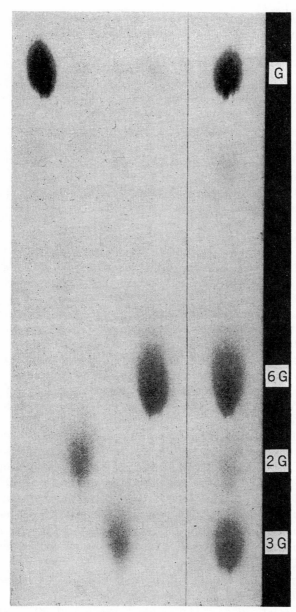

Fig. 6. Unidimensional chromatogram of glucose and three mono-*O*-methyl-D-glucoses (Lenz, 1956). G, Glucose; 2G, 2-*O*-methyl-D-glucose; 3G, 3-*O*-methyl-D-glucose; 6G, 6-*O*-methyl-D-glucose (solvent 2, *d*).

e. tert-Amyl alcohol:n-propanol:water = 4:1:1.5 is employed for the chromatography of methyl-glycosides (Cifonelli, 1954).

3. DETECTION AND QUANTITATIVE ESTIMATION

a. Ammoniacal silver nitrate for methylated sugars. Methylated sugars with the exception of tetramethyl fructopyranose reduce ammoniacal silver nitrate (F. Brown, 1948).

b. p-Anisidine·HCl for methylated sugars. This color reagent consists of 3% *p*-anisidine·HCl in *n*-butanol. The chromatograms, after being sprayed, are heated at 100°C. for 10 minutes (Hough, 1950). Overheating should be avoided.

Many of the methylated sugars may be differentiated simply by the color produced with this reagent; e.g., methyl aldopentose is emerald green, methylated aldohexose is brown with a tint of red, and methylated aldopentose is intense red.

c. Aniline phthalate for methylated sugars. After elution of the methylated sugars from the paper chromatograms, the quantities may be determined colorimetrically by the use of the aniline phthalate reagent described above (Bartlett, 1951).

d. N-Dimethyl-p-aminoaniline·HCl, 0.4% in 2% trichloroacetic acid is sprayed on the chromatogram which is heated for two minutes at 125°C. (Schaefer, 1956).

e. Detection of glycosides (Cifonelli, 1954). The chromatogram is first sprayed with a solution of saturated potassium metaperiodate. It is then sprayed with 0.1 M benzidine in ethanol:0.8 N HCl = 1:1. After about six minutes, nonreducing glycosides result in white spots on a blue background (sensitivity: 2–8 μg.).

f. Quantitative analysis of methylated aldoses. Hirst (1949) describes the following iodometric method for the quantitative determination of methylated aldoses: 1.0 ml. of a 0.1 N solution of iodine is added from a syringe to 5.0 ml. of the sugar solution which should contain no more than 2.5 mg. of sugar. (The spots on the paper containing the sugar are extracted with boiling water for ¾ hour.) Two milliliters of a 0.2 M carbonate buffer (pH 10.6) is added, and the solution is boiled for 2–2½ hours. On cooling, the solution is acidified with 2 N H_2SO_4, and the residual iodine is titrated with a standard solution of $Na_2S_2O_3$.

Another colorimetric method involves the elution of spots with 0.9% methanolic *tetraethylene glycol dimethyl ether* by refluxing for twenty minutes (Schaefer, 1956). The eluate is reacted at 30°C. with 1.0 ml. 2.41% methanolic aniline phthalate until all of the methanol has evaporated. The residue is heated for 35 minutes at 98°C. and dissolved in 95%

ethanol. The color is read at 415 mμ for methylhexoses and at 460 mμ for methylpentoses.

Section IX: Sugar Acetates

Since the penta- and hexaacetates of the sugars are only slightly water-soluble, the filter paper must be pre-treated accordingly (Micheel, 1952b, 1954b, c). Schleicher and Schüll No. 602h paper is dipped into a solution of benzene, acetic anhydride, and sulfuric acid in order to acetylate the cellulose to an acetyl content of 24–25 %. The paper has thus become hydrophobic, and the hydrophobic component of the solvent is the stationary phase for partition chromatography. (See Chapter III for details on the preparation of paper and "reversed chromatography"). n-Butanol: pyridine:water = 3:1:1 v/v resolves a mixture consisting of tetraacetyl-D-glucose and the pentaacetates of D-glucose, D-galactose, D-xylose, and L-arabinose. Butyryl- and benzoyl cellulose paper have been used for the separation of sugar acetates. Other solvents are dioxane:butyl acetate: methanol:water = 6:0.5:2.6:15 and ethyl acetate:water:methanol = 4:20:6.5.

The sugar acetates are saponified after development by exposing the chromatogram to an atmosphere of diethylaminomethanol at 50°C. The liberated sugars are then detected by ammoniacal silver nitrate.

Section X: Deoxy Sugars

1. TECHNIQUE

Deoxy-hexoses, like D-digitoxose and D-diginose, products of hydrolysis of digitalis glucosides (see Chapter VIII), have been separated by paper chromatography (Renkonen, 1956). Whatman No. 1 paper is first dipped into 66 % acetone and is air-dried for five minutes before spotting the samples. Solvents for descending chromatography include toluene:n-butanol:water = 1:9:2 (upper phase) and toluene:methyl ethyl ketone: water = 12:12:1 (upper phase).

2. DETECTION

For the detection of deoxy sugars and glycals the following procedure is recommended (Edward, 1952): The dried chromatogram is first sprayed with a 33 % aqueous solution of HIO_4. After the periodate oxidation, the paper is then sprayed with 1 % alcoholic p-nitraniline (or p-dimethyl-aminobenzaldehyde): concentrated HCl = 4:1 v/v. The chromatogram is then heated at 90°C. for 30 seconds to 2 minutes. The following colors are observed: deoxypentoses, deoxypentosides, and D-ribal are blue-grey; deoxyhexoses, deoxyhexosides, glucal, and galactal are pink-grey.

A simpler procedure consists of a 1 % boric acid spray in 90 % methanol, containing 1 % HCl.   Heating the sprayed chromatogram for 1 to 3 minutes at 100°–105°C. results in gray-blue spots for the deoxy-sugars and purple fluorescence in ultraviolet light (Pöhm, 1956).   Sensitivity: daylight, 2 μg.; ultraviolet, 0.5 μg.

Aniline phthalate spraying and subsequent heating over a hot plate will reveal deoxy-sugars in visible and ultraviolet light (see p. 181) (Renkonen, 1956).

Chapter VII

ALIPHATIC ACIDS

Owing to the volatility of the lower-carbon fatty acids, salts rather than the free acids are separated by paper chromatography. Butanol, phenol, and other conventional solvents have been used for their separation. These acids have also been chromatographed as their respective potassium or sodium hydroxamate derivatives (K. Fink, 1949; A. R. Thompson, 1951b). Spraying reagents for the acids are generally alcoholic or aqueous solutions of acid-base indicators like bromocresol green or, bromophenol blue, and $FeCl_3$ in the case of the hydroxamates.

α-Keto acids have been separated as their 2,4-dinitrophenylhydrazones, or when resolved as the original acids, they are detected with a semicarbazide reagent.

Section I: Volatile Aliphatic Acids

1. PREPARATION OF SAMPLES

Sodium (F. Brown, 1950b), ammonia (Hiscox, 1950; Reid, 1951; Kennedy, 1951; Isherwood, 1953), and diethylamine (Miettinen, 1951; Long, 1951; A. R. Jones, 1953) salts have been employed, and by their use the resolution of volatile fatty acids is easily and quickly accomplished. The latter two salts are preferred because, unlike the sodium ion, the ammonium and diethylamine ions do not obliterate the acetate spot. All three salts, however, minimize the loss of fatty acids due to volatilization.

The formation of the ammonia or ethylamine salts can be accomplished in a number of ways. The usual procedure for qualitative work is to obtain a water extract of the unknown and make it alkaline with ammonia or diethylamine. If the fatty acids are present as sodium or potassium salts, it is better to add an equivalent amount of $(NH_4)_2SO_4$ and then a little excess NH_3 to make the solution alkaline (Kennedy, 1951). The alkaline solution is then applied to the paper, and the chromatogram is developed. The unknown mixture may also be applied to a spot previously dampened with diethylamine (A. R. Jones, 1953). An alcoholic mixture of the acids may be neutralized with 0.1 N ethylamine using bromocresol green indicator. The ethylamine salts are then placed on the filter paper and allowed to dry for 15 minutes prior to chromatography (David, 1955).

For quantitative work, it is usually necessary to effect some sort of preliminary purification of the acids in question. This can be done either by steam distillation, on silica gel columns (Isherwood, 1946) or by anion exchange resins.

2. FILTER PAPER

The filter paper employed for the chromatographic separation of fatty acid salts is usually Whatman Nos. 1 or 4. Prior to the application of the spots the paper may be washed with a 1 % solution of oxalic acid, followed by rinsing with water and drying. This treatment of the filter paper eliminates "ghost" spots in the chromatography of volatile acids as their ammonium salts when the spraying reagent is a solution of acid-base indicator with the pH adjusted below the point of color change (Kennedy, 1951).

If an alkaline indicator solution is employed as a spraying reagent, it is best to purify the paper by chromatographically washing it in succession with $2 N$ acetic acid, distilled water, and $10 N NH_3$. This treatment of the paper does not affect the general movement of the acids but does give better resolution, minimizes tailing of the spots, and eliminates "ghost" spots at the starting line. The sensitivity of methods for the location of acid spots is also improved because the paper has been freed of soluble acidic and reducing impurities (Isherwood, 1953).

Mottling of the chromatogram, after visualization of the spots with an alkaline indicator, can also be prevented by washing the paper prior to development with the alcohol phase of a system of equal volumes of butanol and $1.5 N$ ammonium hydroxide (Duncan, 1953). Ethanol (5 % v/v) added to the butanol phase after separation from the equilibrated system prevents the subsequent formation of an aqueous phase.

The apparatus used by Isherwood (1953) for the chromatographic washing of filter papers consisted of a divided plastic (Perspex) trough which will take a block of about 60 sheets of Whatman No. 1 paper. The design of the trough is such that when the two sides are clamped together the block of paper is held firmly in a slot in the bottom of the trough. Slight gaps which might be present between the paper and the trough are closed by ramming a little filter-paper pulp into the crevices. The trough is then filled, and solvent is allowed to descend through the paper for about 24 hours.

For quantitative work with the acid salts the use of washed paper is essential; however, it is usually not nessary for qualitative analysis.

3. SOLVENTS

a. *1-Butanol:1.5 N aqueous NH₃* = 1:1 v/v. The alcohol layer separates the C_2-C_7 straight-chain fatty acids more successfully than their corresponding sodium salts (F. Brown, 1950b; Reid, 1951) (see Tables I and II).

b. *1-Butanol:ethanol:3 N NH₄OH* = 4:1:5. The alcoholic phase is used to separate the sodium salts of the lower fatty acids (F. Brown, 1950b).

c. 95% Ethanol:concentrated NH_4OH = 100:1. This solvent separates the first eight homologues of the straight-chain fatty acids (Kennedy, 1951) (see Table I).

d. 1-Propanol:concentrated aqueous NH_3 = 7:3 v/v. This solvent separates the ammonium salts of the lower fatty acids (Isherwood, 1953; Hashmi, 1956) (see Table I).

e. 1-Butanol:H_2O:diethylamine = 100:15:1 v/v. This solvent separates the diethylamine salts which increase the sensitivity of the bromophenol blue indicator (Kennedy, 1951) several times as compared with the ammonium salts (A. R. Jones, 1953; Hiscox, 1950) (see Table I).

f. 1-Hexanol:1.5 N aqueous ammonia = 1:1 (Nair, 1953). The alcohol layer separates alkoxy acids (see Table II).

g. Isoöctane:acetone:95% ethanol:concentrated NH_4OH = 40:30:30:1 (Nair, 1953). This solvent separates alkoxy acids (*cf.* Table II).

4. COLOR REAGENTS

The volume of the applied spot varies between 2 and 10 μl. containing 0.5–3.0 μg. of the salt of each fatty acid (Kennedy, 1951). Amounts of as little as 0.01–0.004 μM of the acids are detectable by suitable spraying reagents (Hiscox, 1950).

a. Bromophenol blue (Kennedy, 1951), 50 mg. in 100 ml. of water, made acid with 200 mg. of citric acid. Ammonium and ethylamine salts show as blue spots on a yellow background (Lugg, 1947; Buch, 1952).

b. Bromocresol purple (Reid, 1951), 40 mg. in 100 ml. of a 1:5 dilution of formalin in ethanol, the pH is adjusted to about 5 with 0.1 N NaOH. The sprayed chromatogram is held for 2–3 minutes in an atmosphere saturated with 3% aqueous NH_3, and the acids appear as bright yellow spots on a purple background.

c. Thymol blue (Isherwood, 1953), 100 mg. in 100 ml. of water, pH adjusted to 10 with 0.1 N NaOH. Ammonium salts show up as yellow spots on a blue background. Spraying with this reagent must be done in a CO_2-free atmosphere; otherwise the background color rapidly fades. However, when used in the absence of CO_2 the indicator is very sensitive and will even detect phenols on the paper.

d. Bromocresol green (Lugg, 1947, 1948; Hiscox, 1950; Denison, 1952; Miettinen, 1951), 1 g. in 100 ml. of absolute ethanol. Ethylamine and ammonium salts show up as blue spots on a yellow background. Burton (1954) uses 0.5% of the dye in ethanol and sprays just as the developed chromatogram starts to dry.

e. Bromothymol blue (F. Brown, 1950b). A 0.04% aqueous solution of bromothymol blue, adjusted to pH 7.5 with NaOH, results in yellow spots for anions and deep-blue spots on green background for cations. This reagent suffers from the disadvantage that the spots fade rather rapidly, probably owing to atmospheric carbon dioxide.

f. Methyl red and bromothymol blue (Duncan, 1953; Priori, 1955). Dissolve 200 mg. each of methyl red and bromothymol blue in a mixture of 100 ml. of formalin and 400 ml. of ethanol. Ajdust the pH to 5.2 with 0.1 *N* sodium hydroxide. After spraying the chromatogram, the paper (in cylindrical form) is placed into a cylinder saturated with ammonia vapors. It is necessary to repeat the exposure to ammonia vapors several times in order to obtain a stable background color. Acids show up as red spots on a green background.

g. Universal indicator (BDH; pH 9.5) results in red spots on a blue background (Hashmi, 1956).

h. Detection of halogenated acids (Hashmi, 1956). Chromatograms of iodo-acids are exposed to chlorine gas for five to ten seconds, and yellow spots on a white background result. Bromo-acids are detected by spraying the paper with 0.1 % fluorescein in 75 % ethanol and then exposing the paper to chlorine gas for five seconds. Red spots result due to eosin formation.

i. Silver nitrate (see Chapt. VI for preparation) may be used to distinguish between formic and acetic acids which exhibit almost the same migration in all solvents. Silver nitrate is reduced by formate but not by acetate and produces a characteristic brown spot (Perilä, 1955).

5. Quantitative Analysis

The lower fatty acids, separated as salts, are determined quantitatively by the area method (see Chapt. IV; also Fisher, 1948; Reid, 1951). As the colors produced by the acid-base indicators are not stable, the areas should be marked with a pencil immediately.

The basis of another method of the quantitative estimation of the ammonium salts of organic acids is: If an acid is added to a neutralized solution of an acid indicator of which the anion is distinctively colored, the color due to the anion is inversely proportional to the amount of acid added between 20 and 80 % neutralization (Isherwood, 1953). Thymol blue solution is prepared by adding 1 ml. of a 0.05 M solution of the sodium salt of glycine (made by dissolving 3.75 g. of glycine in 1 liter of 0.05 N NaOH, free from carbonate) to 450 ml. of 35 % v/v aqueous ethanol containing 8 mg. of thymol blue. The solution is stirred by a stream of CO_2-free air, and 1.4 ml. of a 0.1 N NaOH is added to bring the intensity of the blue color to about 80 % of the maximum value as measured in a colorimeter. The solution is stored in a reservoir attached to an automatic burette, and both the bottle and burette are protected against the entry of CO_2. The procedure for a relatively pure solution of the ammonium salts of the acids is as follows (in the case of biological extracts, the acids must first be separated from the bulk of the other solutes): Four milliliters, or a quantity sufficient to give a reading in the colorimeter equivalent to about 40% neutralization of the indicator-buffer solution, are applied to the starting line of a paper chromatogram (Whatman No. 1, washed). The paper is

TABLE I

R_f VALUES OF SOME LOWER FATTY ACIDS

Fatty acid	Solvent[a]			
	1	2	3	4
Formic	0.10	0.31	0.37	—
Acetic	0.11	0.33	0.37	0.28
Propionic	0.19	0.44	0.48	0.41
n-Butyric	0.29	0.54	0.57	0.51
n-Valeric	0.41	0.60	—	0.56
n-Caproic	0.53	0.68	0.69	—
n-Heptanoic	0.62	0.72	—	—
n-Octanoic	0.65	0.76	0.78	—
n-Nonanoic	0.67	—	—	—
α-Bromoacetic	—	—	0.45	—
α-Bromopropionic	—	—	0.52	—
α-Bromobutyric	—	—	0.60	—
α-Iodoacetic	—	—	0.50	—
α-Iodopropionic	—	—	0.55	—
α-Iodobutyric	—	—	0.62	—

[a] Solvent: 1. n-Butanol:1.5 N NH₄OH = 1:1 v/v.
    2. 95% Ethanol:concentrated NH₄OH = 100:1.
    3. n-Propanol:concentrated NH₄OH = 7:3 v/v.
    4. n-Butanol:H₂O:diethylamine = 100:15:1 v/v.

TABLE II

R_f VALUES OF SOME SEMIVOLATILE ALKOXY ACIDS

Alkoxy acid	Solvent[a]		
	1	2	3
Methoxyacetic	0.10	0.18	0.06
Ethoxyacetic	0.19	0.17	0.09
n-Propoxyacetic	0.28	0.09	0.18
n-Butoxyacetic	0.42	0.18	0.26
3-Ethoxypropionic	0.22	0.04	0.17
4-Methoxy-n-butyric	0.19	0.04	0.14
n-Hexanoic	0.58	0.39	0.48
2-Ethyl-n-hexanoic	0.70	0.55	0.71

[a] Solvent: 1. n-Butanol:1.5 N NH₄OH = 1:1 v/v.
    2. n-Hexanol:1.5 N NH₄OH = 1:1 (Nair, 1953).
    3. Isoöctane:acetone:95% ethanol:concentrated NH₄OH = 40:30:30:1 (Nair, 1953).

developed with propanol:aqueous NH_3 ; the proportions depend on the acids to be separated. After development, the chromatograms are suspended in large glass jars and a stream of dry CO_2-free air is blown through for at least 2 hours. The dry papers are then cut into strips corresponding to the chromatograms of the various spots originally applied to the starting line, and the individual acids are located by reference to a guide chromatogram. The piece of paper containing the ammonium salt of the acid (usual size, 3 × 3 cm.) is cut out and placed in a dry colorimeter tube. Three milliliters of 35% v/v aqueous ethanol is added, and a slow stream of CO_2-free air is bubbled through the liquid by means of a fine capillary tube. After 5 minutes, the paper is lifted out of the liquid with a platinum wire, pressed against the side of the tube with a glass rod, and removed. Four milliliters of the thymol blue reagent are added with the tip of the burette being inserted well into the tube. After 1 minute, the capillary tube is withdrawn and the test tube is immediately stoppered. The contents are shaken and the color is measured, using a green filter (Ilford 626). The blank must be cut from the same chromatogram. Results with this method are accurate to ±10% when about 50 mg. of organic acid is being determined.

6. MISCELLANEOUS APPLICATIONS

Derivatives of acetic and formic acids have been tentatively identified as air pollutants by paper chromatography (Tebbens, 1954). Large volume of air samples were drawn through Whatman No. 40 filter paper disks. The papers after a definite time period were extracted with ether, and the extracts were chromatograhped with Solvent (c). Spraying with bromophenol blue, two spots corresponding to the R_f of acetate and formate showed on the chromatogram.

Section II: Aliphatic Acid Hydroxamates

By first converting the volatile aliphatic acids to their respective hydroxamate derivatives, excellent resolution of nine homologous straight-chain acids may be achieved with a pair of solvents. Formic and acetic acid hydroxamates easily separate which cannot be achieved by the chromatography of the acids or their salts.

1. PREPARATION OF DERIVATIVE (Bergmann, 1956)

One milligram of the acid in solution is made basic with NH_4OH, taken to dryness, and extracted twice with 1.0 ml. portions of 0.4 N HCl in ethanol. Ethereal diazomethane is added until the yellow color persists, and esterification (to the methyl ester) is allowed to proceed for ten minutes. The excess diazomethane is then destroyed by adding several

TABLE III
SOLVENTS USED TO SEPARATE HYDROXAMIC ACIDS
(A. R. Thompson, 1951b; Perilä, 1956)

Solvent (v/v composition)	No. of carbon atoms in hydroxamic acids
Butanol:acetic acid:water = 4:1:5 } Amyl alcohol:acetic acid:water = 4:1:5}	1–5
Octyl alcohol:formic acid:water = 3:1:3	2–5
Benzene:formic acid:water = 1:1:1	4–9
Benzene-acetic acid:water = 4:3:4	5–8
n-Butanol:benzene:water = 1:1:1	1–6

drops of 0.4 N alcoholic HCl.   Two milliliters of 2 N NH$_2$OH sulfate:3.5 N NaOH = 1:1 v/v is added, and the solution is left standing at room temperature for 15 minutes.   The solution of the hydroxamate is concentrated over steam and is spotted on Whatman No. 1 filter paper.

2. SOLVENTS

The potassium hydroxamate derivatives of the fatty acids may be separated by one- or two-dimensional chromatography with water-saturated phenol and/or water-saturated isobutyric acid (Fink, 1949).

A. R. Thompson (1951b) has classified several solvents according to their ability to separate the hydroxamates of the fatty acids (see Table III).

The separation of hydroxamic acid derivatives and other non-volatile, water-soluble organic acids is usually accomplished with aqueous alcohols or benzene which contains a "swamp" acid, e.g., acetic acid.   The effect of the acetic acid in such solvents is twofold.   First, it represses the ionization of the hydroxamic acids and thus prevents the formation of "tails" or "comets"; and, second, the addition of acid to a water-immiscible solvent such as butanol usually increases the solubility of the solvent for water and, therefore, generally increases the R_f values.   Fink (1949) and Thompson (1951) have determined the solvent combinations which will separate many of both volatile and non-volatile acids (see Table IV).   For two-dimensional technique the following solvent pair is recommended (Bergmann, 1956): *First direction*: 95% ethanol (plus 5% NH$_3$):pyridine:water = 3:1:1 v/v; *Second direction*: 95% ethanol:dioxane:water:acetic acid = 60:20:19:1 v/v.

3. DETECTION OF HYDROXAMATES

After development, the chromatograms are sprayed with a solution of 1% ferric chloride in 95% ethanol, containing 0.1% HCl.   Hydroxamates form an intense red-purple complex with ferric chloride on a yellow background. The spots are stable if stored in subdued light, and since the color is specific for hydroxamates, it is not necessary to use washed filter paper for chromatography. The method is sensitive to 0.01–0.20 μM hydroxamates.

4. Quantitative Determination of Hydroxamates

Method A: Acidified alcoholic and aqueous ferric chloride solutions are used for the quantitative determination of the acyl phosphates which have been converted to hydroxamate derivatives prior to their chromatographic separation (Stadtmann, 1950). The reagents are prepared as follows:

1. Dissolve 50 g. of $FeCl_3 \cdot 6H_2O$ in 1 liter of 95 % ethanol containing 0.1 mole of HCl.

2. Dissolve 5 g. of $FeCl_3 \cdot 6H_2O$ in 25 ml. of concentrated HCl and dilute to 600 ml. with water.

The dried filter paper is sprayed with reagent 1, after which the spot is cut out, transferred to a colorimeter tube, and 6 ml. of reagent 2 is added. The optical density of the solution is measured with an Evelyn colorimeter at 540 mμ. Quantitative estimation of a mixture of acyl phosphates as the hydroxamates (C_2-C_6) has been achieved by this method.

Method B. The unstained areas, located with the aid of guide spots, are extracted with 5 % sodium acetate (Bergmann, 1956). To the extract are added 0.5 ml. of 1 % sulfanilic acid in 25 % (v/v) aqueous acetic acid, followed by five drops of iodine solution (1.3 g. of I_2 in 100 ml. acetic acid) and left standing for 4 minutes. Excess iodine is destroyed with thiosulfate, and two drops of naphthylamine reagent is added (0.6 % α-naphthylamine in 30 % (v/v) acetic acid). The resultant azo dye solution is diluted with water, and the color is read at 520 mμ.

Method C (Wingerd, 1953[1]). The dried chromatogram is dipped into the ferric chloride reagent (5 % $FeCl_3$ in methanol:acetone = 4:3; filter before use). After color development the spots are outlined in pencil in order to facilitate location of the point of maximum density in each spot. The densities are measured with the Densichron (W. M. Welch Manufacturing Co., Chicago, Illinois). A green filter and a 5-mm. aperture are placed over the light source, and a 13-mm. aperture covered with opal glass is used on the probe. The area of the aperture over the light source is approximately half the area of the spots so that very little movement of the paper is required to get maximum optical density readings. Before measurement of the spot densities, a point of average density is selected on the yellow background and the galvanometer is adjusted to zero at this point. The quantity of a given acid is calculated from a standard curve.

[1] W. Wingerd [1953]. *Unpublished results.*

The standard curve (optical density against concentration) is a straight line over the range 25–180 μM per tube.

5. DETAILED EXPERIMENTAL PROCEDURE (Wingerd, 1953[2])

REAGENTS: *Sodium hydroxide, 0.6 N.*

Acidified methanol, 2.5 ml. of concentrated H_2SO_4 (sp. gr. 1.84) added to 100 ml. of absolute methanol immediately prior to use.

Hydroxylamine hydrochloride, 1.67 N in absolute methanol.

Sodium methoxide, 5.0 N in absolute methanol.

SOLVENTS. *Amyl alcohol:HCOOH:H_2O* $= 75:25:75$ v/v (A. R. Thompson, 1951b).

Ferric chloride (5% in methanol):acetone $= 4:3$, filtered immediately prior to use.

STANDARD SOLUTION. Twenty-five millimoles each of acetic, propionic, butyric, and lactic acids are dissolved in 1 liter of water and the pH adjusted to 12 with NaOH.

FORMATION OF HYDROXAMATES. Quadruplicate samples of aqueous solutions are measured into 10-ml. test tubes. Each aliquot is made alkaline with 1 ml. of 0.6 N sodium hydroxide and evaporated to dryness overnight in a hot air oven at 110°C. After evaporation, 2 ml. of acidified methanol is added to each tube, and the hard cake of salts is finely powdered with a small nickel spatula. It is necessary to break up the salt cake in order to insure the complete solution of the organic acids. The tubes are tightly stoppered, and the esterification is allowed to proceed for at least 24 hours. After the esterification reactions have reached equilibrium, the sodium hydroxamates are prepared from the methyl esters by the addition of 3 ml. of a freshly mixed alkaline solution of hydroxylamine to each tube. Sodium methoxide:hydroxylamine-HCl $= 9:20$ v/v is cooled to 0°C., and the NaCl which forms, is removed by centrifugation. The salt is washed once with methanol, and the washing is added to the supernatant to restore the original volume of the NH_2OH solution.

Preliminary isolation of the acids is necessary when the unknown mixtures contain sugars or other substances which are converted to acids in alkali. The lower fatty acids are conveniently isolated from other substances on silica gel columns (Isherwood, 1946), by steam distillation or by anion exchange resins.

At least 1 hour is allowed for the formation of the hydroxamates. After this period of time, the insoluble sodium sulfate has settled in the tubes and the supernatant solution of hydroxamates is easily drawn into a micropipette.

DEVELOPMENT OF THE CHROMATOGRAM. Two and one-half microliters of each reaction mixture is applied to a sheet of Whatman No. 1 filter

[2] W. Wingerd [1953]. *Unpublished results.*

TABLE IV

R_f VALUES OF HYDROXAMIC ACID DERIVATIVES

Hydroxamic acid derivative	Solvent[a]								
	1	2	3	4	5	6	7	8	9
	(A. R. Thompson, 1951b)						(Fink, 1949)	(Fink, 1949)	(Stadtmann, 1950)
Formic	.42	.26	—	.008	0	0	.45	.57	
Acetic	.50	.34	.30	.11	0	.01	.57	.70	
Propionic	.62	.51	.50	.25	.01	.05	.68	.78	
Butyric	.72	.67	.68	.45	.04	.13	.74	.80	
Valeric	.79	.78	.81	.67	.11	.32	.83	.84	
Caproic (hexanoic)	.84	.86	.83	.81	.26	.61	.87	.90	
Heptanoic	.86	.89	.85	.88	.51	.87			
Octanoic	.88	.89		.90	.77	.95			
Nonanoic	.89	.89	.90	.90	.88	.97			
Decanoic	.90	.90		.92	.92	.97			
Oxalic							.14, .40	.22, .28, .32	
Malonic							.11, .23	.19, .32	
Succinic							.40, .72	.45, .52	
Glutaric							.47	.37, .52	
Adipic							.54, .67	.44, .60	
Pimelic							.60, .73	.52, .69	
Azelaic							.63, .74	.66 streaked	
Sebacic							.89	.74, .89	
Citric							.09, .23	.20, .29	
Tartaric							.10	.19	
Pyruvic							.59, .86	.54, .62, .73	
Acetyl phosphate									.52
Propionyl phosphate									.65
Butyryl phosphate									.76
Valeryl phosphate									.81
Caproyl phosphate									.86

[a] Solvents: 1. 1-Butanol:acetic acid:water = 4:1:5 v/v.
  2. Amyl alcohol:acetic acid:water = 4:1:5 v/v.
  3. Amyl alcohol:formic acid:water = 75:25:75 v/v.
  4. Octyl alcohol:formic acid:water = 75:25:75 v/v.
  5. Benzene:formic acid:water = 75:75:75 v/v.
  6. Benzene:acetic acid:water = 100:75:100 v/v.
  7. Water-saturated isobutyric acid.
  8. Water-saturated phenol.
  9. Water-saturated butanol.

paper (45 cm. wide × 28 cm. long) with a micropipette. Each sample is placed 2 cm. apart along a "starting line" 3 cm. from the bottom of the paper. Samples are not placed closer than 4 cm. from the sides of the paper in order to prevent distortion of the spots which occurs near the edges of the paper. The chromatograph chamber is described in Chapter III. The developing solvent is the alcohol phase of the amyl alcohol:formic acid:water = 75:25:75 v/v. The aqueous phase is placed in a second trough, and the lower edge of a blank sheet of filter paper is suspended in it. In this way the atmosphere of the chamber is more readily saturated with respect to the aqueous phase. After the samples are applied, the paper sheets are hung in the chamber for at least 1 hour prior development. Humidification of the paper is necessary in order to prevent streaking of the spots. The chromatographic separation is carried out at room temperature for 3 hours. In this time the solvent front travels about 16 cm., and lactic, acetic, propionic, butyric and valeric acid hydroxamates are clearly separated into small, compact spots. The chromatograms are dried in a stream of air at room temperature for 1–2 hours before color development. Quantitative estimation may be carried out by any of the previously described procedures; Method C has the advantages of any *in situ* densitometric technique, speed and simplicity.

Section III: Fatty Acid 2,4-Dinitrophenylhydrazides

(Inouye, 1955a)

A mixture of 10 mg. of fatty acids and 0.3 ml. of thionyl chloride is refluxed for thirty minutes and is then vacuum-distilled. To the residue is added 0.1 ml. of 5% 2,4-dinitrophenylhydrazine in dry pyridine. The reaction mixture is warmed briefly and is cooled to room temperature for 20 minutes. Two milliliters of benzene is added, and the excess pyridine is extracted with 10–20 ml. of warm water. The benzene layer is directly applied on filter paper.

After the benzene solution of the phenylhydrazides has been spotted on the paper (e.g., Tokyo No. 2), the paper is then sprayed uniformly with "tetralin." It is developed by the ascending techniques with one of the solvents containing "tetralin" (DuPont Product, tetrahydronaphthalene) and a polar component, like methanol, ethanol, and acetic acid (see Table V). For the detection of the phenylhydrazides, the papers are sprayed with 0.5 N KOH in ethanol, and brown spots result (Fig. 1). Similar results are obtained by chromatographing fatty acid anilides, formed by the reaction between acid chloride and aniline $Mg \cdot Br$. The mobile phase is cyclohexane, and the immobile phase is aqueous methanol or propanol (de Jonge, 1956).

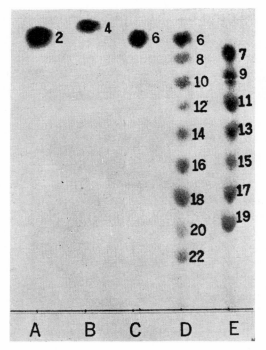

Fig. 1. Paper chromatogram of the 2,4-dinitrophenylhydrazides of saturated fatty acids (Inouye, 1955a). Solvent = methanol:acetic acid:tetralin; numbers refer to the number of carbon atoms in the acids.

Section IV: Non-Volatile Water-Soluble Aliphatic Acids

1. Preparation of Sample

The organic acids may be extracted from plant material with hot 80% aqueous ethanol (Bharucha, 1956) or with 2% H_2SO_4 from foodstuffs (Becker, 1954). Standards may be prepared as 2% solutions in 50% acetone. This solution has excellent storage properties.

2. Filter Paper

The separation of nonvolatile, water-soluble, aliphatic acids is usually accomplished on Whatman No. 1 filter paper. However, Schleicher and Schuell 2043B (Löffler, 1953), Durieux 122 (Cheftel, 1952), Whatman No. 3MM (Palmer, 1955), and acid-washed (0.1 N HCl) Schleicher and Schuell 2045b filter papers (Kalbe, 1954) have been used.

TABLE V
R_f VALUES OF 2,4-DINITROPHENYLHYDRAZIDES OF FATTY ACIDS[a]

Acid	No. of C atoms in acid	Solvent system[b]		
		1	2	3
Acetic	2	0.85	0.93	0.77
Butyric	4	0.88	0.97	0.82
Caproic	6	0.83	0.93	0.81
Heptanoic	7	0.78	0.90	0.78
Caprylic	8	0.74	0.87	0.74
Nonanoic	9	0.69	0.81	0.68
Capric	10	0.64	0.78	0.64
Undecanoic	11	0.57	0.72	0.56
Lauric	12	0.54	0.70	0.51
Tridecanoic	13	0.45	0.62	0.43
Myristic	14	0.42	0.60	0.38
Pentadecanoic	15	0.34	0.52	0.30
Palmitic	16	0.30	0.49	0.25
Heptadecanoic	17	0.25	0.41	0.19
Stearic	18	0.21	0.38	0.15
Nonadecanoic	19	0.16	0.30	0.12
Arachidic	20	0.13	0.27	0.09
Behenic	22	0.08	0.18	0.05

[a] Ascending chromatography at 30°C.
[b] Solvent: 1. 90% Methanol:acetic acid:tetralin = 10:2:1 v/v.
  2. 80% Ethanol:acetic acid:tetralin = 10:2:1 v/v.
  3. 90% Methanol:tetralin = 10:1 v/v (Inouye, 1955).

3. SOLVENTS

The solvent systems most frequently employed are aqueous alcohols which contain a "swamp" acid (see Section I). According to Stark (1951), solvents with a high proportion of low-molecular-weight alcohols and water give R_f values over a narrow range near the solvent boundary. On the other hand, a mixture of benzyl and tert-butyl alcohols without water gives only slight movement. Consequently, it appears that the addition of water is necessary to produce useful separations. Acetone or alcohol must be added to solvents like isoöctane or chloroform to permit the solution of a small amount of water before they can be used to separate acids. Recently, solvent systems have been developed in which ether (Denison, 1952; Jones, 1953), mesityl oxide (Bryant, 1951, 1953), or ethyl acetate (Löffler, 1953) replaces alcohols as the mobile phase. These solvents are fast moving, and, consequently, less time is required to obtain satisfactory development of the chromatogram. Also, owing to the high volitility of these solvents, less time is required to free the paper "swamp" acid after development of the chromatogram. Cheftel (1951, 1952, 1953) has added eucalyptol to the solvent system in order to obtain more rapid evaporation of the formic acid. Denison (1952) removed the swamping acid in 5–10 minutes by blowing steam over the entire surface of the chromatogram. Infrared lamps were used to keep the paper from becoming overloaded with water. The process is actually a steam distillation and, according to the author, the treatment does not decompose the more labile acids such as oxalacetic and α-ketoglutaric acids. The "swamp" acid may also be removed by hanging the paper cylinder into a stove pipe and blowing steam through a manifold from the bottom (Palmer, 1955). By spraying the paper with an indicator reagent (see below), the progress of the steam distillation may be observed by the change in color of the background.

Regardless of the solvent system employed, the number of acids present in many biological systems is too great to obtain satisfactory resolution on one-dimensional chromatograms. Consequently, in order to identify unknown acids it is usually necessary to resolve the mixture with two or more solvents. This can be done either on several one-dimensional chromatograms or on a two-dimensional chromatogram (Fig. 2). In either case, the use of a combination of an alkaline solvent, where the solute moves as an anion, and an acid solvent, where the molecule migrates, will usually give the best separation of the greatest number of acids (Benson, 1950; Overell, 1952; Cheftel, 1952, 1953). Overell (1952) has found that movement in the alkaline solvent is controlled by the number of carboxylic groups. Thus, the monocarboxylic acids move more rapidly than the dicarboxylic acids, and they, in turn, travel further than the tricarboxylic acids. In acidic solvents the hydroxyl groups seem to exert a major effect. Within a series, other factors such as length of carbon chain, govern the relative rate of movement of the acids.

Some of the solvent combinations which have proved most useful in the separation of polycarboxylic, hydroxy, and keto acids are:

a. *1-Butanol:acetic acid.* Water-saturated *n*-butanol to which 1–2 moles of acetic acid are added is a good solvent for malic, tartaric, citric, and succinic acids (Lugg, 1947, 1948).

b. *Isoöctane:95% ethanol:acetone:90% formic acid* = 44:44:11:1 (Stark, 1951).

c. *Chloroform:95% ethanol:90% formic acid* = 65:33:2 (Stark, 1951).

d. *Chloroform:95% ethanol:90% formic acid* = 50:50:1 (Stark, 1951).

e. *1-Butanol:benzyl alcohol:H_2O:formic acid* = 45:45:9:1 (Stark, 1951).

f. *tert-Butyl alcohol:benzyl alcohol:H_2O:formic acid* = 22:68:9:1 (Stark, 1951).

g. *Isopropyl alcohol:tert-butyl alcohol:benzyl alcohol:H_2O:formic acid* = 16:16:48:16:1 (Stark, 1951).

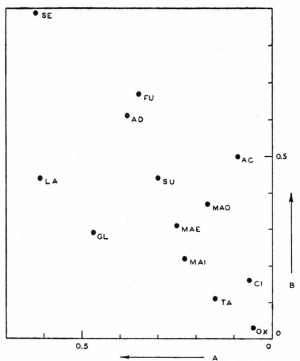

Fig. 2. Schematic drawing of two-dimensional chromatogram of water-soluble organic acids (Cheftel, 1953). A, first direction—ethanol:NH₄OH:water = 80:5:15; B, second direction—ethyl cellosolve:eucalyptol:formic acid = 50:50:20. Ox— oxalic; Ta—tartaric; Ci—citric; Mai—malic; Mae—maleic; Mao—malonic; Su—succinic; Fu—fumaric; Ad—adipic; Se—sebacic; Gl—glycolic; La—lactic; Ac—aconitic acids.

h. *Phenol:H_2O:formic acid* = 75:25:1 (Stark, 1951).

i. *1-Pentanol:5 M formic acid* = 1:1 (Buch, 1952). *1-Pentanol:water:formic acid* = 20:12:1 is refluxed for one hour, the water layer is decanted, and 0.05% 8-quinolinol is added to the organic phase (Resnik, 1955).

k. *Mesityl oxide:H_2O:85% formic acid* = 75:75:36 (Bryant, 1951).

l. *1-Butanol:formic acid:H_2O* = 10:2:15 (Kalyankar, 1952; Shkolnik, 1953).

m. *Ether:acetic acid:H_2O* = 13:3:1 (Denison, 1952).

n. *Ethyl acetate:acetic acid:H_2O* = 3:1:1 (Löffler, 1953) (see Table VI).

o. *2-Ethyl-1-butanol:5 M formic acid* = 2:3 (Jones, 1953).

p. *95% Ethanol:H_2O:concentrated NH_4OH* = 8:1:1 (Jones, 1953).

q. *Methyl cellosolve:eucalyptol:88% formic acid* = 5:5:2 (Cheftel, 1951).

r. *Ethyl cellosolve:eucalyptol:88% formic acid* = 5:5:2 (Cheftel, 1951).

s. *1-Propanol:eucalyptol:88% formic acid* = 5:5:2 (Cheftel, 1951).

t. *Ethyl cellosolve:concentrated $NH_4OH:H_2O$* = 80:5:15 (Cheftel, 1952, 1953).

u. *Ethanol:concentrated $NH_4OH:H_2O$* = 80:5:15 (Cheftel, 1951, 1952, 1953).

v. *Carbon tetrachloride:acetic acid:H_2O* = 4:1:1 (Ohara, 1951).

w. *Ethyl ether:88% formic acid:water* = 5:2:1 (Palmer, 1955).

x. *n-Amyl formate:water:formic acid* = 7:1:2 has been used for the separation of dicarboxylic acids (Kalbe, 1954).

Solvent pairs which have been employed for two-dimensional chromatography are the following:

	First direction	Second direction
1.	v	k
2.	u (or v)	r (see Fig. 2)
3.	v	s
4.	u	t
5.	u	k

(Overell, 1953; Cheftel, 1952, 1953; Elliott, 1954; James, 1955).

4. TECHNIQUES

One- and two-dimensional, ascending, descending, and circular paper chromatography have been employed for the separation of the organic acids. When using volatile solvents, especially those containing ether, it is recommended to develop chromatograms by the ascending technique for a short duration. A one-gallon "pickle jar" serves as an excellent chromatographic tank, being small enough to insure solvent vapor equilibrium conditions during a run (Palmer, 1955; see also Chapter III.). Circular chromatography has also been successfully employed (Rao, 1952; Airan, 1953; Ranjan, 1955).

5. DETECTION

Since most of the solvents used for the resolution of organic acids contain a volatile "swamp" acid, it is necessary to remove this "swamp" acid prior to the employment of an acid-base indicator reagent. This is best accomplished by steaming the papers, taking care not to get the paper wet. A steam manifold is placed below the chromatogram which is hung on a rack by its upper edge. A bank of infrared lamps is placed several inches behind the paper. The "swamp" acid may also be steam-distilled by placing the filter paper in the shape of a cylinder within a stove pipe and introducing steam from the bottom.

Acid-base indicators are generally used to locate free acids on paper chromatograms. However, a number of other reagents, such as ammoniacal silver nitrate, have also been employed. If acid mixtures are separated as ammonium salts, the color reagents listed in Section I are employed. The free acids may be detected by one of the following methods:

a. *Chlorophenol red* (F. Brown, 1951a). A 0.04 % solution in ethanol, adjusted to pH 7 with NaOH. Yellow spots appear on a mauve background. Other indicators used in a similar manner are: *bromocresol green, bromophenol blue, bromothymol blue*, and *methyl red*, the last being adjusted to pH 8 with 0.2 M borate buffer. BDH Universal Indicator and "4.5" Indicator (5 % ethanolic solutions) have also been employed (Nair, 1956).

b. *Ammoniacal silver nitrate* (Buch, 1952). Equal parts of 0.1 N AgNO$_3$ and 0.1 N NH$_4$OH are mixed just prior to use. Spray the chromatogram. Dry at room temperature away from direct sunlight for about 4 hours. Black, gray, yellow, and white spots for different acids appear on a tan background.

c. *Dextrose-ammoniacal silver nitrate* (Gore, 1951). Spray with 1 % dextrose, dry, and spray lightly with a mixture of 0.1 N AgNO$_3$ plus 1.0 N NH$_4$OH v/v. Heat in air draft at 105°C. until the background is black.

d. *Silver nitrate-alkaline phenol* (Löffler, 1953). Spray with 0.1 N AgNO$_3$, dry, and spray with the phenol phase of a mixture of equal parts of water-saturated phenol and 0.05 N NaOH. White spots appear on a brown background.

e. *Aniline-xylose* (Saarnio, 1952). 1 g. of aniline and 1 g. of xylose are dissolved in a minimum quantity of water and added to 100 ml. of methanol. The chromatogram is rapidly dipped in this mixture and dried at room temperature. Brown stains develop when the dry paper is heated for 30 minutes at 105°C.

f. *2,6-Dichlorophenolindophenol*. One-tenth per cent in ethanol is used as a spraying reagent for the organic acids, but the spots (pink on blue background) must be marked immediately before fading (Barnabas, 1955).

g. *p-Dimethylaminobenzaldehyde*. Four per cent in acetic anhydride, plus some crystals of anhydrous sodium acetate, is sprayed on the chromatogram which is heated at 140°C. for 1–2 minutes (Schreier, 1956). The following colors are produced: tartaric acid—red-orange; citric acid— deep red; aconitic acid—wine-red; sensitivity—1 μg.

h. *Ammonium vanadate*. A saturated aqueous solution is used as a spraying reagent, after bromocresol green, as a confirmatory test for tartaric acid. This acid forms brown spots with this reagent, while all other spots disappear (Becker, 1954).

i. *Miscellaneous*. After developing the chromatogram with ethanol:5 % NH$_4$OH = 9:1, the papers are dried at 150°–160°C. for 15 minutes. Dicarboxylic acids form brown spots when viewed in daylight or blue-yellow fluorescence in ultraviolet light (Bina, 1956).

6. Detailed Experimental Procedure

a. Preparation of extract.   Mixtures of organic acids when applied to the chromatogram should be free from contaminating inorganic salts, sugars, and other interfering substances.   Even small amounts of inorganic salt present in the extracts cause sufficient tailing of the spots to interfere with quantitative determinations.   The acids from tissue extracts are, therefore, purified on a column of anion exchange resin (Amberlite IRA-400) and subsequently eluted with ammonium carbonate.   The excess ammonium carbonate is removed by evaporation (Block, 1946).   Five grams of Amberlite IRA-400 is sufficient to absorb 50 mg. each of citric, malic, and succinic acids.   Recovery from the resin is 100% for all acids except succinic where approximately 90% is removed (Bryant, 1953).

b. Paper chromatography.   The conventional descending technique (see Chapter III) is employed with Whatman No. 1 filter paper ($18\frac{1}{4} \times 22\frac{1}{2}$ inches).   Extracts and standard mixtures are applied to the sheet 10 cm. from the upper edge, and the sheets are placed in the tank to equilibrate with the aqueous phase of the solvent system.   Solvent system k (p. 229) is employed.   The chromatogram is developed for 2.5-3 hours and the spots are visualized with bromocresol green (Bryant, 1953; Burton, 1954).   The optimal range of concentrations for individual acids is from 1.0 to 10.0 mg./ml.

The spot area method or one of its modifications (see Chapter IV) is usually employed for the quantitative estimation of non-volatile carboxylic acids when indicators are used to reveal their presence.

7. Miscellaneous Applications

L-Citramalic acid has been identified as a constituent of the peel of the apple by comparing its R_f value with that of malic acid and synthetic citramalic acid (Hulme, 1954).   Citramalic has a slightly faster migration rate than malic acid in three solvent systems that were investigated.   Glycolic acid from etiolated barley shoots has been identified using two-dimensional chromatography (see p. 230) (Elliott, 1954).   The presence of mucic acid has been established by comparing its R_f with that of known mucic acid and malic acid (Anet, 1954).

Section V: α-Keto Acids

The α-keto acids have been separated as the free acids by Magasanik (1950), Wieland (1949), Liberman (1951), and Umbarger (1952).   Although the separation of the keto acids as their carbonyl derivatives is the

TABLE VI

R_f OF ORGANIC ACIDS

Acids	Solvent[a]										
	1	2	3	4	5	6	7	8	9	10[b]	11
Aconitic	0.36	0.81	0.78	—	0.70	0.73	0.02	0.09	—	—	—
Adipic	0.86	—	—	—	—	0.79	0.20	0.38	—	.575	—
Ascorbic	—	—	—	—	0.44	—	—	—	0.32	—	—
Azelaic	—	—	—	—	—	—	—	—	—	.940	—
Caffeic	—	—	—	—	—	—	—	—	—	—	0.63
Chlorogenic	—	—	—	—	—	—	—	—	—	—	0.29
Citric	0.26	0.31	0.37	0.15	0.38	0.23	0.02	0.06	0.46	.055	0.22
Fumaric	0.63	—	0.86	0.90	—	0.82	0.17	0.35	—	.485	0.80
Glutaric	0.78	—	0.80	—	—	—	—	—	—	.465	0.66
Glyceric	—	—	—	—	—	—	—	—	.049	—	—
Glycerate (Ca)	—	—	—	—	—	—	—	—	0.48	—	—
Glycolic	0.59	0.51	—	0.45	—	0.42	0.34	0.37	—	.—	—
Glycolate (K)	—	—	—	—	—	—	—	—	0.64	—	—
Isocitric	—	—	—	—	—	—	—	—	0.46	—	—
Itaconic	—	—	—	—	—	—	—	—	0.82	—	—
α-Ketoglutaric	—	0.63	—	0.36	—	0.63	0.08	0.28	0.69	—	0.25
Lactic	0.72	0.66	0.77	0.72	0.77	0.59	0.48	0.61	0.80	.460[c]	—
Levulinic	0.91	—	—	—	0.94	—	—	—	—	—	—
Maleic	—	—	0.46	—	0.46	0.38	0.13	0.25	0.78	.335	—
Malic	0.42	0.39	0.44	0.25	0.49	0.32	0.09	0.23	0.55	.115	0.30
Malonic	0.48	0.63	0.60	0.52	0.61	0.51	0.07	0.17	0.74	.250	—
Oxalic	0.18	—	0.05	0.12	—	0.02	0.02	0.05	0.18	.135	0.11
Pimelic	—	—	—	—	—	—	—	—	—	.730	—
Pyruvate (K)	—	—	—	—	—	—	—	—	0.83	—	—
Sebacic	—	—	—	—	—	—	—	—	—	1.000	—
Suberic	—	—	—	—	—	—	—	—	—	.845	—
Succinic	0.66	0.70	0.72	0.76	0.78	0.66	0.14	0.30	0.79	.340	0.60
Syringic	0.95	—	—	—	—	—	—	—	—	—	—
Tartaric	0.19	0.22	0.23	0.09	0.26	0.12	0.06	0.15	0.33	.045	0.10
Tricarballylic	0.52	0.63	0.67	—	—	—	—	—	—	—	—

[a] Solvents: 1. Phenol:water:formic acid = 75:25:1.
2. Mesityl oxide:water:formic acid = 75:75:36.
3. Butanol:formic acid:water = 10:2:15.
4. Ether:acetic acid:water = 13:3:1.
5. Ethyl acetate:acetic acid:water = 3:1:1.
6. Ethyl cellosolve:NH₄OH:water = 80:5:15.
7. Ethanol:NH₄OH:water = 80:5:15.
8. CCl₄:acetic acid:water = 4:1:1.
9. Ether:formic acid:water = 5:2:1.
10. n-Amyl formate:water:formic acid = 7:1:2.
11. 1-Pentanol:water:formic acid = 20:12:1.

[b] R_s values are relative to migration of sebacic acid.

[c] Lactic acid produces two spots; R_s 0.460, 0.600.

preferred method, a brief section on the chromatography of the free acids will be included.

1. SOLVENTS FOR SEPARATION OF FREE KETO ACID

a. *1-Butanol:water:propionic acid* = 10:7:5 (Wieland, 1949).

b. *α-n-Dimethylaminoisobutyric nitrile:1-butanol:water* = 4:6:3 (Wieland, 1949).

c. *Water-saturated 1-butanol:HCOOH* = 95:5 (Magasanik, 1950). This solvent separates α-ketoglutaric and pyruvic acids.

d. *Water-saturated 2-butanol:propionic acid* = 95:5 (Umbarger, 1952). The solvent is aged 3–4 weeks to permit esterification equilibrium. The butanol must be free of peroxides or the keto acids will be destroyed during chromatography. This solvent separates α-keto-isovaleric and α-keto-β-methyl-n-valeric acids.

e. *Toluene:acetic acid:H_2O* = 100:5:60 v/v. The layers are separated and an additional 4 ml. of acetic acid is added to the toluene layer (Liberman, 1951). This solvent separates many hydroxy and keto acids of intermediate chain length.

2. COLOR REAGENTS FOR FREE α-KETO ACIDS

a. *o-Phenylenediamine* (Wieland, 1949). The dried filter paper is sprayed with a solution of 0.05 % o-phenylenediamine in 10 % aqueous CCl_3COOH and heated for 2 minutes at 100°. If the paper is overheated, the whole strip fluoresces. α-Keto acids are identified by yellow-green spots which are fluorescent under ultraviolet illumination.

b. *Semicarbazide* (Magasanik, 1950). At the end of the solvent run, the dried filter paper is sprayed with a solution composed of 0.1 % semicarbazide-HCl and 0.15 % sodium acetate. The semicarbazones of the α-keto acids appear as dark shadows on the fluorescing paper when viewed under ultraviolet light. Use Eaton and Dikeman Paper No. 613 (Umbarger, 1952).

c. *Nessler reagent* (Liberman, 1951). The dried filter paper is exposed for a few minutes to ammonia vapor in a closed chamber, the excess ammonia is removed by allowing the paper to stand for 30 minutes, and the spots of ammonium salts are then located by dipping the paper in Nessler solution. Small intensely orange spots against a light background result.

3. QUANTITATIVE ESTIMATION OF FREE α-KETO ACIDS (Umbarger, 1952)

After being sprayed heavily with the semicarbazide reagent (0.1 % semicarbazide and 0.15 % sodium acetate) the papers are dried and the spots are cut out in rectangles of equal size. These rectangles are cut into narrow strips and placed in test tubes. Three milliliters of 0.025 % 2,4-dinitrophenylhydrazine in 0.5 N HCl are added to each tube, followed by 1.00 ml.

of 40 % KOH. After 10 minutes at room temperature, the tubes are shaken for 10 minutes to extract the hydrazones from the paper. The color intensity is read against a filter paper reagent blank at 435 mμ.

Section VI: α-Keto Acid 2,4-Dinitrophenylhydrazones

The separation of the α-keto acids as their 2,4-dinitrophenylhydrazones has several advantages. The derivatives are colored and can be detected on paper chromatograms without further reactions. The α-keto acids can also be more easily extracted from biological samples as carbonyl derivatives which are more stable than the parent keto acids (Cavallini, 1949, 1953; Altmann, 1951; Seligson, 1952; Kulonen, 1952, 1953; Neish, 1953; Fincham, 1953; Virtanen, 1953; El Hawary, 1953; Hockenhull, 1954, and others). Further identification may be made by converting the dinitrophenylhydrazones to their respective amino acids by catalytic hydrogenation (Towers, 1954a; Meister, 1956).

1. PREPARATION OF 2,4-DINITROPHENYLHYDRAZONES

a. Isolation from Blood and Urine (Seligson, 1952; Kvamme, 1954). To 50 ml. of deproteinized sample (metaphosphoric acid for deproteinization) which is diluted about ten times with water is added 2.0 ml. of 0.5 % 2,4-dinitrophenylhydrazine in 6 N HCl. The mixture is allowed to react at room temperature for thirty minutes. It is then transferred to a 125-ml. separatory funnel, and the hydrazones are extracted from the aqueous solution with three 15-ml. portions of chloroform, containing 20 % ethyl alcohol (or with ethyl acetate; Cavallini, 1949).

The combined solvent layers are extracted with 15 ml. of 1 N Na$_2$CO$_3$, and the solvent is discarded. The Na$_2$CO$_3$ solution, containing the hydrazones, is washed with 10 ml. of chloroform-ethyl alcohol (or ethyl acetate); the carbonate solution is acidified in the cold (0–4°C.) with 5 ml. of 6 N HCl. The hydrazones are then extracted from the aqueous layer with three successive portions of chloroform-ethyl alcohol (or ethyl acetate)— 10, 5, and 5 ml. respectively. The three extracts containing the keto acid derivatives are combined and evaporated under a gentle air blast.

b. Isolation from Plant Materials (Virtanen, 1953; Towers, 1954a; Fowden, 1955; Isherwood, 1956). Five to ten grams of strawberry leaves are frozen in a dry-ice bath at -70°C. and are homogenized with 0.6 M HPO$_3$ (*meta*-phosphoric acid) at -2°C. After ten minutes' disintegration in a high-speed blender at 14,000 r.p.m., the macerate is centrifuged, and the residue washed twice with HPO$_3$. To the combined extracts (150–250 ml.) is added 20 ml. 1 % (w/v) 2,4-dinitrophenylhydrazine in 5 N H$_2$SO$_4$, and the reaction is allowed to proceed for 45 minutes. The derivative is extracted four times with 0.4 volume of ether, and the extracts are shaken with 40 ml. of saturated NaHCO$_3$, so that the final pH is 8.4. The bicarbonate extraction is repeated, and any emulsion may be broken up by centrifugation. The combined aqueous phases are adjusted to pH 2.0 with 3 N H_2SO_4 and are extracted three times with 0.5 volume of chloroform, containing 15 % (v/v) ether. The extracts are taken to dryness and redissolved in absolute ethanol.

Chromatography of the phenylhydrazones isolated from plant material is sometimes improved by purifying the derivative prior to chromatography. A solution of the 2,4-dinitrophenylhydrazones is passed through a column of Bentonite-Celite 545 (w/w) or alumina (Virtanen, 1953; Towers, 1954). The derivatives are adsorbed on the column which is washed with ethyl acetate and 95 % ethanol (or ether). The hydrazones are eluted off the column with 1–10 % $NaHCO_3$, acidified with H_2SO_4 and extracted with ethyl acetate.

c. Conversion of 2,4-Dinitrophenylhydrazones to Amino Acids (Towers, 1954a; Meister, 1956). The hydrazones dissolved in ethyl acetate are hydrogenated with PtO_2 catalysts (Adams Catalyst—J. Bishop and Co., Malvern, Pa.) in a Parr Hydrogenation Bomb at 30 lbs./in.^{2} for 6–12 hours. The products are filtered, taken to dryness, and redissolved in a small amount of 80 % ethanol. The amino acids are identified preferably by two-dimensional chromatography (see Chapter V for details). The yields range from 30–97.8 %.

d. Multiple Spots of 2,4-Dinitrophenylhydrazones. Under standard reaction conditions both pyruvic and oxalacetic acids give rise to two *cis-trans* geometrical isomers around the —C—N— bond of the hydrazone, whereas α-ketoglutaric acid gives only one hydrazone (Stewart, 1953; Isherwood, 1954, 1955). The proposed structure of the two isomers has been based on infrared studies:

cis　　　　　　　　　　　　　　　　trans

Towers (1954b) has identified the second spot of pyruvic acid 2,4-dinitrophenylhydrazone as 1-OH-6-NO_2-1,2,3-benzotriazole. The interference of this artifact spot may be minimized by using smaller amounts of 2,4-dinitrophenylhydrazine reagent or by a preliminary separation using the solvent system: *tert*-amyl alcohol:ethanol:water (NH_3 atmosphere) = 9:1:2. If the reaction mixture is heated at 70°C. for 5 minutes or allowed to stand at room temperature for several hours, two hydrazones of α-ketoglutaric acid are also formed. Furthermore, under these conditions, oxalacetic acid decarboxylates to give rise to the two pyruvic hydrazones. Turnock (1953) has also obtained two spots for the hydrazones prepared from phenylpyruvic acid, and Isherwood (1954) found a third spot for pyruvic acid which is due to a polymer.

The appearance of more than one spot for certain α-keto acids which are chromatographed as their hydrazones complicates the separation and particularly the quantitative estimations by this method. No isomerism has been reported for the nitroquinoxalinol derivatives, and, consequently, this may be the preferable compound for use in paper chromatography (see Section VII).

2. SOLVENTS FOR SEPARATION OF 2,4-DINITROPHENYLHYDRAZONES

a. *20% Ethanol* in 1-butanol (Cavallini, 1949).

b. *1-Butanol* saturated with 3% NH$_4$OH (Walker, 1951).

c. *1-Butanol:ethanol:0.5 N NH$_4$OH* = 70:10:20 (El Hawary, 1953).

d. *1-Butanol:1 N NaHCO$_3$* = 1:2 (Seligson, 1952).

e. *tert-Amyl alcohol:1-propanol:concentrated NH$_4$OH* = 65:5:30 (Isherwood, 1954).

f. *2-Butanol:0.8 N NH$_4$OH* = 4:1 (Hockenhull, 1954).

g. *1-Butanol:amyl alcohol:2-octanol* = 1:1:1 or *n-Hexanol* saturated with 0.8 N NH$_4$OH (Hockenhull, 1954).

h. *1-Butanol:ethanol:H$_2$O* = 40:10:50 (Cavallini, 1953).

i. *Glycine:NaOH buffer,* 0.1 M, pH 8.4 (Virtanen, 1953). Separations with this solvent depend on the affinity of the hydrazones for wet cellulose, *i.e.*, adsorption. Therefore, different grades of paper are likely to give different R_f values. This solvent separates dinitrophenylhydrazones of pyruvic, α-ketoglutaric, and oxalacetic acids. Best results are obtained in an atmosphere containing phenol vapors and traces of HCN (see Table VII).

k. *Benzene:tert-pentanol:ethanol:water* = 5:3:1:2 (organic phase), (Isherwood, 1956). This is the recommended solvent for pyruvic acid, using filter paper impregnated with 0.2 M borate buffer, pH 8.2.

l. *tert-Pentanol:ethanol:water* = 5:1:4. This solvent is recommended for α-ketoglutaric acid using paper impregnated with 0.2 M Na phosphate buffer, pH 6.3 (Isherwood, 1956; Altmann, 1951).

Other solvents may be found in Table VII.

3. SPECIAL TECHNIQUES FOR CHROMATOGRAPHY OF 2,4-DINITROPHENYLHYDRAZONES

The phenylhydrazones have been separated on Whatman filter paper Nos. 1, 2, 3 MM, and 4. Altmann (1951) recommends Whatman No. 2.

Washing the paper with buffer solutions improves the resolution of α-keto acid derivatives, provided that the buffers are soluble in the mobile phase of the solvent. Altmann (1951) obtained good results by treating the paper with a glycine:NaOH buffer, 0.1 M, pH 8.2–8.4, and developing with *tert*-amyl alcohol:ethanol. Seligson (1952) found that paper treated with 1 N sodium bicarbonate (pH 8.2) produced the best resolution of the hydrazones when the developing solvent was butanol:1 N NaHCO$_3$ (Solvent d).

Derivatives are usually applied to the paper in ethyl acetate, chloroform, acetone, or ethanol. However, according to Altmann (1951), the use of organic solvents, especially ethyl acetate, for this purpose often results in decarboxylation of certain phenylhydrazones (*e.g.*, the dinitrophenylhydrazone of acetoacetic acid is converted almost completely to the dinitrophenylhydrazone of acetone). Application in phosphate buffer, 0.2 M, pH 7.2, prevents this, but even then the solutions do not keep for more than a day. The derivative formed from about 0.05 μM of α-keto acid is a suitable quantity for detection on paper chromatograms.

4. Detection and Quantitative Evaluation of 2,4-Dinitrophenyl-hydrazones

The 2,4-dinitrophenylhydrazones of the keto acids are visible as yellow spots in daylight, but the color may be accentuated by spraying the paper with 2% ethanolic KOH, resulting in more intense red-brown spots. Inspection of the chromatograms with a Hanovia ultraviolet lamp with an EH-4 arc tube increases the sensitivity of detection to 0.01–0.1 μg.

For the quantitative estimation of the phenylhydrazones the following technique is recommended (Seligson, 1952): Each spot (or transverse streak) which contains about 0.2 μM of acid is cut out, sliced into small pieces, and placed in a bottle. Ten milliliters of 1 N sodium hydroxide is added to each bottle to elute the hydrazones. The bottles are then shaken for 10 minutes. The contents of each vessel are filtered, and the red color is compared photometrically with suitable standards, using a 455-mμ filter.

Section VII: α-Keto Acid 4-Nitro-2-Alkyl-Quinoxalin(3)ols and Oximes

1. Preparation of Quinoxalinol Derivatives (Hockenhull, 1952; Smith, 1953)

The preparation of the nitroquinoxaline derivatives is essentially the same as that for the hydrazones. Sufficient 1,2-diamino-4-nitrobenzene in 2 N HCl is added to a deproteinized solution of α-keto acids. The mixture is

TABLE VII
R_f VALUES OF α-KETO ACIDS AND DERIVATIVES

Compound	Free acids			2,4-Dinitrophenylhydrazones						Nitro-2-R-quinoxalinols	
	1[a]	2	3	4	5	6	7	8	9	10	11
Oxalacetic acid	0.16	0.04	0.08	0.08	0.24	0.06	0.78	0.32; 0.47	0.63; 0.76	0.12	0.13
α-Ketoglutaric acid	0.21	0.07	0.51	0.16	0.12	0.04	0.69	0.33	0.62	0.14	—
Pyruvic acid	0.29	0.46	0.64	0.36	0.41	0.62; 0.80	0.45	0.51	0.75; 0.81	0.65	0.57
α-Ketobutyric acid	—	—	0.76	—	—	—	—	0.63	0.80	0.73	0.74
α-Ketoisovaleric acid	—	—	0.83	—	—	—	—	0.80	0.86	—	—
Dimethylpyruvic acid	0.60	0.78	—	—	—	—	—	—	—	0.86	0.85
Cinnamoylformic acid	0.75	0.95	—	—	—	—	—	—	—	—	—
Acetoacetic acid	—	—	—	0.50	0.55	—	—	—	—	—	—
p-Hydroxyphenylpyruvic acid	—	—	—	0.70	—	—	—	0.75	0.83	—	—
Phenylpyruvic acid	—	—	—	0.78	—	0.91	—	0.87	0.86	—	—
o-Hydroxyphenylpyruvic acid	—	—	—	0.81	—	—	—	—	—	—	—
Acetone	—	—	—	—	0.93	—	—	—	—	—	—
Glyoxylic acid	—	—	—	—	—	—	—	0.39	0.71; 0.77	—	—
β-Sulfopyruvic acid	—	—	—	—	—	—	—	0.18; 0.22	0.62; 0.83	—	—
β-Mercaptopyruvic acid	—	—	—	—	—	—	—	0.47	0.77	—	—
D-α-Keto-β-methylvaleric acid	—	—	—	—	—	—	—	0.77	0.86	—	—
α-Ketoisocaproic acid	—	—	—	—	—	—	—	0.83	0.88	—	—
α-Keto-ϵ-aminocaproic acid	—	—	—	—	—	—	—	0.72	0.95	—	—
α-Keto-γ-methiolbutyric acid	—	—	—	—	—	—	—	0.43	0.82	—	—
β-Indolpyruvic acid	—	—	—	—	—	—	—	0.87	0.83	—	—

[a] Solvents: 1. n-Butanol:water:propionic acid = 10:7:5 (Wieland, 1949).
2. $\alpha \cdot n$-Dimethylaminoisobutyric nitrile:n-butanol:water = 4:6:3 (Wieland, 1949).
3. Water-saturated n-butanol:formic acid = 95:5 (Magasanik, 1950).
4. $tert$-Amyl alcohol:ethanol:water = 5:1:4 (Altmann, 1951).
5. n-Butanol:ethanol:0.5 N NH_4OH = 7:1:2 (El Hawary, 1953).
6. n-Butanol:1 N $NaHCO_3$ = 1:2 (Seligson, 1952).
7. Glycine:NaOH buffer (0.1 M); pH 8.4 (Virtanen, 1953).
8. n-Butanol:water-ethanol = 5:4:1 (Meister, 1956).
9. Methanol:benzene:n-butanol:water = 4:2:2:2 (Meister, 1956).
10. n-Butanol:5 N NH_4OH = 2:1 (Hockenhull, 1953).
11. Benzyl alcohol:5 N NH_4OH = 2:1 (Hockenhull, 1953).

warmed to 60°C. and allowed to stand for 16 hours at room temperature. The nitroquinoxalinol derivatives are extracted and purified in exactly the same way as described for the phenylhydrazones, except that a dilute NaOH solution is used in place of a Na_2CO_3 solution.

2. Solvents for Separation of 4-Nitro-2-R-Quinoxalin(3)ols

a. *Methanol* (Hockenhull, 1952; 1953).

b. *Methanol:H_2O* = 9:1.

c. *Ethanol.*

d. *Ethanol:H_2O* = 9:1.

e. *1-Butanol:5 N NH_4OH* = 2:1.

f. *Amyl alcohol:5 N NH_4OH* = 2:1.

g. *Benzyl alcohol:5 N NH_4OH* = 2:1.

h. *1% Aqueous Na_2CO_3*. Separations depend on adsorption (see Solvent (*i*) under Separation of Hydrazones).

These derivatives are separated on Whatman No. 4 filter paper and are visualized in the same manner as the 2,4-dinitrophenylhydrazones.

3. α-Keto Acid Oximes (Yamafuji, 1953)

The oximes of pyruvic, oxalacetic, and α-ketoglutaric acids have been separated with the solvent amyl acetate:80% formic acid:water = 4:1:1 v/v. The spots are revealed by spraying the chromatogram with 0.035 M $FeCl_3$.

Section VIII: Higher Fatty Acids

1. Preparation of Paper for Reversed Phase Chromatography

A reversed phase partition system (see Chapter III) is generally employed for the paper chromatographic separation of water-insoluble compounds such as the higher fatty acids. In this system the filter paper must repel water and hold the less polar component of solvent system. Some of the methods used to make filter paper water-repellent are as follows:

a. *Rubber latex* (Boldingh, 1948; Ashley, 1955). The filter paper (e.g. Whatman No. 1) is passed through an aqueous solution of 62% liquid latex (Fisher Scientific Co.) and is dried in air. The paper is then washed in methanol or ethanol and stored in acetone.

b. *Silicone* (Kritchevsky, 1951). Paper strips are drawn through a 5% (by volume) solution of Dow Corning Silicon No. 1107 in cyclohexane. These strips are blotted between sheets of absorbent paper to remove excess solution and placed in an oven at 110°C. for 1 hour. The paper is rendered hydrophobic by this treatment, and its properties are not changed by washing with organic solvents.

c. *Octadecyloxymethyl cellulose* (Baker, 1953). The paper is dried by heating for 3 hours at 105°C. and then immersed in toluene containing octadecyloxymethylpyridinium chloride (0.5 % w/v) and left at 90°C. for 3 hours. After draining, the paper is washed with five changes of absolute ethanol and dried. The paper is tested for water repellency by boiling in distilled water. To avoid the formation of acidic fronts, it is advisable to prewash the paper with the developing solvent for at least 24 hours.

d. Paraffin oil (Ashley, 1955). The filter paper is first washed by descending chromatography with methanol, water, acetone, and ether. It is then dried over $CaSO_4$ *in vacuo* and passed through ether solutions of paraffin oil, depending on the length of the carbon chain:

$$7\% \text{ paraffin—}C_{12} \text{ to } C_{18} \text{ acids}$$

$$12\% \text{ paraffin—}C_{18} \text{ to } C_{24} \text{ acids.}$$

The treated papers are stored in a vacuum desiccator over Drierite and paraffin shavings. Papers impregnated with petroleum fraction (190–220°C.) have been used (Perilä, 1955; Wagner, 1955), as well as 12 % olive oil in toluene (Kobrle, 1954).

e. Acetylated paper (see also Chapter III). The paper is immersed in a solution of acetic anhydride in benzene (1:3) which contains 0.1 % concentrated H_2SO_4 (by volume) and heated under reflux for 6 hours at 70°C. After acetylation, the paper is washed with cold water and placed in methanol overnight. It is then soaked for 3 hours in tap water, immersed briefly in distilled water, and dried in air. Before use, the paper is given a final drying for 10 minutes at 110°C. Paper treated in this manner contains about 22 % acetyl and has been employed for the separation of higher fatty acids (C_5-C_{18}) as their hydroxamic acids (Micheel, 1954).

2. Preparation of Higher Fatty Acid Derivatives for Chromatography

As in the separation of the volatile fatty acids and the α-keto acids, better separation may be achieved by resolving a fatty acid derivative rather than the free acid or its salt.

a. Hydroxamates of Higher Fatty Acids (Micheel, 1954). The fatty acids in ether are esterified by adding an ether solution of diazomethane. After evaporation of the ether, the ester residue is dissolved in an alkaline solution of hydroxylamine in methanol. The best proportion of reagent is 1 mole of hydroxylamine hydrochloride and 2 moles of KOH per mole of ester. The reagents in methanol are heated for 2–3 minutes on a water bath, and the KCl is removed by filtration. The excess KOH is neutralized with a tetrahydrofuran:acetic acid (4:1) mixture, and the solution is applied to the paper for chromatographic analysis.

TABLE VIII

SOLVENTS FOR THE SEPARATION OF HIGHER FATTY ACIDS AND DERIVATIVES

No.	Mobile phase	Stationary phase	Paper treatment	Compounds resolved	Reference
1.	Methanol:acetone = 1:1	Rubber	Impregnated with latex	Esters	Boldingh, 1948
2.	Ethanol:water = 75:25	Toluene	Impregnated with toluene and olive oil	C_{10}–C_{22} Acids	Kobrle, 1954
3.	Methanol:water = 85:15, sat. with paraffin oil + 0.001 N HCl	Paraffin	Paraffin paper (equilibration not necessary)	C_{12}–C_{16} Acids	Ashley, 1955
	do. do. = 90:10	do.	do.	C_{14}–C_{20} Acids	do.
	do. do. = 95:5	do.	do.	C_{18}–C_{24} Acids	do.
4.	Methanol:water = 80:20, sat. with "decalin"	Decalin	Octadecyloxymethyl cellulose sprayed with decalin	Acids	Baker, 1953
5.	Acetic acid:water = 9:1, sat. with hydrocarbon (190–220°)	Hydrocarbon (190–220°C.)	Sprayed with kerosene	C_{14}–C_{16} Acids	Wagner, 1955; Perilä, 1955
6.	Methanol:decalin = 8:1	Decalin	Sprayed with decalin	Dinitrophenylhydrazones	Hirayama, 1956
7.	Methanol:decalin:ethyl acetate = 40:7:3	Decalin	Sprayed with decalin	Dinitrophenylhydrazones	Hirayama, 1956
8.	90% Methanol:acetic acid:tetralin = 30:1:3	Tetralin	Equilibrated with tetralin	Mercury compds. of unsat. esters	Inouye, 1955b
9.	Diethylene glycol:acetic acid:tetralin = 60:20:11	do.	do.	do.	do.
10.	Methanol:acetic acid:petroleum ether (140–170°C.) = 30:1:7	Petroleum ether	Equilibrated with petroleum ether	do.	do.
11.	Ethyl acetate:tetrahydrofuran:water = 0.6:3.5:4.7	Tetrahydrofuran	Acetylated paper	Hydroxamates	Micheel, 1954

b. *2,4-Dinitrophenylhydrazones of Acetol Esters* (Hirayama, 1956). (See also Section III of this chapter.) An alcoholic solution of the fatty acids is just acidified with 0.05 N methanolic HCl. Slightly less than the theoretical amount of bromo-acetone is added, and the mixture is refluxed for 30 minutes at 80–90°C. After cooling to 50°C., a slight excess of 2,4-dinitrophenylhydrazine in 2 N methanolic HCl is added and allowed to react for thirty minutes. Benzene is added to the reaction mixture, and after the addition of water, the benzene layer separates and is directly applied to the paper for chromatography.

c. *Mercury Compounds of Unsaturated Fatty Acid Esters* (Inouye, 1955b). The methyl esters of the fatty acids and 20 % excess of mercury (II) acetate in absolute methanol (1–2 ml. methanol/g. mercury (II) acetate) is heated at 80°C. for 30 minutes until the mercuric acetate is almost dissolved. An excess of ether or benzene and a large quantity of water are added, and the mixture is shaken vigorously. The organic phase is applied directly to the filter paper.

3. SOLVENTS FOR HIGHER FATTY ACIDS AND THEIR DERIVATIVES

Due to the water-insolubility of the higher fatty acids and their derivatives, "reversed phase chromatography" is used in all cases. In this technique two solvent phases are employed, *stationary* or *immobile* and *mobile* phases. The stationary phase usually consists of a non-polar substance, and since cellulose paper is strongly hydrophilic, it is necessary to use modified paper for the impregnation of the stationary phase. This procedure requires careful equilibration of the paper with the stationary solvent phase prior to development. The equilibration may be accomplished within the chromatographic chamber or by spraying the paper with the stationary phase immediately prior to solvent development (e.g. decalin or kerosene) (Hirayama, 1956; Wagner, 1955).

The mobile solvent phase is composed of a polar constituent saturated with the stationary phase. Table VIII is a list of solvents, type of paper, and compounds best resolved under the stated conditions. (See Table IX for R_f values.)

4. COLOR REAGENTS FOR HIGHER FATTY ACIDS AND DERIVATIVES

a. *Sudan IV* in 50 % aqueous methanol (Boldingh, 1948) for esters of higher fatty acids.

b. Alkaline 0.4 % solution of *bromothymol blue* in methyl cellosolve for higher fatty acids. Detects 30–50 μg. of each acid (Baker, 1953; Ashley, 1955).

c. *Ferric chloride* solution (see pp. 221–222) for hydroxamic acid derivatives.

d. When the chromatogram is treated successively with *Phenylhydrazine*,

Rhodamine B and aqueous $AgNO_3$ (Kaufmann, 1952), the following characteristic colors are obtained:

Linoleic acid	Reddish brown
Oleic acid	Intense red
Elaidic acid	Intense red
Erucic acid	Dark luminous red
Stearic acid	Faint reddish brown
Undecylenic acid	Intense red wide border
Pelargonic acid Enanthic acid	} Faint reddish brown
Caproic acid Butyric acid Valeric acid	} Rapidly form black spots

e. Quinine, Flurol G, chlorophyll, anthracene, and anthranol (Kaufmann, 1952). These color reagents can be used to distinguish between linoleic and oleic acids. Linoleic gives an intense green fluorescence with these while oleic gives a blue fluorescence.

f. Sodium methionine and thiolacetic acid (Kaufmann, 1952). Preliminary treatment with either of these reagents causes all acids above decanoic to give Rhodamine B fluorescence.

g. Copper (II) acetate (Wagner, 1955; Čmelik, 1956; Perilä, 1955). The chromatograms after development are heated at 80–100°C. and are immersed in 1,000 ml. of water containing 20 ml. of saturated copper (II) acetate. The paper is washed with tap water containing 0.01 % acetic acid. The washed chromatogram is then dipped into a solution of 1.5 % $K_4Fe(CN)_6$. Brown spots on a white background result.

Similar results are achieved by converting the fatty acids to lead (II) salts and exposing the washed papers to H_2S (Ashley, 1955).

h. Diphenylcarbazone (0.2 %) in ethanol, followed by 0.05 N ethanolic nitric acid, yields purple spots for the Hg(II) acetate addition compounds of the unsaturated fatty acid esters (Inouye, 1955b).

Comments. The following mathematical relationship has been established for the R_f of the higher fatty acids (Kobrle, 1954):

Saturated fatty acids

$$R_f = a + bn_c \tag{1}$$

$$(a = 1.42; b = 0.062; n_c = \text{number of carbon atoms})$$

Unsaturated and dicarboxylic acids

$$R_f = a + b(n_c - 2) \tag{2}$$

The exception to this rule is undecylic acid.

TABLE IX

R_f VALUES OF HIGHER FATTY ACIDS AND DERIVATIVES

C atoms	Fatty acid	Hydrox-amates	2,4-DPNH	Free acids		Hg Ac$_2$ addition compounds—unsaturated acids		
	Solvent[a]	1	2	3	4[b]	5	6	7
5	Valeric acid	0.84	—	—	—	—	—	—
6	Caproic acid	0.72	0.67	—	—	—	—	—
7	Enanthic acid	0.64	—	—	—	—	—	—
8	Caprylic acid	0.57	0.60	—	—	—	—	—
9	Pelargonic acid	0.51	—	—	—	—	—	—
10	Capric acid	0.46	0.51	0.80	1.00	—	—	—
11	Undecylic acid	0.40	—	0.80	0.77	—	—	—
12	Lauric acid	0.38	0.43	0.70	0.63	—	—	—
14	Myristic acid	0.34	0.33	0.56	0.48	—	—	—
16	Palmitic acid	0.30	0.25	0.39	0.35	—	—	—
18	Oleic acid	0.30	—	0.46	—	0.17	0.20	0.62
18	Stearic acid	0.24	0.17	0.29	0.26	—	—	—
20	Arachidic	—	0.12	0.16	0.19	—	—	—
10	Sebacic	—	—	0.93	—	—	—	—
9	Azelaic	—	—	0.87	—	—	—	—
18	Elaidic	—	—	0.34	—	—	—	—
18	Linolenic	—	—	0.45	—	0.78	0.87	0.84
22	Erucic	0.22	—	0.14	—	0.07	0.10	0.40
22	Behenic	—	—	—	0.14	—	—	—
24	Lignoceric	—	—	—	0.11	—	—	—
26	Cerotic	—	—	—	0.09	—	—	—
10	9-Decenoic	—	—	—	—	0.67	0.88	0.85
11	10-Undecenoic	—	—	—	—	0.59	0.71	0.84
12	9-Dodecenoic acid	—	—	—	—	0.56	0.65	0.84
14	9-Tetradecenoic acid	—	—	—	—	0.42	0.46	0.80
16	9-Hexadecenoic acid	—	—	—	—	0.27	0.29	0.74
12	2-Dodecenoic acid	—	—	—	—	0.57	0.66	0.85
14	2-Tetradecenoic acid	—	—	—	—	0.43	0.47	0.81
16	2-Hexadecenoic acid	—	—	—	—	0.29	0.30	0.74
18	2-Octadecenoic acid	—	—	—	—	0.17	0.21	0.62
22	Brassidic acid	—	—	—	—	0.08	0.10	0.44
18	Linoleic acid	—	—	—	—	0.57	0.62	0.82
18	β-Eleostearic acid	—	—	—	—	0.77	0.86	0.81
18	Stearolic acid	—	—	—	—	0.75	0.84	0.82
22	Behenolic acid	—	—	—	—	0.50	0.64	0.77
18	Ricinoleic acid	—	—	—	—	0.64	0.53	0.81

[a] 1. Ethyl acetate:tetrahydrofuran:water = 0.6:3.5:4.7; acetylated Whatman No. 1 (25% acetyl) (Micheel, 1954).
2. Methanol:decalin = 8:1.
3. 75% Ethanol; paper impregnated with 12% olive oil in toluene.
4. Acetic acid:water = 9:1; paper saturated with paraffin (190 − 220°C.); circular chromatography.
5. 90% Methanol:acetic acid:tetralin = 30:1:3.
6. Diethylene glycol:acetic acid:tetralin = 60:20:11.
7. Methanol:acetic acid:petroleum ether = 30:1:7.
[b] Given as R_c (migration relative to capric acid).

Section IX: Non-Steroid Lipids

1. PREPARATION OF SAMPLES

Hack (1953) has employed filter paper disks as the solvent support for the separation of lipids in tissue extracts. The total lipid from tissue is obtained by extracting the freeze-dried tissue with $CHCl_3$:methanol $= 4:1$. The filter paper disk is previously extracted with $CHCl_3$:methanol $= 4:1$ and dried. The disk is supported on a Petri dish, and 25 μl. of a $CHCl_3$: methanol solution containing 10^{-2} μM of lipid is placed at the center. The solvent is evaporated by a current of N_2. $CHCl_3$:methanol is added until the lipid spreads to a ring 10 mm. in diameter. Finally, 25-μl. portions of the desired eluent are added at such a rate that the diameter of the wet spot increases about 2 mm. per second. Three portions are generally sufficient to effect as complete a separation as possible with a given solvent. Organic solvents which are most useful as eluents because of their different solvent action are acetone, benzene, chloroform, and methanol.

2. SOLVENTS

For most solvents it is necessary to equilibrate the chromatographic cabinet at least three hours prior to the development of the chromatograms. Table X lists the R_f values of some lipids in several commonly used solvent systems. In general, the solvent systems separate the following classes of compounds: (1) lecithins or lysolecithins, (2) glycerides, (3) phosphatidic acids, and (4) derivatives of lecithins or lysolecithins in which the fatty acids have been removed. In addition to the solvents listed in Table X, the following solvents have been found useful:

a. *Phenol:water* and *n-butanol:morpholine:water* are used to separate the hydrolysis products of lecithin (Clouet, 1952). Ethanolamine- and serine-cephalin may be separated with water-saturated phenol (R_f 0.90 and 0.68, resp.) (Amelung, 1954).

b. *Chloroform:ethanol:water* $= 160:40:5$ or *acetone:methanol* $= 4:1$ v/v completely separate lecithins and cephalins (Bevan, 1951; Amelung, 1954). The cephalins remain near the origin, whereas the lecithins have R_f values of over 0.90.

c. *Lutidine:acetic acid:chloroform* $= 4:1:3.5$ separates some phospholipids. The phospholipids are first dissolved in lutidine:acetic acid $= 3:1$ before being applied to the filter paper (Rouser, 1954).

d. *n-Butanol:ethanol:acetic acid:water* $= 8:2:1:3$ v/v is used to separate acetyl- and butyryl choline by the ascending technique (Henschler, 1956).

e. *Methanol:chloroform* $= 20:80$ separates the glycerophospholipids on silica-impregnated paper (see Techniques below) (Lea, 1955; Mangold, 1955).

f. Two-dimensional solvent systems. Kaufmann and Budwig (1952) have used a two-dimensional development to separate blood lipids. Blood samples are applied to Schleicher and Schüll No. 20436 filter paper, acidified with acetic acid vapors, and the neutral fats are separated by developing the chromatogram with a mixture of methanol and acetone. The phospholipids are then separated along the second dimension by development with a mixture of ethanol and ether. Another solvent combination, phenol-NH_3 and n-propanol-NH_3, gives good separation for glycerylphosphoryl-choline and -ethanolamine (Dawson, 1955a, b).

For the separation of phosphatides on silicic-acid-impregnated paper the following combination is used (Marinetti, 1956): *First direction:* n-butyl ether:acetic acid:chloroform:water $= 40:35:6:5;$ *Second direction:* di-i-butyl ketone:acetic acid:water $= 40:30:7$.

3. TECHNIQUES

For "reversed phase" chromatography it is recommended to use silica- or silicone-impregnated paper (Lea, 1955; Marinetti, 1956). Whatman No. 3 filter paper is immersed in a solution of sodium silicate (50 % aqueous "water glass") for five minutes, drained another five minutes, and transferred to a bath of 6 N HCl for thirty minutes. The paper is washed with water until free of chloride ions, dried at room temperature overnight and at 110°C. for one hour.

Whatman No. 1, previously dried at 200°C. for one hour may be impregnated with silicone by drawing the paper through a 5 % solution of silicone in ether, air-drying the paper, and storing it in a desiccator (Mangold, 1955).

Four microliters of a 2–10 % solution of the phospholipids is spotted on silica-impregnated paper, rolled over a glass rod to prevent cracking, and developed by the descending technique. The paper is first equilibrated with the solvent (methanol:chloroform) for 30 minutes, and the solvent is allowed to migrate about 20 cm. (2 hours).

Ascending development has also been used with Schleicher and Schuell paper No. 2043b (untreated) and saturating the tank with nitrogen to prevent the phosphatides from oxidizing during development (Amelung, 1954).

4. DETECTION

a. Phospholipids. (1)*Rhodamine B* or *G* (0.005 %) in water (Rouser, 1954; Marinetti, 1955). The chromatograms are first washed with water, then dipped into the dye solution, and the excess dye is removed in running water. The spots are viewed in ultraviolet light.

(2) *Modified Hanes-Isherwood Reagent* is prepared from 1 gram ammonium molybdate, 8 ml. of water, 3 ml. of concentrated HCl. Three ml. of 70 %

perchloric acid is added, and the solution is diluted to 100 ml. with acetone. The paper is sprayed with this reagent, heated at 85°C. for 7 minutes and kept in air until blue spots show the position of the phosphatides (Amelung, 1954).

b. *Choline lipids.* (1) *Aqueous 0.05 M Reinecke salt* (Hack, 1953). The chromatogram is immersed for 2 hours or more at room temperature; a pink spot appears at the site of the choline lipid. Thorough rinsing in water removes the excess reagent. The spots may be intensified by spraying the paper with a Na_2O_2 solution in 30 % acetic acid, containing 1 % benzidine; blue spots result (Amelung, 1954).

(2) *0.0001 M Iodine* in aqueous KI (Hack, 1953). Immersion for 1 minute at room temperature produces a transient yellow-brown color.

(3) *Aqueous 0.1 M Potassium dichromate* (Hack, 1953). Immersion for 1 hour at 60°C. results in a faint brownish ring at the site of the choline lipid. This color can be intensified by reacting with a freshly prepared solution of hematein (mix 25 mg. of hematoxylin, 50 ml. of H_2O, and 0.2 ml. of 30 % w/v H_2O and heat to 60°C. for 10 minutes) for 10 minutes at 60°C. Excess reagent must be removed with water at each step.

(4) *Aqueous 0.005 M Phosphomolybdic acid* (Levine, 1951). Immerse the paper for 1 minute, wash with butanol, and then with water. Pass the

TABLE X

R_f VALUES OF LIPIDS AND RELATED COMPOUNDS (Huennekens, 1954; Olley, 1956)

Compound	Solvent[a]			
	1	2	3	4
Unsaturated lecithin (dipalmitoleyl)	0.81	0.89	0.78	0.86
Saturated lecithin	0.87	0.89	0.78	0.86
Unsaturated lysolecithin	0.70	0.87	0.80	0.80
Saturated lysolecithin	0.67	0.89	0.61	0.85
α-Monopalmitin	0.93	0.92	0.91	0.90
α,β-Dipalmitolein	0.93	0.88	0.91	0.92
Phosphatidic acid	Streak	Streak	Streak	Streak
Oleic acid	0.95	0.92	0.94	0.94
Glycerylphosphorylcholine	0.00	0.70	0.25	0.76
β-Glycerophosphate	0.00	0.46	0.03	0.07
Phosphorylcholine	0.00	0.45	0.00	0.08
Choline	0.11	0.72	0.30	0.40

[a] Solvents: 1. 1-Butanol saturated with H_2O.
    2. Ethanol: H_2O = 8:1.
    3. 1-Propanol: H_2O = 8:1.
    4. 1-Propanol: CH_3COOH: H_2O = 8:1:1.

washed paper slowly through a freshly prepared 0.4 % solution of SnCl₂ in 3 *N* HCl. Dark-blue spots appear on a bluish-white background.

(5) *Magnesium dipicrylamine* (0.2 % w/v) in 50 % acetone (Henschler, 1956).

c. Lipids with amine group. The chromatogram is sprayed with 0.4 % *ninhydrin* in 90 % *i*-propanol, plus 5 ml. collidine, and heated to 105° for 10 minutes (Amelung, 1954).

d. Acetal lipids (Plasmalogens). *Aqueous 0.005 M Mercurous chloride* (Hack, 1953). Immersion for 1 minute at room temperature exposes the carbonyl group for reaction with fuchsin-sulfurous acid or with aqueous 2,4-dinitrophenylhydrazine. Excess fuchsin-sulfurous acid is removed with aqueous 0.05 *M* H₂SO₃, and the 2,4-dinitrophenylhydrazine with water.

e. Unsaturated Acids and Aldehydes. *Osmic acid vapors* (Hack, 1953). Expose the chromatograms for 5 minutes. Brown to black spots appear.

f. Esters. *8 % Hydroxylamine-HCl* in 80 % aqueous ethanol is mixed with 2 volumes of 10 % KOH in 90 % ethanol. The chromatogram is sprayed with this solution, dried briefly, and sprayed with a solution composed of 10 g. of FeCl₃·6H₂O, 20 ml. of 10 *N* HCl, and 300 ml. of ether. The esters show up as purple spots on a yellow background (Whittaker, 1952).

g. Neutral Fat. *Nile blue or sudan black.* These dyes stain most of the lipids. A micromethod for the estimation of total lipid in serum by staining with sudan black has been described by Swahn (1952). The sudan black reagent is prepared by adding 100 mg. of dye to 100 ml. of 50 % ethanol. The mixture is boiled, cooled, and filtered. The serum is applied to filter paper and dried. The paper is soaked for 60 minutes in the dye solution, washed three times for 15 minutes with 50 % ethanol, and air-dried. The spots are cut out, eluted with 25 % acetic acid in ethanol, and the color density determined at 590 mµ. Acetylated *Sudan Black B*, prepared from an equivalent amount of dye and acetic anhydride in ether, has been used as a saturated solution in 70 % ethanol or propylene glycol (Casselman, 1954).

h. Glycerides. The chromatograms are sprayed with 1 % α-dextrin in 30 % ethanol, air-dried, humidified for one hour, and exposed to iodine vapors. For unsaturated compounds, yellow spots on a violet background result, while others are white; sensitivity, 20 γ (Mangold, 1955). Di- and triglycerides are first treated with a 1 % aqueous spray of pancreatin and incubated for 24 hours at 37°C. The papers are then sprayed with α-dextrin as before.

Chapter VIII

STEROIDS, BILE ACIDS, AND CARDIAC GLYCOSIDES

The low solubility of steroids and related compounds in water necessitates the use of special techniques in order to separate these compounds by paper chromatography. Two-phase solvent systems have been widely used, and "reversed phase" chromatography has been successfully employed. Keto- and hydroxysteroids may be chromatographed as derivatives (Zaffaroni, 1949; Heftmann, 1950). Adsorption chromatography on alumina-impregnated paper has also been used for the separation of steroids (Bush, 1950). The reader is referred to two excellent review articles on the paper chromatography of steroids (Bush, 1954; Heftmann, 1955).

Section I: Steroids
General Directions

1. PREPARATION OF SAMPLE

  a. Extraction of Cortical Steroids from Blood (Bush, 1953). Citrated or heparinized blood is centrifuged within 12 hours of collection, and a large sample of plasma is withdrawn. This is diluted with an equal volume of water, and the solution is extracted three times with three times its volume of ethyl acetate in a separatory funnel. The ethyl acetate is tested with indicators and is used only if the pH is greater than 6.0. The combined extracts are washed once with 0.1 volume of 0.2 N Na_2CO_3 and once with 0.1 volume of water. One drop of glacial acetic acid is added, and the extract is distilled to near dryness at reduced pressure (45–50°C.) with a fine capillary. Traces of water are removed by adding ethanol toward the end of the distillation.

  Each extract is dissolved in 15–20 ml. of a light petroleum (Skellysolve C):ethyl acetate mixture = 1:1 v/v, and the solution is then passed through 2 g. of silica gel (Davidson, 60 × 200 mesh) in a 1-cm.-diameter column. After a further 10 ml. of petroleum:ethyl acetate is run through the column, the steroids are eluted with 7 ml. of a mixture of ethyl acetate:methanol = 1:1 v/v. This eluate is evaporated in a 2.5-cm.-diameter test tube in a vacuum at 45–50°C. and dissolved in ethylene dichloride and methanol for chromatography on paper.

  b. Extraction of Estrogens from Human Placenta (F. L. Mitchell, 1952). About 200 g. of fresh human placenta is minced and extracted in a Soxhlet apparatus with methanol, which is removed *in vacuo*; the remaining sludge is extracted with ether. Where a hydrolyzate is required, this is obtained by refluxing with 1.5 N hydrochloric acid and subsequent extraction with ether. The ether is washed with 9% sodium bicarbonate, removed *in vacuo*, and the residue is taken up in benzene. At this stage, estriol is separated from estrone and estradiol by thorough extraction of the benzene with water. The water is extracted with ether, and 1 volume of carbon tetrachloride is added to 18 volumes of ether, which is then extracted with N NaOH. The sodium hydroxide extract is brought to pH 9 with H_2SO_4 and extracted with ether, which is evaporated to give the estriol fraction. The estrone and estradiol fraction is obtained by extraction of the benzene with N NaOH and subsequent treatment as for the estriol fraction. The final extracts are dissolved in ethanol for paper chromatography.

c. Spotting of Volumes of 40–100 µl. The problem of concentrating steroid extracts prior to chromatography has been accomplished by various techniques (Bush, 1952; Oertel, 1956). A starting line is drawn several centimeters from one end of the paper and lanes, 5–10 mm. wide, are marked parallel to the direction of flow of solvent. The solutions to be chromatographed are then pipetted along their respective lanes and the solvent is allowed to dry. The sheet is then hung into a small tank, specially kept for this purpose, with the lower edge dipping into a mixture of $CHCl_3$:ethyl acetate (1:1 v/v), containing a small addition of methanol. An ascending chromatogram is thus run with a solvent in which all the steroids move with the front. The solvent is allowed to ascend to the starting line. The result, when dried, is that all the steroids are compressed into small rectangles at the starting line. This preliminary chromatogram takes 5–10 minutes.

A similar procedure may be used for the preliminary concentration of steroids extracted from urine (Oertel, 1956). The dried extract is dissolved in 0.1–1.0 ml. methanol:acetic acid (v/v) to which one drop of *Sudan Red* is added. The total solution is spotted on a strip of Schleicher & Schuell Paper No. 2043b, shaped to a point at the opposite end. The strip is developed by ascending chromatography with methanol:acetic acid (v/v). The migration of the steroids may be followed by the movement of the dye. After 25–30 minutes the steroids have reached the top of the strip, which is dried *in vacuo*. The tip, containing the concentrated steroids, is cut off and inserted into a slit of another strip of paper, which is developed by any of the techniques described below.

d. Total Deposition of Extracts (1–2 ml.). The extract is made light pink by adding a minimal amount of Sudan Red and then evaporated *in vacuo* (in a test tube with side arm) to a small red drop at the bottom of the tube. This drop is taken up onto a three- to five-strand lamp wick, previously cleaned by 8-hour Soxhlet extraction with 90% ethanol. The tube is rinsed down with about 0.1 ml. methanol:ethyl acetate = 1:1 v/v and taken

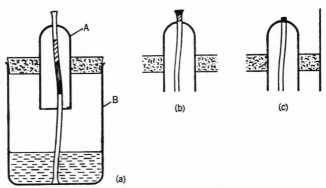

FIG. 1. Concentration of an extract for total deposition; concentration by a "wick chromatogram" (Bush, 1952).

up on the wick. At the third wash the drop will be colorless, indicating complete recovery of the dye and lipoid solutes in the original extract.

The wick is then suspended in a glass cowl (Fig. 1a, A) as shown, with 1–2 cm. emerging. The beaker (B) is filled with a little ethyl acetate, and this is allowed to rise up the wick. In about 15 minutes the dye is concentrated on the emerging zone (Fig. 1b). Immediately before the chromatogram is prepared, the wick is drawn down until only 2–3 mm. emerge (Fig. 1c). When concentrated on this small zone, as indicated by the dye, it is simply painted onto a lane and treated as described above. The reader is also referred to Chapter III, Section "Application of Sample."

2. PREPARATION OF DERIVATIVES

a. Formation of Hydrazones with Girard's Reagent (Zaffaroni, 1949). A convenient sample of the ketosteroid (usually 2.5–5.0 mg.), twice this weight of Girard's reagent T, and 2 ml. of an alcoholic acetic acid solution (10% glacial acetic acid in absolute methanol) are refluxed on a steam bath for 30–60 minutes under anhydrous conditions. After cooling, the refluxed sample is stored in a refrigerator.

An alternate method is more convenient: The ketosteroid, Girard's reagent T, and acidic methanol are incubated at 40°C. for 2 hours. (C3-Ketosteroids do not form a hydrazone with this reagent.) (See Table IV.)

b. Formation of Coupling Compounds with Fast Black-Salt K (Heftmann, 1950). A saturated aqueous solution of diazotized p-nitrobenzeneazodimethoxyaniline (Fast Black-Salt K, obtained from Emil Greiner Co.) is freshly prepared and filtered. One-tenth milliliter of an alcoholic estrogen solution, containing at least 3 μg. of the steroids, is placed in a test tube, 0.2 ml. of the reagent and 0.1 ml. of 20% Na_2CO_3 are added, and the mixture is heated in a boiling water bath for 10 minutes. The estrogen derivative is extracted by adding 0.2 ml. of benzene, shaking the solution, and drawing it up in a medicine dropper. The aqueous phase is expelled and the benzene layer is applied to the paper. A blank containing 0.1 ml. of ethanol in place of the alcoholic estrogen solution is run concurrently.

3. PAPER

In partition chromatographic methods which employ two-phase organic solvent systems it is necessary, in some cases, to impregnate the paper with the stationary phase prior to development. Solvents which have been used for this purpose are propylene glycol, formamide, phenyl cellosolve, and heptanol. The presence of hydrotropic agents, *i.e.,* sodium *p*-toluene-sulfonate, LiCl, or $CaCl_2 \cdot 2H_2O$, in the stationary phase also facilitates the separation of steroids.

a. Propylene Glycol, Formamide, or Phenyl Cellosolve (Zaffaroni, 1950 1951; Neher, 1952). Whatman filter paper No. 1 is washed extensively with water, 95% ethanol, and dried. For the quantitative estimation of urinary steroids, Rubin (1953) refluxed the paper for 48 hours in a Soxhlet apparatus with methanol:benzene = 1:1. The paper is then impregnated with 50% propylene glycol, formamide, or phenyl cellosolve dissolved in methanol; the excess reagent is removed by blotting the paper. Whatman No. 1 paper, impregnated with formamide, is washed in 95% ethanol for one week and is then rinsed with benzene (Mattox, 1956).

b. Heptanol (Schmidt, 1953). Schleicher & Schuell filter paper No. 2043b is washed with distilled water and dried at room temperature. The paper is then placed in a 15–20% solution of heptanol in acetone and dried for 7 hours at room temperature.

c. 1,3-Butanediol (Axelrod, 1953). The paper is dipped in 1,3-butanediol (Eastman Kodak Co.) and blotted between two sheets of absorbent paper.

d. Hydrotropic Agents (Boscott, 1952; Heusghem, 1953). (1) Whatman filter paper No. 3MM is impregnated with a saturated aqueous solution of *p*-toluenesulfonate. (2) Lithium chloride or calcium chloride · $2H_2O$, when added to a mixture of toluene and methanol or ethanol, causes the separation of an alcohol layer. The latter is sprayed on the paper and used in conjunction with the top layer for the paper chromatographic separation of estrogens. (3) The paper is hung in a closed chromatograph chamber, the bottom of which is covered with 0.5 N NH_4OH. When saturation of the paper is complete, the mobile phase is introduced into the chamber without desaturation of the atmosphere.

e. Treatment for Adsorption Chromatography. Alumina (Bush, 1950, 1952). Whatman papers No. 54 or No. 4 are impregnated with alumina by soaking the paper in a 30% solution of $Al_2(SO_4)_3$, made just cloudy with

2 N NaOH, at 60–70°C., hanging it in a cabinet for 15 minutes, and then leaving the paper overnight in an atmosphere saturated with ammonia. The paper is then immersed for 24 hours in a 0.02% aqueous solution of CaCl₂ , continually aspirated with a stream of air to remove the ammonia. This CaCl₂ treatment is the key to reproducible results. The papers treated with CaCl₂ have a pH between 7 and 7.5.

Similar results are achieved by dipping the paper (Schleicher & Schuell No. 2043a) into a 0.5% solution of a mixture of sodium stearate and palmitate ("Szapolit") at 45–50°C. The paper is dried at 70°C. and immersed into a solution of aluminum chloride (22.7 g. AlCl₃·6 H₂O/l.), rinsed with water and dried at 60–70°C. (Kiss, 1956).

f. Treatment for Reversed Phase Chromatography, Silicone (Kritchevsky, 1951, 1952; Markwardt, 1954). The filter paper (Munktell 20, 150G or Schleicher & Schuell, 2043b) is saturated with silicone by drawing the strips through a 5% (v/v) solution of Dow Corning Silicone No. 1107 in cyclohexane. The paper is blotted and dried at 110°C. for one hour. Quilon (Du Pont stearate chromic chloride) may be used in place of silicone.

g. Miscellaneous Treatments. Glass paper, impregnated with silicic acid has been used for cholesterol and its esters (Dieckert, 1954, 1956). The advantage of glass paper is that a spray reagent containing concentrated H₂SO₄ may be employed without disintegrating the paper, as in the case of cellulose paper (See "Detection of Spots.").

Esterification of cellulose (benzoyl-, acetyl-, palmitoyl-, and phthaloyl-cellulose) results in hydrophobic properties of the paper, thus facilitating the chromatography of water-insoluble steroids (Micheel, 1956). The reader is referred to Chapters III and VII for the preparation of this esterified cellulose paper. Acetyl-paper is commercially available (Schleicher & Schuell).

4. SOLVENTS (All solvents are saturated with stationary phase) (See Tables III, IV, and V)

a. Formamide-Treated Paper

(1) *Benzene.*

(2) *Benzene:chloroform* = 9:1; 1:1.

(3) *Chloroform.*

(4) *Benzene:petroleum ether* = 1:1. These solvents are used for the separation of cardiac glycosides, aglucons, adrenal corticosteroids, and ketosteroids (Schindler, 1951; Hassall, 1951; Zaffaroni, 1950, 1951; Hofmann, 1951; Čapek, 1956).

(5) *o-Dichlorobenzene.*

(6) *Methylene chloride.*

(7) *Cyclohexene.*

(8) *Decalin.* Solvents (5), (6), (7), and (8) are used for the separation of estrogens (Axelrod, 1953).

b. Propylene Glycol-Treated Paper

(1) *Toluene.*

(2) *Toluene:methanol* = v/v. Solvents (1) and (2) separate the corticosteroids of the adrenal gland. These solvents are also suitable for the separation of non-steroid estrogens of the hexoestrol series (Zaffaroni, 1950, 1951; Schwarz, 1953; Jellinek, 1953; Reineke, 1956).

(3) *Ligroin.*

(4) *Heptane.* Solvents (3) and (4) are used for the separation of testosterone and its biochemical precursors or the chromatography of corticosteroid acetates (Brady, 1951; Savard, 1953). Ligroin will also separate hydroxy-ketosteroids (Savard, 1953) and the mixture of androst-4-ene-3,17-dione and testosterone (Ofner, 1955).

The urinary steroids etiocholan-3α-ol-17-one, epiandrosterone, and dehydroepiandrosterone cannot be separated, nor can androsterone and etiocholan-3β-ol-17-one be resolved. It is, therefore, of great importance in dealing with unknown mixtures containing these substances that the mixture first be subjected to digitonin separation before chromatography.

Rubin (1953) has chromatographically separated the $\Delta^{9(11)}$-unsaturated 17-ketosteroids from the corresponding saturated ketosteroids by previous oxidation with perbenzoic acid of the unsaturated compounds to the epoxides.

(5) *Benzene:cyclohexane* (v/v) is suitable for the separation of C_{19}-steroids (Kochakian, 1952; Oertel, 1954).

(6) *Methylcyclohexane* is used for deoxy- and dehydrocorticosterone (Touchston, 1955).

c. Ethylene Glycol Monophenyl Ether-Treated Paper.

Heptane is suitable for the separation of the less polar steroids such as saturated or slightly unsaturated compounds whose —OH and —COOH groups are esterified (Neher, 1952). The least polar members of the 17-ketosteroids can also be separated with the heptane:phenyl cellosolve system; however, the chromatograms must be run at 23 ± 2°C., as higher temperatures completely change the character of the resolution of the weakly polar steroids (Rubin, 1953).

d. Heptanol-Treated Paper.

Water saturated with *heptanol* separates the corticosteroids. One part of heptanol and 10 parts of water are shaken vigorously and allowed to stand for several days to obtain complete separation of the phases (Schmidt, 1953).

e. Butanediol-Treated Paper. *Methylcyclohexane* separates allopregnane-3,20-dione and pregnane-3,20-dione. A mixture containing progesterone, androstane-3,17-dione, and 5-isoandrostane-3,17-dione can also be resolved (Axelrod, 1953).

f. Paper Treated with Hydrotropic Agents. (1) *Toluene* separates many neutral ketosteroids and estrogens on paper treated with sodium *p*-toluenesulfonate (Boscott, 1952).

(2) *Chloroform:benzene: N NH₄OH* = 1:9:1 is used with paper saturated with 0.5 *N* NH₄OH to separate the natural estrogens. R_f values for estrone, estradiol, and estriol are 0.89, 0.78 and 0.02, respectively.

g. Alumina-Impregnated Paper. (1) *Benzene* is used to separate estrogenic hormones on alumina-treated paper. Benzene will also separate the acetates of deoxycorticosterone, 11-dehydrocorticosterone, 17-hydroxycorticosterone, and corticosterone (Bush, 1950).

(2) *"Tetralin"* (*tetrahydronaphthalene*) is used to separate estrone, testosterone, and androsterone (Bush, 1950).

(3) *Benzene chloroform* in proportions of 4:1, 3:1, and 2:1 v/v is used to separate a wide variety of steroids (Bush, 1952).

(4) *Acetone* (5% v/v) in benzene separates the 21-acetates of the corticosterone group successfully (see Table V) (Bush, 1952).

(5) *Hexane; hexane:ether* = 19:1; *hexane:ether* = 15:5; and *ether* will separate most of the neutral steroids (Shull, 1952).

(6) *Methanol:CCl₄:water* = 18:5:2 is used for filter paper impregnated with Al stearate-palmitate (Kiss, 1956).

h. Silicone and Quilon-Treated Paper. (1) A solvent prepared by mixing *water, absolute ethanol,* and *chloroform* = 6:10:10 v/v separates a number of steroids on silicone-treated paper. Among these are androstanedione-3,17, Δ⁴-androstenedione-3,17, androsterone, isoandrosterone, dehydroisoandrosterone, and testosterone (Kritchevsky, 1951).

(2) *Ethanol:water* = 8:2 v/v will effect a separation of cholesterol and cholestenone on Quilon-treated paper (Kritchevsky, 1951).

(3) *Methanol:water* systems will separate a large number of steroids on Quilon-treated paper (Kritchevsky, 1952a). The upper limit of dilution for methanol is about 20%. Higher dilutions will not wet the paper. In general, the addition of water to the anhydrous solvent gives a higher R_f value rather than the lower one which might be expected.

(4) *Methanol:water:benzene:petroleum ether* (50–70°C.) = 2:7:3:6 (lower layer) is used to separate estrogen and its esters (Markwardt, 1954). The upper solvent phase is used for the equilibration of the tank.

i. Silicic Acid-Impregnated Glass Paper. *Ethyl ether:isoöctane* = 5:95 gives a good separation of cholesterol and cholesterol acetate (Dieckert, 1956).

j. Untreated Paper. (1) *n-Butanol:tert-butanol:water* = 1:1:1, and

(2) *Water-saturated n-butanol* are the solvents for the ketosteroid hydrazones, formed from Girard's Reagent T (see Section I, 2) (Zaffaroni, 1949; Ruliffson, 1953).

(3) *Toluene:petroleum ether (35–60°C.):methanol:water* = 200:100:30:70 (organic phase) and

(4) *Toluene:petroleum ether:ethanol:water* = 100:200:10:90 are used for the separation of estrogens diazotized with Fast Black-Salt K (see Section I, 2 and Table IV) (Heftmann, 1951). The water layer of both solvents is used for the saturation of the chromatographic tank.

(5) *Methanol and Ethanol Solvents* (Bush, 1952, 1953; Reineke, 1956; Hubener, 1956; Eberlein, 1955) (Fig. 2).

(a) *Petroleum ether (80–100°C.):methanol:water* = 10:8:2.

(b) *Toluene:petroleum ether:methanol:water* = 5:5:7:3; 66.7:3.3:60:40.

(c) *Petroleum ether:benzene:methanol:water* = 66.7:33.3:80:20.

(d) *Toluene:methanol:water* = 10:5:5.

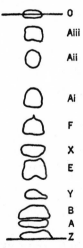

Fig. 2. Whole cortical extract run with system benzene:methanol:water = 10:5:5 v/v on Whatman No. 4 at 34°C. Photograph of the fluorescence developed by spraying with methanolic NaOH (Bush, 1952). *O*, starting line; *Ai, Aii, Aiii*, amorphous fraction components; *F*, 17-hydroxycorticosterone; *X*, unidentified blue fluorescence; *E*, 11-dehydro-17-hydroxycorticosterone; *Y, Z*, unidentified spots; *B*, corticosterone; *A*, 11-dehydrocorticosterone; *Z*, solvent front.

(e) *Benzene:methanol:water* = 10:5:5 and 10:8:2. This solvent separates estrone (0.86), estradiol (0.68), and estriol (0.18)[1] (Puck, 1955).

(f) *Toluene:ethyl acetate:methanol:water* = 9:1:5:5.

(g) *Toluene:petroleum ether:n-butanol:ethanol:water* = 20:10:1.5:1.5:7 and 10:20:1.2:8 for the separation of very polar steroids (Pechet, 1954).

Solvents (a) to (f) are suitable for the separation of the adrenocortical hormones.

(h) *Xylene:methanol* = 3:1 also separates the corticosteroids (Sakal, 1953).

(i) *Petroleum ether* (b.p. 100–120°C.)*:methanol* = 1:1 v/v separates estrone and estradiol in biological extracts if the temperature is kept at 32 ± 0.5°C. Whatman No. 541 filter paper is employed (F. L. Mitchell, 1952).

(j) *Phenol:methanol:water* = 13.5:30:56.5 v/v separates 7-dehydrocholesterol from cholesterol and ergosterol. *Phenol:methanol:water* = 14:30:56 separates ergosterol from cholesterol and 7-dehydrocholesterol (McMahon, 1950).

(6) *n-Butyl acetate:n-butanol:10% acetic acid* is used for the separation of steroid glucuronosides and steroid sulfates (Lewbart, 1955).

k. *Acetylated Cellulose Paper.   Ethyl acetate:tetrahydrofuran:water* = 0.6:3.5:4.7 is used for the separation of androsterone, testosterone, and dehydroandrosterone (Micheel, 1956).

5. TECHNIQUES USED

After the detailed discussion of preparation of samples and derivatives, the modification of paper, and the choice of various solvents, it may be useful to summarize the methods for the chromatographic separation of the steroids:

a. *Partition Chromatography.* For this technique the paper is presaturated with propylene glycol, formamide, and other polar solvents.   Untreated paper may be used with methanol-containing solvents.

b. *Adsorption Chromatography.* Paper impregnated with alumina or aluminum soaps is used.

c. *Reversed Phase Chromatography.* Cellulose or glass paper is impregnated with silicone, "Quilon," or silicic acid.   Esterified cellulose paper has also been employed.

d. *Chromatography of Steroid Derivatives.* Ketosteroid hydrazones (Girard's Reagent T) or steroids diazotized with Fast Black-Salt K may be separated by partition chromatography on untreated paper.

In all of these methods the ascending development method may be the preferred one.   Since most of the solvents contain highly volatile compon

---

[1] ( ) Denotes R_f value.

ents, and since equilibrium conditions must be maintained during a run, it is essential that the chromatographic tanks are absolutely vaporproof. The simplest tank of this type for a short development is a one-gallon "pickle jar" with a metal screw-top which has been coated with paraffin (Palmer, 1955).

In a miniature glass chamber (dimensions: $10 \times 7.5 \times 5$ cm.) the impregnated paper strip is loosely wound around plastic rods, and the leading edge is slipped through a slit in the side of the chamber. The fastest moving substance will be concentrated at the tip which is cut off periodically, eluted, and redeveloped in another solvent (Oertel, 1956a, b).

6. Detection and Identification of Spots (See Table I)

In this section a number of general and specific color reagents, as well as spectrographic techniques, are described. As in all methods of paper chromatography, the migration of the unknown spot may be compared with that of reference compounds. Thus, a characteristic color, absorption spectrum, and R_f value may aid in the final identification of an unknown compound. A set of twenty-four reference steroids for chromatography is available from U.S.P. Reference Standards, 46 Park Avenue, New York 16, N. Y.

a. Alkaline m-Dinitrobenzene (Zimmermann Reaction). The reagent consists of equal volumes ethanolic solutions of 2% *m*-dinitrobenzene and 2.5 *N* KOH. The paper is sprayed with the solution and is dried at 110°C. for 30–60 seconds (Kritchevsky, 1951). Purple-blue spots mark the position of steroids; the spots fade after a few minutes and must be marked immediately.

b. Phosphomolybdic Acid (Kritchevsky, 1952; Reineke, 1956). (Cannot be used with formamide-treated papers.) The dried paper is dipped into a 10% (w/v) solution of phosphomolybdic acid in methanol and heated for five minutes at 90°C. Hydroxysteroids result in blue-black spots on a green background.

c. Silicotungstic Acid and Phosphotungstic Acid (Kritchevsky, 1952; Douste-Blazy, 1952; Bourgain, 1956). The paper is dipped into a 25% alcoholic solution of silicotungstic acid and heated at 110°C. for two to three minutes. Longer heating causes charring of the paper. This reagent is an effective test for many steroids, including sitosterols.

d. Iodine Reagent. The developed chromatogram is dipped for a few seconds into a fresh, saturated solution of iodine in petroleum ether (60–80°C.), kept at 40°C. on a water bath (*Caution!*). There must be complete removal of the solvents, dryness, and neutralization of acids present by a short exposure to ammonia vapors. In order to make the colors more permanent, the chromatogram may be sprayed with a concentrated starch

TABLE I

COLORS PRODUCED BY STEROID CHROMOGENIC SPRAYS[a]

Reagent	Sensitivity γ	Reference letter pp. 259ff	α-Estradiol	β-Estradiol	Estrone	Estriol	17-Ethinyl-estradiol	α-Ketol steroids
15% Fuming sulfuric acid	5	h	Orange-yellow (Yellow-green)	Orange-yellow (Green)	Orange-tan (Green-yellow)	Rose-tan (Pink-green)	Red-brown (Yellow-orange)	—
Benzoyl chloride, zinc chloride	10	i	Orange-tan (Green-yellow)	Orange-red (Yellow)	Orange-brown (Yellow)	Pink-violet (Dark pink)	Pink-red (Orange)	—
Phenolsulfonate phosphoric acid	10	j	Light green (Blue-green)	Green-yellow (Green)	Orange-tan (Violet-pink)	Yellow-pink (Pink red)	Pink-red (Yellow-orange)	—
Nitrous acid, mercuric nitrate	15	k	Yellow-brown (Purple-brown)	Yellow-brown (Vermillion)	Yellow-brown (Purple-brown)	Yellow-brown (Purple-brown)	Yellow-brown (Purple-brown)	—
Antimony pentachloride	15	m	Brown	Purple-blue (Green-brick-red)	Ochre	Yellow-brown	Brown	—
Ferric chloride	20	n	Purple	Wine red	Purple	Purple	Purple	
Tollens	15	e	—	—	—	—	—	Brown
TPTZ	15	f	—	—	—	—	—	Red
KMnO₄	30–70	g	—	—	—	—	—	Brown

[a] ( ) Color refers to fluorescence in ultraviolet light.

solution after all background iodine has disappeared (Bush, 1950). This reagent works with most steroids, and the reaction seems to depend very little on substituent groups in the steroid nucleus.

A modified iodine reagent consists of 0.3 % iodine in 5 % aqueous potassium iodide (Burton, 1951). The dipped chromatogram is washed repeatedly with water until the background is colorless.

  e. *Alkaline Silver Nitrate* (Tollens Reagent). Ten milliliters of 0.1 N silver nitrate, 10 drops of concentrated ammonium hydroxide, and 5 ml. of 10 % NaOH are mixed shortly before use. The dried strips are immersed in this solution for an instant, and after maximum color development, the paper is washed first in 5 % aqueous $Na_2S_2O_3$ solution and then in water to prevent background color (Burton, 1951; Reineke, 1956).

  f. *Triphenyltetrazolium Chloride.* A stock solution of 0.2 % TPTZ in water is stored in the dark. Shortly before use two parts of the stock solution are mixed with one part of 10 % sodium hydroxide (Burton, 1951). This reagent can be used to differentiate between α-ketol and dihydroxyacetone groups of C_{21}-steroids. If the characteristic red spot for α-ketol is obtained with alkaline TPTZ , then another strip of the same chromatogram is passed through aqueous 0.1 N NaOH and placed on a glass plate on a hot plate at 100°C. and covered with a second glass plate. The strip is heated for exactly 3 minutes, the top plate is removed, and the strip allowed to dry on the heated plate. The chromatogram is then treated in the usual way with TPTZ and returned to the heated plate until maximum color is developed. A red spot indicates α-ketol group without added tertiary OH group, whereas no color is produced if a dihydroxy acetone structure is present (Axelrod, 1953).

The red color may be eluted with ethyl acetate:methanol = 7:3 and the optical density determined in a colorimeter at 565 mμ for quantitative analysis (Touchston, 1955).

  g. *Potassium Permanganate* (0.2 %) is made up in 5 % sodium carbonate (Burton, 1951).

  h. *Sulfuric Acid.* Fuming sulfuric acid is pipetted lengthwise onto a glass plate 10 × 60 cm., and the chromatogram strip immersed in the acid with the aid of a glass rod. After 1 minute the strip is observed under an ultraviolet lamp for fluorescence. This reagent is used to detect estrogens (Axelrod, 1953).

Sulfuric acid:acetic acid (v/v) forms a pink ring at the site of cholesterol (Hack, 1953).

  i. *Benzoyl Chloride* (for estrogens). A solution of 5 parts of 40 % w/v zinc chloride in glacial acetic acid is mixed with 7 parts of benzoyl chloride: chloroform v/v. The reaction mixture is applied by same procedure as given for fuming sulfuric acid except that the glass plate is heated on a hot plate until maximum color is attained (Axelrod, 1953).

j. Sodium p-Phenolsulfonate. Two per cent in 85% phosphoric acid. Testing for estrogen is by same procedure as given for benzoyl chloride (Axelrod, 1953).

k. Modified Millon's Reagent. One part of mercury is dissolved in 2 parts of concentrated nitric acid w/w, and 2 volumes of water are added. The testing procedure is the same as that given for benzoyl chloride (Axelrod, 1953).

l. Antimony Trichloride. A saturated solution of $SbCl_3$ in chloroform is sprayed on the paper which is dried at 90°C. for 4 minutes. This reagent identifies Δ^5-unsaturated steroids, 3β-dehydroandrosterone, pregnenolone (Neher, 1951), digitalis glycosides (Lawday, 1952), and cholesterol (Kiss, 1956).

The chromatogram is dipped in a concentrated solution of antimony trichloride in nitrobenzene (25 g. per 5 ml.), gently blotted to remove excess reagent, and heated in an oven at 90°C. for 5 minutes. This reagent reacts instantaneously with non-ketonic, hydroxylated steroids. Non-hydroxylated steroids do not form color products at concentrations normally used in chromatography. Compounds with oxygen groupings at C_{11} appear to give less intense colors, whereas unsaturation at C_5 or C_6 increase the color intensity (Rosenkrantz, 1953).

m. Antimony Pentachloride. The dipping reagent consists of 33% (w/v) $SbCl_5$ in chloroform. The paper is dipped momentarily in the reagent and allowed to dry in air (Axelrod, 1953). A spraying reagent (20%, v/v) produces immediately brilliant blue-green colors for Δ^7-stenols, 7α-, and 7β-diols (Riddell, 1955). Brief heating at 100°C. produces a yellow-brown color for sterols and on prolonged heating for stanols.

n. Ferric Chloride. Two per cent solution in absolute methanol. The testing procedure is the same as that given for benzoyl chloride (Axelrod, 1953).

o. Phosphoric Acid. The dried chromatogram, developed with toluene-propylene glycol, is dipped quickly into 15% H_3PO_4 and heated to 90°C. for 20 minutes. Fluorescent spots, lasting for several hours, indicate the positions of the corticosteroids (Neher, 1951).

p. Anisaldehyde. This reagent consists of 0.5 ml. of anisaldehyde in 50 ml. of glacial acetic acid and 1 ml. of concentrated H_2SO_4. The sprayed chromatogram is heated for 2–5 minutes at 90°C., and those steroids that produce the weakest color with the phosphoric acid reagent are identified. 11-Dehydrocorticosterone is visible in ordinary light; Reichstein U and E spots[2] are visible in ultraviolet light; the spots have a red-brown fluorescence (Neher, 1951).

[2] Reichstein U : Δ^4-pregnene-3,11-dione-17,20,21-triol-20,21-diacetate. Reichstein E : Δ^4-pregnene-3-one-11β,17,20,21-tetrol-20,21-diacetate.

q. Vanillin. The reagent, 25 g. vanillin in 100 ml. of 85% H_3PO_4 , is sprayed on the chromatogram which is heated for 20 minutes at 70°C. (McAleer, 1956). 17α-Hydroxyprogesterone produces a bright orange color, while the 11β compound is negative.

r. Detection of Steroid Hydrazones. The chromatograms of the keto-steroids, coupled with Girard's Reagent T, are dried at room temperature, immersed in iodoplatinate solution, and washed with water (Zaffaroni, 1949). The iodoplatinate solution is made up as follows: 5 ml. of 5% platinum chloride in 1 N HCl, 45 ml. of a 10% potassium iodide solution, and 100 ml. of distilled water are combined and stored in a dark bottle.

The position of the ketosteroids is indicated by purple spots. A suitable blank must be chromatographed, because Girard's Reagent T has a characteristic gray-blue spot.

s. 2,4-Dinitrophenylhydrazine. One hundred and fifty milligrams is dissolved in 25 ml. of distilled water and 22 ml. of concentrated HCl. Enough distilled water is then added to make 100 ml. The chromatogram strip is immersed in reagent, held in the air for 2 minutes, and then blotted (Axelrod, 1953).

A spraying reagent is used for ketosteroids which have no characteristic absorption spectrum in the ultraviolet: 300 mg. 2,4-dinitrophenylhydrazine, 5 ml. ethanol, 0.3 ml. conc. H_2SO_4 ; heated on steam bath until clear solution; diluted to 200 ml. with ethanol (Reineke, 1956). This treatment will not reveal C_{11}-ketosteroids and should be followed, therefore, by Tollens Reagent (See Reagent *e*).

t. Arsenomolybdate Reagent. A solution of 25 g. of ammonium molybdate in 450 ml. of water is mixed with 21 ml. of concentrated sulfuric acid, and a solution of 3 g. of sodium arsenate ($Na_2HAsO_4\cdot7H_2O$) in 25 ml. of water is added. The mixture is incubated at 37°C. for 48 hours and filtered. It is stored in a glass-stoppered brown bottle.

The developed chromatogram is moistened with color reagent by pressing gently with a moistened cloth mounted on washed X-ray film. After removal of the cloth, a ring of filter paper having a short tail at either end is placed around the test strip which lies on a glass plate. The paper ring is kept damp by allowing the tails to dip into distilled water during the incubation. After a warm glass plate has been placed over the test strip and paper ring, the whole arrangement is incubated on a heavy metal base in an electric oven at 70°C. for 30–60 minutes. About 1–2 μg. of a reducing steroid can be detected by this method. The spot color is blue (Schwarz, 1952, 1953).

u. Methanolic Sodium Hydroxide. Chromatograms of α,β-unsaturated ketosteroids, developed by the technique of Bush (1952) (see Detailed Procedures) are sprayed with a solution of 10 g. of NaOH in 100 ml. of 60%

v/v methanol and dried at 60–100°C. Brilliant fluorescent spots in ultra-violet light indicate the positions of the steroids.

v. p-Phenylenediamine Phthalate. About five hundred mg. of *p*-phenylenediamine and 1.6 g. of phthalic acid are added to 100 ml. of water-saturated *n*-butanol. The chromatogram is sprayed with this reagent and heated briefly at about 100°C. Steroids with the Δ⁴-3-keto group in the *A* ring give a brown color with a sensitivity of 2–3 μg. (Bodánsky, 1955).

w. Isotope Derivative Method (Leegwater, 1956). Steroids with a phenolic group in the *A* ring are reacted with p-I^{135} phenylsulfonyl chloride. For example, 10 γ of estrogen is esterified for 15 minutes at room temperature with 2 mg. of "pipsyl chloride" dissolved in 0.4 ml. 75% acetone. The excess reagent is hydrolyzed by adding 2% borax and heating the solution for thirty minutes at 50°C. The derivative is extracted with benzene and chromatographed with the reversed-phase solvent system CCl₄: paraffin oil = 7:2. Spots are detected by autoradiography.

x. Detection of 17,20-Diols (Bush, 1955). The steroid-17,20-diols are oxidized to ketosteroids by dipping the developed chromatogram through a solution of 0.5% Pb(II) acetate in acetic acid and air-drying for 15 minutes. The paper is then passed through 1% *m*-dinitrobenzene in ethanolic *N* KOH and heated to dryness.

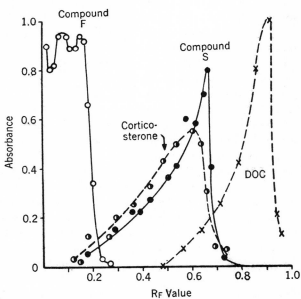

FIG. 3. Superimposed absorbance curves of compound F (O), corticosterone (◑), compound S (●), and 11-deoxycorticosterone (X), developed with water-saturated xylene. Measured at 245 mμ (Tennent, 1951).

TABLE II

ABSORPTION MAXIMA OF SULFURIC ACID CHROMOGENS OF STEROIDS (Zaffaroni, 1950)

Compound	Absorption maxima, mμ
17-Hydroxycorticosterone	280, 395, 475
17-Hydroxy-11-dehydrocorticosterone	280, 343, 415
Corticosterone	285, 330, 373, 455
11-Dehydrocorticosterone	280, 355, 415
17-Hydroxy-11-deoxycorticosterone	285, 535
11-Deoxycorticosterone	285, 370, 440
Allopregnane-3β,11β,17α,21-tetrol-20-one	330, 415, 510
Allopregnane-3β,17α,21-triol-11,20-dione	333, 410
Allopregnane-3β,17α,21-triol-20-one	315, 410
Pregnane-17α,21-diol-3,11,20-trione	270, 340, 415
3-Hydroxy-11-ketoetiocholanic acid	320, 405
3,9-Epoxy-11-ketoetiocholanic acid	290, 405
Δ^4-Androstene-3,11,17-trione	280
Androstane-3,11,17-trione	No maxima

y. Spectrophotometric Identification. Single ketosteroids developed on paper with water-saturated xylene are identified by their ultraviolet absorption curve, obtained at a wavelength of 245 mμ (Tennent, 1951). Some of these results are given in Fig. 3.

α,β-Unsaturated ketosteroids, developed by the partition method of Bush (1952), are also identified by the exposure of the chromatogram to ultraviolet light.

z. Absorption Spectra of Sulfuric Acid Chromogens. Three milliliters of concentrated sulfuric acid is added to 70–90 μg. of the dry steroid in a test tube. The tube is stoppered and allowed to stand at room temperature for 2 hours. The optical density of the solution, from 220 to 600 mμ, is then read in a spectrophotometer, using concentrated sulfuric acid as a blank. Table II summarizes the results obtained with fourteen steroids. The curves are all different with respect to shape and absorption maxima. Acetates and free compounds give identical curves. The absorption spectra of these chromogens are of great value when used in conjunction with the paper chromatographic method of analysis of adrenal steroids and in establishing the identity of compounds isolated from biological sources (Zaffaroni, 1950).

7. QUANTITATIVE ANALYSIS

In order to keep the paper blank at a minimum, it is recommended to wash the filter paper for 24 hours with 2 N ethanolic NaOH by descending chromatography. The paper is then rinsed with distilled water until neutral (Lewis, 1956).

An illustration for the semiquantitative procedure is described, and similar methods may be adaptable to other steroids (Reineke, 1956).

A sample (0.01 ml.) containing 500 μg. each of 11α-OH-4-pregnene-3,20-dione and 4-pregnene-3,20-dione is applied on propylene glycol-treated paper and developed with toluene. The chromatogram is dried at 105°C. for 2 hours and is scanned with an ultraviolet light source to locate the steroids. The detected areas are eluted by shaking with 40 ml. methanol. The solutions are filtered and the optical absorption determined in a Beckman spectrophotometer, Model DU at 224 and 242 mμ. Appropriate paper blanks are treated in the same manner. Concentrations are calculated by the following formula:

$$\frac{RD_{242} - D_{224}}{RK_{42} - K_{224}} (VP) = \text{mg. in aliquot} \tag{1}$$

R = ratio of D/D for paper blank
D = absorbance for sample
K = absorbance of a 1 mg./ml. solution of steroid
P = pipette correction
V = volume of elution solvent

Detailed Procedures

1. PARTITION CHROMATOGRAPHY OF C_{19}- AND C_{21}-KETOSTEROIDS WITH PROPYLENE GLYCOL AS THE STATIONARY PHASE AND LIGROIN AS THE MOBILE PHASE (Savard, 1953)

The descending technique (see Chapter III) where the mobile phase is llowed to run off the chromatogram has had wide use in the paper chromatography of steroids. By this method, the less polar steroids are allowed to run off the paper and are subsequently separated on another chromatogram with a suitable solvent (Hechter, 1953). The original chromatogram is developed until the more polar steroids have separated. The chromatographic procedure of Savard (1953) is an example of this type of separation and is described in detail as follows:

Dried filter paper sheets (Whatman No. 1, 22 × 6 inches), previously extracted in a Soxhlet apparatus with alcohol and benzene, were cut into 1 × 45-cm. strips attached at the upper end to a common base. Approximately 10–100 μg. of steroids, depending on the amount required for subsequent color tests, were applied to the 1-cm. paper strip. In seeking traces of secondary components, higher amounts (up to 1 mg.) were applied without seriously distorting the ensuing chromatogram. For mixtures, it was usual to apply 0.5–1.5 mg. of the ketosteroid mixture and, when larger amounts were to be chromatographed, wider sheets (up to 16 cm.) were used to accommodate as much as 30–40 mg. Distortion occurred only when the final concentration (after chromatography) exceeded 1 mg./sq. cm. for any single component.

The prepared chromatogram strips were impregnated with the stationary solvent (propylene glycol or ethylene glycol phenyl ether) as previously described (see Section I, 3, a). A serious factor influencing mobilities of the steroids was the amount of stationary solvent left in the paper strips. In order to minimize this effect, the blotted strips were left between the sheets of blotting paper with only the upper end and starting lines projecting during the ensuing operation. The steroids (or mixtures), dissolved in benzene or methanol, were applied to the strips in small volumes with the aid of a current of air. The latter solvent was preferred because of its tendency to sweep away the miscible glycol as the steroid solutions were applied; spreading of the zone later became reduced by the backsurge of the glycol after the methanol had evaporated. The paper strips were held in place in the solvent reservoir between two glass plates which projected beyond the edge of the reservoir and were so adjusted that the starting line was located about 1–1.5 cm. beyond the outer edge of the supporting glass plates. After addition of the solvent to the reservoir, a capillary space was provided between the glass plates by means of which the solvent was raised over the "wick" base of the paper to within a centimeter or so of the starting line in a matter of a few seconds. This slight innovation substantially reduced the variations in running times caused by different volumes of solvent in the reservoir.

After the necessary period of time for chromatography, which varied according to the individual steroids being studied (see Table III), the papers were removed from the chambers and suspended in a current of air and allowed to dry. Small strips, about 0.3 cm., were cut from the edge of each and exposed to one or more color reagents.

2. PARTITION CHROMATOGRAPHY WITH AQUEOUS METHANOL AS STATIONARY PHASE (Bush, 1952; Eberlein, 1955)

This method warrants a detailed discussion, because it is one of the first successful adaptations of conventional paper partition chromatography to the separation of steroids by the use of untreated filter paper and aqueous organic solvents.

The temperature during the development is kept at 25–30°C. Saturation of the atmosphere with the solvents is accomplished by covering the walls of the tank with wads of filter paper, continually soaking up the two phases used. Two wads dip into about 2 cm. depth of mobile phase covering the bottom of the tank, and a third into a small basin containing about 600 ml. of stationary phase.

Aliquots of the steroid solutions, containing about 25 μg. of each steroid,

TABLE III

Steroid Mobilities (Reineke, 1956)

Compound	Detection[d]	Development systems[a]								
		1 R_s^b	2 R_s^c	3 R_s^c	4 R_s^b	5 R_f^e	6 R_f	7 R_f	8 R_f	9 R_f
A. C_{19} steroids										
5α-Androstane-3,17-dione	a	2.7	—[f]	—	—	0.76	—	—	—	—
4-Androstene-3,17-dione	b	1.65	—	5.3	—	0.5	0.89	0.78	—	—
1,4-Androstadiene-3,17-dione	c	1.0	—	—	—	0.27	—	0.78	—	—
4,9(11)-Androstadiene-3,17-dione	b	1.65	—	—	—	0.5	—	0.78	—	—
3β-Hydroxy-5-androsten-17-one	d	1.15	—	3.6	—	0.38	0.83	0.65	—	—
Androstane-3,17-dione	d	—	—	—	—	—	—	—	—	1.0
3β-Acetoxy-5-androsten-17-one	d	5.5	—	—	—	0.85	0.99	0.99	—	—
17β-Hydroxy-4-androsten-3-one	b	0.89	1.5	2.0	1.44	0.22	0.74	0.52	—	—
Testololactone	b	0.4	2.8	2.7	1.23	0.043	0.63	0.28	—	—
4-Androstene-3,6,17-trione	b	0.72	—	5.5	1.61	0.13	0.80	0.52	—	—
4-Androstene-3,11,17-trione	b	0.68	—	4.8	1.51	0.11	0.78	0.43	—	—
6β-Hydroxy-4-androstene-3,17-dione	b	—	1.0	0.89	0.74	—	0.43	0.19	0.90	—
11α-Hydroxy-4-androstene-3,17-dione	b	—	0.65	0.49	0.45	—	0.25	0.06	0.82	—
11β-Hydroxy-4-androstene-3,17-dione	b	—	1.50	1.4	1.0	—	0.53	0.26	—	—
14α-Hydroxy-4-androstene-3,17-dione	b	—	0.90	0.79	0.55	—	0.33	0.12	0.87	—
15α-Hydroxy-4-androstene-3,17-dione	b	—	—	0.40	0.41	—	0.22	—	0.82	—
B. C_{19} 17β-hydroxysteroids										
17β-Hydroxy-4-androsten-3-one	b	0.89	1.50	2.0	1.44	0.22	0.74	0.52	—	—
17β-Hydroxy-1,4-androstadien-3-one	c	0.60	1.0	1.35	1.24	0.11	0.69	0.34	—	—
17β-Acetoxy-4-androsten-3-one	b	3.5	—	—	—	0.83	—	—	—	—
17β-Propionoxy-4-androsten-3-one	b	4.25	—	—	—	0.85	—	—	—	—
17β-Cyclopentylpropionoxy-4-androsten-3-one	b	5.85	—	—	—	0.99	—	—	—	—

Compound										
17α-Methyl-17β-hydroxy-4-androsten-3-one	b	1.15	1.80	3.1	1.66	0.33	0.82	0.64	—	—
17α-Ethinyl-17β-hydroxy-4-androsten-3-one	b	0.74[a]	1.80[a]	2.55[a]	1.55[a]	0.16[a]	0.74[a]	0.52[a]	—	—
5-Androstene-3β,17β-diol	d	—	0.38	0.57	—	—	0.62	—	—	—
17β-Hydroxy-4-androstene-3,11-dione	b	—	0.82	0.64	0.65	—	0.31	0.13	—	—
17α-Methyl-17β-hydroxy-4-androstene-3,11-dione	b	—	1.05	1.3	1.0	—	0.56	0.21	—	—
6β,17β-Dihydroxy-4-androsten-3-one	b	—	—	0.13	0.16	—	0.15	—	0.67	—
11α,17β-Dihydroxy-4-androsten-3-one	b	0.16	0.074	0.065	0.09	—	0.07	—	0.47	—
17α-Methyl-11α,17β-dihydroxy-4-androsten-3-one	b	—	—	0.13	0.20	—	0.13	—	0.58	—
11β,17β-Dihydroxy-4-androsten-3-one	b	—	—	0.21	0.28	—	0.21	—	0.74	—
14α,17β-Dihydroxy-4-androsten-3-one	b	—	—	0.18	0.21	—	0.12	—	0.67	—
C. C_{18} steroids										
4-Estrene-3,17-dione	b	1.32	—	1.6	—	0.4	0.74	0.74	—	—
Estrone	d	0.66	1.3	1.86	1.42	0.14[a]	0.68	0.52	—	0.78
17β-Hydroxy-4-estren-3-one	b	0.78	1.3	0.40	1.32	0.14	0.47	0.43	—	—
Estradiol	d	—	—	—	0.68	—	—	0.21	—	—
Estradiol-17α		—	—	—	—	—	—	—	—	0.45
Estradiol-17β		—	—	—	—	—	—	—	—	0.27
11α-Hydroxy-4-estrene-3,17-dione	b	—	—	0.35	0.32	—	0.19	0.05	0.76	—
10ξ,17β-Dihydroxy-4-estren-3-one	b	—	—	—	—	—	0.11	—	0.66	—
11α,17β-Dihydroxy-4-estren-3-one	b	—	—	—	—	—	0.04	—	0.39	—
D. C_{21} steroids										
5α-Pregnane-3,20-dione	a	3.5	—	—	—	0.83	—	—	—	—
5β-Pregnane-3,20-dione	a	3.5	—	—	—	0.83	—	—	—	—
4-Pregnene-3,20-dione	b	2.7	—	6.0	—	0.76	0.95	0.96	—	—
1,4-Pregnadiene-3,20-dione	b	1.65	—	—	—	0.55	—	0.78	—	—
4,6-Pregnadiene-3,20-dione	b	2.7	—	—	—	0.68	—	0.96	—	—
4,9(11)-Pregnadiene-3,20-dione	b	2.7	—	—	—	0.68	—	0.96	—	—
4,16-Pregnadiene-3,20-dione	b	2.7	—	—	—	0.76	—	0.96	—	—

TABLE III—*Continued*

Compound	Detection[d]	Development systems[a]								
		1 R_s[b]	2 R_s[c]	3 R_s[c]	4 R_s[b]	5 R_f•	6 R_f	7 R_f	8 R_f	9 R_f
D. C21 steroids (Continued)										
3α-Hydroxy-5β-pregnan-20-one	e	1.95	—	—	—	0.72	—	0.93	—	—
3β-Hydroxy-5α-pregnan-20-one	e	1.65	—	—	—	0.72	—	0.89	—	—
3β-Hydroxy-5-pregnen-20-one	d	1.65	—	—	—	0.64	—	0.78	—	—
3β-Hydroxy-5,16-pregnadien-20-one	d	1.65	—	—	—	0.61	0.89	0.78	—	—
5α-Pregnane-3,11,20-trione	a	1.25	—	—	—	0.42	0.89	0.78	—	—
5β-Pregnane-3,11,20-trione	a	1.25	—	—	—	0.42	0.82	0.78	—	—
4-Pregnene-3,11,20-trione	b	1.00	—	4.0	—	0.25	—	0.65	—	—
3α-Hydroxy-5β-pregnane-11,20-dione	a	0.79	1.6	2.1	—	0.14	—	0.43	—	—
3β-Hydroxy-5α-pregnane-11,20-dione	a	0.64	1.6	1.9	—	0.11	—	0.34	—	—
3β-Hydroxy-5β-pregnane-11,20-dione	a	0.79	1.6	2.1	—	0.16	—	0.43	—	—
11α-Hydroxy-5α-pregnane-3,20-dione	a	0.64	1.6	1.9	—	0.08	—	0.34	—	—
11α-Hydroxy-5β-pregnane-3,20-dione	a	0.79	1.6	2.1	—	0.12	—	0.43	—	—
11β-Hydroxy-5β-pregnane-3,20-dione	a	1.0	—	3.3	—	0.20	—	0.65	—	—
6β-Hydroxy-4-pregnene-3,20-dione	b	0.63	1.5	1.6	1.12	0.097	0.69	0.34	—	—
11α-Hydroxy-4-pregnene-3,20-dione	b	0.4	1.0	1.0	1.0	0.034	0.47	0.19	—	—
11α-Hydroxy-4,16-pregnadiene-3,20-dione	b	0.4	1.0	1.0	1.04	0.04	0.47	0.19	—	—
11α-Acetoxy-4-pregnene-3,20-dione	b	1.25	—	5.3	—	0.25	—	0.71	—	—
11β-Hydroxy-4-pregnene-2,20-dione	b	0.60	1.8	2.1	1.42	0.11	0.71	0.43	—	—
14α-Hydroxy-4-pregnene-3,20-dione	b	0.60	1.8	2.1	1.32	0.078	0.69	0.34	—	—
15α-Hydroxy-4-pregnene-3,20-dione	b	0.37	1.0	0.77	0.82	0.017	0.40	0.13	—	—
15β-Hydroxy-4-pregnene-3,20-dione	b	0.4	1.1	1.2	1.0	0.036	0.49	0.20	—	—
16α-Hydroxy-4-pregnene-3,20-dione	b	0.4	0.8	0.92	0.74	0.024	0.43	0.15	—	—
17α-Hydroxy-4-pregnene-3,20-dione	b	0.78	1.8	2.55	1.51	0.16	0.78	0.52	—	—
21-Hydroxy-4-pregnene-3,20-dione	f	0.86	—	4.0	1.5	0.23	0.81	0.52	—	—

Compound										
Methyl-3,11-diketo-4,17(20)-(cis)-pregnadien-21-oate	b	1.5	—	5.8	—	0.57	—	0.78	—	—
3α,11α-Dihydroxy-5β-pregnan-20-one	a	0.4	—	0.43	0.74	—	0.41	▲	0.87	—
3β,11α-Dihydroxy-5α-pregnan-20-one	a	0.24	—	0.29	0.63	—	0.29	—	0.87	—
11β,21-Dihydroxy-4,17(20)-pregnadien-3-one	b	—	0.29	0.29	0.47	—	0.31	—	0.87	—
21-Acetoxy-11β-hydroxy-4,17(20)-pregnadien-3-one	b	1.15	—	4.8	—	0.5	—	0.78	—	—
6β-Hydroxy-4-pregnene-3,11,20-trione	b	—	0.91	0.57	0.58	—	0.28	—	—	—
17α-Hydroxy-5β-pregnane-3,11,20-trione	b	0.64	1.5	1.8	—	0.07	0.65	0.37	—	—
17α-Hydroxy-4-pregnene-3,11,20-trione	b	0.4	1.0	1.0	0.89	0.304	0.47	0.19	0.47	—
6β,11α-Dihydroxy-5β-pregnane-3,20-dione	a	—	—	—	0.067	—	0.05	—	0.87	—
3α,17α-Dihydroxy-5β-pregnane-11,20-dione	a	0.35	—	0.27	0.48	—	0.32	0.10		—
6β,11α-Dihydroxy-4-pregnene-3,20-dione	b	—	0.074	0.04	0.05	—	0.04	—	0.38	—
6β,17α-Dihydroxy-4-pregnene-3,20-dione	b	—	—	0.19	0.21	—	0.19	—	0.75	—
11α,17α-Dihydroxy-4-pregnene-3,20-dione	b	—	0.14	0.09	0.13	—	0.09	—	0.61	—
11β,17α-Dihydroxy-4-pregnene-3,20-dione	b	—	0.38	0.29	0.39	—	0.23	—	0.83	—
E. C_{21} 21-hydroxysteroids										
21-Hydroxy-4-pregnene-3,20-dione	f	0.86	—	4.0	1.5	0.23	0.81	0.52	—	—
21-Acetoxy-4-pregnene-3,20-dione	f	1.4	—	—	—	0.55	—	0.89	—	—
21-Acetoxy-4,16-pregnadiene-3,20-dione	f	1.15	—	1.4	0.69	0.50	0.43	0.89	—	—
21-Hydroxy-4-pregnene-3,11,20-trione	f	0.28	—	4.7	1.6	—	0.75	—	0.92	—
21-Acetoxy-4-pregnene-3,11,20-trione	f	0.47	—	0.28	0.19	—	0.21	0.43	0.75	—
6β,21-Dihydroxy-4-pregnene-3,20-dione	f	—	0.23	0.16	0.13	—	0.10	—	0.61	—
11α,21-Dihydroxy-4-pregnene-3,20-dione	f	0.22	0.63	0.49	0.39	—	0.33	—	0.87	—
11β,21-Dihydroxy-4-pregnene-3,20-dione	f	0.17	0.42	0.36	0.25	—	0.21	—	0.77	—
14α,21-Dihydroxy-4-pregnene-3,20-dione	f	—	—	0.12	0.086	—	0.06	—	0.53	—
15α,21-Dihydroxy-4-pregnene-3,20-dione	f	0.28	0.42	0.36	0.35	—	0.33	—	0.87	—
17α,21-Dihydroxy-4-pregnane-3,20-dione	f	—	0.71	0.33	0.35	—	0.30	—	0.87	—
17α-Hydroxymethyl-17aα-hydroxy-D-homo-4-androstene-3,17-dione (D-homo compound S)	b									—

TABLE III—*Continued*

Compound	Detection[d]	Development systems[a]								
		1 R_S[b]	2 R_S[c]	3 R_S[c]	4 R_S[b]	5 R_f[e]	6 R_f	7 R_f	8 R_f	9 R_f
E. C₂₁ 21-hydroxysteroids (Continued)										
21-Acetoxy-11β-hydroxy-4-pregnene-3,20-dione	f	0.4	2.6	2.1	1.36	—	0.71	0.38	—	—
21-Acetoxy-15α-hydroxy-4-pregnene-3,20-dione	f	—	0.92	0.73	0.79	—	0.34	0.10	—	—
21-Acetoxy-17α-hydroxy-4-pregnene-3,20-dione	f	0.49	1.8	1.7	1.5	—	0.73	0.43	—	—
17α,21-Dihydroxy-5β-pregnane-3,11,20-trione	g	0.21	—	0.11	0.11	—	0.21	—	0.75	—
17α,21-Dihydroxy-4-pregnene-3,11,20-trione	f	0.16	—	0.085	0.055	—	0.09	—	0.61	—
17α,21-Dihydroxy-1,4-pregnadiene-3,11,20-trione	f	—	—	—	—	—	—	—	0.57	—
21-Acetoxy-17α-hydroxy-5β-pregnane-3,11,20-trione	g	0.4	1.5[a]	0.64[a]	1.0	—	0.65[a]	0.28[a]	—	—
21-Acetoxy-17α-hydroxy-4-pregnene-3,11,20-trione	f	0.22	0.91[a]	0.39[a]	0.65	—	0.44	0.15	0.95	—
21-Acetoxy-17α-hydroxy-1,4-pregnadiene-3,11,20-trione	h	—	—	—	0.56[a]	—	0.40	0.12	0.90	—
6β,17α,21-Trihydroxy-4-pregnene-3,20-dione	f	—	—	—	—	—	0.24	—	0.22[a]	—
11α,17α,21-Trihydroxy-4-pregnene-3,20-dione	f	—	—	0.01	0.01	—	0.013	—	0.12	—
11β,17α,21-Trihydroxy-4-pregnene-3,20-dione	f	—	—	0.033	0.029	—	0.04	—	0.37	—
11β,17α,21-Trihydroxy-1,4-pregnadiene-3,20-dione	h	—	—	—	0.018	—	0.025	—	0.27	—

21-Acetoxy-3α,17α-dihydroxy-5β-pregnane-11,20-dione	i	—	—	0.11	0.31	—	0.28	—	0.87	—
21-Acetoxy-3β,17α-dihydroxy-5α-pregnane-11,20-dione	i	—	—	0.08	0.23	—	0.21	—	0.87	—
21-Acetoxy-11β,17α-dihydroxy-4-pregnene-3,20-dione	f	0.17	—	0.29[a]	0.39[a]	—	0.34[a]	0.09	0.9	—
21-Acetoxy-11β,17α-dihydroxy-1,4-pregnadiene-3,20-dione	h	—	—	0.15[a]	0.25[a]	—	0.27[a]	0.07	0.82[a]	—
11β,17α,20α,21-Tetrahydroxy-4-pregnen-3-one	b	—	—	—	—	—	—	—	0.09	—
11β,17α,20β,21-Tetrahydroxy-4-pregnen-3-one	b	—	—	—	—	—	—	—	0.12	—
21-Acetoxy-11β,17α,20α-trihydroxy-4-pregnen-3-one	b	—	—	—	0.055	—	0.09	—	0.61	—
21-Acetoxy-4β-bromo-17α-hydroxy-5β-pregnane-3,11,20-trione	g	0.4	—	—	1.42	—	0.71	0.39	—	—
2-Methyl-11β,17α,21-trihydroxy-4-pregnene-3,20-dione	f	—	—	—	0.09	—	0.10	—	0.69	—
21-Acetoxy-9α-fluoro-11β,17α-dihydroxy-4-pregnene-3,20-dione	f	—	—	—	0.23	—	0.27[a]	—	0.9	—
2-Methyl-21-acetoxy-11β,17α-dihydroxy-4-pregnene-3,20-dione	f	—	—	0.64	0.92	—	0.51	0.20	0.96	—
17α,21-Dihydroxy-5β-pregnane-3,11,20-trione-3,20-ethylene glycol diketal	a	0.5	—	1.7	1.26	—	0.60	0.37	—	—
17α,21-Dihydroxy-5-pregnene-3,11,20-trione-3,20-ethylene glycol diketal	a	0.36	—	1.4	1.0	—	0.47	0.23	0.91	—
11β,17α,21-Trihydroxy-5-pregnene-3,20-dione-3,20-ethylene glycol diketal	a	0.28	—	0.66	0.5	—	0.31	0.13	0.61	—
2-Methyl-9α-fluoro-11β,17α,21-trihydroxy-4-pregnene-3,20-dione	f	—	—	—	0.04	—	0.057	—	0.61	—
2-Methyl-21-acetoxy-9α-fluoro-11β,17α-dihydroxy-4-pregnene-3,20-dione	f	—	—	0.49	0.56[a]	—	0.41[a]	0.15	0.95	—

TABLE III—*Concluded*

Compound	Detection[d]	1 R_S[b]	2 R_S[c]	3 R_S[c]	4 R_S[b]	5 R_f[e]	6 R_f	7 R_f	8 R_f	9 R_f
						Development systems[a]				
F. Miscellaneous										
Cortisone		—	—	—	—	—	—	—	—	0.00
trans-Testosterone		—	—	—	—	—	—	—	—	0.77
cis-Testosterone		—	—	—	—	—	—	—	—	0.90
17-Methyltestosterone		—	—	—	—	—	—	—	—	0.87
Dehydroisoandrosterone		—	—	—	—	—	—	—	—	0.94
Progesterone		—	—	—	—	—	—	—	—	1.0
17-Ethinylestradiol		—	—	—	—	—	—	—	—	0.52
Equilenin		—	—	—	—	—	—	—	—	0.40
Equilin		—	—	—	—	—	—	—	—	0.65
Estriol		—	—	—	—	—	—	—	—	0.00
Hexoestrol		—	—	—	—	—	—	—	—	0.48
Dienestrol		—	—	—	—	—	—	—	—	0.48
α,β-Diethylstilbestrol		—	—	—	—	—	—	—	—	0.50

[a] Solvents. 1. Methyl cyclohexane saturated with diethylene glycol mono-ethyl ether.
2. Toluene saturated with propylene glycol-MeOH (v/v).
3. Cyclohexane:Benzene = v/v, saturated with propylene glycol-MeOH (v/v).
4. Benzene, saturated with formamide:MeOH (v/v).
5. Petroleum Ether (86–100):MeOH:water = 5:4:1.
6. Toluene:Petroleum Ether:MeOH:water = 5:5:7:3.
7. Benzene:Petroleum Ether:MeOH:water = 33.3:66.7:80:20.
8. Benzene:methanol:water = 2:1:1.
9. Toluene, saturated with aqueous Na *p*-toluene sulfonate (Boscott, 1952).

[b] Mobility relative to 4-pregnene-3,11,20-trione.

[c] Mobility relative to 11α-hydroxy-4-pregnene-3,20-dione.

[d] Detection (preferred methods):
a. 2,4 Dinitrophenylhydrazine reagent (s. in text).
b. Ultraviolet absorption and 2,4-dinitrophenylhydrazine.
c. Ultraviolet absorption.
d. Phosphomolybdic acid reagent (b in text).
e. 2,4-Dinitrophenylhydrazine and phosphomolybdic acid.
f. Ultraviolet absorption, 2,4 dinitrophenylhydrazine, and Tollens Reagent (e in text).
g. 2,4-Dinitrophenylhydrazine and Tollens Reagent.
h. Ultraviolet absorption and Tollens Reagent.
i. Tollens Reagent.

[e] Mobility relative to solvent front.

[f] R values not given because of nonsuitability of solvent.

[g] Streaked.

TABLE IV

R_f Values of Steroid Derivatives (Zaffaroni, 1949; Heftmann, 1950, 1951)

Steroid	Girard's Reagent T hydrazones		Fast Black-Salt K coupling compd.	
Solvents[a]	1	2	3	4
Pregnanol-5-trione-3,6,20	0	0.02	—	—
17-Hydroxyprogesterone	0.06	0.16	—	—
Pregnanetrione-3,12,20	0.10	0.22	—	—
Progesterone	0.15	0.28	—	—
Δ^4-Pregnenetriol-17α,20,21-one-3	0.35	0.53	—	—
Pregnanedione-3,20	0.46	0.70	—	—
Ethinyltestosterone	0.51	—	—	—
Pregnanol-3α-one-20	0.53	0.74	—	—
Δ^5-Pregnenol-3β-one-20	0.53	—	—	—
Methyltestosterone	0.50	—	—	—
Δ^4-Androstenedione-3,17	0.10	0.17	—	—
Etiocholanedione-3,17	0.42	—	—	—
Androstanedione-3,17	0.42	—	—	—
Androsterone	0.49	—	—	—
Isoandrosterone	0.49	—	—	—
Dehydroisoandrosterone	0.49	—	—	—
Testosterone	0.49	0.69	—	—
cis-Testosterone	0.49	—	—	—
Etiocholanol-3α-one-17	0.49	—	—	—
Androstanol-17α-one-3	—	—	—	—
Androstanone-17	0.59	—	—	—
Androstanone-3	—	—	—	—
Estrone	0.47	—	0.29	0.96
Pregnanediol-3α,12α-one-20	0.46	0.65	—	—
Allopregnanedione-3,20	0.48	—	—	—
Estradiol-17α	—	—	0.32	0.96
Estradiol-17β	—	—	0.09	0.82
Equilin	—	—	0.49	0.96
Equilenin	—	—	0.05	0.80
Estriol	—	—	0	0.10

[a] Solvents: 1. Water-saturated n-butanol.
    2. n-Butanol:tert-butanol:water = 1:1:1.
    3. Petroleum ether:toluene:ethanol:water = 20:10:1:9.
    4. Toluene:petroleum ether:methanol:water = 20:10:3:7.

are spotted on Whatman No. 1 or No. 4 paper. The paper may be shaped in the form of a cylinder and placed in the chromatographic jar containing the solvent phases. The paper should not touch any of the liquid. The tank is wrapped with an electric blanket and is equilibrated at 32°C. for

TABLE V

R_f VALUES OF VARIOUS STEROIDS ON ACTIVATED ALUMINA PAPER (Bush, 1952)

Compound	Solvents[a]			
	1	2	3	4
Progesterone	0.75	0.95	1.0	0.8
Testosterone	0.40	0.60	—	—
Estrone	0.30	0.40	0.9	0.6
Estradiol	0.05	0.15	0.5	0.25
Pregnenolone	—	0.80	—	—
Dehydroandrosterone	—	0.41	—	—
Androsterone	0.25	0.39	—	—
11-Deoxycorticosterone-21-acetate	0.70	0.85	—	0.70
11-Dehydrocorticosterone-21-acetate	0.35	0.60	0.95	0.40
11-Dehydro-17-hydroxycorticosterone-21-acetate	0.05	0.10	0.40	0.10
17-Hydroxycorticosterone-21-acetate	0.02	0.06	0.30	0.05
Corticosterone-21-acetate	—	0.15	0.67	0.20

[a] Solvents: 1. Benzene:CHCl₃ = 3:1 v/v.
      2. Benzene:CHCl₃ = 2:1.
      3. Benzene:CHCl₃ = 1:1.
      4. Benzene:acetone = 19:1.

5–12 hours. The blanket is removed, and the mobile phase is added through a hole in the cover. The paper is developed by the ascending technique for 3–12 hours at room temperature.

At the end of the development, the chromatograms are placed over Ilford Reflex paper No. 50 and exposed briefly to ultraviolet light in the 254-mμ region. In order to overcome the interference of impurities, which absorb light in the same region, the following method is employed:

The chromatograms are sprayed with a solution of 10 g. of NaOH in 100 ml. of 60% v/v methanol and dried at 60–100°. When quite dry, the α,β-unsaturated ketosteroids give a brilliant primrose-yellow fluorescence in ultraviolet light. The fluorescence will fade in several days but may be redeveloped by a second treatment.

Section II: Bile Acids

Bile acids have been separated as anions by use of alkaline solvent systems (Kritchevsky, 1952) and as the unionized molecules by use of acidic solvent systems (Sjövall, 1952). Zaffaroni's method of developing ketosteroids as the Girard's reagent T hydrazone has also been applied to ketobile acids (Tanaka, 1952). Cholic acid has been separated as the hydroxamate (Elliott, 1956a).

1. PREPARATION OF CHOLYLHYDROXAMIC ACID (Elliott, 1956a)

To 0.4 g. of ethyl cholate, dissolved in 3 ml. of dry methanol, are added 0.14 g. of $NH_2OH \cdot HCl$ and 0.1 g. of sodium metal both dissolved in a small amount of dry methanol. The reaction mixture is kept at room temperature for six hours and is neutralized with methanolic HCl. The precipitated NaCl is filtered off. Aliquots of the filtrate are spotted on Whatman No. 3 paper, which has been pre-washed with 2 N acetic acid and water.

2. PAPER

a. Whatman No. 3, washed with 2 N acetic acid, water, then with solvent to be used for development, and finally with water (Elliott, 1956b).

b. Whatman No. 3 MM, washed with ethanol and 10 % acetic acid (Eriksson, 1954).

c. Whatman No. 3 MM, untreated, but equilibrated with stationary and mobile phases 12 hours prior to chromatography (Sjövall, 1955).

d. Whatman Nos. 1, 4, 3 MM, soaked in 70 % acetic acid, heated at 100°C. until almost dry; equilibrated overnight with both phases of solvent prior to chromatography (Sjövall, 1954).

3. SOLVENTS (see Table VI)

a. Isopropyl ether:heptane = 7:3 v/v saturated with 70 % acetic acid is the moving phase, and 70 % acetic acid is the stationary phase. The filter paper is wetted with the stationary phase and then dried at 90°C. for 5 minutes prior to the application of samples. Before development, the paper is left in the chromatographic chamber for 2 hours in an atmosphere saturated with vapors from both phases (Sjövall, 1952, 1954). This solvent is suitable for conjugated bile acids.

b. n-Propyl alcohol:ethanolamine:water = 9:5:5 v/v. (Kritchevsky, 1952).

c. Toluene:acetic acid (glacial):water = 5:5:1 (Beyreder, 1953). The organic phase of this solvent mixture will separate taurocholic, glycocholic, deoxycholic, dehydrocholic, and cholic acids.

d. 1-Butanol:1-propanol:water = 6:2:1 (Tanaka, 1952). This solvent system separates the hydrazones of many keto-bile acids (see Section I for hydrazone formation).

e. Ethylene chloride:n-butanol = 95:5 (stationary phase: 70% acetic acid) for the separation of taurochenodeoxycholic acid and taurodeoxycholic acid (Sjövall, 1955). Descending development.

f. Ethylene chloride:heptane = 2:8 (stationary phase: 70% acetic acid) for the separation of deoxycholic and chenodeoxycholic acids (Sjövall, 1955). Ascending development.

g. n-Butanol:acetic acid:acetone:water is used for the chromatography of taurocholic acid (R_f 0.64) (Elliott, 1956b). The solvent is prepared as follows: (A) *n*-butanol:acetic acid:water = 8:2:1 (top layer), then A:acetone:water = 45:54.5:0.5 v/v.

h. Di-i-propyl ether:n-propanol:acetic acid:water = 20:9:3:2, for the chromatography of cholylhydroxamic acid (Elliott, 1956a).

4. TECHNIQUES USED

Whatman No. 1 which has been previously treated with 70% acetic acid is spotted with an aliquot solution of the free bile acids. The paper is equilibrated overnight in a tank whose walls are lined with filter paper which is soaked with the mobile phase. The tank is tilted at such an angle that the paper (for ascending development) is not in contact with the liquid. At the start of the development, the tank is placed in an upright position. Development time is four hours (Sjövall, 1954).

5. DETECTION OF SPOTS

a. Phosphoric acid (85%):water:ethanol (95%) = 85:25:25 v/v (Kritchevsky, 1952). The developed chromatogram is sprayed and kept at 90°C. for 20 minutes. Generally, cholic and norcholic acids show up as red or brick-colored spots. In ultraviolet light deoxycholic acid exhibits a pink fluorescence and other bile acids exhibit a greenish-yellow fluorescence.

b. Phosphomolybdic acid (10%) in ethanol (Sjövall, 1952, 1954). The sprayed chromatogram is heated at 80–100°C. for a few minutes. The sensitivity for this reagent is 1–3 μg. for cholic, deoxycholic, and chenodeoxycholic acids; 10–20 μg. for lithocholic acid.

c. Antimony trichloride (50%) in glacial acetic acid. This reagent produces a rose-pink spot for taurocholic acid on heating (Elliott, 1956b).

d. $FeCl_3 \cdot 6H_2O$ (10%) in 0.2 N HCl produces brown-purple spots for the hydroxamate derivatives of the bile acids (Elliott, 1956a).

6. QUANTITATIVE ESTIMATION (Eriksson, 1954)

After chromatographing the bile acids on Whatman paper 3 MM by the method of Sjövall (1954), guide strips are visualized with phosphomolybdic acid (see above). The undeveloped areas containing the bile acids are eluted with ethanol, and the extracts are evaporated. To the residues, 65% sulfuric acid is added, and the solutions are heated various lengths of time. Optical densities are determined at the following maxima:

Bile Acid	Treatment	Maximum Absorption
Tauro- and glycodeoxycholic	60 min. at 60°C.	390 mμ
Deoxycholic	15 min. at 60°C.	385
Cholic, taurocholic, and glycocho-⎱	15 min. at 60°C.	320
lic ⎰	or 60 min. at 60°C.	389

Section III: Cardiac Glycosides and Aglycones

1. PREPARATION OF SAMPLE

As an illustration, the extraction of cardiac aglycones from *Strophanthus* seeds is described (Bush, 1952): One gram of the seed is ground in a coffee mill and then extracted in a Soxhlet apparatus with 150 ml. of methanol for 2 hours. The extract is then evaporated to 25 ml., diluted with 5 ml. of water, and extracted three times with 25 ml. of light petroleum. The aqueous solution is then diluted with 30 ml. of 0.1 N H_2SO_4 and refluxed for 30 minutes. After cooling, the solution is extracted twice with 50-ml. portions of $CHCl_3$ and the extract is evaporated to 5 ml. One drop of this extract is usually sufficient for paper chromatography. Other plant juice material may be extracted with a mixture of chloroform:ethanol = 3:1, and aliquots spotted on Schleicher & Schuell Paper No. 2043b (Wichtl, 1956).

2. PAPER

a. Whatman Paper No. 3 MM may be impregnated with ethylene glycol by passing it through a 30% methanolic solution (Rigby, 1956). The paper may also be saturated with propylene glycol as the stationary phase (see Section I, 3, *a*) (Heftmann, 1954).

b. Whatman Paper No. 1 is saturated with formamide. The paper may also be impregnated with silica gel by passing it first through a 20% "water-glass" solution, then rinsing it in 3 N HCl for 24 hours, and drying the paper for 5 hours at 110°C. (Turba, 1954).

The paper may be dipped into the aqueous phase of the solvent used for development (e.g., water saturated with butanol), dried for 10 minutes, and blotted between two sheets of filter paper with the aid of a rubber roller (Schenker, 1954).

3. SOLVENTS (see Table VII)

a. n-Butanol, saturated with water has been used for the separation of highly polar cardiac glycosides and aglycones (Habermann, 1953; Schenker,

TABLE VI

R_f Values of Bile Acids

Bile acid	Solvent[a]					
	1	2	3[b]	4	5	6
Taurocholic	0.00	—	—	0.00	0.06	0.18
Taurochenodeoxycholic	—	—	—	0.00	—	0.29
Taurodeoxycholic	—	—	—	0.00	0.16	0.32
Glycocholic	0.05	—	—	0.03	0.51	—
Glycochenodeoxycholic	—	—	—	0.13	0.68	—
Glycodeoxycholic	—	—	—	0.17	0.68	—
Cholic	0.36	0.71	—	0.28	0.79	—
Hyodeoxycholic	0.67	—	—	0.44	—	—
Chenodeoxycholic	0.78	—	—	0.58	—	—
Deoxycholic	0.75	0.92	—	0.58	0.80	—
Dehydrocholic	—	0.65	—	—	—	—
Norcholic	—	0.69	—	—	—	—
Triformylnorcholic	—	0.92	—	—	—	—
Me 12-ketocholanate	—	—	0.83	—	—	—
Me 12-keto-3-acetoxycholanate	—	—	0.76	—	—	—
Me 12-keto-3-hydroxycholanate	—	—	0.74	—	—	—
Me 3,12-diketocholanate	—	—	0.70	—	—	—
Me 7-keto-3,12-dihydroxycholanate	—	—	0.58	—	—	—
Me 12-hydroxy-3,7-diketocholanate	—	—	0.53	—	—	—
Me 7,12-diketocholanate	—	—	0.42	—	—	—
Me 3-hydroxy-7,12-diketocholanate	—	—	0.23	—	—	—
Me 3,7,12-triketocholanate	—	—	0.09	—	—	—

[a] Solvents: 1. Isopropyl ether:heptane = 7:3 (paper saturated with 70% acetic acid) (Sjövall, 1952).
2. n-Propyl alcohol:ethanolamine:water = 9:5:5 (Kritchevsky, 1952).
3. n-Butanol:n-propanol:water = 6:2:1 (Tanaka, 1952).
4. Amyl acetate:heptane = 5:5 (paper saturated with 70% acetic acid).
5. Amyl acetate:heptane = 8:2.
6. Amyl acetate:heptane = 85:15 (Sjövall, 1955).
[b] Separated as Girard's Reagent T hydrazones.

1954; Hassall, 1951). The butanol is refluxed for two hours with CaO and is then distilled.

b. *n-Butanol:acetic acid:water* = 4:1:5 (upper phase) is used for the separation of saponins (Dutta, 1955).

c. *Petroleum ether (35–60°):toluene:ethanol:water* of different composition has been used to separate sapogenins from sapogenin acetates (Heftmann, 1952).

d. *Chloroform:methanol:water* = 10:2:5 is used for the separation of glycosides and aglycones (Okada, 1952).

e. Benzene:chloroform = 75:25 (formamide paper) has been used for derivatives of digitoxigenin (Turba, 1954).

f. Chloroform:tetrahydrofuran:methylglycol:formamide = 30:45:1.5:9 has been used for the glycosides from *Digitalis purpurea* (Haack, 1956).

g. Xylene:methyl ethyl ketone (v/v) has been used for the glycosides (Wichtl, 1956).

h. Chloroform, saturated with ethylene glycol is another useful solvent for the glycosides. The papers, previously impregnated with ethylene glycol (see above) are saturated with chloroform overnight before development (Rigby, 1956). The tendency of this solvent to separate into two phases is overcome by placing a dry sheet of Whatman paper No. 3 MM on top of the chromatogram. *Toluene*, saturated with propylene glycol, has been used for the glycosides and aglycones (Heftmann, 1954).

4. Techniques Used (Schenker, 1954)

The extracted glycosides are dissolved in ethanol and spotted on Whatman No. 1 paper which has been treated with water, saturated with *n*-butanol. The paper is equilibrated in the tank with both separated phases overnight. The chromatogram is then developed by the descending technique. Since the solvent front is not easily visible, a small amount of dye is added as marker, having an R_f of 1 (1-amino-2-methylanthraquinone). After 11–16 hours at 14°C., the development has been completed.

5. Detection of Spots

a. Alkaline m-Dinitrobenzene. After the separation of cardiac glycosides, developed with a benzene solvent on formamide-treated paper at 15°C. for 24 hours, the paper is dried at 60°C. It is then sprayed with a 10 % solution of *m*-dinitrobenzene in benzene and placed in an oven at 60°C. After drying, the paper is sprayed with methanolic NaOH (6 g. of NaOH dissolved in 25 ml. of water, diluted with 45 ml. of methanol). Purple spots, changing to blue, denote the position of the cardiac glycosides. Since the spots fade within 10 minutes, the positions must be marked immediately (Schindler, 1951).

b. 3,5-Dinitrobenzoic Acid. For the detection of cardiac aglycones, a 1 % solution of 3,5-dinitrobenzoic acid in 0.5 N 50 % v/v aqueous methanolic KOH is very suitable. This reagent gives a purple color which has the advantage of being reasonably permanent (Bush, 1952).

c. Trichloroacetic Acid. After separation of cardiac glycosides, aglycones, and acetates, developed with benzene or toluene on propylene glycol- or formamide-treated paper, the dried chromatograms are sprayed with a 25 % solution of trichloroacetic acid in chloroform. The sprayed sheets are hung in a drying oven at 120°C. for 20 minutes and then inspected in the dark under an ultraviolet lamp (Heftmann, 1952).

TABLE VII

MIGRATION OF CARDIAC GLYCOSIDES AND AGLYCONES

Compound	Solvent[a]						
	1[b]	2[b]	3[b]	4 R_f	5 R_f	6 R_f	7 R_f
Strophanthidin			13.6				
Sarverogenin			32.4				
Sarmentogenin			8.0				
Strophanthidol			14.0				
Sarmentocymarin	4.1	7.5	>37				
Sarverosid	8.5	17					
Cymarol	3.7	8					
Cymarin	5.5	11					
Emicymarin	1.5	1.5					
Digitalinum verum				0.17			
Gitoxigenin glycoside				0.24			
Gitoxin				0.29	0.29		0.80
Glucogitaloxin				0.53			
Strospesid				0.71			
Verodoxin				0.81			
Digitoxin					0.69	0.22	0.95
Gitaloxin					0.55		
Digitoxigenin					0.81	0.50	0.90
Gitoxigenin					0.42		0.55
Digitoxigenin glyco- side						0.42	
Digitoxigenin acetate						0.91	

[a] Solvents: 1. Benzene, saturated with formamide (formamide paper).
  2. Benzene:chloroform = 9:1, saturated with formamide.
  3. Chloroform, saturated with formamide (Schindler, 1951).
  4. Chloroform:tetrahydrofuran:methylglycol:formamide = 30:45:1.5:9 (Haack, 1956).
  5. Xylene:methyl ethyl ketone, v/v, saturated with formamide (ascending development) (Wichtl, 1956).
  6. Benzene:chloroform = 75:25 (formamide paper) (Turba, 1954).
  7. Chloroform, saturated with ethylene glycol (Rigby, 1956).
[b] As cm. from start.

d. Blood. For the detection of steroid sapogenins the chromatogram is sprayed evenly with whole blood or a blood cell suspension in saline. The sapogenins appear as lighter or darker spots (depending on their concentration) on a tan background (Heftmann, 1952).

e. Triphenyltetrazoliumchloride (TPTZ) (0.2%) in N NaOH detects keto-triol cardiac glycosides (Turba, 1954).

f. Anisaldehyde:acetic acid: H_2SO_4 = 0.5:50:1, v/v is sprayed on the dried paper which is heated at 90°C. for several minutes (Günzel, 1955/56).

g. Sodium periodate (2%): $KMnO_4$ *(1%)* = 4:1, made up freshly in 2%

Na_2CO_3 (pH adjusted to 7.2), is sprayed on the paper, left for 5–6 minutes, and washed with running water.   Brown spots on a white background indicate the location of saponins (Dutta, 1955).

   h. Ultraviolet Absorption (Bernasconi, 1955).   Glycosides and aglycones possessing a coumalin ring (e.g., bufotalin, hellebrigenin) exhibit a maximum absorption at 300 mμ.   Using a mercury high pressure lamp and suitable filters, the dry chromatogram may be placed on top of photocopy paper, covered with 3 mm. thick "Plexiglas" and given an exposure time of 35 seconds at a focal distance of 100 cm.   White spots on a black background result.   The following filters have been used: (1) "Plexiglas" and Pyrex-glass to filter out light below 300 mμ.   (2) Three hundred grams of $CoSO_4 \cdot 7H_2O$ and 500 g. of $NiSO_4 \cdot 7H_2O$ are dissolved in 2 liters of water and poured into a 20 mm. thick filter.   (3) CG (Corning Glass $\#$ 9863) red filter.   Combination of all three filters gives good transmission between 300 and 350 mμ with a maximum at 325 mμ.

Chapter IX

PURINES, PYRIMIDINES AND RELATED SUBSTANCES

The separation and identification of purines, pyrimidines, and related substances by paper chromatography have aided greatly in obtaining the proof of structure of nucleic acids, nucleotides, and nucleosides. The nucleic acids are usually hydrolyzed, and the hydrolysis products may be resolved by one- and two-dimensional chromatography. Recently, however, the nucleoproteins, nucleic acids, and nucleotides have also been separated by paper electrophoresis (see Part II) (Davidson, 1952; Deimel, 1952; Irvin, 1953). For the detection of these compounds, the following techniques may be applied: phosphate reagents for the nucleotides; mercuric nitrate-H_2S reagent for the purines and pyrimidines; spectrographic techniques due to the characteristic absorption bands of purines and pyrimidines in the ultraviolet. The last technique is also the basis for the quantitative determination of these compounds. The reader is referred to an excellent review article on the chromatography of nucleotides and related substances (Markham, 1954).

1. Preparation of Samples

a. Hydrolysis of Nucleic Acids. (i) Acid hydrolysis. Nucleic acids are hydrolyzed with 72 % w/w aqueous perchloric acid at 100°C. for 60 minutes, with pure formic acid at 175°C. for 30 minutes, with 1 N HCl at 100°C. for 1 hour (J. D. Smith, 1950, 1951), or with 2 % H_2SO_4 at 100°C. for 3 hours. Hydrolysis with 1 N HCl liberates the following compounds from nucleic acid: adenine, guanine, cytidylic, and uridylic acids.

Deoxyribonucleic acids are hydrolyzed in a sealed tube with concentrated formic acid at 175°C. for 2 hours. Adenine, thymine, cytosine, and guanine, among other bases, are liberated by this procedure (Uzman, 1954).

(ii) Alkaline hydrolysis. The nucleic acids are hydrolyzed to nucleotides by boiling with 1 N NaOH for 18 hours. The hydrolyzate is applied to the paper but must be neutralized when the ammonium sulfate solvent is employed (see Tables I and IV) (Markham, 1951a).

Detailed directions for the hydrolysis of yeast nucleic acid to nucleotides are as follows (Dimroth, 1952): 100 g. of yeast nucleic acid is hydrolyzed at 100°C. for 48 hours with Cd(OH)$_2$ which is freshly precipitated from 100 g. of CdCl$_2$. The volume of the reaction mixture is 700 ml. After hydrolysis, the hot suspension is filtered, and the residue is decomposed by precipitating the Cd^{++} with H_2S. The CdS is filtered off, and the filtrate is aerated to remove any traces of H_2S. The yield is 9.6 g. of a nucleotide mixture: cytidylic, adenylic, guanylic, and uridylic acids.

(*iii*) *Acid- and base-hydrolysis.* A sample of ribonucleic acid may be hydrolyzed by three methods, each yielding different decomposition products (Crosbie, 1953).

(1) Ten milligrams of ribonucleic acid is digested with 0.1 ml. of 72% w/w $HClO_4$ at 100°C. for 1 hour. The hydrolyzate is made up to a volume of 1.0 ml. and is chromatographed with 65% isopropanol:HCl (2 N with respect to HCl). The following results are obtained:

	R_f
Guanine	0.33
Adenine	0.48
Cytosine	0.57
Uracil	0.73

(2) Twenty milligrams of the sample of ribonucleic acid is hydrolyzed for 1 hour with 1.0 ml. of N HCl, and the hydrolyzate is again chromatographed with acidic isopropanol. The following R_f values are obtained:

	R_f
Guanine	0.33
Adenine	0.48
Cytidylic acid	0.76
Uridylic acid	0.91

(3) Ten milligrams ribonucleic acid is hydrolyzed with 1.0 ml. of 0.3 N KOH. The digest is adjusted to pH 3.6 with 60% w/w $HClO_4$, and the precipitated $KClO_4$ is removed by centrifugation. The supernatant solution, containing ribonucleotides, is analyzed by paper electrophoresis (see Part II).

b. *Isolation of Deoxyribonucleic Acids.* The source material is incubated for 16–20 hours at 37°C. in a small volume of 1 N NaOH. The insoluble material is removed by centrifugation, the supernatant liquid is brought to pH 4 with acetic acid, and 1 volume of ethanol is added. The resultant precipitate, containing deoxyribonucleic acid, is collected by centrifugation, dissolved in dilute NaOH, and protein is removed by shaking the solution with a mixture of $CHCl_3$:octanol = 8:1 v/v. A further precipitation with acetic acid and ethanol completes the purification (J. D. Smith, 1951).

c. *Preparation of Yeast Ribonucleic Acid.* (Markham and Smith, 1952*b*; Sevag, 1938). Baker's yeast is treated with ethanol and ethanol:ether = 1:1 v/v and dried. The dry yeast is boiled in water, adjusted to pH 8–8.4, for 20 minutes. An equal volume of ethanol is added to the cooled suspension, and the precipitate is centrifuged off. The supernatant is adjusted to pH 4.5 with a small amount of dilute acetic acid. The impure nucleic acid is treated further by the addition of 0.25 volume of chloroform and 0.1 volume of amyl alcohol (anti-foam) to the solution. This mixture is shaken for 15–60 minutes, and upon centrifugation two layers form. The lower layer represents a stable protein-chloroform gel. The upper layer is decanted.

d. *Purification of Yeast Ribonucleic Acid.* One and one-half grams of yeast nucleic acid (Merck) is dissolved in 40 ml. of water by the addition of 1.5 ml. of 2 N ammonia. The filtered solution is dropped with mechanical stirring into 86 ml. of 95 % ethanol containing 0.5 ml. of concentrated HCl. The precipitate, collected by centrifugation, is washed with 12.5 ml. of 66 % ethanol and redissolved in 25 ml. of water and 1.6 ml. of 2 N ammonia. The precipitate, obtained from the filtered solution by the addition of 50 ml. of ethanol and 0.4 ml. of concentrated HCl, is suspended in 2.5 ml. of water and is dialyzed against running water (14 hours) and several changes of ice-cold distilled water (20 hours). The ribonucleic acid is collected, washed with 66, 98, and 100 % ethanol and with ether, and dried *in vacuo* over P_2O_5 (Vischer, 1948).

e. *Extraction of Purines from Urine* (Weissmann, 1954). Urine, adjusted to pH 2, is passed through Dowex 50 (H^+), washed with water, and eluted with 200 ml. of 1 N NH_4OH. The eluate is concentrated, adjusted again to pH 2 with H_2SO_4, and 2 ml. of 1 M $AgNO_3$ is added. The precipitate is washed with small amounts of water and extracted with hot 0.05 M HCl. The extract is taken to dryness and redissolved in 0.80 ml. of 1 M HCl. Guanine, xanthine, adenine, and other purines are extracted in this manner.

2. PAPER

Whatman No. 1 and Schleicher and Schuell No. 597 filter papers, usually without any special pretreatment, are used (Kream, 1952). When it is intended to extract the separated substances, it is, however, recommended to wash Whatman No. 1 filter paper with dilute HCl, followed by a thorough water rinse (Deutsch, 1953). Long sheets of Whatman No. 1 filter paper (20 × 60 cm.) are used for the separation of adenosine and inosine phosphates (Krebs, 1953). Other filter papers which have been used include Whatman No. 4 (washed with dilute acetic acid and water) and Whatman No. 3 MM (Baddiley, 1956; Weissmann, 1954).

3. SOLVENTS FOR ONE-DIMENSIONAL CHROMATOGRAPHY (see also Tables I and V)

a. *1-Butanol:water:morpholine:diethylene glycol* = 45:20:15:10 v/v (Vischer, 1948).

b. 1-Butanol:diethylene glycol:water = 4:1:1 v/v. When this solvent is used, the spot containing the purine and pyrimidine samples must be neutralized with ammonia. Guanine should not be present in amounts larger than 10 μg., because it is only slightly soluble in a neutral medium (Vischer, 1948).

c. 1-Butanol:urea. 1-Butanol is saturated with a 10% aqueous solution of urea (Carter, 1950). This solvent is used in an atmosphere saturated with water vapor. The limitation of this solvent and most other organic solvents is the inability to move ribonucleotides.

d. Na₂HPO₄:isoamyl alcohol. A 5% aqueous solution of Na_2HPO_4 is saturated with isoamyl alcohol, and the layers are separated. A vessel of sufficient capacity is used so that both phases exist as thin layers (1.0 cm. aqueous phase, 0.5 cm. non-aqueous phase). Other 5% salt solutions used are ammonium citrate (pH 3.6 and 9.6) and KH_2PO_4.

e. 1-Butanol:formic acid:water. A solvent consisting of 77% *n*-butanol:13% H_2O:10% formic acid v/v moves purines but leaves nucleotides at the starting line (J. D. Smith, 1950).

f. 1-Butanol:boric acid. 1-Butanol saturated with 4% boric acid does not move ribosides, *e.g.*, uridine, but moves purines, pyrimidines, and deoxyribosides (Rose, 1951).

g. 2-Propanol:water:HCl. To 65 ml. of absolute 2-propanol, concentrated hydrochloric acid is added to give a final concentration of 2 *N*. The solution is made up to a total volume of 100 ml. with distilled water (J. D. Smith, 1951; Wyatt, 1951).

h. (1) *Isobutyl alcohol:acetic acid:water* = 20:0.8 15 v/v; (2) *1-butanol: acetic acid:water* = 74:19:50 v/v; (3) *formic acid:ethanol:water* = 15:80:5 v/v (Simonis, 1953).

i. Isobutyric acid:water:acetic acid = 100:50:1 v/v (Turba, 1951).

j. 2-Propanol:80% saturated (NH₄)₂SO₄:M Na acetate = 2:80:18 v/v has been used in the tentative identification of the 2',3'-anhydrides of cytidylic and uridylic acids (Markham, 1951*b*).

k. Solvents for Orotic Acid (Leone, 1950)

Solvent	R_f
1-Butanol:formic acid:water = 77:10:13 v/v	0.21
1-Butanol:ethanol:formic acid:water = 50:15:10:25 v/v	0.40
1-Propanol:formic acid:water = 70:10:20 v/v	0.50
1-Propanol:water = 60:40 v/v	0.66
Isoamyl alcohol (sat. with water):formic acid = 90:10 v/v	0.21

l. Recommended Solvents for Nucleotides (Pabst, 1956) (see Table IV)

(1) Ten ml. of concentrated NH_4OH and 329 ml. water are mixed with 661 ml. *i*-butyric acid; the pH is adjusted to 3.7.

TABLE I

SOLVENTS FOR PURINES, PYRIMIDINES, AND RELATED COMPOUNDS

Solvent	Mixture to be resolved	Reference
1. Isopropanol:HCl [cf 3 (g)]	Cytidine from guanine and adenine	Markham, 1951
	5-Hydroxymethylcytosine	Wyatt, 1952
2. 7.45 M tert-Butanol:0.8 N HCl	Uridine + cytidylic acid	Markham, 1951
3. Sat. $(NH_4)_2SO_4$:H_2O : isopropanol = 79:10:2 (v/v)	Guanine, adenine, cytidine	Markham, 1951
4. n-Butanol, sat. with water	Adenylthiomethylpentose $(R_f = 0.56)$	Weygand, 1953
5. n-Butanol:H_2O:ethylene glycol:acetic acid = 5:1:5:2 (v/v)	AMP, ADP, ATP	Turba, 1951
6. Amyl alcohol, saturated with water	Thiouracil, methylthiouracil, propylthiouracil	Lederer, 1952a
7. n-Propanol:NH_4OH:H_2O = 60:30:10 (v/v)	Inosine and adenosine phosphates	Webster, 1953; Baddiley, 1956
8. 0.5% Lauryl amine in amyl alcohol	Inosinic acid, adenosine-2- and 3-phosphates, adenosine	Snellman, 1951
9. 95% Ethanol:1M NH_4Ac = 75:30 v/v.	ATP, ADP, AMP	Paladini, 1952
10. n-Butanol:diethylene glycol:H_2O = 4:1:1 (v/v) (NH_3 atmosphere)	Hypoxanthine, adenine	Kream, 1952
11. n-Butanol:diethylene glycol:0.1 N HCl = 4:1:1 (v/v)	Xanthine, guanine	Kream, 1952
12. Pyridine:water = 2:1 (v/v)	DPN, DPNH, TPN, TPNH	Burton, 1954
13. i-Butyric acid:0.5N NH_4OH = 10:6 (v/v)	Cytidine-5-ph Adenosine-5-ph	Baddiley, 1956
14. Propanol:water:trichloroacetic acid:22% NH_4OH = 75:20:5:0.3 (v/v)	ATP, ADP, AMP, IDP, ITP, P-P, PO_4^{---}	Cerletti, 1955
15. Dimethylformamide:n-butanol:water (v/v/v)	Purine riboside	M. P. Gordon, 1956
16. Methanol:conc. HCl:water = 7:2:1 (v/v)	Purines and pyrimidines	Kirby, 1955a
17. Methanol:ethanol:conc. HCl:water = 50:25:6:19 (v/v)	Purines and pyrimidines	Kirby, 1955a
18. i-Propanol:water = 7:3 (v/v) (NH_3 atm.)	Substituted nucleotides	Heppel, 1955
19. sec-Butyl alcohol:tert butyl alcohol:water = 5:1:5.6 (v/v) (upper phase)	Pyrimidines and reduction products	Fink, 1956

(2) Seventy-seven g. of ammonium acetate is dissolved in approximately 750 ml. water, adjusted to pH 7.5 with NH_4OH, and diluted to one liter. Three-hundred ml. of this solution is mixed with 700 ml. 95 % ethanol.

(3) Six-hundred g. of ammonium sulfate is dissolved in one liter of 0.1 M sodium phosphate buffer (pH 6.8) and 20 ml. of *n*-propanol is added.

m. n-Butanol:n-propanol:25 % NH₃:water = 35:25:35:10 for the separation of nucleotides and sugar phosphates (Gerlach, 1955 b).   Multiple, descending development (twice) is employed.

4. Solvents for Two-Dimensional Chromatography

a. The first solvent is composed of 90 % v/v wet *1-butanol* and 10 % glacial *formic acid* v/v (Markham, 1949a, c)   This is followed by water-saturated *butanol* in an atmosphere of ammonia.

b. Phenol:2-propanol:formic acid:water = 80:10:10:100 v/v.   The upper layer of this mixture is used after letting it separate for 24 hours. The solvent for second development is 7.45 *M tert-butanol:0.8 N HCl* in water (Boulanger, 1951).   This combination gives good separation of uridylic, guanylic, cytidylic, and adenylic acids.

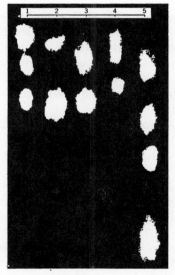

Fig. 1.   Photograph of chromatogram showing separation of nucleic acid derivatives.   Ultraviolet illumination (Markham, 1949).   Solvent: water-saturated *n*-butanol:formic acid = 1:1 v/v.   1, Uric acid, 6,8-dihydroxypurine, hypoxanthine; 2, guanine, adenine; 3, adenosine, adenine; 4, cytidine, cytosine; 5, xanthine, 3-methylxanthine, 3,7-dimethylxanthine   (theobromine),   1,3,7-trimethylxanthine (caffeine).

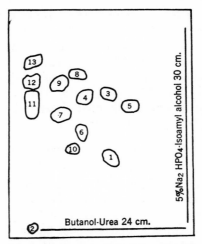

Fig. 2. Two-dimensional chromatogram of yeast nucleic acid derivatives (Carter, 1950): 1, adenine; 2, guanine; 3, uracil; 4, cytosine; 5, thymine (not a component of yeast nucleic acid); 6, adenosine; 7, guanosine; 8, uridine; 9, cytidine; 10, xanthine; 11, adenylic acids a + b; 12, guanylic acid; 13, cytidylic and uridylic acids.

c. (1) *1-Butanol* saturated with 10% aqueous *urea*; (2) 5% Na_2HPO_4 saturated with *isoamyl alcohol* (Carter, 1950) (see Fig. 2).

d. A large number of nucleotides, nucleosides, and free bases are resolved by two-dimensional chromatography with the following solvent system:

First direction (18.5 × 22-inch Whatman No. 1)

    (long direction) 1-Butanol:acetic acid:water = 8:2:2 v/v, 4 inches from bottom edge.

    (same direction) Acetone:1-butanol:H_2O = 8:1:1 v/v.

Second direction

    Saturated $(NH_4)_2SO_4$:2-propanol:H_2O = 79:2:19 v/v (Dorough, 1954).

e. (1) *Isopropyl ether*:90% w/v *formic acid* = 90:60 v/v; (2) *isobutyric acid*:*N* NH_4OH:0.1 *M Versene* = 100:60:1.6, v/v (Krebs, 1953).

f. (1) *1-Propanol*:NH_3:H_2O = 60:30:10 v/v; (2) saturated $(NH_4)_2$-SO_4:H_2O:*2-propanol* = 79:19:2 v/v (Deutsch, 1953). This solvent pair gives good resolution of inosine and adenosine phosphates.

g. (1) *n-Butanol*:*0.6M* NH_4OH = 6:1 v/v; (2) *n-butanol*:*formic acid*:*water* = 77:11:12 v/v have been used for the separation of purines in urine (Weissmann, 1954).

5. Techniques Used

One- and two-dimensional techniques have been employed for the separation of purines, pyrimidines, nucleotides, and nucleosides. An example for one-dimensional chromatography is depicted in Fig. 1, and for two-dimensional development in Fig. 2.

a. Special Techniques have been devised for the prior removal of inorganic phosphate from a sample of inosine- and adenosine phosphates, since the presence of inorganic phosphate interferes in the detection of the nucleotides (see Section 6: Detection of Spots) (Krebs, 1953; Gerlach, 1955a).

Whatman No. 1 filter paper (20 × 60 cm.), washed with Versene and water prior to chromatography, is folded 38 cm. from one end and the edges are fastened with paper clips. The samples to which P^{32}-phosphate is added as a marker are spotted 2–3 cm. from the fold. The chromatogram is first developed for 3–4 hours by the ascending technique with *isopropyl ether*:90 % *HCOOH* = 9:6 v/v. The phosphates which have moved to the front are located by scanning with a radiation monitor and are cut off the paper horizontally. The remaining chromatogram is now developed with the second solvent (*isobutyric acid*:N NH_4OH:0.1 M *Versene* = 100:60:1.6) by descending chromatography for 16–18 hours. The paper is dried at 80°C. for 20 minutes, and the spots are detected by molybdate spray or ultraviolet illumination. The following R_f values are observed by this technique:

Compound	R_f
AMP	1.00
ADP	0.80
ATP	0.66
IMP	0.53
IDP	0.39
ITP	0.26

In a similar fashion, the pyrimidines can be separated from the purines by a preliminary 3-hour chromatography with water or 0.01 M phosphate buffer (pH 7.1) as solvent. The pyrimidines travel about twice as fast as the purines. The purines are located with an ultraviolet lamp and are cut off in a line parallel to the points of application. The filter paper is unrolled, and the pyrimidines are chromatographed in the usual manner (Zamenhof, 1952).

b. Circular Paper Chromatography (Giri, 1953e). A 25 milligram sample is hydrolyzed with 3 ml. of 6 N HCl in an autoclave at 15 pounds pressure for 6 hours. The excess acid is removed by evaporation. Five microliters of the hydrolyzate are spotted on a pencil-drawn circumference around the center of a Whatman No. 1 24-cm. disk. A wick is either attached or cut out; the solvent is 1-butanol:acetic acid:water = 4:1:5 v/v (see Chapter III for details of technique). Identification of nitrogen bases is made by the ultraviolet contact print method of Markham (1949a, c, 1951a).

6. Detection of Spots

Amounts of purines and pyrimidines as small as 1 μg. in 5 μl. volume have been successfully resolved and detected (Markham, 1949a). The recommended range for separation and quantitative estimation of purines and pyrimidines within an experimental error of 4–6 % is 5–50 μg. (Vischer, 1948). The upper limit for the resolution of a single spot by paper chromatography is 200 μg. per component (Carter, 1950).

a. *Molybdic Acid Reagent for Nucleotides.* This reagent, which is also used for the identification of the sugar phosphates (see Chapter VI), consists of the following (Hanes, 1949; Boulanger, 1951): 5.0 ml. of perchloric acid (sp. gr. 1.61), 10.0 ml. of 1 N HCl, 25 ml. of 4 % $(NH_4)_2MoO_4$, and 60 ml. of water.

The dried chromatogram is sprayed with the reagent, and after a preliminary drying in a current of warm air it is heated for 7 minutes at 85°C. To develop the color of the spots more fully, the paper is allowed to regain moisture from the air and is exposed to hydrogen sulfide gas for 5–10 minutes. The recommended method for the formation of "molybdenum-blue" is the exposure of the sprayed and dried chromatogram to ultraviolet illumination.

"Unknown phosphate" spots should be treated with reservation when using this or subsequent reagents, since these spots may be due to $H_2PO_4^-$, HPO_4^{--}, or PO_4^{-3}. One means of differentiating between organic and inorganic phosphate is that the spot due to orthophosphate forms an immediate yellow spot even prior to the "reduction" step (Curry, 1953).

b. *Cysteine:Sulfuric Acid Reagent* (Modified Dische Reagent). The reagent consists of a solution of 0.5 g. of cysteine hydrochloride in 100 ml. of 3 N H_2SO_4. The air-dried chromatogram is sprayed with this solution, and after 5–10 minutes' heating at 85°C. pink spots appear, indicating the position of deoxyribonucleosides (Buchanan, 1951).

c. *Mercuric Nitrate Reagent.* After the development of the chromatograph containing purine samples, the paper is dried and washed with ether. The paper is then sprayed with 0.25 M $Hg(NO_3)_2$ in 0.5 N nitric acid, washed with 0.5 N HNO_3 and water, and dipped into an aqueous ammonium sulfide solution. Black spots of mercuric sulfide indicate the positions of the purines, e.g., guanine, adenine, and xanthine (Vischer, 1947).

After the mercuric nitrate treatment the paper may also be exposed to gaseous H_2S or held over a container filled with aqueous ammonium polysulfide.

Since the mercury compounds of xanthine, uric acid, and their derivatives are water-soluble, a modified procedure is used, eliminating the washing step (Dikstein, 1956): The chromatogram is first sprayed with 0.25 % Hg(II) acetate in 95 % ethanol acidified with a few drops of glacial acetic acid. The paper is then sprayed with 0.05 % diphenylcarbazone in 95 %

ethanol and heated at 90°C. until the background color fades.   The paper should not be heated too long since the spots will fade.

d. *Specific Reagent for Adenine-Compounds* (Gerlach, 1955c).   The dried chromatogram is sprayed with 0.07 % aqueous $KMnO_4$, placed in an atmosphere of chlorine gas for 15 seconds, and dried at 100°C. for 5 minutes. Yellow-orange spots result.   When the paper is next sprayed with 3 N KOH, the spots turn red.   The sensitivity for this reagent is 0.2 γ for adenine and 0.3 γ for bound adenine, e.g., AMP, ADP, ATP.

e. *1,2-Naphthoquinone-4-Sulfonic Acid* (Folin's Reagent).   Two-tenths per cent in half-saturated Na_2CO_3 forms violet spots with adenine and blue spots with guanine (Boser, 1954).

f. *Detection of Pyridine Nucleotides* (Burton, 1954; Chaykin, 1956). Oxidized pyridine nucleotides (DPN, TPN) are detected by treating the chromatogram with 1 M aqueous KCN.   Ultraviolet illumination produces fluorescent spots of the pyridine nucleotides; adenine-containing compounds exhibit a quenching effect (Burton, 1954).

DPN is reduced to DPNH by applying a mixture of alcohol, alcohol dehydrogenase, and buffer, pH 9, to the paper.   Strong fluorescence indicates the presence of DPNH.   The presence of DPNH can be confirmed by oxidizing it enzymatically as above, but using pH 7.0 buffer.   Blue quenching indicates the formation of DPN.

g. *Detection of Pyrimidine Reduction Products* (Fink, 1956).   The chromatogram is first sprayed with 0.5 N NaOH (for hydrolysis) and then with p-dimethylaminobenzaldehyde reagent (1 g. DMAB, 10 ml. conc. HCl, 100 ml. ethanol).   After 2–6 hours at room temperature, yellow spots are formed.

h. *Detection of Thiouracils*.   Thiouracils are detected by one of two methods (Lederer, 1952a).   (A) The chromatogram is exposed to iodine vapors, and dark-brown spots on a yellow background appear. (B) The chromatogram is sprayed first with an alcoholic solution of dichlorobenzoquinonechlorimide, followed by 0.1 N alkali.   Orange-yellow spots are formed.

i. *Isotope Derivative Method* (Fresco, 1955).   The unknown sample, containing pyrimidines, is treated with I^{131}-"pipsyl" chloride ("pipsyl" = p-iodophenylsulfonyl), and the reaction mixture is diluted wtih 50 % acetone.   Another aliquot of the unknown sample is reacted with S^{35}-"pipsyl" chloride.   Both solutions are extracted with ether after acidification, the extracts are concentrated to a small volume and are chromatographed. The dried strips are counted with and without Al filters (see Chapter III for counting techniques).   The ratio of the two counts should be constant for a pure spot or band.

j. *Spectrographic Techniques* (see also Chapter III).   These techniques are based on the absorption of ultraviolet light by purines, pyrimidines, and related compounds. The compounds may be detected directly on the filter paper with one of the following light sources:

Hanovia "Homesun" lamp (450 watts, 200 volts, mercury arc) gives a high emission at 253.7 mμ. Two filters, one containing $CoSO_4$-$NiSO_4$ solutions, the other gaseous chlorine, are used in line with this lamp (Markham, 1949c; J. D. Smith, 1951). In order to check the instrument, a test spot of adenine on Whatman No. 1 paper is printed with this light source; 1 μg. of adenine should be detected by this method.

SL Mineralight, Model V-41 (Ultra-Violet Products, Inc.), is employed with a 253.7-mμ short-wave filter, *e.g.*, Corning No. 9863 (Holiday, 1949; Goeller, 1950).

Mazda mercury lamp (80 watts, MB/V; British Thompson Houston) has been used by J. D. Smith (1950).

Monochromatic light at 257 mμ and 275 mμ is obtained from the rotating Cd electrodes of an ultraviolet microscope using a quartz condenser with a corrected aperture (Edström, 1951, 1952).

The ultraviolet absorbing spots may be intensified by holding the illuminated chromatogram against a fluorescent screen made from zinc orthosilicate (Feigelson, 1956).

k. Contact Print Techniques. The developed chromatogram is pinned on photographic paper, *e.g.*, Ilford Reflex Document Paper No. 50, which is then exposed to one of the above light sources. The distance from the light source (see above) to the chromatogram is 120 cm., and the exposure time is 2–90 minutes (Markham, 1949; Burma, 1951). The photographic paper is developed with Kodak D153 developer. It is best, however, to make several preliminary test exposures and choose the best distance and exposure. An ultraviolet scanner camera is commercially available (Labline Co., Chicago 22, Illinois).

7. Quantitative Methods

a. Elution of Spots (This step is applicable only to Methods (c) and (d) below). Small rectangles are removed from an untreated portion of the paper with the guidance of a parallel strip treated with an appropriate reagent (see above) to locate the positions of the purines and other nitrogenous bases. The spots are extracted for 24 hours with 5.0 ml. of the following solutions, designed for several groups of compounds (Carter, 1950): 0.1 *N* HCl for uracil, thymine, and cytosine; 1.0 *N* HCl for adenine and guanine; 1 *N* NH$_4$OH for adenosine, guanosine, uridine, cytidine, adenylic, guanylic, cytidylic, and uridylic acids. The extracted spots are analyzed by spectrographic techniques.

b. Area Technique (Tennent, 1951). The absorbance curve of a mixture of purines and pyrimidines is obtained directly from the paper strip fed through the Beckman spectrophotometer in a special adapter fitting into

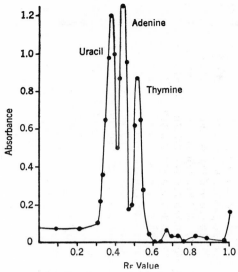

Fig. 3.   Absorbance curve of a mixture of uracil, adenine, and thymine developed with water-saturated butanol in the presence of ammonia.   Measured at 260 mμ (Tennent, 1951).

TABLE II

MOLAR EXTINCTION COEFFICIENTS FOR PURINES, PYRIMIDINES
AND RELATED COMPOUNDS
(Assembled by Dorough and Seaton, 1954)

Compound	Maximum absorption, Å.	$E \times 10^{-3}$ (0.1 M HCl)
Adenine	2600	13.6
Guanine	2500	10.0
Hypoxanthine	2500	9.03
Uric acid	2850	11.7
Xanthine	2650	7.93
Cytosine	2750	10.1
Thymine	2650	7.67
Uracil	2600	8.06
Adenosine	2600	14.2
Cytidine	2800	13.0
Guanosine	2550	12.2
Inosine	2470	11.8
Thymidine	2650	10.1
Uridine	2620	9.93
Xanthosine	2620	8.90
Adenylic acid	2550	15.1
Cytidylic acid	2780	12.7
Inosinic acid	2470	10.7
Uridylic acid	2620	9.89

TABLE III
R_f Values of Nucleic Acid Derivatives

Compound	1	2	3	4	5	6	7	8	9	10	11	12	13	14	15	16	17	18	19	20	21
Adenine	0.36	0.32	0.69	0.37	0.53	0.44	0.42	0.41		0.55	0.44	0.45	0.52	0.58	0.65	0.55		0.56	0.83	0.64	0.56
Guanine	0.25	0.21	0.50	0.37	0	0.02	0.02	0.05		0.53	0.49	0.50	0.54	0.63	0.56	0.63		0.39	0.70	0.36	0.23
Uracil	0.68		0.72	0.72	0.78	0.73	0.74	0.35		0.56	0.62	0.61	0.64	0.68	0.66	0.64		0.50	0.67	0.62	0.54
Cytosine	0.47		0.83	0.72	0.79	0.73	0.74	0.29		0.42	0.62	0.60	0.64	0.68	0.65	0.64		0.60	0.80	0.57	0.42
Thymine	0.77		0.72	0.72	0.77	0.73	0.74	0.52		0.70	0.71	0.70	0.72	0.77	0.73	0.71		0.63	0.78	0.81	0.54
Adenosine			0.68	0.52	0.58	0.54	0.53	0.28		0.47	0.36	0.38	0.46	0.57	0.57	0.54	0.48	0.72	0.91	0.57	0.56
Guanosine			0.66	0.59	0.68	0.62	0.64	0.17		0.36	0.37	0.35	0.38	0.53	0.52	0.49		0.27	0.59	0.42	0.25
Uridine			0.80	0.80	0.88	0.79	0.80	0.23		0.53	0.59	0.59	0.61	0.66	0.63	0.63		0.34	0.60	0.65	0.35
Cytidine	0.50		0.86	0.77	0.88	0.76	0.80	0.17		0.38	0.42	0.43	0.47	0.50	0.51	0.50		0.39	0.73	0.61	0.44
Adenylic acid "a"			0.74	0.65	0.72	0.74	0.74			0.48	0.49	0.20	0.06	0.35	0.31	0.20	0.69				
Adenylic acid "b"			0.74	0.60	0.81	0.67	0.63										0.61				
Guanylic acid			0.80	0.73	0.87	0.79	0.78			0.07	0.07	0.07	0.05	0.67	0.43	0.18					
Cytidylic acid		0.61	0.89	0.82	0.93	0.85	0.86			0.10	0.09	0.08	0.07	0.26	0.26	0.13					
Uridylic acid		0.79	0.89	0.82	0.93	0.85	0.86			0.16	0.15	0.17	0.10	0.43	0.39	0.21					
Hypoxanthine	0.31		0.63	0.49	0.52	0.57	0.59	0.29		0.45	0.45	0.45	0.48	0.59	0.56	0.53		0.45	0.69	0.46	0.37
Xanthine	0.25		0.52	0.45	0.56	0.49	0.42	0.12		0.12	0.39	0.54	0.41	0.59	0.60	0.58		0.34	0.60	0.34	0.24
Cytosine deoxyriboside	0.63					0.77			0.23												
5-Methylcytosine deoxyriboside						0.76			0.25												
Thymine deoxyriboside						0.78			0.51												
Uracil deoxyriboside						0.79			0.38												
Adenine deoxyriboside						0.55			0.35												
Guanine deoxyriboside						0.62			0.21												
Hypoxanthine deoxyriboside						0.70			0.23												
2-Deoxyribose						0.87			0.36												
2-Deoxygalactose						0.86			0.23												

Solvent[a]

5-Methylcytosine	0.55						
Adenylic acid-5	0.46	0.62	0.44	0.08	0.28	0.27	0.20
ADP		0.04	0.05	0.05	0.07	0.08	0.07
ATP			0.40	0.05	0.05	0.08	0.08	0.70
Xanthosine	0.37	.038	0.27	0.18	0.56	0.40	0.32
Inosine	0.37	0.39	0.37	0.41	0.56	0.52	0.49
Inosinic acid	0.86						
Thymidine	0.60	0.75	0.86	0.54			

[a] Solvents:
1. 65% v/v Aqueous isopropanol:2.0 N HCl (Wyatt, 1951).
2. tert-Butanol:const. boiling HCl: H_2O = 700:132:168 v/v (Smith, 1950).
3. 5% Ammonium citrate (pH 3.6) in isoamyl alcohol (Carter, 1950).
4. 5% Ammonium citrate* (pH 9.6) in isoamyl alcohol (Carter, 1950).
5. 5% KH_2PO_4 in isoamyl alcohol (Carter, 1950).
6. 5% Na_2HPO_4 in isoamyl alcohol (Carter, 1950; Buchanan, 1951).
7. 5% KH_2PO_4* (pH 7.0) in isoamyl alcohol (Carter, 1950).
8. n-Butanol saturated with a 10% aqueous urea solution (Carter, 1950).
9. Water-saturated n-butanol (Buchanan, 1951).
10. n-Propanol:tetrahydrofurfuryl alcohol:0.10 M ammonium acetate (pH 3.02) = 2:1:1 v/v (Carpenter, 1952).
11. n-Propanol:tetrahydrofurfuryl alcohol:0.08 M potassium citrate (pH 3.02) = 2:1:1 v/v (Carpenter, 1952).
12. n-Propanol:tetrahydrofurfuryl alcohol:0.08 M potassium citrate (pH 5.66) (Carpenter, 1952).
13. n-Propanol:tetrahydrofurfuryl alcohol:0.08 M potassium citrate (pH 7.92) (Carpenter, 1952).
14. Isoamyl alcohol:tetrahydrofurfuryl alcohol:0.08 M potassium citrate (pH 3.02) = 1:1:1 v/v (Carpenter, 1952).
15. Isoamyl alcohol:tetrahydrofurfuryl alcohol:0.08 M potassium citrate (pH 5.66) (Carpenter, 1952).
16. Isoamyl alcohol:tetrahydrofurfuryl alcohol:0.08 M potassium citrate (pH 7.92) (Carpenter, 1952).
17. 0.5% Laurylamine in amyl alcohol (Snellman, 1951).
18. Isobutyric acid:water:25% NH_4OH = 400:208:0.4 v/v (Löfgren, 1952).
19. n-Butanol:isobutyric acid:25% NH_4OH:H_2O = 75:37.5:2.5:25 v/v (Löfgren, 1952).
20. n-Butanol:morpholine:diethylene glycol:H_2O = 9:3:2:4 v/v (Löfgren, 1952).
21. n-Butanol:piperidine:diethylene glycol:diethyl carbitol:water = 8:3:1:2:4 v/v (Löfgren, 1952).

* Adjusted to desired pH with concentrated NH_4OH.

the compartment for the absorption cells (see Chapter III). The areas under the curves are measured and compared to those of curves from a mixture of known composition. The relative accuracy is ±5% when the areas of different substances on the same strip are compared (Fig. 3). *Density* plotted against *log concentration* gives a straight line (see Maximum Color Density, Chapter IV) (Paladini 1952).

The filter paper strips are in some cases impregnated with paraffin oil; the excess oil is removed by blotting. This technique increases the transmittance of the paper. It is also recommended, when phenol is one of the developing solvents, to wash the paper strip with ether prior to scanning.

A similar apparatus is described for the detection of guanine, cytosine, adenine, and thymine at 2537 Å (Hashimoto, 1952).

  c. Differential Extinction Technique (Vischer, 1948). The acidic extracts from the filter paper are placed into 1-cm. quartz cells, and their absorption

TABLE IV

R_f VALUES OF PURINE- AND PYRIMIDINE NUCLEOTIDES

Compound	Solvents[a]			
	1	2	3	4
Des-DPN	0.65	—	—	—
Des-DPNH	0.39	—	—	—
DPN	0.63	0.35	0.13	0.31
DPNH	0.76	—	—	—
TPN	0.51	0.21	0.03	0.44
TPNH	0.24	—	—	—
Nicotinamide mononucleotide	0.33	—	—	—
Nicotinamide riboside	0.77	—	—	—
2-Phosphoadenosine diphosphoribose	0.13	—	—	—
Adenosine	0.89	0.76	0.63	0.13
Adenylic acid "a"	0.28	—	—	—
Adenylic acid "b"	0.28	—	—	—
5-Adenylic acid	0.41	—	—	—
Adenosine diphosphoribose	0.80	—	—	—
ATP (adenosine-triphosphate)	—	0.20	0.04	0.48
ADP	—	0.30	0.07	0.37
AMP	—	0.45	0.15	0.29
CTP (cytidine-triphosphate)	—	0.07	0.04	0.77
CDP	—	0.13	0.07	0.71
CMP	—	0.28	0.13	0.67
Cytidine	—	0.59	0.65	0.56
UTP (uridine-triphosphate)	—	0.08	0.04	0.77
UDP	—	0.13	0.09	0.71
UMP	—	0.23	0.18	0.64
Uridine	—	0.47	0.73	0.54

[a] Solvents: 1. Pyridine:water = 2:1 v/v (Burton, 1954).
  2, 3, 4. See p. 287 and 289, *l*. (1), (2), and (3).

in the ultraviolet measured in a Beckman photoelectric quartz spectrophotometer. An HCl extract of the paper serves as the blank. It is preferable to estimate the purine contents of the extracts from the difference in the extinction values read at the absorption maximum and at 290 mμ. From the difference in the extinction values of a solution of known composition, it is possible to estimate the contents of the unknown extract within ±8% accuracy. The absorption maximum for adenine is 262.5 mμ, and for guanine 249 mμ.

A sample computation which follows is based on a proportion between readings of the unknown extracts and those with purine solutions containing 10 μg./ml.

	Extinction at wavelength		Difference in extinction,
	262.5 mμ	290 mμ	Δ
Adenine, unknown concentration	0.311	0.017	0.294
Adenine, 10 μg./ml.	0.930	0.030	0.900

$$\frac{\mu\text{g. in unknown solution}}{10 \ \mu\text{g.}} = \frac{\Delta_x}{\Delta} = \frac{0.294}{0.900}$$

$$\mu\text{g. unknown solution} = \frac{0.294 \times 10}{0.900} = 3.27 \ \mu\text{g.}$$

TABLE V

R_f OF NUCLEIC ACID DERIVATIVES

(R_f thymine deoxyriboside = 1) (Tamm, 1953)

Compound	Solvent			
	1	2	3	4
Adenine	0.72	0.42	0.78	
Guanine	0.17	0.43	0.28	
Hypoxanthine	0.23	0.72	0.29	
Cytosine	0.50	0.91	0.51	
Uracil	0.55	0.94	0.60	
Thymine	1.02	0.88	1.08	
Adenine deoxyriboside	0.84	0.67	0.79	1.21
Guanine deoxyriboside	0.19	0.76	0.23	0.89
Hypoxanthine deoxyriboside	0.19	0.94	0.22	0.94
Cystosine deoxyriboside	0.56	0.99	0.56	1.11
Uracil deoxyriboside	0.51	1.01	0.52	0.89
Thymine deoxyriboside	1.00	1.00	1.00	1.00
Deoxyadenylic acid				0.92
Deoxyguanylic acid				0.49
Deoxycytidylic acid				0.74
Deoxy-5-methylcytidylic acid				1.26
Deoxythymidylic acid				0.61

[a] Solvents: 1. n-Butanol sat. with NH$_4$OH:H$_2$O = 1:4 v/v.
2. Water.
3. n-Butanol:6.0 N NH$_3$ = 6:1 v/v.
4. Isobutyric acid:ammonium isobutyrate (pH 3.6) = 1:1 v/v.

d. Maximum Extinction Technique (J. D. Smith, 1950; Markham, 1951c). The spots containing the chemically unchanged nucleic acid derivatives are extracted for 18 hours with 5 ml. of 0.1 N HCl. The optical density is read, and the values for the extinction coefficients in Table II are used.

e. Densitometric Analyses. (1) A quantitative spot test of nucleic acids is as follows (Kanngiesser, 1953): 20-μl. samples of the nucleic acid are spotted on Whatman No. 1 filter paper and dried. The paper is dipped for 5–10 seconds into a molybdenum blue reagent[1] and washed with methanol to remove any phosphatides. The pH of the last rinse should be about 7. The color of the spot is measured with a densitometer; a plot of density against concentration yields a straight line (see Chapter IV).

(2.) The yellow color of the pyrimidine reduction products resulting from the p-dimethylaminobenzaldehyde spray [see 6 (g)] is measured directly on the paper with a Perkin-Elmer flame photometer, modified for transmission spectrophotometry (Fink, 1956).

8. MISCELLANEOUS APPLICATIONS

Carbon-14-DPN and C[14]-TPN (di- and triphosphopyridine nucleotides) have been prepared by incubating *L. plantarum* with C[14]-nicotinic acid for 18 hours (Boone, 1954). The cells were washed with water, adjusted to pH 4, and centrifuged. The washings were taken to dryness *in vacuo* and redissolved in a small amount of water. This solution was subjected to descending chromatography using two solvents, (1) n-butanol, saturated with water and (2) 60 % aqueous n-propanol. The nucleotides after chromatography were detected by their characteristic fluorescence (Kodicek, 1951). Radioactive substances were detected by autoradiography. The radioactive regions with R_f 0.26 and 0.15 in Solvent (2) were identified as C[14]-DPN and C[14]-TPN, respectively.

---

[1] Molybdenum blue reagent (Zinsadze, 1935): (I) 40.11 g. of MoO_3 is added to one liter of 25 N H_2SO_4. The mixture is boiled gently until the solution is clear. (II) To 500 ml. of I is added 1.78 g. of molybdenum powder. The suspension is boiled for 15 minutes, cooled, decanted, and made up to 500 ml. I and II are mixed so that 5.0 ml. of the mixture corresponds to 5.0 ml. of 0.1 N $KMnO_4$.

Chapter X

PHENOLS, AROMATIC ACIDS, AND INDOLE COMPOUNDS

Section I: Phenols and Aromatic Acids

For the separation of the simpler phenols the presence of acids in the organic phase of the solvent seems to produce "tailing." Better results have been obtained with neutral or slightly basic solutions. The separation of more complex phenols, *i.e.* pyrogallol tannins, is complicated by their oxidation in the presence of bases. The addition of a strong organic acid to the solvent forms more clearly defined spots (Asquith, 1951).

In the resolution of acid mixtures, a volatile organic acid is usually used in the developing solvent to depress the ionization of individual acids. After the paper is removed from the chromatographic chamber, it is heated to volatilize this acid. Then the chromatogram is sprayed with an acid-base indicator to reveal the positions of the acids. If an individual acid has another functional group any other suitable spraying reagent may be used.

1. PREPARATION OF SAMPLE

Standard solutions of phenols and organic acids are dissolved in volatile organic solvents (ethyl ether, methanol, and others) at a concentration of 0.5–1.0%. About 5–20 μg. of each substance should be deposited on the paper, although as little as 1 μg. may be detected.

a. Extraction from Urine (D. Robinson, 1951; Armstrong, 1956). A measured amount of urine is treated with 0.1 volume of concentrated HCl and heated with refluxing for 20 minutes to hydrolyze ethereal sulfates. After cooling, the urine is extracted continuously for 6 hours with ether. Unconjugated phenolic acids may also be extracted with ethyl acetate from acidified urine (pH 1) which has been saturated with NaCl. The phenols are re-extracted with 10% $NaHCO_3$, the pH is adjusted to 1–2, and the phenols are again extracted with ethyl acetate. Aminophenols are removed from the extract with 2 N HCl and the residual nitrophenols transferred to 2 N NaOH. The latter is acidified, and the nitrophenols transferred to 10 ml. of ether which is then used for paper chromatography.

The metabolic products of hydroxybenzoic acids in urine were identified by Bray (1950). The urine is acidified with 0.2 volume of 2 N H_2SO_4 and continuously extracted for 6 hours to concentrate the unconjugated phenols. The acid content of the urine is then adjusted to 2 N, and the urine is hydrolyzed by boiling under reflux for 1 hour and again continuously extracted with ether for 20 hours to remove phenols originally conjugated.

301

The residues after removal of solvent from the two extracts are separately taken up in 5 ml. of acetone.

Hydroxy acids may be concentrated by extracting the ether solutions with saturated $NaHCO_3$ solutions (Boscott, 1952).

Biological samples may often be analyzed without previous concentration. Kelemen (1950) applied 2.5–20 μl. of urine to the paper to analyze for aromatic amino acids.

b. *Isolation from Processed Foods* (Safina, 1954). About 25–50 g. of the material to be analyzed is acidified with H_2SO_4 and deproteinized by the addition of 2–3 ml. of a solution containing 15 % $K_4Fe(CN)_6$ and 30 % $ZnSO_4$. The mixture is heated at 100°C. and filtered. The filtrate is extracted with ether:petroleum ether (v/v), the extract is dried over anhydrous Na_2SO_4 and evaporated *in vacuo*. The residue is dissolved in 75 % methanol and subjected to chromatography.

c. *Isolation of Chlorogenic Acid* (Ruckenbrod, 1954). Plant material is first boiled in 96 % ethanol for one minute to destroy phenoloxidase activity. The plant particles are then crushed with sand and extracted three times with 70 % ethanol (ten times the weight of sample) at 50–55°C. The extracts are concentrated to a total volume of 10 ml., and 10 μl. aliquots are spotted on paper for chromatography.

d. *Preparation of Colored Derivatives.* Hossfeld (1951) found that satisfactory qualitative separation of many simple phenols could be accomplished by applying paper chromatography to a mixture of the sodium salts of phenylazo dyes derived by coupling the phenols, pure or in mixture, with diazotized sulfanilic acid. For the preparation of individual dyes, the method of Cheronis (1942) may be followed: Sulfanilic acid (2.6 g.), 20 ml. of water, and 3 ml. of 6 N NaOH are brought into solution. One gram of $NaNO_2$ is added with stirring, and this mixture is slowly poured into a beaker which contains 30 ml. of water, 40 g. of crushed ice, and 2 ml. of concentrated H_2SO_4. After thirty minutes standing (temperature should not rise above 5°C.), a slight excess of the phenol is added, and the diazotization is allowed to proceed for 15 minutes. Twelve ml. of 6 N NaOH and 50 ml. of saturated NaCl solution are added, the mixture is cooled for 10 minutes, and the crystallized dye is filtered by suction.

The preparation of diazo dyes from a mixture of phenols is accomplished in a similar manner as has just been described. No attempt is made, however, to isolate a crystalline product, but the reaction product is acidified with an excess of HCl, and any unreacted phenols are removed by benzene or chloroform extraction.

2. SOLVENTS (See Tables I, II, and III)

a. *1-Butanol:pyridine:saturated NaCl* = 1:1:2 (organic phase). This solvent is used to separate phenolic acids and phenols (Evans, 1949).

b. 1-Butanol (saturated with) ammonium carbonate buffer (3.0 *N*).   This solvent gives good separation of a number of aromatic acids (Fewster, 1951).

c. 1-Butanol:ethanol:3.0 N ammonium carbonate buffer = 40:11:19; *butanol:benzene:3.0 N ammonium carbonate buffer* = 80:5:15 v/v (Fewster, 1951).

d. 1-Butanol, saturated with 5 N NH₄OH (Lederer, 1949c).

e. 1-Butanol:concentrated NH₄OH = 4:1 v/v is used for the separatioɪ of methylol phenols (Freeman, 1952).

f. 1-Butanol, saturated with 0.005 N NH₄OH is used for the chromatography of hydroxybenzoic acids, *m-* and *p*-hydroxyhippuric acids.

g. sec-Butanol:2% aqueous Na₂CO₃ (v/v) separates phenols diazotized with sulfanilic acid (see Table II) (Chang, 1952).

h. 1-Butanol:acetic acid:water = 4:1:5 v/v is a suitable solvent for many phenols (Bate-Smith, 1949; Gaffney, 1954).

i. 1-Butanol:benzene:concentrated NH₄OH = 50:2:48 v/v is used to separate phenols and aminophenols from their respective glycosides (Myers, 1954).

j. 1-Butanol:dioxane:2 N NH₄OH = 4:1:5 v/v is used for the separation of thyroacetic acids (Wilkinson, 1956).

k. Methyl ethyl ketone:water (v/v) separates the phenols which are coupled with diazotized sulfanilic acid (Hossfeld, 1951).

l. Benzene:acetic acid:water = 2:2:1 v/v (organic phase) is used for the separation of hydroxybenzoic acids (Bray, 1950).

m. m-Cresol:acetic acid:water = 50:2:48 v/v (organic phase) (Bate-Smith, 1949).

n. Ethyl acetate:formic acid:water = 10:2:3 v/v (organic phase *after* phases are allowed to separate for 6 hours) gives the following R_f values for chlorogenic and caffeic acid, respectively: 0.60 and 0.85. (Svendson, 1951).

o. Acetic acid (2%) is used for the separation of cinnamic acid derivatives (A. H. Williams, 1955).

p. i-Amyl alcohol:xylene:water = 40:60:50 v/v plus 16.25% acetic acid is a suitable solvent for di- and trihydroxyphenols (Wagner, 1953).

q. Benzene:cyclohexane = 1:12 v/v plus 1% CH₃OH is a good solvent for simple phenols, provided that the filter paper is previously impregnated with 4% NaOH (Schleede, 1955).

r. Formamide:water = 60:40 v/v, pH 3.5; buffered with formic acid gives the following R_f values for ellagɪc and flavellagic acids: 0.6 and 0.27, respectively (Hathway, 1956a).

s. Methyl ethyl ketone:cineole:formic acid:water = 50:50:20:16 v/v is a suitable solvent for ʟ-quinic acid (1,3,4,5-tetrahydroxycyclohexane-2-carboxylic acid) (Anet, 1953).

t. Phenol:water = 3:1 (w/v), plus 0.9 % formic acid separates dihydro-shikimic, shikimic, and L-quinic acids (Hathway, 1956b).

u. Petroleum ether (40–60°C.):formic acid = 2:1 v/v will separate *tert*-butyl methoxyphenol, -quinol, -*p*-benzoquinone, *n*- and *p*-methoxyphenol (Dawe, 1956).

v. Two-dimensional Chromatography Solvent Systems (1) *First direction:* benzene:acetic acid:water = 2:2:1; *second direction:* 20 % (w/v) HCl or 22 % w/v KHCO₃ (Boscott, 1952; Kirby, 1953).

2. *First direction:* sec-butanol:2 % Na₂CO₃ (v/v); *second direction:* 1-butanol:ethanol:water = 20:6:20 v/v; this system will separate *o*-cresol and *m*-cresol (Chang, 1952).

3. TECHNIQUES

Separations of phenols and aromatic acids have generally been carried out with Whatman No. 1 or Whatman No. 4 paper. Except in specific applications, Whatman No. 4 is preferable, since the solvent rate through the paper is greater and thus the time required for a given experiment is shortened.

Treatment of the paper with Na₂CO₃ or Na₂HPO₄ solutions facilitates the separation of acidic compounds, *i.e.*, phenol and carboxylic acids, from non-acid substances (Newcombe, 1953). For the separation of the dyes as Na salts, formed by the reaction of phenols and diazotized sulfanilic acid, Whatman No. 1 paper is first sprayed with 4 % Na₂CO₃ and dried before proceeding with the solvent development (Hossfeld, 1951).

Circular paper chromatography has been employed for a mixture of phenols and organic acids using the solvent 1-pentanol:glacial acetic acid: water = 4:1:5 v/v (Barnabas, 1954).

An interesting technique of two dimensional chromatography of phenols involves both ZnCO₃-impregnation and reversed phase development on the same chromatogram (Green, 1955): A sheet of Whatman No. 1 (25 cm.²) is immersed in a solution containing 40 g. of ZnCO₃, 30 g. of (NH₄)₂CO₃, 500 ml. water, and 200 ml. concentrated NH₄OH. The paper is air-dried and then heated at 95°C. for three hours.

The solvent for the first direction is dry benzene using the ascending development. The dry paper is next immersed in 5 % ethyl oleate in petroleum ether (40–60°C.), care being taken to impregnate only the area which has not been traversed by the substances during the first development. The second direction is developed with 40 % (v/v) ethanol for sixteen hours.

4. DETECTION

If a synthetic mixture is prepared, good spots can usually be obtained with 5–20 μg. of each substance. Quantities as low as 1 μg. can be detected if necessary.

a. Diazotized Sulfanilic Acid (Ames, 1952). Twenty-five ml. of freshly prepared 5 % $NaNO_2$ is slowly added at 0°C. to 5.0 ml. of sulfanilic acid solution (0.9 g. of sulfanilic acid and 9 ml. of concentrated HCl, diluted to 100 ml. with water). The dried chromatogram is lightly sprayed with this reagent, and while the paper is still damp, it is sprayed with 20 % Na_2CO_3 (cf Chapter V).

b. Diazotized p-Nitraniline (Bray, 1950). Twenty-five milliliters of a solution of *p*-nitraniline (0.3 %) in HCl (80 % w/v) is mixed with 1.5 ml. of sodium nitrite solution (5 % w/v) just before spraying. Subsequently, the strip is sprayed with Na_2CO_3 solution (20 % w/v). This reagent is suitable for detection of hydroxybenzoic acids and aminohydroxybenzoic acids.

c. Coupling with β-Naphthol (Myers, 1954). For the detection of aminophenols, the chromatogram is first sprayed with a 1 % (w/v) solution of HNO_2, followed after five minutes by 1 % (w/v) β-naphthol in N NaOH; red colors result.

d. Coupling with N-(1-naphthyl) ethylenediamine (Bray, 1955, 1956). The chromatogram is sprayed with a reagent composed of the following: 2 N HCl, 0.1 % $NaNO_2$, 0.5 % ammonium sulfamate, and 0.1 % N-(1-naphthyl) ethylenediamine·2 HCl.

e. Sucrose. Two grams is mixed with 10 ml. of concentrated HCl and 90 ml. of absolute ethanol. Complete solution is not achieved, but the suspension is sprayed on the chromatogram. The paper is then heated for 1 minute at 85–95°C. It produces characteristic colors with many di- and trihydroxyphenols (Roux, 1951).

f. Ammoniacal Silver Nitrate (0.1 N). This is a convenient reagent for any easily oxidizable compounds. Thus, many complex phenols, such as the pyrogallol tannins, and many hydroxybenzoic acids produce black spots on the white background (Bray, 1950; Asquith, 1951).

g. NaOH Solution (1 N). When various nitrophenols are sprayed with this reagent, characteristic colors are produced (Robinson, 1951).

h. Methyl Red Indicator. Five parts of 0.1 % alcoholic methyl red solution is mixed with 10 parts of 0.667 M phosphate buffer solution of pH 7.0. Aromatic acids give pink spots on a yellow background. Many other indicators, *e.g.* bromocresol green, bromophenol blue, etc., may be used (Fewster, 1951; Azouz, 1955).

i. FeCl₃ Solution (0.1 % w/v). This is a general reagent for phenols, but it is inferior to other spraying agents (Bray, 1950; Roberts, 1951; Keup, 1952). A 2 % ethanolic solution of $FeCl_3$ produces green spots for chlorogenic and caffeic acids with a sensitivity of 10 μg. (Svendson, 1951).

j. p-Dimethylaminobenzaldehyde, 500 mg. in 1 ml. of concentrated HCl and 100 ml. of absolute ethanol (Reddi, 1953; Sundaram, 1954). The composition of another mixture is 4 % *p*-dimethylaminobenzaldehyde in acetic anhydride containing a few crystals of sodium acetate. After spraying the paper, the chromatogram is heated for 1–2 minutes at 130–150°C. This reagent is very sensitive for the detection of hippuric acid which gives an orange colored spot. Quantitative estimations can be made by elution of the azlactone with methanol and determination of the color density at 460 mμ (Gaffney, 1954; Haberland, 1954).

k. Nitrobenzenediazonium fluoroborate. A 1% solution of the reagent in acetone is painted on the chromatogram with a brush. After drying briefly, the chromatogram is painted with a 0.1 N solution of potassium hydroxide in methanol, causing colored spots to appear for phenols. For preparation of the reagent, 14 g. of *p*-nitraniline is dissolved by heating with 30 ml. of concentrated HCl and 30 ml. of water. It is then cooled to 5°C., and a solution of 8 g. of NaNO$_2$ in 20 ml. of water is added at once. Sixty milliliters of 40% fluoroboric acid is added, and the fluffy yellow precipitate is separated by filtration, washed successively with fluoroboric acid, alcohol, and ether, and dried in a vacuum desiccator (Freeman, 1952).

l. tetra-Azotized di-o-anisidine. A 1% solution (w/v) in 0.5 N NaHCO$_3$ gives brown purple spots for quinol and its glucoside, arbutin (Myers, 1954).

m. 2,6-Dichloroquinonechlorimide (2% alcoholic solution), followed by one of the following sprays: saturated NaHCO$_3$ (pH 8), borax (pH 9), or Na$_2$CO$_3$ (pH > 10) (Azouz, 1955). This reagent is used to differentiate halogenated benzenes.

n. Sodium Nitrite; 2% in 50% ethanol or 1% in 10% acetic acid is used to detect chlorogenic and caffeic acids (Svendson, 1951; Ruckenbrod, 1954). On exposure to ammonia, red-yellow spots appear; sensitivity, 5 μg.

o. Ultraviolet Absorption and Fluorescence. When chromatograms are viewed with a Hanovia U.V. Light (2536 A), provided with a "Chance 0 X 7 Filter", 1,2-dihydroxynaphthalenes appear as dark spots, while 1-naphthol, 2-naphthol and derivatives cause fluorescence after being exposed to NH$_3$ vapors (Boyland, 1956b).

5. QUANTITATIVE METHODS

Reference to Chapter IV on Quantitative Methods of Analysis will suggest many procedures which may be followed in analyzing the completed paper chromatogram. Depending on the accuracy desired and the properties of individual substances, a suitable method may be worked out. Thus, the areas of the spots may be measured and compared to those of standards. The color density procedure may be used, or corresponding areas of the paper which have not been treated with a color-producing reagent may be eluted with a suitable solvent and the washings analyzed by any standard chemical methods.

Spots containing unreacted phenols may be eluted with methanol and reacted with diazotized sulfanilamide (Wagner, 1953). Optical densities

TABLE I

R_f VALUES OF AROMATIC ACIDS, PHENOLS, AND RELATED COMPOUNDS

Compound	Solvent[a]										
	1	2	3	4	5	6	7	8	9	10	11
I. Aromatic Acids											
o-Hydroxy											
benzoic (salicylic acid)	0.78	0.88	0.66	0.90	0.43	0.65	—	0.95	0.84	—	—
hippuric	0.22	0.43	0.68	0.86	0.30	—	—	—	—	—	—
phenylacetic	0.76	0.57	0.86	0.91	0.49	—	—	—	—	—	—
mandelic	0.58	0.13	0.82	0.54	0.30	—	—	—	—	—	—
	(0.68)	—	(0.88)	(0.68)	—	—	—	—	—	—	—
phenylpropionic	0.70	0.74	0.77	0.91	0.72	—	—	—	—	—	—
cinnamic	0.35	0.70	0.44	0.93	0.75	—	—	—	—	—	—
phenyllactic	0.59	0.29	0.84	0.85	0.28	—	—	—	—	—	—
phenylpyruvic	dec.	0.21	0.85	0.70	0.43	—	—	—	—	—	—
phenylpyruvic lactone	0.54	0.88	0.44	0.85	0.87	—	—	—	—	—	—
m-Hydroxy											
benzoic	0.39	0.53	0.70	0.88	0.50	—	—	—	—	—	—
hippuric	0.33	0.09	0.75	0.78	0.19	—	—	—	—	—	—
phenylacetic	0.46	0.49	0.83	0.92	0.46	—	—	—	—	—	—
mandelic	0.37	0.07	0.87	0.68	0.19	—	—	—	—	—	—
phenylpropionic	0.54	0.61	0.77	0.92	0.68	—	—	—	—	—	—
cinnamic	0.44	0.58	0.39	0.93	0.60	—	—	—	—	—	—
phenyllactic	0.51	0.12	0.86	0.82	0.21	—	—	—	—	—	—
phenylpryuvic	dec.	0.13	streaks	0.74	dec.	—	—	—	—	—	—
p-Hydroxy											
benzoic	0.23	0.55	0.54	0.87	0.68	—	—	—	—	—	—
hippuric	0.15	0.07	0.72	0.78	0.18	—	—	—	—	—	—
phenylacetic	0.42	0.49	0.82	0.92	0.50	—	—	—	—	—	—
mandelic	0.33	0.07	0.87	0.68	0.16	—	—	—	—	—	—
phenylpropionic	0.51	0.61	0.73	0.93	0.69	—	—	—	—	—	—
cinnamic	0.28	0.58	0.31	0.93	0.67	—	—	—	—	—	—
phenyllactic	0.45	0.13	0.85	0.82	0.19	—	—	—	—	—	—

[a] Solvents: 1. *i*-Propanol:concentrated NH_4OH:H_2O = 8:1:1 v/v (Armstrong, 1956).
    2. Benzene:propionic acid:water = 2:2:1 v/v (Armstrong, 1956).
    3. 20% KCl (Armstrong, 1956).
    4. *n*-Butanol:acetic acid:water = 8:2:2 v/v (Armstrong, 1956).
    5. *n*-Butanol:pyridine:dioxane:water = 70:20:5:5 v/v (Armstrong, 1956).
    6. *n*-Butanol:pyridine:sat. NaCl = 1:1:2 v/v (Evans, 1949).
    7. Benzene:acetic acid:water = 2:2:1 v/v (Robinson, 1951).
    8. *n*-Butanol:acetic acid:water = 4:1:5 v/v (Bate-Smith, 1949; Gaffney, 1954; Smith, 1955).
    9. *m*-Cresol:acetic acid:water = 50:2:48 v/v (Bate-Smith, 1949).
    10. *n*-Butanol:NH_4OH = 4:1 v/v (Freeman, 1952a).
    11. Ethylmethylketone:2 *N* NH_4OH = 2:1 v/v (J. N. Smith, 1955).

TABLE I—*Continued*

Compound	Solvent[a]										
	1	2	3	4	5	6	7	8	9	10	11
3-Methoxy-4-hydroxy											
benzoic (vanillic acid)	0.22	0.80	0.66	0.89	0.60	—	—	0.92	0.81	—	—
hippuric	0.16	0.18	0.66	0.74	0.16	—	—	—	—	—	—
phenylacetic	0.39	0.66	0.82	0.88	streaks	—	—	—	—	—	—
mandelic	0.28	0.16	0.84	0.71	0.20	—	—	—	—	—	—
phenylpropionic	0.43	0.81	0.74	0.91	0.65	—	—	—	—	—	—
cinnamic	0.27	0.80	0.35	0.88	0.63	—	—	—	—	—	—
Protocatechuic acid	0.06	0.16	0.73	0.83	streaks	—	—	0.85	0.35	—	—
Gentisic	0.68	0.26	0.53	0.89	0.34	0.51	—	—	—	—	—
α-Resorcylic	0.24	0.09	0.64	0.78	0.39	—	—	—	—	—	—
β-Resorcylic	0.39	0.38	0.48	0.92	0.34	0.55	—	0.93	0.54	—	—
γ-Resorcylic	0.77	0.11	0.50	0.54	0.48	—	—	—	—	—	—
Gallic	dec.	0	streaks	0.60	dec.	0.43	—	0.68	0.08	—	—
Syringic	0.18	0.79	0.57	0.87	dec.	—	—	—	—	—	—
Homogentisic	—	0.09	0.90	0.75	0.34	—	—	—	—	—	—
Caffeic	—	0.19	0.36	0.78	0.53	—	—	—	—	—	—
Kynurenic	0.52	0.16	0.37	0.55	0.21	—	—	0.64	—	—	—
Xanthurenic	0.08	0.03	0.24	0.53	0.23	—	—	0.69	—	—	—
3-OH-Anthranilic	—	0.38	streaks	0.85	0.65	—	—	0.90	—	—	—
5-OH-Indoleacetic	0.32	0.16	0.58	0.76	0.45	—	—	—	—	—	—
Pyrogallol carboxylic	—	—	—	—	—	0.71	—	—	—	—	—
Tannic acid	—	—	—	—	—	0.99	—	—	—	—	—
Quinolinic	—	—	—	—	—	—	—	—	0.50	—	—
Anthranilic	—	—	—	—	—	—	0.26	—	—	—	—
Mandelic	—	—	—	—	—	—	0.28	—	—	—	—
p-Aminobenzoic	—	—	—	—	—	—	0:09	—	—	—	—
Hippuric	—	—	—	—	—	—	0.31	—	—	—	—
o-Coumaric	—	—	—	—	—	—	0.27	—	—	—	—
Sulfanilic	—	—	—	—	—	—	0.11	—	—	—	—
Cinnamic	—	—	—	—	—	—	0.62	—	—	—	—
Phenylpropionic	—	—	—	—	—	—	0.57	—	—	—	—
Phenylacetic	—	—	—	—	—	—	0.44	—	—	—	—
Benzoic	—	—	—	—	—	—	0.41	—	—	—	—
II. Phenols											
Phenol	—	—	—	—	—	0.97	—	—	—	0.93	
Catechol	—	—	—	—	—	0.96	—	0.91	0.74	—	—
Resorcinol	—	—	—	—	—	0.97	—	0.91	0.63	—	—

TABLE I—*Continued*

Compound	Solvent[a]										
	1	2	3	4	5	6	7	8	9	10	11
Hydroquinone	—	—	—	—	—	0.96	—	0.88	0.69	—	—
Pyrogallol	—	—	—	—	—	0.94	—	0.77	0.34	—	—
Hydroxyquinol	—	—	—	—	—	0.48	—	—	—	—	—
Phloroglucinol	—	—	—	—	—	0.96	—	0.76	0.16	—	—
Orcinol	—	—	—	—	—	—	—	0.91	0.75	—	—
o-Hydroxybenzyl alcohol	—	—	—	—	—	—	—	—	—	0.84	—
m-Hydroxybenzyl alcohol	—	—	—	—	—	—	—	—	—	0.81	—
p-Hydroxybenzyl alcohol	—	—	—	—	—	—	—	—	—	0.79	—
2,6-Dimethylolphenol	—	—	—	—	—	—	—	—	—	0.67	—
2,4-Dimethylolphenol	—	—	—	—	—	—	—	—	—	0.61	—
2,4,6-Trimethylolphenol	—	—	—	—	—	—	—	—	—	0.34	—
p-Cresol	—	—	—	—	—	—	—	—	—	0.92	—
p-Cresolmonomethylol	—	—	—	—	—	—	—	—	—	0.89	—
2,6-Dimethylol-p-cresol	—	—	—	—	—	—	—	—	—	0.82	—
o-Cresol	—	—	—	—	—	—	—	—	—	0.93	—
2,4-Dimethylol-o-cresol	—	—	—	—	—	—	—	—	—	0.79	—
m-Cresol	—	—	—	—	—	—	—	—	—	0.94	—
III. *Conjugated Phenols*											
m-Aminophenyl sulfuric acid	—	—	—	—	—	—	—	0.33	—	—	0.35
m-Aminophenyl glucoside	—	—	—	—	—	—	—	0.33	—	—	0.23
m-Aminophenol	—	—	—	—	—	—	—	0.75	—	—	0.90
m-Hydroxyphenylsulfamic acid	—	—	—	—	—	—	—	0.22	—	—	0.15
p-Aminophenyl sulfuric acid	—	—	—	—	—	—	—	0.33	—	—	0.10
p-Aminophenol	—	—	—	—	—	—	—	0.64	—	—	0.81
p-(2,4-Dihydroxyphenyl)azophenyl sulfuric acid	—	—	—	—	—	—	—	0.78	—	—	0.11

TABLE I—*Concluded*

Compound	Solvent[a]										
	1	2	3	4	5	6	7	8	9	10	11
p-(2,4-Dihydroxy-phenyl)azo-phenol	—	—	—	—	—	—	—	0.90	—	—	0.25
3-Quinolyl sul-furic acid	—	—	—	—	—	—	—	0.74	—	—	0.82
3-Hydroxyquino-line	—	—	—	—	—	—	—	0.88	—	—	0.70
6-Quinolyl sul-furic acid	—	—	—	—	—	—	—	0.54	—	—	0.62
6-Hydroxyquino-line	—	—	—	—	—	—	—	0.77	—	—	0.90
7-Quinolyl sul-furic acid	—	—	—	—	—	—	—	0.58	—	—	0.62
7-Hydroxyquino-line	—	—	—	—	—	—	—	0.74	—	—	0.90
8-Quinolyl sul-furic acid	—	—	—	—	—	—	—	0.56	—	—	0.61
8-Quinolyl gluco-side	—	—	—	—	—	—	—	0.55	—	—	0.50
8-Hydroxyquino-line	—	—	—	—	—	—	—	0.70	—	—	0.90
7-Coumarinyl sul-furic acid	—	—	—	—	—	—	—	0.53	—	—	0.78
7-Coumarinylglu-coside	—	—	—	—	—	—	—	0.67	—	—	0.46
7-Hydroxycou-marin (um-belliferone)	—	—	—	—	—	—	—	0.95	—	—	0.64
4-Methylcouma-rin-7-yl sul-furic acid	—	—	—	—	—	—	—	0.66	—	—	0.90
7-Hydroxy-4-methylcou-marin	—	—	—	—	—	—	—	0.90	—	—	0.77

are determined using the following Zeiss filters: for resorcinol—S 50; for phloroglucinol—S 47; for thymol and guiacol—S 50.

Colored spots produced by nitrobenzenediazonium fluoroborate (Reagent 4 (k)) are marked with a soft pencil 20–40 minutes after drying and weighed quantitatively several hours later. Comparison with standards·results in an experimental error of no more than ±5.5 % (Freeman, 1952). Semi-

TABLE II
R_f Values of Phenylazobenzene-Sulfonic Acid Dyes
(Chang, 1952)

Phenol	Solvent sec-butanol:2% Na_2CO_3 (v/v)
Acetoguaiacone	0.11
2,6-Dimethoxyphenol	0.12
Guaiacol	0.19
Phenol	0.30
o-Chlorophenol	0.37
o-Hydroxybenzaldehyde	0.39
α-Naphthol	0.43
o-Cresol	0.43
m-Cresol	0.43
2,6-Dimethylphenol	0.48
2,4-Dichlorophenol	0.63
p-Methylguaiacol	0.64
2,5-Dimethylphenol	0.66
o-Ethylphenol	0.75
m-Ethylphenol	0.76
p-Ethylguaiacol	0.80
Eugenol	0.81
3,5-Dimethylphenol	0.83
o-Phenylphenol	0.84
m-Phenylphenol	0.86
p-Phenylphenol	0.89
p-Cresol	0.89
2,3,5-Trimethylphenol	0.90
Dihydroeugenol	0.93
2,3,4-Dimethylphenol	0.94
β-Naphthol	0.95
p-Ethylphenol	0.95
Thymol	0.96
4-(α-Methylbenzyl)-2-phenylphenol	0.98
2,4-Dimethylphenol	0.99

quantitative determinations of colored spots have been made by measuring the spot size with a planimeter after projection from a photographic enlarger (20 × magnification) (Boyland, 1956b). A standard curve is constructed by plotting concentration against "spot area."

For the quantitative estimation of chlorogenic and caffeic acids, the spots, which are detected by their fluorescence in ultraviolet light, are extracted with 10 ml. water, filtered, and the optical density determined at the following wave lengths: 324 mμ for chlorogenic acid and 290 mμ for caffeic acid (Ruckenbrod, 1954).

TABLE III
R_f Values of Chlorinated Phenols and Related Compounds
(Azouz, 1955; Bray, 1956)

Compound	Solvent[a]				
	1	2	3	4	5
2,3-Dichlorophenol	—	0.84	—	—	—
3,4-Dichlorophenol	—	0.95	—	—	—
3,4-Dichlorocatechol	0.54	0.62	—	—	—
4,5-Dichlorocatechol	0.42	0.52	—	—	—
2,3-Dichloroquinol	0.38	—	—	—	—
2,5-Dichlorophenol	0.93	—	—	—	—
2,5-Dichloroquinol	0.33	—	—	—	—
2,3-Dichlorophenylmercapturic acid	—	0.70	—	—	—
3,4-Dichlorophenylmercapturic acid	—	0.75	—	—	—
2,4-Dichlorophenol	—	0.85	—	—	—
2,6-Dichlorophenol	—	0.73	—	—	—
3,5-Dichlorophenol	—	0.94	—	—	—
4-Chlorocatechol	0.33	—	—	—	—
3-Chlorocatechol	0.41	—	—	—	—
4-Chlororesorcinol	0.19	—	—	—	—
Chloroquinol	0.17	—	—	—	—
3,5-Dichlorocatechol	0.51	—	—	—	—
2,6-Dichloroquinol	0.39	—	—	—	—
L-2-Chlorophenylmercapturic acid	—	0.56	—	—	—
L-3-Chlorophenylmercapturic acid	—	0.61	—	—	—
L-4-Chlorophenylmercapturic acid	—	0.60	—	—	—
L-2,4-Dichlorophenylmercapturic acid	—	0.61	—	—	—
L-2,6-Dichlorophenylmercapturic acid	—	0.53	—	—	—
L-3,5-Dichlorophenylmercapturic acid	—	0.65	—	—	—
2-Chlorothiophenol	—	0.50	—	—	—
3-Chlorothiophenol	—	0.61	—	—	—
4-Chlorothiophenol	—	0.59	—	—	—
2,4-Dichlorothiophenol	—	0.02	—	—	—
2,6-Dichlorothiophenol	—	0.56	—	—	—
3,5-Dichlorothiophenol	—	0.39	—	—	—
2-Chloro-3-nitrophenol	—	—	0.75	—	0.69
3-Chloro-2-nitrophenol	—	—	1.0	—	0.69
3-Chloro-4-nitrophenol	—	—	0.07	—	0.69
4-Chloro-3-nitrophenol	—	—	0.14	—	0.87
o-Nitrophenol	—	—	1.0	—	0.57
2-Amino-3-chlorophenol	—	—	—	0.95	—
3-Amino-2-chlorophenol	—	—	—	0.91	—
3-Amino-4-chlorophenol	—	—	—	0.83	—

[a] Solvents: 1. Benzene:acetic acid:water = 1:1:2 v/v.
  2. n-Butanol:ethanol:3 N (NH$_4$)$_2$CO$_3$ buffer = 40:11:19 v/v.
  3. Petroleum ether (90°C.) saturated with 98% formic acid.
  4. Chloroform:acetic acid:water = 2:1:1 v/v.
  5. n-Butanol:3 N(NH$_4$)$_2$CO$_3$:3 N NH$_4$OH = 4:3:3 v/v.

TABLE III—*Continued*

Compound	Solvent[a]				
	1	2	3	4	5
4-Amino-3-chlorophenol	—	—	—	0.67	—
o-Chloroaniline	—	—	—	1.0	—
o-Aminophenol	—	—	—	0.17	—
N-Acetyl-S-(2-nitrophenyl)-L-cysteine	—	—	0.0	—	0.39
2-Chloro-4-nitrophenol	—	—	0.53	—	0.66
2-Chloro-6-nitrophenol	—	—	1.0	—	0.60
3-Chloro-5-nitrophenol	—	—	0.16	—	0.84
4-Chloro-2-nitrophenol	—	—	1.0	—	0.66
m-Nitrophenol	—	—	0.09	—	0.81
2-Amino-4-chlorophenol	—	—	—	0.62	—
2-Amino-6-chlorophenol	—	—	—	0.93	—
3-Amino-5-chlorophenol	—	—	—	0.51	—
4-Amino-2-chlorophenol	—	—	—	0.45	—
m-Chloroaniline	—	—	—	1.0	—
m-Aminophenol	—	—	—	0.4	—
2-Chloro-5-nitrophenol	—	—	0.50	—	0.69
5-Chloro-2-nitrophenol	—	—	1.0	—	0.66
p-Nitrophenol	—	—	0.02	—	0.59
2-Amino-5-chlorophenol	—	—	—	0.51	—
5-Amino-2-chlorophenol	—	—	—	0.70	—
p-Chloroaniline	—	—	—	1.0	—
p-Aminophenol	—	—	—	0.2	—
N-Acetyl-S-(4-nitrophenyl)-L-cysteine	—	—	0.0	—	0.42

Section II: Indoles and Related Compounds

Plant growth substances are hormone-like chemicals which play an important role in the regulation of growth and maturation of plants. There is considerable evidence that many different hormones are produced by plants, but only two, ethylene and 3-indoleacetic acid, have been chemically identified with certainty (P. W. Zimmerman, 1953). Some of the more frequently used terms for plant growth substances are plant hormones, auxins, phytohormones, and growth regulators. These have been applied not only to the naturally occurring hormones but also to all chemicals which are physiologically active when applied to plants. Only derivatives of indole will be discussed here.

Other indoles of biological importance are those which are excreted by animals, probably as a result of tryptophan metabolism. For example the excretion of serotonin (5-hydroxytryptamine) by man may in some way be connected to mental processes (Bodansky, 1955).

1. PREPARATION OF SAMPLE

a. *Isolation from Plant Material* (Bennet-Clark, 1953; Vlitos, 1953; Weller, 1954; Stowe, 1954; Kefford, 1955). The plant sample is frozen to $-10°C$. with "dry ice" and macerated at this temperature with small amounts of ethanol. After allowing the mixture to stand at $-10°C$. for 24 hours, it is centrifuged, the residue is washed several times with ethanol, and the alcohol is evaporated at reduced pressure. The residue is adjusted to pH 3 with H_3PO_4 and extracted for $1\frac{1}{2}$ hours with ether which is shaken immediately before use with acidic $FeSO_4$. The ether extract is shaken 3 times with 5% $NaHCO_3$, the bicarbonate extracts adjusted to pH 3 with H_3PO_4, re-extracted with ether, and washed with small amount of H_3PO_4 at pH 3. The final extract is evaporated with a stream of nitrogen and redissolved in sodium-dried ether.

The alcohol extract may be further purified by adsorption on an alumina column and elution with ether (A. Fischer, 1954). The elutate is chromatog aphed on Schleicher and Schuell Paper Nos. 2071 ar 2230 with appropriate solvents (see below), re-extracted from the paper with ether, and the individual zones are chromatographed for final identification.

An alternate procedure is as follows: Ground, sweet corn is extracted with 50% acetone at cold-room temperature. The extract is salted out with NaCl (250 g. NaCl/1.5 liters of solution), and the acetone layer is concentrated *in vacuo* to $\frac{1}{10}$ its original volume. The indoles are next extracted with ether, and after evaporation, the remaining amber oil is chromatographed. *CAUTION:* Indoles, especially those isolated from plant sources, must be kept under nitrogen during evaporation of solutions and stored in the cold in dark containers. These compounds are extremely labile and lose their biological activity when tested with *Avena* coleoptiles (See Section 4).

b. *Isolation of Indoles from Urine* (Armstrong, 1954; Dalgliesh, 1956). Acidified urine is extracted with ethyl acetate, the extract is shaken with 10% $NaHCO_3$, acidified, and re-extracted with ethyl acetate. The extracts may be further purified by passing them through a column of deactivated charcoal, and eluting the indoles with aqueous phenol.

2. SOLVENTS (see also Table V)

a. *i-Propanol:concentrated NH_4OH:water* = 10:1:1 v/v (Bennet-Clark, 1952; Müller, 1953; Stowe, 1953, 1954; Vlitos, 1953). This solvent or others with minor changes in the proportions of constituents has found wide use in the one-dimensional chromatography of indoles isolated from plant material.

b. *i-Propanol:water* = 10:1 or 10:2 v/v in the presence of NH_3 (Bennet-Clark, 1952, 1953; Terpstra, 1953). This solvent separates 3-indoleacetic acid and 3-indoleacetonitrile. As an equilibrating solvent, use Solvent (a) (Kefford, 1955).

c. n-Propanol:concentrated NH₄OH:water = 6:3:1 v/v or 16:1:3 v/v has been successfully used for the separation of 5-hydroxytryptamine (serotonin), *N*-methyl-5-hydroxytryptamine, bufotenin, and tryptamine (Jerchel, 1951; Luckwill, 1952; Weller, 1954; Rodnight, 1956).

d. n-Butanol:acetic acid:water = 4:1:5 v/v (organic phase) (Mitoma, 1956; Schreier, 1956; Boyland, 1956a; Dalgliesh, 1955a,b). This solvent is useful for the separation of metabolic products from tryptophan, e.g., anthranilic acid, kynurenine.

e. n-Butanol (water-saturated):concentrated NH₄OH = 7:1 v/v (Müller, 1953; Pacheco, 1953; Terpstra, 1953).

f. n-Butanol:pyridine:water = 1:1:1 v/v (Jepson, 1954b).

g. n-Butanol:water:formic acid = 81:12:7 v/v (Jacoby, 1956). This solvent will resolve ʟ-kynurenine, kynurenic acid, and anthranilic acid.

h. Methanol:n-butanol:benzene:water = 2:1:1:1 v/v (Jepson, 1954b; Mason, 1953). NaOH (0.05 N) may be substituted for water in this solvent.

i. Methanol:n-butanol = 4:2 v/v (Benassi, 1951).

j. Ethyl acetate:pyridine:water = 4:2:4 v/v is recommended for the chromatography of plant indoles (Müller, 1953).

k. Methyl ethyl ketone:pyridine/water = 70:15:15 v/v (Jerchel, 1951; Müller, 1953). This solvent separates indoleacetic acid and tryptophan.

l. Two-Dimensional Solvent Systems. (1) *First direction: i*-propanol: NH₄OH:water = 80:5:15 v/v; *second direction: n*-butanol:acetic acid: water = 4:1:5 v/v. This pair of solvents will separate indole, skatole and indolealdehyde (Fischer, 1954). Jepson (1955) uses the same solvents in the following proportions: *first direction:* 20:2:1; *second direction:* 12:3:5.

(2) *First direction: i*-propanol:acetic acid:water = 7:2:1 v/v; *second direction:* butanol:NH₄OH:water = 75:5:20 v/v (organic phase) (Decker, 1955).

(3) *First direction:* (long dimension-15 hours development) *n*-butanol: acetic acid:water = 4:1:5 v/v; *second direction:* 20% (w/v) aqueous KCl (3-4 hours development) (Dalgliesh, 1956). This solvent system is especially suitable for the separation of a large number of urinary indoles and related substances.

3. TECHNIQUES

Both the ascending and descending techniques, as well as two-dimensional chromatography, have been employed for the separation of indole compounds. Development is best carried out in a light-subdued room or by covering the glass cylinder with opaque material. For discerning work it may be recommended to fill the chromatographic tank with nitrogen and keep the temperature at about 15°C. 3-Indolylpyruvic acid breaks down during chromatographic development even under these conditions

TABLE IV

DETECTION AND SENSITIVITY OF INDOLE COMPOUNDS

(Sen, 1954)

Compound	Fluorescence in ultraviolet light	Color reactions with							
		FeCl$_3$-HClO$_4$		p-dimethylamino benzaldehyde		KNO$_2$-HNO$_3$		Cinnamaldehyde, HCl	
		Color	(μg.)	Color	(μg.)	Color	(μg.)	Color	(μg.)
Indole	Pale green	Orange red	3	Light red	3	Red	3	Pinkish brown	3
2-Methylindole	Green	Pinkish yellow		Scarlet					
3-Methylindole	Light blue	Pinkish brown	3	Blue	1	Yellow	3	Light brown	3
Indole-3-aldehyde	Pale yellow	Light brown	3	Light brown	3	Yellow	10	Yellow	3
Indole-3-carboxylic acid	Blue	Orange	1	Pink	1	Red	3	Orange	3
Indole-3-acetic acid	Ash	Pink	1	Bluish pink	1	Red	3	Yellowish brown	1
Indole-3-propionic acid	Light blue	Light brown	1	Bluish green	1	Yellow	3	Light brown	1
Indole-3-butyric acid	Light blue	Brown	1	Bluish green	1	Yellow	3	Light brown	1
Indole-3-acetamide	Yellowish brown	Pink	1	Pinkish brown	1	Pinkish brown	1	Yellowish brown	3
Indole-3-acetonitrile	Greenish blue	Green	3	Yellow	1	Ashy brown	3	Yellow	5
Indole-3-butyronitrile	Violet	Orange brown	3	Bluish light brown	1	Orange	10	Yellowish brown	10
Tryptophan	Yellowish green (after treatment with HClO$_4$)	Light brown	1	Pink	1	Yellow	1	Light brown	3
Tryptamine		Dull brown				Yellow	3		
Gramine	Grey	Pinkish blue	5	Yellow	1				

Acetyl tryptophan	Light blue	Light brown		Ash					
Isatin	Brown	Yellow	5	Yellow	3	Yellow	3	Light yellow	3
Dihydroxyindole	Brown			Yellow		Yellow	50		
N-acetyl isatin	Brown			Light yellow				Light yellow	5
N-acetyl indoxyl	Blue	Light brown	10	Orange	3	Light brown	10	Brown light	3
Indoxyl-acetate	Green	Blue	1	Greyish brown	3	Light ash	10	Brown	1
Indican	Light violet	Blue	3	Brownish orange	3	Yellow	10	Yellowish pink	1
Indican glucoside	Yellow			Pale yellow					
Indigotin	Light blue	Blue		Black					
Indigo disulfonate	Light blue	Blue		Black					
Indigo tetrasulfonate	Light blue	Blue		Black					

(Bentley, 1956), and the apparent physiological activity of biograms is mainly due to the action of breakdown products.

When a 1 % indoleacetic acid solution is exposed to ultraviolet light for a short time, the resultant chromatogram reveals several additional spots when sprayed with the perchloric acid-FeCl₃ reagent (see below). Only 10 % of the original biological activity is recovered on the paper (Mayr, 1956)

4. DETECTION (See Table IV)

   a. *Dimethylaminobenzaldehyde* (Ehrlich's Reagent).   (1) *Spray Reagent:* 0.5 % DMAB in 1 % alcoholic HCl or 1 % DMAB in 1 N aqueous HCl (Reddi, 1953; Vlitos, 1953).   Spraying the chromatogram next with concentrated NH_4OH causes the spot due to indican to turn from brown to red (orange fluorescence) (Decker, 1955).

   (2) *Dipping Reagent:* Two g. DMAB dissolved in 100 ml. of concentrated HCl:acetone = 10:90.   The reagent is made up just before use.   The chromatograms are dipped into this reagent and dried at 40°C.   The sensitivity of this reagent is 0.05 μg. for serotonin and other indoles; Rodnight, 1956).

   b. *Croconic Aldehyde* (2 %) in acetone or ethanol.   The sprayed papers are exposed to HCl vapors, and reddish-brown spots result for the indoles (Jerchel, 1951; Vlitos, 1953).

   c. *Cinnamaldehyde* (Sen, 1954; Müller, 1953; Terpstra, 1953).   Five ml. of cinnamaldehyde is dissolved in 95 ml. of ethanol and 5 ml. of concentrated HCl.   The sprayed chromatograms are heated at 65°C. for 3–10 minutes.

   d. *FeCl₃-HClO₄ Reagent* (Salkowski Reaction) (Linser, 1956; Bennet-Clark, 1952, 1953; Bolle-Jones, 1954; Yamaki, 1952; Sen, 1954).   Two ml. of 0.05 M FeCl₃ is added to 100 ml. 5 % HClO₄.   Red-violet colors result for indoles, changing to blue-yellow after 24 hours.

   e. *Nitrose Reaction* (Sen, 1954; Linser, 1956).   One g. of KNO₂ is dissolved in 20 ml. concentrated HNO₃ and 80 ml. 95 % ethanol.   Blue-yellow spots result for the indoles.

   f. *1-Nitroso-2-naphthol* (0.1 %) in 95 % ethanol followed by nitrose-reaction spray (see above) produces violet spots on a faint yellow background for 5-hydroxy-indoles, like serotonin (Udenfriend, 1955).

   g. *Diazotized Sulfanilic Acid and Nitraniline* (Stowe, 1954) (See Section I of this chapter, p. 305 for the preparation).   These reagents react with most indole compounds giving characteristic colors.

   h. *Detection of Serotonin* (Shepherd, 1953).   5-Hydroxytryptamine is visualized with a reagent composed of 0.1 % of potassium dichromate:37 to 41 % formaldehyde = 9:1 v/v.   The sprayed chromatogram is heated

TABLE V

R_f VALUES OF INDOLE COMPOUNDS

Compound	Solvent[a]						
	1	2	3	4	5	6	7
Indican	—	0.34	—	—	—	—	—
Tryptophan	0.50	0.44	0.62	0.42	0.24	0.18	0.34
N-Methyltryptophan	0.56	—	0.66	—	0.39	—	—
N-Acetyltryptophan	0.88	—	0.68	0.58	0.46	—	—
Tryptamine	0.71	—	0.78	0.82	0.82	0.65	0.72
1-Methyl tryptamine	0.70	—	0.75	0.85	—	—	—
2-Methyl tryptamine	0.72	—	0.78	0.85	—	—	—
α-Methyl tryptamine	0.78	—	0.82	0.89	0.87	—	—
α-Ethyltryptamine	0.84	—	0.86	0.89	—	0.79	—
α,α-Dimethyltryptamine	0.83	—	0.87	0.90	0.89	—	—
N,N-Dimethyltryptamine	0.76	—	0.80	0.92	—	—	—
5-Hydroxytryptamine	0.47	0.38	0.70	0.65	0.57	0.52	—
5-Methoxytryptamine	0.60	—	0.73	—	0.76	—	—
6-Methoxytryptamine	0.62	—	0.75	—	0.76	—	—
5,6-Dimethoxytryptamine	0.50	—	0.66	—	0.63	—	—
Gramine	0.74	—	0.76	—	—	0.80	—
Indole	0.97	—	0.97	0.93	0.93	0.79	0.78
Skatole	0.97	—	0.97	0.95	0.95	0.9	—
Indole-3-carboxylic acid	—	—	—	—	—	0.20	0.62
Indole-3-acetic acid	0.90	—	0.80	0.52	0.38	0.25	0.43
Indole-3-propionic acid	0.92	—	0.86	0.59	0.45	0.35	0.49
Indole-3-butyric acid	0.95	—	0.91	0.65	0.55	0.44	0.53
Indolylacetonitrile	0.93	—	—	0.92	—	0.75	—
Indole-3-aldehyde	0.90	—	—	—	—	0.72	0.46
5-Hydroxyindoleacetic acid	0.77	—	0.70	0.31	0.20	0.17	—
Indoxyl sulfate	0.45	0.25	0.78	0.71	0.61	—	—
Indolyl-3-pyruvic acid	—	—	—	—	—	0.12	—
Anthranilic acid	—	0.90	—	—	—	—	—
3-OH-Anthranilic acid	—	0.84	—	—	—	—	—
5-OH-Anthranilic acid	—	0.54	—	—	—	—	—
L-Kynurenine	—	0.37	—	—	—	—	—
D-Kynurenine	—	0.31	—	—	—	—	—
L-3-OH-Kynurenine	—	0.29	—	—	—	—	—
D-3-OH-Kynurenine	—	0.24	—	—	—	—	—
L-5-OH-Kynurenine	—	0.17	—	—	—	—	—
D-5-OH-Kynurenine	—	0.14	—	—	—	—	—
Indole-3-butyronitrile	—	—	—	—	—	—	0.79
Indole-3-lactic acid	—	—	—	—	—	0.30	0.33
Indole-3-acrylic acid	—	—	—	—	—	—	0.80
5-OH-Tryptophan	—	—	—	—	—	0.11	—
7-OH Indoleacetic acid	—	—	—	—	—	0.09	—

[a] Solvents: 1. n-Butanol:acetic acid:water = 60:15:25 v/v (Jepson, 1954b).

    2. n-Butanol:acetic acid:water = 4:1:5 v/v (Dalgliesh, 1955a; Shepherd, 1953).

    3. n-Butanol:pyridine:water = 1:1:1 v/v (Jepson, 1954).

    4. i-Propanol:NH₄OH:water = 8:1:1 v/v (Jepson, 1954).

    5. i-Propanol:NH₄OH:water = 20:1:2 v/v (Jepson, 1954).

    6. i-Propanol:NH₄OH:water = 10:1:1 v/v (Stowe, 1954).

    7. i-Propanol:NH₄OH:water = 80:5:15 v/v (Vlitos, 1953.)

for 5 minutes at 100–110°C. and is viewed with an ultraviolet light source, where the compound produces a golden-yellow fluorescent spot.

An alternate procedure involves the spraying of the chromatogram with 10 % methanolic xanthydrol:acetic acid (v/v) and exposing the paper to HCl vapors. Serotonin forms a blue spot (Schreier, 1956).

i. Biological Tests. The extension of *Avena* coleoptiles grown on 3 % sucrose solutions in the dark can be used for both qualitative and quantitative measurement of indole compounds (Bennet-Clark, 1952; Luckwill, 1952; Müller, 1953; Yamaki, 1952).

j. Ultraviolet Illumination. Kynurenine, kynurenic acid, 3-hydroxyanthranilic acid, and related compounds are detected as blue fluorescent spots under ultraviolet illumination (Reddi, 1953; Dalgliesh, 1951; Mason, 1951, 1953; Benassi, 1951).

5. QUANTITATIVE METHODS

After chromatography, the papers are dried and sprayed with a solution of 1 % dimethylaminobenzaldehyde dissolved in N HCl. The color density of the spots is measured at 560 mμ and a quantitative estimation is made by the maximum density method (see Chapter IV) (Vlitos, 1953; Rodnight, 1956). Plant indoles may also be eluted with water after locating the area with the aid of guide strips and a suitable color reagent. The absorption is measured in a spectrophotometer at 280 mμ and compared with standard solutions (Müller, 1953). Spots whose color has been developed with methanolic xanthydrol (see h. above) are eluted with acetic acid:methanol = 2:1 and the optical density determined at 580 mμ (Schreier, 1956). This method is suitable for the estimation of serotonin.

Chapter XI

NATURALLY OCCURRING PIGMENTS

Section I: Porphyrins

Historically speaking, the chloroplast pigments were the first compounds which were separated by adsorption chromatography. The ready availability and the natural coloration of these compounds were important factors for Michael Tswett's brilliant experiments first reported at the meeting of the Warsaw Society of Natural Sciences in 1903 (Hesse and Weil, 1954). A detailed description of adsorption chromatography of plant pigments is not within the scope of this chapter; however, it is noted that many techniques of paper chromatography of the plant pigments are adaptations of Tswett's adsorption column techniques. For example, the use of sugar-impregnated paper substitutes a thin sheet of paper for a glass tube (Sporer, 1954), or glass paper has been used with petroleum ether as developing solvent (Strain, 1953).

Urinary porphyrins and porphyrin esters may be separated by two-dimensional and horizontal techniques. Using one-dimensional development, it has been found that the R_f values are inversely proportional to the number of carboxyl groups (Dunning, 1956; Kehl, 1951).

The reader is referred to a comprehensive review on the paper chromatography of chlorophyll pigments (Douin, 1953). For a general discussion on urinary porphyrins, including a picture of scale models of closely related porphyrins, a review by Falk (1954a) is recommended.

1. PREPARATION OF SAMPLE

a. Isolation of Porphyrins. In order to separate and identify the porphyrin pigments of Molluscan shells, the material is treated as follows prior to chromatography (Nicholas, 1949): The shells are broken and decalcified for 24 hours by treating them either with concentrated HCl or a mixture of H_3PO_4 (sp. gr. 1.75):water $= 1:1$ v/v. The acid extracts are filtered and adjusted with water to contain 1–2.5 N acid. The porphyrins are separated by adsorption chromatography on a talc column suspended in 2 N HCl. The eluate is evaporated to dryness, and the residue is taken up in acetone and passed through another talc column made up with distilled water. The column is washed with water until the washings no longer give a test for chloride ions. The column is then eluted with a 10 N ammonia solution. Aliquot portions of the eluate are applied to the paper.

The extraction of porphyrins from urine is as follows (Nishikawa, 1952; Corwin, 1954): To 10 ml. of urine in a centrifuge tube is added 2 ml. of 10 % lead acetate. The precipitate is centrifuged and washed with 5 ml. of water. The pigments are extracted from the precipitate with 1 ml. of 15 % HCl. The extract is dried *in vacuo* over pellets of NaOH, the residue is taken up in 0.2 ml. of 10 N NH$_4$OH, and an aliquot of this solution is spotted on paper for chromatography.

b. Preparation of Porphyrin Methyl Esters (Kehl, 1954*a,b*). Two ml. of blood, 10 ml. of urine or 5 g. of feces are extracted with ethyl acetate: acetic acid (v/v). The extracts are concentrated *in vacuo* under nitrogen which is being passed through pyrogallol to remove any traces of oxygen. Twenty-five ml. of dry methanol and dry HCl gas are added to the residue, and esterification is allowed to proceed for one hour with refluxing. Twenty-five ml. of chloroform is then added, and the excess methanol-HCl is washed out with small amounts of water to neutrality. The chloroform extract is taken to dryness, and the methyl esters are redissolved in 30 μl. of chloroform for chromatography.

c. Isolation of Chlorophylls (Chiba, 1954). Chlorophylls a and b are extracted from leaves by grinding them in a mortar with sand and gradually adding ethyl ether in the ratio of 50 ml. solvent per 1 g. of fresh weight of the material. The extract is filtered and washed several times with distilled water. The ether extract is concentrated *in vacuo* to a convenient volume.

2. PAPER

Whatman No. 1 and Schleicher and Schuell No. 2043b papers have been used without pretreatment for the chromatography of porphyrins and their methyl esters (Kehl, 1954*b*).

In order to repress the decomposition of chlorophyll during chromatographic development, Whatman No. 1 paper is impregnated with sucrose by dipping the paper into an 18 % aqueous solution of sucrose, followed by drying at 100° (Sporer, 1954). Untreated Eaton and Dikeman filter paper No. 301 or glass-fiber paper (Reeve Angel & Co.) may also be used for the separation of chloroplast pigments (Strain, 1953). Better results are achieved by using paper impregnated with methanol or "Vaseline" (see Chapters III, VII, and VIII; reversed phase chromatography). A 5 % solution of "Vaseline" in petroleum ether is poured over the paper which is then dried in the hood.

3. SOLVENTS (See also Tables I and II)

a. 2,5-Dimethylpyridine (lutidine):water (v/v) (NH$_3$ atmosphere) is used for the chromatography of porphyrins (Kehl, 1951). A commercial mixture of 2,4- and 2,5-dimethylpyridine has been used in place of pure 2,5-

dimethylpyridine; saturation of the chamber with NH_3 is not necessary (Nicholas, 1949, 1951; Eriksen, 1953).

b. *Kerosene:chloroform* $= 100:65$ v/v and *kerosene:n-propyl alcohol* $= 5:1$ when used in succession for a unidimensional development will separate the methyl esters of coproporphyrins I and III, protoporphyrin IV, mesoporphyrin IX, and uroporphyrin I. For development with the first solvent the chamber is saturated with chloroform; for development with the second solvent the chamber is saturated with kerosene (Chu, 1951, 1953; Lucas, 1954). Better resolution is obtained if this pair of solvents is used for two-dimensional development (Bogorad, 1953; Michalec, 1956).

Falk (1953, 1954b) has found that after development by the method of Chu (1951) the main natural porphyrins are separated with the exception of uroporphyrins I and III which remain together near the origin. Consequently, these investigators cut the paper parallel with the base line, just above the uroporphyrins. This lower portion is then developed with kerosene:dioxane $= 8:3$ in a direction at right angles to the direction of the previous development. The uroporphyrin esters I and III move in the kerosene:dioxane solvent with R_f values of about 0.02 and 0.5, respectively.

c. *Ethanol and Methanol.* Ethanol (80 %) plus a few drops of concentrated HCl is the mobile phase (stationary phase: ether) for the separation of natural porphyrins on filter paper disks (Serchi, 1953). Thirty-three per cent ethanol and methanol have been used for the chromatography of bilirubin (R_f 0.7–0.8) (Kawai, 1953). Absolute methanol separates the isomeric coproporphyrins in urine (Nishikawa, 1952). Methanol (80 %) is used for chloroplast pigments on paper impregnated with "Vaseline" (Strain, 1953).

d. *Petroleum ether (30–60):chloroform* $= 3:1$ v/v for porphyrin methyl esters (Rappoport, 1955).

e. *Heptane:ethylene dichloride:tert-butanol* $= 20:1:1.5$ v/v gives good separation of the porphyrin methyl esters by horizontal chromatography (see Fig. 1) (Rappoport, 1955).

f. *Petroleum ether:n-propanol* $= 100:0.5$ v/v separates the following plant pigments in about 20–40 minutes development: neoxanthin, chlorophyll b, violaxanthin, chlorophyll a, lutein and zeaxanthin, carotenes— arranged in order of increasing mobility (Strain, 1953). Eaton and Dikeman No. 301 paper or glass fiber paper is employed with this solvent.

g. *Petroleum ether* is used for the chloroplast pigments on filter paper which is previously sprayed with 80 % methanol (Strain, 1953).

h. *Toluene:95 % ethanol* $= 20:0.1$ v/v gives the following R_f values for chlorophylls a and b, respectively: 0.47, 0.28 (Chiba, 1954, 1955). *n*-Propanol (0.5 %) in *n*-hexane will also separate chlorophylls a and b on paper impregnated with sucrose (Sporer, 1954).

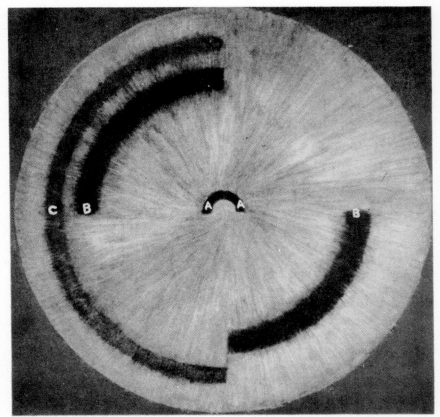

Fig. 1. Horizontal Chromatogram of Porphyrin Methyl Esters (Rappoport, 1955), viewed under ultraviolet illumination. A: coproporphyrin I; B: coproporphyrin III; C: protoporphyrin IX.

i. Carbon tetrachloride:isoöctane = 7:3 v/v, for porphyrins (Blumer, 1956).

4. TECHNIQUES

Most solvents used for the chromatography of porphyrins are highly volatile. It is necessary, therefore, to choose a chromatographic cabinet with a tight-fitting, vapor-proof lid. Since equilibrium conditions must be maintained during the development phase, it is recommended to use the ascending technique. An efficient method for the pre-equilibration of the chromatographic tank is the use of an inverted bell jar with a vacuum desiccator lid (Dunning, 1956). The paper sheets are tacked to wooden disks which are held by a wooden dowel rod fitted through a vented cork. The system is rapidly evacuated, the solvent is allowed to boil briefly, the chamber is sealed, the papers are lowered into the solvent, and the development is allowed to proceed.

Horizontal development is accomplished by clamping the paper disk between two glass plates, weighted down by a number of lead bricks. The solvent is fed through a small hole in the center of the top plate by means of a hypodermic syringe (see Fig. 1) (Rappoport, 1955).

The chromatography of the plastid pigments is preferably carried out in a darkened tank or in a refrigerator at 5°C. It is recommended to fill the tank with nitrogen or CO_2 to retard decomposition of the pigments (Sporer, 1954).

5. Detection and Quantitative Evaluation of Spots

The porphyrins may be observed as red spots in ordinary light when sufficient concentrations are applied or with ultraviolet illumination as pink fluorescent spots (Nicholas, 1949). The spots may be quantitatively evaluated by a visual or photometric comparison of their color densities or areas with those of spots of known concentration (see Chapter IV). The porphyrins may also be identified by their characteristic ultraviolet absorption spectra (Kehl, 1951). This latter method should be amenable to semi-quantitative analysis.

6. Detailed Experiments

This detailed descripton of an experiment should serve only to illustrate one successful resolution of porphyrins.

Schleicher and Schuell No. 2043b filter paper, 30 × 40 cm., is employed. Samples of a volume 1–3 μl. are applied to the paper, 3 cm. from the bottom edge, 5 cm. from the sides of the paper, and 2 cm. distance between drops. The porphyrins are separated with the lutidine:water (v/v) solvent, with or without 25 % ammonia in a beaker in the chamber (Kehl, 1951; Nicholas, 1951). The apparatus should be kept in the shade, as direct sunlight causes decomposition of the porphyrins and a resulting decrease in fluorescence of the spots. The chromatogram is allowed to develop for 12–16 hours at 19–25°C. The filter paper is dried in a stream of warm air and observed in daylight or ultraviolet illumination (Kehl, 1951).

Lind (1953) separated the plastid pigments in leaves by two-dimensional chromatography. Three solvents were employed for development along the first dimension. First, *acetone* is used to move all pigments into a line at the top of the original circular spot. Second, *Skellysolve* B moves the carotenes with the solvent front while the other pigments move only slightly. Third, 1 % *1-propanol* in Skellysolve B v/v separates chlorophyll b from chlorophyll a and the xanthophylls. The chromatogram is developed along the second dimension with 25 % chloroform in Skellysolve B

TABLE I
R_f VALUES OF PORPHYRINS

Compound	Solvents[a]			
	1	2	3	4
Uroporphyrin	0.26	—	—	—
Coproporphyrin	0.54	—	—	—
Cobalt protoporphyrin	0.6	—	—	—
Heminporphyrin	0.7	—	—	—
Protoporphyrin	0.84	0.75	0.80	0.96
Mesoporphyrin	0.86	0.82	0.82	0.96
Hematoporphyrin	0.87	0.30	0.05	0.05
Deuteroporphyrin	0.88	—	—	—
Etioporphyrin	1.0	—	—	—
All porphyrin esters	1.0	—	—	—
Chlorin a₂ (methyl ester)	—	0.55	0.32	0.77
Mesochlorin	—	0.88	0.89	0.96
Pyrrochlorin	—	0.96	0.97	0.96
Rhodochlorin	—	0.90	0.91	0.96
Dioxyprotoporphyrin	—	0.34	0	0
Dioxymonovinylhydroxyethyldeuteroporphyrin	—	0.26	0	0
Monovinylhydroxyethyldeuteroporphyrin	—	0.40	0.28	0
Pyrroporphyrin	—	0.92	0.96	0.96
Rhodoporphyrin	—	0.77	0.82	0.96

[a] Solvents: 1. 2,5-Dimethylpyridine:water v/v (Kehl, 1951).
    2. Kerosene:chloroform = 4:2.6 v/v.
    3. Kerosene:n-propanol = 6:1 v/v.
    4. Trichloroethylene (Barrett, 1956).

TABLE II
R_f VALUES OF PORPHYRIN METHYL ESTERS

	Solvents[a]	
	1	2
Uroporphyrin I	0.17	0.37
Uroporphyrin III	— (0.14)[b]	0.40, 0.54
Coproporphyrin I	0.47 (0.41)	0.37
Coproporphyrin III	0.67	0.34
Protoporphyrin I	—	0.29
Protoporphyrin III	—	0.22
Protoporphyrin IX	0.84 (0.82)	—
Mesoporphyrin IX	0.90 (0.90)	—
Deuteroporphyrin IX	0.88	—

[a] Solvents: 1. Kerosene:chloroform = 100:65 v/v, then same direction kerosene:n-propanol = 5:1 v/v (Chu, 1951).
    2. 80% ethanol v/v (Serchi, 1953).
[b] R_f values by Kehl and Günter (1954b).

(the chloroform is thoroughly washed with water and dried with $CaCl_2$). In this solvent the carotenes again move with the solvent front and the xanthophylls are separated from chlorophyll a, which is almost stationary.

Section II: Flavonoid Pigments, Anthocyanins, and Pterins

A large number of naturally occurring flavonoid pigments have been separated by paper chromatography and identified by a study of R_f values in various solvents (see Tables IV and V) (Wender, 1949; Gage, 1951; Paris, 1952; Casteel, 1953; Jorgenson, 1955; Barber, 1956; Nordström, 1956).

1. PREPARATION OF SAMPLE

Non-anthocyanin pigments are extracted from flower petals with methanol, whereas anthocyanins are best isolated with methanol containing 1% HCl (Geissman, 1954). Leucoanthocyanins are first converted to anthocyanidins by heating the leaf tissue with 2 N HCl on a steam bath for 20 minutes (Bate-Smith, 1954). The aqueous acid solution is extracted with isoamyl alcohol.

2. PAPER

Whatman No. 1 filter paper is commonly employed for the chromatography of the flavonoids. Schleicher and Schuell No. 597 has been recommended for the separation of quercetin and isoquercetin isolated from apricots (Williams, 1953).

3. SOLVENTS

A wide variety of solvents for one-dimensional chromatography is listed in Tables IV and VI. The following additional solvents are suitable for two-dimensional chromatography:

a. *First direction:* n-butanol:27% acetic acid (v/v); *second direction:* m-cresol:acetic acid:water = 50:2:48 v/v (organic phase) (Geissman, 1954).

b. *First direction:* ethyl acetate:acetic acid:water = 50:2:50 v/v; *second direction:* n-butanol:acetic acid:water = 4:1:5 v/v (Oshima, 1952).

4. TECHNIQUES

Twelve to eighteen microliters of an alcohol solution of the mixture, containing 7–40 μg. of each pigment, is spotted on the filter paper which is then developed by conventional techniques. Solvent development is usually carried out for a period of 8–22 hours, allowing the solvent front to advance 35–40 cm. from the origin.

Horizontal chromatography has been employed for the separation of rutin, isoquercitrin, quercitrin, and quercetin (see Table V) (Oshima, 1952). The solvent is ethyl acetate:acetic acid:water = 4:1:5 v/v.

TABLE III

FLAVONOIDS; COLORS PRODUCED BY CHROMOGENIC SPRAYS (CASTEEL, 1953)

Compound	Untreated		Chromogenic spraying reagent[a]													
			1		2		3		4		5		6		7	
	vis.	u.v.	vis.	u.v.	vis.	u.v.	vis.	u.v.	vis.	u.v.	vis.	u.v.	vis.	u.v.	vis.	u.v.
Hesperitin	...	PG	I	G	PY	Y	...	T	T	BK	BO	G	T	T	T	G
Kaempferitin	...	POB	Y	YG	PY	YO	PY	OY	olive	BK	Y	YG	PY	Y	Y	YG
Myricetin	Y	Y	DY	YG	Y	DG	PY	O	T	BK	G	OB	O	BK	T	G
Myricitrin	DY	B	PY	YO	Y	OY	DY	B	olive	BK	BO	DB	DV	B	ochre	DB
Pinobanksin	PY	YB	I	G	PY	Y	PY	YB	T	BK	Y	YG	...	T	PYG	G
Pinocembrin	...	PG	PI	YG	...	Y	PY	Y	T	BK	cream	YG	...	Y	T	G
Rhoifolin	Y	O	...	YG	PY	YO	PY	OY	T	BK	Y	YG	PY	Y	Y	YG
Teetochrysin	PY	PDV	Y	Y	PY	OB	PY	T	T	BK	Y	PO	PY	PRB	PY	YB

Colors: B, brown; Bk, black; D, dark; G, green; I, ivory; O, orange; P, pale; R, red; T, tan; V, violet; Y, yellow; ... no appreciable color.
[a] Color reagents: 1. 1% alcoholic aluminum chloride.
2. 1% alcoholic thorium chloride.
3. 1% basic lead acetate.
4. 1% alcoholic ferric chloride.
5. 1% aqueous sodium carbonate.
6. 1% lead acetate.
7. Benedict's solution.

Flavonoids may also be separated by paper electrophoresis using borate buffers (see Part II) (Hashimoto, 1952).

5. DETECTION

Most of the flavonoid compounds exhibit characteristic fluorescent colors on the developed chromatogram when examined under ultraviolet light. In addition, the original color of these compounds in visible and ultraviolet light may be altered or enhanced with the following color reagents: (see also Table III)

a. 1 % alcoholic *ferric chloride.*

b. 1 % alcoholic *thorium chloride.*

c. 1 % aqueous *basic lead acetate.*

d. 1 % aqueous *lead acetate.*

e. 1 % aqueous Na_2CO_3 .

f. $0.1 \ N \ AgNO_3 : 5 \ N \ NH_4OH \ = \ 1:1$ v/v.

g. 1 % alcoholic *aluminum chloride.*

h. *Benedict's solution.*[1]

i. 1 % alcoholic *ferric perchlorate.*

j. $2 \ N \ KOH$ in ethanol.

k. *Tetraphenyldiboronoxide.* For the identification of flavones, the chromatogram is dipped into a saturated petroleum ether solution of tetraphenyldiboronoxide (F. Heyl and Co., Hildesheim, Germany), followed by dipping the paper into a 1–2 % aqueous solution of a tertiary ammonium salt like β-phenoxy-ethyldimethylammonium bromide (Neu, 1956).

6. DETAILED EXPERIMENTAL PROCEDURES

a. *Identification of Quercetin from Apricot* (B. L. Williams, 1953). An impure extract from apricot fruits is chromatographed on Schleicher and Schuell paper No. 597 with *acetic acid:water* = 6:4 v/v. The fluorescent spots or bands at R_f 0.40 are cut out and eluted with 95 % ethanol. The eluate is concentrated *in vacuo*, crystallized from water, and dried over P_2O_5 . An alcoholic solution of the crystals is rechromatographed in several solvents, and on the basis of the R_f values the identity of quercetin is established.

b. *Separation of Quercetin and Rutin* (Naghski, 1951; Kariyone, 1953). Quercetin is separated from rutin by descending chromatography using serated sheets of Whatman No. 1 and one of the following solvents: *ethyl acetate* saturated with water; *ethyl acetate:benzene:water* = 35:15:50 v/v.

---

[1] Preparation of Benedict's solution (Hawk, Oser, Summerson, *Practical Physiological Chemistry*, 12th edition, The Blakiston Co., 1947): 173 g. of Na citrate and 100 g. of Na_2CO_3 are dissolved in 800 ml. of hot water, and the solution is filtered if necessary. 17.3 g. of $CuSO_4$ is dissolved in 100 ml. of water, and this solution is added slowly, with stirring to the carbonate-citrate solution. The volume is made up to 1 liter.

TABLE IV

R_f VALUES OF FLAVONOID PIGMENTS (GAGE, 1951; PARIS, 1952; CASTEEL, 1953)

Substance	|	|	|	|	Solvent[a]	|	|	|	|	|	|
	1	2	3	4	5	6	7	8	9	10	11
Flavonol aglycones											
Gossypetin	0.59	0.09	0.07	....	0.21	....	0.06	0.51	0.12	0.07	0.43
Kaempferol	0.90	0.74	0.53 (0.75)[b]	0.17	0.85	0.05	0.09	0.77	0.10	0.04	0.50
Morin	0.71 (0.83)	0.65	0.17 (0.25)	....	0.87 (0.81)	0.12	0.26	0.58	0.27	0.13	0.68
Nortangeretin	0.79	0.92	0.72	....	0.76	....	0.08	0.60	0.10	0.04	0.54
Patuletin	0.81	0.13	0.43	....	0.78	....	0.10	0.76	0.10	0.06	0.50
Quercetagetin	0.17	0.06	0.09	....	0.22	....	0.24	0.61	0.19	0.13	0.63
Quercetin	0.81 (0.94)	0.42	0.22	0.05	0.78	0.05	0.06	0.67	0.07	0.04	0.40
Rhamnetin	0.92	0.71	0.63	0.96	0.80	0.07	0.08	0.73	0.08	0.03	0.60
Robinetin	0.41	0.25	0.10	....	0.56	0.05	0.07	0.58	0.08	0.03	0.32
Flavonol	0.98	1.00	0.99	....	0.96	....	....	0.94?	....	....	0.86
Galangin	0.98	0.93	0.92	....	0.96	....	....	0.92	0.15	....	0.75
Myricetin	0.78	0.20	0.06	....	0.54	....	....	0.45	0.12	....	0.31
Ulexflavonol	0.93		0.95		0.92						
Ulexogenol	0.89		0.86		0.82						
Adansoniagenine		0.77	....		0.76						
Opuntiagenine	0.95				0.68						
Scoparol					0.83						
Rhamnetol	0.92	0.70			0.90						
Aphloiol	0.07		0.31		0.52						
Quercetol	0.83		0.31		0.75						
Equisporol	0.02		0.08		0.25						
Equisporonol	0.04		0.11		0.30						

Flavonol Glycosides

Gossypin	0.02	0.81	0.25	....	0.87	0.16	0.13	0.54	0.14	0.17	0.44
Gossypitrin	0.11	0.39	0.08	....	0.49	0.27	0.40	0.79	0.46	0.24	0.74
Isoquercitrin	0.40	0.51	0.24	0.05	0.72	0.28	0.42	0.80	0.45	0.27	0.74
Quercemeritrin	0.50	0.52	0.27	....	0.72	....	....	0.80	0.45	0.27	0.73
Quercitrin	0.50 (0.54)	0.56	0.33	0.05	0.82	0.54	0.55	0.79 (0.88)	0.46 (0.58)	0.45	0.74
Robinin	0.21	0.55	0.35	0.14	0.51	0.77	0.72	0.76	0.77	0.71	0.84
Rutin	0.15	0.45	0.21	0.07	0.57	0.54	0.60	0.83	0.62	0.45	0.75
Xanthorhamnin	0.02	0.70	0.27	0.08	0.50	0.69	0.66	0.83	0.68	0.58	0.82
Kaempferitin	0.26	0.82	0.63		0.79			0.89	0.77		0.86
Myricitrin	0.35	0.48	0.17		0.74			0.87	0.52		0.73

Flavone aglycones

Acacetin	0.94	0.96	0.95	0.94	0.92	....	0.00	0.80 (0.90)	0.00	0.00	0.71 (0.79)
Apigenin	0.87	0.89	0.87	....	0.91	....	0.12	0.89	0.15	0.00	0.66
Auranetin	0.92	0.93	0.99	0.94	0.91	....	....	0.99	0.63	0.34	0.90
Chrysin	0.86	0.93	0.95	....	0.93	....	0.00	....	0.00	0.00	0.75
Genkwanin	0.93	0.96	0.98	0.94	0.91	0.02	0.00	0.78	0.00	0.00	0.72
Isowogonin	0.92	0.74	0.99	....	0.90	0.11	0.00	0.87	0.00	0.00	0.81
Norwogonin	0.85	0.94	0.99	....	0.88	....	0.21	0.83	0.26	0.00	0.73
Oroxylin A	0.97	0.98	0.98	....	0.94	0.02	0.00	0.88	0.00	0.00	0.84
Wogonin	0.94	0.97	0.99	0.94	0.92	....	0.00	0.88	0.00	0.00	0.79
Baicalein	0.97	....	0.99		0.90			0.83	0.24		0.79
Tectochrysin	0.98	0.99	0.98		0.97			0.94	0.27[c]		0.89
Apigenol	0.95	0.92			0.91						
Luteolol	0.93	0.67			0.84						
Gentiacauleol	0.94	0.94			0.93						
Paspalol	0.92	0.74			0.92						
Homoeriodictyol	0.97	0.95	0.93	0.08	0.91	0.32	0.49	0.92	0.55	0.29	0.80
3,3',4',5,7-Pentahydroxy-flavanone	0.79	0.62	0.42	....	0.84	....	0.57	0.87	0.13	0.00	0.73

TABLE IV *Continued*

Substance	Solvent[a]										
	1	2	3	4	5	6	7	8	9	10	11
Butin	0.98	0.88?	0.79?		0.91			0.93?	0.55		0.81?
Hesperitin	0.97	0.96	0.97		0.94			0.94	0.50		0.85
Katsuranin	0.97	0.87	0.76		0.93			0.95	0.63		0.82
Liquiritigenin	0.97	0.92	0.91?		0.95			0.95	0.62?		0.86?
Pinobanksin	0.98	0.97	0.94		0.96			0.95	0.68		0.87
Pinocembrin	0.99	0.98	0.98		0.97			0.97	0.58		0.88
Pinostrobin	0.99	0.99	0.98		0.97			0.96	0.52		0.92
7-Hydroxyflavanone	0.98	....	0.97		0.95			0.96	....		0.89?
Flavanone glycosides											
Hesperidin	0.77 (0.12)	0.85	0.40 (0.66)	0.17	0.40 (0.63)	0.80	0.79	0.63 (0.86)	0.82	0.17	0.89
Naringin	0.51	0.75	0.58	0.16	0.70	0.81	0.75	0.86	0.80	0.77	0.88
Neohesperidin	0.38	0.75	0.67	0.16	0.67	0.80	0.79	0.88	0.81	0.72	0.90
Flavane aglycones											
D-Catechin	0.91	0.35	0.16	0.11	0.74	....	0.65	0.79	0.41	0.51	0.68
L-Epicatechin	0.80	0.59	0.83	0.00	0.65	....	0.54	0.72	0.55	0.38	0.68
Flavone glycosides											
Diosmin	0.07	0.77?	0.62		0.54			0.67			
Rhoifolin	0.08	0.85	0.61		0.69			0.88			0.87
Flavonol heterosides											
Rutoside	0.09		0.22		0.59						
Quercitroside	0.38		0.55		0.81						
Xanthorhamnoside	0.02				0.44						
Scoparoside	0.16		0.61		0.40						
Ulexoside	0.13				0.80						
Opuntiaflavonoside	0.14				0.59						

Compound	1	2	3	4	5	6	7	8	9	10	11
Adansoniaflavonoside	0.40				0.69						
Equisporonoside	0.17	0.55	0.29		0.26						
Flavone heterosides											
Apioside	0.06				0.65						
Gentiacauloside	0.07				0.83						
Luteololglucoside b	0.09				0.74						
Paspaloside					0.78						
Isoflavones											
Genisteol	0.95				0.88						
Orobol	0.93				0.84						
Isoflavone heterosides											
Iridoside	0.15				0.39						
Miscellaneous compounds											
Hesperidin methylchalcone	0.79	0.96	0.96	....	0.87	....	0.82	0.95	0.92	0.14	0.89
Phloretin	0.93	0.81	0.84	0.81	0.93	....	0.45	0.91	0.42	0.00	0.73
2′,3,4-Trihydroxychalcone	0.93	0.85	0.88	0.77	0.90	0.08	0.15	0.81	0.19	0.06	0.68
Esculetin	0.78	0.85	0.76	....	0.82	....	0.66	0.73	0.60	0.38	0.74
Pomiferin	0.96	0.98	0.96	0.06	0.95	....	0.00	0.89	0.00	0.00	0.78

[a] Solvents: 1. Ethyl acetate saturated with water.
   2. Phenol saturated with water.
   3. m,p-Cresols saturated with water.
   4. Chloroform saturated with water.
   5. 1-Butanol:acetic acid:water = 4:1:5 v/v.
   6. Chloroform:isobutanol:water = 2:4:4 v/v.
   7. 2-Propanol:water = 22:78 v/v.
   8. 2-Propanol:water = 6:4 v/v.
   9. Acetic acid:water = 15:85 v/v.
   10. n-Heptane:1-butanol:water = 29:14:57 v/v.
   11. Acetic acid:water = 6:4 v/v.

[b] Figures in parentheses indicate two different R_f values reported by several independent investigators.

[c] Question mark indicates the appearance of multiple spots, making the identification doubtful.

TABLE V

R_f VALUES OF FLAVONES (CIRCULAR PAPER CHROMATOGRAPHY) (OSHIMA, 1952)

Substance	Solvent[a]	
	1	2
Baicalein	0.97	0.97
Naringenin	0.98	0.95
Kaempferol	0.99	0.95
Hesperitin	0.98	0.92
Quercetin	0.97	0.81
Myricetin	0.96	0.52

TABLE V—*Continued*

Substance	Solvent[a] 1	2
Quercitrin (quercetin-3-rhamnoside)	0.83	0.93
Myricitrin (myricetin-3-rhamnoside)	0.68	0.87
Isoquercitrin (quercetin-3-glucoside)	0.41	0.84
Naringin (naringenin-7-rhamnoglucoside)	0.26	0.72
Multiflorin (kaempferol-rhamnoglucoside)	0.16	0.81
Rutin (quercetin-3-rhamnoglucoside)	0.11	0.64
Baicalin (baicalein-7-glucuronic acid ester)	0.08	0.38
Hesperidin (hesperitin-7-rhamnoglucoside)	0.00	0.00

[a] Solvents: 1. Ethyl acetate:acetic acid:water = 50:2:50 v/v.
  2. n-Butanol:acetic acid:water = 4:1:5 v/v.

TABLE VI

R_f VALUES OF ANTHOCYANIDINS

(Bate-Smith, 1954)

Compound	Solvents[a] 1	2	3
Pelargonidin	0.80	0.68	0.82
Cyanidin	0.69	0.50	0.69
Paeonidin	0.72	0.63	0.87
Delphinidin	0.35	0.30	0.52
Petunidin	0.45	0.45	0.75
Malvidin	0.53	0.60	0.90

[a] Solvents: 1. n-Butanol:2 N HCl = v/v.
  2. Water:acetic acid:concentrated HCl = 10:30:3 v/v.
  3. m-Cresol:5.5 N HCl:acetic acid = 1:1:1 v/v.

Quercetin drips off with these solvents, whereas rutin moves only about 2–3 inches. It is purified by alternate crystallizations from ethanol and water. Quercetin is estimated quantitatively by evaporating an aliquot of the eluate and adding 10 ml. of absolute ethanol and 3 ml. of 0.1 M AlCl$_3$. The color is read after 20 minutes in a colorimeter at 440 mμ.

c. *Identification of Narcissin* (isorhamnetin-3-rutinoside) (Kotake, 1956). An unknown flavonoid pigment of lily (*L. auratum*) was identified as narcissin on the basis of R_f values in a number of solvents:

22% i-propanol	0.61
water-saturated phenol	0.77
water-saturated ethyl acetate	0.46
n-butanol:acetic acid:water = 4:1:5	0.62

d. Separation of Pterins and Synthetic Derivatives. Good (1949) and Renfrew (1950) identified small quantities of pterins from butterfly wings by paper chromatography. These studies were extended to some synthetic pteridines. The mixture is applied to the paper from 0.1% solutions in 0.5 N NH$_4$OH. Butanol:acetic acid:water and n-butanol:morpholine: water = 3:1:3 v/v are the best solvents tested. After chromatographic development, the paper is dried and viewed under ultraviolet light. In the case of xanthopterin, three spots are usually obtained, of which (c) is ascribed to xanthopterin itself, (b) is a decomposition product of xanthopterin and (a) is unknown. The R_f values and some fluorescent colors are listed in Table VII.

TABLE VII

R_f VALUES OF SOME PTERINS AND PTERIDINES

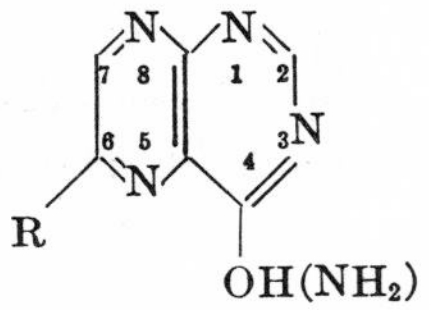

OH(NH$_2$)

| | Solvent | | |
| | Butanol:morpholine | Butanol:acetic acid | |
R_6	4-OH	4-OH	4-NH$_2$
—CH$_2$COOH	0.32	0.13	0.10
—CH(COOH)CH$_2$COOH	0.33	0.10	0.13
—CH$_3$	0.38	0.18	0.26
—C$_6$H$_5$	0.50	0.41	0.42
OH(Xanthopterin)	0.5–0.6	0.38	
Dihydroxanthopterin	0.5–0.6		
Leucopterin	0.25–0.30	0.12	
Rhizopterin		0.56	

Color of fluorescence	
Leucopterin	Pale blue
Xanthopterin	Yellow-green
Rhizopterin	Bright blue

Chapter XII

MISCELLANEOUS ORGANIC SUBSTANCES

Although this manual is not intended to be a complete review of the literature, it seems necessary to describe some of the experiments which have been done in fields not already covered. Thus, we come to the necessary task of writing a chapter on the separations of miscellaneous organic substances. However, the authors hope that the index will enable the reader to locate information on any particular subject with a minimum of effort. Sharp divisions of organic substances are not always possible, and repetitions may occur. Thus nicotinic acid will be covered in this chapter and Chapter XIII (Vitamins); polyphenols will appear in this chapter and also in Chapter X (Phenols). The reader is referred to a complete annual bibliography on paper chromatography compiled by and available from Schleicher and Schuell (Dassel/Einbeck, Germany).

Alcohols

The alcohols are separated by paper chromatography as the following derivatives: xanthogenates, 3,5-dinitrobenzoates, and nitrophthalates. Each of these procedures is outlined below.

a. Alcohol Xanthogenates (Kariyone, 1951, 1952). A few drops of the alcohol are shaken in a test tube with 0.5 ml. of pure CS_2 and 0.1 g. of KOH for several minutes. The liquid phase of the reaction mixture is evaporated, and the residue is dissolved in a drop of water. The resulting solution of xanthogenate (ROCSSK) is chromatographed with 1-butanol saturated with 2% KOH. For ethyl and methyl xanthogenates the solvent is 1-butanol saturated with 5% $NaHCO_3$. For a simple mixture containing only a few alcohol xanthogenates, circular paper chromatography (see Chapter III) is the preferred method.

In the case of solid alcohols, the xanthogenate derivatives are dissolved in formamide. The resulting R_f values are those of the ammonium salts, as seen by the following equation:

$$ROCSSK + HCONH_2 + H_2O \rightarrow ROSSNH_4 + HCOOK$$

The xanthogenates are detected by a brown luminescence when exposed to ultraviolet illumination. They also yield a yellow-blue color when reacting with Grote's reagent (1931): 0.5 g. of sodium nitroprusside is dissolved in 10 ml. of water at room temperature; 0.5 g. of $NH_2OH \cdot HCl$ is added, followed by 1 g. of $NaHCO_3$. After evolution of gas has ceased, 2 drops of bromine are added, the excess of bromine being removed by aeration.

The solution is filtered and made up to 25 ml. The solution is stable for 2 weeks. The spots on the chromatogram are extracted with 5 % NaHCO₃ and reacted with twice the volume of Grote's reagent.

b. *3,5-Dinitrobenzoates* (Meigh, 1952; Sundt, 1957). The preparation of the 3,5-dinitrobenzoates of the volatile alcohols is as follows (Shriner and Fuson, *Systematic Identification of Organic Compounds*, 2nd edition, p. 138, John Wiley and Sons, New York, 1940).

About 0.5 g. of 3,5-dinitrobenzoyl chloride[1] is mixed with 1 ml. of the alcohol in a test tube, and the mixture is boiled gently for five minutes. Then 10 ml. of water is added, and the solution is cooled in an ice bath until a precipitate forms. The precipitate is washed with 2 % Na₂CO₃ and may be recrystallized from ethanol-water.

The 3,5-dinitrobenzoates are dissolved in chloroform (0.1 %), and 10–100 μl. are spotted on Schleicher and Schuell Paper No. 2043b, previously saturated with 50 % N,N-dimethylformamide in acetone and dried at room temperature. The papers are first equilibrated in the tank with dimethylformamide saturated with decalin. They are then developed by the descending technique with decalin (DuPont Product), saturated with dimethylformamide.

The 3,5-dinitrobenzoates are detected after chromatography by the following techniques: The chromatogram is soaked in a 0.002 % methanol solution of Rhodamine 6 GBN·500 (I.C.I. Ltd.). The paper is drained and dried at 100°C. The dinitrobenzoates are seen as dark spots on a yellow fluorescent background when viewed under ultraviolet light. Table I lists the R_f values of a number of alcohol 3,5-dinitrobenzoates. The 3,5-dinitrobenzoates are also detected by spraying the chromatogram with a 0.5 % alcoholic solution of α-naphthylamine (Rice 1951). The spots may also be observed at 2540 Å by placing the chromatogram on top of a fluorescent screen. This screen may be prepared by soaking a piece of filter paper in a 0.1 % alcoholic solution of fluorescein, made just basic with 10 % KOH.

c. *Alcohol Nitrophthalates and Diphenates* (Momose, 1951; Siegel, 1953).

PREPARATION OF DERIVATIVES. *3,6-Dinitrophthalates*. 0.1–1 g. of the alcohol (or mixture) is dissolved in 0.1–0.2 ml. of dry pyridine. 3,6-Dinitrophthalic anhydride is added in excess. The mixture is heated to 50°C. for the lower alcohols and to 100°C. for the higher and polyhydric alcohols. The excess anhydride is decomposed by the addition of 1 drop of water. Two to three milliliters of ether is now added, and the pyridine is removed by extraction with 2–3 ml. of 5 % HCl. The ether residue is taken to dryness and dissolved in *n*-butanol, ready for spotting on paper for chromatography.

---

[1] Five-tenths 3,5-dinitrobenzoic acid is reacted for 4 minutes by gentle heating with 1 g. of PCl₅ .

3-Nitrophthalate. 0.4 g. of 3-nitrophthalic anhydride and 0.2–0.3 ml. of the alcohol are heated in boiling water in a sealed tube. The reaction mixture is dissolved in ether and washed twice with diluted Na_2CO_3. The precipitated derivative may be dissolved in diluted HCl or *n*-butanol as above.

Diphenates. An excess of diphenic acid anhydride is heated with the alcohol in a sealed flask for 2 hours. After the reaction, the diphenate derivatives are distilled *in vacuo*.

CHROMATOGRAPHIC TECHNIQUE. Whatman filter papers No. 1 and 4 and Schleicher and Schuell No. 2043b, coarse and fine, are recommended for the chromatographic separation of these alcohol derivatives. The following solvents are used:

Isoamyl alcohol:concentrated $NH_4OH:H_2O$ = 30:15.5 v/v for 3-nitrophthalates and diphenates (see Table I).

TABLE I

R_f VALUES OF ALCOHOL DERIVATIVES

	Solvent[a]			
	1	2	3	3
	3,5-	3,5-		
	Dinitro-	Dinitro-	3-Nitro-	
Alcohol	benzoate	benzoate	phthalate	Diphenate
Methanol	0.24	0.21	0.15	0.24
Ethanol	0.39	0.40	0.26	0.37
Propanol-1	0.46	0.50	0.42	0.48
Propanol-2	0.51	0.52	0.35	0.47
Butanol-1	0.57	0.64	0.55	0.56
2 Me-propanol-1	0.55	—	0.53	0.55
Butanol-2	0.61	—	0.48	0.54
Pentanol-1	0.66	0.72	0.64	0.61
2-Me-butanol-1	—	—	0.61	0.59
3-Me-butanol-1	0.65	—	0.63	0.60
Pentanol-2	—	—	0.59	0.58
Cyclopentanol	—	—	0.49	0.55
Hexanol-1	0.72	0.79	0.67	0.65
Cyclohexanol	—	—	0.57	0.62
Heptanol-1	—	—	0.70	0.69
Benzyl alcohol	—	—	0.50	0.49
2-C_6H_5-EtOH-1	—	—	0.52	0.56
3-C_6H_5-propanol-1	—	—	0.55	0.60
Allyl alcohol	—	—	0.32	0.41
Cinnamic alcohol	—	—	0.50	0.53

[a] Solvent: 1. Heptane:methanol (Meigh, 1952).
2. Decalin:dimethylformamide (Sundt, 1957).
3. Isoamyl alcohol: $NH_4OH:H_2O$ = 30:15:5 v/v (Siegel, 1953).

1-Butanol saturated with N acetic acid for 3,6-dinitrophthalates of lower alcohols.

1-Butanol:acetic acid:H_2O = 8:1:2 v/v for 3,6-dinitrophthalates of higher alcohols.

COLOR REAGENTS. *3,6-Dinitrophthalates.* The paper is sprayed with *N* NaOH and then with ethyl acetoacetate to produce orange-red spots.

3-Nitrophthalate and diphenates. A spraying reagent composed of a 0.02 % solution of 4-methylumbelliferone (pH 8–9) in 33 % ethanol produces fluorescent spots in ultraviolet light.

Ketones and Aldehydes

Aldehydes and ketones are separated by paper chromatography as carbonyl compounds or their derivatives, e.g., 2,4-dinitrophenylhydrazones.

1. PAPER

Whatman filter paper No. 1 is usually employed. Several instances have been reported where pretreatment of the paper has resulted in better resolution of the 2,4-dinitrophenylhydrazones and of the free aldehydes as follows:

a. A heavy grade of filter paper is soaked in sodium silicate solution (Bé 42° diluted with 2 volumes of water) and is drained of surplus liquid (Kirchner, 1950). The paper is then washed for 5 minutes in 6 *N* HCl followed by a brief water rinse. The paper is dried at 110°C. and pressed between weighted glass plates to flatten it. Whatman No. 7 filter paper may be dipped into a solution of 10 % phenoxyethanol in acetone, blotted, and air-dried. Good resolution of the 2,4-dinitrophenylhydrazones is achieved with this paper and the solvent heptane, saturated with the stationary phase (Lynn, 1956).

b. Similar improvement is noted when filter paper is first impregnated with borate buffer (0.1 *M*, pH 8.7) (Wachtmeister, 1951). 3,4- and 2,4-Dihydroxybenzaldehydes are resolved on this borate-impregnated paper as a result of the interaction of the isomer with two adjacent hydroxyl groups, forming a more soluble, acidic complex. The R_f values of these two aldehydes are 0.28 and 0.92, respectively, with *n*-butanol:acetic acid:H_2O = 4:1:5.

c. The filter paper is first sprayed with a dilute aqueous solution of $NaHSO_3$ and is dried. Aldehydes are more reactive with bisulfite than ketones, and, therefore, the mobility of the aldehydes is more retarded than that of the ketones (Newcombe, 1953). Vanillin, acetovanillone, veratraldehyde, and acetoveratrone are separated with the organic phase of hexane:-chloroform:water = 9:1:10 v/v.

A variation of this technique is the streaking of a band of 41 % sodium metabisulfite on the paper, just above the applied sample containing a mixture of aldehydes and ketones (Reaville, 1955). Whatman No. 1 paper is used. The chromatogram is developed with n-butyl ether, and the aldehydes (vanillin and p-hydroxybenzaldehyde) will not migrate above the "bisulfite block."

2. DETAILED EXPERIMENTAL PROCEDURES

a. *Chromatography of 2,4-Dinitrophenylhydrazones* (Buyske, 1956). For the identification of carbonyl compounds in tobacco smoke, the smoke is first condensed by passing it through four liquid-air traps. The condensate is dissolved in 200 ml. of methanol, containing 2 g. of 2,4-dinitrophenylhydrazine and 0.5 ml. of 1 N HCl. The mixture is refluxed for two hours, and 1 ml. of the solution is streaked on a sheet of Whatman No. 1 paper, impregnated with dimethylformamide. Descending development is employed with n-hexane, saturated with N,N-dimethylformamide, as solvent. The bands can be seen in daylight or may be intensified by a spray of 10 % aqueous alkali, resulting in red-brown bands. Spectrographic analysis may be applied after eluting the derivatives with methanol in a Soxhlet extractor.

A list of additional solvents for the 2,4-dinitrophenylhydrazones is given in Table II.

b. *Chromatography of Salicylaldehyde Derivatives* (Mentzner, 1953). To 2 ml. of a solution containing at least 0.5 μg. of ketone, add 2 ml. of 11.3 N KOH and 1 ml. of 10 % salicylaldehyde. Heat at 50°C. for one-half hour with stirring; a red or orange color appears. Cool, acidify with HCl, and extract with ether. Wash with H_2O, dry over anhydrous Na_2SO_4, and evaporate to 1 ml. Chromatograph with ether:petroleum ether = 35:64 v/v or with benzene:xylene = 75:25 v/v. Treat the paper with 5 % NaOH. Acetone gives two spots; methyl ethyl ketone gives four spots.

c. *Chromatography of Hydroxamic Acid Derivatives* (Uno, 1951). Hydroxamic acid of aldehyde is prepared by mixing aldehyde in absolute ethanol with benzenesulfohydroxamic acid and sufficient NaOH to make the reaction mixture basic. Hydroxamic acids are separated with isoamyl alcohol:acetic acid:H_2O = 5:1:1 or butanol:acetic acid:H_2O = 5:1:1. Aliphatic aldehydes, C_1—C_5, can be separated as well as vanillin, veratrum aldehyde, benzaldehyde, furfural, and methyl furfural.

d. *Chromatography of Girard Derivatives* (Zaffaroni, 1949; Seligman, 1954). A convenient sample of the ketone or aldehyde, twice this weight of Girard's Reagent T or P, and 2 ml. of 10 % glacial acetic acid in absolute methanol are refluxed on a steam bath for 30–60 minutes under anhydrous

TABLE II

R_f Values of Aldehydes, Ketones, and Derivatives

Compound	Solvent[a]								
	2,4-Dinitro-phenylhydrazone					Gi-rard T	Gi-rard P	Free aldehyde and ketone	
	1	2	3	4	5	6	6	7	8
Formaldehyde	0.60	0.09	0.75	—	00.6	0	0	—	—
Acetaldehyde	0.56	0.18	—	—	0.67	—	0.19	—	—
Acetone	0.42	0.30	0.85	—	—	—	0.19	—	—
Isobutyraldehyde	0.32	—	—	—	—	0.37	0.38	—	—
Methyl ethyl ketone	0.31	0.43	0.90	0.38	—	—	0.29	—	—
Cyclopentanone	0.29	—	—	—	—	—	—	—	—
Cyclohexanone	0.23	—	—	—	—	—	—	—	—
2,2-Dimethylcyclohexanone	0.15	—	—	—	—	—	—	—	—
n-Propionaldehyde	—	0.32	0.57	—	0.91	—	0.29	—	—
n-Butyraldehyde	—	0.42	0.85	—	—	0.36	0.38	—	—
n-Valeraldehyde	—	0.54	0	—	—	—	—	—	—
n-Caproaldehyde	—	0.57	—	—	—	—	—	—	—
Methyl-n-propyl ketone	—	0.53	0.90	0.54	—	—	—	—	—
Methyl-n-butyl ketone	—	0.65	—	—	—	—	—	—	—
Furfural (Furfuraldehyde)	—	0.06	0.57	—	0.70	0.29	0.28	—	—
Acrolein	—	0.21	—	—	—	—	—	—	—
Crotonaldehyde	—	0.22	—	—	0.90	—	—	—	—
2,4-Dinitrophenylhydrazine	—	—	0.05	—	0.32	—	—	—	—
Salicylaldehyde	—	—	0.30	—	—	0.48	—	—	—
Cinnamaldehyde	—	—	0.48	—	—	—	—	—	—
Benzaldehyde	—	—	0.68	—	0.81	0.45	—	—	—
Isovalerylaldehyde	—	—	0.84	—	—	—	—	—	—
Decyl aldehyde	—	—	0.86	—	—	—	—	—	—
Nonyl aldehyde	—	—	0.87	—	—	—	—	—	—
Methyl isopropyl ketone	—	—	0.91	0.48	—	—	—	—	—
Glycolaldehyde	—	—	0	—	—	—	—	—	—
Biacetyl	—	—	0	—	—	—	—	—	—
Methyl glyoxal	—	—	—	—	0.20	—	—	—	—
Glyoxal (bis)	—	—	—	—	0.23	—	—	—	—
Girard Reagent	—	—	—	—	—	0.09	0.10	—	—
p-Anisaldehyde	—	—	—	—	—	0.41	—	—	—
5-Methyl-2-furfural	—	—	—	—	—	0.39	0.35	—	—
p-Hydroxy benzaldehyde	—	—	—	—	—	0.36	—	—	—
Di-n-propyl ketone	—	—	—	—	—	0.51	0.51	—	—
Methyl heptyl ketone	—	—	—	—	—	0.59	0.62	—	—
5-Carboxyvanillin	—	—	—	—	—	—	—	0.12	0.37
5-Formylvanillin	—	—	—	—	—	—	—	0.20	0.53
Dehydrovanillin	—	—	—	—	—	—	—	0.31	streak
Syringaldehyde	—	—	—	—	—	—	—	0.37	0.79
Vanillin	—	—	—	—	—	—	—	0.44	0.87
Vanillovanillone	—	—	—	—	—	—	—	0.47	0.86
Acetovanillone	—	—	—	—	—	—	—	0.60	0.85

TABLE II—*Continued*

^a Solvents: 1. Ethanol:petroleum ether = 80:20 (Sykora, 1953).
  2. Anhydrous methanol:heptane = 1:1 (Meigh, 1952).
  3. 5% Ether in petroleum ether (65–110°) (Rice, 1951).
  4. Ethyl ether:petroleum ether (110°C.) = 5:95—sodium silicate paper (Kirchner, 1950).
  5. Dibutyl ether:dimethylformamide:tetrahydrofuran = 85:15:4 (*Fresh*) (Schmitt, 1956).
  6. *n*-Butanol:ethanol:water = 27:3:10 (Seligman, 1954).
  7. *n*-Butanol, saturated with 2% aq. NH₄OH (Pearl, 1954).
  8. *n*-Butanol:pyridine:water = 10:3:3 (Pearl, 1954).

conditions.   After cooling, 1 μl. of the solution (about 1 %) is spotted on Whatman No. 1 paper and developed for 18 hours with butanol:ethanol: water = 27:3:10 (see Table II).

   e. Chromatography of Aldehydes and Ketones.   The separation of vanillin and syringaldehyde produced by the oxidation of lignins with nitrobenzene in alkaline medium is important in lignin chemistry.   Bland (1949) separated these two aldehydes on Whatman No. 1 paper using petroleum ether (100–110°C.) saturated with water as solvent.   Stone (1951) adapted this technique to the separation of the aldehydes from other components of the oxidation reaction mixture.   He also included *p*-hydroxybenzaldehyde.   The aldehydes were applied to paper strips in 0.01-ml. spots. Two developing solvents were found suitable, petroleum ether saturated with water and *n*-butyl ether saturated with water.   The former separated vanillin and syringaldehyde in 16 hours, the latter in 1.5 hours.   The R_f values obtained are shown below.

| | R_f values | | |
Solvent	Vanillin	Syringaldehyde	*p*-Hydroxy benzaldehyde
n-Butyl ether:water	0.64	0.37	0.64
Petroleum ether:water	0.39	0.12	0.01

   Mixtures of the three aldehydes could be separated in a satisfactory way by using the upper layer of petroleum ether (100–120°C.):*n*-butyl ether: water = 6:1:1 v/v.

   The composition of vanilla extracts was determined by paper chromatography, using Whatman No. 1 paper and 1-butanol saturated with ammonia as solvent (Lagneau, 1953).   The aldehydes were detected by a spraying reagent composed of a saturated solution of 2,4-dinitrophenylhydrazine in dilute HCl:ethanol = 1:1 v/v.   The following R_f values were observed: vanillin, 0.42; ethylvanillin, 0.55; heliotropin, 0.89.

   Vanillin and syringaldehyde are resolved with the solvent ethanol:*n*-butanol:25 % amyl alcohol:water = 80:80:11:29 v/v.   The aldehydes are revealed with a saturated solution of 2,4-dinitrophenylhydrazine in 2 *N* HCl.

TABLE III
COLORS OF SPOTS PRODUCED BY ORCINOL REAGENT (BEVENUE, 1952)

| | Temperature and duration of heating | | | | |
| | 25°C. | 50°C. | | 100°C. | |
Aldehyde	5-10 min.	1 min.	10 min.	1 min.	5 min.
Cinnamaldehyde	OY	O	Y	O	Y
p-Dimethylaminobenzaldehyde	R	R	R	R	Pu-Br
p-Hydroxybenzaldehyde	S	S	S	O Br	O Br
2,3-Dimethoxybenzaldehyde	B	B	B	B	B
2-Hydroxy-3-methoxybenzaldehyde	B	B	B	B	B
Anisaldehyde	P	P	P	P	P
Protocatechuic aldehyde	P	P	P	P	P
Vanillin	P	P	P	P	P
Veratraldehyde	P	P	P	P	G
Ethyl vanillin	P	P	P	L	Br
2,4-Dihydroxybenzaldehyde	P	P	P	O	Y
Phenylacetaldehyde	N	N	N	N	Y
Formaldehyde	—	—	—	—	B
Piperonal	P	P	P	L	Br

Colors: B-buff; Br-brown; G-gray; L-lavender; N-no color; O-orange; P-pink; Pu-purple; R-red; S-salmon; Y-yellow.

3. DETECTION AND QUANTITATIVE EVALUATION

The carbonyl derivatives are mostly colored and need no further treatment for detection on the chromatogram. For the visualization of free aldehydes and ketones several spraying reagents may be recommended:

(1) *2,4-Dinitrophenylhydrazine* (0.4 %) in 2 N HCl (Bland, 1949).

(2) *Orcinol reagent* (Bevenue, 1952). The reagent consists of 0.5 g. of orcinol, 15 g. trichloroacetic acid, dissolved in water, saturated with *n*-butanol. The chromatograms are sprayed with this reagent and heated at different temperatures for various lengths of time, resulting in characteristic colors for various aldehydes (see Table III).

(3) *Ammoniacal silver nitrate* (Mühlberger, 1954). 5 % aqueous silver nitrate:25 % NH_4OH = 9:1 produces a violet color for eugenol when exposed to ultraviolet light.

(4) *Hydrazine reagent* (Mühlberger, 1954). Aqueous saturated hydrazine sulfate:25 % HCl = 9:1 results in a light green spot for anisaldehyde under ultraviolet light and a yellow spot for cinnamaldehyde in daylight. Eugenol does not react.

(5) *Ferric chloride* (Pearl, 1954). A 5 % solution produces a blue color for vanillin and related compounds.

(6) *Quantitative evaluation* (Bland, 1949). The quantitative determination of the aldehydes is carried out on a strip of paper 6 inches wide and 22 inches long. A line is drawn across the paper 4.5 inches from one end, and another is drawn down the length of the paper 1 inch from one edge. A known volume of the mixture of aldehydes to be analyzed is spotted along the base line in the wide (5-inch) lane. After the chromatogram is developed, the narrow strip is cut off, sprayed to reveal the position of the aldehydes, and these segments are cut from the main chromatogram in 2–3-inch wide strips. The strips of paper containing the pure aldehydes are rolled up and extracted in small Soxhlet extractors for 2 hours with 25 ml. of ethanol. Four milliliters of 0.2% alcoholic KOH is added to the extract, which is made up to 50 ml. The optical density is measured at the appropriate wavelength with a Beckman spectrophotometer. These wavelengths are 352 mμ for vanillin, 368 mμ for syringaldehyde, and 335 mμ for *p*-hydroxybenzaldehyde. The amount of aldehyde present is then read directly from standard curves.

Urea, Guanidine Bases, and Related Compounds

This section is partly based on Williams and associates' work (R. J. Williams, 1951) dealing with urinary excretory products. The preparation of the sample prior to spotting on the paper may involve desalting by electrolysis or ion exchange treatment (see Chapters III and V for details), but the use of buffered phenol solvent (see below) minimizes the effect of interfering inorganic salt ions.

1. SOLVENTS (See also Figure 1 and Table IV).

(1) *Phenol.* 100 g. of phenol is saturated with an aqueous solution containing 6.3% sodium citrate and 3.7% sodium (or potassium) dihydrogen phosphate.

(2) *1-Butanol:acetic acid.* 80 ml. of 1-butanol, 20 ml. of glacial acetic acid, and 20 ml. of water. This is freshly prepared for each development.

(3) *Butanol:ethanol.* 80 ml. of 1-butanol, 20 ml. of 95% ethanol, and 20 ml. of water.

(4) *1-Butanol:acetic acid:pyridine:water* = 4:1:1:2.

(5) *1-Butanol:6 N HCl* = 7:3 v/v.

(6) *Isobutyric acid.* 80 ml. of isobutyric acid and 20 ml. of water.

(7) *Lutidine.* 65 ml. of 2,6-lutidine and 35 ml. of water.

(8) *n-Propanol:water* = 8:2 (Zahn, 1953). This solvent gives the following R_f values for methylol compounds: dimethylolurea, 0.47; *o*-methylolphenol, 0.93; *N*-methylolacetamide, 0.69; hexamethylolmelamine, 0.60.

(9) *Methyl ethyl ketone:petroleum ether:water* = 9:4:3 (organic layer)

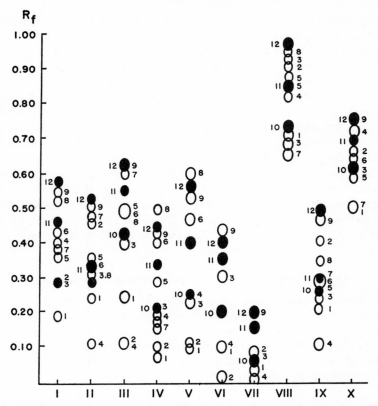

FIG. 1. Diagram of R_f values of guanidine derivatives (ascending development, Whatman No. 1) (Roche, 1954). Key: *Solvents:* I. pyridine:isoamyl alcohol:acetic acid:water = 8:4:1:4; II. pyridine:isoamyl alcohol:NH₃:water = 8:4:1:4; III. pyridine:isoamyl alcohol:water = 8:4:7; IV. butanol:acetic acid:water = 73:10:17; V. butanol:acetic acid:water = 50:12:50 (organic layer); VI. butanol:formic acid: water = 63:20:17; VII. butanol:NH₃:water = 25:8:17 (organic layer); VIII. phenol, saturated with water; IX. propanol:20% NH₃:water = 73:20:7; X. butanol:ethanol: acetic acid:water = 8:4:1:1. *Compounds:* ○ Monosubstituted derivatives—1. arginine; 2. agmatine; 3. glycocyamine; 4. arcaine; 5. arginine (H⁺); 6. guanidopropionic acid; 7. taurocyamine; 8. guanidobutyric acid; 9. methylguanidine. ● Disubstituted guanidine derivatives—10. creatine; 11. guanidine; 12. dimethylguanidine.

for the separation of cyanamide and its derivatives on Whatman 3 MM paper (Milks, 1956).

(10) *n-Propanol:NH₄OH:water* = 6:3:1, for the separation of creatine, arginine, taurocyamine, creatine phosphate, and related compounds (Hobson, 1955).

TABLE IV
R_f VALUES OF GUANIDINES AND RELATED COMPOUNDS

Compound	Solvent[a]					
	1	2	3	4	5	6
Acetamide	0.30	—	—	—	—	—
Creatine	0.91	0.36	0.33	—	0.49	—
Creatinine	0.90	0.55	0.54	—	—	—
Glycocyamine	—	0.35	0.30	0.103	0.42	—
Guanidine	0.66	0.54	0.50	—	—	—
Urea	0.78	0.55	—	—	—	0.35
Arginine	—	0.09	0.21	0.053	0.40	—
Agmatine	—	0.10	0.34	0.144	—	—
Arcaine	—	0.18	0.46	0.278	—	—
Canavanine	—	—	0.19	—	—	—
Dimethylguanidine	—	—	0.60	—	—	—
Methylguanidine	—	—	0.60	0.483	—	—
Octopine	—	—	—	0.022	—	—
Potassium cyanoureate	—	—	—	—	—	0.04
Biguanide	—	0.01	—	—	—	0.08
Melamine	—	—	—	—	—	0.08
Ammonium thiocyanate	—	—	—	—	—	0.38
Thiourea	—	0.44	—	—	—	0.49
Cyanamide	—	—	—	—	—	0.61
Taurocyamine	—	—	—	—	0.54	—
Creatine phosphate	—	—	—	—	0.29	—
Arginine phosphate	—	—	—	—	0.24	—
Glycocyamine phosphate	—	—	—	—	0.21	—

[a] Solvent: 1. Buffered phenol (R. J .Williams, 1951).
2. Butanol:acetic acid:water = 4:1:5 (Williams, 1951; List, 1956).
3. Butanol:acetic acid:pyridine:water = 4:1:1:2 (Makisumi, 1952).
4. Butanol:water:acetic acid = 78:17:5 — paper is impregnated with 0.066 N NaOH (Roche, 1951).
5. Propanol:NH$_4$OH:water = 6:3:1 (Hobson, 1955).
6. Butanol:ethanol:water = 4:1:1 (Milks, 1956).

2. DETECTION

Besides the usual reagents for amino acids (ninhydrin) and acid-bases (bromocresol green, etc.), the following more specific color reagents are recommended:

(1) *Phenol-hypochlorite (PHC)*. Chromatograms are first sprayed with 5% phenol in 95% ethanol. After drying, the sheets are sprayed with 5.25% sodium hypochlorite (Clorox). The colors develop immediately, for urea (5 μg.; 4 yellow-green), arginine (orange), and chloride ions (1 μg.; blue).

(2) *Sakaguchi reagent* (Roche, 1954; Hobson, 1955). The chromatogram is first sprayed with a fresh solution of α-naphthol (0.2 ml. 40% NaOH, 0.2 ml. 40% urea, 0.2 ml. saturated alcoholic solution of α-naphthol, diluted with distilled water to 10.0 ml.). The paper is then sprayed with a 30% hypobromite stock solution (stock solution: 0.9 ml. Br_2 in 100 ml. 10% NaOH). Monosubstituted guanidines react with this reagent (orange-red color).

For creatine alone, the paper is sprayed with 5% (w/v) α-naphthol in 2.5 N NaOH, dried, and then sprayed with 0.1% fresh diacetyl; red spots appear after 1–2 minutes (Hobson, 1955).

(3) *Alkaline ferricyanide-nitroprusside* (FCNP) (Kirby-Berry, 1951). Equal volumes of 10% NaOH, 10% sodium nitroprusside, and 10% potassium ferricyanide solutions are mixed. The mixture is diluted with 3 volumes of water. After standing for 20 minutes, the initial dark color changes to a pale yellow indicating the reagent is ready for use. The reagent is kept under refrigeration. Creatine, guanidine, and glycocyamine give orange colors against a light yellow background. Creatinine gives a blue color.

(4) *Dimethylaminobenzaldehyde* (1%) in 2% alcoholic HCl is sprayed on the paper which is heated at 60°C. for 1–2 minutes. One microgram of urea produces a lemon-yellow spot (Marini-Bettolo, 1956).

(5) *Picric acid* (Acker, 1955). For creatine alone, the chromatogram is first heated at 100°C., then sprayed with 2 N NaOH, and next with 1.2% picric acid. In order to convert creatine to creatinine, the chromatogram is exposed to HCl vapors for two hours.

(6) *Pentacyanoaminoferrate* (PCAF) (List, 1956). The spray reagent is made by adding 5 ml. of 20% NaOH to 15 ml. 1% $Na_3Fe(CN)_5NH_3$ (PCAF) and 1 drop of 30% H_2O_2. The reagent is stable for 24 hours.

PCAF is prepared by dissolving 10 g. of sodium nitroprusside in 40 ml. of concentrated NH_4OH and keeping the mixture at 0°C. for 24 hours. The solution is filtered, and absolute alcohol is added to the clear filtrate until a precipitate forms. The precipitated PCAF is stored *in vacuo* over H_2SO_4 in the dark.

Guanidines give red to yellow spots with this reagent whose sensitivity of detection is 0.5–10 μg. for arginine, agmatine, arcaine, creatine, glycocyamine, and thiourea.

(7) *Schiff's Reagent for Methylol Compounds* (Zahn, 1953). Schiff's reagent: 0.5 g. of fuchsin is dissolved in 500 ml. of water; 500 ml. of water saturated with SO_2 is added, and the solution allowed to stand overnight. The chromatogram is sprayed with Schiff's reagent; after drying at room temperature, the paper is sprayed with a saturated solution of ammonium chloride. After the chromatogram is heated at 110°C. for several minutes, the methylol compounds are revealed.

3. Detailed Experimental Procedures

(1) *Creatine and creatinine* (R. J. Williams, 1951). For the determination in urine, the butanol-ethanol solvent is used. Color development is carried out with alkaline picric acid reagent as follows: The chromatogram is sprayed with 0.5 N H_2SO_4 and heated for 1 hour at 100°C. It is then sprayed with a 1.3 % solution of picric acid in 95 % ethanol which is combined immediately before use with $\frac{1}{5}$ volume of 10 % NaOH. Creatine and creatinine appear as orange spots against a yellow background. After the solvent has traveled 3 inches, interfering substances are not present in the creatinine spot.

Pure creatinine in a standard solution is added in varying amounts to samples of urine, and quantitative estimations are made using the color comparison or spot area methods (see Chapter IV).

(2) *Creatine* (R. J. Williams, 1951). Creatine, when present in urine, can be estimated using the lutidine solvent. After development, the paper is dried, sprayed with 1.3 % picric acid, and then heated for 1 hour at 110°C. in order to convert the creatine to creatinine. Finally the sheet is sprayed with a 1 N NaOH solution. The characteristic orange color of creatinine is produced. No interference occurs, since the R_f value of creatine in this solvent is 0.27 whereas that of creatinine is 0.56.

(3) *Urea* (R. J. Williams, 1951). Chromatograms of urine developed with phenol give a bright green spot after spraying with 5.25 % sodium hypochlorite (Clorox). There are no other materials giving this test with an R_f value close to that of urea. The color and intensity of the spot is markedly affected by the amount of phenol present on the sheet when sprayed with sodium hypochlorite. Best results are obtained by drying the sheets of paper for 8 minutes at 90°C. Quantitative estimations are made by using a standard urea solution on the same sheet by the methods described in Chapter IV.

Thioureas

The thioureas are separated by paper chromatography with water-saturated chloroform (Kjaer, 1953). Two microliters of a 1 % alcoholic solution of the samples is placed on Whatman filter paper No. 1. It is necessary to equilibrate the chromatographic chamber by lining the walls of the chamber with filter paper soaked in water-saturated chloroform for 16–18 hours prior to development. The ascending technique is recommended, and the development is completed in 110–120 minutes.

The thioureas are detected with one of the following color reagents: *Grote's reagent* (Grote, 1931) (see ALCOHOLS, pp. 337–338). The dried chromatograms are sprayed with Grote's reagent and are heated at 100°C. The thioureas appear as deep-blue spots, fading in a few days. Quantita-

TABLE V

R_{PH} OF THIOUREAS (R_f OF N-PHENYLTHIOUREA $= 1.0$) (KJÆR, 1953)

(Solvent: water-saturated chloroform)

Compound	R_{PH}
Thiourea	0
N-Methylthiourea	0.4
N-Ethylthiourea	0.15
N-n-Propylthiourea	0.42
N-Isopropylthiourea	0.41
N-n-Butylthiourea	0.84
N-Isobutylthiourea	0.76
N-DL-sec-Butylthiourea	0.74
N-$tert$-Butylthiourea	1.00
N-Isopentylthiourea	1.07
N-Benzylthiourea	0.90
N-β-Phenylethylthiourea	1.10
N-Allylthiourea	0.26
N-α-Methallylthiourea	0.62
N-$trans$-Crotylthiourea	0.78
N-3-Butenylthiourea	0.61
N-p-Bromophenylthiourea	1.00
N-p-Iodophenylthiourea	1.06
N-o-Tolylthiourea	1.19
N-m-Tolylthiourea	1.25
N-p-Tolylthiourea	1.22
N-Ethylenethiourea	0.26
Trimethylthiourea	1.21
N-Methyl-4-morpholine thiocarboxamide	1.17
N-Ethyl-4-morpholine thiocarboxamide	1.27
N-Allyl-4-morpholine thiocarboxamide	1.31
N-Methyl-1-piperidine thiocarboxamide	1.37
N-Methyl-1-pyrrolidinethiocarboxamide	1.35
N-Ethyl-1-pyrrolidinethiocarboxamide	1.37
Tetramethylthiourea	1.43
Thioacetamide	0.25
Thiobenzamide	0.79
Thiosemicarbazide	0
4-Methylthiosemicarbazide	0.20
1,1,4-Trimethylsemicarbazide	1.32
1-Phenylthiosemicarbazide	0.55
Thiobarbituric acid	0
5-Ethylthiobarbituric acid	0
5,5-Diethylthiobarbituric acid	1.30
5-Methyl-5-allylthiobarbituric acid	1.19
5,5-Diallylthiobarbituric acid	1.37
N',N''-Dimethylthiourea	0.42
N',N''-Methyl ethyl thiourea	0.89
N',N''-Diethylthiourea	1.24
N',N''-Methyl butyl thiourea	1.35
N',N''-Dibutylthiourea	1.41
N',N''-Methyl phenyl thiourea	1.40
N',N''-Ethyl phenyl thiourea	1.41
N'-Dimethylthiourea	0.60

tive estimation may be made by extraction of spots and photometric density determinations, with an accuracy of ±5 %.

Iodine-azide reagent (Feigl, 1954). The dried chromatograms are first sprayed with a 1 % starch solution and, while still damp, sprayed with Feigl's iodine-azide reagent (3 g. of sodium azide dissolved in 100 ml. of 0.1 N iodine solution). Colorless spots on a blue background reveal thioureas.

Relative R_f values for a number of thioureas may be found in Table V.

Imidazoles

Imidazole compounds may be separated on Whatman No. 52 paper by the descending development technique. The following solvent mixtures have been employed (Ames, 1952; Cowgill, 1955) (see also Table VI):

(1) *Ethanol:ether:water:conc.NH_4OH* = 4:5:1:0.1;

(2) *Acetone:chloroform:water:concentrated NH_4OH* = 30:5:4:0.2;

(3) *Acetic acid:n-butanol:ethyl acetate:water* = 1:1:1:1. Two-dimensional chromatography has been used with the following solvent combinations:

First direction: Solvent (3); *second direction*: Solvents (1) or (2);

First direction: Solvent (1); *second direction*: Solvent (2).

The imidazoles may be detected by one of the following techniques or a combination of all three in the order given:

(1) *Ultraviolet absorption*. Carboxyimidazoles, its methyl esters, and aldehydo-imidazoles appear as blue spots when viewed under ultraviolet illumination (Cowgill, 1955).

(2) *Iodine spray*. The papers are sprayed with a 1 % iodine solution in 95 % ethanol, dried at room temperature overnight or heated at 100°C. for thirty minutes. The spots are marked immediately; they appear as brown spots in daylight and brown-blue in ultraviolet light. After the colors have faded, the papers may be sprayed again (Cowgill, 1955).

(3) *Diazonium spray* (Ames, 1952). SOLUTION A: 25 ml. of freshly prepared 5 % $NaNO_2$ is slowly added at 0°C. to 5.0 ml. of a sulfanilic acid solution (0.9 g. of sulfanilic acid plus 9 ml. of concentrated HCl, diluted to 100 ml. with distilled water).

SOLUTION B: 5 % aqueous Na_2CO_3. The dried chromatogram is lightly sprayed with solution A, and while the paper is still damp it is sprayed with solution B. Colored spots formed by imidazoles are suitable for quantitative estimation by densitometry (see Chapter IV).

Miscellaneous Organic Bases

1. CHOLINE AND CHOLINE ESTERS

Since choline, ethanolamine, and serine are encountered as a mixture after hydrolyzing phospholipids, a suitable solvent should separate these

TABLE VI

R_f VALUES AND DIAZO COLORS FOR IMIDAZOLES (AMES, 1952)

Compound	Diazo color	Solvent[a]	
		1	2
Histidine	Red	0.22	0.12
4(5)-Carboxyimidazole	Yellow	0.23	0.29
Carnosine	Red	0.24	0.06
2-Thiolhistidine	Red	0.25	0.15
[Imidazolyl-4(5)]-lactic acid	Red	0.26	0.27
Ergothionine	Red	0.27	0.26
Guanine	Orange	0.27	0.35
[Imidazolyl-4(5)]-pyruvic acid	Red	0.31	0.31
[Imidazolyl-4(5)]-acrylic acid	Red	0.34	0.69
NH₄Cl	Yellow	0.39	0.41
4(5)-Amino-5(4)-carboxamide imidazole	Blue	0.52	0.51
Histamine	Red	0.65	0.10–0.28
Histidinol	Red	0.65	0.10–0.28
Histidine methyl ester	Red	0.75	0.45
4(5)-Hydroxymethylimidazole	Red	0.75	0.56
Imidazole	Red-orange	0.88	0.58

[a] Solvents: 1. n-Propyl alcohol:0.2 N NH₄OH = 3:1 v/v.
2. n-Propyl alcohol:N acetic acid = 3:1 v/v.

compounds. Such a solvent is described by Munier (1951): *n-butanol: glycolmonochlorohydrin:NH₄OH:water* = 50:10:5:16. The following R_f values are observed: choline, 0.30; ethanolamine, 0.64; serine, 0.16.

Choline esters are separated either by the ascending or descending technique on Whatman No. 4 paper with a variety of solvents, listed in Table VII (Whittaker, 1952; Augustinsson, 1953).

DETECTION. (1) *Phosphomolybdic Acid* (Levine, 1951; Hawke, 1953). The dried paper chromatogram is immersed in a 1–2% w/v solution of phosphomolybdic acid in ethanol:chloroform v/v. The paper is then washed in running water for 15–20 minutes and dried at 20°C. The choline phosphomolybdate, thus formed on the paper, is reduced with 1% w/v SnCl₂ in 3 N HCl. Blue spots on a pale blue background result. Choline is estimated semiquantitatively by the area method (see Chapter IV).

(2) *Dipicrylamine* (Malyoth, 1951; Augustinsson, 1953; Ackermann, 1955). *Spray Reagent*: 0.4% of Mg dipicrylamine in 50% acetone. Choline and its esters produce dark-yellow spots on a light-yellow background, but fade in about a week. *Dipping Reagent*: The chromatogram is placed for one hour in a 0.6% aqueous solution of Mg dipicrylamine. The background is washed off with water, until pale yellow, and choline shows up as a red spot.

(3) *Iodine.* When the dried chromatogram is exposed to iodine vapors, nitrogenous bases form brown spots; this reagent is not specific for choline (Munier, 1951).

(4) *Hydroxamate-FeCl₃ Reaction* (Whittaker, 1952).

Reagent A: 20 g. $NH_2OH \cdot HCl$ is dissolved in 50 ml. of water and diluted to 200 ml. with 95% ethanol. *Reagent B*: Ethanolic KOH. *Reagent C*: 10 g. of $FeCl_3 \cdot 6H_2O$ is dissolved in 20 ml. of 10 N HCl and shaken with 200 ml. of ether until a homogenous suspension results. *Procedure*: Reagents A and B are mixed in the proportion of 2:1, and the resulting KCl precipitate is filtered off. The chromatogram is sprayed with this reagent, dried, and sprayed with Reagent C. Brown spots on a yellow background indicate the positions of choline esters.

(5) *Quantitative Estimation.* The hydroxamate-FeCl₃ reaction is suitable for the quantitative estimation of choline esters by the maximum density method. (See Chapter VII for details.)

An alternative procedure is as follows (Augustinsson, 1953): Spots, located by the color development of a parallel guide strip, are eluted with 10^{-4} M HCl. Acetylcholine is estimated by mixing the eluate with 3.5 M NaOH:2 M $NH_2OH \cdot HCl$ v/v. The pH is adjusted to 1.4, and 1.0 ml of 0.37 M $FeCl_3$ is added. The color density is determined at 540 mμ.

2. ALIPHATIC AMINES (see also Chapter V)

Aliphatic amines and/or their salts are separated on paper with the butanol:acid acid:water solvent of different compositions (see Table VIII). When chromatographing amine halide salts, it is recommended to include the respective halogen acid in the organic solvent in order to prevent the appearance of "ghost" spots due to halide (Ukai, 1953).

The aliphatic amines are detected by spraying the chromatogram with a 1% solution of acetoacetylphenol in *n*-butanol and the subsequent appearance of fluorescent spots (Baker, 1952).

Another spraying reagent for aliphatic amine hydrochlorides is 1% ammoniacal silver nitrate solution, followed by 10% aqueous acetic acid and distilled water rinses. After exposing the wet papers to ultraviolet light, the amine halides show up as black spots, due to elemental silver (Dal Nogare, 1956).

3. HYDRAZINE AND RELATED COMPOUNDS

Solvents for the separation of hydrazine derivatives by horizontal chromatography are:

(1) *n-Butanol:acetic acid:water* = 4:1:5 (organic phase) and

(2) *i-Amyl alcohol:acetic acid:water* = 10:1.5:10 (Hinman, 1956) (see Table IX).

(3) For the separation of hydrazine, hydroxylamine, phenylhydrazine,

and phenylhydroxylamine, Pollard (1956) recommends the preparation of the following solvent which is mixed in this manner in order to minimize esterification: 15 ml. of water, 4 ml. concentrated HCl, 50 ml. of diethyl ether, and 30 ml. of methanol. For this solvent Whatman No. 1 paper is soaked for four days in 2 N HCl and is then washed ten times with distilled water.

For the detection of hydrazines the following reagents are recommended:

(1) *Ehrlich's Reagent* (Hinman, 1956). Fifty milligrams of dimethylaminobenzaldehyde is added to 100 ml. of ethanol and 1 ml. of concentrated HCl. The sprayed papers are heated at 90–95°C. for 10 minutes, and orange fluorescent spots become visible in ultraviolet light.

(2) *Ammoniacal Silver Nitrate* (Hinman, 1956). 5 N NH$_4$OH:0.1 N AgNO$_3$ = v/v.

(3) *Picryl Chloride* (Pollard, 1956). Five-tenths per cent (w/v) ethanolic picryl chloride is sprayed on the chromatograms which are dried and exposed to ammonia vapors. Phenylhydrazine and phenylhydroxylamine appear as brown spots; semicarbazide forms a red spot, while hydroxylamine gives a blue color.

4. AROMATIC AMINES (see Table VIII)

Whatman No. 1 filter paper and the following solvents are employed to resolve DOPA, hydroxytyramine, N-methylhydroxytyramine, tyrosine, and tyramine: n-butanol, saturated with acetic acid; n-butanol, saturated with 5 % trichloroacetic acid; n-butanol, saturated with N HCl; n-butanol: 25 % methylamine = 8:5 v/v (Correale, 1953).

For the chromatography of chloroaniline, Whatman No. 1 filter paper is prewashed with the developing solvent, methanol:i-amyl alcohol:benzene:2 N HCl = 35:17.5:35:12.5.

Hydroxyphenylalkylamines and chloroaniline are detected by diazotization with sulfanilamide (see Chapters V and X) or by the following:

The chromatogram is first sprayed with 1 % p-dimethylaminobenzaldehyde in 1 N HCl. Yellow spots are formed. More intense coloration is achieved by the following successive sprays: (1) 1 % NaNO$_2$ in 1 N HCl; (2) 0.2 % N-(1-naphthyl)ethylenediamine·2HCl. A magenta-colored dye results (Bleidner, 1954).

o- and p-Chloroaniline may be coupled with β-naphthol by diazotization and resolved with *water:pyridine* = 4:1, using a filter paper wedge, as depicted in Figure 2 (Kitahara, 1954).

5. PICOLINES AND LUTIDINES

Picolines and lutidines may be revealed by the following procedure (Baudet, 1952): Filter paper, prior to chromatography, is dipped into a

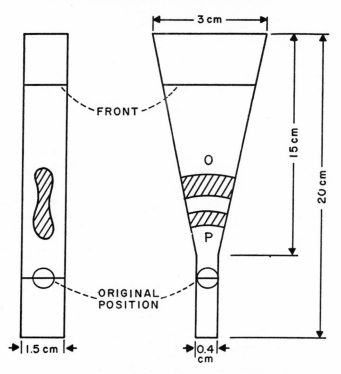

Fig. 2. Resolution of *o*- and *p*-chloroaniline, diazotized with β-naphthol (Kitahara, 1954). *Left:* no resolution by strip technique; *right:* separation using "wedge technique".

solution containing 5 g. of $CuCl_2$, 20 ml. of glycerol, and 100 ml. of water. After the excess moisture is removed by blotting, the paper is dried in air. A mixture of lutidines and picolines is chromatographed with ether in an atmosphere of ether; the development is completed in 20–30 minutes. The compounds are resolved as their copper complexes and are identified by their characteristic colors as follows: α-picoline, green; β-picoline, orange; γ-picoline, bright blue; 2,6-lutidine, mauve; 2,3-lutidine, yellow; 2,4-lutidine, blue; 2,5-lutidine, pale blue.

Piperazine and Hexamethylenetetramine (Castiglioni, 1953). Ten micrograms of each component is spotted on Whatman No. 1 paper which is developed with 1-butanol:water = v/v (1% KCN added). The compounds are detected by exposing the chromatogram to iodine vapors, with piperazine giving a red color and hexamethylenetetramine a yellow color. The R_f values are 0.08 and 0.20, respectively, with the butanol solvent.

TABLE VII

R_f VALUES FOR CHOLINE ESTERS

Compound[a]	Solvent[b]							
	1	2	3	4	5	6	7	8
Acetylcholine	0.14	0.17	0.24	0.46	0.33	0.46	0.18	0.36
Acetyl-β-methylcholine	0.19	0.23	0.35	0.56	0.37	0.55		
Propionylcholine	0.22	0.27	0.35	0.59	—	0.57		
Butyrylcholine	0.28	0.29	0.43	0.66	0.46	0.66		
Benzoylcholine	0.28	0.30	0.43	0.65	0.49	0.71		
Lactylcholine	0.18							
Valerylcholine		0.55						
Choline	0.09	0.13	0.24	0.38	0.25	0.38	0.14	0.31
Acetylthiocholine iodide						0.58		
Carbaminoylcholine						0.30	0.07	0.14
Succinyldicholine iodide						0.12		
Salicylcholine						0.64	0.82,	0.97,
							0.60	0.69
Acetylsalicylcholine						0.67		
Acetylthiamine						0.33		
Betaine						0.46		

[a] Chlorides, unless stated otherwise.
[b] Solvents: 1. 1-Butanol saturated with water (Whittaker, 1952).
2. 1-Butanol:1-propanol:water = 4:2:1 v/v (Whittaker, 1952).
3. 1-Propanol:water = 9:1 v/v (Whittaker, 1952).
4. 1-Propanol:formic acid:water = 8:1:1 v/v (Whittaker, 1952).
5. 1-Propanol:benzyl alcohol:water = 5:2:2 v/v (Whittaker, 1952).
6. 1-Butanol:ethanol:acetic acid:water = 8:2:1:3 v/v (Augustinsson, 1953).
7. Ethyl acetate:pyridine:water = 50:35:15 v/v.
8. Ethyl acetate:pyridine:water = 50:30:20 v/v (Malyoth, 1951).

6. QUINOLINES (J. N. Smith, 1955)

Quinolines and conjugates are chromatographed on Whatman papers No. 1 or 4 with a variety of solvents (Table X). These compounds are detected by their characteristic colors in ultraviolet light after HCl or NH$_3$ exposure. Another color reagent is 0.1% aqueous *Brentamine Fast Blue B salt*, followed by saturated NaHCO$_3$.

Alkaloids

1. PREPARATION OF SAMPLES

The following procedure is recommended for the isolation of alkaloids from urine (Jatzkewitz, 1953, 1956): 10 ml. of urine is adjusted to pH 9–10 with dilute Na$_2$CO$_3$. The alkaloids are extracted with 10 ml. of isoamyl- or amyl acetate, and the sample is centrifuged. Several drops of 15% formic acid are added to the organic phase, and the sample is again centri-

TABLE VIII
R_f VALUES OF ORGANIC AMINES (BAKER, 1952)

Compound	1-Butanol:acetic acid:water	
	5:1:4 v/v	2:1:1 v/v
Benzylamine	0.70	0.66
n-Hexylamine	0.80	
n-Heptylamine	0.83	
n-Octylamine	0.85	
n-Decylamine	0.87	
Tryptamine·HCl		0.39
Tyramine·HCl		0.58
2-Hydroxyethylamine		0.48
1-Phenylethylamine		0.72
2-Phenylethylamine		0.72
2-Aminoheptane		0.76
Ethylenediamine		0.39
Trimethylenediamine		0.39
Hexamethylenediamine		0.48
2-Amino-2'-hydroxydiethylamine		0.42
Noradrenaline·HCl		0.34
Cobefrin·HCl		0.42
Butanefrin·HCl		0.50
Norephedrine		0.53
Paredrin		0.64
Propadrine		0.68
Dexedrine		0.74

fuged.   The alkaloids are thereby converted to the formate derivatives which are water-soluble.   Aliquots of the water phase are applied on Schleicher and Schüll paper No. 2043b.

The alkylpyridines are converted to their respective pyridine carboxylic acids prior to chromatography (Jerchel, 1953).   One gram of the alkyl-pyridine is added dropwise to a 4–6 % aqueous $KMnO_4$ solution at 60–100°C.   The oxidation is allowed to proceed for several hours.   The reaction mixture is filtered, and the precipitated MnO_2 is extracted several times with hot water.   The filtrate and washings are acidified with acetic acid, evaporated to dryness, and extracted with sec-butanol.   Aliquot portions of the extract are spotted on filter paper.

Pyridine aldehydes may be chromatographed as such or as their dimedone derivatives.   The latter are prepared by boiling the sample with a 10 % solution of dimedone (5,5-dimethylcyclohexanedione-1,3) (Jerchel, 1953).

For the isolation of tobacco alkaloids, 50–100 g. of leaves are macerated in a Waring blendor with 50 % acetone (overall concentration) (Jeffrey,

TABLE IX
R_f VALUES OF HYDRAZINE DERIVATIVES (HINMAN, 1956)

| | Solvent[a] | | |
| | 1 | 2 | |
Compound	Circular chroma- tography	Circular chroma- tography	Ascending chroma- tography
1,2-Diformylhydrazine	0.26		
1,2-Diacetylhydrazine	0.48		
1,2-Dipropionylhydrazine	0.81		
1,2-Dibutyrylhydrazine	0.91		
1,2-Diformyl-1,2-dimethylhydrazine	0.60		
1,2-Diacetyl-1,2-dimethylhydrazine	0.74		
1-Formyl-2,2-dimethylhydrazine	0.72		
1-Acetyl-2,2-dimethylhydrazine	0.76		
1-Benzoyl-2,2-dimethylhydrazine	0.88		
Hydrazine·2HCl	0	0.39	0.16
Methylhydrazine sulfate	0.13	0.47	0.17
1,1-Dimethylhydrazine·HCl	0.29	0.53	0.20
1,2-Dimethylhydrazine·2HCl	0.27	0.57	0.23
Trimethylhydrazine·HCl	—	0.42	0.23
1,2-Diethylhydrazine·2HCl	0.30	0.55	0.25

[a] Solvents: 1. i-Amyl alcohol:acetic acid:water = 10:1.5:10.
2. n-Butanol:acetic acid:water = 4:1:5.

TABLE X
R_f VALUES OF QUINOLINE DERIVATIVES (J. N. SMITH, 1955)

| | Solvent[a] | | |
Compound	1	2	3
Quinolyl-6-glucuronide	0.25	—	—
2-Quinolonyl-6-glucuronide	0.38	—	—
4-Quinolonyl-6-glucuronide	0.34	—	—
6-Hydroxyquinoline	0.86	0.88	—
2,6-Dihydroxyquinoline	0.78	0.59	—
4,6-Dihydroxyquinoline	0.78	0.41	—
6-Hydroxyquinolyl-5-sulfuric acid	0.53	—	—
3-Hydroxyquinoline	—	—	0.30
2,3-Dihydroxyquinoline	—	—	0.18
2,4-Dihydroxyquinoline	0.83	—	—

[a] Solvents: 1. n-Butanol:acetic acid:water = 4:1:5.
2. Benzene:n-butanol:concentrated NH_4OH = 2:5:2.
3. Benzene:ethanol:water = 5:1:4.

1955). The slurry is filtered, and aliquots of the clear filtrate are applied to the paper.

2. PAPER

Due to the low water-solubility of the alkaloids, the filter paper may be pretreated by several alternate procedures. The impregnation of paper with suitable buffers will also aid, in many cases, in the final identification of alkaloids.

a. Formamide-Impregnated Paper. Schleicher and Schuell No. 2043b paper has been impregnated with formamide for the separation of alkaloid-aglycones (Tuzson, 1956). Ergot alkaloids have been chromatographed on Whatman No. 1 paper impregnated with formamide, containing 4% benzoic acid (Pöhm, 1954). For the separation of *Rauwolfia* alkaloids, Whatman No. 1 is dipped into acetone:formamide = 3:1. The paper is blotted between two sheets of filter paper, and the sample, dissolved in chloroform, is spotted (Grant, 1955).

b. Silicone-Impregnated Paper is employed for the separation of 2-isopropyl-4-methyl-6-hydroxypyrimidinyldiethyl phosphate and 2-isopropyl-4-methyl-6-hydroxypyrimidinyldiethyl thionophosphate (Vigne, 1955).

c. Dimethylphthalate-Impregnated Paper (Stoll, 1954). Whatman No. 1 paper is saturated with 10% dimethylphthalate in isopropyl ether. The paper is drained no longer than fifteen minutes, since the phthalate will volatilize, and the sample of ergot alkaloids is immediately spotted.

d. Buffered Paper. Whatman No. 1 paper is dipped into 0.1 *M* phosphate buffer (pH 6.5):acetone (v/v), blotted and dried (Jeffrey, 1955). Goldbaum (1956) has buffered Whatman No. 2 paper with McIlvaine's phosphate-citrate buffers of pH 3.0, 5.0 and Sørenson's phosphate buffers of pH 6.5, 7.5. Butanol, saturated with the appropriate buffer is used as developing solvent. Morphinane derivatives may be separated on Whatman No. 1, saturated with phosphate buffer, pH 6.32 and citrate buffer, pH 8.09 (Brossi, 1955).

A strip of Whatman No. 1 paper may be divided into buffered zones (McIlvaine's buffer—double strength), ranging from pH 6.4 to 4.2. Each buffered zone is separated by a thin area of untreated paper. By chromatographing alkaloids on this multibuffered paper, each substance tends to form a salt at the pH of its isoelectric point and ceases to move (Schmall, 1956).

e. Washed Paper. Whatman No. 1 or 3 MM is washed with *N* HCl and water for the chromatography of the alkaloids of hemlock (Cromwell, 1956).

3. SOLVENTS (see Table XI)

a. Butanol:HCl. Twenty ml. of concentrated HCl is added to 100 ml. of 1-butanol, and the mixture is shaken with water until saturation is achieved. Atropine and related compounds are separated by this solvent (Munier, 1951). Nicotine, pyrrolidine, and pyridine are separated as their chlorohydrates.

1-Butanol saturated with 0.1 N HCl separates cardiazole (R_f = 0.86) and coramine (R_f = 0.32) (Kaiser, 1953). n-Butanol (100 ml.) and 4 ml. of concentrated HCl are saturated with water. This solvent separates a mixture of chlorohydrates of corynanthine, yohimbine, and related substances.

b. Butanol:acetic acid. Fourteen ml. of glacial acetic acid is added to 100 ml. of n-butanol, and the mixture is saturated with water. This solvent is suitable for the separation of sparteine and genisteine. n-Butanol:acetic acid:water = 4:1:3 is used for descending "Durchlauf chromatography" of mustard oil glucosides (Schultz, 1956). The same solvent of the composition 6:1:3 has been used for circular chromatography of tobacco alkaloids (Tewari, 1954).

c. n-Butanol:formic acid:water = 12:1:7 separates alkaloids isolated from urine (Jatzkewitz, 1953,1956) (see Table XI).

d. Butyl Acetate:methanol:0.25% NH₄OH = 95:5:25 for the separation of nicotine transformation products (Porter, 1949).

e. n-Butanol:concentrated NH₄OH = 4:1 gives the following R_f values: aspirin—0.49; caffeine—0.68; phenacetine—0.93 (Castiglioni, 1955a).

f. Butyl acetate:butanol:acetic acid = 85:15:30 gives the following R_f values: papaverine—0.57; narcotine—0.70 (Thies, 1955).

g. n-Propanol:formic acid:ethyl benzoate = 6:2:4, saturated with water, is used for the chromatography of tropic acid (Schindler, 1956).

h. tert-Amyl alcohol:water = 10:2 to which is added 0.3 g. ethyl p-aminobenzoate/120 ml. of solvent. The tank is presaturated with tert-amyl alcohol, and Whatman No. 1 (pH 6.5) is used for the separation of nicotine, anabasine, and nornicotine (Jeffrey, 1955).

i. Amylene hydrate:n-butyl ether:water = 80:7:13 for Whatman No. 1 paper (pH 6.32) and 50:7:43 for paper, impregnated with pH 8.09 buffer. These solvents are employed for the separation of morphinane derivatives (Brossi, 1955).

j. Formamide:water = 4:6; adjusted to pH 4 or 5.2 with formic acid, will separate the ergot alkaloids (Stoll, 1954). The formamide should be vacuum-distilled before use, and the development carried out in subdued light. The paper is saturated with dimethylphthalate.

k. Benzene, saturated with formamide for the separation of protoveratrine A and B on formamide-impregnated paper (Grant, 1955).

l. Benzene:chloroform = 1:2 for the separation of alkaloids from Solanum, like solanidine (R_f 0.56), tomatidine (R_f 0.85) (Tuzson, 1956). Schleicher and Schuell paper 2043b is impregnated with formamide.

m. Cyclohexane:n-butanol:acetic acid:water = 40:2:20:10 is shaken thoroughly and allowed to separate for 24 hours. The paper is impregnated with the lower, aqueous phase, and the organic layer is used as the developing solvent for solanidiene (R_f 0.18) and solasodiene (R_f 0.25) (Tuzson, 1956).

n. Two-Dimensional Solvent System (Boscott, 1955). *First direction*: *n*-hexyl ether:methyl isobutylketone:acetic acid:water = 20:5:2:18; tank must be equilibrated; *second direction*: 10% (v/v) acetic acid in aqueous 5% sodium acetate, saturated with *n*-butyl ether; no equilibration necessary. This solvent pair has been found suitable for the separation of reserpine and related compounds.

4. TECHNIQUES

Either the ascending or descending development technique may be employed for the chromatography of alkaloids. A novel technique for the semiquantitative determination of auramine has been described by Mori (1954). A narrow passage is defined on a filter paper strip by areas saturated with paraffin. The substances travel through this rectangular narrow passage, resulting in elongated instead of round spots. The length of the developed colored zone may be related to the concentration.

The number of glycol groups in *Veratrum* alkaloids may be calculated from the change in R_M (see Chapter II for definition) by running two parallel chromatograms on paper impregnated with formamide plus boric acid and formamide alone (Macek, 1955). Since glycol-borate complexes are highly polar, the migration on the formamide-borate paper will be greatly retarded. Also a change in ΔR_M on acetylation gives an indication of the number of glycol groups which are blocked.

5. DETECTION

a. Dragendorff Reagent (Munier, 1951; Kaiser, 1953; Jatzkewitz, 1953; Grant, 1955). This is the most widely used color reagent for the detection of alkaloids, including those isolated from *Rauwolfia*: *Solution A*: 0.8 g. of bismuth subnitrate, 10 ml. of glacial acetic acid, and 40 ml. of water. *Solution B*: 40% (w/v) aqueous KI.

Spraying reagent: 5 ml. each of Solutions *A* and *B* are mixed with 20 ml. of glacial acetic acid and diluted to 100 ml. with distilled water. Alkaloids form red-orange spots.

An alternate procedure for the preparation of the Dragendorff Reagent has been described by Thies (1954, 1955) who claims several advantages over the above reagent:

Stock solution: 2.6 g. of basic bismuth carbonate and 7.0 g. of dry NaI are boiled with 25 ml. of glacial acetic acid for a few minutes. The solution is allowed to cool overnight, filtered, and 20 ml. of the clear supernatant mixed with 80 ml. of ethyl acetate. This serves as the stock solution.

Dipping reagent: 20 ml. of stock solution, 50 ml. acetic acid, and 120 ml. of ethyl acetate; 10 ml. of water is added dropwise.

Spraying reagent: 10 ml. of stock solution; then proceed as for dipping reagent.

This reagent is suitable for quantitative estimation of alkaloids using a densitometer at maximum absorption at 5080 Å.

b. Detection of Pyridinecarboxylic Acids (Jerchel, 1953): (1) 0.05% *Alcoholic Fluorescein.* The sprayed chromatogram is viewed under ultraviolet light, with a "Schott-UG5" filter, absorbing most of the visible spectrum. The acids appear as dark spots on a green-yellow fluorescent background. Sensitivity: 25 μg./ml.

(2) 4% Alcoholic solution of *bromophenol blue* is made just alkaline with $NaHCO_3$. Pyridinecarboxylic acids appear as yellow spots on a blue-green background. Sensitivity: 20–40 μg./ml.

(3) The chromatogram is sprayed with a 2% alcoholic solution of *2,4-dinitrofluorobenzene* and heated for 10–15 minutes at 110°C. It is then sprayed with 5% NaOH and the following colored spots are observed: nicotinic acid, red-brown (fades in 3 minutes); isonicotinic acid, violet (fades in 3 minutes); pyridine, violet; β-picoline, rust brown; γ-picoline, green-black; aldehyde collidine, blue-black; quinoline, no color.

(4) The chromatogram is first exposed to the vapors of an ethereal solution of *cyanogen bromide*. It is then sprayed with the following solution: 2 g. of $p\text{-}NH_2C_6H_4COOH$, 75 ml. of 0.75 N HCl, and 25 ml. of ethanol. Nicotinic acid produces a yellow spot. (Caution! CNBr is very toxic).

c. Color Reagent for Pyridinealdehydes (Jerchel, 1953): 10% alcoholic solution of dimedone (5,5-dimethylcyclohexanedione-1,3). The chromatogram is dried and then sprayed with a 5% aqueous solution of $FeCl_3$. Violet-red brown spots result. Sensitivity: 50 μg. of monoaldehyde per ml. of solution; 20 μg. of dialdehyde per ml. of solution.

d. Ehrlich's Reagent (Stoll, 1954). Chromatograms of ergot alkaloids are dried for 45 minutes at 100°C. They are then dipped into warm 0.5% *p*-dimethylaminobenzaldehyde in cyclohexane, air-dried, and exposed to HCl vapors. Blue-violet spots result.

e. Detection of Reserpine and Related Compounds (Boscott, 1955). These compounds appear as fluorescent spots after the paper has been treated

TABLE XI

R_f Values of Alkaloids (Munier, 1949; Tso, 1953; Jatzkewitz, 1953; Boscott, 1955)

Compound	Solvent[a]						
	1	2	3	4	5	6	7
Morphine	0.04	0.07	—	0.31	—	—	—
Codeine	0.46	0.51	—	—	—	—	—
Thebaine	0.68	0.67	—	—	—	—	—
Narcotine	0.81	0.80	—	—	—	—	—
Papaverine	0.80	0.72	—	—	—	—	—
Cryptopine	0.63	0.60	—	—	—	—	—
Strychnine	0.73	0.69	—	—	—	—	—
Brucine	0.49	0.52	—	—	—	—	—
Quinine	0.87	0.80	—	—	—	—	—
Quinidine	0.91	0.80	—	—	—	—	—
Cinchonine	0.90	0.79	—	—	—	—	—
Cinchonidine	0.78	0.81	—	—	—	—	—
Cinchonamine	0.81	0.84	—	—	—	—	—
Nicotine	0.44	0.50	—	0.23	0.33	—	—
Piperine	0.95	0.90	—	—	—	--	—
Berberine	0.30	0.35	—	—	—	—	—
Colarnine	0.35	0.47	—	—	—	—	—
Hydrastinine	0.24	0.40	—	—	—	—	—
Eserine	0.78	0.72	—	—	—	—	—
Atropine	0.63	0.63	—	—	—	—	—
Yohimbine	0.67	0.72	—	—	—	—	—
Pilocarpine	0.40	0.47	—	—	—	—	—
Boldine	0.49	0.59	—	—	—	—	—
Corynantheine	0.91	0.85	—	—	—	—	—
Chelidonine	0.68	0.67	—	—	—	—	—
Conessine	0.51	0.53	—	—	—	—	—
Gelsemine	0.65	0.69	—	—	—	—	—
Delphenine	0.84	0.88	—	—	—	—	—
Sparteine	0.63	0.69	—	—	—	—	—
Veratrine	0.89	0.85	—	—	—	—	—
Caffeine	0.69	0.67	0.72	—	—	—	—
Theobromine	0.41	0.42	0.45	—	—	—	—
Theophylline	0.64	0.59	0.57	—	—	—	—
Trigonelline	0.08	0.13	0.09	—	—	—	—
Ephedrine	0.70	0.66	0.90	—	—	—	—
Hordenine	0.53	0.52	0.88	—	—	—	—
Betaine	0.14	0.17	0.11	—	—	—	—
Choline	0.19	0.23	0.10	—	—	—	—
Nicotinamide	0.71	0.65	0.65	—	0.86	—	—
Dilaudid	—	—	—	0.32	—	—	—
"Eukodal"	—	—	—	0.34	—	—	—

TABLE XI—*Continued*

Compound	Solvent[a]						
	1	2	3	4	5	6	7
Dicodid	—	—	—	0.39	—	—	—
Cliradon	—	—	—	0.61	—	—	—
Pervitin	—	—	—	0.65	—	—	—
Dolantin	—	—	—	0.70	—	—	—
Dromoran	—	—	—	0.71	—	—	—
Polamidon	—	—	—	0.80	—	—	—
4-Methylamino-1-(3-pyridyl)-1-butanol	—	—	—	—	0.12	—	—
"N-Methylmyosmine"	—	—	—	—	0.13	—	—
Nornicotine	—	—	—	—	0.17	—	—
Anabasine	—	—	—	—	0.21	—	—
Metanicotine	—	—	—	—	0.25	—	—
xynicotine	—	—	—	—	0.30	—	—
"N-Methylanabasine"	—	—	—	—	0.36	—	—
Dihydronicotyrine	—	—	—	—	0.36	—	—
Isonicotinic acid	—	—	—	—	0.51	0.65	—
3-Acetylpyridine	—	—	—	—	0.61	—	—
Nicotinic acid	—	—	—	—	0.62	0.71	—
β-Picoline	—	—	—	—	0.87	—	—
Myosmine	—	—	—	—	0.92	—	—
2,3'-Dipyridyl	—	—	—	—	0.95	—	—
2-Methyl-6-(3-pyridyl)-tetrahydro-1,2-oxazine·HCl	—	—	—	—	0.96	—	—
Nornicotyrine	—	—	—	—	0.97	—	—
Nicotyrine	—	—	—	—	0.98	—	—
α-Picolinic acid	—	—	—	—	—	0.59	—
2-Methylpyridine-5-carboxylic acid	—	—	—	—	—	0.69	—
6-Methylpyridine-2-carboxylic acid	—	—	—	—	—	0.52	—
2,3-Pyridinedicarboxylic acid	—	—	—	—	—	0.57	—
2,4-Pyridinedicarboxylic acid	—	—	—	—	—	0.60	—
3,4-Pyridinedicarboxylic acid	—	—	—	—	—	0.50	—
2,5-Pyridinedicarboxylic acid	—	—	—	—	—	0.71	—
2,6-Pyridinedicarboxylic acid	—	—	—	—	—	0.49	—
α-Pyridinealdehyde	—	—	—	—	—	0.68[b] (0.86)	—
β-Pyridinealdehyde	—	—	—	—	—	0.67 (0.90)	—
γ-Pyridinealdehyde	—	—	—	—	—	0.59 (0.86)	—
6-Methylpyridine-2-aldehyde	—	—	—	—	—	0.64 (0.90)	—

TABLE XI—*Concluded*

Compound	Solvent[a]						
	1	2	3	4	5	6	7
2,6-Pyridinedialdehyde	—	—	—	—	—	0.83 (0.93)	—
Ajmaline	—	—	—	—	—	—	0.76
Deserpine	—	—	—	—	—	—	0.41
Methyl reserpate	—	—	—	—	—	—	0.52; 0.76
Rauwolscine	—	—	—	—	—	—	0.63
Reserpine	—	—	—	—	—	—	0.34
Rescinnamine	—	—	—	—	—	—	0.26
Serpentine	—	—	—	—	—	—	0.5

[a] Solvents: 1. Four ml. of glacial acetic acid is added to 100 ml. of n-butanol, and the mixture is saturated with water at 20° C.
2. Ten ml. of glacial acetic acid is added to 100 ml. of n-butanol, and the mixture is saturated with water.
3. n-Butanol:ethanol:NH$_4$OH:H$_2$O = 90:10:1:97 v/v are mixed, and the upper phase is used.
4. n-Butanol:formic acid:water = 12:1:7 v/v.
5. *tert*-Amyl alcohol:0.2 M acetate buffer, pH 5.6 = 1:1 v/v.
6. *sec*-Butanol:formic acid:water = 75:15:10 v/v.
7. 10% Acetic acid in 5% sodium acetate, satured with n-butyl ether.
[b] Dimedate derivative.

with 3% sodium nitroprusside in 50% aqueous trichloroacetic acid. *Ehrlich's Reagent* (see d above) may also be used.

f. Sodium Nitroprusside (1%, w/v), neutralized with 10% Na$_2$CO$_3$ results in red spots for γ-coniceine and piperidines (Cromwell, 1956).

g. β-Naphthylamine (1%) in ethanol, followed by exposure to cyanogen bromide results in the identification of nicotine and related compounds (Tso, 1953). p-Aminobenzoic acid may be used in place of naphthylamine (Leiserson, 1955).

h. Iodoplatinic Acid Reagent (Goldbaum, 1956). Alkaloids and other basic drugs are revealed as dark spots by spraying the chromatogram with the following reagent: 45 ml. 10% KI, 5 ml. 5% PtCl$_6^{--}$, and 100 ml. of water.

6. DETAILED EXPERIMENTAL PROCEDURE

For the chromatography of nicotine and related compounds the following procedure is recommended (Leiserson, 1955):

Whatman Paper No. 1 is sprayed with a buffer composed of 95 ml. 0.2 M acetic acid and 905 ml. of 0.2 M sodium acetate, adjusted to pH 5.6. Ten to 50 μg. samples of the solutes are spotted, and the paper is hung in a water-saturated atmosphere for hydration. The chromatogram is then developed by the ascending technique with *n*-butanol, saturated with pH 5.6 acetate buffer. The walls of the chromatographic tank are lined with paper soaked with the water phase of the solvent.

After the development, the paper is air-dried, sprayed with 1 % alcoholic *p*-aminobenzoic acid, again air-dried, and placed in a tank containing cyanogen bromide. Colored spots for the alkaloids result.

Nicotinic Acid and Related Compounds

(See also Chapter XIII)

1. PREPARATION OF SAMPLES

a. Isolation from Urine. Ten milliliters of urine is concentrated *in vacuo* at 55–60°C. The residue is extracted with 1.0 ml. of water and is centrifuged. Ten to forty microliters of the clear supernatant are chromatographed on Whatman No. 1 paper (Reddi, 1953).

b. Isolation of Trigonelline from Coffee (Kogan, 1953). To 5–10 g. of ground coffee are added 200 ml. of water and 50 ml. of 0.05 N H_2SO_4 . The mixture is boiled gently for 20 minutes, and 25 g. of MgO is added. The resultant mixture is boiled for another 20 minutes and filtered through Whatman No. 12. Twenty microliters of the filtrate are chromatographed on Whatman No. 1 paper.

2. SOLVENTS

Besides the solvents listed in Table XII, the following have also been used for the chromatography of pyridine carboxylic acids and derivatives:

a. n-Butanol:Acetic Acid:Water = 4:1:1 results in the following R_f values: picolinic acid—0.63; nicotinic acid—0.89; *iso*-nicotinic acid— 0.76 (Chakrabarti, 1956).

b. n-Butanol:Acetic Acid:Water = 4:1:5 for the separation of pyridoxine, pyridoxamine, and nicotinic acid (Maiwald, 1956).

c. 10% NH₃:n-Butanol = 2:10 is a good solvent for the separation of pyridine carboxylic acid hydrazides, except for isonicotinic acid hydrazide, which decomposes to the amide (Itai, 1954).

d. i-Propanol:Water = 85:15 for the metabolites of *isoniazid* (isonicotinic acid hydrazide) (Defranceschi, 1954). 65% Isopropanol in HCl (final concentration of HCl is 2 N) results in the following fluorescent spots when viewed in ultraviolet light: caffeine (R_f 0.78), trigonelline (R_f 0.59), and chlorogenic acid (R_f 0.86) (Kogan, 1953).

3. DETECTION (Caution! CNBr is very toxic.)

a. Ultraviolet Absorption. After chromatographic development, the paper is dried in an oven at 105°C. and laid on a photographic plate.

With appropriate filters, ultraviolet light of 260–270 mμ wavelength is directed on the chromatogram, and the spots of nicotinic acid, nicotinamide, trigonelline, and tryptophan are revealed as white spots on a black background (Munier, 1951; Allouf, 1952). N-Methyl-2-pyridone-3-carboxylic acid and its amide are detected by monochromatic light of 313 mμ. The CoSO₄-NiSO₄ filter used for the detection of purines and pyrimidines (see Chapter IX) is replaced by one filled with saturated CuSO₄.

b. *CNBr-PABA Treatment* (Kodicek, 1951; Reddi, 1953). The dried chromatograms are exposed for 1 hour to CNBr vapors. They are then sprayed with the following solution: 2 g. of *p*-aminobenzoic acid dissolved in 75 ml. of 0.75 N HCl, diluted to 100 ml. with 96 % ethanol. The tertiary pyridine compounds appear as fluorescent spots in ultraviolet light. Quaternary nicotinyl compounds fluoresce in ultraviolet light when the chromatograms are exposed to vapors from a mixture (1:1) of ethyl methyl ketone:ammonia.

c. *4-Chloro-1,3-Dinitrobenzene* (1 %) in methanol is sprayed on the paper, followed after ten minutes by 3 N NaOH (Maiwald, 1956). The following colors result: nicotinamide—wine-red; nicotinic acid—orange yellow; pyridoxine—light yellow; sensitivity 10 μg. Pyridoxal phosphate results in a fading light-yellow color, while pyridoxamine is negative.

d. *CuSO₄-Benzidine Reagents* (Chakrabarti, 1956). This technique has been developed for the detection of picolinic-, nicotinic-, and iso-nicotinic acid. The chromatogram is first sprayed with 0.2 % anhydrous CuSO₄ in 36 % ethanol and dried at 60°C. After the paper is sprayed with 0.1 % benzidine in 50 % ethanol, blue spots on a light brown background result.

e. *Color Reagent for Isonicotinoyl Hydrazide* (Rapi, 1953). *Stock Solution.* The reagent is prepared as follows: 0.1 g. of Na₂S₂O₄ is dissolved in a few milliliters of water, and 1 ml. of 10 % Na₂CO₃ is added. One-tenth gram of 1-amino-2-naphthol-4-sulfonic acid is then added, and the solution is diluted to 100 ml. with water. The reagent is stored in the dark.

Color Development. The chromatogram is first sprayed with the 20 % trichloroacetic acid:30 % Na₂CO₃:water = 1:1:2 v/v. The paper is heated at 50°C. for 1–2 minutes and is then sprayed with stock solution: water:30 % Na₂CO₃ = 1:2:1 v/v.

f. *Miscellaneous Reagents.* Nicotinic acid compounds may be revealed by first spraying the chromatogram with 0.5 % alcoholic N-(*1-naphthyl*) *ethylenediamine·2HCl* and then exposing the paper to an atmosphere of CNBr. Yellow spots result (Johnson, 1953). The sensitivity of this method is 40 μg./ml. N'-Methylnicotinuric acid betaine and N'-methyl-nicotinamide are revealed by streaking the chromatogram with 20 % KOH and viewing the paper under *ultraviolet light* with a Corning filter No. 587

TABLE XII

R_f VALUES OF NICOTINIC ACID AND RELATED COMPOUNDS

Compound	Solvent[a]						
	1	2	3	4	5	6	7
Nicotinic acid	0.30	0.21	—	—	0.68	0.66	—
Nicotinamide	0.67	0.69	—	—	0.55	—	—
Nicotinuric acid	0.13	0.11	—	—	—	—	—
N'-Methylnicotinamide chloride	0.05	—	0.71	0.47	—	—	—
Trigonelline	0.07	—	—	—	0.16	—	—
Diethylnicotinamide	—	—	0.90	—	—	—	—
N'-Methylnicotinuric acid betaine	—	—	0.57	0.26	—	—	—
Carbamyl-N',2'-hydroxyethylpyridinium bromide	—	—	0.74	0.36	—	—	—
DPN	—	—	0.43	0.10	—	—	—
TPN	—	—	0.30	0	—	—	—
3-Carbamyltetraacetyl-N'-D-glucosidylpyridinium bromide	—	—	0.94	0.84	—	—	—
3-Carbamyl-N'-ribosidylpyridinium bromide	—	—	0.62	0.33	—	—	—
N-Methyl-2-pyridone-5-carboxylic acid	—	—	—	—	0.70	—	—
N-Methyl-2-pyridone-5-carboxylic amide	—	—	—	—	0.57	—	—
N-Methyl-2-pyridone-3-carboxylic acid	—	—	—	—	0.79	—	—
Pyridoxine	—	—	—	—	0.74	—	—
Picolinic acid	—	—	—	—	—	0.47	—
Isonicotinic acid	—	—	—	—	—	0.54	—
Quinolinic acid	—	—	—	—	—	0.28	—
Cinchomeronic acid	—	—	—	—	—	0.29	—
2,4-Pyridine dicarboxylic acid	—	—	—	—	—	0.17	—
Picolinic acid hydrazide	—	—	—	—	—	—	0.64
Nicotinic acid hydrazide	—	—	—	—	—	—	0.49
Isonicotinic acid hydrazide	—	—	—	—	—	—	0.37[b]
Quinolinic acid hydrazide	—	—	—	—	—	—	0.07
Cinchomeronic acid hydrazide	—	—	—	—	—	—	0.13
2,4-Pyridine dicarboxylic acid hydrazide	—	—	—	—	—	—	0
Hydrazine	—	—	—	—	—	—	0.15

[a] Solvents: 1. n-Butanol:acetone:water = 45:5:50 v/v (Johnson, 1953).
2. n-Butanol:saturated with water (Kodicek, 1951).
3. 60% Acetone (Kodicek, 1951).
4. 80% Acetone (Kodicek, 1951).
5. Isobutanol:98% formic acid:water = 100:20:45 v/v (Allouf, 1952).
6. n-Butanol:acetic acid:water = 4:1:2 (Itai, 1954).
7. 10% NH_3:n-butanol = 2:10 (Itai, 1954).
[b] Isonicotinic acid hydrazide is decomposed to the amide.

(Johnson, 1953). Chromatograms containing pyridoxine are sprayed with a dilute solution of ferric chloride producing yellow fluorescent spots (Allouf, 1952).

Adrenaline and Related Compounds

1. PREPARATION OF SAMPLE

Plasma is first extracted with n-butanol which in turn is extracted with 0.05 N HCl. The pH is first adjusted to 3 with Dowex 50 ion exchange resin and then to pH 8.4 with dilute alkali. This solution is passed through a column of acid-washed alumina, the eluate concentrated *in vacuo* and extracted with acidified acetone (1 ml. concentrated HCl in 100 ml. of acetone). Five μl. aliquots are spotted on paper for chromatography (Weil-Malherbe, 1954).

For the isolation of hydroxytryptamine from urine, the following procedure is used (von Euler, 1951): The urine is boiled for 20 minutes at pH 2 in order to split conjugated catechol amines. The liberated amines are taken up in n-butanol by repeated extractions and concentrations by evaporation *in vacuo*. The butanol extracts are further purified by passing them through a starch column, using n-butanol:1 N HCl (v/v) as developing solvent. The eluates are evaporated to dryness and redissolved in water.

When trichloroacetic acid is employed for deproteinization of a gland extract for the chromatography of adrenaline, Shepherd (1952) has observed an additional spot on a chromatogram developed with n-butanol: acetic acid:water. This "unknown" spot is probably due to an artifact of the trichloroacetic acid treatment.

2. PAPER

Adrenaline and related compounds have been chromatographed as their hydrochlorides on untreated Whatman No. 1 paper and Schleicher and Schuell No. 597 (James, 1948; Goldenberg, 1949). For more discerning work, Whatman No. 1 paper is washed for 24 hours in 0.5 N HCl, rinsed with water, washed another 24 hours in 0.1 % Versene, rinsed with water, and air-dried (Goldstein, 1956).

3. SOLVENTS (See also Table XIII)

a. n-Butanol:Acetic Acid: Water = 4:1:5 (Schayer, 1951; 1953). This solvent is used for the metabolic breakdown products of adrenaline.

b. Phenol:0.1 N HCl (Goldstein, 1956). The phenol must be freshly distilled. Water-saturated phenol may also be employed (James, 1948;

Goldenberg, 1949). When phenol is used, the tank is equilibrated with 5 N HCl, saturated with phenol (Weil-Malherbe, 1954).

c. *n-Butanol:1 N HCl* (v/v) (von Euler, 1951).

4. TECHNIQUE

Ascending or descending development technique is used. When the sample containing adrenaline and related compounds is spotted, a stream of dry nitrogen should be used for drying instead of air. This precaution prevents the oxidation of these compounds. For this reason also, the chromatographic tank is flushed with CO_2 (dry ice) 30 minutes before the start of the development.

5. DETECTION

a. Potassium Ferricyanide. The dried chromatogram is sprayed with a 0.44 % solution of potassium ferricyanide in phosphate buffer, pH 7.8. Oxidation of the adrenalines is immediate and leads to a brownish red spot with noradrenaline and a bright red spot with adrenaline. Methyl adrenaline is revealed by a bleached spot on a reddish background (James, 1948).

A modification of this reagent is as follows (Shepherd, 1953): 0.66 % aqueous potassium ferricyanide:40 % formic acid = 9:1 v/v. The sprayed chromatogram is heated at 100°C. for 5 minutes and is viewed under ultraviolet light. Brightly colored fluorescent spots result. The sensititivy of this reagent is 0.5 μg.

The definition of the spots may be improved by using an additional spray after the ferricyanide treatment. This reagent consists of 5.0 g. of anhydrous ferric sulfate, 75 ml. of 85 % phosphoric acid, and water to a final volume of 1 liter. The spots on the chromatogram, containing adrenaline and related compounds, turn to a brilliant blue, owing to Prussian blue formation (Goldenberg, 1949).

b. β-Naphthoquinone-4-Sulfonate. The dried chromatogram is sprayed with a solution of 0.5 g. of sodium β-naphthoquinone-4-sulfonate dissolved in 100 ml. of 0.2 M borate buffer at pH 8.9. This reagent is freshly prepared before use. Noradrenaline produces a blue color, adrenaline a pink color, and dihydroxyphenylalanine a yellow color which changes to blue-gray (Glazko, 1951). The reagent will detect 2 μg. of adrenaline. Quantitative evaluation of the resulting spots is feasible by relating the areas of the zones to the log concentration (see Chapter IV).

c. Ninhydrin. Ninhydrin (see Chapter V) gives a strong coloration with noradrenaline, but a very weak one with adrenaline. This may be used as a confirmatory test.

d. Potassium Mercury (II) Thiocyanate. A colorimetric test for adrenaline

TABLE XIII
ADRENALINE AND RELATED COMPOUNDS

Compound	R_f	
	Phenol: H_2O	Butanol: acetic acid: H_2O
Noradrenaline	0.22, 0.30[a]	0.28
Dihydroxyphenylalanine	0.23, 0.35	0.19
Hydroxytyramine	0.32, 0.45	0.39
Corbasil	0.41	—
Adrenaline	0.44, 0.50	0.36
N-Methyl corbasil	0.71	—
Epinine	0.76	—
Methyl adrenaline	0.80	—
m-Hydroxyphenylethanolamine		0.56

[a] Two values for the R_f factor are those reported by different authors (James, 1948; Goldenberg, 1949).

may be useful for paper chromatography (Salgó, 1953): 21.6 g. of yellow mercuric oxide and 39 g. of KCNS are mixed to a paste with 200 ml. of water. Dilute sulfuric acid is added until a clear solution is obtained which is diluted to 1 liter with water. It is important to keep the solution slightly alkaline during the preparation of the reagent. The reagent gives a deep red color when heated with a sample containing adrenaline.

Aromatic Sulfur Compounds

1. SOLVENTS

Several solvents used for the chromatographic separation of sulfa drugs are listed in Table XIV. Additional solvents are as follows:

a. 1-Butanol: Acetic Acid: H_2O = 50:15:35 v/v for sulfaguanidine (R_f = 0.55) and sulfamerazine (R_f = 0.85) (Steel, 1951).

b. 1-Butanol saturated with *borate-carbonate buffer*, pH 10 (Mizuno, 1953).

c. Ethyl Acetate: NH_4OH: Acetone = 10:10:8 (L. C. Mitchell, 1955). This solvent is used for the separation of cyclohexylsulfamate (R_f 0.19), saccharin (R_f 0.38), and dulcin (R_f 0.92). Another solvent for the separation of saccharin and dulcin is *n*-butanol: NH_4OH = 4:1 (Castiglioni, 1955*b*).

2. DETECTION

One of the color reagents for the detection of the sulfa drugs is the modified Ehrlich *p*-dimethylaminobenzaldehyde reagent. The preparation of this reagent is as follows: 0.5 g. of *p*-$(CH_3)_2NC_6H_4CHO$ is dissolved in 5 ml. of 2 *N* HCl and diluted to 250 ml. with water. Sulfonamides appear as yellow spots when the chromatogram is sprayed with this solution. Succinylsulfathiazole and septazine do not react, as neither compound has a free amino group (de Reeder, 1953).

When the spots containing the sulfa drugs are eluted for assaying, the following procedure is adopted: To the eluate is added 1 ml. of 0.75 M disodium acid citrate and 2 ml. of 2% alcoholic p-dimethylaminobenzalde-hyde. The resultant yellow color is compared to that of a standard solution by colorimetry (Morris, 1941; San, 1952). A second method of detection of the sulfa drugs involves diazotization on the paper chromato-gram. The paper is first sprayed with a solution of 0.2% $NaNO_2$ in 10% trichloroacetic acid. This is followed by a reagent consisting of 0.2% 1-amino-8-naphthol-5,6-disulfonic acid. Red spots on a white background are formed (Kutzim, 1952). N-Dimethyl-α-naphthylamine may be used as the coupling reagent (Steel, 1951).

For the detection of homosulfamine, the paper is first sprayed with dilute NaOH and then 0.5% potassium naphthoquinonesulfonate, re-sulting in an orange spot (Mitsuno, 1955).

Saccharin forms a blue spot when sprayed with 0.1% alcoholic α-naph-thylamine, plus 4–5 drops of saturated Cu(II)acetate and 2–3 drops of acetic acid (Castiglioni, 1955b).

TABLE XIV

R_f Values for Sulfa Drugs

Compound	Solvent[a]		
	1	2	3
Sulfaguanidine	0.43	0.36	—
Sulfathiazole	0.48	0.46	0.47
Sulfanilamide	0.56	0.42	0.55
Sulfadiazine	0.24	0.50	0.24
Sulfamethazine	0.48	0.48	0.65
Sulfamerazine	0.34	0.50	0.42–0.46
Sulfacetamide	0.71	0.44	—
Sulfapyridine	0.70	0.51	0.65
Sulfaguanidine	—	—	0.30
Na sulfadiazine	—	0.13	—
Na sulfamerazine	—	0.20	—
Na sulfamethazine	—	0.30	—
Na sulfathiazole	—	0.34	—
Na sulfapyridine	—	0.48	—

[a] Solvents: 1. Organic phase: 1-butanol:acetic acid:H_2O = 50:15:60 v/v; p-dimethylaminobenzaldehyde is added to a final concentration of 0.5% (R. Robinson, 1951).
2. Organic phase: 1-butanol:NH_4OH:H_2O = 4:1:3 v/v (R. Robinson, 1951; de Reeder, 1953).
3. 1-Butanol saturated with water:pyridine = 8:1 v/v (de Reeder, 1953).

Barbiturates

1. Isolation from Urine

A sample of urine is extracted at pH 11 with diethyl ether, and the extracts are discarded. The pH is adjusted to 3 with dilute HCl, and the barbiturates are extracted with ether. Aliquot volumes of this extract are applied to filter paper for chromatography (Riebeling, 1954). In place of ether, chloroform may be used for the isolation of barbiturate metabolites from urine (Allgén, 1954).

2. Solvents (See also Table XV)

Whatman No. 1 and Schleicher and Schuell No. 2045b papers have been used with the following solvents:

a. *i-Amyl alcohol:NH₄OH:ethylene glycol* = 10:10:1 (NH₃ atmosphere) (Allgén, 1954).

b. *Hexyl alcohol*, saturated with NH_4OH is used to resolve a mixture of barbiturates containing diallyl-, isoamyl ethyl-, and phenylallyl barbituric acid, barbital, aprobarbital, phenobarbital, mephobarbital, cyclobarbital, and hexobarbital (Allgén, 1953).

c. *n-Butanol:25% NH₄OH:water* = 84:8:8 (Riebeling, 1954).

3. Detection

The chromatogram containing the barbiturates is sprayed with 0.5 N NaOH and may be visualized in ultraviolet light owing to the quenching effect of the barbiturates at pH 9–10 (Grieg, 1952). The dried chromatogram is placed in firm contact with a fluorescent screen and placed in front of a low-pressure mercury lamp with a 2537-Å filter. The barbiturates appear as black spots on the fluorescent screen.

Barbiturates may also be detected as cobalt complexes by spraying the chromatogram with 1 % alcoholic Co(II)nitrate, heating for 1–2 minutes at 80°C., and exposing the papers to piperidine vapors. Violet spots result which fade in several days (Hübner, 1954).

Tannins and Polyphenols

(See also Chapter X, Section I)

The naturally occurring tannins are extracted with water and are subjected to uni- and two-dimensional paper chromatography. The tannins and polyphenols are detected by their fluorescence in ultraviolet light, by the reaction with $FeCl_3$, or by the enzymatic oxidation using polyphenoloxidase.

TABLE XV

R_f VALUES OF BARBITURATES (HÜBNER, 1954)

Compound	Solvent[a]			
	1	2	3	4
Veronal (diethylbarbituric acid)	0.77	0.69	0.58	0.31
Eldoral (piperidinylethylbarbituric acid)	—	—	—	0.34
Luminal (phenylethyl barbituric acid)	0.70	0.67	0.56	0.39
Cyclohexenylethyl barbituric acid	—	0.81	—	0.49
Phenylallyl barbituric acid	0.69	0.77	0.61	0.50
Isopropylallyl barbituric acid	—	—	—	0.52
sec-Butyl-β-bromoallyl barbituric acid	—	—	—	0.55
Isopropylbromopropenyl barbituric acid	—	—	—	0.56
Cycloheptenylethyl barbituric acid	—	—	0.63	0.64
N-Methylethylphenyl barbituric acid	0.84	0.80	0.75	0.68
Cyclohexenylmethyl N-methyl barbituric acid	0.88	0.87	0.76	0.70

[a] Solvents: 1. Ethanol: NH₄OH = 95:5.
2. i-Propanol: NH₄OH = 95:5.
3. n-Butanol: NH₄OH = 90:10.
4. Amyl alcohol: n-butanol (v/v), saturated with NH₄OH.

1. PREPARATION OF TANNINS (Roberts and Wood, 1951)

Plucked, minced tea shoots are squeezed by hand through cheese cloth. The extract is centrifuged, and the filtrate is rapidly heated to 100°C. and cooled to room temperature. This solution is centrifuged or filtered, if necessary, concentrated *in vacuo*, and aliquots are spotted on filter paper sheets. Tannins may also be extracted from dried tea leaves with three times the weight of water.

For the isolation of chlorogenic acid, potato peelings are extracted with 95% ethanol in a Waring blendor. The extracts are taken to dryness *in vacuo*, redissolved in water, and spotted on filter paper (Johnson, 1951, 1952).

2. CHROMATOGRAPHY AND SOLVENTS

Spots (20–35 μl.) of the solution are applied to Whatman filter paper No. 1 and subjected to two-dimensional paper chromatography, using the following solvents (see Chapter III for two-dimensional technique): *phenol* saturated with water; *1-butanol:acetic acid* = 4:1 plus water just short of saturation. Water alone may be substituted for phenol (Oshima, 1954).

Other solvents are:

a. n-Butanol:Ethyl Acetate:NH₄OH = 1:8:1 or 2:2:1 for the separation of lichen substances, like pulvic acid, vulpinic acid, pinastric acid, calycin, and epanorin (Mitsuno, 1955).

b. n-Butanol, saturated with concentrated NH₄OH is used for the chromatography of depsides, depsidones, and usnic acid. *n*-Butanol: acetone:water = 5:1:2 is also used for these compounds (Mitsuno, 1953).

c. Two-Dimensional Solvent System: First Direction: 6% acetic acid containing 2% formic acid; *second direction:* benzyl alcohol:*tert*-butanol: *i*-propanol:water = 3:1:1:1 (White, 1952). This system will separate chebulagic acid, chebulinic acid, corilagin, gallic acid, ellagic acid, chebulic acid, 3,6-digalloylglucose, and β-glucogallin. (See Table XVI for solvents and R_f values.)

d. Adsorption Chromatography. Tannins may also be separated by adsorption paper chromatography, employing paper which is impregnated with Al(OH)₃ and ethanol as developing solvent (Vanyarkho, 1953).

3. DETECTION (Roberts, 1951, 1953).

a. Ferric Salts. One-tenth per cent w/v aqueous $FeCl_3$ or 0.2% w/v agueous $FeNH_4(SO_4)_2 \cdot 12H_2O$. Tannins with catechol grouping result in green spots, whereas those with pyrogallol grouping result in gray-blue spots. The colors are further intensified by exposure of the sprayed chromatogram to NH₃ vapors. Catechin and epicatechin turn dark blue (see also Torii, 1950–1951).

b. Ammoniacal Silver Nitrate. Silver nitrate (0.1 *N*): 5 *N* NH₄OH is a more general, but nonspecific, spraying reagent for polyphenols.

c. Potassium Cyanide. One per cent aqueous KCN spray results in fading pink spots for gallic acid and fading orange-pink spots for catechin gallates.

d. Ammonia. Exposure of the dried chromatograms to vapors of ammonia causes temporary yellow spots for anthoxanthins and chlorogenic acid.

e. Polyphenoloxidase Spray (Siegelman, 1955). Polyphenols which are separated on paper are made visible by spraying the chromatogram with a solution of polyphenoloxidase (PPO).

Preparation of PPO: 300 g. of cored apples are homogenized for 2 minutes with 300 ml. of cold 0.1 *M* phosphate buffer (pH 6), containing 0.005 *M* ascorbic acid and crushed ice. The homogenate is filtered and centrifuged at 13,000 × g for 15 minutes. The sediment is suspended in 0.2 *M* phosphate buffer and washed twice as before. The residue is finally suspended in 50 ml. 0.2 *M* phosphate buffer in a tissue grinder and poured into an atomizer sprayer.

The chromatograms are sprayed with PPO suspension, placed in a humid-chamber for 2 hours, and the following substrates show up as brown spots: catechol, chlorogenic acid, caffeic acid, esculetin, D-catechin, eriodictyol, and taxifolin.

TABLE XVI

R_f Values of Polyphenols (Roberts, 1951; Mitsuno, 1953)

Substance	Solvent[a]			
	1	2	3	4
L-*epi* Gallocatechin	0.3	0.45	—	—
DL-Gallocatechin	0.3	0.6	—	—
Gallic acid	0.15	0.7	—	—
Gallocatechin-α-gallate	0.2	0.7	—	—
L-*epi*-Gallocatechin gallate	0.3	0.7	—	—
L-*epi*-Catechin gallate	0.5	0.9	—	—
Catechin	0.5	0.75	—	—
L-*epi*-Catechin	0.5	0.68	—	—
Lecanoric acid	—	—	0.33	—
Evernic acid	—	—	0.61	—
Divaricatic acid	—	—	0.83	—
Sphaerophorin	—	—	0.88	—
Perlatolic acid	—	—	0.93	—
Obtusatic acid	—	—	0.60	—
Barbatic acid	—	—	0.65	0.87
Diffractaic acid	—	—	0.80	0.83
Baeomycesic acid	—	—	0.50	0.64
Squamatic acid	—	—	0.28	0.28
Atranorin	—	—	0.63	—
Olivetoric acid	—	—	0.74	—
Microphyllic acid	—	—	0.91	—
Thamnolic acid	—	—	—	0.37
Lobaric acid	—	—	0.54	—
α-Collatolic acid	—	—	0.66	—
Alectoronic acid	—	—	0.45	—
Salazinic acid	—	—	—	0.50
Stictic acid	—	—	—	0.52
Norstictic acid	—	—	—	0.62
Protocetraric acid	—	—	—	0.45
Fumarprotocetraric acid	—	—	—	0.38
Physodalic acid	—	—	—	0.68
Psoromic acid	—	—	—	0.62
Usnic acid	—	—	0.92	—
Orsellic acid	—	—	0.15	—
Everninic acid	—	—	0.53	—
Divaric acid	—	—	0.41	—
Divaricatinic acid	—	—	0.77	—
Olivetol-carboxylic acid	—	—	0.55	—
Sphaerophorol-carboxylic acid	—	—	0.80	—
Methyl orsellate	—	—	0.62	—
β-Orcinol-carboxylic acid	—	—	0.33	—
Rhizonic acid	—	—	0.64	—
β-Orcinol-carboxylic acid dimethyl ether	—	—	0.66	—
Orcinol-dicarboxylic acid monomethyl ether	—	—	0.04	—

[a] Solvents: 1. Phenol saturated with water.
2. n-Butanol:acetic acid = 4:1 plus water short of saturation.
3. n-Butanol saturated with concentrated NH_4OH.
4. n-Butanol:acetone:water = 5:1:2.

f. Detection of Chlorogenic Acid. (1) The chromatogram is first sprayed with 1 % w/v $NaNO_2$ dissolved in 10 % v/v acetic acid and then with N NaOH (Roberts, 1953). (2) The chromatogram is sprayed with a saturated solution of 3,5-*dinitrosalicylic acid* in 50 % ethanol, containing 2 % NaOH (Johnson, 1951). A bright yellow spot is produced. (3) The chromatogram is observed with an *ultraviolet light* source with a 365 mμ filter before and after exposure of the chromatogram to NH_3 vapors (Johnson, 1951). Chlorogenic acid is thus observed as a blue-green fluorescent spot with an R_f value of 0.54 using n-butanol:acetic acid:water = 4:1:5 as solvent (Weurman, 1953).

g. Semiquantitative Estimation (Forsyth, 1955). Polyphenols from cacao are developed with water on Whatman No. 1 paper by the descending method. Guide strips are detected with $FeCl_3$, and areas containing polyphenols (unreacted) are cut out and titrated in 10 ml. 1 % H_2SO_4 with 0.01 N $KMnO_4$ until the purple color persists for one minute. (-)-*epi* Catechin and leucocyanadin 1 are used as standards.

Coumarins

A detailed study of the coumarins and related compounds is that of Swain (1953). Whatman No. 1 filter paper, plain or buffered with 0.1 M Na_2HPO_4 or 0.1 M Na_3BO_3, is used (see Table XVII). A large variety of solvents is employed and is listed with the R_f values of the coumarins in Table XVII. Most coumarins may be seen as fluorescent spots in ultraviolet light; the fluorescence may be intensified by the exposure of the chromatogram to ammonia vapors or by spraying it with 2 N NaOH. Coumarins and furocoumarins may also be separated on Whatman No. 1 paper, impregnated with propylene glycol, using petroleum ether (60–70°C.) as developing solvent (Riedl, 1952).

Owing to the insolubility of coumarins in water, the paper chromatography of this class of compounds presents considerable difficulty. A solvent composed of petroleum ether (b.p. 65–70):benzene:95 % methanol = 25:20:10 tends to overcome some of these problems (Svendson, 1952). It is essential, however, to have the chromatographic tank fully saturated with the phases of the solvent. This is accomplished by inserting two blank pieces of filter paper into the tank, one saturated with petroleum ether:benzene and the other with 95 % methanol. A 3-hour development results in good resolution.

Coumarin and other vanilla-like substances (Mitchell, 1953) can be separated with commercial-grade mixed octanes on paper which has been previously treated with a solution containing 2 ml. of formamide, 5 ml. of ethanol, and 93 ml. of ethyl ether. Chromogenic agents for these compounds include methanolic KOH and 0.5 % hydrazine sulfate in 2 %

TABLE XVII

R_f Values of Coumarins and Related Compounds (Swain, 1953)

Compounds	Solvent[a] 1	2	3	4	5	6	7	8	9	10	11	12	13	14	15	16	17	18	19	20	21
Coumarin	.98	.97	.92	.86	.98	.87	.87	.88	.92	.94	.94	.93	.95	.87	.84	.81	.67	.76	.74	.87	.73
Umbelliferone	.95	.94	.89	.83	.92	.84	.65	.83	.90	.73	.89	.90	.28	.66	.75	.73	.57	.60	.66	.84	.77
Skimmin	.90	.81	.52	.22	.54	.33	.20	.31	.09	.04	.10	.12	.07	.61	.84	.85	.72	.82	.73	.80	
Herniarin	.98	.98	.91	.87	.98	.85	.87	.87	.92	.94	.94	.94	.95	.87	.79	.76	.50	.67	.63	.84	
Aesculetin	.72	.81	.79	.65	.80	.32	.11	.29	.44	0	.14	.75	0	.31	.63	.65	.34	.48	.54	.65	
Scopoletin	.96	.96	.83	.73	.91	.76	.40	.71	.85	.36	.79	.83	.06	.59	.70	.70	.50	.51	.60	.78	
Daphnetin	.84	.83	.81	.68	.83	.60	.10	.40	.74	0	.58	.78	.02	.38	.69	.70	.61	.54	.62	.72	
Limettin	.97	.97	.92	.89	.98	.88	.89	.88	.94	.95	.95	.96	.96	.88	.67	.40	.11	.39	.44	.87	
Ostruthin	.96	.98	.93	.95	.97	.95	.92	.93	.95	.97	.95	.97	.96	.88	.36	.07	.05	.10	.18	.93	
Osthol	.98	.98	.92	.91	.97	.92	.89	.90	.96	.96	.94	.89	.96	.89	.72	.71	.17	.53	.66	.91	
Bergapten	.98	.97	.88	.88	.97	.88	.91	.88	.94	.96	.95	.94	.96	.86	.65	.59	.19	.45	.38	.81	
Xanthotoxin	.96	.97	.87	.88	.96	.87	.85	.86	.93	.95	.94	.93	.95	.84	.76	.67	.33	.58	.57	.83	
Imperatorin	.98	.97	.91	.92	.97	.91	.91	.92	.91	.96	.95	.96	.97	.90	.65	.50	.22	.47	.59	.90	
o-Coumaric acid	.66	.81	.90	.90	.92	.72	.20	.23	.78	.01	.18	.93	0	.39	.74	.69	.86	.58	.81	.81	
p-Coumaric acid	.67	.81	.88	.88	.90	.62	.16	.18	.77	.01	.12	.90	0	.32	.69	.65	.81	.49	.79	.78	
Caffeic acid	.33	.46	.78	.73	.75	.28	0	.05	.21	0	.03	.80	0	.19	.60	.57	.78	.38	.78	.69	
Ferulic acid	.77	.89	.84	.81	.90	.54	.11	.13	.55	.01	.13	.90	0	.26	.68	.63	.78	.48	.77	.74	
Chlorogenic acid	.49	.33	.61	.31	.54	.05	0	.04	0	0	0	.31	0	.10	.78	.76	.89	.64	.81	.75	
Phloroglucinol	.32	.16	.69	.56	.52	.70	.60	.65	.62	.50	.68	.68	.18	.35	.72	.69	.52	.61	.68	.80	
Aesculin	.80	.64	.49	.21	.44	.30	.03	.12	.04	0	.02	.08	0	.34	.78	.80	.81	.69	.76	.77	
Fraxin																					.44
Fraxetin																					.73
Scopolin																					.33

TABLE XVII—*Continued*

a Solvent: 1. Phenol:water.
2. *m*-Cresol:acetic acid:water = 50:2:48.
3. 1-Butanol:acetic acid:water = 4:1:5.
4. Amyl alcohol:acetic acid:water = 4:1:5.
5. Benzyl alcohol:acetic acid:water = 4:1:5.
6. 1-Butanol:water.
7. 1-Butanol:water (borate paper).
8. 1-Butanol:water (phosphate paper).
9. Ethyl acetate:water.
10. Ethyl acetate:water (borate paper).
11. Ethyl acetate:water (phosphate paper).
12. Ethyl acetate:2 N HCl = 1:1.
13. Ethyl acetate:2 N NH₃ = 1:1.
14. 1-Propanol:concentrated NH_4OH = 7:3.
15. Aqueous phase: 1-butanol:acetic acid:H_2O = 4:1:5.
16. Aqueous phase: 1-benzyl alcohol:acetic acid:H_2O = 4:1:5.
17. Water.
18. 10% acetic acid.
19. Isopropanol:water = 1:4.
20. Isopropanol:water = 2:3.
21. 1-Butanol:acetic acid:water = 60:15:30 (K. Krebs, 1953).

HCl. The former reagent is not applicable to piperonyl; the latter is not applicable to coumarin and vanitrope.

The following colored spots are observed in ultraviolet light before and after spraying the chromatograms with 1 % alcoholic KOH:

Compound	Ultraviolet illumination	
	Plain	KOH spray
Pimpinellin	Yellow	Brown fluorescence
Isopimpinellin	Yellow	Weak brown-yellow
Isobergapten	Blue fluorescence	Yellow, then bluish
Bergapten	Blue fluorescence	Yellow

Synthetic Dyes and Dye Intermediates

1. pH INDICATORS

Lederer (1950*a*), Taira (1951–1952), and Franglen (1955) have separated many pH indicators on Whatman No. 1 and 3 MM filter papers. The solvents and R_f values are listed in Table XVIII. Graichen (1951) has separated fluoresceins on Whatman No. 1. Mixtures such as "universal indicator" are easily separated with the simplest equipment and make excellent material for classroom demonstrations. Phenolphthalein and thymolphthalein remain colorless during solvent development and are detected on the chromatogram by exposing the paper to NH_3 vapors.

2. FOOD COLORS

A comprehensive study of the identification of coal tar colors by paper chromatography was undertaken by Tilden (1952, 1953). Whatman No. 1

TABLE XVIII

R_f VALUES OF INDICATOR DYES (LEDERER, 1950a; TIARA, 1951–1952; GRAICHEN, 1951; FRANGLEN, 1955)

Indicator	Solvents[a]						
	1	2	3	4	5	6	7
Congo red	—	0.0	0.0	—	—	—	—
Indigo carmine	0.0	0.0	0.0	0.32	—	—	—
Chlorophenol red	—	0.17	0.01	—	0.09	0.67	—
Phenol red	—	0.18	0.01	0.73	0.06	0.54	—
Cresol red	—	0.41	0.12	—	0.12	0.67	—
Bromcresol purple	0.68	0.43	0.10	0.58	0.19	0.76	—
Bromcresol green	0.84	0.47	0.24	—	0.32	0.79	—
Bromphenol blue	—	0.55	0.19	0.57	0.27	0.74	—
Methyl orange	0.77	0.55	0.26	—	—	—	—
Methyl red	0.73	0.59	0.33	0.41	—	—	—
Neutral red	—	0.66	0.53	—	—	—	—
Bromthymol blue	0.93	0.79	0.63	0.37	0.50	0.88	—
Methyl violet	0.95	0.88	0.86	0.01	—	—	—
Thymol blue	1.0	0.90	0.75	0.37	0.70	0.85	—
Phenolphthalein	1.0	0.92	0.89	0.10	—	—	—
Thymolphthalein	1.0	0.92	0.92	—	—	—	—
Bromphenol red	—	—	—	—	0.11	0.68	—
Metacresol purple	—	—	—	—	0.16	0.66	—
Fluorescein	—	—	—	—	—	—	0.18
Dibromofluorescein	—	—	—	—	—	—	0.26
							(0.24)
Tetrabromofluorescein	—	—	—	—	—	—	0.45
							(0.34)
Tetraiodofluorescein	—	—	—	—	—	—	0.52
Tetrachlorotetrabromofluorescein	—	—	—	—	—	—	0.64

[a] Solvents: 1. Isopropanol (NH₃ atmosphere).
      2. n-Butanol (NH₃ atmosphere).
      3. n-Amyl alcohol (NH₃ atmosphere).
      4. 3% Aqueous NaCl.
      5. tert-Amyl alcohol: NH₄OH = 20:5.
      6. tert-Amyl alcohol: acetic acid: water = 20:5:5.
      7. n-Butanol: water: NH₄OH: ethanol = 200:88:2:40.

filter paper is recommended. Among twenty developing solvents, the following are listed: (1) phenol: acetic acid: water = 150:2:48 w/v; (2) phenol: water = 8:2 v/v; (3) n-butanol: NH_4OH: water: 70% ethanol = 200:2:88:40 v/v.

Additional solvents have been recommended by Hashimoto (1953), Ishida (1953), and Anderson (1953): (4) phenol: ethanol: water = 40: 25:40; (5) phenol: water: formic acid = 66:32:2, and (6) n-butanol: acetic acid: water = 4:1:5.

Bengal Rose (tetraiododichlorofluorescein) has been chromatographed with 65–70% methanol (R_f 0.82) and 50–70% propanol (R_f 0.91–0.97) (Valenciano, 1955).

Two-dimensional chromatography is capable of resolving a large number of water-soluble food colors (Sclar, 1955). The solvent system is: *First direction:* water:methyl cellosolve acetate = 2:3 or 1:4; *Second direction:* 10% ethanol plus 0.125% NaCl.

Artificial coloring matter in preserves has been chromatographed on filter paper impregnated with $CaCO_3$, then $(NH_4)_2CO_3$, and washed with water free of $CaCl_2$. The developing solvent is 90% ethanol (Monselise, 1954).

For positive identification, the spots are eluted with 70% ethanol and the absorption curve determined in a Beckman spectrophotometer. The following R_f values are selected, using phenol:water.

FDC* red 2	0.27
FDC yellow 5	0.34
FDC orange I	0.87
Brilliant Scarlet (C.I. No. 185)	0.29

* FDC = Food, Drug, and Cosmetic designation.

The acridines are separated on Whatman No. 1 paper by the ascending technique using the following solvents: (1) *1-butanol:acetic acid:water* = 4:1:5 v/v; (2) *caprylic alcohol:1.5 N* NH_4OH v/v. The spots are detected with an ultraviolet light source, and the following R_f values are obtained with the above solvents (Lederer, 1952b):

	Solvent	
	1	2
Acriflavine	0.57	0.01
Proflavine	0.56	0.17
Monoacrin (5-aminoacridine)	0.82	0.81
Atebrin	0.78	0.93

3. ANTHRAQUINONE PIGMENTS

Shibata (1950) separated and identified many anthraquinone pigments with petroleum ether (45–70°C.) saturated with 97% methanol. An acetone solution of the mixture of hydroxyanthraquinone pigments is placed on the paper. After solvent development for 5–6 hours (30 cm.), the paper strip is sprayed with a solution of 0.5% magnesium acetate in methanol. Orange-red, purple, or violet spots are produced, depending on the positions of the hydroxyl groups on the anthraquinone nucleus. Table XIX shows the R_f factors and colors produced.

4. Napththoquinones (Sproston, 1954; Canady, 1956).

An alcoholic solution of substituted naphthoquinones is spotted on a 1-cm. diameter filter paper disk which is then attached to a 2 × 18-inch Whatman No. 1 filter paper strip. The disk is fastened to the larger strip between two slits, 6.5 cm. from one end of the strip. A developing solvent of the following composition is used throughout: fusel oil (Fisher amyl alcohol):pyridine:water = 3:2:1.5. The naphthoquinones are detected by spraying the chromatogram with a 5% aqueous solution of NaOH. Table XX lists the R_f values of naphthoquinones and the color produced by the chromogenic spray.

Menadione and related compounds have been separated on Whatman No. 2 paper with concentrated NH_4OH as solvent by the ascending method. The compounds appear as blue-purple spots but must be marked immediately since the colors fade as the ammonia volatilizes.

5. Photographic Developers

A mixture of photographic developers is separated by paper chromatography with 1-butanol:acetic acid:H_2O = 4:1:5 v/v (Pannell, 1953). The mixture to be spotted contains 1–10 μg. of each compound. The spots are detected after chromatography either by a spraying reagent of 2% aqueous ammoniacal silver nitrate or 5% phosphomolybdic acid.

TABLE XIX

R_f Values and Colors for Anthraquinones (Shibata, 1950)[a]

Compound	R_f values	Color of spot
Chrysophanol	0.92	Orange
Physcion	0.89	Orange
Quinizarin	0.89	Purple
2-Methylquinizarin	0.92	Purple
Emodin	0.52	Pink
Rubiadin	0.49	Orange-yellow
Aloe-emodin	0.15	Orange
Rhein	0	Orange
Alizarin	0.04	Violet
Endocrocin	0.0	Pink
Purpurin	0.03	Purple
Dihydroxymethylanthraquinone	0.92	Orange
Tetrahydroxyanthraquinone	0.02	Orange
Rhodocladonic acid	0	Orange
Anthragallol	0	Gray
Rufigallic acid	0	Grayish violet

[a] Solvent: Petroleum ether (45–70°C.), saturated with 97% methanol.

TABLE XX
R_f VALUES OF SUBSTITUTED NAPHTHOQUINONES AND COLORS PRODUCED BY AQUEOUS NaOH

Compound	Solvent[a]		Color[b]
	1	2	
1,4 Naphthoquinones			
Unsubstituted	0.85	0.46	OB
2-Methyl-	0.87	0.34	OB
2-Methoxy-	0.81	—	O
2,3-Dimethoxy-	0.84	—	PuP
2-Methoxy-3-OH-	0.37	—	PuP
2-Hydroxy-	0.47	—	O
2-Methyl-3-acetyl-	0.83	—	PaB
3-Methyl-6-succino-	0.53	—	P
2,3-Dichloro-	0.41	—	Y
Ferric 2-Cl-3-OH-	0.42	—	OP
2-Amino-	0.82	—	YB
2-Amino-3-Cl-	0.83	—	O
2-Acetylamino-	0.83	—	POB
2-Dimethylamino-	0.83	—	O
2-Chloro-3-dimethylamino-	0.87	—	OP
2-Chloro-3-ethylamino-	0.88	—	—
2-Chloro-3-*n*-decylamino-	0.91	—	PaY
2-(*N*-Acetanilido)-3-Cl-	0.89	—	PaOB
2-Methylmercapto-	0.84	—	Y
Benzoquinones			
p-Benzoquinone	0.87	—	PaB
p-Toluquinone	0.85	0.73	YB
p-Xyloquinone	0.97	—	PaB
2,5-Dichloro-*p*-benzoquinone	0.28	—	PaY
2,3,5,6-Tetrachloro-*p*-benzoquinone	0.22	—	PaY
3,4,5,6-Tetrachloro-*o*-benzoquinone	0.90	—	PaYB
1,2-Naphthoquinone-3-sulfonic acid	—	0.85	Pu

[a] Solvents: 1. Fusel oil:pyridine:water = 3:2:1.5 (Sproston, 1954).
   2. Concentrated NH_4OH (Canady, 1956).
[b] Colors: B, brown; O, orange; P, pink; Pa, pale; Pu, purple; R, red; Y, yellow.

The following R_f values for photographic developers are observed:

Hydroquinone disulfonate	0
p-Methylaminophenol sulfonate	0.09
Hydroquinone sulfonate	0.15
Quinone sulfonate	0.34
p-Aminophenol·HCl	0.43
p-Phenylenediamine·HCl	0.55
p-Methylaminophenol sulfate	0.61
Hydroquinone	0.80

Organic Pesticides

1. BENZENEHEXACHLORIDES (HEXACHLOROCYCLOHEXANES)

Method 1 (L. C. Mitchell, 1952): Owing to the insolubility of these compounds in water, reversed phase chromatography is recommended. α, β, γ, and δ-Benzenehexachlorides are spotted singly and as a mixture on Whatman filter paper No. 1. The top and bottom of the paper sheet is clipped to glass rods and is sprayed with the stationary phase, acetic anhydride: ethyl ether = 1:9 v/v. The chromatogram is immediately developed with the mobile phase for 90 minutes. The mobile phase is mixed octanes (Phillips petroleum):acetic anhydride = 100:6 v/v. The developed chromatogram is dried at room temperature, sprayed with N KOH, and heated at 130–133°C. for 30 minutes. The paper is sprayed after 12 hours with a solution of 0.05 N AgNO$_3$:dilute HNO$_3$ = 1:3 v/v. After the paper has been exposed to sunlight, darkened spots indicate the position of the benzenehexachlorides with the following R_f values: β-benzenehexachloride, 0.51; δ-benzenehexachloride, 0.65; γ-benzenehexachloride, 0.77; α-benezenehexachloride, 0.84. Other pesticides giving a positive test with this color reagent are chlordane, DDT, heptachlor, methoxychlor, and toxaphene.

Method 2 (Moynihan, 1951): A mixture of five isomers of hexachlorocyclohexane and heptachlorocyclohexane has been separated as follows:

Filter paper strips are dipped into acetic anhydride and the excess is pressed out between filter papers. n-Hexane saturated with acetic anhydride is then used as the developing solvent. Clear separations are obtained in 6–16 hours. After development, the strips are sprayed with a solution prepared by shaking a saturated aqueous solution of FeSO$_4$ with 5 volumes of glacial acetic acid and centrifuging the suspension. On heating, the positions of the separated constituents show up as brown spots.

Method 3 (Bridges, 1956): Whatman No. 1 paper is washed with distilled water overnight in order to remove any halides. The air-dried paper is dipped into a 5% ethereal solution of Paraffinum Molle Album, drained, and dried. The benzenehexachlorides are dissolved in acetone and applied at the top of the paper strip. The mobile solvent phase is 70% aqueous methanol, and development is allowed to proceed for 18 hours. For the detection of the benzenehexachlorides, the papers are dipped into redistilled monoethanolamine, heated at 100°C. for 1 hour, and then dipped into 0.1 N silver nitrate, acidified with nitric acid (AgNO$_3$:concentrated HNO$_3$ = 10:1). The papers are exposed to ultraviolet light (254 mμ) for final color development. The R_f values for the isomers are: α, 0.33; β, 0.00; γ, 0.40; δ, 0.58. It is essential to remove all of the monoethanolamine before color development.

2. ALDRIN, ISODRIN, DIELDRIN, ENDRIN, ETC. (L. C. Mitchell, 1953a, 1956; Klein, 1956).

The technique for the separation of these pesticides is again the "reversed phase" development due to the water-insolubility of these compounds. The solvents are as follows:

Stationary phase: (1) 1, 2, and 5% soybean oil in ether; (2) 20% acetic anhydride in ether.

Mobile phase: (1) acetone:water = 4:1; (2) acetonitrile:water = 7:3; (3) pyridine:water = 3:2; (4) *n*-heptane; (5) 95% ethanol. Table XXI lists the R_f values of some representative pesticides in this class.

The color reagent for aldrin and related compounds had to be modified in the following manner: The dry chromatogram is sprayed with 0.05 N $AgNO_3$ in ethanol and is left at room temperature for 30 minutes. It is then sprayed with 37% formaldehyde and dried at room temperature for half an hour. The paper is next sprayed with N KOH in methanol and heated at 130–133°C. for 30 minutes. The final spray consists of concentrated HNO_3:30% H_2O_2 = v/v. The paper is left at room temperature overnight, and after exposure to sunlight, black spots are observed. By using 16 sheets of paper (8 × 8") and applying 21 spots of 10 μl. on each sheet, endrin has been identified by infra-red spectroscopy after eluting the zones, located by parallel strips, with *n*-pentane.

3. COMPONENTS OF DILAN (L. C. Mitchell, 1954)

The same procedure as Method 1 for benzenehexachlorides, is used for the separation of the components of Dilan, using the following solvents: *Stationary phase:* dimethyl formamide:ethyl ether = 15:85 v/v. *Mobile phase:* mixed octanes (Phillips Petroleum Co., Bartlesville, Oklahoma).

Chromogenic Spray. (1) 11 g. of KOH and 5.0 ml. of water, made up to 100 ml. with methanol. (2) 1 g. of $FeSO_4 \cdot 7H_2O$ dissolved in 50 ml. of water and 20 ml. of concentrated HCl; the solution is diluted to 100 ml. with water.

The dried chromatogram is sprayed with (1), left at room temperature for 10 minutes, and sprayed with (2). The spots must be marked immediately. The following R_f values are observed: prolan, 0.56; bulan, 0.70.

4. DDT AND RELATED COMPOUNDS

DDT and hexachlorohexane (HCH) have been resolved on Schleicher and Schuell Paper No. 2043b, dipped into 2% ethereal Vaseline. The samples are dissolved in acetone, and the solvent is 96% ethanol: water:NH_4OH = 80:15:5 (Gruch, 1954). The R_f values are: DDT, 0.63 and HCH, 0.87.

DDT, *p,p'*-DDT, DDA, DDD, DDE, 4,4'-dichlorobenzophenone, and

2,4'-dichlorobenzophenone have been separated on Whatman No. 1, impregnated with 0.5 % soybean oil in ether (Mitchell, 1956). The mobile solvent is 70 % 2-methoxyethanol in water.

DDT is detected by the chromogenic spray (KOH-FeSO$_4$) described above for the detection of components of Dilan. It may also be detected by bioassay techniques by cutting the strip into 1 cm. segments, eluting each segment with water, and testing the toxicity on the larvae of *Aedes aegypti*.

Another method for detection of DDT and related compounds is the following (Mitchell, 1956): 1.7 g. of AgNO$_3$ is dissolved in a small volume of water. Ten ml. of 2-phenoxyethanol and 50 ml. of 95 % ethanol are added, and the solution is diluted to 200 ml. with water. (If cloudy, ethanol is added dropwise until clear.) The chromatograms are sprayed with this reagent and exposed to ultraviolet light, resulting in black spots.

Bromine analogues of DDT, containing Br[82], are separated on Whatman paper No. 1, which is conditioned for reversed phase chromatography (Winteringham, 1950). The filter paper is dipped into ether containing 2.5 % w/v Vaseline, blotted, and dried. By the descending technique, using as solvent ethanol:water:NH$_4$OH (d 0.88) = 80:15:5 v/v, the following R_f values are achieved: $(BrC_6H_4)_2CHCCl_3$, 0.44; $(BrC_6H_4)_2C{=}CCl_2$, 0.35; $(BrC_6H_4)_2CHCOOH$, 0.75. Detection is by autoradiography (See Chapter III) or by scanning with a Geiger-Müller tube with a thin end-window.

5. ORGANIC PHOSPHATE PESTICIDES (See Table XXII)

a. Extraction of Parathion (Fiori, 1956). Ten grams of the biological material is homogenized in a mortar with sand, then diluted with 20 ml. of water, 20 ml. ethanol and 50 ml. of 20 % trichloroacetic acid. The mixture is shaken for 30 minutes and centrifuged for 15 minutes. The supernatant is filtered, the alcohol is evaporated, and the remaining aqueous solution is passed through a column of acid-alumina. The adsorbed Parathion is eluted with ether, the effluent is evaporated, and the residue dissolved in benzene or ethanol to be spotted on Schleicher and Schuell paper 2043b.

b. Chromatography. Method 1: Parathion and pyrethrin-type insecticides are separated by reversed phase paper chromatography (Winteringham, 1952; Metcalf, 1953). Whatman filter paper No. 1 is soaked for 30 minutes in a solution of the following composition: ethanol:water: concentrated HCl = 45:50:5 v/v. The paper is then neutralized in dilute NH$_4$OH, washed with water, drained, and dried. The washed paper is next impregnated with Vaseline.

The recommended solvent for pyrethrin derivatives is ethanol:water:5 %

NH₄OH = 45:50:5 v/v, and the chromatography is carried out in an atmosphere of nitrogen.

Method 2: In the case of parathion and related phosphate esters, Whatman No 1 is impregnated with Dow Silicone 550 by immersing the paper in a 5%. solution of silicone in *n*-hexane.

The compounds are resolved with a solvent consisting of chloroform:ethanol:water = 10:10:6 v/v. The spots are detected by spraying the chromatogram with a 5% alcoholic solution of KOH and heating the paper at 105°C. for 2–3 minutes.

Method 3: Whatman No. 1 filter paper is immersed in 4% mineral oil in ethyl ether and air-dried. The parathion insecticides are separated with ethanol:acetone:water = 1:1:2 (Cook, 1954).

Method 4: Whatman No. 1 is equilibrated with the aqueous phase of the solvent 5% ethyl ether in water-saturated petroleum ether (Fiori, 1956). Parathion is then developed by the ascending technique in 2–3 hours at 20°C.

c. Detection. *Method 1:* The chromatogram is first sprayed with 0.002 M N-bromosuccinimide in methyl chloroform or acetone, dried, and sprayed with an alcoholic solution of 3×10^{-4} M fluorescein. Green fluorescent spots on a pink background result for Systox (sensitivity 1–2 μg.), Methyl Parathion (2 μg.), and related compounds (Cook, 1954; Otter, 1955).

Method 2: A bioautographic method for cholinesterase inhibitors (e.g., Systox, Parathion) has been developed by Cook (1955). Three strips of Whatman No. 1 filter paper of the same dimension as the chromatogram are arranged as depicted in Fig. 3. Strip ≠1 is soaked with water; Strip ≠2 is the chromatogram; Strip ≠3 is dipped into 1 part human plasma, 3 parts water, 0.1 part 0.1 N NaOH, and 0.25 parts indicator (0.15 g. bromothymol blue in 25 ml. 0.1 N NaOH); Strip ≠4 is dipped into a solution of 0.10 g. acetylcholine chloride in 25 ml. of water. Strips ≠1, 2, and 3 are laid together in the order shown, and after 5–10 minutes, Strip ≠4 is laid on top of the stack. Enzyme activity is indicated by yellow regions (acetic acid), while the inhibitor shows up as blue regions.

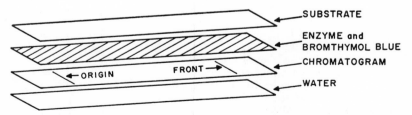

FIG. 3. Diagram of arrangement of chromatogram and reagent-treated paper strips for location of *in vitro* cholinesterase inhibitors on chromatogram (Cook, 1955).

TABLE XXI
R_f VALUES OF CHLORINATED PESTICIDES (MITCHELL, 1953a, 1956)

Compound	Solvent[a]				
	1	2	3	4	5
Aldrin	0.49	0.42	0.25	—	—
Dieldrin	0.61	0.66	0.45	0.67	0.46
				0.93	
Isodrin	—	—	0.32	—	—
Endrin	—	—	0.51	—	—
Captan	—	—	—	0.28	0.69
Spergon	—	—	—	0.33	0.45
Aramite	—	—	—	0.43	0.57
Lindane	—	—	—	0.48	0.46
Tritisan	—	—	—	0.80	0.29

[a] Solvents: 1. Acetone:water = 4:1 (stationary phase—soybean oil).
2. Acetonitrile:water = 7:3 (stationary phase—soybean oil).
3. Pyridine:water = 3:2 (stationary phase—soybean oil).
4. n-Heptane (stationary phase—acetic anhydride).
5. 95% Ethanol (stationary phase—soybean oil).

TABLE XXII
R_f VALUES OF PHOSPHOROUS INSECTICIDES (COOK, 1954)[a]

Compound	R_f
EPN Insecticide	0.35
Parathion	0.52
Diazinon	0.61
Chlorothion	0.70
Methyl parathion	0.85
Malathion	0.93

[a] Solvent: stationary phase—4% mineral oil; mobile phase—ethanol:acetone:water = 1:1:2.

TABLE XXIII
R_f VALUES OF PYRETHRINS AND DERIVATIVES (QUAYLE, 1956)[a]

Compound	R_f
Pyrethrin I	0.85
Pyrethrin II	0.70
trans-Chrysanthemic acid	0.54
cis-Chrysanthemic acid	0.56
Chrysanthemum dicarboxylic acid	0
Methyl pyrethrate	0.73
α-DL-trans-Allethrin	0.82
Allethrolone	0.09

[a] Solvent: Petroleum ether (80–100°C.), saturated with CH_3OH.

6. PYRETHRIN-TYPE INSECTICIDES (Quayle, 1956).

Pyrethrins and their derivatives are separated by ascending chromatography with the solvent petroleum ether (80–100°C.), saturated with methanol. Whatman No. 1 paper is equilibrated with both solvents overnight in the chromatographic chamber under reduced pressure. (See Table XXIII.)

For the detection of these compounds, the papers are dipped into 0.1% aqueous $KMnO_4$, washed with water, and partially dried. The papers are then treated with 0.5% aqueous benzidine·HCl. An intensely blue color forms for unsaturated compounds.

Polymers

1. POLYAMIDES (NYLON, PERLON) (Ayers, 1953; Zahn, 1955/56)

Twenty-five microliters of a 1% solution of several polyamides in 10% w/v formic acid is spotted on Whatman paper No. 54. The chromatogram is developed with 88% w/w formic acid in a water-saturated atmosphere Another solvent is pyridine:water = 7:3, using Schleicher and Schuel Paper No. 2043b and descending development for 20 hours.

Detection. Method 1: The spots are revealed by dipping the chromatogram in a 0.1% solution of Solacet Fast Blue 2BS in 0.1% acetic acid and heating the paper at 80°C. for 5 minutes. The following R_f values are observed: Nylon 6 (polycaproamide), 0.8; Nylon 66 (polyhexamethylenediamine adipamide), 0.4; Nylon 610 (polyhexamethylenediamine sebacamide), 0.3; Perlon U (polyurethan), 0.

Method 2: This detection technique is based on the conversion of carbonamides to chloramides by chlorine. The dried chromatograms are exposed to chlorine gas, previously bubbled through H_2SO_4 and $KMnO_4$. The papers are briefly exposed to NH_3 until the background is white (2–3 seconds). The chromatograms are then dipped into a water-saturated solution of o-tolidine:0.50 N KI (v/v) (pH 5–6) and washed with water until blue spots appear. The spots are marked immediately. Cyclic amides of ε-aminocaproic acid are exposed to Cl_2 for 10 minutes and ammonia for one minute; Perlon is exposed to Cl_2 for 2–3 minutes and NH_3 for 3–4 seconds. Orlon gives no color with this reagent.

2. NATURAL RUBBER AND RESINS

Owing to the insolubility of rubber and resins in water, it is necessary to impregnate the filter paper with a hydrophobic material prior to chromatography.

In the case of the resins, Whatman No. 1 is impregnated with kerosene (180–200°C.) by immersing the paper into a 25% solution of kerosene in ether (Mills, 1952). Then 0.2 mg. of the resin is dissolved in acetone or chloroform and is spotted on the treated paper. The developing solvent is the lower layer of isopropanol:water:kerosene = 6.5–7.5:2.5:1 v/v. The chromatogram is then sprayed with 50 % w/v phenol in CCl_4 and is exposed to bromine vapors. The colored spots, due to the resins, are stable if the chromatogram is kept in the dark. The following resins have been chromatographed individually by this technique:dammar, mastic, sandarac, rosin, elemi, copal.

Natural rubber has been chromatographed in the following manner (Banigan, 1953): Whatman paper No. 1 is drawn through a 5 % solution of methyltrichlorosilane in benzene. The paper is blotted and dried at 65°C. for 2 hours. The rubber is applied to the paper as a 1 % solution in benzene. Cyclohexanone is recommended as developing solvent. The spots are detected by the following technique: The developed chromatogram is dried at 65°C. and is immersed in a 0.25 % solution of "oil blue NA (Calco)" in 50 % aqueous ethanol. The reagent is first dissolved in a minimum volume of butanol before the addition of the ethanol. The solution is filtered, if necessary. A brief rinse in 50 % ethanol removes the excess dye but leaves the rubber as a blue-purple spot on a white background.

Detergents

(Holness, 1955)

n-Alkyl sulfates have been separated by chromatography on Whatman No. 1 paper by the ascending technique with aqueous ethanol as solvent. Octyl-, decyl-, and dodecyl sulfates have been separated with 15 % ethanol. Tetradecyl-, hexadecyl-, and octadecyl sulfates have been resolved with 40 % ethanol. The anions are detected by spraying the chromatograms with an aqueous solution of pinacryptol yellow; under ultraviolet light these compounds show up as bright orange fluorescent spots.

n-Alkylpyridinium halides and alkyl trimethylammonium halides (cationic detergents) have been separated with 30 % ethanol, containing 5 % concentrated HCl. The cations are detected by a spraying reagent composed of an aqueous solution of Rhodamine BS, containing a commercially available optical bleach. The sprayed papers are exposed to NH_3, and bright fluorescent spots are visible with ultraviolet illumination.

Chapter XIII

ANTIBIOTICS AND VITAMINS[1]

Section I: Antibiotics

The general techniques of paper chromatography are applicable to experiments involving antibiotics. In many cases stringent requirements are necessary for reproducible results. The relative humidity in the chromatographic chamber is important. When long periods of solvent development are necessary, temperature control is essential. The types of solvents used are similar to those in other applications. Sometimes, a compound that will react with substances being separated is added to the developing solvent. Thus, in the separation of streptomycin and related compounds, p-toluenesulfonic acid is added to the solvent to form the sulfonates, which are more efficiently separated. Water-saturated ether is used as the solvent for penicillin separations. The penicillins are soluble in both water and ether, but the salts are insoluble in ether. By impregnating the paper with a suitable buffer it is possible to change the R_f factors of each entity. In neutral solutions, the penicillin salts are insoluble in the ether and their R_f values are practically zero. As the buffer pH is lowered, more of the free penicillin that is more soluble in the mobile liquid phase is formed. Thus, the R_f factor increases. The buffer pH usually used is 6.0–6.7, since it has been observed that over this range very little change in distance traveled by the penicillin occurs (Karnovsky, 1949).

When possible, spraying reagents are employed to produce visible colored spots on the completed chromatogram. More often, the zones of inhibition of growth on agar plates must be used.

General Directions

1. QUANTITIES USED

The quantity of each antibiotic needed depends on the method of detection that follows solvent development. Penicillin and streptomycin are usually detected by microbiological assay; therefore, small amounts (1–2 units) of each penicillin and 3–12 units of streptomycin and related compounds are used. Color tests are used for sulfonamides and chloromycetin so that larger amounts are necessary. Five to twenty micrograms is suitable, although samples obtained from biological sources may be analyzed with less.

[1] This subject has been reviewed by T. S. G. Jones (1954).

2. Paper

Whatman papers Nos. 1, 2, and 4 have been used extensively as well as Eaton and Dikeman No. 613 and Schleicher and Schüll Nos. 112 and 2043a.

3. Solvents

1. *1-Butanol:phenol:pyridine* = 95.5:2.5:2 (Glazko, 1950).
2. *1-Butanol:water* + *acetic acid* = 100:14 + 2.5% (G. N. Smith, 1950).
3. *Ether* saturated with water (Goodall, 1946; Karnovsky, 1949; Thorn, 1950; Glister, 1950). This solvent is especially valuable for separation of penicillins.
4. *Ether*, anydrous, for penicillins (Kluener, 1949).
5. *1-Butanol:ammonia:water* = 4:1:5 for separating the sulfonamides and sulfones (Longenecker, 1949).
6. *1-Butanol:water:piperidine:1-toluenesulfonic acid* = 100:14:2.3:2.3 v/v/v/w (Winsten, 1948). This solvent is useful for separating streptomycins.
7. *1-Butanol:water:p-toluenesulfonic acid* = 100:14:2.3 (Peterson, 1950).
8. *1-Butanol* saturated with $M/15$ phosphate buffer, pH 5.8 (Brockmann, 1953), for the separation of rhodomycins A and B.
9. *1,1-Dibutyl ether* saturated with 10% aqueous sodium naphthalene-1,6-disulfonate (Brockmann, 1953). The paper (Schleicher and Schüll No. 2043a) is sprayed with 10% Na naphthalenedisulfonate. This solvent is used to separate the actinomycin polypeptides.

4. Separation and Detection of Penicillins

In order to obtain suitable resolution of penicillin mixtures the paper must be buffered at a pH of about 6.0. According to Karnovsky (1949), K_2HPO_4 is made up at 20% w/v and the pH is adjusted to 6.2 by the addition of 85% phosphoric acid. The paper is then blotted and hung up to dry. Other workers use buffer solutions of 20–30% concentration of phosphate at pH 6–7.

The humidity in the chamber must be controlled for good separation of the penicillins. The practice is to equilibrate the paper strips with an atmosphere saturated with water vapor for 15 minutes before beginning the solvent development. This is obviously too short a time for complete equilibration.

The first separation of penicillin entities with ether as solvent was carried out at 4–5°C. (Goodall, 1946). Excellent separations are still being obtained at this temperature for a solvent development of about 24 hours (Karnovsky, 1949; Thorn, 1950). However, it has been shown that the separations can be carried out at room temperature in 3–4 hours. The advantages of the latter procedure are obvious (Winsten, 1947; Kluener, 1949; Glister, 1950).

The solution of penicillins which is to be analyzed should be such that no more than two units are applied to the paper. Stock solutions of penicillins X, G, F, dihydro F, and K can be conveniently prepared at concentrations of 100 units/ml. in 1 % potassium phosphate buffer, pH 6.0 (Kluener, 1949). Application of 5 µl. of each solution is made. The penicillin broth to be analyzed should also have concentrations of penicillins similar to those above.

No sufficiently sensitive color-producing reagent has been found for the penicillins so that microbiological techniques are generally used with *B. subtilis* or *S. aureus* as the test organism. Assay plates may be made in many ways. Glister (1950) used sheets of plate glass 19 × 14 inches. Half-inch-wide strips were cemented to form walls. Kluener (1949) used trays 12¼ inches long, 4 inches wide, and ½ inch deep, consisting of a quarter-inch bar aluminum frame with a transparent glass bottom. The glass bottom was installed by slotting the bar aluminum, inserting the glass, and sealing with putty. The trays were provided with lids that contained holes to maintain proper humidity conditions. Winsten (1948) used a plate consisting of a galvanized iron frame 18 inches long and 11 inches wide and ¾-inch-high walls. The edge of the frame was ¾-inch wide. A sheet of window glass was placed in the iron frame and held there by waterproof adhesive tape 1 inch wide.

In penicillin assay, the agar and spore suspension may be prepared as follows (Karnovsky, 1949): The nutrient medium consists of 1 g. of glucose, 1.5 g. of meat extract, 6 g. of Bacto-peptone, 3 g. of yeast extract, and 15 g. of agar per liter of water. The *B. subtilis* spore suspension consists of 3 g. of peptone and 3 g. of meat extract per liter inoculated with *B. subtilis*, Marburg type, and incubated for 6 days on a shaker at 30°C. The suspension is then pasteurized at 80°C. for 10 minutes and stored in the refrigerator until required. The agar medium is seeded just prior to pouring the plates by first heating to about 70°C. Precautions should be taken to ensure uniformity of depth of seeded agar over the entire plate. When many plates are poured, an equal volume should be added to each so that the depth of medium is the same in each case. After pouring, all plates are stored in the cold room until needed.

After chromatography, the dried strips of paper are laid on the assay plates which are then returned to the cold room for 3 hours, after which they are incubated at 30°C. until the inhibiton zones are well defined (about 12 hours).

In the quantitative evaluation of the resulting inhibiton zones, the maximum width of each zone may be measured and related to concentration.

Alternatively, the paper strip may be cut into small uniform squares after solvent development and these may be serially plated and the resulting zones measured (Karnovsky, 1949) (see Chapter IV).   Penicillins G, F and dihydro F produce spots of the same shape; therefore, a standard curve for G can be used for the determination of the other two.   Penicillin K produces a zone having much greater ellipticity than the others; therefore a separate standard curve must be prepared for this compound.   Penicillin X is usually present in very small quantities in mixtures, and it may be neglected.   If larger amounts are present, a standard curve should be made.

Two standard solutions are prepared—a high standard containing 5000 *B. subtilis* units each of sodium penicillin G and K per milliliter, and a low standard containing 50 *B. subtilis* units of sodium penicillin G and K per milliliter.   The solutions are made in 1 % phosphate buffer, pH 6.5.

Whatman No. 1 paper strips[2] (30 × 1 cm.) are impregnated with potassium phosphate buffer, pH 6.2, and dried.   Identical volumes of the standards are applied to separate strips with a 2-μl. pipette.   The test sample is applied to a third strip with the same pipette.   The concentrations of penicillins in the test sample should be between those of the standards. With concentrated samples this may be achieved by preliminary dilution with 1 % phosphate buffer to approximately 5000 *B. subtilis* units per milliliter.   When the test sample is of low activity, as with culture filtrates, it is necessary to superimpose several spots, drying between applications, in order to keep a small concentrated spot.

When the spots are dry, the strips are hung in the developing chamber previously saturated with water and ether at room temperature.   They are developed for 3½–4 hours with water-saturated ether.

In the meantime assay plates should be poured with agar seeded with *B. subtilis* spores and stored in the cold.   When development is complete, the strips are removed and placed on the surface of the *B. subtilis*-seeded agar.   Diffusion is allowed to proceed for one-half hour, and then the plates are incubated at 27°C. overnight.   The plates are photographed and the zone areas or widths are measured.

The areas or maximum widths of the zones are plotted against concentration (in units) for the standards and the unknown concentrations are determined from this plot (Fig. 1).

5. SEPARATION AND DETECTION OF STREPTOMYCINS

Streptomycin assay agar may be obtained from Difco Laboratories in dehydrated form.   To the sterile assay plates, a uniform layer of uninoculated streptomycin agar is poured.   After solidification, the streptomycin

---

[2] The superiority of sheets or wide bands of filter paper over narrow strips is discussed in Chapters IV and V.

agar inoculated with 1.0 m. of a *B. subtilis* (Illinois) spore suspension containing approximately 5×10^{10} spores per milliliter is superimposed as a seed layer. The plates are stored at 4°C. until used. Plates are incubated at 37°C. for 15 hours to obtain a satisfactory growth (Peterson, 1950). Many modifications of the procedures for preparation of plates are reported in the literature.

After incubation, the glass plates are removed from the supporting frame and laid on sheets of high-contrast photographic paper for the preparation of contact prints. Subsequent measurements, such as zone diameter or area, are then made from the print.

In most cases the contrast between the areas of growth and the clear agar is very low. The procedure of Drake (1950) produces excellent prints. Plane polarized light illuminates the tray, which has a dead black surface beneath it and a polarizer at the camera lens crossed with the polarizer at the light source. Two 200-watt lamps in reflectors or a fluorescent strip lamp serves as a light source when fitted with a sheet of Polaroid. In order to obtain precise crossing of the polarizers, a view camera is used and the exposure is made on high-contrast negative material such as Contrast Process Ortho or Kodalith.

A 1-inch square is placed on the plate before photography in order to form a size scale for measurement of the areas of zones of inhibition and distance traveled by the zones.

To date, chromatographic work on the antibiotics has been mostly of a

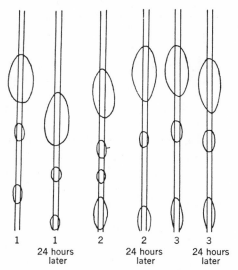

1	1	2	2	3	3
	24 hours later		24 hours later		24 hours later

FIG. 1. Separation of penicillins (Kluener, 1949).

qualitative or semiquantitative nature.   Many improvements in the analysis of mixtures are possible, especially after the substances have been eluted from the paper.   Hiscox (1951) has shown that when streptomycin and dihydrostreptomycin are heated in acid solution, absorption maxima exist in the ultraviolet region.   Numerous other techniques are possible where fluorescent substances exist or where colored derivatives may be formed.

In practice, 2–4 μl. of an unknown solution containing 0.1–120 streptomycin units is applied to separate strips of Whatman No. 1 paper (or equal intervals on a large sheet).[3]

The test sample may be a culture filtrate, provided that the salt concentration does not exceed approximately 50 μg. per streptomycin unit.   If larger amounts of salts are present, one compound may produce two zones on the resulting chromatogram.   This salt effect could be compensated, however, by using a developing solution consisting of 2 % p-toluenesulfonic acid in n-butanol previously saturated with 1–2.5 % aqueous NaCl.   2.5 % NaCl was found best for very low potency beers of 5–50 units/ml.

Standard solutions of streptomycin, mannosidostreptomycin, dihydrostreptomycin, and neomycin A may be applied to other strips.   The concentration of each applied should be 0.2–1.0 unit.

Butanol:water:p-toluenesulfonic acid (or butanol:aqueous NaCl:p-toluenesulfonic acid, if the salt concentration of the test sample is high) is used as the developing solvent.   Peterson (1950) reported that no more than four 5 $\times$ 22-inch strips should be developed before the solvent is renewed.   Water is lost to the paper, the equilibrium is disturbed, and poor resolution and slower mobility result if the same solvent is used continuously.

Development with solvent is carried out for 17–24 hours.   The paper is then air-dried and laid directly on agar plates seeded with *B. subtilis*.   After 8 minutes, the paper strip is removed and the plate allowed to incubate for 16–24 hours at 37°.

The zones of inhibition were recorded by photographing the plates (Drake, 1950).

The concentration of streptomycin antibiotics in solutions to be tested varies from 300 units/ml. up to as high as 12,000 units/ml. (Winsten, 1948).   A total of 2–120 units of antibiotics is applied to the paper.   In general 0.2–0.5 unit of each antibiotic will give a clear spot on the agar plate from which semiquantitative data can be obtained.

6. CHLOROMYCETIN AND ITS DEGRADATION PRODUCTS

In the study of chloromycetin and its decomposition products in broth solutions, preliminary separation using a liquid-liquid extraction procedure

[3] See footnote p. 394.

was employed to separate the material into basic, acidic, and neutral components. The most satisfactory concentrations to be used can then be ascertained by running four to five chromatograms side by side using 5, 10, 15, 20, and 25 μl. of solution. Each spot should be completely dried before further aliquots are added to the paper. Chloromycetin itself, since it contains a nitro group, can be reduced, diazotized, and coupled to form a colored derivative (G. N. Smith, 1950). The strip is first sprayed with a solution made by mixing 3 ml. of $SnCl_2$ (15 %) with 15 ml. of concentrated HCl and 180 ml. of H_2O. This solution must be prepared fresh. The strips are air-dried and sprayed with a solution of 1 g. of p-dimethylamino-benzaldehyde dissolved in a mixture of 30 ml. of ethanol, 3 ml. of concentrated HCl, and 180 ml. of 1-butanol. On air-drying, the areas containing NO_2-compounds appear as yellow spots.

Chloromycetin gives a bright yellow spot if first sprayed with 0.25 % stannous chloride in N HCl, dried, and then treated with 2 % w/v p-dimethyl-aminobenzaldehyde in 1.2 N HCl (Sokolski, 1953) after chromatography with 1-butanol:acetic acid (solvent 2; see p. 392).

7. AUREOMYCIN, TERRAMYCIN, ACTINOMYCINS, ETC.

The antibiotics may be separated by 1-butanol:acetic acid and revealed with the $SnCl_2$:p-dimethylaminobenzaldehyde method (see Chloromycetin). Aureomycin gives a dirty yellow spot, and terramycin gives a blue-green spot (Sokolski, 1953).

The tetracyclines are separated on paper with the organic phase of butyl acetate:methyl isobutyl ketone:1-butanol:water = 5:15:2:22 v/v to which 2 volumes of formic acid are added before use (Fischbach, 1955). The chromatograms are sprayed with 5 % ferric chloride in methanol, and viewed under u.v. light.

The antibiotics may also be visualized using the *starch-iodine reaction* as follows: (1) Spray with dilute sodium hypochlorite (chlorox:water = 1:20 v/v) and air dry. (2) Dip into 95 % ethanol and air dry. (3) Spray with freshly prepared starch iodide (1 % soluble starch:1 % KI = 1:1 v/v).[4] Acetylated neomycins show deep blue against a colorless background (Pan, 1956; cf. Berti, 1954; Hickey, 1954; and Stiffney, 1955).

The actinomycins are separated with dibutyl ether (solvent 9; see p. 392) and revealed by ninhydrin (Brockmann, 1953). Vining (1954) described the following procedure for the separation and identification of the actinomycins: *Solvent:* 1-dibutyl ether:ethyl acetate:2 % aqueous naphthalene-β-sulfonic acid = 3:1:4 v/v. *Method:* Whatman No. 1 paper is dipped into the aqueous phase of the above solvent and is blotted between sheets

---

[4] This reaction is also useful for detecting peptides which do not have a free amino group.

of filter paper. The actinomycins are applied to the paper in acetone.
After development with the organic phase of the solvent, the deep red
color of the naphthalene-β-sulfonate facilitates detection of the active
zones (Vining, 1954; cf. Gregory, 1955 for other useful solvents).

Circulins and polymixins are separated with 1-butanol:acetic acid:
water = 49.5:1.0:49.5 v/v and revealed with ninhydrin (Dowling, 1952).
Hypoglycins are separated with aqueous phenol (Hassall, 1954).

8. SULFONAMIDES (see also Chapter XII)

Although the sulfonamides are not truly antibiotics, they are included
here as a matter of convenience.

PAPER. Whatman No. 1; Schleicher and Schüll No. 2043b (G. Wagner,
1952).

SOLVENT. *1-Butanol:concentrated NH$_4$OH:H$_2$O* = 40:10:50 v/v. If
the sulfonamides are present in plasma, 100 mg. of nonaethyleneglycol-
monostearate should be added to the solvent (Longenecker, 1949).

COLOR REAGENTS. (1) *p-Dimethylaminobenzaldehyde*, 1 g. in 100 ml. of
3 % HCl.

2. *N-(1-Naphthyl) ethylenediamine·2HCl.* Dissolve 100 mg. of reagent
in 100 ml. of 95 % 1-butanol. Store in a brown bottle. The sulfonamides
on the developed chromatogram are diazotized with HONO (100 mg. of
NaNO$_2$ in 100 ml. of glacial acetic acid containing 1 drop of concentrated
HCl), then sprayed with the naphthylethylenediamine solution.

Stock solutions of sulfonamides are prepared by suspending 0.1 g. of
each compound in about 50 ml. of water, adding sufficient concentrated
ammonia to effect solution, and diluting to 100 ml. with distilled water. A
3–10-μl. sample is applied to the paper. Plasma samples from animals
which have been fed the drugs may be analyzed directly (Longenecker,
1949).

The following R_f values have been reported: sulfadiazine, 0.17; sulfa-
merizine, 0.30; sulfathiazole, 0.38; and p,p'-sulfonyldianiline, 1.0 (Longenecker, 1949).

Section II: Vitamins

1. VITAMIN A AND RELATED SUBSTANCES

QUANTITIES. One microgram of each carotinoid per spot.

PAPER. Whatman No. 54 impregnated with alumina. The paper is
dipped into Al$_2$(SO$_4$)$_3$ solution [65 g. of Al$_2$(SO$_4$)$_3$ per liter]. The excess
fluid is then allowed to drain off, and the papers are dipped into 2
N NH$_4$OH. The immersion in ammonia should not be hurried, as the precipitated aluminum hydroxide on the surface hinders the diffusion of NH$_3$

into the body of the paper. If heavy impregnation of the paper is desired, it is placed in NH_3 overnight. The paper is then washed with water for at least 5 hours and dried (Datta, 1949).

Whatman No. 54 impregnated with 10% w/v Dow Corning silicone stopcock grease in methylene chloride may also be used. Dry at 50°C. (J. Brown, 1953).

SOLVENTS. *Acetonitrile:water* = 93:7; 60:40; 50:50 w/v (J. Brown, 1953a) for silicone paper.

Petroleum ether (b.p. 80–100°C.) for alumina-treated paper (Datta, 1949).

COLOR REAGENTS. *Antimony trichloride.* In the determination of vitamin A, its esters, anhydrovitamin A, retinene, and other chromogens the positions of the resulting spots can be located by rapidly spraying the paper with Carr-Price reagent (saturated solution of antimony trichloride in chloroform) (Datta, 1949). Blue colors are produced that may be compared directly with standards, or the areas of the spots may be measured. Once the positions of the spots have been determined on one strip, the corresponding areas on other strips may be cut out and the substances eluted with $CHCl_3$. Addition of the Carr-Price reagent to the eluates will then produce the blue colors which may be read in a photoelectric colorimeter with a 620-mμ filter.

Since vitamin A is characterized by selective absorption in the ultraviolet, the intensity of this band, whose maximum is at 328 mμ, serves as a measure of vitamin A content.

SPECTROPHOTOMETRY. The chromatograms may be read directly in the Beckman spectrophotometer at 328 mμ, using the apparatus described in Chapter III (J. Brown, 1953b).

Comment. It is advisable to carry out all chromatography in the absence of actinic rays and oxygen. The strips should be dried in a jar containing dry ice (CO_2). Vitamin A alcohol and its esters have been separated (Kaiser, 1956).

2. VITAMIN D

PAPER. Whatman No. 2 coated with 5% v/v liquid paraffin in petroleum ether.

SOLVENT. *Ethylene monoethyl ether:n-propanol:methanol:water* = 35:10:30:25 v/v (Kodicek, 1954).

1-Propanol:methanol:water = 15:82:3 v/v (Kodicek, 1954).

COLOR REAGENTS. 24% antimony trichloride in $CHCl_3$. Heat to maximum color. View under ultraviolet (320 mμ) before spraying. Vitamins D_2 and D_3 give strong yellow colors with iodine in $C_2H_4Cl_2$ in the presence of mercurous *p*-chlorobenzoate (Lyness, 1955).

Quantitative Estimation of Vitamin D (Kodicek, 1954). The non-saponifiable fraction is purified via magnesium oxide:kieselguhr (1:1) column with petroleum ether (b.p. 40–60°C.):acetone = 99.5:0.5 v/v. After removal of the solvent, the residue is taken up in methanol, excess digitonin is added, and the precipitate is washed with petroleum ether. The solvent is removed, and the residue is dissolved in 0.2 ml. of ethanol and chromatographed. The vitamin D spot is cut out, eluted with 5 ml. of methanol, and read at 265 mμ. Recovery, 92 ± 12%. High quantities of vitamin A interfere.

3. Vitamin E (Tocopherols)

Paper. Whatman No. 1 is dipped in 2.5% w/v of Vaseline in ether, or into 3% w/v liquid paraffin in petroleum ether (b.p. 40–60°C.), or into 600 mg. of ferric undecylate per liter of petroleum ether, or into 10% w/v silicone stopcock grease in methylene chloride. These procedures result in reverse phase chromatograms. Whatman No. 1 paper may also be impregnated with $ZnCO_3$ by dipping the paper into $ZnCO_3$ solution (20 g. $(NH_4)_2CO_3$, 600 ml. water, 25 g. $ZnCO_3$, 150 ml. NH_4OH; filter) and drying it overnight at 100°C. (Green, 1955).

Separation of samples. Plant oils are hydrolyzed in the presence of pyrogallol to prevent oxidation of the tocopherols. The sterols are removed by crystallization at −15°C. from methanol. Carotenes are removed on floridin treated with stannous chloride (1.5–2.0 g. of floridin is boiled with 250 mg. of $SnCl_2$ plus 5–8 ml. of 10 N HCl, put into the chromatogram tube, and washed with 5 ml. of ethanol followed by five washings with 5-ml. portions of benzene). After removal of the solvent, the tocopherols are taken up in ethanol.

Solvent. *75% Ethanol* v/v (J. A. Brown, 1951, 1952); 77% ethanol (Harrison, 1956).

75% Ethanol in solvent saturated with nitrogen (Eggitt, 1953).

Acetone:water = 80:20 v/v (Guerillot, 1953).

Acetonitrile:H_2O = 93:7; 60:40; 50:50 (J. Brown, 1953a). The atmosphere of the chamber must be saturated with solvent.

Cyclohexane for $ZnCO_3$-paper (Green, 1955).

Color reagents. *2,2'-Diphenyl:ferric chloride 0.25%* w/v. 2,2'-Diphenyl in ether is sprayed on the chromatogram, followed by 0.1% w/v $FeCl_3$ in ethanol (J. A. Brown, 1952). Tocopherols give transient bright red spots.

Silver nitrate. 1.7 g. of $AgNO_3$ in 50 ml. of water plus 33 ml. of methanol plus 17 ml. of concentrated NH_4OH (J. A. Brown, 1952).

o-Dianisidine. Spray with 2% w/v Na_2CO_3 followed by diazotized o-dianisidine (J. A. Brown, 1952).

Potassium ferricyanide. Spray with 2% HCl, then with 0.05% aqueous $K_3Fe(CN)_6$ (Guerillot, 1952).

Quantitative Determination. The spots are cut out and extracted with 3 ml. of absolute ethanol at room temperature in the dark for 1 hour. Then 0.5 ml. of 0.2 % $FeCl_3$ in ethanol and 0.5 ml. of α,α'-dipyridyl, 0.5 % w/v in ethanol, are added. The solution, free from filter paper shreds, is read at 520 mμ within 2 minutes (Eggitt, 1953). The red color is exceedingly light sensitive.

Comment. The following R_f values have been reported with 75 % ethanol on paraffin-treated paper (Eggitt, 1953): α-tocopherol, 0.24; β-tocopherol, 0.48; γ-tocopherol, 0.48; δ-tocopherol, 0.65. α-Tocopherol has been determined in human blood (Delmas, 1956). Green and Dam (1954) have reported the separation of vitamin K and related compounds.

4. THIAMINE, TRIPHOSPHOTHIAMINE,[5] ETC.

PAPER. Whatman No. 1 washed with dilute (0.2 %) Versene (Eggleston, 1952) at pH 8.5, followed by thorough washing with water.

SOLVENTS. *1-Butanol:acetic acid:water.*

10 % Potassium chloride:95 % ethanol = 3:2 (Miyaki, 1952).

Ethylacetate:pyridine:water = 50:35:15 or 50:30:20 (Malyoth, 1952).

Pyridine:water:isobutanol = 2:5:3 v/v (Rossi-Fanelli, 1952) for triphosphothiamine (TPT).

1-Propanol:0.1 N HCl = 2:1 (Heyndrickx, 1953).

1-Propanol:H₂O:M acetate (pH 5) = 70:20:10 v/v (Siliprandi, 1954).

1-Propanol:0.5 M acetate (pH 4.5) = 60:40 v/v (Siliprandi, 1954).

1-Propanol:H₂O:M acetate (pH 5) = 65:20:15 v/v (Siliprandi, 1954).

p-Toluenesulfonic acid:tert-pentanol:water = 2:60:30 w/v/v (Hanes, 1949).

COLOR REAGENT. *Alkaline ferricyanide.*[5a] Mix 5 volumes of 55 % ethanol, 5 volumes of 10 % NaOH, and 0.1 volume of 2.5 % $K_3Fe(CN)_6$. View under ultraviolet light (Beran, 1951; Cacioppo, 1950; Rossi-Fanelli, 1952; Kiessling, 1953b).

Alkaline ferricyanide. 5 % $K_3Fe(CN)_6$ in 2 N NaOH (Heyndrickx, 1953).

p-Aminophenolacetate. The chromatogram is sprayed with freshly diazotized p-$NH_2C_6H_4OOCCH_3$ and then with dilute NaOH (Miyaki, 1952).

Dipicrylamine. Dissolve 0.2 ml. of 0.5 N Mg salt of dipicrylamine in 50 ml. of methanol, and add 49 ml. of water and 1 ml. of concentrated NH_4OH (Malyoth, 1952). This reagent is a general one for quaternary amines.

Potassium bismuth iodide. Boil 5 g. of $KBiI_4$ in 100 ml. of water plus 0.5 ml. of concentrated HCl. Filter when cold. Spray, dry, and respray. Remove background color by extraction with ether containing a little water. This reagent is useful for thiamine, thiamine phosphates, oxy- and chloro-

---

[5] Phosphoric esters may be revealed by spraying with molybdate reagent (see Chapter VI) followed by spraying with 0.1% ascorbic acid (Ganguli, 1953a).

[5a] Recommended

thiamines, morphine, strychnine, brucine, choline, nicotine, betaine, etc. Bartley, (1954).

Experimental Technique

A mixture of thiamine and its phosphates is chromatographed on Whatman No. 1 paper with the solvent, ethanol:water = 4:1 v/v (Viscontini, 1951; Kiessling 1953b).[6] The chromatogram is dried at 100°C., and the spots are detected by one of the following methods: (1) ultraviolet light (250 mμ); (2) Dragendorff reagent (see Chapter XII, alkaloids); (3) 5 % alkaline potassium ferricyanide in ethanol; blue spots in ultraviolet light.

Thiamine is converted to thiochrome with CNBr prior to circular chromatography. (CNBr reagent: 10 % KCN is added dropwise to saturated bromine water until color disappears.) The spots of thiamine, while still damp, are exposed to CNBr and NH$_3$ for 20 minutes. 1-Butanol:acetic acid:water = 4:1:5 is used as developing solvent. Both thiamine and riboflavin are resolved and detected by viewing the chromatogram in ultraviolet light (Giri, 1955c).

5. RIBOFLAVIN (see Table I)

PREPARATION OF SAMPLE. For the analysis of riboflavin, its nucleotides and derivatives, an aqueous protein-free and salt-free flavine solution is recommended. Homogenized tissue is denatured by boiling for 3 minutes, half of its weight of $(NH_4)_2SO_4$ is added, and the protein precipitate is centrifuged off. The free flavine is then concentrated by extraction into liquid phenol, and returned to water by the addition of ether to the phenol layer. A spot of this solution is then applied to the paper (Crammar, 1948).

Photolysis products of riboflavin solutions have been studied by subjecting irradiated samples to paper chromatography (Hais, 1949).

SOLVENTS. *1-Butanol:acetic acid:water* = 4:1:5 (Crammar, 1948; Hais, 1949; Yagi, 1950, 1951).

1-Propanol:pyridine:water = 1:3:1 (Blair, 1954).

tert-Butyl alcohol:pyridine:water = 50:15:35 (Blair, 1954).

COLOR REAGENT. Riboflavin and related compounds may be seen directly on the chromatograms under ultraviolet light, especially after spraying the paper with 0.05 N NaOH (Heyndrickx, 1953).

Riboflavin may be extracted from the paper with a dilute acid solution and its concentration determined by measuring its fluorescence in a fluorophotometer. The vitamin may also be determined by measurement of the growth stimulation of *Lactobacillus casei*. The area of growth on the microbiological plate may then be measured.

[6] *cf* Giri (1953a), Marten (1955), Siliprandi (1954) and Jones A. (1954).

TABLE I

RIBOFLAVIN AND RELATED COMPOUNDS (HAIS, 1949;
CRAMMAR, 1948; YAGI, 1953)

Substance	Solvent[a] 1	2	3	4	Fluorescence ultraviolet light
Riboflavin	0.5	0.85	0.33	—	Yellow
Flavin mononucleotide	0.03	0.41	—	—	Green blue
Flavin adenine dinucleotide	0.01	0.55	0.02	—	Green blue
Lumiflavin	0.46	0.82	0.46	0.50	Yellow
Lumichrome	0.67	0.92	0.67	0.68	Green-blue
Riboflavin phosphate	—	—	0.09	—	Green-yellow

[a] Solvents: 1. Water-saturated benzyl alcohol.
   2. Water-saturated 2,4-lutidine.
   3. n-Butanol:acetic acid:water = 4:1:5 v/v.
   4. Isobutanol:acetic acid:water = 4:1.5 v/v.

6. NICOTINIC ACID (NIACIN) AND ITS DERIVATIVES

PAPER. Whatman No. 1 or 4.

SOLVENTS. *Acetone:water* = 80:20; 60:40 (Kodicek, 1951).

1-Butanol:acetic acid:water (see Chapter V).

1-Butanol:acetone:water = 45:5:50 (B. C. Johnson, 1953).

1-Butanol:methanol:benzene:water = 2:1:1:1 (Radhakrishnamurthy, 1953).

1-Butanol saturated with 1.5 N ammonia (Huebner, 1951).

1-Butanol saturated with 0.2 N ammonium hydroxide (Leifer, 1950).

1-Butanol, water-saturated (Kodicek, 1951; Quagliariello, 1951).

2-Butanol:water = 1:1 (Kodicek, 1951).

Ethanol:0.1 N acetic acid = 1:1 (Zatman, 1953).

Ethyl methyl ketone:acetic acid:water = 49:1:50 (Kodicek, 1951).

1-Propanol:0.1 N HCl = 2:1 (Heyndrickx, 1953).

1-Propanol:water = 80:20 (Holman, 1954).

COLOR REACTIONS. *Cyanogen bromide (König's test).* Titrate cold bromine-water with ice-cold 10% NaCN until the color disappears (Kodicek, 1951). Commercial CNBr can also be used (Bolling, 1949). Expose the dried chromatogram to CNBr vapors in a chamber for 1 hour. Nicotinic acid and many of its derivatives give yellow colors. The color can be intensified by spraying with:

2% p-Aminobenzoic acid (2 g. of p-aminobenzoic acid in 75 ml. of 0.75 N HCl, diluted to 100 ml. with ethanol) (Kodicek, 1951).

1% Benzidine in aqueous ethanol (1:1) (Huebner, 1951).

p-Aminoacetophenone, 1% w/v in aqueous ethanol (1:1) (Cuthbertson, 1953).

3-Methyl-1-phenylpyrazol-5-one, saturated aqueous solution (Cuthbertson, 1953).

Picryl chloride, 1.5% w/v in ethanol (Cuthbertson, 1952, 1953). Expose to NH_3 vapors to give red spots; when dipped into acetic acid only hydrazides remain.

1-Fluoro-2,4-dinitrobenzene, 1% v/v in ethanol (Cuthbertson, 1953).

1-Chloro-2,4-dinitrobenzene, 1% w/v in ethanol (Cuthbertson, 1953). Heat at 100°C. for 1 hour, then spray with 0.7% alcoholic KOH (Heyndrickx, 1953). For hydrazides only.

p-Nitroaniline, diazotized, followed by spraying with 20% Na_2CO_3 (Cuthbertson, 1953). For hydrazides only.

Hypobromite-sulfamate-naphthylethylenediamine. Spray with NaOBr: 4 ml. of 2.5 N NaOH plus H_2O to 45 ml., add 2 ml. of Br_2 solution (12.5 g. of NaBr plus 12.5 g. of Br_2 diluted to 100 ml. with water), dilute to 50 ml.; prepare every few days. Air-dry for 15 minutes, then heat for 5 minutes at 100°C. Spray with 1:1 v/v 2.4 N NaOH plus 0.1% $NaNO_3$. After 1 minute, spray with 1:1 v/v 0.5% NH_4 *sulfamate* plus 0.1 N-(1-naphthyl)-ethylenediamine·HCl. Each spray must be prepared fresh before use (Holman, 1954).

Methyl ethyl ketone:ammonia = 1:1. On exposure to the vapors of this reagent for 1 hour, quaternary nicotinamide derivatives show as bluish-white fluorescent spots at 0.05 μg. (Kodicek, 1951).

SPECTROPHOTOMETRY. Direct quantitative measurement on the chromatograms (J. A. Brown, 1952; see Chapter III).

Comment. Among the compounds which have been identified by these methods are nicotinic acid, isonicotinic acid, niacinamide, isoniacinamide, nicotinic acid hydrazide, isoniazide, nicotinoglycine, isonicotinoglycine, nicotinuric acid, dimethylnicotinamide (coramine), isopropylisonicotinic acid hydrazide, N^1-methylnicotinamide, N^1-methylnicotinuric acid betaine, carbamyl-N^1-2'-hydroxyethylpyridinium bromide, diphosphopyridine nucleotide, triphosphopyridine nucleotide, 3-carbamyl-tetraacetyl-N^1-D-glucosidylpyridinium bromide, and 3-carbamyl-N^1-ribosidylpyridinium bromide.

7. PANTOTHENIC ACID[7]

SOLVENT. *1-Butanol*, water-saturated (Crokaert, 1948).

COLOR REAGENT. Spray with 0.5% sodium β-naphthoquinone-4-sulfonate adjusted to pH 9.2–9.4 with sodium tetraborate (Folin's reagent) (Frame, 1943). Heat at 100°C. for 10 minutes. Allow the chromatogram to stay in the light for several hours to bleach the background color (Crokaert, 1948).

[7] cf. Pierpont (1955).

8. PYRIDOXINES

PAPER.   Schleicher and Schüll No. 507; Whatman No. 1.

SOLVENTS.   *1-Butanol*, water-saturated (Winsten, 1948).

n-Amyl alcohol:acetone:water = 2:1:2 v/v (Snyder, 1953).

Isoamyl alcohol:pyridine:water = 2:1:2 (Snyder, 1953).

ASSAY.   *Microbiological.*   A solution containing 1–5 μg. each of pyridoxal, pyridoxamine, and pyridoxine is applied to the paper and the chromatogram is developed.   After drying for 15 minutes at 65°C. the paper strip is laid on the agar plate seeded with *Saccharomyces carlsbergensis*, strain 4228.   The nutrient agar (Atkin, 1943) contains all factors necessary for the growth of the organism with the exception of the vitamin B_6 group. The agar plates are prepared as follows: A bottom layer of the nutrient agar is made by pouring 300 ml. of the agar medium on a plate 11 × 18 inches. This is allowed to harden.   Then a 200-ml. portion of the nutrient agar cooled to 48–50°C. is seeded with 10 ml. of sterile saline to which has been added a loopful of a 24-hour culture of the yeast.   The seeded agar is then poured on the hardened underlayer and allowed to cool.   (With such a plate, eight separate strips may be laid side by side on agar.)   The paper chromatogram is allowed to soak for 5 minutes on the surface of the moist agar in order to transfer the various B_6 members from the strip to the agar plate.   The strip is then removed and the agar plate incubated overnight at 27–30°C.   Well-defined zones of growth mark the position of the various forms of B_6.   The area of each zone is a measure of the concentration of each constituent.   The R_f factors observed are 0.18 for pyridoxamine, 0.68 for pyridoxal, and 0.75 for pyridoxine.   Since the R_f values of the latter two are fairly close, there is some overlapping of zones.

Chemical.   *2,6-Dichloroquinonechlorimide.*   Spray with 0.1 % in benzene. Expose to NH_3 vapors from boiling NH_4OH solution (Snyder, 1953).   Vitamin B_6 appears blue.   Sensitivity, 1 μg.

Phenylhydrazine in acetic acid may be used to detect pyridoxal by the usual aldehyde reaction (Snyder, 1953; see Chapter XII).

p-Dimethylaminobenzaldehyde (*Ehrlich's* reagent) (see Chapter V; Dalgliesh, 1952).

Ethyl-1-naphthylamine (*Ekman's* reagent) (see Chapter V; Dalgliesh, 1952).

9. FOLIC ACID, ITS DERIVATIVES[8] AND ANTAGONISTS

PAPER.   Eaton and Dikeman No. 613; Whatman No. 1.

SOLVENTS.   *Ethanol:1-butanol:ammonia:water* = 50:15:10:25 v/v for growth factors for *Leuconostoc citrovorum* 8081.   (Doctor, 1953).

[8] cf. Toennies (1956).

Isopropyl alcohol:ammonia:water = 70:10:20 (Fountain, 1953).

0.1 M Phosphate buffer, pH 7.0 (Nichol, 1953).

1-Butanol:acetic acid:water = 8:1:1 (Zakrzewski, 1953).

1-Butanol:morpholine:water = 3:1:3 (Zakrzewski, 1953).

2,4,6-Collidine, water-saturated (Zakrzewski, 1953).

Isoamyl alcohol:5% KH$_2$PO$_4$ (Wieland, 1952). The strips are developed with a two-phase system consisting of the aqueous phase and the non-aqueous phase (1 cm. of aqueous phase, 0.5 cm. of organic phase or the reverse) (Carter, 1950).

Isoamyl alcohol:5% Na$_2$HPO$_4$ (O. P. Wieland, 1952). Use as described above.

ASSAY. The folic acid vitamins and their antagonists are assayed by bioautographic techniques. Thus for amethopterin, Difco folic acid assay agar plates plus 0.5 μg. of pteroylglutamic acid per milliliter are seeded with *S. faecalis* or *L. citrovorum* 8081 (ATCC 8043). Bioautographs of the inhibition zones are observed after 16 hours (Fountain, 1953). The contrast may be improved by including approximately 200 μg. of 2,3,5-triphenyltetrazolium chloride per milliliter of medium (Nichol, 1953). (See Section I of this chapter for other bioautographic techniques.)

The chromatogram is sprayed with 10% titanium chloride in concentrated HCl mixed with 15% Na citrate. The excess TiCl$_3$ is destroyed by oxidation in air, after which the paper is treated with 0.2% NaNO$_2$ in 0.1 N HCl followed by 0.2% 1-naphthylamine or N-(1-naphthyl)ethylenediamine (Komenda, 1953).

10. COBALAMINS

PAPER. Whatman No. 1 plain, impregnated with 0.66 M KH$_2$PO$_4$ buffer at pH 4.6 (Woodruff, 1950) or moistened with 1% KCN solution (Patte, 1953).

SOLVENTS. *1-Butanol*, water-saturated (Winsten, 1949).

1-Butanol, pH 4.6 phosphate buffer (Woodruff, 1950).

2-Butanol:acetic acid:H$_2$O:5% w/v NaCN = 100:1:50:0.25 v/v (Ford, 1955).

2-Butanol:concentrated NH$_4$OH:H$_2$O:5% w/v NaCN = 100:1:50:0.25 v/v (Ford, 1955).

2-Propanol:water = 70:30 w/v, in the presence of 25 ml. of 1% KCN and 4 ml. of 50% H$_2$SO$_4$ (Patte, 1953).

Other useful solvents have been described by Ganguli (1956), Friedrich (1955) and Phillipe (1952).

BIOASSAY. The strips are allowed to dry in air for 1 hour at 30–35°C. They are then laid on the agar plates seeded with *L. leichmannii* 313. After the moist agar has leached the strips for 5 minutes, the paper is removed and the plate is incubated overnight at 37°C. The edges of the zones

TABLE II

Vitamin	Test	$R_f{}^a$	Minimum concentration $\mu g.$
Inositol	AgNO₃—NH₄OH	0.14	5.0
B₁₂		0.25	1.5
Choline	Iodine vapor	0.34, 0.44	3.0
Pantothenic acid	β-Naphthoquinone-4-sulfonate	0.36	80.0
Riboflavin		0.40	0.8
Niacin	CNBr	0.44	0.5
Niacinamide	CNBr	0.73	2.0
Thiamine		0.47	4.0
Biotin	Dilute acid KMnO₄	0.64	4.0
Pyridoxine		0.73	1.5
β-Aminobenzoic acid	Ehrlich's reagent	0.80	0.5

^{a} R_f: Solvent is 1-butanol : methanol : benzene : water = 2 : 1 : 1 : 1.

formed in the agar are outlined with a sharp instrument, and contact photographic prints are then prepared with Kodagraph contact standard paper to make a permanent record (Winsten, 1949). Agar may be replaced by nutrient gelatin plates seeded with *Escherichia coli*, B_{12}-dependent (Tarr, 1952). The B_{12} content is calculated from the diameter of the spots of growth. The error is approximately $\pm 17\%$ calculated from the mean of eight chromatograms (Patte, 1953; *cf*. Chapter IV).

Comment. All work involving vitamin B_{12} should be carried out in a dim light (Tarr, 1952).

11. OTHER VITAMINS OF THE B GROUP

Table II summarizes some of the methods and reactions for the various B vitamins. The R_f values are those obtained using 1-butanol:methanol: benzene:water = 2:1:1:1 with circular chromatograms (Radhakrishnamurthy, 1953).

Choline may also be detected by spreading a fresh 1% aqueous solution of potassium ferrocyanide over the paper, followed by treatment with 0.5% cobalt chloride (Heyndrickx, 1953). The sensitivity is approximately 10 μg. of choline.

12. ASCORBIC ACID (VITAMIN C) AND RELATED COMPOUNDS

PAPER. Whatman No. 1

SOLVENTS.[9] *Phenol:acetic acid:water* = 100:1:100. Use the lower layer (Mapson, 1949). Run in the presence of NaCN (see Table III).

[9] cf. Mitchell (1953a) and Schmidt (1955).

TABLE III

ASCORBIC ACID AND RELATED COMPOUNDS (MAPSON, 1949)

Compound	R_f values	Color reaction	
		Indophenol	AgNO$_3$—NH$_3$
Ascorbic acid	0.35	White	Black
Isoascorbic acid	0.40	White	Black
Hydroxytetronic acid	0.62	White	Black
Reductone	0.66	White	Black
Reductic acid	0.78	White	Black
Dehydroascorbic acid	0.38	—	Brown

1-Butanol-acetic acid:water = 250:60:250 in H_2S atmosphere (Tegethoff, 1953).

COLOR REAGENTS. *2,6-Dichlorophenolindophenol.* Dissolve 800 mg. of dye in 1 liter of water and dilute with an equal volume of ethanol (Mapson, 1949).

Ammoniacal silver nitrate. Add 10 ml. of 0.2 N AgNO$_3$ to 10 ml. of 10 % NaOH solution, and then add concentrated NH$_4$OH drop by drop to dissolve the silver oxide (Mapson, 1949).

Both solvents and either color reaction may be used to separate and identify ascorbic acid, isoascorbic acid, hydroxytetronic acid, reductone, reductic acid, and dehydroascorbic acid.

Ammonium molybdate. Dissolve 150 g. of ammonium molybdate in 1 liter of 1 % NH$_4$OH. To 3.0 ml. of this solution, add 2.0 ml. of N HCl-citrate buffer (pH 3.8) and 3 drops of concentrated H$_2$SO$_4$. The test is reported to be specific for ascorbic acid (Heimann, 1953).

Cacotheline (Merck). Spray with 2 % w/v aqueous cacotheline, heat to 110°, ascorbic acid forms violet spots (Tegethoff, 1953).

Another method for the separation of ascorbic acid and related compounds is that of Mitchell, 1953a:

PAPER. Whatman No. 1 or 4 stabilized by spraying with 1 % w/v *m*-phosphoric acid and drying in air.

SOLVENT. *Acetonitrile:acetone:water:acetic acid* = 80:5:15:1 v/v.

COLOR REAGENT. *Ammoniacal silver nitrate.* Dissolve 5 g. of AgNO$_3$ in water, add 10 ml. of NH$_4$OH, and dilute to 100 ml. with water.

R_f VALUES. D-Glucoascorbic acid, 0.23; L-ascorbic acid, 0.37; D-isoascorbic acid, 0.43.

Quantitative Determination of Ascorbic Acid (Strohecker, 1955). Ascorbic acid is extracted from the biological sample with oxalic acid. Up to 60 μl. of the extract and 20 μl. of a 1 % standard solution are spotted on Schleicher and Schuell Paper No. 2042bM. The solvent is the upper phase of 2 g. oxalic acid, 60 ml. water, 40 ml. 1-butanol, plus 1–2 mg. KCN.

The paper is developed for $5\frac{1}{2}$ hours by the descending technique. At the end of the run, the paper is dried at 105°C. for two minutes. A parallel marker is sprayed with molybdate reagent (see above), and untreated areas are eluted with 5–10 ml. of 0.5–1.0% oxalic acid under a stream of CO_2. These extracts are titrated with 0.001 N 2,6-dichloroindophenol.

13. BIOTIN AND RELATED COMPOUNDS (Wright, 1954).

Ten to 20 μl. of biotin in 50% ethanol (about 10 μg.) is spotted on Whatman No. 1 paper which is developed by the ascending technique for 16–18 hours with 1-butanol:acetic acid:water = 4:1:5. Since no satisfactory color reagent for biotin is available, sections of the chromatogram are cut out, eluted with 25 ml. of basal medium, and the microbiological activity is determined using the organism *Neurospora crassa*.

Chapter XIV

INORGANIC SEPARATIONS

This chapter will be a brief outline of the separation of inorganic ions by paper chromatography. No attempt has been made at an exhaustive search of the literature on the subject, and the interested reader is referred to the book, *Chromatographic Methods of Inorganic Analysis*, by McOmie and Pollard (1953).

Inorganic separations on filter paper have been studied extensively by many investigators. In fact, it is possible to conduct a course in qualitative analysis based on the separations obtained with suitable solvents and the identification of the individual zones made possible by color-producing reagents. Very often, mixtures of cations may be completely resolved on paper. Subsequent qualitative and quantitative determination of each element can then be carried out by suitable means (see also Chapter IV). Alternatively, groups of metals may be separated, and individual cations determined by other analytical means. Thus, in polarography, quantitative determination of each ion in a mixture is sometimes complicated by the presence of interfering ions. Separation of the sample into two or more fractions can produce mixtures which may be easily analyzed by this method. By combining paper chromatography with other analytical techniques, almost any sample can be studied.

Most of the work to date has been done on untreated filter paper, although impregnation of the paper with reagents has been found useful in certain applications. Flood (1949) impregnated the paper with alumina, forming an adsorption column for the separation of cations. Laskowski (1951) and Fernando (1953) dipped paper into 8-hydroxyquinoline prior to chromatography. By impregnating filter paper with electrolytes (*e.g.*, KNO_3, NaCl, etc.) better separation of many cations is achieved (Lederer, 1952c). This improvement may be due to complex formation of cations with Cl^- on the paper (Tewari, 1954b). When Whatman No. 1 is impregnated with a precipitating agent (e.g. KI and K_2CrO_4), no correlation could be obtained between the band width at the beginning and end of the solvent development (Chatterji, 1956).

A common observation in the chromatography of inorganic ions and organic acids is the occurrence of multiple spots for a single ion species. For example, when Cd^{++} salts are chromatographed with solvents containing NH_4OH, as many as three spots have been observed (Erdem, 1954, 1955). The explanation is that several $Cd^{++}NH_3$ complexes have been formed whose equilibrium is rapidly attained in solution but is detained by cellulose adsorption. For this reason one should start with salts in which the anion corresponds to the anion of an acid or salt in the solvent (Pollard, 1955a). In the presence of a complexing agent, the acidity of the solvent should be sufficiently low and the concentration of the complexing agent sufficiently high to insure a single metal-complex. It is also necessary to remove any metal impurities in the paper by a prewashing step. One should bear in mind that a chemical reaction between solute and solvent affects the R_f value and the final spot size which are important factors in quantitative work (Pickering, 1955).

The rate of movement of a given cation along the paper depends on its partition coefficient between the mobile organic phase and the stationary aqueous phase. Some simple operations can be carried out using a system such as butanol-water. Usually, however, a strong acid is added to the developing solvent in order to prevent hydrolysis and the existence of ions in complex and simple form at the same time. This avoids "tailing" of individual zones (Lederer, 1949d; Burstall, 1950). Other workers have added complexing agents to the solvent to be used. In this case, the solubility of the metal complex in the organic solvent determines the rate of movement of a zone along the papers, rather than the solubility of the metal ion or salt itself (Pollard, 1951).

To locate the spots on a completed chromatogram, any reagent which produces a color or fluorescence, or quenches fluorescence, may be used. A general spraying agent for most cations is a mixture of kojic acid and 8-hydroxyquinoline. H_2S produces colored spots with all metals that form colored sulfides. Other general reagents include dithizone, alizarin, potassium iodide.

Reference to Tables I and II will enable the investigator to decide on a suitable solvent for his problem. Not too much attention should be paid to the actual R_f values, but rather to the relative values that indicate whether separations will occur. The predictions made from the study of single cations are found to hold for most of the cations when mixed. There are a few instances where interference occurs, e.g., As, Sb, and Sn, or when a very large excess of one salt is present with smaller quantities of other cations. However, even in these cases, suitable spot tests will correctly identify each cation.

General Directions

1. QUANTITIES USED

Individual cation mixtures containing 20–200 μg. of each metal are generally employed. However, if a fluorescent spray is used to detect the spots, quantities as low as 1 μg. can be easily detected. Pollard (1951) reports that the optimum quantity of material to use is 0.02 ml. of 0.1 N

solutions of Ag^+, Hg^+, Hg^{++}, Pb^{++}, Bi^{+++}, Cu^{++}, Cd^{++}, Al^{+++}, Fe^{+++}, Zn^{++}, Mn^{++}, Co^{++}, Ni^{++}, As^{+++}, Sb^{+++}, and 0.02 μl. of 0.2 N solutions of Ca^{++}, Sr^{++}, Ba^{++}, Mg^{++}, K^+, Na^+, Sn^{++}, Sn^{4+}, Cr^{+++}. For separation of the platinum metals, Burstall (1950) applied 25–50 μg. of each metal, Au, Os, Pt, Pd, Rh, and Ir to the paper. One microgram of Se can be detected in the presence of 1000 μg. of Te. One microgram of Au may be detected in several hundred times the amount of each of the platinum metals. One microgram of Hg may be isolated from large quantities of other cations. One microgram of Sc may be detected in 1000 μg of the rare earths. Twenty micrograms of uranium can be isolated from many common metals (Lewis, 1951). About 5 μg. of K can be separated from the other alkali and alkaline earth metals (Beerstecher, 1950). Two micrograms of either Be or Al in a large excess of the other can be detected (Osborn, 1949). Ten to two hundred micrograms of each of F, Cl, Br, and I can be detected in the presence of the others.

For best results the concentration of the cation should be about 1 %, and the initial spot should contain about 60 μg. If tailing of spots results, the concentration should be decreased to 0.5 % (Sommer, 1955).

2. PAPER

Whatman papers Nos. 1, 3, 54, and 541 have been used. No distinct advantage of one paper over the others has been observed. Pollard (1951) reports that the advantage in using No. 54 is the increased rate of flow of solvent through this paper. However, Whatman No. 1 has been used more than any other single type paper. Schleicher and Schuell (S. & S.) papers are listed in the order of increasing R_f values caused by the different textures of these papers: S. & S. 45, S. & S. 43, and S. & S. 2040b (Sommer, 1955).

Whatman No. 1 is impregnated, prior to chromatography, with 8-quinolinol and derivatives thereof, by dipping the paper into a 2 % pyridine or alcoholic solution of the quinolinols (Fernando, 1953). The resolution of a number of cations on this modified filter paper appears greatly improved. Whatman No. 1 has also been impregnated with a 2 % ethanolic solution of 4-hydroxybenzthiazole (Fernando, 1955). If not commercially available, 4-hydroxybenzthiazole may be synthesized by the method of Erlenmeyer (1942). Aminated and phosphorylated paper has been employed for the separation of Fe, Cu, and Ni (Kember, 1955b; experimental paper available from W. and R. Balston, Ltd.).

Ion exchange paper (impregnated with Dowex 50-H^+) is used for the separation of selenite and tellurite ions with a variety of organic and inorganic acid solvents (Lederer, 1955, 1956a). Le, Ce, and Y nitrates may be resolved on this paper with 3 % aqueous citrate buffer, pH 3.

3. SOLVENTS (See also Tables I and II)

Most solvents used for the chromatography of inorganic ions may be divided into three classes (Lederer, 1956b): 1) Solvents containing strong acids; 2) solvents with weak acids, bases, or complexing agents; 3) solvents for nonequilibrium conditions as in gradient-elution analysis. The nature of the organic component and the concentration of the mineral acid have varying effects on the R_f values of inorganic ions (Sommer, 1955). Ethanol, n-propanol, isopropanol, n-butanol, sec- and tert-butanol, pentanol, isopentanol, acetone, methylethylketone have been successfully employed, together with HCl. Glycols and glycerol are not suitable. A useful composition is alcohol:water:concentrated HCl = 8:1:1.

The addition of NH_4OH to pure solvents results in an increase in mobility for Ag and Ni due to complex formation (Pickering, 1956).

Other solvent combinations and their applications are as follows:

1. *1-Butanol:benzoylacetone:nitric acid* is prepared by dissolving 5 g. of benzoylacetone in 50 ml. of n-butanol and then shaking with 50 ml. of 0.1 N HNO_3.

2. *Dioxane:antipyrine:nitric acid* is prepared by dissolving 1 g. of antipyrine in a mixture of 100 ml. of pure dioxane, 1 ml. of concentrated HNO_3, and 2.8 ml. of H_2O (Pollard, 1951).

3. *1-Butanol:20% HCl* is prepared by mixing 20 ml. of concentrated HCl with 80 ml. of n-butanol. This solvent has been used to separate many common cations in the form of their 8-hydroxyquinolinates (Reeves, 1951).

4. *1-Butanol:N HCl* is prepared by saturating n-butanol with 1 N HCl (Lederer, 1948, 1949).

5. *1-Butanol:3 N HCl* (Burstall, 1950). This solvent separates mixtures containing Pb, Hg, Bi, Cu, and Cd.

6. *Acetylacetone:HCl:acetone* is made by adding 0.1 part of concentrated HCl and 5.0 parts of acetone to 15 parts of acetylacetone saturated with water v/v. This solvent proved efficient in separating mixtures of As, Sn, and Sb (Burstall, 1950).

7. *Acetone:HCl* is prepared by adding 5 parts of H_2O and 8 parts of concentrated HCl to 87 parts of acetone (Burstall, 1950). This solvent is used to separate mixtures containing Zn, Mn, Co, and Ni (see Fig. 1).

8. *Methyl ethyl ketone:8% HCl* is prepared by mixing 8 parts of concentrated HCl with 92 parts of methyl ethyl ketone. It is used to separate Cu, Fe, Mn, Co, and Ni (Burstall, 1950).

9. *Methyl ethyl ketone:30% HCl* v/v. This solvent resolves the platinum metals (Burstall, 1950) (see Fig. 1).

10. *Pyridine:H_2O* is prepared by adding 10 parts of H_2O to 90 parts of pyridine v/v. Burstall (1950) used this solvent to separate mixtures of the anions—fluoride, chloride, bromide, and iodide.

TABLE I

TABLE I
R_f VALUES OF CATIONS

Cations	Solvent[a]									
	1	2	3	4	5	6	7	8	9	10
Ag	0.10	0.78	0.08	0	0					
Hg^+	0.24	0	0.43							
Pb	0.03	0	0.15			0.27				
Hg^{++}	0.31	0	0.42	0.84		0.81				
Bi	0.02	0	0.63	0.51		0.59				
Cu	0.22	0.76	0.24	0.40	0.1	0.20			0.71	
Cd	0.05	0.76	0.18	0.83		0.77				
As	0.43	0.65	0.18				0.2			
Sb	0	0.38	0.65				0.5			
Sn^{++}	0.58	0	0.77				1.0			
Sn^{++++}	0.55	0	0.58							
Al	0.03	0	0.03	0.03	0.07					
Cr^{+++}	0.03	0	0.01		0.07					
Fe^{+++}	0.95	0	0.10	0.93					0.93	
Zn	0.05	0.75	0.08	0.78	0.77			0.9		
Mn	0.07	0.71	0.09					0.3	0.18	
Co	0.06	0.74	0.05	0.19				0.6	0.54	
Ni	0.03	0.76	0.05	0.04				0.07	0.01	
Ca	0.05	0.52	0.10							
Sr	0.04	0.40	0.04							
Ba	0.02	0.26	0.02							
Mg	0.06	0.65	0.04		0.11					
K	0.05	0.32	0.03							
Na	0.06	0.42	0.04							
Pd					0.6					0.60
Pt					0.8					0.80
Au					1.1					0.93
Rh										0.10
Ir										0.10
Ti					0.07					
V					0.17					
Rare earths					0.03					
Be					0.33					
In					0.30					
Te^+					0.00					
Te^{+++}					1.11					

[a] Solvents: 1. 1-Butanol:benzoylacetone (Pollard, 1951).
  2. Collidine:water (Pollard, 1951).
  3. Dioxane:antipyrine (Pollard, 1951).
  4. Metals first precipitated with 8-hydroxyquinoline and then developed with butanol:20% HCl (Reeves, 1951).
  5. 1-Butanol:1 N HCl (Lederer, 1949d).
  6. 1-Butanol:3 N HCl (Burstall, 1950).
  7. Acetylacetone:HCl:acetone (Burstall, 1950).
  8. Acetone:8% HCl (Burstall, 1950).
  9. Methyl ethyl ketone:8% HCl (Burstall, 1950).
  10. Methyl ethyl ketone:30% HCl (Burstall, 1950).

TABLE II

R_f VALUES OF ANIONS

Anion	Solvent[a]			
	1	2	3	4
Fluoride	0.00	—	0	—
Chloride	0.23	0.24	0.10	—
Bromide	0.47	0.36	0.16	—
Iodide	0.71	0.47	0.30	0.99
Chlorate	—	0.42	—	0.98
Bromate	—	0.25	0.13	—
Iodate	—	0.09	0.03	—
Nitrite	—	0.25	0.20	—
Nitrate	—	0.40	0.24	—
Arsenite	—	0.19	0.21	—
Arsenate	—	0.05	0	—
Carbonate	—	0.06	—	—
Phosphate	—	0.04	0	—
Chromate	—	0	0	—
Thiocyanate	—	0.56	0.45	—
Sulfate	—	0.07	0	—
Sulfide	—	—	0	—
Thiosulfate	—	—	0	—
Periodate	—	—	0	—
Oxalate	—	—	0	—
Ferricyanide	—	—	0	0.91
Ferrocyanide	—	—	0	1.00
Picrate	—	—	0.7	—
Tetraborate	—	—	—	0.74
Dichromate	—	—	—	0.17
Selenite	—	—	—	0.78
Tellurite	—	—	—	0.91
Molybdate	—	—	—	0.38
Phosphate	—	—	—	0.82
Perrhenate	—	—	—	0.94
Tungstate	—	—	—	—

[a] Solvents: 1. Pyridine:10% H_2O (Burstall, 1950).
2. Butanol:pyridine:1.5 N NH_3 = 2:1:2 v/v (Pollard, 1951).
3. Butanol:1.5 N NH_4OH (Lederer, 1949a,b).
4. n-Butanol:40% HBr:water = 10:1:9—organic phase + 10 ml. 40% HBr (Kertes, 1956).

11. *1-Butanol:pyridine:NH_3* is prepared by mixing 2 parts of n-butanol, 1 part pyridine, and 2 parts 1.5 N NH_4OH (Pollard, 1951). It is used for the common anions.

12. *1-Butanol:NH_3* is prepared by saturating n-butanol with 1.5 N NH_4OH (Lederer, 1949). The upper layer is used to separate anions.

13. *Methanol:concentrated HCl* = 100:5 v/v, for Ba and Sr (Fourage, 1955).

14. *Tetrahydrofuran:concentrated HCl* = 50:15 for UO_2^{++} (R_f 0.976),

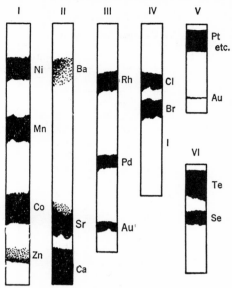

FIG. 1.   Separation of cations (Burstall, 1950)[a]: I, separation of Zn, Co, Mn, and Ni; II, separation of Ba, Sr, and Ca; III, separation of Rh, Pd, and Au; IV, separation of Cl, Br, and I; V, separation of Au from Pt metals; VI, separation of Te and Se.

Cu^{++} (0.777), VO_2^{++} (0.555), Mn^{++} (0.506), and Ni^{++} (0.274) (Hartkamp, 1955).

15. *Isobutyl methyl ketone:pentanol:concentrated HCl* = 6:1:3 for Rh, Pd, and Pt.   Ir and Rh which do not separate are resolved with *n*-butanol, saturated with 3 *N* HCl plus several drops of H_2O_2 (Kember, 1955a).

16. *n-Butanol, saturated with water:acetic acid* = 100:14 plus 5 g. oxine for the separation of lanthanons (Pollard, 1954a).

17. *n-Butanol:pyridine:diethylaniline:5 N HCl* = 5:1:0.5:1.5 for Mn, Co, Ni, Zn (chlorides) by circular chromatography (Barnabas, 1955a).

18. *Ethanol:methanol* (v/v) for K, Na, NH_4^+, and Li by ascending or circular chromatography (Barnabas, 1954).

19. *2-Methyltetrahydrofuran* is shaken with excess of water.   Fifty ml. of this solvent is placed in a 250 ml. flask, and 1.25 ml. of concentrated HNO_3 is added by submerging the top of a pipette below the surface of the liquid (CAUTION!).   This solvent moves U^{+6} with the solvent front, while 31 other cations (radioisotopes) stay near the origin (Raaen, 1955).

[a] Solvents:
  I. Acetone:water:HCl = 87:5:8 v/v.
  II. Pyridine:water (v/v):KCNS (w/v) = 79:20:1.
  III. Methylethyl ketone:HCl = 7:3 v/v.
  IV. Acetone:pyridine:water = 70:20:10 v/v.
  V. Ethyl ether:(dry)HCl:methanol = 90.5:2:7.5 v/v (w/v for HCl).
  VI. Butanol:methanol = 6:4 v/v.

20. *Ethanol:methanol:1.94 N HNO₃* = 3:7:10 for Se^{+6} (R_f 0.92), Se^{+4} (0.79), Te^{+6} (0.00), and Te^{+4} (0.67) (Veselý, 1955).

4. SPECIAL TECHNIQUES

This section is confined to special techniques of paper chromatography and does not include other methods of separating inorganic ions, like electrochromatography, developed by Strain (1951) and others.

a. Inorganic Capillary Analysis. Porous paper impregnated with $Al(OH)_3$ is used as adsorbent (Flood, 1949). The impregnation is carried out by dipping the paper in a solution of sodium aluminate (0.1–1.0 mole/liter). The paper is then dried, and $Al(OH)_3$ is formed by dipping the paper into a saturated solution of $NaHCO_3$. The paper is washed for several days in distilled water, dried over a period of some days, and finally cut into strips.

The solution is sucked up in one end of the strip to a height of 1–3 cm. The paper is then treated with water until a height of 10 cm. or more is wetted. Two or three times the length of the adsorption zone is sufficient to give a constant length of zone. During the passage of water, the adsorption zone does not leave the lower end of the paper. Finally, the chromatographic zones are visualized by brushing with suitable reagents.

The following sequence of adsorption is found for cations:

H^+ Sn^{4+} Sb^{+++} TiO^{++} Bi^{+++}	Sn^{++} As^{++}	Fe^{+++} Cr^{+++} Hg^{++}	UO^{++}	Pb^{++}	VO^{++} Al^{+++}

Ag^+	Cu^{++}	Zn^{++}	Cd^{++}	Ca^{++} Ni^{++} Fe^{++}	Tl^+	Mn^{++}.

The sequence of anion adsorption is:

OH^-	PO_4^{---} F^-	$Fe(CN)_6^{4-}$ SO_4^{--}	CrO_4^{--}	$Fe(CN)_6^{---}$	Ac^-	CNS^- Cl^- I^-	NO_3^- ClO_4^-.

The zone length, h, is a linear function of the concentration, c, of the ion in solution. For cations of the same valency, decreasing adsorption tendency seems to run parallel with increasing molar zone lengths. Increasing valency increases the molar zone length.

If we add to a solution of M_1 a less strongly adsorbable cation M_2, an elongation of the chromatographic zone of M_1 is observed. The reason is that a mixed zone of M_1 and M_2 is formed. The relative elongation h/h_0 is a function of the concentration ratio M_1/M_2 in solution. The tendency to form a mixed zone increases with decreasing difference in adsorption affinity. Only when the difference in adsorption tendency is considerable will the zone length of a cation be apparently independent of the presence of other cations.

Flood has shown that it is possible to separate cations by using complex-forming reagents, since electrically neutral molecules or negatively charged complex ions show a negligible adsorption tendency on paper not previously treated with acid. If an excess of sodium glycinate is added to a solution of Cu and Zn or Co or Cd, the Cu forms a more stable complex and is completely separated from the other cation. Ni-Co mixtures can be readily separated, as well as Co-Cd and Ag-Cu mixtures.

b. Chromatography on Modified Paper. Whatman No. 1 paper, impregnated with substituted 8-quinolinols, is used for the separation of a number of cations as their chlorides (Fernando, 1953). Twenty microliters of a solution containing 1 mg./ml. of each constituent is applied to the paper which is developed with ethanol for 16–20 hours. The position of the spots is revealed by the color or fluorescence produced under ultraviolet light. Table III lists the R_f values of several cations chromatographed on paper, saturated with various substituted 8-quinolinols.

2-Thenoyltrifluoroacetone-metal-chelates are separated on Whatman No. 1 paper impregnated with NaCl or Al_2O_3 (Berg, 1954, 1955). The chelates are prepared by adding a 10 % ethanolic solution of TTFA to a hot solution of the cations dissolved in buffered sodium acetate (pH 7.5). The developing solvent is benzene:methanol:acetic acid = 68:30:2 for NaCl-paper. Fe and Cu complexes are colored. Mn is detected by streaking the paper first with 0.05 N NaOH and then benzidine (0.05 g. benzidine·HCl in 10 ml. acetic acid, made up to 100 ml. with water). A blue color results. Co is detected with a 1 % aqueous Na_2S spray (black). Ni is detected with 1 % alcoholic dimethylglyoxime, containing a trace of ammonia.

TABLE III

R_f VALUES OF CATIONS ON 8-QUINOLINOL-IMPREGNATED PAPER (FERNANDO, 1953)

(Solvent:ethanol)

	8-Quinolinol-						
Cation	8-Quino-linol	2-CH$_3$	3-CH$_3$	4-CH$_3$	2-C$_6$H$_5$	2-styryl	5-sulfonic acid
Fe^{+++}	0.98	0.89	0.93	0.92	0.10	0.18	0
Co^{++}	0.95	0	0.92	0.91	0.92	0.10	0
Ni^{++}	0.76	0.90	0.91	0.91	0.91	0.10	0.05
Cu^{++}	0	0	0	0	0.84	0	0
Cd^{++}	0	0	0	0	0.12	0.05	0
Zn^{++}	0.05	0.07	0.08	0.05	0.79	0.06	0.05
Al^{+++}	0.94	0.73	0.92	0.84	0	0	0.06
Bi^{+++}	0.63	0.71	0.90	0.37	0.15	0.40	0

Diphenylthiocarbazones ("dithizones") are separated on Whatman No. 1 impregnated with diphthalate buffer, pH3 (50 ml. of 0.1 M potassium diphthalate, 20.32 ml. 0.1 N HCl, made up to 100 ml. with water) (Venturello, 1954). The chelates are prepared by reacting the metal nitrates with 1.5 % dithizone solution in chloroform and evaporating the solution. Methanol is used as developing solvent.

Filter paper may be impregnated with salts, e.g., NaCl, KNO_3, and NH_4NO_3. The developing solvent must contain the common anion of this salt for optimum results (Lederer, 1952c). Table IV shows a comparison of R_f values of a number of cations chromatographed on plain and impregnated paper.

c. *Circular Paper Chromatography.* A number of cations may be separated by circular filter paper chromatography (Rutter technique), experimental details of which are described in Chapter III. One advantage of this method over the ascending or descending chromatography is its short time development. Whatman No. 41 12.5 cm. filter paper disks are used and only require $1\frac{1}{2}$ hours' development for fair separation (E. C. Martin, 1951) (see Table V). The solvent used contains thiocyanic acid which forms complexes with many cations. The preparation of the solvent is as follows: 50 g. of KCNS is dissolved in 50 ml. of water. The solution is filtered, and 100 ml. of n-butanol is added. 9.5 ml. of concentrated H_2SO_4 is added dropwise, and the precipitated K_2SO_4 is removed by careful decantation. The filtered butanol-rich layer is used.

The cations are spotted as nitrates; each spot contains 50 μg. of each component. After development, the chromatogram is exposed to NH_3 and H_2S vapors.

The Rutter technique has also been applied to the separation and quantitative estimation of aluminum alloys (Venturello, 1952). Whatman No. 1 12.5 cm. filter paper disks and 1-butanol:2 N HCl v/v are employed. The cations are detected by specific sprays, e.g., dimethylglyoxime for Al, dithizone for Zn and Pb, and Cupron for Fe and Cu (see Section 6). Good resolution is achieved for Cu, Fe, Ni, Zn, and Pb. The widths of the bands are measured densitometrically and are found to be proportional to log concentration (see Chapter IV). Comparison between spectroscopic analysis and paper chromatography reveals less than 4.5 % variation.

Airan (1953) has separated Co, Ni, and Cu by this technique using methyl ethyl ketone: concentrated HCl = 75:25 as solvent. Other examples of circular inorganic chromatography are cited by Tewari (1954a), Murthy (1955), and Barnabas (1955). Excellent resolution is obtained with ethanol:methanol (v/v) for the cations Mg, Ca, Sr, and Ba.

d. *Gradient Elution Analysis* (Lederer, 1953b). A novel technique has been developed for the separation of Hg, Cd, Bi, Fe, Ni, Cu, and Co. A

TABLE IVa

R_f VALUES OF CATIONS ON PLAIN AND IMPREGNATED PAPERS (LEDERER, 1952c)

(Solvent:n-butanol:N HCl)

Cation	Paper not impregnated	Paper impregnated with N NaCl
Ag^+	0.0	0.0
Pb^{++}	0.0 tail	0.04
Hg^{++}	0.79	0.36
Cu^{++}	0.09	0.13
Cd^{++}	0.61	0.23
Bi^{+++}	0.59	0.09
Sb^{+++}	0.70 tail	0.70
Fe^{+++}	0.19	0.74
Co^{++}	0.08	0.09
Ni^{++}	0.08	0.08
Mn^{++}	0.11	0.07
MoO_4^{--}	0.32	0.62
Ti^{4+}	0.08	0.04
V^{5+}	0.22 tail	0.39 tail
UO_2^{++}	0.15	0.39
Ba^{++}	0.01	0.01
Rh^{+++}	0.15	0.06
Pd^{++}	0.65	0.07
Pt^{4+}	0.07	0.22
Ru^{6+}	0.14	0.04
Au^{+++}	0.82	1.0

TABLE IVb

R_f VALUES OF CATIONS ON PLAIN AND IMPREGNATED PAPERS (LEDERER, 1952c)

(Solvent:n-butanol:1.5 N HNO$_3$)

Cation	Paper not impregnated	Paper impregnated with KNO$_3$	Paper impregnated with NH$_4$NO$_3$
UO_2^{++}	0.30	0.50	0.74
Fe^{+++}	0.05	0.06	0.12
Cu^{++}	0.05	0.08	0.07
Co^{++}	0.07	0.07	0.07

large jar (30 cm. high) is used as the chromatographic chamber for ascending chromatography. 1-Butanol saturated with N HCl is placed at the bottom of the jar and is agitated by means of a magnetic stirrer. The spotted filter paper, rolled into a cylinder, is placed into the tank, and concentrated HCl is added dropwise with a burette fitted through a hole in the cover. The rate of addition of HCl is in relation to the speed of development, i.e., 2-ml. portions per centimeter of solvent ascent for the first 11 cm. Then the rate of addition is increased to 4 ml./cm. ascent.

TABLE V

R_f Values of Cations Separated by Circular Paper Chromatography
(E. C. Martin, 1951; Venturello, 1952)

Cation	(n-Butanol:HCNS)	(n-Butanol:2 N HCl v/v)
Fe^{+++}	1.00	0.37
Ni^{++}	0.42	0.34
Co^{++}	1.00	—
Cr^{+++}	0.23	—
Cu^{++}	1.00	0.37
Cd^{++}	1.00	—
As^{+++}	0.54	—
Sb^{+++}	0.96	—
Bi^{+++}	0.96	—
Hg^{++}	1.00	—
Pb^{++}	—	0.48
Ag^+	1.00	—
Zn^{++}		0.87

The cations are detected on the paper by spraying it with $(NH_4)_2S$. One disadvantage of the gradient elution analysis of this mixture is the formation of "comets" by Fe^{+++}.

e. "Rear-Phase Chromatography" (Pollard, 1955b). This technique which is described in Chapter III, has been applied to the separation of thionic acids. Some chromatographic solvents separate into acidic and basic zones during development, and, for this reason, the actual chromatography of the spots is delayed until the phase boundary has reached a desirable distance from the starting point. This technique allows the sample to be spotted after the phase boundary has been established, without removing the paper from the tank.

The solvent for the separation of thionic acids is *tert*-butanol:acetone: water = 15:65:20 plus 0.5 g. anhydrous potassium acetate and several drops of bromocresol purple-phenol red indicators. The dye is a marker for the phase boundary. The paper is allowed to equilibrate for ten hours, the phase boundary is established in 24 hours, and the actual chromatographic period lasts 15 hours. The following distances, measured from the origin, are obtained under these conditions: $S_2O_3^{--}$ 2.3–3.8 cm.; $S_3O_6^{--}$ 9.5–11.1 cm.; $S_5O_6^{--}$ 14.4–16.0 cm.; $S_4O_6^{--}$ 12.1–14.3 cm.; $S_6O_6^{--}$ 16.9–19.7 cm. (see Fig. 2, p. 437)

5. Preparation of Samples

In general, cation mixtures should be made up as chlorides or nitrates, since salts of these anions are usually soluble and show little tendency to hydrolyze. Burstall (1950) used solutions of the chlorides except for the separation of Se and Te, and Th, Sc, and the rare earths, in which case the metals were dissolved in dilute HNO_3 . For almost all the separations he carried out, Pollard (1951) used mixtures of the cations present as nitrates.

To prepare an unknown mixture for chromatography, a 2 % solution of the unknown is made either by dissolving the solid in distilled water and then slightly acidifying it with one or two drops of 2 N HNO_3 , or a few milliliters of 2 N HNO_3 or 50 % HNO_3 and diluting the product to the necessary concentration with distilled water. The pH should be adjusted to about 1. If the unknown mixture will not completely dissolve in the above solvents, then the insoluble portion can be removed by centrifuging and treated separately, while the soluble portion is analyzed in the usual manner (Pollard, 1951). Burstall (1950) prepared his solutions by dissolving the chlorides of the metals in aqueous HCl.

In the analysis of anion mixtures, solutions may be prepared using Na or K salts or the free acids.

To resolve a mixture of the noble metals, Lederer (1948) dissolved the mixture or alloy in aqua regia, added an equal volume of water, and applied a drop of the resulting solution to the filter paper.

Reeves (1951) formed complexes of Ag, Al, Ni, Co, Cu, Bi, Zn, Cd, Hg, and Fe with 8-hydroxyquinoline and submitted the resulting mixture to chromatography. He dissolved the metal salts in 0.1 N acetic acid or in an acetic acid:sodium acetate buffer solution and added a 4 % solution of 8-hydroxyquinoline in ethanol in slight excess. The solutions were heated gently (50–70°C.) for 5–10 minutes, and then filtered. Excess reagent was removed from the precipitates by washing with hot water.

The thiocyanate complexes of Fe, Co, V, and Cu are separated with pyridine or ether as solvents (Beck, 1953).

6. Detection of Cations (See Tables VIa, VIb and VII)

Many of the color reagents for the detection of inorganic ions are adaptations of spot tests found in Feigl's book (1956), and the reader may refer to this reference for additional reagents which this space does not permit to enumerate.

1. *Hydrogen sulfide.* A spray of ammoniacal aqueous H_2S will reveal as colored sulfides the following cations: Ag^+, Hg^+, Hg^{++}, Pb^{++}, Bi^{+++}, Cu^{++}, Cd^{++}, As^{+++}, Sb^{+++}, Fe^{+++}, Co^{++}, and Ni^{++} (LeStrange, 1954). Aqueous solutions of yellow ammonium sulfide or sodium sulfide may also be used (Kertes, 1956; Heros, 1955).

2. *8-Hydroxyquinoline*, alcoholic solution, followed by exposure to NH_3 (Sommer, 1955). The following metal ions are detected by their yellow fluorescence in ultraviolet light: Mg, Ca, Sr, Ba, Be, Al, Zr, Sn, Cd, and Zn. The following ions are detected as dark spots: Mn, Ni, Co, Fe, Bi, Cu, Cr, Th, U, Ti, Hg, and Pb.

TABLE VIa
COLORS OF SPOTS WITH BENZIDINE REAGENT (H. MILLER, 1952)

Compound	Color
Cerium ammonium sulfate	Brown
Cobalt acetate	Red
Cobalt nitrate	Gray
Ferric chloride	Brown
Nitric acid	Brown
Potassium dichromate	Brown, gray[a]
Potassium ferricyanide	Blue
Potassium periodate	Brown
Potassium permanganate	Brown
Phosphoric acid	Brown
Silver nitrate	Brown, purple
Sulfuric acid	Brown
Uranium acetate	Brown

[a] Double spots with 1-butanol:acetic acid: $H_2O = 4:1:5$.

TABLE VIb
COLOR REAGENTS FOR INORGANIC IONS (CARLESON, 1954)

Ion	Reagent	Special Conditions
Cu, Co, Ni	Saturated rubeanic acid in ethanol	$+NH_3$
Zn, Tl^{+3}, Hg, Mn, Cr	1% Diphenylcarbazide in ethanol	
Cd, Tl, As^{+3}	15% Dithizone in $CHCl_3$	$+NH_3$
Ag, Hg	0.03% Dimethylaminobenzal-rhodanin in ethanol	$+NH_3$
Au	0.5% p,p'-Tetramethyldi-aminodiphenylmethane in 5% citric acid	
Ca, Sn, Sb^{+5}, BO_3^-, Zr, Y, Pr, Th, Ti	0.1% Alizarin in ethanol	$+NH_3$
Be, Ga, Al, La, Fe	0.1% Aluminon in ethanol	$+NH_3$
Mg	0.01% Quinalizarin in ethanol	$+NH_3$
As^{+5}, Pd, Sb^{+5}	α,α'-Dipyridyliodide	
Pd, Pt, Bi^{+3}	Cinchoniniodide	
Ti	5% Aqueous chromotropic acid	
Sb^{+3}, Sn^{+2}	5% Aqueous phosphomolybdic acid	
Ce^{+3}, VO_4^{-3}, VO^{+2}, MoO_4^{-2}, WO_4^{-2}	5% Pyrogallol in ethanol	
Ir, CrO_4, MnO_4, $Cr^{+3}(H_2O_2)$	NH_3, then 2% o-toluidine	
Cs, Rb, K	Dipicrylamine	
Li, Na	0.1 M Aqueous violuric acid	
UO_2^{+2}	$K_4Fe(CN)_6$	$+NH_3$

TABLE VII

R_f VALUES AND COLOR OF SPOTS FOR ALKALI AND ALKALI EARTH METALS
(ERLENMEYER, 1951)

(96% Ethanol: 2 N acetic acid = 8:2)

Cation	Color with violuric acid	R_f
Li	Red-violet	0.76
Na	Violet-bright red	0.56
K	Violet	0.45
Be	Yellow-green	0.86
Mg	Yellow-pink	0.76
Ca	Orange	0.68
Sr	Red-violet	0.55
Ba	Light red	0.43

Another spray is prepared by dissolving 5 g. of 8-hydroxyquinoline and 1 g. of kojic acid in 1 liter of 60% ethanol. After spraying, the paper is exposed to NH_3 (Pollard, 1951).

3. *Dithizone* is prepared by dissolving 1–2 mg. of dithizone in 100 ml. of CCl_4. Using this reagent, Burstall (1950) obtained the following colored zones: Hg, pink; Cd, purple; Bi, purple; Cu, purplish brown; Pb, weak red; As, yellow; Sn, purple; Sb, red.

4. *Ammoniacal quinalizarin* may be prepared by dissolving 0.05 g. of quinalizarin in 100 ml. of 0.1 N NaOH and holding the strip over NH_3. Be gives a blue zone, Cr a red one, and the rare earths give blue colors (Lederer, 1949d).

5. *Rubeanic acid:benzidine* is prepared by mixing equal volumes of a 0.25% solution of rubeanic acid in alcohol and 1% benzidine in 10% aqueous acetic acid. The following colors are produced on spraying: Ni, blue; Mn, pale blue; Co, yellow; Cu, gray-green (Lewis, 1951).

6. *Sodium rhodizonate* (5% in water) is also used as a color reagent. Brownish red spots are produced with Ba and Sr. Pb forms a violet spot (Pollard, 1951). The paper must be neutral (Sommer, 1955).

7. *Stannous chloride* is prepared in a dilute acid solution. This reagent reduces the following to the metals to locate the spots: Pt, Pd, Au, Rh, Te, and Se (Burstall, 1950).

8. *Potassium ferrocyanide* is prepared as a dilute aqueous solution. Prussian blue color is produced with Fe^{+++}. Cu and U produce brown spots. Zn can be detected as a white spot on a reddish background (Pollard, 1951; Lederer, 1949d).

9. *Benzidine* is prepared by dissolving 0.05 g. of benzidine base or hydrochloride in 10 ml. of acetic acid, diluting to 100 ml. with water, and filter-

ing. This base can be converted by a number of oxidizing reagents into a blue product. The following cations may be detected: Au^{+++}; Tl^{+++}; chromium after conversion to chromate; Mn^{4+}, after first spraying paper with dilute alkali and then heating; Ce^{+++}.

A wide variety of inorganic compounds gives colored spots when the chromatogram, after being sprayed with the benzidine reagent, is heated at 85°C. for 30 minutes (H. Miller, 1952) (see Table VIa).

10. *Detection of K, Rb, Cs* (Beerstecher, 1950; C. C. Miller, 1951). 11.4 g. of hydrated cobalt acetate, 16.2 g. of hydrated lead (II) acetate, 20 g. of sodium nitrite, and 2 ml. of glacial acetic acid are dissolved in 150 ml. of water. This solution, mixed with 25 % methanol, is used as spraying reagent, and the resultant yellow background is bleached by washing the paper with cold water.

11. *Detection of Na and Li* (Pollard, 1951; C. C. Miller, 1951). The chromatogram is sprayed with an aqueous solution of *Zn uranyl acetate* and 25 % methanol. Na and Li are viewed in ultraviolet light.

12. *Violuric acid reagent.* 0.1 M aqueous solution of violuric acid (5-isonitrosobarbituric acid) is a fairly specific spraying reagent for the alkali and alkali-earth metal cations (Erlenmeyer, 1951) (see Table VII). However, Co^{++} produces a green-yellow and Cu^{++} a yellow-brown spot with this reagent (von Hahn, 1951).

13. *Aluminon reagent* (Quentin, 1953). 1 g. of Aluminon and 1 g. of ammonium acetate are dissolved in 100 ml. of water. The chromatogram is sprayed with this reagent and exposed to ammonia vapors. The reagent is specific for Al.

14. *Detection of thallium* (Diller, 1953). The chromatogram is sprayed with a 10 % aqueous solution of KI to which a small amount of NH_4OH has been added. Yellow spots result for Tl; sensitivity for this reagent is 0.03 μg.

Spraying the paper with 5 % *thioglycolic acid-β-aminonaphthalid* in acetone and subsequent exposure to NH_3 vapors result in yellow spots for Tl. Viewing the spots in ultraviolet light results in a black quenching effect. The sensitivity of this reaction is 0.5 μg.

15. *Detection of rare earths.* The rare earths, as well as Al, Fe, Ca, Th, and Sc, may be detected with an aqueous or alcoholic solution of *alizarin* (Lederer, 1949d, 1953a). The dried paper is placed in an atmosphere of NH_3 for 10 minutes and then sprayed with an alcoholic solution of alizarin followed by 1 N acetic acid. Th and Sc are detected as violet-blue spots. The rare earths give a similar color as thorium, but a redder tint is obtained with scandium (Burstall, 1950).

16. *Detection of Sn^{++}* (Anderson, 1953). A newly developed spraying reagent for Sn^{++} is 2 % aqueous *6-nitro-2-naphthylamine-8-sulfonic acid.*

Sn^{++} when viewed under ultraviolet light gives an intense blue fluorescence; this reagent is specific for Sn^{++}.

17. *Miscellaneous reagents.* *1.2% Dimethylglyoxime* in ethanol for Ni^{++}; *1.2% Cupron* in ethanol for Fe and Cu (Venturello, 1952).

18. *Potassium iodide* (0.2%), aqueous, as a spraying reagent gives the following colored spots: Hg—red, yellow; Bi—brown, yellow; Sb—brown; Cu—brown. Arsenic shows up as a brown spot after the paper has been sprayed with concentrated HCl (Pfeil, 1955).

19. *Quercetin* (0.2%), alcoholic, followed by concentrated NH_4OH, causes the following colors to form: Cu—gray-brown; Hg—gray; Ag—black-brown. These ions appear as dark violet spots in ultraviolet light (Weiss, 1954).

20. *Detection of germanium* (Ladenbauer, 1954). The paper is sprayed with 0.05% phenylfluorone in ethanol:concentrated HCl = 75:25. The preparation of phenylfluorone (9-phenyl-2,3,7-trihydroxy-6-fluorone) is as follows:

Eight g. of benzaldehyde and 20 g. of hydroquinone are dissolved in 200 ml. of ethanol. Thirty-two g. of H_2SO_4 in 160 ml. of water are added, and the solution is warmed for 5–6 hours on a water bath. On cooling, the sulfate precipitates. The mixture is made slightly basic (red color), then acidified with several drops of H_2SO_4, warmed, and diluted with water. The free base separates and is washed with hot water; 35% yield.

21. *Pyrocatechol* (0.05%) ethanolic solution is used as a dipping reagent and gives a blue-purple spot on a yellow background for the following ions: Al, Fe, Sb, Bi, Th, Zr, V, Cr, Mo, W; sensitivity—0.1 μg. (Macek, 1956).

22. *Hematoxylin* (0.2%), ethanolic; must be made up fresh before use. The following cations have been tested with this spraying reagent to give red-blue colors: Fe, Zn, Mn, Co, Ca, Pb, Cd, Cu, and Ag (Hood, 1957).

23. *Successive Spraying Technique.* In the separation of complex inorganic mixtures, the investigator will undoubtedly find that one color reagent will not produce the most satisfactory spots for all ions involved. If ions are very far apart on the completed chromatogram, it is often possible to treat one half of the strip with one reagent and the other half with another. Usually, the best procedure is to run at least four identical chromatograms at a time. Then, suitable reagents may be used on each strip to locate the desired spots.

An example of the above procedure may be shown by the work of Pollard (1951). A mixture containing Ag, Pb, Ni, Cu, Sb, and Ba on three separate paper strips was chromatographed with butanol-benzoylacetone solvent. After drying, one strip was treated with potassium chromate and then with H_2S gas. Pb and Ag formed yellow and red zones, respectively. The same strip was held over NH_3, and the Ag spot faded. On spraying with rhodizonic acid and then dilute HCl, Ba formed a red zone, Pb a violet zone, and Ag a red zone. The second strip was treated with rubeanic acid and then held over NH_3. Ni produced a blue zone, and Cu an olive-green one. The third strip was sprayed with ammonium sulfide, treated with concentrated HCl to dissolve the sulfides, and then sprayed with phosphomolybdic acid. Sb produced a royal blue zone.

7. DETECTION OF ANIONS

a. Halides and Thiocyanate. After resolving a mixture containing Cl^-, I^-, Br^-, and SCN^-, Lederer (1949a) and Ando (1952) detected the spots in the following way: First, the paper is sprayed with a mixture of 0.1 N *ferric nitrate* and 3 % H_2O_2, which reveals SCN^- as a red spot and I^- as a blue one; next, the whole paper is sprayed with 0.1 N $AgNO_3$ which discolors the spots originally formed and precipitates all four ions as insoluble silver salts within the filter paper. The paper is then washed with dilute HNO_3 to remove excess Ag ions and held over H_2S. Black AgS is formed wherever silver halides have been precipitated.

An alternate procedure is as follows (Mitchell, 1955):

Solution A: 170 mg. of $AgNO_3$ (85 mg. for dilute solutions of halides), 1 ml. water, 5 ml. NH_4OH, diluted to 200 ml. with ethanol.

Solution B: (fresh) 13 mg. pyrogallol in 200 ml. ethanol.

Procedure: The chromatogram is sprayed with Solution A and then Solution B.

b. Phosphates. The detection of inorganic phosphates is a modification of Hanes-Isherwood's (1949) established procedure for the detection of sugar phosphates (Ando, 1952). The chromatogram is first sprayed with a 0.4 % w/v solution of ammonium molybdate in 8 % HNO_3 and is heated at moderate temperatures (80°C.) for 5–10 minutes. The dried paper is next sprayed with 0.05 % benzidine in 10 % acetic acid and then exposed to NH_3 vapors. Meta- and orthophosphates result in blue spots; the color for pyrophosphate is purplish red.

Instead of benzidine, $SnCl_2$ solution may be substituted as the reducing spray (Westman, 1952; Bonnin, 1952). The stock solution is composed of 10 g. of $SnCl_2$ in 25 ml. of concentrated HCl. The spraying solution consists of 1 ml. of stock solution and 200 ml. of N H_2SO_4. The chromatogram is next hung in an atmosphere of H_2S.

Crowther (1954) substitutes ultraviolet irradiation for the reducing solution, resulting in deep-blue spots for the phosphates. Silicic acid may also be detected by spraying the paper with $(NH_4)_2MoO_4$ (pH 1.5) and keeping it in a moist atmosphere overnight. For highly condensed acids, the chromatogram is first sprayed with NaOH or Na_2CO_3 for prior hydrolysis (Baumann, 1956).

c. Diphenylamine (Servigne, 1956). Diphenylamine in concentrated H_3PO_4 detects *bromate* and *iodate* ions (blue-green). Diphenylamine in concentrated HCl results in an indigo-blue spot for chlorate ion.

d. Miscellaneous. Nitrate, sulfate, and oxalate may be revealed as red spots by universal indicator. Ammoniacal silver nitrate (0.1 N) may be used to detect arsenite and phosphate as yellow spots. A mixture of KI and HCl may be used to detect nitrite, bromate, iodate, and periodate as red zones. Fluoride may be detected by spraying with $Fe(SCN)_3$. Its position is revealed as a white spot on a red background (Lederer, 1949*b*).

e. Sulfates. The chromatogram is first sprayed with a $BaCl_2$ solution (100 mg. $BaCl_2$ in 50 ml. of 70 % ethanol). The paper is then sprayed with a *sodium rhodizonate* solution (10 mg. sodium rhodizonate in 20 ml. of 50 % ethanol). Sulfates result in yellow spots on a reddish background (Burma, 1953).

8. QUANTITATIVE ESTIMATION

a. Elution Methods. A number of successful techniques for the quantitative estimation of inorganic ions separated by paper chromatography consist of the elution of spots and subsequent microanalyses (see Lacourt, 1956, for a review). Some applications of elution analysis are briefly described below:

1. *Aluminum.* One milliliter of a fresh 0.2 % w/v solution of Aluminon and 1.0 ml. of ammonium buffer (pH 4.7) are added to the eluate. The color is read after 15 minutes at 520 mμ (Lacourt, 1952).

2. *Fe, Ti.* One milliliter of a fresh aqueous solution of 4 % w/v "Tiron" and 5 ml. of sodium acetate buffer (pH 4.7) are added to the eluate. The optical density is determined for Ti at 410 mμ and for Fe at 560 mμ. The reported error is ± 2 % (Lacourt, 1952).

3. *Cadmium.* The spot containing Cd is eluted with boiling 1 % HCl and the eluate is digested with $HClO_4$. Cd is then determined by polarography (Davies, 1951).

4. *Chromium.* The Cr spot or band is eluted with 2 N H_2SO_4 oxidized with 0.1 N $KMnO_4$, and the excess $KMnO_4$ decomposed with $NaNO_2$. The Cr color is then developed with 1 % ethanolic diphenylcarbazide and read at 540 mμ in a spectrophotometer at 0.02 mm. slit width (Lacourt, 1954*a*).

5. *Cobalt and Tungsten.* Cobalt is eluted from the paper and titrated with standardized $Pb(NO_3)_2$. Tungsten is determined by the toluene-dithiol method in the Beckman spectrophotometer at 630 mμ (Lacourt, 1953, 1954*b*).

6. *Phosphate* (Koberlein, 1955). Condensed phosphates are eluted from

the paper, ashed, hydrolyzed with 10 % H_2SO_4, and the color developed with molybdic acid-$SnCl_2$ is read at 278 mμ.

7. *Miscellaneous Ions.* Au, Cu, and PO_4^{-3} have been determined by microtechniques after elution from the chromatogram. (Anderson, 1951; Kember, 1951; Lewis, 1951; Westman, 1952).

b. *Reflectance Method* (Vaeck, 1953, 1954). This method for the quantitative determination of nickel in microgram quantities warrants a detailed description, as it represents one of the first reported techniques employing the reflectance measurements of colored spots on a chromatogram. Most of the other direct quantitative estimations involve the measurement of area or color density of the spots (see Chapter IV) (see LeStrange, 1954, for reflectance densitometer).

1. *Requirements for highest accuracy.* (*i*) The substance must be evenly distributed over the entire surface of the spot. (*ii*) Chromatographic technique must separate all interfering ions. (*iii*) The color development must be one of high sensitivity and stability. (*iv*) An accurate measurement of the reflectance from a constant area of the spot must be possible.

2. *Chromatographic technique.* The sample, containing 1-25 mg. of Ni, is dissolved in 3 N HCl and is spotted on Whatman No. 1 paper with a total volume of 45 μl. from a 0.2-ml. micropipette. Three standards (3, 10, and 20 mg. per 100 ml.) and two unknowns are spotted. The filter paper (23 $\times$ 23 cm.) is fastened at two edges with cotton thread in the form of a cylinder and is developed by the ascending technique. The solvents are acetone:25 % HCl:acetylacetone = 90:10:2 or acetone:6 N HCl = 90:10 v/v. The development is allowed to proceed for 2 hours; Ni in both solvents has an R_f of 0.03.

The paper is dried for 30 minutes each at room temperature and at 50–60°C. in an oven. The paper is then neutralized by exposure to NH_3 vapors. It is then sprayed on both sides with a freshly prepared reagent composed of 0.05 % rubeanic acid in ethanol containing 5 % v/v concentrated NH_4OH. Ni produces blue spots which are stable for over a month.

3. *Color measurements.* Reflectance measurements are carried out with the reflectance attachment to the Beckman spectrophotometer, Model DU. An additional requirement is that the illuminated surface must be smaller than the colored spot.

A 27-mm. circle is drawn with a pencil around the spot, which is then cut out. The circle is placed in one compartment of the diffuse reflectance attachment, and a blank paper spot of the same size is placed in the second compartment. Reflectance is read at 625 mμ (minimum reflectance) and 0.5-mm. slit width. A background of eight layers of Whatman No. 1 is used. A standard curve should be constructed each time from spots developed on the same chromatogram. A plot of K/S (see below) versus concentration yields a straight line. The precision of the Ni determination by this technique is ±3 %.

4. *Theory.* The method of reflectance measurement is based on the Kubelka-Munk law:

$$R_\infty = 1 + \frac{K}{S} - \left[\left(1 + \frac{K}{S}\right)^2 - 1\right]^{\frac{1}{2}}, \tag{1}$$

where R_∞ = monochromatic reflectance of material of infinite thickness.

K = absorption coefficient (incident energy lost by absorption).

S = scattering coefficient (incident energy lost by scattering).

Expanding and rewriting equation 1:

$$\frac{K}{S} \approx kc = \left[\frac{(1 - R_\infty)^2}{2R_\infty}\right]_{total} - \left[\frac{(1 - R_\infty)^2}{2R_\infty}\right]_{paper}, \tag{2}$$

where c = amount of dye present.

Reflectance measurements of chromatograms cannot follow the Kubelka-Munk law exactly, because the readings are against a paper blank and the material is not opaque. However, a plot of K/S versus concentration yields a straight line between the limits 3–20 mg. of Ni per 100 ml. K/S values are obtained from D. B. Judd, *Color in Business, Science, and Industry*, John Wiley and Sons, New York, 1952.

c. Direct Transmission Density Methods. Quantitative estimation may be made by the techniques described in detail in Chapter IV, by comparing the color density of unknowns with that of standard mixtures directly on the filter paper (Beerstecher, 1950; Venturello, 1952).

1. *Determination of Cobalt* (Vaeck, 1955).

Principle: The colored spots are scanned on the chromatogram; the height or area of the curves is plotted against "concentration."

Chromatographic Solvent: Acetone (fresh):*n*-butanol:25 % HCl:acetylacetone = 56:30:12:2.

Spraying Solution: 0.03 % Ethanolic solution of rubeanic acid plus 5 % concentrated NH_4OH.

Standards: 0.1 % Co from $CoCl_2 \cdot 6H_2O$ in 6 N HCl. 10 μl. spots to contain 0.4, 0.8, 1.2, 1.6, and 2.0 μg. Co^{++}.

Unknown Sample: The unknown is dissolved in HNO_3, taken to dryness, and redissolved in 3 N HCl.

Procedure: Whatman No. 1 paper, 23 × 23 cm. is used. Four unknown and 4 standards are spotted 5 cm. from the edge at right angles to the machine direction. The chromatogram is developed by the ascending cylinder technique (see Chapter III), after the paper has been humidified for one hour at 65 % relative humidity. The development takes $2\frac{1}{2}$

hours. The paper is dried, exposed to NH_3, sprayed with rubeanic acid. The paper is cut into 2 cm. wide strips which are then scanned with a Photovolt Densitometer or in a Beckman spectrophotometer at 422 mμ. The areas are measured with a planimeter. The accuracy is 5 % for alloys containing 0.2 % Co.

2. *Direct Photometry of Circular Chromatograms* (Bergami, 1954). The following ions are separated by circular chromatography with the solvent composed of 0.5 g. benzoylacetone, 50 ml. *n*-butanol, and 50 ml. 0.1 *N* HNO_3:Pb, Ag, Cu, Cd, Co, Ni, Te. The zones are visualized with spraying reagents listed in "Detection of Cations." The filter paper is made transparent by treating it with paraffin oil: α-Br-naphthalene, and transmission density readings are taken every millimeter. Optical density is plotted against concentration, and by a comparison with standards, the concentration of unknowns may be estimated.

3. *Estimation of Cobalt and Copper* (Lacourt, 1955). Brief mention is made of this technique in which the colored zones are cut out and mounted between the wall of the spectrophotometric cell and a glass adapter which is wetted with a few drops of water to eliminate gas bubbles. This method is more laborious than the two previously described.

Experimental Details

The R_f tables in this chapter indicate what separations are possible by developing inorganic mixtures in one direction using one solvent. However, if after solvent development the paper is dried and developed with a second solvent in the *same* direction, improved separations are often possible. An example of this technique is the resolution of a mixture containing Al, Bi, and Fe. In butanol:benzoylacetone solvent, Fe has a high R_f value but Al and Bi remain together at the starting point. If the paper is then dried and developed with dioxane:antipyrine solvent, Bi moves and separates from the Al. The R_f values after movement are Fe, 0.95; Bi, 0.6; and Al, 0.06. It is apparent from the R_f table that neither solvent will give such a good separation. It should be possible to apply this one way-two solvent procedure to many separations (Pollard, 1951).

Two-dimensional chromatograms are of great value in improving separations. Pollard (1951) has analyzed many cation mixtures by using collidine as the first solvent and butanol:benzoylacetone as the second solvent. The position of the cations after movement are usually in accordance with the prediction from their movements in the two separate solvent mixtures.

Although the purpose of this chapter has been to suggest general procedures for the analysis of any mixture, there are special separations which may best be considered individually. A number of these are summarized in Table VIII and illustrated in Fig. 2.

TABLE VIII

EXAMPLES FOR THE SEPARATION OF INORGANIC IONS

	Mixture	R_f	Solvent	Color reagent	Remarks	Reference
1	Cd	0.24	1-Butanol:0.1 N NH$_4$OH: collidine = 5:4:1 v/v			Pollard, 1951
	Zn	0.06				
2	Th	0.03	1-Butanol:N HNO$_3$ v/v plus 0.5% benzoylacetone		Separated as nitrates	Pollard, 1951
	V	0.27				
3	Ca	0.93	(1) Pyridine:KCNS = 96:4 w/v	Ca–Na rhodizonate		Arden, 1948
	Sr	0.61	(2) Pyridine:water:KCNS = 79:20:1	Sr–Na rhodizonate		Burstall, 1950
	Ba	0.48	(3) Isopropanol:water:6 N HCl = 4:3:3	Ba–alizarin		Surak, 1953
4	K	0.07	1-Butanol:N HNO$_3$ = v/v plus 1% acetylacetone			Pollard, 1951
	Ti	0.55				
	V	0.17				
	Mo	0.63				
	Fe	0.40				
5	Cu	0.37	1-Butanol:2 N HCl = v/v	Cu–Cupron–green	Circular paper chromatography	Venturello, 1952
	Fe	0.37		Fe–Cupron–yellow		
	Ni	0.34		Ni–dimethylglyoxime–red		
	Zn	0.87		Zn–dithizone–violet		
	Pb	0.48		Pb–dithizone–pink		

	Ions	R_f	Solvent	Reagent	Notes	Reference
6	Au Pt Pd	1.0 0 0	Ether saturated with HCl		Descending—Au drips off strip	Anderson, 1951
7	Cu, Ag, Au, Pt, Rh, Hg, Bi	Cu-1.0; all others-0	1-Butanol saturated with 2 N NH₄OH and dimethylglyoxime	Gravimetric microanalysis	Descending—Cu drips off strip	Anderson, 1951
8	Al Ti Fe	0.07-0.20 0.26-0.47 0.90-1.0	Amyl alcohol:benzene:conc. HCl = 6:1:3 v/v	Aluminon Tiron Tiron		Lacourt, 1952
9	SiO_3, BO_3, MoO_4		Conc. HCl:acetone = 5:95; tank saturated with conc. HCl:butanone-2 = 5:95			Lacourt, 1951
10	Ag Pb	0.5-0.9 0.1	1-Butanol:pyridine:H_2O = 10:1:2			Harasawa, 1951
11	Fe, Al, Be	1.0	Methyl ethyl ketone:conc. HCl = 85:15	8-Hydroxyquinoline	Ca, Mg ions interfere	Rao, 1953
12	Sb^{5+} Sn^{4+}	0 0.7	1-Butanol:HCl:H_2O = 100:4:20		Sb^{+++} and Sn^{++} are separated with water being replaced by 3% H_2O_2	Harasawa, 1951
13	Cu Co[a]	0.64, 0.51, 0.46, 0.40	1-Butanol:acetic acid:ethyl acetoacetate:H_2O = 10:5:2:15	Violuric acid		v. Hahn, 1951

TABLE VIII—*Continued*

Mixture	R_f	Solvent	Color reagent	Remarks	Reference
14　Ni Co Mn Fe Zn		Acetone:conc. HCl = 100:5	Dimethylglyoxime Dimethylglyoxime Dimethylglyoxime $K_4Fe(CN)_6$ Dithizone		Oka, 1951
15　La Ce Pr Nd Sm Eu Gd Dy Ho Er Yb Ac Y Sc	0.31 0.38 0.38 0.22 0.47 0.49 0.43 0.62 0.56 0.60 0.59 0.08 0.59 0.97	1-Butanol:acetylacetone:acetic acid:water = 100:30:5:65	Aqueous alizarin	Rare earths precipitated as hydroxides and dissolved in N acetic acid	Lederer, 1953a
16　Pb As Hg Cu Zn Tl	0 0.68 0.71 0.82 0.84 0.35	Methanol:25% H_2SO_4:H_2O = 7:1:4	10% KI or thioglycolic acid-β-aminonaphthalid		Diller, 1953

17	Ni, Ba, Sr, Ca, Al Mn Mg Co Zn Fe	0 0.67 0.15 0.69 0.90 1.0	Acetone:ethyl acetate:H_2O: conc. HCl = 45:45:5:5	Aluminon and Morin for Al		Quentin, 1953
18	Al Zn	0.38	tert-Butanol:water = 70:30 adjusted to pH 3 with HCl	Aluminon Dithizone		Surak, 1953
19	Fe Co Mn Ni	1.00 0.33 0.11 0.05	Acetone:6 N HCl:water = 87:8:5	$K_4Fe(CN)_6$ and 0.2% nitroso-β-naphthol 0.05% benzidine 1.0% dimethylglyoxime		Surak, 1953
20	K Ti V Mo Fe	0.07 0.55 0.17 0.63 0.40	1-Butanol:N HNO_3 v/v plus 1% acetylacetone			Pollard, 1951
21	Te Se	0.05 0.5	1-Butanol:abs. methanol = 6:4 v/v	$SnCl_2$:Te-black Se-orange		Burstall, 1950
22	U		Tetrahydrosylvane:HNO_3 saturated with water		SO_4 and PO_4 interfere	Lewis, 1951
23	Al Ga In Zn		1-Butanol:saturated with 3 N HCl	Aluminon Aluminon Dithizone Dithizone		

TABLE VIII (*continued*)

	Mixture	R_f	Solvent	Color reagent	Remarks	Reference
24	Sn Fe Mo	0.93 0.60 0.5	n-Butanol, sat. with 3 N HCl	0.5% Alizarin in ethanol Sn-red; Fe-yellow; Mo-purple	Descending development; separated as chlorides	Kolier, 1954
25	Ba Sr Ca Mg Be	0.05–0.14 0.17–0.27 0.44–0.51 0.55–0.64 0.78–0.93	Methanol:n-butanol:s-collidine:6N acetic acid = 4:2:2:2	8-Hydroxyquinoline: Ca-green; Mg-yellow; Be-yellow. Sodium rhodizonate for Ba and Sr.	Suitable for semi quantitative work	Magee, 1955

a Co produces triple spots.

1. SEPARATION OF LI, NA, K (Burma, 1953)

The alkali metals have been separated as sulfates or citrates, using 70 % ethanol as solvent. The spots on the chromatogram may be detected as follows:

a. Sulfates. The chromatogram is first sprayed with a $BaCl_2$ solution (100 mg. of $BaCl_2$ in 50 ml. of 70 % ethanol). The paper is then sprayed with a *sodium rhodizonate* solution (10 mg. of sodium rhodizonate in 20 ml. of 50 % ethanol). Sulfates result in yellow spots on a reddish background.

b. Citrates. The dry chromatogram is sprayed with an indicator solution composed of 50 mg. of bromphenol blue and 200 mg. of citric acid dissolved in 100 ml. of 70 % ethanol. The alkali citrates give blue spots on an orange-yellow background.

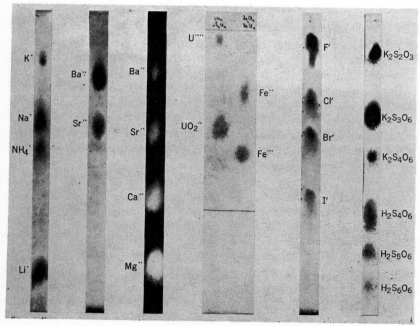

FIG. 2. Separation of inorganic ions by paper chromatography (Pollard, 1954b): (from left to right) (1) solvent, *methanol : n-butanol* = 7:3, (2) solvent, *methanol : iso-propanol : formic acid : water* = 50:30:2:15 plus 2.5 g. ammonium formate; spraying reagent; sodium rhodizonate; (3) solvent, same as (2); spraying reagent:8-hydroxy-quinoline + NH₃— viewed in ultra violet light; (4) solvent, *ether : methanol : concen-trated HCl : water* = 50:30:4:15; spraying reagents: *left—NH₃* , then $K_3Fe(CN)_6$; *right*—8-hydroxyquinoline, NH₃ , ultra violet light; (5) solvent, *n-butanol : pyridine : water : NH₄OH* = 4:2:saturated:1 (organic phase-upper layer); (6) solvent, *iso-propanol : acetone : water* = 5:2:3 plus 2 g. potassium acetate; spraying procedure: silver nitrate, warmed, "hypo dip".

K, Rb, Cs, and NH$_4$ ions have also been separated with phenol saturated with 20 % v/v HCl (Steel, 1954). Whatman No. 4 filter paper and the descending technique are employed. A mixture containing 50 μg. of each material is streaked on the paper.

The alkali metals are detected by spraying the chromatogram with 10 % aqueous *cobaltinitrite* in 5 % acetic acid, followed by a water wash of 2–3 minutes. The cations appear as yellow spots; sensitivity is 5 μg. The color reaction is rendered more sensitive with a second spraying reagent, 0.1 % alcoholic α-nitroso-β-naphthol, made alkaline with dilute NaOH. Brown spots on a green background result. The R_f values of the alkali metals are K, 0.19; Rb, 0.27; Cs, 0.43; NH$_4$, 0.11.

Table IX lists the R_f values of the alkali sulfates and citrates.

2. SEPARATION OF U, TH, PR (Sarma, 1949–1951)

The chlorides of U, Th, and Pr are dissolved in water and are chromatographed by the descending technique on Whatman No. 1 filter paper strips with one of the following solvents: (1) isobutanol:saturated with 4 N HCl; (2) ether:HNO$_3$ = 9:1 v/v.

After development, the strips are sprayed with 1 % aqueous ferrocyanide; U shows up as a brown spot. When the same paper is exposed to ammonia vapors and sprayed with 1 % alcoholic alizarin, Th is revealed by a violet color, and Pr as bluish violet. After a spray of 1 N acetic acid the color due to the rare earths diminishes. The following R_f values are observed:

	(1)	(2)
U	0.31	0.82
Th	0.09	0.44
Pr	0.02	0.00

3. SEPARATION OF INORGANIC PHOSPHATES (Karl-Kroupa, 1956; Grunze, 1954; Gauthier, 1955)

a. Paper. Untreated Whatman No. 30 or Schleicher and Schuell 589, orange ribbon, may be used for the chromatography of phosphates. Schleicher and Schuell 2040a is washed with dilute HCl and water. Whatman Nos. 1 and 4 may be washed with 8-hydroxyquinoline.

b. Solvents. 1. *Dioxane:isopropanol:water* = 15:5:10 plus 0.5 g. boric acid adjusted to pH 7.2 with NaOH.

2. *Isopropanol:trichloroacetic acid.* Isopropanol:water = 75:25 + 5 g. trichloroacetic acid + 0.3 ml. 20 % NH$_3$. Another combination of this solvent is; isopropanol:water:20 % aq. trichloroacetic acid:25 % NH$_3$ = 70:10:20:0.3.

3. *Isopropanol:isobutanol:water:25 % NH$_3$* = 40:20:39:1.

4. *Isobutanol:ethanol:water:25 % NH$_3$* = 30:30:39:1.

c. *Detection*. The modified Hanes-Isherwood reagent is composed of 5 ml. 60% $HClO_4$, 1 ml. concentrated HCl, 1 g. ammonium heptamolybdate·4 H_2O, diluted to 100 ml. with water. The sprayed chromatograms are exposed to ultraviolet light for color development.

d. *Structural Analysis*. For Solvents 1 and 2 the expression P_K is directly proportional to the number of P atoms. The following equations have been developed:

$$P_K = \frac{\text{Distance of substance}}{\text{Distance of } PO_4^{---}} \times 100 \qquad (3)$$

$$\log P_K = -kn, \qquad (4)$$

where k = constant and n = number of P atoms

e. *Quantitative Estimation* (Crowther, 1954). Spots containing phosphates are eluted with 0.1 N NH_4OH and hydrolyzed with N H_2SO_4. One ml. of 12.5% ammonium molybdate and 1 ml. of 0.6% hydrazine·HCl are added to the hydrolyzate, and the developed color is read in a suitable photometer at 830 mμ.

4. SEPARATION OF HALOGENS (Ando, 1952; Mitchell, 1955)

For the identification of halides in organic compounds, the following procedure is recommended: The organic halogen compound is decomposed by sodium fusion, and the resulting NaOH solution is spotted on filter paper, containing no traces of chloride. The solvent giving best separations is 1-butanol:picoline:water = 1:1:0.8 v/v. Ascending chromatography is used. For the detection of the halides, the paper is first sprayed with 0.2 N aqueous silver nitrate. The excess silver nitrate is washed off with 0.1 N HNO_3, and the chromatogram is finally sprayed with 0.2 N H_2S or exposed to H_2S vapors. The R_f values obtained are Cl^-, 0.19; Br^-, 0.27; I^-, 0.56. The solvent 2-methoxyethanol (Cellosolve):NH_4OH = 95:5 will resolve Cl^-, Br^-, I^-, F^- and also the cations K^+ and Na^+.

5. CHROMATOGRAPHY OF ACETYLACETONE METAL CHELATES (Berg, 1955)

a. *Preparation of Chelates*. A solution of Co, Cu, and Ni salts is adjusted to pH 7 with sodium acetate and shaken with acetylacetone. The Ni-chelate is extracted with *n*-butanol, and the extract is washed with water to remove any unreacted Ni. Co- and Cu-chelates are extracted with methyl isopropyl ketone and washed with water.

Alternately, 60 ml. of 2% Co, Cu, and Ni nitrates are treated with 20 ml. 3% H_2O_2 and heated on a steam bath for 15 minutes. The pH is adjusted to 7, and 20 ml. of acetylacetone:ethanol (v/v) is added. The mixture is heated for a few minutes and treated with 50 ml. of methyl isopropyl ketone-*n*-butanol (v/v) on a steam bath for 30 minutes. After several hours the green organic layer is spotted on paper for chromatography.

b. Chromatography of Acetylacetone-Metal Complexes. A solution of the mixed complexes is spotted on Whatman No. 1 paper and dried in air for one hour. The paper is developed with cyclohexane:dioxane:methanol = 84:10:6. Cu and Co are detected with 0.3% ethanolic dithiooxamide and NH_3 vapor, while Ni is detected with 1% ethanolic dimethylglyoxime and NH_3. The R_f values are Co—0.88, Cu—0.57, and Ni—0.01.

Similar results are achieved with the metal complexes (Fe, Cu, Ni, Co, Mn) of 2-thenoylperfluorobutyrylmethane and 2-furoylperfluorobutyrylmethane. The solvents for these chelates are mixtures of petroleum ether, methanol, and dioxane (Berg, 1955).

6. CHROMATOGRAPHY OF MOLYBDENUM (V AND VI) (Candela, 1956)

Whatman No. 1 is soaked for one hour in 2 *N* HCl and washed with glass-distilled water 20 times. $MoCl_6$ and $Mo(CNS)_5$ solutions are separated with water:acetic acid = 10:1, plus 10 g. KCNS. The spots are detected by exposure of the paper to HCl fumes. The R_f values are Mo^{+6}—0.35 and Mo^{+5}—0.85. For quantitative estimation the areas containing Mo are cut out and disintegrated by shaking with 30 ml. 10% KCNS in 2 *N* HCl. This is heated at 40–45°C. for 10 minutes, cooled, shaken with 10 ml. ethyl acetate, and the emulsion is broken by centrifugation. The extracted color is read in a photometer.

Molybdenum oxinates, prepared from 8-hydroxyquinoline, may be resolved with ethanol as solvent (Stevens, 1956*a*).

7. CHROMATOGRAPHY OF IRON (II AND III) (Stevens, 1956*b*)

Acid-washed Whatman No. 1 and *n*-butanol:ethanol:acetic acid:water = 40:25:25:35 are used after an overnight equilibration. The iron salts are adjusted to pH 4 prior to chromatography. Development time (descending) is 2–3 hours. For the detection of Fe, the paper is exposed to water vapor containing a small quantity of oxine. Fe forms green-black spots with the following R_f values: Fe^{+2}—0.25 and Fe^{+3}—0.85.

8. ESTIMATION OF ARSENIC BY CHROMATOGRAPHY (Elbeigh, 1955)

Descending chromatography on Whatman No. 1 paper is employed. The solvent consists of 1 g. ammonium borate, 1 g. ammonium tartrate, 0.5 g. mannitol, all dissolved in 50 ml. of water. This solution is mixed with 50 ml. of *n*-butanol, shaken, the organic layer used for development, and the water phase for equilibration of the tank.

Standard solution of $NaAsO_3$ are chromatographed along with the unknown sample. The color development of the chromatogram is as follows: *Solution A:* 5% glycerol in ethanol, containing 1% HNO_3. *Solution B:* 5% aqueous $AgNO_3$ to which is added concentrated NH_4OH with stirring until the original precipitate has redissolved.

Color Development: The paper is sprayed with Solution A and after drying with Solution B. After irradiation with ultraviolet light, brown spots, due to $AgAsO_4$, appear whose color density can be read directly on the paper with a densitometer.

TABLE IX

R_f VALUES OF ALKALI SULFATES AND CITRATES (BURMA, 1953)

(70% ethanol)

Substance	R_f
Li_2SO_4	0.58
Na_2SO_4	0.41
K_2SO_4	0.21
Li citrate	0.59
Na citrate	0.41
K citrate	0.29

TABLE X

R_f VALUES OF INORGANIC PHOSPHATES

	Solvent[a]				
	1	2	3[b]	4	5
Monophosphate (ortho)	0.14	0.21	1.0	0.69	0.73
Di-	—	—	—	0.44	0.53
Tri-	—	—	0.37	0.29	0.39
Tetra-	—	—	—	0.17	0.29
Penta-	—	—	—	0.11	0.22
Hexa-	—	—	—	0.07	0.16
Hepta-	—	—	—	0.04	0.11
Octa-	—	—	—	—	0.08
Trimeta-	—	—	0.60	0.20	0.32
Tetrameta-	—	—	0.89	0.08	0.18
Pyro-	—	0.15	0.49	—	—
Hypophosphite	0.61	—	—	—	—
Phosphite	0.22	—	—	—	—
Metaphosphate	—	0	—	—	—

[a] Solvents: 1. *n*-Butanol:dioxane:N NH_4OH = 1:1:1 v/v (Bonnin, 1952).
  2. *n*-Butanol:acetic acid:water = 4:1:5 v/v (Ando, 1952).
  3. *n*-Propanol:water:NH_4OH (sp. gr. 0.90) = 6:1:3 v/v (Westman, 1952).
  4. Isopropanol:water = 75:25 + 5 g. trichloroacetic acid + 0.3 ml. 20% NH_3 (Grunze, 1953).
  5. Isopropanol:water:20% aq. TCA:25% NH_3 = 70:10:20:0.3 (Grunze, 1953).
[b] R_f values for solvents are based on the R_f of PO_4^{-3} = 1.

9. DETECTION OF MOISTURE IN ALCOHOL (Stringer, 1951)

An application of "capillary analysis" may not properly be included in a book on paper chromatography. However, the technique is novel and may be cited in this chapter on inorganic separations.

A strip of paper is impregnated, in two bands, with $K_3Fe(CN)_6$ and below it, $FeSO_4$. Alcohol is allowed to ascend, and the ferrous sulfate, thus eluted by any water which may be present is carried to the upper zone to give a blue color. The method can detect as little as 0.1 % moisture in alcohol.

Bibliography for Part I

Abdel-Akher, M., and Smith, F. [1951]. *J. Am. Chem. Soc.* **73**, 5859-5860.
Acher, R., Fromageot, C., and Jutisz, M. [1950]. *Biochim. et Biophys. Acta* **5**, 81-88.
Acher, R., and Crocker, C. [1952]. *Biochim. et Biophys. Acta* **9**, 704-705.
Acher, R., and Laurila, U. R. [1953]. *Bull. soc. chim. biol.* **35**, 413-418.
Acker, L., Diemair, W., Pfeil, D., and Schiffner, G. [1955]. *Z. anal. Chem.* **148**, 10-14.
Ackerman, B. J., and Cassidy, H. G. [1954]. *Anal Chem.* **26**, 1874-1876.
Ackermann, R., and Ackermann, D. [1955]. *Z. physiol. Chem.* **300**, 92-96.
Acland, J. D. [1952]. *Nature* **170**, 32-33.
Adams, H. W., and Stuart, R. G. [1951]. *Analyst* **76**, 553.
Ågren, G., and Nilsson, T. [1949]. *Acta Chem. Scand.* **3**, 525-538.
Airan, J. W. [1953a]. *Current Sci. (India)* **22**, 51.
Airan, J. W. [1953b]. *J. Univ. Bombay* **A21**, 5-8.
Airan, J. W., and Barnabas, J. [1953c]. *Sci. and Culture (Calcutta)* **18**, 438.
Airan, J. W., Joshi, G. V., Barnabas, J., and Master, R. W. P. [1953d]. *Anal. Chem.* **25**, 659-660.
Akabori, S., Ohno, K., and Narita, K. [1952]. *Bull. Chem. Soc. Japan* **25**, 214-218; from [1954]. *Chem. Abstr.* **48**, 1468.
Åkerfeldt, S. [1954]. *Acta Chem. Scand.* **8**, 521-522.
Albanese, A. A., and Lein, M. [1949]. *Science* **110**, 163-164.
Albon, N., and Gross, D. [1952]. *Analyst* **77**, 410-412.
Albright, E. C., Larson, F. C., and Deiss, W. P. [1953]. *Proc. Soc. Exptl. Biol. Med.* **84**, 240-244.
Alcock, M., and Cannell, J. S. [1956]. *Nature* **177**, 327-328.
Algeri, E. J., and Walker, J. T. [1952]. *Am. J. Clin. Pathol.* **22**, 37-40.
Algeri, E. J., and McBay, A. J. [1953]. *Am. J. Clin. Pathol.* **23**, 654-660.
Allgén, L. G. [1953]. *Svensk Farm. Tidskr.* **57**, 188-190; from [1953] *Chem. Abstr.* **47**, 7017.
Allgén, L. G. [1954]. *Acta Chem. Scand.* **8**, 1101.
Allouf, R., and Munier, R. [1952]. *Bull. soc. chim. biol.* **34**, 196-203.
Altmann, S. M., Crook, E. M., and Datta, S. P. [1951]. *Biochem. J.* **49**, lxiii.
Ambe, K. S., Kulkarni, L., and Sohonie, K. [1954]. *J. Sci. Ind. Research (India)* **13B**, 380-382.
Amber-Hi-Lites [Jan. 1953]. Rohm and Haas Co., Philadelphia, Pennsylvania.
Amelung, D., and Böhm, P. [1954]. *Z. physiol. Chem.* **298**, 199-209.
Ames, B. N., and Mitchell, H. K. [1952]. *J. Am. Chem. Soc.* **74**, 252-253.
Aminoff, D., and Morgan, W. T. J. [1948]. *Nature* **162**, 579-580.
Andersch, M. A. [1953]. *Federation Proc.* **12**, 168.
Anderson, J. R. A., and Lederer, M. [1951]. *Anal. Chim. Acta* **5**, 321-324.
Anderson, J. R. A., and Garnett, J. L. [1953a]. *Anal. Chim. Acta* **8**, 393-396.
Anderson, J. R. A., and Martin, E. C. [1953b]. *Anal. Chim. Acta* **8**, 530-537.
Ando, T., Ito, J., Ishii, S., and Soda, T. [1952a]. *Bull. Chem. Soc. Japan* **25**, 78-79; from [1953] *Chem. Abstr.* **47**, 9860.
Ando, T., and Shinichi, I. [1952b]. *Bull. Chem. Soc. Japan* **25**, 106-109; from [1953] *Chem. Abstr.* **47**, 1538.
Anet, E. F. L. J., and Reynolds, T. M. [1953]. *Nature* **172**, 1188-1189.

Anet, E. F. L. J., and Reynolds, T. M. [1954]. *Nature* **174,** 930.

Ansell, G. B., and Richter, D. [1954]. *Biochem. J.* **57,** 70–73.

Arden, T. V., Burstall, F. H., Davies, G. R., Lewis, J. A., and Linstead, R. P. [1948]. *Nature* **162,** 691–692.

Armstrong, M. D., and Robinson, K. S. [1954]. *Arch. Biochem. Biophys.* **52,** 287.

Armstrong, M. D., Shaw, K. N. F., and Wall, P. E. [1956]. *J. Biol. Chem.* **218,** 293–303.

Aronoff, S., and Vernon, L. [1950]. *Arch. Biochem.* **28,** 424–439.

Aronoff, S. [1956]. "Techniques of Radiobiochemistry." Iowa State College Press, Ames, Iowa.

Arroyave, G., and Axelrod, L. R. [1954]. *J. Biol. Chem.* **208,** 579–589.

Aschan, O. [1884]. *Ber.* **17,** 421.

Ashley, B. D., and Westphal, U. [1955]. *Arch. Biochem. Biophys.* **56,** 1–10.

Asimov, I. [1955]. *Astounding Sci. Fiction* **56** (September), 112–123.

Aso, K., Shibasaki, K., Matsuda, K., and Yamauchi, F. [1951]. *J. Fermentation Technol. (Japan)* **29,** 74–77; from [1953] *Chem. Abstr.* **47,** 1864.

Asquith, R. S. [1951]. *Nature* **168,** 738–739.

Asselineau, J., Choucroun, N., and Lederer, E. [1950]. *Biochim. et Biophys. Acta* **5,** 197–203.

Asselineau, J. [1952]. *Bull. soc. chim. France* pp. 884–891.

Astrup, T., Stage, A., and Olsen, E. [1951]. *Acta Chem. Scand.* **5,** 1343–1348.

Atkin, L., Schultz, A. S., Williams, W. L., and Frey, C. N. [1943]. *Ind. Eng. Chem., Anal. Ed.* **15,** 141–144.

Atkinson, H. F. [1948]. *Nature* **162,** 858.

Auclair, J. L., and Dubreuil, R. [1952]. *Can. J. Zool.* **30,** 109–113.

Augustinsson, K. B., and Grahn, M. [1953]. *Acta Chem. Scand.* **7,** 906–912.

Awapara, J. [1948]. *Arch. Biochem.* **19,** 172–173.

Awapara, J. [1949]. *J. Biol. Chem.* **178,** 113–116.

Awapara, J., Landua, A. J., and Fuerst, R. [1950]. *J. Biol. Chem.* **183,** 545–548.

Axelrod, L. R. [1953a]. *J. Biol. Chem.* **201,** 59–69.

Axelrod, L. R. [1953b]. *J. Biol. Chem.* **205,** 173–184.

Axelrod, L. R. [1953c]. *J. Am. Chem. Soc.* **75,** 4074–4075.

Ayers, C. W. [1953]. *Analyst* **78,** 382–383.

Azouz, W. M., Parke, D. V., and Williams, R. T. [1953]. *Biochem. J.* **55,** 146–151.

Azouz, W. M., Parke, D. V., and Williams, R. T. [1955]. *Biochem. J.* **59,** 410–415.

Baar, S., and Bull, J. P. [1953]. *Nature* **172,** 414–415.

Baar, S. [1954]. *Biochem. J.* **58,** 175–176.

Bacon, E. E., and Bacon, J. S. D. [1954]. *Biochem. J.* **58,** 398–402.

Bacon, J. S. D., and Edelman, J. [1951]. *Biochem. J.* **48,** 114–126.

Baddiley, J., Cantoni, G. L., and Jamieson, G. A. [1953]. *J. Chem. Soc.* pp. 2662–2664.

Baddiley, J., Buchanan, J. G., Carss, B. Mathias, A. P., and Sanderson, A. R. [1956]. *Biochem. J.* **64,** 599–603.

Baker, R. G. [1953]. *Biochem. J.* **54,** xxxix.

Baker, W., Harborne, J. B., and Ollis, W. D. [1952]. *J. Chem. Soc.* pp. 3215–3217.

Baldridge, R. C., and Lewis, H. B. [1953]. *J. Biol. Chem.* **202,** 169–176.

Balinga, B. R., Krishnamurthy, K., Rajagopalan, R., and Giri, K. V. [1955]. *J. Indian Inst. Sci.* **37A,** 18–22.

Balston, J. N., and Talbot, B. E. [1952]. "A Guide to Filter Paper and Cellulose Powder Chromatography," 145 pp. H. Reeve Angel, London.

Bandursky, R. S., and Axelrod, B. [1951]. *J. Biol. Chem.* **193**, 405–410.

Bangham, D. R. [1956]. *Biochem. J.* **62**, 550–51.

Banigan, T. F., Jr. [1953]. *Science* **117**, 249–250.

Barber, G. A. [1956]. *Arch. Biochem. Biophys.* **64**, 401–11.

Barnabas, J. [1954]. *Naturwissenschaften* **41**, 453–454.

Barnabas, J. [1955a]. *Naturwissenschaften* **42**, 153.

Barnabas, J., and Joshi, D. V. [1955b]. *Anal. Chem.* **27**, 443–444.

Barnabas, T., Badve, M. G., and Barnabas, J. [1954]. *Naturwissenschaften* **41**, 478–479.

Barnabas, T., Badve, M. G., and Barnabas, J. [1955]. *Anal. Chim. Acta* **12**, 542–543.

Barieto, R. C. R. [1955]. *Rev. Quim. ind. (Rio de Janeiro)* **274**, 13, 17; from [1956] *Chem. Abstr.* **50**, 1963.

Barrett, J. [1956]. *Biochem.* **64**, 626–639.

Barrollier, J. [1955]. *Naturwissenschaften* **42**, 486.

Barrollier, J., Heilman, J., and Watzke, E. [1956]. *Z. physiol. Chem.* **304**, 21–25.

Bartlett, J. K., Hough, L., and Jones, J. K. N. [1951]. *Chem. & Ind.* (London) p. 76.

Bartley, W. [1954]. *Biochem.* **56**, 379–387.

Barton, G. M., Evans, R. S., and Gardner, J. A. F. [1952]. *Nature* **170**, 249–250.

Bate-Smith, E. C. [1948]. *Nature* **161**, 835–838.

Bate-Smith, E. C. [1949]. *Biochem. Soc. Symposia (Cambridge, Engl.)* **3**, 62.

Bate-Smith, E. C., and Westall, R. G. (1950). *Biochim. et Biophys. Acta* **4**, 427–440.

Bate-Smith, E. C. [1954]. *Biochem. J.* **58**, 123–132.

Baudet, J. [1952]. *Compt. rend.* **234**, 2454–2456.

Bauer, L. [1952]. *Naturwissenschaften* **39**, 88.

Baumann, H. [1956]. *Naturwissenschaften* **43**, 300–331.

Bayly, R. J., Bourne, E. J., and Stacey M. [1951]. *Nature* **168**, 510–511.

Bayly, R. J., and Bourne, E. J. [1953]. *Nature* **171**, 385–387.

Bealing, F. J., and Bacon, J. S. D. [1953]. *Biochem. J.* **53**, 277–285.

Beck, M. T. [1953]. *Acta Chim. Acad. Sci. Hung.* **3**, 187–189; from [1953] *Chem. Abstr.* **47**, 12095.

Beck, M. T., and Ébrey, P. [1954]. *Acta Chim. Acad. Sci. Hung.* **4**, 231–233.

Becker, E. [1954]. *Z. Lebensm.-Untersuch. u.-Forsch.* **98**, 249–257.

Beerstecher, E., Jr. [1950]. *Anal. Chem.* **22**, 1200–1202.

Benassi, C. A. [1951]. *Boll. soc. ital. biol. sper.* **27**, 420–421.

Benesch, R., Benesch, R. E., Gutcho, M., and Laufer, L. [1956]. *Science* **123**, 981.

Bennet-Clark, T. A., Tambiah, M. S., and Kefford, N. P. [1952]. *Nature* **169**, 452–453.

Bennet-Clark, T. A., and Kefford, N. P. [1953]. *Nature* **171**, 645–647.

Benson, A. A., Bassham, J. A., Calvin, M., Goodale, T. C., Haas, V. A., and Stepka W. [1950]. *J. Am. Chem. Soc.* **72**, 1710–1718.

Benson, A. A., Bassham, J. A., Calvin, M., Hall, A. G., Hirsch, H. E., Kawaguchi., S., Lynch, V., and Tolbert, N. E. [1952]. *J. Biol. Chem.* **196**, 703–716.

Bentley, H. R., and Whitehead, J. K. [1950]. *Biochem. J.* **46**, 341–345.

Bentley, J. A., Farrar, K. R., Housley, S., Smith, G. F., and Taylor, W. C. [1956]. *Biochem. J.* **64**, 44–49.

Beran, M., and Šicho, V. [1951]. *Chem. listy* **45**, 154–156; from [1951] *Chem. Abstr.* **45**, 9589.

Berenblum, I., and Chain, E. [1938]. *Biochem. J.* **32**, 295–298.

Berg, E. W., and McIntyre, R. T. [1954]. *Anal. Chem.* **26**, 813–814.

Berg, E. W., and Strassner, J. E. [1955]. *Anal. Chem.* **27,** 127–129; **27,** 1131–1134.

Bergamini, C. [1953]. *Sperimentale, Sez. chim. biol.* **4,** 38–44; from [1954] *Chem. Abstr.* **48,** 6501.

Bergamini, C., and Versorese, W. [1954]. *Anal. Chim. Acta* **10,** 328–334.

Bergamini, C. and Rovai, A. [1956]. *Anal. Chim. Acta* **15,** 43–45.

Bergmann, F. [1952]. *Anal. Chem.* **24,** 1367–1369.

Bergmann, F., and Segal, R. [1956]. *Biochem. J.* **62,** 542–546.

Bergner, K. G., and Sperlich, H. [1953]. *Z. Lebensm.-Untersuch. u.-Forsch.* **97,** 253–263; from [1954] *Chem. Abstr.* **48,** 2273.

Berl, W. G., ed. [1951]. "Physical Methods in Chemical Analysis," Vol. II. Academic Press, New York.

Berlingozzi, S., Serchi, G., and Adembri, G. [1951]. *Sperimentale, Sez. chim. biol.* **2,** 89–94; from [1952] *Chem. Abstr.* **46,** 9070.

Berlingozzi, S., and Serchi, G. [1952a]. *Sperimentale, Sez. chim. biol.* **3,** 1–5; from [1952] *Chem. Abstr.* **46,** 10039f.

Berlingozzi, S., Serchi, G., Michi, P., and Rapi, G. [1952b]. *Sperimentale, Sez. chim. biol.* **3,** 45–95; from [1953] *Chem. Abstr.* **47,** 9916.

Berlingozzi, S., Rapi, G., and Monti, L. [1953]. *Sperimentale, Sez. chim. biol.* **4,** 27–37; from [1954] *Chem. Abstr.* **48,** 6323.

Bernasconi, R., Sigg, H. P., and Reichstein, T. [1955]. *Helv. Chim. Acta* **38,** 1767–1775.

Berridge, N. J., Newton, G. G. F., and Abraham, E. P. [1952]. *Biochem. J.* **52,** 529–535.

Berry, H. K., and Cain, L. [1949]. *Arch. Biochem.* **24,** 179–189.

Bersin, T., and Müller, A. [1952]. *Helv. Chim. Acta* **35,** 475–478.

Bertetti, J. [1953]. *Ann. Chim. (Rome)* **43,** 351–360.

Bertetti, J. [1954]. *Ann. chim. (Rome)* **44,** 495–499.

Berti, T., and Cima, L. [1954]. *Boll. ist. sieroterap. milan.* **33,** 643–647.

Bevan, T. H., Gregory, G. I., Malkin, T., and Poole, A. G. [1951]. *J. Chem. Soc.* 841–842.

Bevenue, A., and Williams, K. T. [1951]. *Arch. Biochem. Biophys.* **34,** 225–227.

Bevenue, A., and Williams, K. T. [1952]. *Chemist Analyst* **41,** 5–7.

Beyreder, J., and Rettenbacher-Däubner, H. [1953]. *Monatsh.* **84,** 99–101; from [1953] *Chem. Abstr.* **47,** 5475.

Bharucha, F. R., and Joshi, G. V. [1956]. *Naturwissenschaften* **43,** 327.

Bickel, H., and Souchon, F. [1955]. "Die Papierchromatographie in der Kinderheilkunde" (*Arch. Kinderheilk., Beih.* **31**). Enke, Stuttgart.

Bidwell, R. G. S., Krotkov, G., and Reed, G. B. [1952]. *Can. J. Botany* **30,** 291–305.

Bidwell, R. G. S., Krotkov, G., and Reed, G. B. [1954]. *Arch. Biochem. Biophys.* **48,** 72–83.

Bighi, C., and Trabanelli, G. [1955]. *Ann. chim. (Rome)* **45,** 109–114; **45,** 115–122.

Bina, K., and Kalamár, J. [1956]. *Naturwissenchaften* **43,** 36.

Binger, H. P., Sullivan, J. T., and Jensen, C. O. [1954]. *J. Agr. Food Chem.* **2,** 696–700.

Bird, R., and Hopkins, R. H. [1954]. *Biochem. J.* **56,** 86–99; **56,** 140–146.

Biserte, G., and Osteux, R. [1951]. *Bull. soc. chim. biol.* **33,** 50–63.

Bito, Y. [1956]. *J. Biochem. (Tokyo)* **43,** 523–529.

Black, R. A., Rosen, A. A., and Adams, S. L. [1953]. *J. Am. Chem. Soc.* **75,** 5344–5346.

Blackburn, S., and Robson, A. [1950]. *Chem. & Ind. (London)* pp. 614–615.

Blackburn, S., and Lowther, A. G. [1951]. *Biochem. J.* **48,** 126–128.

Blair, J. A., and Graham, J. [1954]. *Biochem. J.* **56**, 286–287.
Blake, G. G. [1955]. *Anal. Chim. Acta* **13**, 562–565.
Blake, G. G. [1956]. *Anal. Chim. Acta* **14**, 329–335; **15**, 232–236.
Bland, D. E. [1949]. *Nature* **164**, 1093.
Bleidner, W. E. [1954]. *J. Agr. Food Chem.* **2**, 682–684.
Block, R. J., Darrow, D. C. and Cary, M. K. [1934]. *J. Biol. Chem.* **105**, 455–461.
Block, R. J. [1946]. *Arch. Biochem.* **11**, 235–248.
Block, R. J. [1948]. *Science* **108**, 608–609.
Block, R. J. [1949]. *Proc. Soc. Exptl. Biol. Med.* **72**, 337–341.
Block, R. J. [1950]. *Anal. Chem.* **22**, 1327–1332.
Block, R. J. [1951*a*]. *Arch. Biochem. Biophys.* **31**, 266–272.
Block, R. J. [1951*b*]. *J. Dairy Sci.* **34**, 1–10.
Block, R. J., and Bolling, D. [1951*c*]. "The Amino Acid Composition of Proteins and Foods," 576 pp. C. C Thomas, Springfield, Illinois.
Block, R. J., and Van Dyke, H. B. [1952]. *Arch. Biochem. Biophys.* **36**, 1–4.
Block, R. J., and Weiss, K. W. [1956]. "Amino Acid Handbook," 386 pp. C. C Thomas, Springfield, Illinois.
Block, R. J., and Mandl, R. H. [1957]. *Contribs. Boyce Thompson Inst.* **18**, 477–482.
Blumer, M. [1956]. *Anal. Chem.* **28**, 1640–1644.
Bodánsky, A., and Kollonitsch, J. [1955]. *Nature* **175**, 729–730.
Bodansky, O. [1955]. *Ann. Rev. Biochem.* **24**, 627–652.
Bode, F., and Hübener, H. J. [1952*a*]. *Nature* **170**, 501.
Bode, F., Hübener, H. J., Brückner, H., and Hoeres, K. [1952*b*]. *Naturwissenschaften* **39**, 524–525.
Bode, F. [1955]. *Biochem. Z.* **326**, 433–435.
Böhm, P., and Richarz, G. [1954]. *Z. physiol. Chem.* **298**, 110–120.
Boggs, L., Cuendet, L. S., Ehrenthal, I., Koch, R., and Smith, F. [1950]. *Nature* **166**, 520–521.
Boggs, L. A. [1952]. *Anal. Chem.* **24**, 1673–1675.
Bogorad, L., and Granick, S. [1953]. *J. Biol. Chem.* **202**, 793–800.
Boissonnas, R. A. [1950]. *Helv. Chim. Acta* **33**, 1966–1982.
Boissonnas, R. A. [1952]. *Helv. Chim. Acta* **35**, 2226–2228.
Boldingh, J. [1948]. *Experientia* **4**, 270–271.
Boldingh, J. [1949]. *Discussions Faraday Soc.* **7**, 162.
Bolle-Jones, E. W. [1954]. *Nature* **173**, 127–128.
Bolling, D., Sober, H. A., and Block, R. J. [1949]. *Federation Proc.* **8**, 185.
Boman, H. G. [1952]. *Nature* **170**, 703–704.
Bonetti, E., and Dent, C. E. [1954]. *Biochem. J.* **57**, 77–81.
Bonetti, R. [1953]. *Giorn. biochem.* **2**, 410.
Bonino, G. B., and Carassiti, V. [1951]. *Nature* **167**, 569–570.
Bonnin, A., and Süe, P. [1952]. *Compt. rend.* **234**, 960–961.
Boone, I. U., Turney, D. F., and Woodward, K. T. [1954]. *Science* **120**, 312–314.
Booth, J., Boyland, E., and Manson, D. [1955]. *Biochem. J.* **60**, 62–71.
Boscott, R. J. [1951]. *Biochem. J.* **48**, xlvii–xlviii.
Boscott, R. J. [1952*a*]. *Abstr. 2nd Inter. Congr. Biochem., Paris* p. 349.
Boscott, R. J. [1952*b*]. *Chem. & Ind. (London)* pp. 472–473.
Boscott, R. J., and Kar, A. B. [1955]. *Nature* **176**, 1077–1078.
Boser, H. [1954]. *Z. physiol. Chem.* **296**, 10–18; **298**, 145–150.
Boulanger, P., and Montreuil, J. [1951*a*]. *Bull. soc. chim. biol.* **33**, 784–790.
Boulanger, P., and Biserte, G. [1951*b*]. *Bull. soc. chim. biol.* **33**, 1930–1939.
Boulanger, P., and Biserte, G. [1952*a*]. *Bull. soc. chim. France* pp. 830–844.

Boulanger, P., and Montreuil, J. [1952b]. *Bull. soc. chim. France* pp. 844–852.

Boulanger, P., Biserte, G., and Courtot, F. [1952c]. *Bull. soc. chim. biol.* **34**, 366–379.

Bourgain, L. [1956]. Private communication.

Bowden, C. H., and Maclagan, N. F. [1954]. *Biochem. J.* **56**, vii–viii.

Bowden, C. H., Maclagan, N. F., and Wilkinson, J. H. [1955]. *Biochem. J.* **59**, 93–97.

Boyarkin, A. N. [1956]. *Z. physiol. Chem.* **304**, 21–25.

Boyland, E., Manson, D., Solomon, J. B., and Wiltshire, G. H. [1953]. *Biochem. J.* **53**, 420–423.

Boyland, E., Sims, P., and Williams, D. C. [1956a]. *Biochem. J.* **62**, 546–550.

Boyland, E., and Solomon, J. B. [1956b]. *Biochem. J.* **63**, 679–683.

Brackett, J. W., Jr., and Bradford, L. W. [1952]. *J. Criminal Law, Criminol. Police Sci.* **43**, 530.

Bradbury, J. H. [1956]. *Nature* **178**, 912–913.

Bradfield, A. E., and Flood, A. E. [1950]. *Nature* **166**, 264–265.

Brady, R. O. [1951]. *J. Biol. Chem.* **193**, 145–148.

Brante, G. [1949]. *Nature* **163**, 651–652.

Brattsten, I., and Nilsson, A. [1951]. *Arkiv Kemi* **3**, 337–345.

Bray, H. G., Thorpe, W. V., and White, K. [1951a]. *Biochem. J.* **46**, 271–275.

Bray, H. G., Thorpe, W. V., and Wood, P. B. [1951b]. *Biochem. J.* **48**, 394–399.

Bray, H. G., Craddock, V. M., and Thorpe, W. V. [1955]. *Biochem. J.* **60**, 225–232.

Bray, H. G., James, S. P., and Thorpe, W. V. [1956]. *Biochem. J.* **64**, 38–44.

Bregoff, H. M., Roberts, E., and Delwiche, C. C. [1953]. *J. Biol. Chem.* **205**, 565–574.

Bremner, J. M., and Kenten, R. H. [1951]. *Biochem. J.* **49**, 651–655.

Breyhan, T. [1953]. *Naturwissenschaften* **40**, 271–272.

Bricas, E., and Fromageot, C. [1953]. *Advances in Protein Chem.* **8**, 1–125.

Bridges, R. G., Harrison, A., and Winteringham, F. P. W. [1956]. *Nature* **177**, 86.

Brimley, R. C., and Barrett, F. C. [1953]. "Practical Chromatography," 128 pp. Reinhold, New York.

Brockmann, H., and Musso, H. [1951]. *Naturwissenschaften* **38**, 11–12.

Brockmann, H., and Patt, P. [1953a]. *Naturwissenschaften* **40**, 221–222.

Brockmann, H., and Gröne, H. [1953b]. *Naturwissenschaften* **40**, 222–223.

Brockmann, H. Bohnsack, G., and Gröne, H. [1953c]. *Naturwissenschaften* **40**, 223–224.

Brossi, A., Häfliger, O., and Schnider, O. [1955]. *Arzneimittel-Forsch.* **5**, 62–66.

Brown, F., Hirst, E. L., Hough, L., Jones, J. K. N., and Wadman, H. [1948]. *Nature* **161**, 720.

Brown, F., and Hall, L. P. [1950a]. *Nature* **166**, 66–67.

Brown, F. [1950b]. *Biochem. J.* **47**, 598–600.

Brown, F. [1951a]. *Nature* **167**, 441.

Brown, F., and Blaxter, K. L. [1951b]. *Chem. & Ind. (London)* 633–634.

Brown, F. [1952a]. *Biochem. J.* **51**, 237–239.

Brown, F. [1952b]. *Biochem. J.* **52**, 523–526.

Brown, F. [1953a]. *Chem. & Ind. (London)* p. 174.

Brown, F. [1953b]. *J. Sci. Food Agr.* **4**, 161–165.

Brown, F., and Jackson, H. [1954]. *Biochem. J.* **56**, 399–406.

Brown, H. C., Johnson, H. S., and Podall, H. [1954]. *J. Am. Chem. Soc.* **76**, 5556–5557.

Brown, J. A., and March, M. M. [1952]. *Anal. Chem.* **24**, 1952–1956.

Brown, J. A. [1953a]. *Anal. Chem.* **25**, 774–777.

Brown, J. A., and Marsh, M. M. [1953b]. *Anal. Chem.* **25**, 1865–1869.

Brown, R., Johnson, A. W., Robinson, E., and Tyler, G. J. [1952]. *Biochem. J.* **50**, 596–600.

Brown, R. J. [1952]. *Anal. Chem.* **24**, 384–388.

Brown, W. G. [1939]. *Nature* **143**, 377–378.

Brüggemann, J., and Drepper, G. [1952]. *Naturwissenschaften* **39**, 301–302.

Bruschweiler, H., Minkoff, G. J., and Salooja, K. C. [1953]. *Nature* **172**, 909.

Bryant, F., and Overell, B. T. [1951]. *Nature* **168**, 167–168.

Bryant, F., and Overell, B. T. [1953]. *Biochim. et Biophys. Acta* **10**, 471–476.

Bryson, J. L., and Mitchell, T. J. [1951]. *Nature* **167**, 864.

Buch, M. L., Montgomery, R., and Porter, W. L. [1952]. *Anal. Chem.* **24**, 489–491.

Buchanan, J. G., Dekker, C. A., and Long, A. G. [1950]. *J. Chem. Soc.* pp. 3162–3167.

Buchanan, J. G. [1951]. *Nature* **168**, 1091.

Buchanan, J. G. [1953]. *Arch. Biochem. Biophys.* **44**, 140–149.

Bull, H. B., Hahn, J. W., and Baptist, V. H. [1949]. *J. Am. Chem. Soc.* **71**, 550–553.

Buras, E. M., and Hobart, S. R. [1955]. *Anal. Chem.* **27**, 1507–1508.

Burma, D. P. [1951]. *Nature* **168**, 565–566.

Burma, D. P. [1952]. *J. Indian Chem. Soc.* **29**, 567–572.

Burma, D. P. [1953a]. *Anal. Chem.* **25**, 549–553.

Burma, D. P. [1953b]. *Anal. Chim. Acta* **9**, 513–517.

Burma, D. P., and Chakrabortty, H. C. [1955]. *Anal. Chim. Acta* **13**, 248–252.

Burmistrov, S. I. [1946]. *Zhur. Anal. Khim.* **1**, 265–271; from [1949] *Chem. Abstr.* **43**, 5344.

Burrows, S., Grylls, F. S. M., and Harrison, J. S. [1952]. *Nature* **170**, 800–801.

Burstall, F. H., Davies, G. R., Linstead, R. P., and Wells, R. A. [1950]. *J. Chem. Soc.* pp. 516–528.

Burstall, F. H., and Wells, R. A. [1951]. *Analyst* **76**, 396–410.

Burton, H. S. [1954]. *Nature* **173**, 127.

Burton, R. B., Zaffaroni, A., and Keutmann, E. H. [1951]. *J. Biol. Chem.* **188**, 763–771.

Burton, R. M., and San Pietro, A. [1954]. *Arch. Biochem. Biophys.* **48**, 184–188.

Bush, I. E. [1950]. *Nature* **166**, 445–446.

Bush, I. E. [1952a]. *Biochem. J.* **50**, 370–378.

Bush, I. E., and Taylor, D. A. H. [1952b]. *Biochem. J.* **52**, 643–648.

Bush, I. E., and Sandberg, A. A. [1953]. *J. Biol. Chem.* **205**, 783–793.

Bush, I. E. [1954]. *Brit. Med. Bull.* **10**, 229–236.

Bush, I. E. [1955]. *Biochem. J.* **59**, xiv.

Butler, G. W. [1951]. *Anal. Chem.* **23**, 1300–1304.

Buyske, D. A., Owen, L. H., Wilder, P., and Hobbs, M. E. [1956]. *Anal. Chem.* **28**, 910–912.

Cacioppo, F., and LaGrutta, G. [1950]. *Boll. soc. ital. biol. sper.* **26**, 1011–1012; **26**, 1347–1349; both from [1952] *Chem. Abstr.* **46**, 558.

Caldwell, P. C. [1953]. *Biochem. J.* **55**, 458–467.

Caldwell, P. C. [1955]. *Biochem. J.* **60**, xii–xiii.

Calvin, M., and Benson, A. A. [1949]. *Science* **109**, 140–142.

Calvo, J. M. [1955]. *Euclides (Madrid)* **15**, 208–212.

Campani, M., Arezio, G., and Cameroni, R. [1952]. *Atti. soc. lombarda sci. med. e biol.* **7**, 113–115; from [1953] *Chem. Abstr.* **47**, 5310.

Canady, W. J., and Roe, J. H. [1956]. *J. Biol. Chem.* **220**, 563–570.
Candela, M. I., Hewitt, E. J., and Stevens, H. M. [1956]. *Anal. Chim. Acta* **14**, 66–69.
Cantoni, G. L. [1953]. *J. Biol. Chem.* **204**, 403–416.
Čapek, A., Hanč, O., Macek, K., Tadra, M., and Riedl-Tůmová, E. [1956]. *Naturwissenschaften* **43**, 471.
Carangal, A. R. [1955]. *Philippine Agriculturist* **39**, 1–16.
Carleson, G. [1954]. *Acta Chem. Scand.* **8**, 1673–1692.
Carpenter, D. C. [1952]. *Anal. Chem.* **24**, 1203–1204.
Carsten, M. E. [1952]. *J. Am. Chem. Soc.* **74**, 5954–5959.
Carter, C. E. [1950]. *J. Am. Chem. Soc.* **72**, 1466–1471.
Casselman, W. G. B. [1954]. *Biochim. et Biophys. Acta* **14**, 450.
Cassidy, H. G. [1957]. "Fundamentals of Chromatography," 447 pp. Interscience, N. Y.
Casteel, H. W., and Wender, S. H. [1953]. *Anal. Chem.* **25**, 508–509.
Castiglioni, A., and Nivoli, M. [1953]. *Z. anal. Chem.* **138**, 187–188, from [1953] *Chem. Abstr.* **47**, 5848.
Castiglioni, A., and Vietti, M. [1955a]. *Z. anal. Chem.* **144**, 112–113.
Castiglioni, A. [1955b]. *Z. anal. Chem.* **145**, 188–189.
Catch, J. R., Jones, T. S. G., and Wilkenson, S. [1949]. *Ann. N. Y. Acad. Sci.* **51**, 917.
Cathcart, J. A., and Reynolds, D. D. [1951]. *J. Am. Chem. Soc.* **73**, 3504.
Cavallini, D., Frontali, N., and Toschi, G. [1949]. *Nature* **163**, 568–569; **164**, 792–793.
Cavallini, D., and Frontali, N. [1953]. *Ricerca sci.* **23**, 807–819; from [1953] *Chem. Abstr.* **47**, 9863.
Cavallini, D., and Frontali, N. [1954]. *Biochim. et Biophys. Acta* **13**, 439–445.
Cerbulis, J. [1954]. *Arch. Biochem. Biophys.* **49**, 442–450.
Cerbulis, J. [1955]. *Anal. Chem.* **27**, 1400–1401.
Ceriotti, G. [1955]. *Nature* **175**, 897–898.
Cerletti, P., and Siliprandi, N. [1955]. *Ricerca Sci.* **25**, 208–490.
Chakrabarti, J. K., and Guha, A. K. [1956]. *Nature* **178**, 538.
Chakrabortty, H. C., and Burma, D. P. [1956]. *Anal. Chim. Acta* **15**, 451–456.
Chang, W. H., Hossfeld, R. L., and Sandstrom, W. M. [1952]. *J. Am. Chem. Soc.* **774**, 5766–5767.
Charalampous, F. C., and Mueller, G. C. [1953]. *J. Biol. Chem.* **201**, 161–173.
Chargaff, E., Levine, C., and Green, C. [1948]. *J. Biol. Chem.* **175**, 67–71.
Chargaff, E., Magasanik, B., Doniger, R., and Vischer, E. [1949]. *J. Am. Chem. Soc.* **71**, 1513–1514.
Chatterji, A. C., and Bhagwan, H. [1956]. *Z. anal. Chem.* **149**, 339–345.
Chaykin, S., Meinhart, J. O., and Krebs, E. G. [1956]. *J. Biol. Chem.* **220**, 811–829.
Cheftel, R. I., Munier, R., and Macheboeuf, M. [1951]. *Bull. soc. chim. biol.* **33**, 840–845.
Cheftel, R. I., Munier, R., and Macheboeuf, M. [1952]. *Bull. soc. chim. biol.* **34**, 380–387.
Cheftel, R. I., Munier, R., and Macheboeuf, M. [1953]. *Bull. soc. chim. biol.* **35**, 1085–1093; **35**, 1095–1099.
Chen, Y. T., Isherwood, F. A., and Mapson, L. W. [1953]. *Biochem. J.* **55**, 821–823.
Chernick, S. S., Chaikoff, I. L., and Abraham, S. [1951]. *J. Biol. Chem.* **193**, 793–802.
Cheronis, N. D. [1942]. "Semimicro and Macro Organic Chemistry: A Laboratory Manual," 388 pp. Crowell, New York.
Chiba, Y., and Noguchi, I. [1954]. *Cytologia (Tokyo)* **19**, 41–44.

Chiba, Y. [1955]. *Arch. Biochem. Biophys.* **54**, 83–92.
Chu, T. C., Green, A. A., and Chu, E. J. H. [1951]. *J. Biol. Chem.* **190**, 643–646.
Chu, T. C., and Chu, E. J. H. [1953]. *J. Am. Chem. Soc.* **75**, 3021–3023.
Chu, T. C., and Chu, E. J. H. [1954]. *J. Biol. Chem.* **208**, 537–541.
Cifonelli, J. A., and Smith, F. [1954]. *Anal. Chem.* **26**- 1132–1134.
Cifonelli, J. A., and Smith, H. F. [1955]. *Anal. Chem.* **27**, 1501–1502.
Clark, E. W. [1954]. *J. Econ. Entomol.* **47**, 934.
Clarkson, T. W., and Keneh, J. E. [1956]. *Biochem. J.* **62**, 361–372.
Clayton, R. A., and Strong, F. M. [1954]. *Anal. Chem.* **26**, 1362–1363.
Clayton, R. A. [1956]. *Anal. Chem.* **28**, 904–908.
Clingman, A. L., and Sutton, D. A. [1952]. *Fuel* **31**, 259–260; from [1954] *Chem. Abstr.* **48**, 4372.
Clouet, D. H. [1952]. *Federation Proc.* **11**, 197.
Čmelik, S., and Bartl, Z. [1956]. *Z. physiol. Chem.* **305**, 170–176.
Cohen, A. S., and Kantor, N. [1955]. *Am. J. Clin. Pathol.* **25**, 1328–1330.
Cohn, D. V., Buckaloo, G. W., and Carter, W. E. [1955]. *Nucleonics* **13**(8), 48.
Consden, R., Gordon, A. H., and Martin, A. J. P. [1944]. *Biochem. J.* **38**, 224–232.
Consden, R., Gordon, A. H., and Martin, A. J. P. [1946]. *Biochem. J.* **40**, 580–582.
Consden, R., Gordon, A. H., and Martin, A. J. P. [1947]. *Biochem. J.* **41**, 590–596.
Consden, R., and Gordon, A. H., [1948a]. *Nature* **162**, 180–181.
Consden, R. [1948b]. *Nature* **162**, 359–361.
Consden, R. [1948c]. *Nature* **162**, 1007.
Consden, R., and Stanier, W. M. [1952]. *Nature* **169**, 783–785.
Consden, R. [1954]. *Brit. Med. J.* **10**, 177–182.
Conway, E. J. [1947]. "Microdiffusion Analysis and Volumetric Error," 357 pp. C. Lockwood, London.
Cook, J. W. [1954]. *J. Assoc. Offic. Agr. Chemists* **37**, 984–989.
Cook, J. W. [1955]. *J. Assoc. Offic. Agr. Chemists* **38**, 150–153; **38**, 826–832.
Correale, P., and Cortese, I. [1953]. *Naturwissenschaften* **40**, 57–58.
Corwin, L. M., and Orten, J. M. [1954]. *Anal. Chem.* **26**, 608–609.
Cowgill, R. W. [1955a]. *Biochem. et Biophys. Acta* **16**, 614.
Cowgill, R. W. [1955b]. *Anal. Chem.* **27**, 1519–1521.
Craig, L. C. [1950]. *Anal. Chem.* **22**, 1346–1352.
Cramer, F. [1950]. *Angew. Chem.* **62**, 73–75.
Cramer, F. [1954]. "Papier Chromatographie," 136 pp. Verlag Chemie, Weinheim.
Crammar, J. L. [1948]. *Nature* **161**, 349–350.
Cremer, H. D., and Tiselius, A. [1950]. *Biochem. Z.* **320**, 273–283.
Crippa, A. [1953]. *Ist. botan. univ. Lab. crittogam., Pavia, Atti* **10**, 173–177; from [1954] *Chem. Abstr.* **48**, 3187.
Crokaert, R. [1948]. *Arch. intern. physiol.* **56**, 189–191.
Cromwell, B. T. [1956]. *Biochem. J.* **64**, 259–266.
Crosbie, G. W., Smellie, R. M. S., and Davidson, J. N. [1953]. *Biochem. J.* **54**, 287–292.
Crowther, J. P. [1954a]. *Nature* **173**, 486.
Crowther, J. P. [1954b]. *Anal. Chem.* **26**, 1383–1386.
Crumpler, H. R., and Dent, C. E. [1949]. *Nature* **164**, 441–442.
Crumpler, H. R., Dent, C. E., Harris, H., and Westall, R. G. [1951]. *Nature* **167**, 307–308.
Csobán, G. [1950]. *Magyar Kém. Folyóirat* **56**, 449–451; from [1952] *Chem. Abstr.* **46**, 1384.
Curry, A. S. [1953]. *Nature* **171**, 1026–1027.

Curry, A. S., and Powell, H. [1954]. *Nature* **173**, 1143–1144.

Curzon, G., and Giltrow, J. [1953]. *Nature* **172**, 356–357.

Curzon, G., and Giltrow, J. [1954]. *Nature* **173**, 314–315.

Cuthbertson, W. F. J., and Smith, E. Lester [1949]. *Biochem. J.* **44**, v–vi.

Cuthbertson, W. F. J., and Ireland, D. M. [1952]. *Biochem. J.* **52**, xxxiv.

Cuthbertson, W. F. J., Ireland, D. M., and Wolff, W. [1953]. *Biochem. J.* **55**, 669–671.

Dakshinamurti, K. [1954]. *Current Sci. (India)* **23**, 89.

Dalgliesh, C. E., Knox, W. E., and Neuberger, A. [1951]. *Nature* **168**, 20–22.

Dalgliesh, C. E. [1952a]. *J. Chem. Soc.* pp. 3940–3942.

Dalgliesh, C. E. [1952b]. *Biochem. J.* **52**, 3–14.

Dalgliesh, C. E. [1955a]. *Arch. Biochem. Biophys.* **58**, 214–226.

Dalgliesh, C. E. [1955b]. *Biochem. J.* **61**, 334–337.

Dalgliesh, C. E. [1956]. *Biochem. J.* **64**, 481–485.

Dal Nogare, S. [1956]. *Anal. Chem.* **28**, 903.

Das, D. B., Choudhury, P. K. R., and Wareham, J. T. [1952]. *Sci. and Culture (Calcutta)* **18**, 197.

Datta, S. P., and Overell, B. G. [1949a]. *Biochem. J.* **44**, xlii.

Datta, S. P., Overell, B. G., and Stack-Dunne, M. [1949b]. *Nature* **164**, 673–674.

Datta, S. P., Dent, C. E., and Harris, H. [1950]. *Science* **112**, 621–623.

Dautrevaux, M., and Biserte, G. [1955]. *Compt. rend.* **240**, 1153–1155.

David, S., and Monnier, J. [1955]. *Bull. soc. chim. France* pp. 797–798.

Davidson, J. N., and Smellie, R. M. S. [1952]. *Biochem. J.* **52**, 594–599.

Davies, D. A. L. [1955]. *Biochem. J.* **59**, 696–704.

Davies, R. L. [1951]. *Nature* **168**, 834.

Dawe, J. C., Denz, F. A., and Kennedy, T. H. [1956]. *Biochem. J.* **64**, 777–782.

Dawson, R. M. C. [1953]. *Biochem. J.* **55**, xii.

Dawson, R. M. C. [1955a]. *Biochem. J.* **59**, 5–8.

Dawson, R. M. C. [1955b]. *Biochem. J.* **60**, 325–328.

Decker, P., and Riffart, W. [1950]. *Chem.-Ztg.* **74**, 261; from [1951] *Chem. Abstr.* **45**, 6528.

Decker, P. [1951a]. *Naturwissenschaften* **38**, 287–288.

Decker, P., Riffart, W., and Oberneder, G. [1951b]. *Naturwissenschaften* **38**, 288.

Decker, P., and Sano, I. [1955]. *Z. physiol. Chem.* **300**, 245–251; **300**, 252–260.

Defranceschi, A., and Zamboni, V. [1954]. *Biochim. et Biophys. Acta* **13**, 304–530.

Deimel, M., and Maurer, W. [1952]. *Naturwissenschaften* **39**, 489–490.

de Jonge, A. P. [1956]. *Chem. Weekblad* **52**, 37–43.

de Ley, J. [1955]. *Naturwissenschaften* **42**, 96.

Delmas, L. [1956]. *Compt. rend.* **242**, 2595–2598.

Demorest, H. L., and Baskin, R. [1954]. *Anal. Chem.* **26**, 1531.

Denison, F. W., and Phares, E. F. [1952]. *Anal. Chem.* **24**, 1628–1629.

Dent, C. E. [1947a]. *Biochem. J.* **41**, 240–253.

Dent, C. E., Stepka, W., and Steward, F. C. [1947b]. *Nature* **160**, 682–683.

Dent, C. E. [1948]. *Biochem. J.* **43**, 168–180.

Dent, C. E., and Rose, G. A. [1949]. *Biochem. J.* **44**, 610–618.

de Reeder, P. L. [1953]. *Anal. Chim. Acta* **8**, 325–336.

Deutsch, A., and Nilsson, R. [1953]. *Acta Chem. Scand.* **7**, 858–861.

DeVay, J. E., Chang, W. H., and Hossfeld, R. L. [1951]. *J. Am. Chem. Soc.* **73**, 4977–4978.

de Verdier, C. H., and Ågren, G. [1948]. *Acta Chem. Scand.* **2**, 783–796.

de Vries, G. [1954]. *Nature* **173**, 735–736.

de Vries, G., and Van Dalen, E. [1955]. *Anal. Chim. Acta* **13**, 554–561.

de Whalley, H. C. S. [1950]. *Intern. Sugar J.* **52**, 127; **52**, 151; **52**, 267.

de Whalley, H. C. S., Albon, N., and Gross, D. [1951]. *Analyst* **76**, 287–300.

Dieckert, J. W., and Reiser, R. [1954]. *Science* **120**, 678.

Dieckert, J. W., and Reiser, R. [1956]. *J. Am. Oil Chemists' Soc.* **33**, 123–126.

Dierick, W., Stockx, J., and Vandendriessche, L. [1956]. *Naturwissenschaften* **43**, 82–83.

Dihlmann, W. [1953]. *Naturwissenschaften* **40**, 342–343.

Dikstein, S., Bergmann, F., and Chaimovitz, M. [1956]. *J. Biol. Chem.* **221**, 239–251.

Diller, H., and Rex, O. [1953]. *Z. anal. Chem.* **137**, 241–244.

Dimler, R. J., Schaefer, W. C., Wise, C. S., and Rist, C. E. [1952]. *Anal. Chem.* **24**, 1411–1414.

Dimroth, K., Jaenicke, L., and Vollbrechtshausen, I. [1952]. *Z. physiol. Chem.* **289**, 71–77.

Dirkx, J. [1952]. *Biochim. et Biophys. Acta* **8**, 194–201.

Dixon, H. B. F. [1956]. *Biochem. J.* **64**, 47P.

Doctor ,V. M., and Couch, J. R. [1953]. *J. Biol. Chem.* **200**, 223–231.

Doebbler, G. F. [1953]. *Texas J. Sci.* **5**, 443–448; from [1954] *Chem. Abstr.* **48**, 5920.

Doman, N. G., and Kagan, Z. S. [1952]. *Biokhimiya* **17**, 719–724; from [1953] *Chem. Abstr.* **47**, 4795.

Done, J., and Fowden, L. [1952]. *Biochem. J.* **51**, 451–458.

Dorough, G. D., and Seaton, D. L. [1954]. *J. Am. Chem. Soc.* **76**, 2873–2877.

Douin, R. [1953]. *Rev. gén. botan.* **60**, 777–797.

Douste-Blazy, L., Polonovski, J., and Valdiguie, P. [1952]. *Compt. rend.* **235**, 1643–1645.

Dowling, J. H., Koffler, H., Reitz, H. C., Peterson, D. H., and Tetrault, P. A. [1952]. *Science* **116**, 147–148.

Dragúnová, I., and Langer, P. [1956]. *Nature* **178**, 537–538.

Drake, N. A. [1950]. *J. Am. Chem. Soc.* **72**, 3803.

Drake, N. A., Haines, W. J., Knauff, R. E., and Nielson, E. D. [1956]. *Anal. Chem.* **28**, 2036–2038.

Drell, W. [1953]. *J. Am. Chem. Soc.* **75**, 2506.

Drell, W. [1955]. *J. Am. Chem. Soc.* **77**, 5429–5431.

Dreywood, R. [1946]. *Ind. Eng. Chem., Anal. Ed.* **18**, 499.

Drèze, A., and deBoeck, A. [1952]. *Arch. intern. physiol.* **60**, 201.

Drèze, A., and Reith, W. S. [1956]. *Biochem. J.* **63**, 22P.

Dubois, M., Gilles, K., Hamilton, J. K., Rebers, P. A., and Smith, F. [1951]. *Nature* **168**, 167.

Dubois, M., Gilles, K. A., Hamilton, J. K., Rebers, P. A., and Smith, F. [1956]. *Anal. Chem.* **28**, 350–356.

Duff, R. B., and Eastwood, D. J. [1950]. *Nature* **165**, 848–849.

Duggan, E. L. [1956]. *Anal. Chem.* **28**, 714–720.

Duncan, R. E. B., and Porteous, J. W. [1953]. *Analyst* **78**, 641–646.

Dunn, D. B., and Smith, J. D. [1955]. *Nature* **175**, 336–337.

Dunning, H. N., and Carlton, J. K. [1956]. *Anal. Chem.* **28**, 1362–1366.

Durant, J. A. [1952]. *Nature* **169**, 1062–1063.

Durrum, E. L., Paul, M. H., and Smith, E. R. B. [1952]. *Science* **116**, 428–430.

Durso, D. F., and Mueller, W. A. [1956]. *Anal. Chem.* **28**, 1366–1368.
Dutta, N. L. [1955]. *Nature* **175**, 85.
Eastham, M. [1949]. *Biochem. J.* **45**, xiii–xiv.
Eberlein, W. R., and Bongiovanni, A. M. [1955]. *Arch. Biochem. Biophys.* **59**, 90–96.
Edman, P. [1950]. *Acta Chem. Scand.* **4**, 283–293.
Edman, P. [1953]. *Acta Chem. Scand.* **7**, 700–701.
Edström, J. E. [1951]. *Nature* **168**, 876–877.
Edström, J. E. [1952]. *Biochim. et Biophys. Acta* **9**, 528–530.
Edward, J. T., and Waldron, D. M. [1952]. *J. Chem. Soc.* pp. 3631–3634.
Edward, J. T., and Nielsen, S. [1953]. *Chem. & Ind. (London)* 197.
Eggitt, P. W. R., and Ward, L. D. [1953]. *J. Sci. Food Agr.* **4**, 176–179.
Eggleston, L. V., and Hems, R. [1952]. *Biochem. J.* **52**, 156–160.
Ehrmantrout, H. C., and Weinstock, A. [1954]. *Biochim. et Biophys. Acta* **15**, 589–590.
Ekman, B. [1948]. *Acta Chem. Scand.* **2**, 383–384.
Elbeih, I. I. M. [1955]. *Chemist Analyst* **44**,(1), 20–21.
El Hawary, M. F. S., and Thompson, R. H. S. [1953]. *Biochem. J.* **53**, 340–347.
Elliott, D. C. [1954]. *J. Exptl. Botany* **5**, 353–356.
Elliott, W. H. [1956]. *Biochem. J.* **62**, 427–433; **62**, 433–436.
Elodi, P. [1954]. *Acta Physiol. Acad. Sci. Hung.* **6**, 225–233.
England, A., and Cohn, E. J. [1935]. *J. Am. Chem. Soc.* **57**, 634–637.
Erbring, H., and Patt, P. [1954]. *Naturwissenschaften* **41**, 216.
Erdem, B., and Erlenmeyer, H. [1954]. *Helv. Chim. Acta* **37**, 2220–2224.
Erdem, B. [1955]. *Rev. fac. sci. univ. Istanbul* **20C**, 332–345; **20C**, 346–348.
Eriksen, L. [1953]. *Scand. J. Clin. & Lab. Invest.* **5**, 155–157; from [1953] *Chem. Abstr.* **47**, 10603.
Eriksson, S., and Sjövall, J. [1954]. *Acta Chem. Scand.* **8**, 1099.
Erlenmeyer, H., and Überwasser, H. [1942]. *Helv. Chim. Acta* **25**, 515–521.
Erlenmeyer, H., von Hahn, H., and Sorkin, E. [1951]. *Helv. Chim. Acta* **34**, 1419–1421.
Erspamer, V. [1952]. *Nature* **169**, 375–376.
Evans, G. G., and Reith, W. S. [1954]. *Biochem. J.* **56**, 111–116.
Evans, R. A., Parr, W. H., and Evans, W. C. [1949]. *Nature* **164**, 674–675.
Falk, J. E., and Benson, A. [1953]. *Biochem. J.* **55**, 101–104.
Falk, J. E. [1954a]. *Brit. Med. J.* **10**, 211–214.
Falk, J. E., and Benson, A. [1954b]. *Arch. Biochem. Biophys.* **51**, 528–530.
Faraday Society. [1949]. "Chromatographic Analysis," 336 pp. Gurney and Jackson, London.
Fearon, W. R. [1944]. *Biochem. J.* **38**, 399–402.
Fearon, W. R., and Boggust, W. A. [1954]. *Analyst* **79**, 101–102.
Feigelson, P. [1956]. Private communication.
Feigl, F. [1954]. "Spot Tests," 4th ed., Vols. I and II. Elsevier, Houston, Texas.
Feigl, F. [1956]. "Spot Tests in Organic Analysis," 5th ed. Van Nostrand, Princeton, New Jersey.
Feingold, D. S., Avigad, G., and Hestrin, S. [1956]. *Biochem. J.* **64**, 356–361.
Felix, K., and Krekels, A. [1952]. *Z. physiol. Chem.* **290**, 78–80.
Fernando, Q., and Phillips, J. P. [1953]. *Anal. Chem.* **25**, 819–820.
Fernando, Q. [1955]. *Anal. Chim. Acta* **12**, 432–435.
Fewster, M. E., and Hall, D. A. [1951]. *Nature* **168**, 78–79.
Fincham, J. R. S. [1953]. *Biochem. J.* **53**, 313–320.
Fink, K., and Fink, R. M. [1949]. *Proc. Soc. Exptl. Biol. Med.* **70**, 654–656.

Fink, K., Henderson, R. B., and Fink, R. M.   [1951].   *Proc. Soc. Exptl. Biol. Med.* **78**, 135–141.

Fink, K., Henderson, R. B., and Fink, R. M.   [1952].   *J. Biol. Chem.* **197**, 441–452.

Fink, R. M., Dent, C. E., and Fink, K.   [1947].   *Nature* **160**, 801–803.

Fink, R. M., and Fink, K.   [1948].   *Science* **107**, 253–254.

Fink, R. M., Cline, R. E., McGaughey, C., and Fink, K.   [1956].   *Anal. Chem.* **28**, 4–6.

Fiori, A. [1956].   *Nature* **178**, 423.

Fischbach, H., and Levine, J.   [1955a].   *Science* **121**, 602–603.

Fischbach, H., and Levine, J.   [1955b].   *Antibiotics and Chemotherapy* **5**, 640–642.

Fischer, A., and Behrens, M.   [1952].   *Z. physiol. Chem.* **291**, 14–15.

Fischer, A.   [1954].   *Planta* **43**, 288–314.

Fischer, F. G., and Dörfel, H.   [1953].   *Biochem. Z.* **324**, 544–566.

Fischer, F. G., and Dörfel, H.   [1954].   *Z. physiol. Chem.* **297**, 164–178.

Fischer, F. G., and Dörfel, H.   [1955a].   *Z. physiol. Chem.* **301**, 224–234.

Fischer, F. G., and Nebel, H. G.   [1955b].   *Z. physiol. Chim.* **302**, 10–19.

Fisher, R. B., Parsons, D. S., and Morrison, G. A.   [1948].   *Nature* **161**, 764–765.

Fisher, R. B., Parsons, D. S., and Holmes, R.   [1949].   *Nature* **164**, 183.

Fitzpatrick, W. H.   [1949].   *Science* **109**, 469.

Flavin, M., and Anfinsen, C. B.   [1954].   *J. Biol. Chem.* **211**, 375–390.

Fletcher, E., and Malpress, F. H.   [1953].   *Nature* **171**, 838–839.

Fletcher, K., and Stanley, P. S.   [1955].   *Nature* **175**, 730.

Fleury, P. F., Courtois, J. E., and Malangeau, P.   [1953].   *Bull. soc. chim. biol.* **35**, 537–540; from [1954] *Chem. Abstr.* **48**, 781.

Flood, A. E., Hirst, E. L., and Jones, J. K. N.   [1947].   *Nature* **160**, 86–87.

Flood, A. E., Hirst, E. L., and Jones, J. K. N.   [1948].   *J. Chem. Soc.* 1679–1683.

Flood, H.   [1949].   *Discussions Faraday Soc.* **7**, 190–195.

Folk, J. E.   [1956].   *Arch. Biochem. Biophys.* **61**, 150–157.

Ford, J. E., Holdsworth, E. S., and Kohn, S. K.   [1955].   *Biochem. J.* **59**, 86–93.

Forsyth, W. G. C., and Webley, D. M.   [1948a].   *Nature* **162**, 150–151.

Forsyth, W. G. C.   [1948b].   *Nature* **161**, 239–240.

Forsyth, W. G. C.   [1950].   *Biochem. J.* **46**, 141–146.

Forsyth, W. G. C.   [1953].   *Nature* **172**, 726–727.

Forsyth, W. G. C.   [1955].   *Biochem. J.* **60**, 108–111.

Fosdick, L. S., and Blackwell, R. G.   [1949].   *Science* **109**, 314–315.

Fourage, J.   [1955].   *Anal. Chim. Acta* **12**, 231–238.

Fountain, J. R., Hutchison, D. J., Waring, G. B., and Burchenal, J. H.   [1953].   *Proc. Soc. Exptl. Biol. Med.* **83**, 369–373.

Fowden, L., and Penney, J. R.   [1950].   *Nature* **165**, 846–847.

Fowden, L.   [1951a].   *Biochem. J.* **48**, 327–333.

Fowden, L.   [1951b].   *Nature* **167**, 1030–1031.

Fowden, L., and Done, J.   [1953].   *Biochem. J.* **55**, 548–553.

Fowden, L.   [1955a].   *Nature* **176**, 347–348.

Fowden, L., and Webb, J. A.   [1955b].   *Biochem. J.* **59**, 228–234.

Fowden, L.   [1956].   *Biochem. J.* **64**, 323–332.

Fowler, H. D.   [1951].   *Nature* **168**, 1123–1124.

Frame, E. G., Russell, J. A., and Wilhelmi, A. E.   [1943].   *J. Biol. Chem.* **149**, 255–270.

Frame, E. G., and Rausch, V. L.   [1952].   *Bull. Univ. Minn. Hospital* **23/28**, 532–543.

Franglen, G. T.   [1955].   *Nature* **175**, 134.

Frank, H., and Petersen, H.   [1955].   *Z. physiol. Chem.* **299**, 1–5.

Franklin, A. E., and Quastel, J. H. [1950]. *Proc. Soc. Exptl. Biol. Med.* **74,** 803–808.

Franklin, A. E., Quastel, J. H., and Van Straten, S. F. [1951]. *Nature* **168,** 687–689.

Freeman, J. H. [1952]. *Anal. Chem.* **24,** 955–959; **24,** 2001–2002.

French, D., Knapp, D. W., and Pazur, J. H. [1950]. *J. Am. Chem. Soc.* **72,** 5150–5152.

French, D., and Wild, G. M. [1953]. *J. Am. Chem. Soc.* **75,** 2612–2616.

Fresco, J. R., and Warner, R. C. [1955]. *J. Biol. Chem.* **215,** 751.

Fridhandler, L., and Quastel, J. H. [1955]. *Arch. Biochem. Biophys.* **56,** 424–440.

Friedman, S., McFarland, J. E., Bhattacharyya, P. K., and Fraenkel, G. [1955]. *Arch. Biochem. Biophys.* **59,** 484.

Friedrich, W., and Bernhauer, K. [1955]. *Z. Naturforsch.* **10b,** 6.

Frierson, W. J., and Jones, J. W. [1951]. *Anal. Chem.* **23,** 1447–1452.

Frierson, W. J., Thomason, P. F., and Raaen, H. [1954]. *Anal. Chem.* **26,** 1210–1211.

Fromageot, C., Jutisz, M., and Tessier, P. [1949]. *Bull. soc. chim. biol.* **31,** 689–695.

Fromageot, C., Jutisz, M., Meyer, D., and Pénasse, L. [1950]. *Compt. rend.* **230,** 1905–1906; [1950]. *Biochim. et Biophys. Acta* **6,** 283–289.

Fujisawa, Y. [1951]. *J. Osaka City Med. Center* **1,** 7–13; from [1954] *Chem. Abstr.* **48,** 13550.

Fuller, R. C. [1956]. *Science* **124,** 1253.

Gaffney, G. W., Schreier, K., DiFerrante, N., and Altman, K. I. [1954]. *J. Biol. Chem.* **206,** 695–698.

Gage, T. B., Douglass, C. D., and Wender, S. H. [1951]. *Anal. Chem.* **23,** 1582–1585.

Gage, T. B., and Wender, S. H. [1950]. *Anal. Chem.* **22,** 708–711.

Gaillard, B. D. E. [1953]. *Nature* **171,** 1160.

Gale, E. F., and van Halteren, M. B. [1951]. *Biochem. J.* **50,** 34–43.

Ganguli, N. C. [1953a]. *Science and Culture (India)* **19,** 100–101; from [1954] *Chem. Abstr.* **48,** 3206.

Ganguli, N. C. [1953b]. *Naturwissenschaften* **40,** 624.

Ganguli, N. C. [1954a]. *Nature* **174,** 189–190.

Ganguli, N. C. [1954b]. *Naturwissenschaften* **41,** 282.

Ganguli, N. C. [1955a]. *Naturwissenschaften* **42,** 486.

Ganguli, N. C. [1955b]. *Anal. Chim. Acta* **12,** 335–341.

Ganguli, S., and Roy, S. C. [1956]. *Arch. Biochem. Biophys.* **64,** 67–73.

Gardner, K. J. [1955]. *Nature* **176,** 929.

Gassner, F. X., and Hopwood, M. L. [1952]. *Proc. Soc. Exptl. Biol. Med.* **81,** 37–43.

Gauthier, P. [1955]. *Bull. soc. chim. France* p. 981.

Geissman, T. A., Jorgensen, E. C., and Johnson, B. L. [1954]. *Arch. Biochem. Biophys.* **49,** 368–388.

Geldmacher-Mallinckrodt, M., and Weinland, H. [1953]. *Z. physiol. Chem.* **292,** 65–72.

Gendre, T., and Lederer, E. [1952]. *Biochim. et Biophys. Acta* **8,** 49–55.

Gerlach, E., and Weber, E. [1955a]. *Arch. exptl. Pathol. Pharmakol. Naunyn-Schmiedeberg's* **224,** 496–522.

Gerlach, E., Weber, E., and Döring, H. J. [1955b]. *Arch. exptl. Pathol. Pharmakol. Naunyn-Schmiedeberg's* **226,** 9–17.

Gerlach, E., and Döring, H. J. [1955c]. *Naturwissenschaften* **42,** 344.

Gerok, W. [1955]. *Z. physiol. Chem.* **299,** 112–128.

Geschwind, I. I., and Li, C. H.   [1952].   *J. Am. Chem. Soc.* **74,** 834–835.
Gibbons, G. C., and Boissonnas, R. A.   [1950].   *Helv. Chim. Acta* **33,** 1477–1481.
Gillespie, J. M., Jermyn, M. A., and Woods, E. F.   [1952].   *Nature* **169,** 487–488.
Giovannozzi-Sermanni, G.   [1956].   *Nature* **177,** 586–587.
Giri, K. V.   [1951*a*].   *Current Sci. (India)* **20,** 295–296.
Giri, K. V., and Prasad, A. L. N.   [1951*b*].   *Nature* **167,** 859–860.
Giri, K. V., and Prasad, A. L. N.   [1951*c*].   *Nature* **168,** 786–787.
Giri, K. V., and Rao, N. A. N.   [1952*a*].   *J. Indian Inst. Sci.* **34A,** 95–105.
Giri, K. V., Krishnamurthy, K., and Venkatasubramanian, T. A.   [1952*b*].   *Current Sci. (India)* **21,** 11–12.
Giri, K. V., Krishnamurthy, K., and Venkatasubramanian, T. A.   [1952*c*].   *Current Sci. (India)* **21,** 44–45.
Giri, K. V., Krishnamurthy, K., and Venkatasubramanian, T. A.   [1952*d*].   *Lancet* **263,** 562–563.
Giri, K. V., Krishnamurthy, K., and Venkatasubramanian, T. A.   [1952*e*].   *J. Indian Inst. Sci.* **34A,** 209–217.
Giri, K. V., Prasad, A. L. N., Devi, S. G., and Ram, J. S.   [1952*f*].   *Biochem. J.* **51,** 123–128.
Giri, K. V., Radhakrishnan, A. N., and Vaidyanathan, C. S.   [1952*g*].   *Nature* **170,** 1025–1026.
Giri, K. V., Radhakrishnan, A. N., and Vaidyanathan, C. S.   [1952*h*].   *Anal. Chem.* **24,** 1677–1678.
Giri, K. V.   [1953*a*].   *Current Sci. (India)* **22,** 373.
Giri, K. V.   [1953*b*].   *Nature* **171,** 1159.
Giri, K. V., and Rao, N. A. N.   [1953*c*].   *Current Sci. (India)* **22,** 114–116.
Giri, K. V., and Rao, N. A. N.   [1953*d*].   *J. Indian Inst. Sci.* **35A,** 343–353.
Giri, K. V., Krishnaswamy, P. R., Kalyankar, G. D., and Rao, P. L. N.   [1953*e*].   *Experientia* **9,** 296–297.
Giri, K. V., Krishnamurthy, K., and Rao, N. A. N.   [1953*f*].   *J. Indian Inst. Sci.* **35A,** 93–98.
Giri, K. V.   [1954].   *Nature* **173,** 1194–1195.
Giri, K. V.   [1955*a*].   *J. Indian Inst. Sci.* **37A,** 1–13.
Giri, K. V.   [1955*b*].   *Experientia* **11,** 165–166.
Giri, K. V. and Balakrishnan, S.   [1955*c*].   *Anal. Chem.* **27,** 1178–1180.
Giri, K. V., and Parihar, D. B.   [1955*d*].   *Nature* **175,** 304–305.
Giri, K. V., Nagabhushanam, A., Nigam, V. N., and Belavadi, B.   [1955*e*].   *Science* **121,** 898.
Glazko, A. J., Dill, W. A., and Rebstock, M. C.   [1950].   *J. Biol. Chem.* **183,** 679–691.
Glazko, A. J., and Dill, W. A.   [1951].   *Nature* **168,** 32.
Glazko, A. J., and Dill, W. A.   [1953].   *Anal. Chem.* **25,** 1782.
Glegg, R. E., Eidinger, D., and Leblond, C. P.   [1953].   *Science* **118,** 614–616.
Glegg, R. E., and Eidinger, D.   [1954].   *Anal. Chem.* **26,** 1365–1367.
Glister, G. A., and Grainger, A.   [1950].   *Analyst* **75,** 310–314.
Godin, P.   [1954].   *Nature* **174,** 134.
Goeller, J. P., and Sherry, S.   [1950].   *Proc. Soc. Exptl. Biol. Med.* **74,** 381–382.
Goldbaum, L. R., and Kazyak, L.   [1956].   *Anal. Chem.* **28,** 1289–1290.
Goldenberg, M., Faber, M., Alston, E. J., and Chargaff, E. C.   [1949].   *Science* **109,** 534–535.
Goldstein, M., and Abelin, I.   [1956].   *Helv. Chim. Acta* **39,** 158–167.
Good, P. M., and Johnson, A. W.   [1949].   *Nature* **163,** 31.

Goodall, R. R., and Levi, A. A. [1946]. *Nature* **158**, 675.

Goodban, A. E., Stark, J. B., and Owens, H. S. [1953]. *J. Agr. Food Chem.* **1**, 261–264.

Goppelsroeder, F. [1909]. *Kolloid-Z.* **4**, 23–27, 94–123, 191–197, 236–252, 312–315.

Gorbach, G., and Demmel, H. [1956]. *Mikrochim. Acta* 1264–1276.

Gordon, A. H., Gross, J., O'Connor, D., and Pitt-Rivers, R. [1952]. *Nature* **169**, 19–20.

Gordon, H. T., and Hewel, C. A. [1955]. *Anal. Chem.* **27**, 1471–1474.

Gordon, H. T., Thornburg, W., and Werum, L. N. [1956]. *Anal. Chem.* **28**, 849–855.

Gordon, H. T. [1957]. Private communication.

Gordon, M. P., and Brown, G. B. [1956]. *J. Biol. Chem.* **220**, 927–937.

Gordon, S., and Nardi, G. L. [1954]. *J. Lab. Clin. Med.* **43**, 827–830.

Gore, D. N. [1951]. *Chem. & Ind. (London)* p. 479.

Gottschalk, A., and Ada, G. L. [1956]. *Biochem. J.* **62**, 681–686.

Goulden, J. D. S. [1954]. *Nature* **173**, 646.

Gourevitch, A., and Lein, J. [1952]. *Federation Proc.* **11**, 221.

Graichen, C. [1951]. *J. Assoc. Offic. Agr. Chemists* **34**, 795–799.

Grant, E. W., and Kennedy, E. E. [1955]. *J. Am. Pharm. Assoc., Sci. Ed.* **44**, 129–132.

Grassmann, W. [1951a]. *Naturwissenschaften* **38**, 200–206.

Grassmann, W., Hannig, K., and Knedel, M. [1951b]. *Deut. med. Wochschr.* **76**, 333–336, [1951]. from *Chem. Abstr.* **45**, 6680.

Grassmann, W., and Deffner, G. [1953a]. *Z. physiol. Chem.* **293**, 89–98.

Grassmann, W., and Hormann, H. [1953b]. *Z. physiol. Chem.* **292**, 24–32.

Grassmann, W., and Hannig, K. [1953c]. *Z. physiol. Chem.* **292**, 32–50.

Grassmann, W., Hannig, K., and Plöckl, M. [1955]. *Z. physiol. Chem.* **299**, 258–276.

Gray, H. E., and Fraenkel, G. [1953]. *Science* **118**, 304–305.

Gray, R. A. [1952]. *Arch. Biochem. Biophys.* **38**, 305–316.

Green, J., and Marcinkiewicz, S. [1955a]. *Nature* **176**, 1172–1173.

Green, J., Marcinkiewicz, S., and Watt, P. R. [1955b]. *J. Sci. Food Agr.* **6**, 274–282.

Green, J. P., and Dam, H. [1954]. *Acta Chem. Scand.* **8**, 1341–1346.

Green, J. W. [1954]. *J. Am. Chem. Soc.* **76**, 5791–5792.

Greenway, R. M., Kent, P. W., and Whitehouse, M. W. [1953]. *Research (London)* **6**, Suppl. No. 1, 6S.

Gregory, F. J., Vining, L. C., and Waksman, S. A. [1955]. *Antibiotics & Chemotherapy* **5**, 409–416.

Gregory, G. F. [1955]. *Science* **121**, 169.

Grieg, A. [1952]. *Nature* **170**, 845.

Grodsky, G., and Tarver, H. [1956]. *Nature* **177**, 223–225.

Gross, J., and Leblond, C. P. [1951]. *Endocrinology* **48**, 714–725.

Gross, J., and Pitt-Rivers, R. [1953]. *Biochem. J.* **53**, 645–650.

Grote, I. W. [1931]. *J. Biol. Chem.* **93**, 25–30.

Gruch, W. [1954]. *Naturwissenschaften* **41**, 39–40.

Grüttner, R. [1954]. *Klin. Wochschr.* **32**, 263–264, from [1954]. *Chem. Abstr.* **48**, 6900.

Grunze, H., and Thilo, E. [1954]. *Sitzber. deut. Akad. Wiss. Berlin, Kl. Math. u. allgem. Naturw.* **1953**, No. 5, 1–25.

Günzel, C., and Weiss, F. [1955]. *Z. anal. Chem.* **148**, 250–251.

Guerillot, J., Guerillot-Vinet, A., and Delmas, L. [1952]. *Compt. rend.* **235**, 1295–1297.

Guggenheim, M. [1940]. "Die Biogenen Amine," 510 pp. Nordeman, Basel.

Gurvich, A. E. [1955]. *Biokhimiya* **20**, 550–553.

Gustafsson, C., Sundman, J., and Lindh, T. [1951]. *Paper and Timber (Finland)* **33**, 1.

Haack, E., Kaiser, F., Gube, M., and Springler, H. [1956]. *Naturwissenschaften* **43**, 301–302.

Haberland, G. L., Bruns, F., and Altman, K. I. [1954]. *Biochim. et Biophys. Acta* **15**, 578.

Habermann, E., Müller, W., and Schreglmann, A. [1953]. *Arzneimittel-Forsch.* **3**, 30–33; from [1953] *Chem. Abstr.* **47**, 5479.

Hack, M. H. [1953]. *Biochem. J.* **54**, 602–605.

Hackman, R. H., and Trikojus, V. M. [1952]. *Biochem. J.* **51**, 653–656.

Hackman, R. H., and Lazarus, M. [1955]. *Biochim. et Biophys. Acta* **17**, 148.

Hagdahl, L., and Tiselius, A. [1952]. *Nature* **170**, 799–800.

Hagdahl, L., and Danielson, C. E. [1954]. *Nature* **174**, 1062–1063.

Hais, I. M., and Pecáková, L. [1949]. *Nature* **163**, 768.

Hais, I. M., and Horesovsky, O. [1954]. *Chem. listy* **48**, 549–551.

Hale, D. K. [1955]. *Chem. & Ind. (London)* pp. 1147–1148.

Hall, D. A., and Wewalka, F. [1951]. *Nature* **168**, 685–687.

Hall, D. A. [1952]. *Biochem. J.* **51**, 499–504.

Hamerman, D. [1955a]. *Science* **122**, 924–925.

Hamerman, D., Bartz, K. W., and Reife, A. [1955b]. *Anal. Chem.* **27**, 1524–1525.

Hamilton, P. B., and Ortiz, P. J. [1950]. *Anal. Chem.* **22**, 948–949.

Hanes, C. S., and Isherwood, F. A. [1949]. *Nature* **164**, 1107–1112.

Hanes, C. S., Hird, F. J. R., and Isherwood, F. A. [1950]. *Nature* **166**, 288–292.

Hannan, R. S., and Lea, C. H. [1951]. *Nature* **168**, 744–745.

Harasawa, S. [1951a]. *J. Chem. Soc. Japan, Pure Chem. Sect.* **72**, 236–239; from [1952] *Chem. Abstr.* **46**, 850.

Harasawa, S. [1951b]. *J. Chem. Soc. Japan, Pure Chem. Sect.* **72**, 423–426; from [1952] *Chem. Abstr.* **46**, 1917.

Hardwicke, J. [1954]. *Biochem. J.* **57**, 166–171.

Hardy, T. L., and Holland, D. O. [1952]. *Chem. & Ind. (London)* p. 855.

Hardy, T. L., Holland, D. O., and Nayler, J. H. C. [1955]. *Anal. Chem.* **27**, 971–974.

Harris, G., and MacWilliam, I. C. [1954]. *Chem. & Ind. (London)* p. 249.

Harrison, W. H., Gander, J. E., Blakley, E. R., and Boyer, P. D. [1956]. *Biochim. et Biophys. Acta* **21**, 150–158.

Hartkamp, H., and Specker, H. [1955]. *Naturwissenschaften* **42**, 534–535.

Hashimoto, Y., and Mori, I. [1952a]. *Nature* **170**, 1024–1025.

Hashimoto, Y., Mori, I., and Kimura, M. [1952b]. *Nature* **170**, 975–976.

Hashimoto, Y., and Mori, I. [1953a]. *Nature* **172**, 542–543.

Hashimoto, Y., and Shimizu, S. [1953b]. *J. Pharm. Soc. Japan* **73**, 767–769; from [1953] *Chem. Abstr.* **37**, 10141.

Hashizume, T. [1954]. *Nature* **173**, 645.

Hashmi, M. H., and Cullis, C. F. [1956]. *Anal. Chim. Acta* **14**, 336–338.

Haslewood, G. A. D., and Sjövall, J. [1954]. *Biochem. J.* **57**, 126–130.

Hassall, C. H., and Martin, S. L. [1951]. *J. Chem. Soc.* pp. 2766–2767.

Hassall, C. H., Reyle, K., and Feng, P. [1954a]. *Nature* **173**, 356–357.

Hassall, C. H., and Magnus, K. E. [1954b]. *Experientia* **10**, 425–426.

Hathway, D. E. [1956a]. *Nature* **177**, 747–748.

Hathway, D. E. [1956b]. *Biochem. J.* **63**, 380–387.

Hattori, S., and Shirova, T. [1951]. *Arch. Biochem. Biophys.* **34**, 121–134.

Haugaard, G., and Kroner, T. D. [1948]. *J. Am. Chem. Soc.* **70**, 2135–2137.

Hausmann, W. [1952]. *J. Am. Chem. Soc.* **74**, 3181–3182.

Hawke, J. C., and Lea, C. H. [1953]. *Biochem. J.* **54**, 479–483.

Haworth, R. D., MacGillivray, R., and Peacock, D. H. [1951]. *Nature* **167**, 1068.

Hawthorne, J. R. [1947]. *Nature* **160**, 714–715.

Hayworth, R., and Bacon, J. S. D. [1955]. *Biochem. J.* **61**, 225–232.

Heath, H. [1953]. *Biochem. J.* **54**, 689–694.

Hecht, E., and Mink, C. [1952]. *Biochim. et Biophys. Acta* **8**, 641–653.

Hechter, O., Solomon, M. M., Zaffaroni, A., and Pincus, G. [1953]. *Arch. Biochem. Biophys.* **46**, 201–214.

Hedén, C. G. [1950]. *Nature* **166**, 999–1000.

Heftmann, E. [1950]. *Science* **111**, 571–572.

Heftmann, E. [1951]. *J. Am. Chem. Soc.* **73**, 851–852.

Heftmann, E., and Levant, A. J. [1952a]. *J. Biol. Chem.* **194**, 703–709.

Heftmann, E., and Hayden, A. L. [1952b]. *J. Biol. Chem.* **197**, 47–55.

Heftmann, E., Berner, P., Hayden, A. L., Miller, H. K., and Mosettig, E. [1954]. *Arch. Biochem. Biophys.* **51**, 329–339.

Heftmann, E. [1955]. *Chem. Revs.* **55**, 679–711.

Heimann, W., Strohecker, R., and Matt, F. [1953]. *Z. Lebensm.-Untersuch. u.-Forsch.* **97**, 263–270.

Hellmann, H. [1951]. *Z. physiol. Chem.* **287**, 205–209.

Henschler, D. [1956]. *Z. physiol. Chem.* **305**, 34–41.

Heppel, L. A., and Whitfield, P. R. [1955]. *Biochem. J.* **60**, 1–7.

Heros, E., and Amy, L. M. [1955]. *Bull. soc. chim. France* pp. 367–369.

Hesse, G., and Weil, H. [1954]. "Michael Tswett's erste chromatographische Schrift." Woelm, Eschwege.

Heusghem, C. [1953]. *Nature* **171**, 42–43.

Heyndrickx, A. [1953]. *J. Am. Pharm. Assoc., Sci. Ed.* **42**, 680–681.

Heyns, K., and Anders, G. [1951]. *Z. physiol. Chem.* **287**, 1–18.

Heyns, K., Koch, W., and Köningsdorf, W. [1952]. *Naturwissenschaften* **39**, 381.

Heyrovský, A. [1956]. *Biochim. et Biophys. Acta* **21**, 180.

Hickey, R. J., and Phillips, W. F. [1954]. *Anal. Chem.* **26**, 1640–1642.

Hiller, E., Zinnert, F., and Frese, G. [1952]. *Biochem. Z.* **323**, 245–250.

Hiller, E., and Zinnert, F. [1953]. *Biochem. Z.* **324**, 93–95.

Hinman, R. L. [1956]. *Anal. Chim. Acta* **15**, 125–128.

Hirayama, O., and Noda, M. [1956]. *Abura Kagaku* **5**, 16–18.

Hird, F. J. R., and Trikojus, V. M. [1948]. *Australian J. Sci.* **10**, 185–187; from [1948] *Chem. Abstr.* **42**, 8852.

Hirst, E. L., Hough, L., and Jones, J. K. N. [1949]. *J. Chem. Soc.* 928–933.

Hiscox, D. J. [1951]. *Anal. Chem.* **23**, 923–924.

Hiscox, E. R., and Berridge, N. J. [1950]. *Nature* **166**, 522.

Hobson, G. E., and Rees, K. R. [1955]. *Biochem. J.* **61**, 549–552.

Hockenhull, D. J. D., and Floodgate, D. G. [1952]. *Biochem. J.* **52**, 38–40.

Hockenhull, D. J. D. [1953a]. *Nature* **171**, 982.

Hockenhull, D. J. D., Hunter, G. D., and Herbert, M. W. [1953b]. *Chem. & Ind. (London)* p. 127.

Hockenhull, D. J. D., Herbert, M., and Walter, A. D. [1954]. *Biochem. J.* **56**, 73–82.

Hofmann, H., and Staudinger, H. J. [1951]. *Naturwissenschaften* **38**, 213.

Hofmann-Credner, D. [1953]. *Naturwissenschaften* **40**, 623.

Hôjô, S. [1950]. *Igaku to Seibutsugaku* **17**, 85–88; from [1951] *Chem. Abstr.* **45**, 1188.

Holiday, E. R., and Johnson, E. A. [1949]. *Nature* **163**, 216–217.

Holman, W. I. M. [1954]. *Biochem. J.* **56**, 513–520.

Holness, H., and Stone, W. R. [1955]. *Nature* **176**, 604.

Honda, K., Miura, K., and Tamaokhi, T. [1952]. *J. Agr. Chem. Soc. Japan* **26**, 453–456; from [1953] *Chem. Abstr.* **47**, 6481.

Honer, C. J., and Tuckey, S. L. [1953]. *J. Dairy Sci.* **36**, 1233–1240.

Hood, S. L. [1957]. Private communication.

Horne, R. E., and Pollard, A. L. [1948]. *J. Bacteriol.* **55**, 231–234.

Horner, L., Emrich, W., and Kirschner, A. [1952]. *Z. Elektrochem.* **56**, 987–995; from [1953] *Chem. Abstr.* **47**, 5837.

Horrocks, R. H. [1949a]. *Nature* **164**, 444.

Horrocks, R. H., and Manning, G. B. [1949b]. *Lancet* **256**, 1042–1045.

Hossfeld, R. L. [1951]. *J. Am. Chem. Soc.* **73**, 852–854.

Hotchkiss, R. D. [1948]. *J. Biol. Chem.* **175**, 315–332.

Hough, L., Jones, J. K. N., and Wadman, W. H. [1948]. *Nature* **162**, 448.

Hough, L. [1950a]. *Nature* **165**, 400.

Hough, L., Jones, J. K. N., and Wadman, W. H. [1950b]. *J. Chem. Soc.* pp. 1702–1706.

Housewright, R. D., and Thorne, C. B. [1950]. *J. Bacteriol.* **60**, 89–100.

Hubener, H. J., Fukushima, D. F., and Gallagher, T. F. [1956]. *J. Biol. Chem.* **220**, 499–511.

Huebner, C. F. [1951]. *Nature* **167**, 119–120.

Hübner, G., and Pfeil, E. [1954]. *Z. physiol. Chem.* **296**, 225–228.

Huennekens, F. M., Hanahan, D. J., and Uziel, M. [1954]. *J. Biol. Chem.* **206**, 443–447.

Hulme, A. C., and Arthington, W. [1952]. *Nature* **170**, 659–660.

Hulme, A. C. [1953]. *Nature* **171**, 610–611.

Hulme, A. C. [1954]. *Biochem. et Biophys. Acta* **14**, 36–43.

Hunter, G. [1951]. *Biochem. J.* **48**, 265–270.

Hunter, I. R., Houston, D. F., and Owens, H. S. [1956]. *Anal. Chem.* **28**, 283–284.

Huygens, R., and Casimir, J. [1953]. *Bull. inst. agron. et stas. recherches Gembloux* **21** (3/4), 8–13; also [1954]. *Chem. Abstr.* **48**, 9273.

Iacobellis, M. [1955]. *Arch. Biochem. Biophys.* **59**, 199–206.

Ingalls, A. G. [1953]. *Sci. American* **188**, 102–106.

Ingram, V. M. [1953]. *J. Biol. Chem.* **202**, 193–201.

Inoue, Mitsuji [1953]. *Nagasaki Igakkai Zassi* **28**, 1283–1285; from [1954] *Chem. Abstr.* **48**, 7088.

Inoue, Yoshiyuki, and Noda, M. [1950]. *J. Agr. Chem. Soc. Japan* **23**, 368; from [1952] *Chem. Abstr.* **46**, 6408.

Inoue, Yoshiyuki, and Noda, M. [1955a]. *Bull. Agr. Chem. Soc. Japan* **19**, 214–219.

Inoue, Yoshiyuki, Noda, M., and Hirayama, O. [1955b]. *J. Am. Oil Chemists' Soc.* **32**, 132–135.

Irion, W., and Moosmüller, E. [1953]. *Z. anal. Chem.* **140**, 416–421.

Irreverre, F., and Martin, W. [1954]. *Anal. Chem.* **26**, 257–261.

Irvin, J. L., and Irvin, E. M. [1953]. *Federation Proc.* **12**, 223–224.

Isherwood, F. A., and Jermyn, M. A. [1951]. *Biochem. J.* **48**, 515–524.

Isherwood, F. A., and Hanes, C. S. [1953]. *Biochem. J.* **55**, 824–830.

Isherwood, F. A. [1954a]. *Brit. Med. Bull.* **10**, 202–210.

Isherwood, F. A., and Cruickshank, D. H. [1954b]. *Nature* **173**, 121-122; **174**, 123–126.

Isherwood, F. A., and Jones, R. L. [1955]. *Nature* **175**, 419–421.

Isherwood, F. A., and Niavis, C. A. [1956]. *Biochem. J.* **64**, 549–558.
Ishida, Y., Inagaki, N., Shiota, A., and Watanabe, R. J.[1953]. *Pharm. Soc. Japan* **73**, 736ᴸ740; from [1953] *Chem. Abstr.* **47**, 10141.
Itai, T., Oba, T., and Kamiya, S. [1954]. *Eisei Shikenjo Hôkoku* **72**, 87–90.
Iyer, G. Y. N. [1954]. *Indian J. Med. Research* **42**, 225–229.
Jaarma, M. [1954]. *Acta Chem. Scand.* **8**, 860–862.
Jacoby, W. B., and Bonner, D. M. [1956]. *J. Biol. Chem.* **221**, 689–695.
James, W. O. [1948]. *Nature* **161**, 851–852.
James, W. O., and Elliott, D. C. [1955]. *Nature* **175**, 89.
Janot, M. M., Saïas, E., and Foucher, M. [1953]. *Bull. soc. chim. biol.* **35**, 1101–1110.
Jatzkewitz, H. [1953]. *Z. physiol. Chem.* **292**, 94–100.
Jatzkewitz, H., and Lenz, U. [1956]. *Z. physiol. Chem.* **305**, 53–60.
Jax, P., and Aust, H. [1953]. *Milchwiss. Ber.* pp. 145–189; from [1954] *Chem. Abstr.* **48**, 7218.
Jeanes, A., Wise, C. S., and Dimler, R. J. [1951]. *Anal. Chem.* **23**, 415–420.
Jeffrey, R. N., and Eoff, W. H. [1955]. *Anal. Chem.* **27**, 1903–1905.
Jellinek, P. H. [1953]. *Nature* **171**, 750–751.
Jensen, H., and Evans, E. A., Jr. [1935]. *J. Biol. Chem.* **108**, 1–9.
Jepson, J. B., and Stevens, B. J. [1953a]. *Nature* **172**, 772.
Jepson, J. B., and Smith, I. [1953b]. *Nature* **172**, 1100–1101.
Jepson, J. B., and Smith, I. [1954a]. Society of Chemical Industry Meeting, Kings College, London, Jan. 15.
Jepson, J. B., Smith, I., and Stevens, B. J. [1954b]. Private communication.
Jepson, J. B. [1955]. *Lancet* 1009–1011.
Jepson, J. B., and Smith, I. [1956]. *Nature* **177**, 84.
Jerchel, D., and Müller, R. [1951]. *Naturwissenschaften* **38**, 561–562.
Jerchel, D., and Jacobs, D. [1953]. *Angew. Chem.* **65**, 342–344.
Jermyn, M. A., and Isherwood, F. A. [1949]. *Biochem. J.* **44**, 402–407.
Jermyn, M. A. [1953]. *Australian J. Biol. Sci.* **6**, 77–97.
Joftes, D. L., and Warren, S. [1956]. *Science* **124**, 1155.
Johanson, R. [1953]. *Nature* **172**, 956–957.
Johnson, B. C., and Lin, P. H. [1953]. *J. Am. Chem. Soc.* **75**, 2971–2973.
Johnson, G., Mayer, M. M., and Johnson, D. K. [1951]. *Food Research* **16**, 169–180.
Johnson, G., and Schaal, L. A. [1952]. *Science* **115**, 627–629.
Johnson, G. R. A., Stein, G., and Weiss, J. [1951]. *J. Chem. Soc.* p. 3275.
Jollès, P., and Fromageot, C. [1952]. *Biochim. et Biophys. Acta* **9**, 287–292.
Jones, A. R., Dowling, E. J., and Skraba, W. J. [1953]. *Anal. Chem.* **25**, 394–396.
Jones, A., Taylor, M. P., and Gore, D. N. [1954]. *Chem. & Ind. (London)* p. 461–462.
Jones, J. I. M., and Michael, S. E. [1950]. *Nature* **165**, 685.
Jones, N. R. [1955]. *Biochem. J.* **60**, 81–87.
Jones, T. S. G. [1948]. *Biochem. J.* **42**, lix–lx.
Jones, T. S. G. [1954]. *Brit. Med. Bull.* **10**, 224–228.
Jorgenson, E. C., and Geissman, T. A. [1955]. *Arch. Biochem. Biophys.* **54**, 72–82.
Jutisz, M. [1952]. *Bull. soc. chim. France* pp. 821–830.
Jutisz, M., Privat de Garilhe, M., Suquet, M., and Fromageot, C. [1954]. *Bull. soc. chim. biol.* **36**, 117–125.
Kaiser, Emil, Maxwell, L. C., Landmann, W. A., and Hubata, R. [1953]. *Arch. Biochem. Biophys.* **42**, 94–101.
Kaiser, Elizabeth, and Kagan, B. M. [1956]. *Arch. Biochem. Biophys.* **63**, 118–121.
Kaiser, H., and Jori, H. [1953]. *Pharm. Ztg.-Nachr.* **89**, 331; from [1953] *Chem. Abstr.* **47**, 12492.

Kalbe, H. [1954]. *Z. physiol. Chem.* **297**, 19–44.

Kalkwarf, D. R., and Frost, A. A. [1954]. *Anal. Chem.* **26**, 191–195.

Kalyankar, G. D., Krishnaswamy, P. R., and Sreenivasaya, M. [1952]. *Current Sci. (India)* **21**, 220–222.

Kanngiesser, W. [1951]. *Naturwissenschaften* **38**, 503–504.

Kanngiesser, W. [1953]. *Z. physiol. Chem.* **291**, 247–249.

Kariyone, T., Hashimoto, Y., and Kimura, M. [1951a]. *Nature* **168**, 511.

Kariyone, T., and Hashimoto, Y. [1951b]. *Nature* **168**, 739.

Kariyone, T., Shimizu, S., and Hashimoto, Y. [1952]. *Nature* **170**, 422.

Kariyone, T., Hashimoto, Y., and Kimura, M. [1953]. *Yakugaku Zasshi* **73**, 253–256.

Karl-Kroupa, E. [1956]. *Anal. Chem.* **28**, 1091–1097.

Karler, A. [1952]. *U. S. Atomic Energy Comm.* **UCRL-1838**, May 29.

Karnovsky, M. L., and Johnson, M. J. [1949]. *Anal. Chem.* **21**, 1125.

Katz, J., and Chaikoff, I. L. [1954]. *J. Biol. Chem.* **206**, 887–900.

Kaufmann, H. P. [1950]. *Fette u. Seifen* **52**, 713–721; from [1951] *Chem. Abstr.* **45**, 8271.

Kaufmann, H. P., and Budwig, J. [1952]. *Fette u. Seifen* **54**, 156–165; from [1952] *Chem. Abstr.* **46**, 8703.

Kawai, K., [1953]. *Igaku Kenkyuu* **23**, 572–581; from [1953] *Chem. Abstr.* **47**, 8119.

Kawerau, E. [1950]. *Biochem. J.* **47**, xxiii.

Kawerau, E. [1951a]. *Biochem. J.* **48**, 281–283.

Kawerau, E., and Wieland, T. [1951b]. *Nature* **168**, 77–78.

Kawerau, E. [1956]. *Chromatog. Methods* **1**(2), 7–8.

Kay, R. E., Harris, D. C., and Entenman, C. [1956]. *Arch. Biochem. Biophys.* **63**, 14–25.

Kefford, N. P. [1955]. *J. Exptl. Botany* **6**, 129–151.

Kehl, R., and Stich, W. [1951]. *Z. physiol. Chem.* **289**, 6–10.

Kehl, R., and Günter, B. [1954a]. *Naturwissenschaften* **41**, 118.

Kehl, R., and Günter, B. [1954b]. *Z. physiol. Chem.* **297**, 254–257.

Kelemen, E., Tanos, B., and Halmagyi, D. [1950]. *Biochem. J.* **47**, 138–139.

Kellner, W., Hellmuth, H., and Martin, H. [1954a]. *Naturwissenschaften* **41**, 304–305

Kellner, W., and Hellmuth, H. [1954b]. *Naturwissenschaften* **41**, 527.

Kember, N. F., and Wells, R. A. [1951]. *Analyst* **76**, 579–587.

Kember, N. F., and Wells, R. A. [1955a]. *Analyst* **80**, 735–751.

Kember, N. F., and Wells, R. A. [1955b]. *Nature* **175**, 512–513.

Kemble, A. R., and Macpherson, H. T. [1952]. *Nature* **170**, 664.

Kemble, A. R., and Macpherson, H. T. [1954]. *Biochem. J.* **56**, 548–555.

Kennedy, E. P., and Barker, H. A. [1951]. *Anal. Chem.* **23**, 1033–1034.

Kent, P. W., Lawson, G., and Senior, A. [1951]. *Science* **113**, 354–355.

Kerby, G. P. [1953]. *Proc. Soc. Exptl. Biol. Med.* **83**, 263.

Kertes, S., and Lederer, M. [1956]. *Anal. Chim. Acta* **15**, 543–547.

Keston, A. S., Udenfriend, S., and Levy, M. [1947]. *J. Am. Chem. Soc.* **69**, 3151–3152.

Keston, A. S., Udenfriend, S., and Levy, M. [1950]. *J. Am. Chem. Soc.* **72**, 748–753.

Keup, W. [1952]. *Z. physiol. Chem.* **291**, 223–228.

Khabas, I. M., and El'kin, S. B. [1955]. *Byull. Eksptl. Biol. i Med.* **40**(7), 79; from [1956] *Chem. Abstr.* **50**, 3160.

Khan, N. A., Baker, B. E., and Van Horn, W. F. [1955]. *J. Agr. Food Chem.* **3**, 853–855.

Kiessling, H. [1954]. *Acta. Chem. Scand.* **8**, 859–860.

Kiessling, K. H. [1953a]. *Nature* **172,** 1187-1188.

Kiessling, K. H., and Lindahl, G. [1953b]. *Arkiv Kemi* **6,** 271-272; from [1954] *Chem. Abstr.* **48,** 4622.

Kilgour, G. L., and Dutton, G. G. S. [1953]. *Can. J. Chem.* **31,** 1260-1261.

Kimbel, K. H. [1953]. *Naturwissenschaften* **40,** 200-201.

Kirby, K. S., Knowles, E., and White, T. [1953]. *J. Soc. Leather Trades' Chemists* **37,** 283.

Kirby, K. S. [1955a]. *Biochim. et Biophys. Acta* **18,** 575-576.

Kirby, K. S., and White, T. [1955b]. *Biochem. J.* **60,** 582-590.

Kirby-Berry, H., Sutton, H. E., Cain, L., and Berry, J. S. [1951]. *Texas Univ. Publ.* No. **5509,** 22-55.

Kirchner, J. G., and Keller, G. J. [1950]. *J. Am. Chem. Soc.* **72,** 1867-1868.

Kirk, P. L., and Duggan, E. L. [1954]. *Anal. Chem.* **26,** 163-176.

Kiss, P., and Széll, T. [1956]. *Naturwissenschaften* **43,** 448.

Kitahara, S., and Hiyama, H. [1954]. *Sci. and Ind. (Japan)* **28,** 341.

Kjaer, A., and Rubenstein, K. [1953a]. *Acta Chem. Scand.* **7,** 528-536.

Kjaer, A., and Rubenstein, K. [1953b]. *Nature* **171,** 840-841.

Klatzkin, C. [1952]. *Nature* **169,** 422.

Klein, A. M., Laug, E. P., Tighe, J. F., Ramsey, L. L., Mitchell, L. C., and Kunze, F. M. [1956]. *J. Assoc. Offic. Agr. Chemists* **39,** 242-253.

Klenk, E., and Lauenstein, K. [1952]. *Z. physiol. Chem.* **291,** 249-258.

Kludas, K. H. [1954]. *Chem. Tech. (Berlin)* **6,** 39; from [1954] *Chem. Abstr.* **48,** 6326.

Kluener, R. G. [1949]. *J. Bacteriol.* **57,** 101-109.

Knight, C. A. [1951]. *J. Biol. Chem.* **190,** 753-756.

Koberlein, W., and Mair-Waldburg, H. [1955]. *Z. Lebensm.-Untersuch. u.-Forsch.* **102,** 231-235.

Kobrle, V., and Zahradnik, R. [1954]. *Chem. listy* **48,** 1189-1196.

Koch, G., and Weidel, W. [1956]. *Z. physiol. Chem.* **303,** 213-223.

Kochakian, C. D., and Stidworthy, G. [1952]. *J. Biol. Chem.* **199,** 607-612.

Kodicek, E., and Reddi, K. K. [1951]. *Nature* **168,** 475-477.

Kodicek, E., and Ashby, D. R. [1954]. *Biochem. J.* **57,** xii-xiii.

Köiw, E., and Grönwall, A. [1952]. *Scand. J. Clin. & Lab. Invest.* **4,** 244-246.

Kofranyi, E. [1955]. *Z. physiol. Chem.* **299,** 129-138.

Kogan, L., DiCarlo, F. J., and Maynard, W. E. [1953]. *Anal. Chem.* **25,** 1118-1120.

Kolier, I., and Ribaudo, C. [1954]. *Anal. Chem.* **26,** 1546-1549.

Komenda, J. [1953]. *Chem. listy* **37,** 1877-1878; from [1954] *Chem. Abstr.* **48,** 3850.

Kosikowsky, F. V., and Dahlberg, A. C. [1954]. *J. Dairy Sci.* **37,** 167-172.

Kotake, M., Sakan, T., Nakamura, N., and Senoh, S. [1951]. *J. Am. Chem. Soc.* **73,** 2973-2974.

Kotake, M., and Arakawa, H. [1956]. *Naturwissenschaften* **43,** 327-328.

Kowkabany, G. N., and Cassidy, H. G. [1950]. *Anal. Chem.* **22,** 817-819.

Kowkabany, G. N., and Cassidy, H. G. [1952]. *Anal. Chem.* **24,** 643-649.

Kowkabany, G. N. [1954]. *Advances in Carbohydrate Chem.* **9,** 303-353.

Kream, J., and Chargaff, E. [1952]. *J. Am. Chem. Soc.* **74,** 4274-4277.

Krebs, H. A., and Hems, R. [1953]. *Biochim. et Biophys. Acta* **12,** 172-1 0.

Krebs, K., and Wankmüller, A. [1953]. *Naturwissenschaften* **40,** 623-6 4.

Krishnamurthy, K., Venkitasubramanian, T. A., and Giri, K. V. [1952]. *Current Sci. (India)* **21,** 252.

Krishnamurthy, K., and Swaminathan, M. [1954]. *J. Sci. Indian Research* **13B,** 374-376.

Krishnamurthy, K., and Swaminathan, M. [1955a]. *J. Sci. Ind. Research* **14C**, 79–80.

Krishnamurthy, K., and Swaminathan, M. [1955b]. *Anal. Chem.* **27**, 1396–1399.

Kritchevsky, D., and Calvin, M. [1950]. *J. Am. Chem. Soc.* **72**, 4330.

Kritchevsky, D., and Kirk, M. R. [1952a]. *Arch. Biochem. Biophys.* **35**, 346–351.

Kritchevsky, D., and Kirk, M. R. [1952b]. *J. Am. Chem. Soc.* **74**, 4484–4486.

Kritchevsky, D., and Kirk, M. R. [1952c]. *J. Am. Chem. Soc.* **74**, 4713.

Kritchevsky, T. H., and Tiselius, A. [1951]. *Science* **114**, 299–300.

Kritsman, M. G., and Lebedeva, M. B. [1950]. *Ukrain. Biokhim. Zhur.* **22**, 430–434; from [1954] *Chem. Abstr.* **48**, 2159.

Kruh, J., Dreyfus, J. C., and Schapira, G. [1952]. *Bull. soc. chim. biol.* **34**, 773–777.

Kubelka, P., and Munk, F. [1931]. *Z. tech. Physik* **12**, 593–601.

Kühn, A. [1955]. *Naturwissenschaften* **42**, 529–530.

Kulonen, E., Carpén, E., and Ruokolainen, T. [1952]. *Scand. J. Clin. & Lab. Invest.* **4**, 189–197; from [1953] *Chem. Abstr.* **47**, 1766.

Kulonen, E. [1953]. *Scand. J. Clin. & Lab. Invest.* **5**, 72–74; from [1953] *Chem. Abstr.* **47**, 7573.

Kunkel, H. G., and Tiselius, A. [1951]. *J. Gen. Physiol.* **35**, 89–118.

Kuroda, Y. [1951]. *J. Biochem. (Japan)* **38**, 115–118; from [1951] *Chem. Abstr.* **45**, 9097.

Kutzim, H. [1952]. *Naturwissenschaften* **39**, 135.

Kvamme, E., and Hellman, L. [1954]. *Anal. Chem.* **26**, 1995–1996.

Lacourt, A., Sommereyns, G., Degeyndt, E., Baruh, J., and Gillard, J. [1949]. *Nature* **163**, 999–1000.

Lacourt, A., Sommereyns, G., and Claret, M. [1951]. *Mikrochemie ver. Mikrochim. Acta* **38**, 444–455.

Lacourt, A., Sommereyns, G., and Wantier, G. [1952]. *Analyst* **77**, 943–954.

Lacourt, A., Sommereyns, G., Stadler-Denis, A., and Wantier, G. [1953]. *Mikrochemie ver. Mikrochim. Acta* **40**, 268–284.

Lacourt, A., and Sommereyns, G. [1954a]. *Mikrochim. Acta* pp. 550–583.

Lacourt, A., and Sommereyns, G. [1954b]. *Mikrochim. Acta* pp. 604–629.

Lacourt, A., and Heyndryckx, P. [1955]. *Nature* **176**, 880–881.

Lacourt, A. [1956]. *Mikrochim. Acta* pp. 700–733.

Ladenbauer, I.-M., Bradacs, L. K., and Hecht, F. [1954]. *Mikrochim. Acta* pp. 388–402.

Lagneau, C. [1953]. *Ann. fals. et fraudes* **46**, 432–437; from [1954] *Chem. Abstr.* **48**, 3590.

Laidlaw, R. A., and Reid, S. G. [1952]. *J. Sci. Food Agr.* **3**, 19–25.

Lakshminarayanan, K. [1954a]. *Arch. Biochem. Biophys.* **49**, 396–399.

Lakshminarayanan, K. [1954b]. *Arch. Biochem. Biophys.* **51**, 367–370.

Lambou, M. G. [1956]. *Anal. Chem.* **28**, 1216.

Landua, A. J., Fuerst, R., and Awapara. [1951]. *Anal. Chem.* **23**, 162–168.

Landucci, J. M., and Pimont, M. [1953]. *Bull. soc. chim. biol.* **35**, 1041–1044.

Langer, A. [1956]. *Anal. Chem.* **28**, 426–427.

Laskowski, D. E., and McCrone, W. C. [1951]. *Anal. Chem.* **23**, 1579–1582.

Latner, A. L. [1952]. *Biochem. J.* **51**, xii.

Lautsch, W., Manecke, G., and Broser, W. [1953]. *Z. Naturforsch.* **8b**, 232–236.

Lawday, D. [1952]. *Nature* **51**, 415–416.

Lawson, A., Morley, H. W., and Woolf, K. I. [1950]. *Biochem. J.* **47**, 513–518.

Lea, C. H., Rhodes, D. N., and Stoll, R. D. [1955]. *Biochem. J.* **60**, 353–363.

Lebez, D. [1953]. *Bull. sci. Conseil acad. RPF Yougoslavie* **1,** 44–45; from [1954] *Chem. Abstr.* **48,** 5249.

Lederer, E., and Lederer, M. [1953]. "Chromatography: A Review of Principles, and Applications," 460 pp. Elsevier, Houston, Texas.

Lederer, E., and Lederer, M., [1957]. "Chromatography: A Review of Principles and Applications," 2nd ed. 711 pp. Van Nostrand, Princeton, New Jersey.

Lederer, M. [1948]. *Nature* **162,** 776–777.

Lederer, M. [1949a]. *Science* **110,** 115–116.

Lederer, M. [1949b]. *Australian J. Sci.* **11,** 174.

Lederer, M. [1949c]. *Australian J. Sci.* **11,** 208–209.

Lederer, M. [1949d]. *Australian J. Sci.* **12,** 78.

Lederer, M. [1950a]. *Science* **112,** 504–505.

Lederer, M. [1950b]. *Nature* **165,** 529–530.

Lederer, M., and Silberman, H. [1952a]. *Anal. Chim. Acta* **6,** 133–134.

Lederer, M. [1952b]. *Anal. Chim. Acta* **6,** 267–269.

Lederer, M. [1952c]. *Anal. Chim. Acta* **7,** 458–461.

Lederer, M. [1953a]. *Compt. rend.* **236,** 1557–1559.

Lederer, M. [1953b]. *Nature* **172,** 727.

Lederer, M. [1955]. *Anal. Chim. Acta* **12,** 142–145.

Lederer, M., and Kertes, S. [1956a]. *Anal. Chim. Acta* **15,** 226–231.

Lederer, M. [1956b]. *Mikrochim. Acta* 43–53.

Leegwater, D. C. [1956]. *Nature* **178,** 916–917.

Leifer, E., Langham, W. H., Nye, J. F., and Mitchell, H. K. [1950]. *J. Biol. Chem.* **184,** 589–592.

Leiserson, L., and Walker, T. B. [1955]. *Anal. Chem.* **27,** 1129–1130.

Lemieux, R. U., and Bauer, H. F. [1954]. *Anal. Chem.* **26,** 920–921.

Lenz, R. W., and Holmberg, C. V. [1956]. *Anal. Chem.* **28,** 7–8.

Leone, E., and Scale, E. [1950]. *Bol. soc. ital. biol. sper.* **26,** 1223–1224; from [1951] *Chem. Abstr.* **45,** 7622.

LeStrange, R. J., and Müller, R. H. [1954]. *Anal. Chem.* **26,** 953–959

Levenbook, L. [1957]. *Anal. Chem.* **29,** 1719–1720.

Levine, C., and Chargaff, E. [1952]. *J. Biol. Chem.* **192,** 465–479; **192,** 481–483.

Levy, A. L., and Chung, D. [1953]. *Anal. Chem.* **25,** 396–399.

Levy, A. L. [1954a]. *Nature* **174,** 126–127.

Levy, A. L. [1954b]. *Biochim. et Biophys. Acta* **15,** 589.

Levy, M. F. [1954]. *Anal. Chem.* **26,** 1849–1850.

Lewbart, M. L., and Schneider, J. J. [1955]. *Nature* **176,** 1175.

Lewis, B. [1956a]. *Biochim. et Biophys. Acta* **20,** 396.

Lewis, B. [1956b]. *Biochim. et Biophys. Acta* **20,** 417.

Lewis, J. A., and Griffiths, J. M. [1951]. *Analyst* **76,** 388–395.

Lewis, P. R. [1952]. *Biochem. J.* **52,** 330–338.

Li, C. H., and Ash, L. [1953]. *J. Biol. Chem.* **203,** 419–424.

Liberman, L. A., Zaffaroni, A., and Stotz, E. [1951]. *J. Am. Chem. Soc.* **73,** 1387–1388.

Light, A., and Simpson, M. V. [1956]. *Nature* **177,** 225.

Lind, E. F., Lane, H. C., and Gleason, L. S. [1953]. *Plant Physiol.* **28,** 325–328.

Lindberg, B., Misiorny, A., and Wachtmeister, C. A. [1953]. *Acta Chem. Scand.* **7,** 591–595.

Linderstrøm-Lang, K., and Holter, H. [1933]. *Compt. rend. trav. lab. Carlsberg* **19** (14), 1-12.

Linser, H., and Kiermayer, O. [1956]. *Biochim. et Biophys. Acta* **21,** 382.

Lissitsky, S. [1955]. *Bull. soc. chim. biol.* **37,** 89–96.

List, P. H. [1956]. *Z. physiol. Chem.* **303,** 27–29.

Livingston, C. H., Payne, M. G., Fults, J. L., and Blouch, R. M. [1953]. *Science* **118,** 56–57.

Lockhart, I. M. [1956]. *Nature* **177,** 393–394.

Löffler, J. E., and Reichl, E. H. [1953]. *Mikrochim. Acta* pp. 79–88.

Loeffler, W., and Wunderly, C. [1953]. *J. Clin. Pathol.* **6,** 282–285.

Löfgren, M. [1952]. *Acta Chem. Scand.* **6,** 1030–1035.

Lohmann, D. [1956]. *Z. physiol. Chem.* **305,** 192–195.

Long, A. G., Quayle, J. R., and Stedman, R. J. [1951]. *J. Chem. Soc.* pp. 2197–2201.

Longenecker, W. H. [1948]. *Science* **107,** 23–24.

Longenecker, W. H. [1949]. *Anal. Chem.* **21,** 1402–1405.

Loring, H. S., Levy, L. W., and Moss, L. K. [1956]. *Anal. Chem.* **28,** 539–540.

Lotz, W. E., Gallimore, J. C., and Boyd, G. A. [1952]. *Nucleonics* **10,** 28–31.

Lowther, A. G. [1951]. *Nature* **167,** 767–768.

Lucas, J., Vassilaros, L., and Petraitis, L. [1954]. *Federation Proc.* **13,** 256.

Luckwill, L. C. [1952]. *Nature* **169,** 375.

Lüderitz, O., and Westphal, O. [1952a]. *Z. Naturforsch.* **7b,** 136–138.

Lüderitz, O., and Westphal, O. [1952b]. *Z. Naturforsch.* **7b,** 548–554; from [1953] *Chem. Abstr.* **47,** 4415.

Lugg, J. W. H., and Overell, B. T. [1947]. *Nature* **160,** 87–88.

Lugg, J. W. H., and Overell, B. T. [1948]. *Australian J. Sci. Research* **A1,** 98–111.

Lugg, J. W. H., and McEvoy-Bowe, E. [1957]. *Nature* **176,** 1076.

Lyness, W. I., and Quackenbush, F. W. [1955]. *Anal. Chem.* **27,** 1978–1980.

Lynn, W. S., Jr., Steele, L. A., and Staple, E. [1956]. *Anal. Chem.* **28,** 132–133.

Ma, R. M., and Fontaine, T. D. [1949]. *Science* **110,** 232–233.

McAleer, W. J., and Kozlowski, M. [1956]. *Arch. Biochem. Biophys.* **62,** 196–197.

McAllister, R. A. [1951]. *Nature* **167,** 863.

McCollum, E. V., and Rider, A. A. [1952]. *Arch. Biochem. Biophys.* **40,** 20–21.

McCready, R. M., and McComb, E. A. [1954]. *Anal. Chem.* **26,** 1645–1647.

McDonald, H. J., Bermes, E. W., Jr., and Shepherd, H. G., Jr. [1957]. *Chromatog. Methods* **2**(1), 1-5.

McDonough, S. [1954]. *Nature* **173,** 645–646.

Macek, K., and Tadra, M. [1952]. *Chem. listy* **46,** 450–452; from [1952] *Chem. Abstr.* **46,** 11049.

Macek, K. and Vejdêlek, Z. J. [1955]. *Nature* **176,** 1173–1174.

Macek, K., and Morávek, L. [1956]. *Nature* **178,** 102–103.

McCready, R. M., and McComb, E. A. [1954]. *Anal. Chem.* **26,** 1645–1647.

McFarren, E. F. [1951a]. *Anal. Chem.* **23,** 168–174.

McFarren, E. F., Brand, K., and Rutkowski, H. R. [1951b]. *Anal. Chem.* **23,** 1146–1149.

McFarren, E. F., and Mills, J. A. [1952]. *Anal. Chem.* **24,** 650–653.

McGeown, M. G., and Malpress, F. H. [1952]. *Biochem. J.* **52,** 606–611.

McIntire, F. C., Roth, L. W., and Shaw, J. L. [1947]. *J. Biol. Chem.* **170,** 537–544

McKee, H. S. [1952]. Private communication.

McKee, H. S., and Urbach, G. E. [1953]. *Australian J. Biol. Sci.* **6,** 369–378.

McKerns, K. W. [1951]. *Can. J. Med. Sci.* **29,** 59–62.

McMahon, J. M., Davis, R. B., and Kalnitsky, G. [1950]. *Proc. Soc. Exptl. Biol. Med.* **75,** 799–801.

Magasanik, B., and Umbarger, H. E. [1950]. *J. Am. Chem. Soc.* **72,** 2308–2309.

Magasanik, B. [1953]. *J. Biol. Chem.* **205,** 1007–1026.

Magee, R. J., and Headridge, J. B. [1955]. *Analyst* **80,** 785–788.

Maiwald, L., and Maske, H. [1956]. *Z. physiol. Chem.* **306**, 143–144.

Makisumi, S. [1952]. *J. Chem. Soc. Japan, Pure Chem. Sect.* **73**, 737–739; from [1953] *Chem. Abstr.* **47**, 5848.

Malpress, F. H., and Morrison, A. B. [1949]. *Nature* **164**, 963.

Malyoth, E. [1951]. *Naturwissenschaften* **38**, 478.

Malyoth, G., and Stein, H. W. [1951]. *Biochem. Z.* **322**, 165–167.

Malyoth, G., and Stein, H. W. [1952]. *Biochem. Z.* **323**, 265.

Mangold, H. K., Lamp, B. G., and Schlenk, H. [1955]. *J. Am. Chem. Soc.* **77**, 6070–6072.

Mann, T., and Leone, E. [1953]. *Biochem. J.* **53**, 140–148.

Mapson, L. W., and Partridge, S. M. [1949]. *Nature* **164**, 479–480.

Mapson, L. W., and Goddard, D. R. [1951]. *Biochem. J.* **49**, 592–601.

Mapson, L. W., and Isherwood, F. A. [1956]. *Biochem. J.* **64**, 13–22.

Marchal, J. G., and Mittwer, T. [1951]. *Compt. rend. soc. biol.* **145**, 417–421.

Marinetti, G. V., and Stotz, E. [1955]. *J. Am. Chem. Soc.* **77**, 6668–6670.

Marinetti, G. V., and Stotz, E. [1956]. *Biochim. et Biophys. Acta* **21**, 168–170.

Marini-Bettolo, G. B., and Trabacchi, G. [1956]. *Biochim. et Biophys. Acta* **21**, 258–264.

Markees, S. [1954]. *Biochem. J.* **56**, 703–704.

Markham, R., and Smith, J. D. [1949a]. *Nature* **163**, 250–251.

Markham, R., and Smith, J. D. [1949b]. *Nature* **164**, 1052.

Markham, R., and Smith, J. D. [1949c]. *Biochem. J.* **45**, 294–298.

Markham, R., and Smith, J. D. [1951a]. *Biochem. J.* **49**, 401–406.

Markham, R., and Smith, J. D. [1951b]. *Nature* **168**, 406–408.

Markham, R., and Smith, J. D. [1952a]. *Biochem. J.* **52**, 552–557.

Markham, R., and Smith, J. D. [1952b]. *Biochem. J.* **52**, 558–565.

Markham, R. [1954]. *Brit. Med. J.* **10**, 214–217.

Markwardt, R. [1954]. *Naturwissenschaften* **41**, 139.

Mars, P. H. [1953]. *Pharm. Weekblad* **88**, 319–320; from [1953] *Chem. Abstr.* **47**, 8585.

Marshak, A., and Vogel, H. J. [1951]. *J. Biol. Chem.* **189**, 597–605.

Marten, G. [1955]. *Intern. Z. Vitaminforsch.* **25**, 392–401.

Martin, A. J. P., and Synge, R. L. M. [1941a]. *Biochem. J.* **35**, 91–121.

Martin, A. J. P., and Synge, R. L. M. [1941b]. *Biochem. J.* **35**, 1358–1368.

Martin, A. J. P. [1947]. *Endeavour* **6**, 21–28.

Martin, A. J. P., and Mittelmann, R. [1948]. *Biochem. J.* **43**, 353–358.

Martin, A. J. P. [1949]. *Biochem. Soc. Symposia (Cambridge, Engl.)* **3**, 4.

Martin, E. C. [1951]. *Anal. Chim. Acta* **5**, 511–512.

Masamune, H., Yoshizawa, Z., and Maki, M. [1951]. *Tôhoku. J. Exptl. Med.* **53**, 237–241; from [1951] *Chem. Abstr.* **45**, 9576.

Masamune, H., and Maki, M. [1952]. *Tôhoku J. Exptl. Med.* **55**, 299–310; from [1953] *Chem. Abstr.* **47**, 11303.

Mason, M., and Berg, C. P. [1951]. *J. Biol. Chem.* **188**, 783–788.

Mason, M. [1953]. *J. Biol. Chem.* **201**, 513–518.

Matsukawa, T., and Yurugi, S. [1953a]. *Science* **118**, 109–111.

Matsukawa, T., Yurugi, S., and Matsuoka, T. [1953b]. *Science* **118**, 325–327.

Matsuo, Y. [1953]. *Nature* **171**, 1021–1022.

Matthias, W. [1954]. *Naturwissenschaften* **41**, 17–18.

Matthias, W. [1956]. *Naturwissenschaften* **43**, 351–352.

Mattox, V. R., Mason, H. L., and Albert, A. [1956]. *J. Biol. Chem.* **218**, 359–364.

Mavrodineanu, R., Sanford, W. W., and Hitchcock, A. E. [1955]. *Contribs. Boyce Thompson Inst.* **18**, 167–172.

Mayr, H. H. [1956]. *Planta* **46**, 512–515.

Meigh, D. F. [1952a]. *Nature* **169**, 706–707.

Meigh, D. F. [1952b]. *Nature* **170**, 579.

Meister, A., and Abendschein, P. A. [1956]. *Anal. Chem.* **28**, 171–173.

Mellon, E. F., Korn, A. H., and Hoover, S. R. [1953]. *J. Am. Chem. Soc.* **75**, 1675–1678.

Mendenhall, R. M. [1956]. *Chromatog. Methods* **1**(2), 2–3.

Mentzer, C., Molho, D., and Molho-Lacroix, L. [1953]. *Bull. soc. chim. France* pp. 636–640.

Metcalf, R. L., and March, R. B. [1953]. *Science* **117**, 527–528.

Metzenberg, R. L., and Mitchell, H. K. [1954]. *J. Am. Chem. Soc.* **76**, 4187.

Meyer, H., and Riklis, E. [1953]. *Nature* **172**, 543.

Michalec, C. [1955]. *Naturwissenschaften* **42**, 509–510.

Michalec, C., and Komárková, A. [1956]. *Naturwissenschaften* **43**, 19.

Micheel, F., and van de Kamp, P. [1952a]. *Angew. Chem.* **64**, 607–608.

Micheel, F., and Schweppe, H. [1952b]. *Naturwissenschaften* **39**, 380.

Micheel, F., and Schweppe, H. [1954a]. *Angew. Chem.* **66**, 136–137.

Micheel, F., and Schweppe, H. [1954b]. *Mikrochim. Acta* pp. 53–63.

Micheel, F., and Albers, P. [1954c]. *Mikrochim. Acta* pp. 489–493.

Micheel, F., and Albers, P. [1956]. *Chem. Ber.* **80**, 140–146.

Michl, H. [1953]. *Naturwissenschaften* **40**, 390.

Micks, D. W. [1954]. *Nature* **174**, 217–218.

Miettinen, J. K., and Virtanen, A. I. [1949]. *Acta Chem. Scand.* **3**, 459–464.

Miettinen, J. K., and Virtanen, A. I. [1951]. *Ann. Acad. Sci. Fennicae* Ser. A, II, **41**, 1–9, from [1952]. *Chem. Abstr.* **46**, 11500.

Miettinen, J. K., and Virtanen, A. I. [1952]. *Physiol. Plantarum* **5**, 540–557.

Miettinen, J. K., Kari, S., Moisio, T., Alfthan, M., and Virtanen, A. I. [1953a]. *Suomen Kemistilehti* **26B**, 26–30.

Miettinen, J. K. [1953b]. *Suomen Kemistilehti* **26B**, 49–63.

Miettinen, J. K., and Moisio, T. [1953c]. *Acta Chem. Scand.* **7**, 1225–1238.

Milks, J. E., and Janes, R. H. [1956]. *Anal. Chem.* **28**, 846–849.

Miller, C. C., and Magee, R. J. [1951]. *J. Chem. Soc.* pp. 3183–3187.

Miller, H., and Kraemer, D. M. [1952]. *Anal. Chem.* **24**, 1371–1372.

Miller, J. M., and Rockland, L. B. [1952]. *Arch. Biochem. Biophys.* **40**, 416–423.

Milletti, M. [1953]. *Ann. chim.* (*Rome*) **43**, 338–344; from [1954] *Chem. Abstr.* **48**, 1875.

Mills, G. L. [1952]. *Biochem. J.* **50**, 707–712.

Mills, J. S., and Werner, A. E. A. [1952]. *Nature* **169**, 1064.

Mitchell, F. L. [1952]. *Nature* **170**, 621–622.

Mitchell, F. L., and Davies, R. E. [1954]. *Biochem. J.* **56**, 690–698.

Mitchell, H. K., and Haskins, F. A. [1949]. *Science* **110**, 278–279.

Mitchell, L. C. [1952]. *J. Assoc. Offic. Agr. Chemists* **35**, 920–927; **35**, 928.

Mitchell, L. C., and Patterson, W. I. [1953a]. *J. Assoc. Offic. Agr. Chemists* **36**, 553–558; **36**, 1127–1130.

Mitchell, L. C. [1953b]. *J. Assoc. Offic. Agr. Chemists* **36**, 1123–1127; **36**, 1183–1186.

Mitchell, L. C. [1954]. *J. Assoc. Offic. Agr. Chemists* **37**, 216–217.

Mitchell, L. C. [1955]. *J. Assoc. Offic. Agr. Chemists* **38**, 832–835; **38**, 943–946.

Mitchell, L. C. [1956]. *J. Assoc. Offic. Agr. Chemists* **39**, 484–489; **39**, 980–990.

Mitoma, C., Weissbach, H., and Udenfriend, S. [1956]. *Arch. Biochem. Biophys.* **63**, 122–130.

Mitsuno, M. [1953]. *Pharm. Bull.* (*Tokyo*) **1**, 170–173.

Mitsuno, M. [1955]. *Pharm. Bull. (Tokyo)* **3**, 60–62.

Miura, K. [1950–1951]. *J. Agr. Chem. Soc. Japan* **24**, 369–371; from [1952] *Chem. Abstr.* **46**, 11040.

Miyaki, K., Momiyama, H., and Hayashi, M. [1952a]. *J. Pharm. Soc. Japan* **72**, 688–692; from [1952] *Chem. Abstr.* **46**, 9147.

Miyaki, K., and Momiyama, H. [1952b]. *J. Pharm. Soc. Japan* **72**, 1061–1062; from [1952] *Chem. Abstr.* **46**, 11296.

Miwa, T., and Zeitlin, H. [1955]. *Anal. Chem.* **27**, 1357.

Mizuno, K. [1952]. *Ann. Repts. Takeda Research Lab.* **11**, 1–7; from [1953] *Chem. Abstr.* **47**, 4796.

Moilanen, M., and Richtzenhain, H. [1954]. *Acta Chem. Scand.* **8**, 704.

Momose, T., and Torigoe, M. [1951]. *J. Pharm. Soc. Japan* **71**, 977–979; from [1952] *Chem. Abstr.* **46**, 1921.

Monselise, J. J., and Miranda, D. [1954]. *Inds. agr. et aliment. (Paris)* **71**, 223–224.

Montreuil, J., and Boulanger, P. [1953]. *Compt. rend.* **236**, 337–339.

Moore, A. M., and Boylen, J. B. [1953]. *Science* **118**, 19–20.

Moore, S., and Stein, W. H. [1948]. *J. Biol. Chem.* **176**, 367–388.

Mori, I. [1953]. *J. Pharm. Soc. Japan* **73**, 958–961; from [1954] *Chem. Abstr.* **48**, 792.

Mori, I. [1954a]. *J. Pharm. Soc. Japan* **74**, 213–214; from [1954] *Chem. Abstr.* **48**, 5709.

Mori, I. [1954b]. *Science* **119**, 653–654.

Morris, C. J. O. [1941]. *Biochem. J.* **35**, 952–959.

Morris, D. L. [1948]. *Science* **107**, 254–255.

Morris, N. J., and Mason, A. C. F. [1956]. *Anal. Chem.* **28**, 2038.

Morrison, R. I. [1953]. *Biochem. J.* **53**, 474–478.

Mortimer, D. C. [1952]. *Can. J. Chem.* **30**, 653–660.

Mortreuil, M., and Khouvine, Y. [1954]. *Bull. soc. chim. biol.* **36**, 425–428.

Moynihan, P., and O'Colla, P. [1951]. *Chem. & Ind. (London)* p. 407.

Mühlberger, F. H. [1954]. *Z. anal. Chem.* **143**, 21–30.

Müller, D. C. [1952]. *Analyst* **77**, 933–942.

Mueller, J. H. [1950]. *Science* **112**, 405–406.

Müller, R. [1953]. *Beitr. Biol. Pflanz.* **30**(1), 1–32.

Münz, T. [1954]. *Naturwissenschaften* **41**, 553.

Müting, D. [1952]. *Naturwissenschaften* **39**, 303.

Mukherjee, S., and Srivastava, H. C. [1952]. *Nature* **169**, 330.

Munier, R., and Macheboeuf, M. [1949]. *Bull. soc. chim. biol.* **31**, 1144–1162.

Munier, R., and Pénasse, L. [1950]. *Comt. rend.* **230**, 1176–1177.

Munier, R., and Macheboeuf, M. [1951]. *Bull. soc. chim. biol.* **33**, 846–856; **33**, 857–861; **33**, 862–867.

Murata, A. [1955]. *Nippon Kagaku Zasshi* **76**, 517–520.

Murthy, A. R. V., and Narayan, V. A. [1955]. *Naturwissenschaften* **42**, 439.

Myers, C. M., and Smith, J. N. [1954]. *Biochem. J.* **56**, 498–503.

Mylius, F. [1887]. *Z. physiol. Chem.* **11**, 306–347.

Myrbäck, K., and Willstaedt, E. [1953]. *Arkiv Kemi* **6**, 417–425; from [1954] *Chem. Abstr.* **48**, 6490.

Naftalin, L. [1948]. *Nature* **161**, 763.

Naghski, J., Fenske, C. S., Jr., and Couch, J. F. [1951]. *J. Am. Pharm. Assoc., Sci. Ed.* **40**, 613–616.

Nair, J. H., III. [1953]. *Anal. Chem.* **25,** 1912.

Nair, K. K., and Muthe, P. T. [1956]. *Naturwissenschaften* **43,** 106.

Nakabayashi, T. [1952]. *J. Agr. Chem. Soc. Japan* **26,** 140-141; from [1954] *Chem. Abstr.* **48,** 5941.

Nakajima, S., and Okuyama, G. [1956]. *Yakugaku Zasshi* **76,** 620-624.

Nakamura, N. [1951]. *J. Chem. Soc. Japan, Pure Chem. Sect.* **72,** 789-790; from [1953] *Chem. Abstr.* **47,** 5916.

Nanninga, L., and Bink, B. [1951]. *Nature* **168,** 389-390.

Neher, R., and Wettstein, A. [1951]. *Helv. Chim. Acta* **34,** 2278-2285.

Neher, R., and Wettstein, A. [1952]. *Helv. Chim. Acta* **35,** 276-283.

Neish, W. J. P. [1953]. *Rec. trav. chim.* **72,** 105-118; from [1953] *Chem. Abstr.* **47,** 8163.

Nettleton, R. M., Jr., and Mefferd, R. B. [1952]. *Anal. Chem.* **24,** 1687.

Neu, R. [1956]. *Naturwissenschaften* **43,** 82.

Neuberg, C., Strauss, E., and Lipkins, L. E. [1944]. *Arch. Biochem.* **4,** 101-104.

Neuberger, A. [1938]. *Biochem. J.* **32,** 1435-1451.

Newcombe, A. G., and Reid, S. G. [1953]. *Nature* **172,** 455-456.

Newton, G. G. F., and Abraham, E. P. [1953]. *Biochem. J.* **53,** 597-604.

Nichol, C. A., Zakrzewski, S. F., and Welch, A. D. [1953]. *Proc. Soc. Exptl. Biol. Med.* **83,** 272-277.

Nicholas, R. E. H., and Comfort, A. [1949a]. *Biochem. J.* **45,** 208-210.

Nicholas, R. E. H., and Rimington, C. [1949b]. *Scand. J. Clin. & Lab. Invest.* **1,** 12-18.

Nicholas, R. E. H., and Rimington, C. [1951]. *Biochem. J.* **48,** 306-309.

Nicholson, D. E. [1949]. *Nature* **163,** 954.

Nielsen, N., Sandegren, E., and Ljungdahl, L. [1949]. *Nature* **164,** 1055.

Nishikawa, S. [1952-53]. *J. Japan Biochem. Soc.* **24,** 52-54; from [1953] *Chem. Abstr.* **47,** 12489.

Noggle, G. R. [1953]. *Arch. Biochem. Biophys.* **43,** 238-239.

Nordby, G. L., and Luck, J. M. [1956]. *J. Biol. Chem.* **219,** 399-404.

Nordström, C. G., and Swain, T. [1956]. *Arch. Biochem. Biophys.* **60,** 329-344.

Norris, F. C., and Campbell, J. J. R. [1949]. *Can. J. Research* **C27,** 253-261.

Novellie, L. [1950]. *Nature* **166,** 1000.

Noworytko, J., and Sarnecka-Keller, M. [1955]. *Acta biochim. polon.* **2,** 91-105; from [1956] *Chem. Abstr.* **50,** 16531.

Oehme, F. [1956]. *Z. anal. Chem.* **150,** 93-99.

Oertel, G., and Hein, H. [1954]. *Z. physiol. Chem.* **297,** 249-253.

Oertel, G. W. [1956a]. *Naturwissenschaften* **43,** 17-18.

Oertel, G. W. [1956b]. *Naturwissenschaften* **43,** 251.

Ofner, P. [1955]. *Biochem. J.* **61,** 287-297.

Ogawa, T., and Ohno, M. [1950]. *J. Chem. Soc. Japan* **53,** 170-172; from [1952] *Chem. Abstr.* **46,** 10257.

Ohara, M., and Suzuki, Y. [1951]. *Science (Japan)* **21,** 362-363; from [1951] *Chem. Abstr.* **45,** 10286.

Ohtsu, T., and Mizuno, D. [1952]. *Japan. J. Med. Sci. & Biol.* **5,** 37-44; from [1952] *Chem. Abstr.* **46,** 10051.

Oka, Y., and Murata, A. [1951]. *J. Chem. Soc. Japan, Pure Chem. Sect.* **72,** 657-660, 757-758; from [1952] *Chem. Abstr.* **46,** 6030, 6037.

Okada, M., Yamada, A., and Kometani, K. [1952]. *J. Pharm. Soc. Japan* **72,** 930-936; from [1953] *Chem. Abstr.* **47,** 3324.

Olley, J. [1956]. *Biochem. J.* **62**, 5P.

Opieńska-Blauth, J., Madecka-Borkowska, I., and Borkowski, T. [1952]. *Nature* **169**, 798–799.

Oreskes, I., and Saifer, A. [1955]. *Anal. Chem.* **27**, 854–856.

Ortega, M. [1952]. *Anales real acad. farm.* **18**, 449–458; from [1953] *Chem. Abstr.* **47**, 7374.

Ortegren, V. H. [1954]. *Anal. Chem.* **26**, 943–944.

Osborn, G. H., and Jewsbury, A. [1949]. *Nature* **164**, 443–444.

Oshima, Y., and Nakabayashi, T. [1951]. *J. Agr. Chem. Soc. Japan* **25**, 212–215; from [1953] *Chem. Abstr.* **47**, 7952.

Oshima, Y., Nakabayashi, T., and Imagawa, H. [1952]. *Nippon Nôgei-kagaku Kaishi* **25**, 478–495.

Oshima, Y., Yoshihara, S., and Sakanoto, Y. [1953]. *Nippon Nogei-kagaku Kaishi* **27**, 102–104.

Oshima, Y., Nakabayashi, T., and Ishibashi, S. [1954]. *Nippon Nôgei-kagaku Kaishi* **28**, 269–274; Oshima, Y., Nakabayashi, T., Hada, N., and Matsuyama, S. [1954]. *Ibid.* 618–621; Oshima, Y., Nakabayashi, T., and Hada, N. [1954]. *Ibid.* 621–624.

Otter, I. K. H. [1955]. *Nature* **176**, 1078.

Overell, B. T. [1952]. *Australian J. Sci.* **15**, 28–29.

Pabst. Circ. [1956]. **OR.–10** (January), 1–21.

Pachéco, H. [1953]. *Compt. rend.* **237**, 110–111.

Pacsu, E., Mora, T. P., and Kent, P. W. [1949]. *Science* **110**, 446–447.

Paladini, A. C., and Leloir, L. F. [1952a]. *Anal. Chem.* **24**, 1024–1025.

Paladini, A. C., and Leloir, L. F. [1952b]. *Biochem. J.* **51**, 426–430.

Palmer, J. K. [1955]. *Conn. Agr. Expt. Sta. Bull.* **589**, 12–14.

Pan, H.-P. [1956]. *Arch. Biochem. Biophys.* **64**, 311–314.

Pan, S. C., Nicholson, L. W., and Kolachov, P. [1953]. *Arch. Biochem. Biophys.* **42**, 406–420.

Pan, S. C., and Dutcher, J. D. [1956]. *Anal. Chem.* **28**, 836–838.

Pannell, J. H., and LuValle, J. E. [1953]. *Anal. Chem.* **25**, 1566.

Papastamatis, S. C., and Williams, J. F. [1951]. *Nature* **167**, 724–725.

Pardee, A. B. [1951]. *J. Biol. Chem.* **190**, 757–762.

Parihar, D. B. [1954]. *Naturwissenschaften* **41**, 427.

Parikh, S. N., and Godbole, A. N. [1954a]. *J. Maharaja Sayajirao Univ. Baroda* **3**(2), 27–31.

Parikh, S. N., Parikh, J. M., and Godbole, A. N. [1954b]. *Current Sci. (India)* **23**, 53.

Paris, R. [1952]. *Bull. soc. chim. biol.* **34**, 767–772.

Parke, T. V., and Davis, W. W. [1952]. *Anal. Chem.* **24**, 2019–2020.

Parke, D. V., and Williams, R. T. [1955]. *Biochem. J.* **59**, 415–422.

Partridge, S. M. [1946]. *Nature* **158**, 270.

Partridge, S. M. [1948]. *Biochem. J.* **42**, 238–249.

Partridge, S. M. [1949]. *Nature* **164**, 443.

Partridge, S. M., and Swain, T. [1950]. *Nature* **166**, 272–273.

Pasieka, A. E., and Morgan, J. F. [1955]. *Biochim. et Biophys. Acta* **18**, 236–240.

Pasieka, A. E., and Morgan, J. F. [1956a]. *Biochim. et Biophys. Acta* **19**, 366–371.

Pasieka, A. E., and Morgan, J. F. [1956b]. *Proc. Soc. Exptl. Biol. Med.* **92**, 96–99; **93**, 54–57.

Patte, F. [1953]. *Ann. pharm. franç.* **11**, 37–44; from [1953] *Chem. Abstr.* **47**, 6482.

Patton, A. R., and Foreman, E. M. [1949a]. *Science* **109**, 339.

Patton, A. R., Foreman, E. M., and Wilson, P. C. [1949b]. *Science* **110**, 593–594.

Patton, A. R. [1950]. *J. Chem. Educ.* **27**, 60–61.

Patton, A. R., and Chism, P. [1951]. *Anal. Chem.* **23**, 1683–1685.

Payne, W. J., and Kieber, R. [1954]. *Arch. Biochem. Biophys.* **52**, 1–4.

Pazur, J. H., and French, D. [1952]. *J. Biol. Chem.* **196**, 265–272.

Pazur, J. H. [1953]. *J. Biol. Chem.* **205**, 75–80.

Pazur, J. H., and Budovich, T. [1955]. *Science* **121**, 702–703.

Pearl, I. A., and Beyer, D. L. [1954]. *J. Am. Chem. Soc.* **76**, 2224; **76**, 6106–6108.

Pechet, M. M. [1954]. *Science* **121**, 39–40.

Peeters, G., Coussens, R., and Sierens, G. [1954]. *Naturwissenschaften* **41**, 428.

Pereira, A., and Serra, J. A. [1951]. *Science* **113**, 387–388.

Pereira, A. [1952]. *Cereal Chem.* **29**, 478–481.

Perilä, O. [1955]. *Acta Chem. Scand.* **9**, 864–865.

Perilä, O. [1956]. *Acta Chem. Scand.* **10**, 143–144.

Pernis, B., and Wunderly, C. [1953]. *Biochim. et Biophys. Acta* **11**, 209–214.

Perrone, J. C. [1951]. *Nature* **167**, 513–515.

Peterson, D. H., and Reineke, L. M. [1950]. *J. Am. Chem. Soc.* **72**, 3598–3603.

Petronici, C., and Safina, G. [1953]. *Conserve e deriv. agrumari (Palermo)* **2**(5), 3–11; from [1953] *Chem. Abstr.* **47**, 11297.

Pew, J. C. [1948]. *J. Am. Chem. Soc.* **70**, 3031–3034.

Pfeil, E., Ploss, G., and Saran, H. [1955]. *Z. anal. Chem.* **146**, 241–243.

Pfennig, N. [1954]. *Naturwissenschaften* **41**, 62–63.

Philippe, J., Benoist, D., and Patte, P. [1952]. *Congr. intern. biochim. 2e Congr., Paris* pp. 16–17.

Phillips, D. M. P. [1948]. *Nature* **162**, 29.

Phillips, D. M. P. [1954]. *Biochim. et Biophys. Acta* **13**, 560–563.

Phillips, J. D., and Pollard, A. [1953]. *Nature* **171**, 41–42.

Piantanida, M., and Muić, N. [1953]. *Arch. Biochem. Biophys.* **46**, 110–118.

Piantanida, M., Meniga, A., and Muić, N. [1955]. *Arch. Biochem. Biophys.* **57**, 334–339.

Pickering, W. F., and Jacobs, E. B. [1955]. *Anal. Chim. Acta* **12**, 436–442.

Pickering, W. F. [1956]. *Anal. Chim. Acta* **15**, 337–342.

Pierpont, W. S., Hughes, D. E., Baddiley, J., and Mathias, A. B. [1955]. *Biochem. J.* **61**, 368–374.

Piper, E. A., and Arnstein, H. R. V. [1956]. *Biochem. J.* **64**, 57P.

Pöhm, M., and Fuchs, L. [1954]. *Naturwissenschaften* **46**, 63.

Pöhm, M., and Weiser, R. [1956]. *Naturwissenschaften* **43**, 582.

Pokrovskiĭ, A. A. [1954]. *Byull. Eksptl. Biol. i Med.* **38**(12), 69–70; from [1955] *Chem. Abstr.* **49**, 6358.

Pollard, F. H., and McOmie, J. F. W. [1951a]. *Endeavour* **10**, 213–221.

Pollard, F. H., McOmie, J. F. W., and Elbeih, I. I. M. [1951b]. *J. Chem. Soc.* pp. 466–470.

Pollard, F. H., and McOmie, J. F. W. [1953]. "Chromatographic Methods of Inorganic Analysis," 192 pp. Academic Press, New York.

Pollard, F. H., McOmie, J. F. W., and Stevens, H. M. [1954a]. *J. Chem. Soc.* pp. 3435–3440.

Pollard, F. H. [1954b]. *Brit. Med. J.* **10**, 187–191.

Pollard, F. H., McOmie, J. F. W., Martin, J. V., and Hardy, C. J. [1955a]. *J. Chem. Soc.* pp. 4332–4337.

Pollard, F. H., McOmie, J. F. W., and Jones, D. J. [1955b]. ·J. Chem. Soc. pp. 4337–4340.

Pollard, E. H., and Banister, A. J. [1956]. Anal. Chim. Acta 14, 70–73.

Polson, A. [1948]. Biochim. et Biophys. Acta 2, 575–581.

Polson, A., van Rooy, P. J., and Marais, E. J. [1951]. Onderstepoort J. Vet. Research 25, 31–38; from [1952] Chem. Abstr. 46, 3905.

Popenoe, E. A., and du Vigneaud, V. [1953]. J. Biol. Chem. 205, 133–143.

Porath, J., and Flodin, P. [1951]. Nature 168, 202–203.

Porter, W. L., Naghski, J., and Eisner, A. [1949]. Arch. Biochem. 24, 461–463.

Porter, W. L. [1954a]. Anal. Chem. 26, 439–440.

Porter, W. L., and Hoban, N. [1954b]. Anal. Chem. 26, 1846–1848.

Pratt, J. J., Jr., and Auclair, J. L. [1948]. Science 108, 213–214.

Price, T. D., and Hudson, P. B. [1954]. Anal. Chem. 26, 1127–1132.

Price, T. D., Hudson, P. B., and Ashman, D. F. [1955a]. Nature 175, 45–49.

Price, T. D., and Hudson, P. B. [1955b]. Nucleonics 13, 54–58.

Price, T. D., and Dietrich, L. S. [1956]. Chromatog. Methods 1(1), 2–6.

Pridham, J. B. [1956]. Anal. Chem. 28, 1967–1968.

Priori, O. [1955]. Boll. lab. chim. provinciali (Bologna) 6(2), 45–46.

Procházka, Ž. [1950]. Chem. listy 44, 43; from [1951] Chem. Abstr. 45, 5561.

Proom, H., and Woiwod, A. J. [1951]. J. Gen. Microbiol. 5, 681–686.

Proom, H., and Woiwod, A. J. [1953a]. Chem. & Ind. (London) pp. 311–315.

Proom, H., and Woiwod, A. J. [1953b]. Nature 171, 42.

Puck, A. [1955]. Klin. Wochschr. 33, 865–867.

Quagliariello, G., Guerritore, D., and Porcellati, G. [1951]. Boll. soc. ital. biol. sper. 27, 1688–1691; from [1953] Chem. Abstr. 47, 8809.

Quastel, J. H., and Van Straten, S. F. [1952]. Proc. Soc. Exptl. Biol. Med. 81, 6–9.

Quayle, J. R. [1956]. Nature 178, 375–376.

Quenten, K. E. [1953]. Z. anal. Chem. 140, 92–102.

Quilley, E. [1952]. J. Pharm. and Pharmacol. 4, 624–630.

Raacke-Fels, I. D. [1953]. Arch. Biochem. Biophys. 43, 289–298.

Raaen, H. P., and Thomason, P. F. [1955]. Anal. Chem. 27, 936–944.

Radhakrishnamurthy, R., and Sarma, P. S. [1952]. J. Sci. Ind. Research (India) 11B, 279–282; from [1953] Chem. Abstr. 47, 11082.

Radhakrishnamurthy, R., and Sarma, P. S. [1953]. Current Sci. (India) 22, 209–210.

Ramachandran, L. K., and McConnell, W. B. [1955]. Nature 176, 931–932.

Ranjan, S., and Raja Rao, T. [1955]. Naturwissenschaften 42, 581.

Rao, C. L., and Shankar, [1953]. Anal. Chim. Acta 8, 491–492.

Rao, P. S., Beri, R. M., and Rao, P. R. [1951]. Proc. Indian Acad. Sci. 34A, 236–239; from [1952] Chem. Abstr. 46, 9020.

Rao, T., and Giri, K. V. [1953]. J. Indian Inst. Sci. 35A, 77–92; 35A, 93–98.

Rao, V. K. M. [1952]. J. Sci. Ind. Research (India) 11B, 277–279.

Rao, V. K. M. ·[1953]. Experientia 9, 151–156.

Rapi, G. [1953]. Sperimentale, Sez. chim. biol. 4, 11–22; from [1953] Chem. Abstr. 47, 10604.

Rappoport, D. A., Calvert, C. R., Loeffler, R. K., and Gast, J. H. [1955]. Anal. Chem. 27, 820–822.

Rau, K. R., and Sober, H. A. [1954]. J. Am. Chem. Soc. 76, 1328–1331.

Rautanen, N. [1948]. Ann. Acad. Sci. Fennicae, Ser. A, II. Chem. 33, 1–66; from [1950] Chem. Abstr. 44, 4088.

Reaville, E. T., and Shreve, G. W. [1955]. *Anal. Chem.* **27**, 565–566.
Reddi, K. K., and Kodicek, E. [1953]. *Biochem. J.* **53**, 286–294.
Redfield, R. R., and Barron, E. S. G. [1952]. *Arch. Biochem. Biophys.* **35**, 443–461.
Redfield, R. R. [1953]. *Biochim. et Biophys. Acta* **10**, 344–345.
Reed, L. J. [1950]. *J. Biol. Chem.* **183**, 451–458.
Reed, L. J., DeBusk, B. G., Johnston, P. M., and Gretzendaner, M. E. [1951]. *J. Biol. Chem.* **192**, 851–865.
Reese, E. T., and Gilligan, W. [1953]. *Arch. Biochem. Biophys.* **45**, 74–82.
Reeves, W. A., and Crumpler, T. B. [1951]. *Anal. Chem.* **23**, 1576–1578.
Regna, P. P., and Murphy, F. X. [1950]. *J. Am. Chem. Soc.* **72**, 1045–1046.
Reichl, E. R., and Löffler, J. E. [1954]. *Mikrochim. Acta* pp. 226–230.
Reichl, E. R. [1956]. *Mikrochim. Acta* pp. 955–965.
Reid, R. L., and Lederer, M. [1951]. *Biochem. J.* **50**, 60–67.
Reid, W. W. [1950]. *Nature* **166**, 569.
Reindel, F., and Hoppe, W. [1953]. *Naturwissenschaften* **40**, 221; **40**, 245.
Reindel, F., and Hoppe, W. [1954]. *Ber.* **87**, 1103–1107.
Reineke, L. M. [1956]. *Anal. Chem.* **28**, 1853–1858.
Reinhardt, F. [1954]. *Mikrochim. Acta* pp. 219–222.
Reitsema, R. H. [1954]. *Anal. Chem.* **26**, 960–963.
Renfrew, A. G., and Piatt, P. C. [1950]. *J. Am. Pharm. Assoc., Sci. Ed.* **39**, 657–659.
Renkonen, O., and Schindler, O. [1956]. *Helv. Chim. Acta* **39**, 1490–1493.
Resnik, F. E., Lee, L. A., and Powell, W. A. [1955]. *Anal. Chem.* **27**, 928–931.
Rheinboldt, H. [1921]. *In* "Methoden der Organischen Chemie" (Houben-Weyl, ed.), 2nd ed., Vol. 1, pp. 272–291. G. Thieme, Leipzig.
Rhuland, L. E., Work, E., Denman, R. F., and Hoare, D. S. [1955]. *J. Am. Chem. Soc.*, **77**, 4844–4846.
Rice, R. G., Keller, G. J., and Kirchner, J. G. [1951]. *Anal. Chem.* **23**, 194–195.
Ricketts, C. R., Walton, K. W., and Saddington, S. M. [1954]. *Biochem. J.* **58**, 532–536.
Riddell, C., and Cook, R. P. [1955]. *Biochem. J.* **61**, 657–671.
Riebeling, C., and Burmeister, H. [1954]. *Klin. Wochschr.* **32**, 1057.
Riedl, K., and Neugebauer, L. [1952]. *Monatsh.* **83**, 1083–1087; from [1953] *Chem. Abstr.* **47**, 9967.
Riemschneider, R., and Weygand, C. [1955]. *Monatsh.* **86**, 201–209.
Rienits, K. G. [1953]. *Biochem. J.* **53**, 79–85.
Rigby, G. J., and Bellis, D. M. [1956]. *Nature* **178**, 415.
Riley, J. F. [1954]. *Nature* **174**, 882–883.
Roberts, E., and Frankel, S. [1950]. *J. Biol. Chem.* **187**, 55–63.
Roberts, E. A. H., and Wood, D. J. [1951]. *Biochem. J.* **49**, 414–422.
Roberts, E. A. H., and Wood, D. J. [1953]. *Biochem. J.* **53**, 332–336.
Roberts, H. R., and Carleton, F. J. [1956]. *Anal. Chem.* **28**, 11–16.
Roberts, H. R. and Kolor, M. G. [1957]. *Abstr. Amer. Chem. Soc. Meeting, Brooklyn, N. Y.*, Feb. 17.
Robinson, D., Smith, J. N., and Williams, R. T. [1951]. *Biochem. J.* **50**, 221–227.
Robinson, D., Smith, J. N., and Williams, R. T. [1955]. *Biochem. J.* **59**, 153–159.
Robinson, R. [1951]. *Nature* **168**, 512–513.
Roche, J., Jutisz, M., Lissitzky, S., and Michel, R. [1950]. *Compt. rend.* **231**, 723–725.
Roche, J., Félix, W., Robin, Y., and Thoai, N.-V. [1951]. *Compt. rend.* **233**, 1688–1689.
Roche, J., Lissitzky, S., and Michel, R. [1953]. *Biochim. et Biophys. Acta* **11**, 220–226.
Roche, J., Thoai, N.-V., and Hatt, J. L. [1954]. *Biochim. et Biophys. Acta* **14**, 71–75.
Roche, J., Michel, R., and Wolff, W. [1955]. *Comp. rend.* **240**, 251–253.

Rockland, L. B., and Dunn, M. S.   [1949a].   *J. Am. Chem. Soc.* **71,** 4121–4122.

Rockland, L. B., and Dunn, M. S.   [1949b].   *Science* **109,** 539–540.

Rockland, L. B., and Dunn, M. S.   [1950].   *Science* **111,** 332–333.

Rockland, L. B., Blatt, J. L., and Dunn, M. S.   [1951].   *Anal. Chem.* **23,** 1142–1146.

Rockland, L. B., and Underwood, J. C.   [1956].   *Anal. Chem.* **28,** 1679–1684.

Rodnight, R.   [1956].   *Biochem. J.* **64,** 621–626.

Rogina, B., and Briski, B.   [1954].   *Kem. ind. (Zagreb)* **3,** 253–256; from   [1955] *Chem. Abstr.* **49,** 6361.

Rohdewald, M., and Zechmeister, L.   [1951].   *Enzymologia* **15,** 109–114; from   [1953] *Chem. Abstr.* **47,** 4387.

Rohdewald, M., and Weber, M.   [1956].   *Z. physiol. Chem.* **306,** 90–95.

Roland, J. F., and Gross, A. M.   [1954].   *Anal. Chem.* **26,** 502–505.

Rose, I. A., and Schweigert, B. S.   [1951].   *J. Am. Chem. Soc.* **73,**.5903.

Rosenberg, I. N.   [1952].   *Proc. Soc. Exptl. Biol. Med.* **80,** 751–756.

Rosenkrantz, H.   [1953].   *Arch. Biochem. Biophys.* **44,** 1–8.

Rossi-Fanelli, A., Siliprandi, N., and Fasella, P.   [1952].   *Science* **116,** 711–713.

Rossi-Fanelli, A., Mondovi, B., and Boffi, V.   [1953].   *Boll. soc. ital. biol. sper.* **29,** 1330–1333; from   [1954]   *Chem. Abstr.* **48,** 5252.

Rouser, G., and Morrison, M.   [1953].   *Federation Proc.* **12,** 261–262.

Rouser, G., Marinetti, G., and Berry, J. F.   [1954].   *Federation Proc.* **13,** 286.

Roux, D. G.   [1951].   *Nature* **168,** 1041–1042.

Rovery, M., and Fabre, C.   [1953].   *Bull. soc. chim. biol.* pp. 541–546.

Rubin, B. L., Dorfman, R. I., and Pincus, G.   [1953].   *J. Biol. Chem.* **203,** 629–645.

Ruckenbrod, H.   [1954].   *Planta* **46,** 19–45.

Ruliffson, W. S., Lang, H. M., and Hummel, J. P.   [1953].   *J. Biol. Chem.* **201,** 839–846.

Rutter, L.   [1950].   *Analyst* **75,** 37–42.

Rydon, H. N., and Smith, P. W. G.   [1952].   *Nature* **169,** 922–923.

Saarnio, J., Niskasaari, E., and Gustafsson, C.   [1952].   *Suomen Kemistilehti* **25B,** 25–29.

Saeman, J. F., and Locke, E. G.   [1953].   Private communication.

Safina, G., and Petronici, C.   [1954].   *Conserve e deriv. agrumari (Palermo)* **3**(12), 172–174.

Saifer, A., and Oreskes, I.   [1953].   *Anal. Chem.* **25,** 1539–1544.

Saifer, A., and Oreskes, I.   [1954].   *Science* **119,** 124–125.

Saifer, A., and Oreskes, I.   [1956].   *Anal. Chem.* **28,** 501–504.

Sakal, E. H., and Merrill, E. J.   [1953].   *Science* **117,** 451–452.

Sakan, T., Nakamura, N., and Senoh, S.   [1951a].   *J. Chem. Soc. Japan* **72,** 745–747; from [1952] *Chem. Abstr.* **46,** 11106.

Sakan, T., Nakamura, N., and Senoh, S.   [1951b].   *J. Inst. Polytech. Osaka City Univ.*, *Ser. C.* **2,** 33–37; from   [1952]   *Chem. Abstr.* **46,** 7075.

Salander, R. C., Piano, M., and Patton, A. R.   [1953].   *Anal. Chem.* **25,** 1252–1253.

Salgó, É.   [1953].   *Z. anal. Chem.* **138,** 101–106; from   [1953]   *Chem. Abstr.* **47,** 6478.

San, G. L., and Ultée, A. J.   [1952].   *Nature* **169,** 586.

Sanger, F.   [1945].   *Biochem. J.* **39,** 507–515.

Sanger, F., and Tuppy, H.   [1951].   *Biochem. J.* **49,** 463–481.

Sanger, F., and Thompson, E. O. P.   [1953].   *Biochem. J.* **53,** 353–366.

Sansone, G., and Cusmano, F.   [1951].   *Boll. soc. ital. biol. sper.* **27,** 1369–1370; from   [1952]   *Chem. Abstr.* **46,** 6176.

Sarak, J. G., Leffler, N., and Martinovich, R.   [1953].   *J. Chem. Educ.* **30,** 20–21.

Sarma, B. [1949–51]. *Trans. Bose Research Inst. Calcutta* **18**, 105.

Saroja, K., Venkataraman, R., and Giri, K. V. [1955]. *Biochem. J.* **60**, 399–403.

Sattler, L., and Zerban, F. W. [1952a]. *Anal. Chem.* **24**, 1862.

Sattler, L., Zerban, F. W., Clark, G. L., Chu C.-C., Albon, N., Gross, D., and deWhalley, H. C. S. [1952b]. *Ind. Eng. Chem.* **44**, 1127–1135.

Sato, T. R., Kisieleski, W. E., Norris, W. P., and Strain, H. H. [1953]. *Anal. Chem.* **25**, 438–446.

Savard, K. [1953a]. *J. Biol. Chem.* **202**, 457–477.

Savard, K., Burstein, S., Rosenkrantz, H., and Dorfman, R. I. [1953b]. *J. Biol. Chem.* **202**, 717–725.

Schaefer, W. C., and van Cleve, J. W. [1956]. *Anal. Chem.* **28**, 1290–1293.

Schauer, H. K., Bulirsch, R., and Decker, P. [1955a]. *Naturwissenschaften* **42**, 626–627.

Schauer, H. K., and Bulirsch, R. [1955b]. *Z. Naturforsch.* **10b**, 683–693.

Schauer, H. K., and Bulirsch, R. [1956]. *Naturwissenschaften* **43**, 34.

Schayer, R. W. [1951]. *J. Biol. Chem.* **189**, 301–306.

Schayer, R. W., Kennedy, J., and Smiley, R. L. [1953]. *J. Biol. Chem.* **202**, 39–43.

Schenker, E., Hunger, A., and Reichstein, T. [1954]. *Helv. Chim. Acta* **37**, 680–685.

Schindler, H., and Herb, M. [1956]. *Naturwissenschaften* **43**, 83.

Schindler, O., and Reichstein, T. [1951]. *Helv. Chim. Acta* **34**, 108–116.

Schlack, P., and Kumpf, W. [1926]. *Z. physiol. Chem.* **154**, 125–170.

Schleede, D. [1955]. *Brennstoff-Chem.* **36**, 78–79.

Schmall, M., Wollish, E. G., and Shafer, E. G. E. [1956]. *Anal. Chem.* **28**, 1373–1376.

Schmidt, F., and Bauriedl, H. U. [1956]. *Naturwissenschaften* **43**, 470.

Schmidt, G., and Thannhauser, S. J. [1943]. *J. Biol. Chem.* **149**, 369–385.

Schmidt, H., Staudinger, H., and Bauer, V. [1953]. *Biochem. Z.* **324**, 128–133.

Schmidt, H., and Staudinger, H. [1955]. *Biochem. Z.* **326**, 343–349.

Schmitt, W. J., Moriconi, E. J., and O'Connor, W. F. [1956]. *Anal. Chem.* **28**, 249.

Schneider, F., and Erlenmann, G. A. [1951]. *Zucker-Beihefte* No. **3**, 40–41; from [1952] *Chem. Abstr.* **46**, 381.

Schreier, K., and Gaedke, K. [1956a]. *Naturwissenschaften* **43**, 130.

Schreier, K., and Hack, W. [1956b]. *Naturwissenschaften* **43**, 178–179.

Schultz, O. E., and Wagner, W. [1956]. *Z. Naturforsch.* **11b**, 73–78.

Schute, J. B. [1953a]. *Mededel. Vlaam. Chem. Ver.* **15**, 1–12; from [1953] *Chem. Abstr.* **47**, 6218.

Schute, J. B. [1953b]. *Nature* **171**, 839–840.

Schwartz, D. P., and Pallansch, M. J. [1957]. *Anal. Chem.* in press.

Schwarz, V. [1952a]. *Biochem. J.* **52**, xiii.

Schwarz, V. [1952b]. *Nature* **169**, 506–507.

Schwarz, V. [1953]. *Biochem. J.* **53**, 148–152.

Schwerdtfeger, E. [1953]. *Naturwissenschaften* **40**, 201.

Schwerdtfeger, E. [1954]. *Naturwissenschaften* **41**, 18.

Schwimmer, S., and Bevenue, A. [1956]. *Science* **123**, 543–544.

Sclar, R. N., and Freeman, K. A. [1955]. *J. Assoc. Offic. Agr. Chemists* **38**, 796–809.

Scott, J. E., and Golberg, L. [1954]. *Chem. & Ind. (London)* pp. 48–49.

Seligman, R. B., Edmonds, M. D., and Lee, L. A. [1954] *Chem. & Ind. (London)* p. 1195.

Seligson, D., and Shapiro, B. [1952]. *Anal. Chem.* **24**, 754–755.

Sen, S. P., and Leopold, A. C. [1954]. *Physiol. Plantarum* **7**, 98–108.

Sendroy, J., Jr., and Cecchini, L. P. [1952]. *Proc. Soc. Exptl. Biol. Med.* **81**, 478–483.

Sendroy, J., Jr., and Cecchini, L. P. [1953]. *Arch. Biochem. Biophys.* **45**, 161–168.
Serchi, G., and Rapi, G. [1952]. *Sperimentale, Sez. chim. biol.* **3**, 107–123; from [1953] *Chem. Abstr.* **47**, 2814.
Serchi, G. [1953]. *Ann. chim. (Rome)* **43**, 253–255; from [1953] *Chem. Abstr.* **47**, 12129.
Servigne, Y. [1956]. *Mikrochim. Acta* pp. 750–759.
Serro, R. F., and Brown, R. J. [1954]. *Anal. Chem.* **26**, 890–892.
Sevag, M. G., Lackman, D. B., and Smolens, J. [1938]. *J. Biol. Chem.* **124**, 425–436.
Shamrai, E. F., Gavrilova, E. A., and Kravchenko, V. V. [1951]. *Biokhimiya* **16**, 604–610; from [1952] *Chem. Abstr.* **46**, 3603.
Shepherd, D. M., and West, G. B. [1952]. *Nature* **169**, 797.
Shepherd, D. M., and West, G. B. [1953]. *Nature* **171**, 1160; **172**, 357.
Shibata, S., Takito, M., and Tanaka, O. [1950]. *J. Am. Chem. Soc.* **72**, 2789–2790.
Shibatani, A., and Fukuda, M. [1951]. *J. Biochem. (Japan)* **38**, 181–198; from [1951] *Chem. Abstr.* **45**, 8933.
Shkol'nik, R. Ya. [1953]. *Doklady Akad. Nauk S.S.S.R.* **90**, 847–849.
Shull, G. M., Sardinas, J. L., and Nubel, R. C. [1952]. *Arch. Biochem. Biophys.* **37**, 186–198.
Siegel, A., and Schlögl, K. [1953]. *Mikrochemie ver. Mikrochim. Acta* **40**, 383–389.
Siegelman, H. W. [1955]. *Arch. Biochem. Biophys.* **56**, 97–102.
Siliprandi, D., and Siliprandi, N. [1954]. *Biochim. et Biophys. Acta* **14**, 52–61.
Silver, D. Z., and Bookman, R. [1956]. *Anal. Chem.* **28**, 556.
Simon, K. [1954]. *Med. Monatsschr.* **8**; 107–11; from [1954] *Chem. Abstr.* **48**, 7100.
Simonart, P., and Chow, K. Y. [1951]. *Enzymologia* **14**, 356–361; from [1953] *Chem. Abstr.* **47**, 3358.
Simonart, P., and Chow, K Y. [1952]. *Neth. Milk Dairy J.* **6**, 206–213; from [1953] *Chem. Abstr.* **47**, 2811.
Simonis, W., and Schwinck, L. [1953]. *Naturwissenschaften* **40**, 245–246.
Singer, A. J., and Kenner, L. [1951]. *Anal. Chem.* **23**, 387–388.
Sisakyan, N. M., Bezinger, E. N., Garkavi, P. G., and Kivman, G. Ya. [1954] *Doklady Akad. Nauk S.S.S.R.* **96**, 343–346; from [1954] *Chem. Abstr.* **48**, 10821.
Sjöquist, J. [1953]. *Acta Chem. Scand.* **7**, 447–448.
Sjövall, J. [1952]. *Acta Chem. Scand.* **6**, 1552–1553.
Sjövall, J. [1954]. *Acta Chem. Scand.* **8**, 339–345.
Sjövall, J. [1955]. *Arkiv Kemi* **8**, 299–301.
Slotta, K. H., and Primosigh, J. [1951]. *Nature* **168**, 696–697.
Slotta, K., H., and Primosigh, J. [1952]. *Mem. Inst. Butantan (São Paulo)* **24**, 85–100; from [1954] *Chem. Abstr.* **48**, 1456.
Sluyterman, L. Æ., and Veenendaal, H. J. [1949]. *Rec. trav. chim.* **68**, 717–720; from [1950] *Chem. Abstr.* **44**, 4363.
Smellie, R. M. S., and Davidson, J. N. [1951]. *Biochem. J.* **49**, xv.
Smith, A. M., and Agiza, A. H. [1951]. *Analyst* **76**, 623–627.
Smith, E. Lester, and Page, J. E. [1948]. *J. Soc. Chem. Ind. (London)* **67**, 48–51.
Smith, E. Lester [1952]. *Nature* **169**, 60–62.
Smith, Elaine L., and Tuller, E. F. [1955]. *Arch. Biochem. Biophys.* **54**, 114–120.
Smith, G. N., and Worrel, C. S. [1950]. *Arch. Biochem.* **28**, 1–9.
Smith, I. [1953]. *Nature* **171**, 43–44.
Smith, I. [1955]. *Paint Technol.* **19**, 375–380.
Smith, J. D., and Markham, R. [1950]. *Biochem.* **46**, 509–513.
Smith, J. D., and Wyatt, G. R. [1951]. *Biochem. J.* **49**, 144–148.

Smith, J. N. [1955a]. *Biochem. J.* **60**, 436–442.

Smith, J. N., and Williams, R. T. [1955b]. *Biochem. J.* **60**, 284–290.

Smith, M. J. H., and Taylor, K. W. [1953]. *Biochem. J.* **55**, xxx–xxxi.

Smith, P. B., and Pollard, A. L. [1952]. *J. Bacteriol.* **63**, 129–132.

Snellman, O., and Gelotte, B. [1951]. *Nature* **168**, 461–462.

Snyder, J. Q., and Wender, S. H. [1953]. *Arch. Biochem. Biophys.* **46**, 465–469.

Sober, H. S. [1950]. Private communication.

Sokolski, W. T., Koffler, H., and Tetrault, P. A. [1953]. *Arch. Biochem. Biophys.* **43**, 236.

Solms, J. [1955]. *Helv. Chim. Acta* **38**, 1127–1133.

Solomons, I. A., and Regna, P. P. [1950]. *J. Am. Chem. Soc.* **72**, 2974–2977.

Sommer, G. [1955]. *Z. anal. Chem.* **147**, 241–266.

Somogyi, M. [1945]. *J. Biol. Chem.* **160**, 61–73.

Souchon, F. [1952a]. *Z. ges. exptl. Med.* **118**, 219–229; from [1953] *Chem. Abstr.* **47**, 1269.

Souchon, F., and Grunau, G. [1952b]. *Z. ges. exptl. Med.* **119**, 641–646; from [1953] *Chem. Abstr.* **47**, 7021.

Soutar, T. H., and Hampton, E. [1954]. *Nature* **174**, 801–802.

Spoerl, E., and Carleton, R. [1954]. *J. Biol. Chem.* **210**, 521–529.

Sporer, A. H., Freed, S., and Sancier, K. M. [1954]. *Science* **119**, 68–69.

Sproston, T., and Bassett, E. G. [1954]. *Anal. Chem.* **26**, 552–553.

Stadtman, E. R., and Barker, H. A. [1950]. *J. Biol. Chem.* **184**, 769–793.

Stanley, P. G. [1953]. *Nature* **171**, 933–934.

Stark, J. B., Goodban, A. E., and Owens, H. S. [1951]. *Anal. Chem.* **23**, 413–415.

Steel, A. E. [1951]. *Nature* **168**, 877.

Steel, A. E. [1954]. *Nature* **173**, 315–316.

Stein, W. H., and Moore, S. [1951]. *J. Biol. Chem.* **190**, 103–106.

Stevens, B. J., Smith, I., and Jepson, J. B. [1954]. Private communication.

Stevens, B. J., Smith, I., and Jepson, J. B. [1956]. *Biochem. J.* **62**, 8P.

Stevens, H. M. [1956a]. *Anal. Chim. Acta* **14**, 126–130.

Stevens, H. M. [1956b]. *Anal. Chim. Acta* **15**, 538–542.

Stewart, H. B. [1953]. *Biochem. J.* **55**, xxvi.

Stiffney, A. V., and Williams, W. L. [1955]. *J. Assoc. Offic. Agr. Chemists* **38**, 870–874.

Stockli, A. [1954]. *Helv. Chim. Acta* **37**, 1581–1585.

Stoffyn, P. J., and Jeanloz, R. W. [1954]. *Arch. Biochem. Biophys.* **52**, 373–379.

Stoll, A., and Rüegger, A. [1952]. *Helv. Physiol. et Pharmacol. Acta* **10**, 385–394; from [1953] *Chem. Abstr.* **47**, 448.

Stoll, A., and Rüegger, A. [1954]. *Helv. Chim. Acta* **37**, 1725–1732.

Stone, J. E., and Blundell, M. J. [1951]. *Anal. Chem.* **23**, 771–774.

Stowe, B. B., and Thimann, K. V. [1953]. *Nature* **172**, 764.

Stowe, B. B., and Thimann, K. V. [1954]. *Arch. Biochem. Biophys.* **51**, 499–515.

Strack, E., Friedel, W., and Hambsch, K. [1956]. *Z. physiol. Chem.* **305**, 166–169.

Strain, H. H. [1951]. *Anal. Chem.* **23**, 25–38.

Strain, H. H. [1952]. *Anal. Chem.* **24**, 356–360.

Strain, H. H. [1953]. *J. Phys. Chem.* **57**, 638–640.

Strain, H. H., Sato, T. R., and Engelke, J. [1954]. *Anal. Chem.* **26**, 90–100

Strain, H. H., and Sato, T. Y. [1956]. *Anal. Chem.* **28**, 687–694.

Stringer, J. E. C. [1951]. *Nature* **167**, 1071–1072.

Ströle, U. [1955]. *Z. anal. Chem.* **144**, 256–264.

Strohecker, R., Heimann, W., and Matt, F. [1955]. *Z. anal. Chem.* **145,** 401–417.
Sulser, H., and Hogel, O. [1953]. *Mitt. Lebensm. u. Hyg.* **44,** 79–123; from [1953] *Chem. Abstr.* **47,** 7125.
Sundaram, T. K., Radhakrishnamurthy, R., Shanmugasundaram, E. R. B., and Sarma, P. S. [1953]. *Proc. Soc. Exptl. Biol. Med.* **84,** 544–546.
Sundman, J., Saarnio, J., and Gustafsson, C. [1951]. *Paper and Timber (Finland)* **31,** 467–471; from [1951] *Chem. Abstr.* **45,** 2199.
Sundt, E., and Winter, M. [1957]. *Anal. Chem.* **29,** 851–852.
Suzuki, S. [1951]. *Igaku to Seibutsugaku* **20,** 64–65; from [1951] *Chem. Abstr.* **45,** 10290.
Svendson, A. B. [1951]. *Pharm. Acta Helv.* **26,** 253–258.
Svendson, A. B. [1952]. *Pharm. Acta Helv.* **27,** 44–48.
Swahn, B. [1952]. *Scand. J. Clin. & Lab. Invest.* **4,** 247–249; from [1953] *Chem. Abstr.* **47,** 1766.
Swain, T. [1953]. *Biochem. J.* **53,** 200–208.
Sýkora, V., and Procházka, Ž. [1953]. *Chem. listy* **47,** 1674–1675; from [1954] *Chem. Abstr.* **48,** 3852.
Synge, R. L. M., and Wood, J. C. [1955]. *Biochem. J.* **60,** XV–XVI.
Tabone, J., Robert, D., and Troestler, J. [1948]. *Bull. soc. chim. biol.* **3,** 547–552.
Tabone, J., Robert, D., Thomassey, S., and Mamounas, N. [1950]. *Bull. soc. chim. biol.* **32,** 529–534.
Tabone, J., Mamounas, N., and Thomassey, S. [1951]. *Bull. soc. chim. biol.* **33,** 1557–1559.
Taira, T., Yamatodani, S., and Fujii, S. [1951–1952]. *J. Agr. Chem. Soc. Japan* **25,** 121–123; from [1953] *Chem. Abstr.* **47,** 6302.
Takeda, S., and Shibatani, A. [1951]. *Science (Japan)* **21,** 136–137; from [1952] *Chem. Abstr.* **46,** 54.
Tamm, C., Shapiro, H. S., Lipshitz, R., and Chargaff, E. [1953]. *J. Biol. Chem.* **203,** 673–688.
Tanaka, K., and Takeda, K. [1952]. *J. Biochem. (Tokyo)* **39,** 333–337.
Tarr, H. L. A. [1952]. *Can. J. Technol.* **30,** 265–279.
Tauber, H., and Petit, E. L. [1952]. *J. Am. Chem. Soc.* **74,** 2865–2867; [1952] *Proc. Soc. Exptl. Biol. Med.* **80,** 143–144.
Tauber, H., Vannier, W. E., Petit, E. L., and Magnuson, H. J. [1953]. *Exptl. Med. and Surg.* **11,** 230–239; from [1954] *Chem. Abstr.* **48,** 6009.
Taurog, A., Chaikoff, I. L., and Tong, W. [1949]. *J. Biol. Chem.* **178,** 997–998.
Taurog, A., Tong, W., and Chaikoff, I. L. [1950]. *J. Biol. Chem.* **184,** 83–97.
Taurog, A., Briggs, F. N., and Chaikoff, I. L. [1952]. *J. Biol. Chem.* **194,** 655–668.
Tauxe, W. N., Moser, A. H., and Boyd, G. A. [1954]. *Science* **120,** 149–150.
Tebbens, B., and Torrey, J. D. [1954]. *Science* **120,** 662–663.
Tegethoff, B. [1953]. *Z. Naturforsch.* **8b,** 374–376.
Teige, C. [1950]. *Věstník Kralov. Ceské Spoleĕnosti Nauk Třida Mat. přirod.* **1949**(5), 13 pp.; from [1954] *Chem. Abstr.* **48,** 5022.
Tennent, D. M., Whitla, J. B., and Florey, K. [1951]. *Anal. Chem.* **23,** 1748–1749.
Terpstra, W. [1953]. *Koninkl. Ned. Akad. Wetenschap. Proc.* **C56,** 206–213.
Tewari, S. N. [1953]. *Kolloid-Z.* **133,** 132; from [1954] *Chem. Abstr.* **48,** 4355.
Tewari, S. N. [1954a]. *Z. anal. Chem.* **141,** 401–404.
Tewari, S. N. [1954b]. *Naturwissenschaften* **41,** 217; **41,** 229.
Thies, H., and Reuther, F. W. [1954]. *Naturwissenschaften* **41,** 230.
Thies, H., and Reuther, F. W. [1955]. *Naturwissenschaften* **42,** 462; **42,** 487.
Thompson, A. R. [1951a]. *Nature* **168,** 390–391.

Thompson, A. R. [1951b]. *Australian J. Sci. Research* **B4**, 180–186.

Thompson, J. F., and Steward, F. C. [1951b]. *Plant Physiol.* **26**, 421–440.

Thompson, J. F., Zacharius, R. M., and Steward, F. C. [1951a]. *Plant Physiol.* **26**, 375–397.

Thompson, J. F., and Marion, M. V. [1956]. *Anal. Chem.* **28**, 288.

Thomson, R. H. K. [1952]. *Biochem. J.* **51**, 118–123.

Thorn, J. A., and Johnson, M. J. [1950]. *J. Am. Chem. Soc.* **72**, 2052–2058.

Tilden, D. H. [1952]. *J. Assoc. Offic. Agr. Chemists* **35**, 423–435.

Tilden, D. H. [1953]. *J. Assoc. Offic. Agr. Chemists* **36**, 802–810.

Toennies, G., and Kolb, J. J. [1951]. *Anal. Chem.* **23**, 823–826.

Toennies, G., and Kolb, J. J. [1956a]. *Nature* **177**, 281–282.

Toennies, G., Usdin, E., and Phillips, P. M. [1956b]. *J. Biol. Chem.* **221**, 855–872.

Toribara, T. Y. [1953]. *Anal. Chem.* **25**, 1286.

Toribara, T. Y., and Di Stefano, V. [1954]. *Anal. Chem.* **26**, 1519–1521.

Torii, H. and Furuya, K. [1950–1951]. *J. Agr. Chem. Soc. Japan* **24**, 178–181; from [1952] *Chem. Abstr.* **46**, 10483.

Touchston, J. C., and Hsu, C. T. [1955]. *Anal. Chem.* **27**, 1517–1521.

Towers, G. H. N., Thompson, J. F., and Steward, F. C. [1954a]. *J. Am. Chem. Soc.* **76**, 2392–2396.

Towers, G. H. N., and Mortimer, D. C. [1954b]. *Nature* **174**, 1189.

Trevelyan, W. E., Procter, D. P., and Harrison, J. S. [1950]. *Nature* **166**, 444–445.

Troll, W., and Cannan, R. K. [1951]. *Federation Proc.* **10**, 260–261.

Tso, T. C., and Jeffrey, R. N. [1953]. *Arch. Biochem. Biophys.* **43**, 269–285.

Turba, F., and Enenkel, H. J. [1950]. *Naturwissenschaften* **37**, 93.

Turba, F., and Turba, M. [1951]. *Naturwissenschaften* **38**, 188–189.

Turba, F., and Scholtissek, C. [1954]. *Z. physiol. Chem.* **296**, 87–96.

Turba, F., and Grundlack, G. [1955]. *Biochem. Z.* **326**, 322–324.

Turnock, D. [1953]. *Nature* **172**, 355–356.

Tuzson, J. [1956]. *Naturwissenschaften* **43**, 198.

Udenfriend, S. [1950]. *J. Biol. Chem.* **187**, 65–69.

Udenfriend, S., and Velick, S. F. [1951]. *J. Biol. Chem.* **190**, 733–740.

Udenfriend, S., Weissbach, H., and Clark, C. T. [1955]. *J. Biol. Chem.* **215**, 337.

Ujejski, L., and Waygood, E. R. [1955]. *Can. J. Chem.* **33**, 687–91.

Ukai, T., and Ohasi, I. [1951]. *Ann. Rept. Fac. Pharm. Kanzawa Univ.* **1**, 35–37; from [1953] *Chem. Abstr.* **47**, 9863.

Ultee, A. J., Jr. [1952]. *Chem. Weekblad.* **48**, 821; from [1953] *Chem. Abstr.* **47**, 4239.

Umbarger, H. E., and Magasanik, B. [1952]. *J. Am. Chem. Soc.* **74**, 4253–4259.

Underwood, J. C., and Rockland, L. B. [1954]. *Anal. Chem.* **26**, 1553–1563.

Uno, H., and Koyama, A. [1951]. *J. Fermentation Technol. (Japan)* **29**, 219–221; from [1953] *Chem. Abstr.* **47**, 1008.

Urbach, K. F. [1949a]. *Proc. Soc. Exptl. Biol. Med.* **70**, 146–152.

Urbach, K. F. [1949b]. *Science* **109**, 259–260.

Usdin, E. [1955]. *Chemist Analyst* **44**(1), 27.

Uzman, L. L., and Desoer, C. [1954]. *Arch. Biochem. Biophys.* **48**, 63–71.

Vaeck, S. V. [1953]. *Nature* **172**, 213–214.

Vaeck, S. V. [1954]. *Anal. Chim. Acta* **10**, 48–67.

Vaeck, S. V. [1955]. *Anal. Chim. Acta* **12**, 443–454.

Vaidyanathan, C. S., and Kalyankar, G. D. [1955]. *J. Indian Inst. Sci.* **A37**, 304–318.

Valenciano, O. A., and Ibarra, A. [1955]. *Rev. asoc. bioquím. arg.* **20,** 145–155.
Vámos, L. [1953]. *Magyar Kém. Folyóirat* **59,** 253–254; from [1954] *Chem. Abstr.* **48,** 506.
van Erkelens, P. C. [1953]. *Nature* **172,** 357–358.
Van Gulik, W. J. [1956]. *Nature* **178,** 994.
van Halteren, M. B. [1951]. *Nature* **168,** 1090–1091.
van Os, G. A. J. [1952]. *Biochim. et Biophys. Acta* **9,** 111–112.
Vanyarkho, L. G., and Garanina, V. A. [1952]. *Aptechnoe Delo* **3,** 22-25.
Vas, K. [1951]. *Acta Chim. Acad. Sci. Hung.* **1,** 335–342; from [1954] *Chem. Abstr.* **48,** 4368.
Vavruch, I. [1949–1950]. *Listy Cukrovar* **66,** 299–301; from [1953] *Chem. Abstr.* **47,** 9219.
Velick, S. F., and Udenfriend, S. [1951]. *J. Biol. Chem.* **190,** 721–731.
Venner, H. [1955]. *Naturwissenschaften* **42,** 179–180.
Venturello, G., and Ghe, A. M. [1952]. *Anal. Chim. Acta* **7,** 261–267; **7,** 268–273.
Venturello, G., and Ghe, A. M. [1954]. *Anal. Chim. Acta* **10,** 335–345.
Vernon, L. P., and Aronoff, S. [1952]. *Arch. Biochem. Biophys.* **36,** 382–398.
Veselý, F., Šmirous, F., and Vepřek-Šiška, J. [1955]. *Chem. listy* **49,** 1661–1663.
Vigne, J. P., Tabau, R. L., and Fondorai, J. [1955]. *Bull. soc. chim. France* p. 1282.
Vining, L. C., and Waksman, S. A. [1954]. *Science* **120,** 389–390.
Virtanen, A. I., Miettinen, J. K., and Kunttu, H. [1953]. *Acta Chem. Scand.* **7,** 38–44.
Virtanen, A. I., and Berg, A. M. [1954a]. *Acta Chem. Scand.* **8,** 1085–1086.
Virtanen, A. I., Uksila, E., and Matikkala, E. J. [1954b]. *Acta Chem. Scand.* **8,** 1091–1093.
Vischer, E., and Chargaff, E. [1947]. *J. Biol. Chem.* **168,** 781–782.
Vischer, E., and Chargaff, E. [1948]. *J. Biol. Chem.* **176,** 703–714.
Viscontini, M., Bonetti, G., Ebnöther, C., and Kamer, P. [1951]. *Helv. Chim. Acta* **34,** 1384.
Vlitos, A. J., and Meudt, W. [1953]. *Contribs. Boyce Thompson Inst.* **17,** 197–202.
von Arx, E., and Neher, R. [1956]. *Helv. Chim. Acta* **39,** 1664–1670.
von Euler, U. S., Hamberg, U., and Hellner, S. [1951]. *Biochem. J.* **49,** 655–658.
von Euler, U. S., and Eliasson, R. [1952]. *Nature* **170,** 664–665.
von Hahn, H., Sorkin, E., and Erlenmeyer, H. [1951]. *Experientia* **7,** 358.
von Schindler, O., and Reichstein, T. [1951]. *Helv. Chim. Acta* **34,** 108–116.
Wachtmeister, C. A. [1951]. *Acta Chem. Scand.* **5,** 976–978; from [1952] *Chem Abstr.* **46,** 8565.
Wade, H. E., and Morgan, D. M. [1953]. *Nature* **171,** 529–530.
Wade, H. E., and Morgan, D. M. [1955]. *Biochem. J.* **60,** 264–270.
Wadman, W. H., Thomas, G. H., and Pardee, A. B. [1954]. *Anal. Chem.* **26,** 1192–1195.
Wagner, Günther [1952]. *Arch. Pharm.* **285,** 409–421.
Wagner, Günther [1953]. *Arch. Pharm.* **286,** 269–277.
Wagner, H., Abisch, L., and Bernhard, K. [1955]. *Helv. Chim. Acta* **38,** 1536–1541.
Wako, H. [1953]. *Tôhoku J. Exptl. Med.* **57,** 191–197; from [1953] *Chem. Abstr.* **47,** 10079.
Waldron, D. M. [1952]. *Nature* **170,** 461–462.
Walker, D. G., and Warren, F. L. [1951]. *Biochem. J.* **49,** xxi.
Walker, D. M. [1952]. *Biochem. J.* **52,** 679–683.

Walker, J. B., and Myers, J. [1953]. *J. Biol. Chem.* **203**, 143–152.

Walker, T. K., Hall, A. N., and Hopton, J. W. [1951]. *Nature* **168**, 1042–1043.

Wallenfels, K. [1950]. *Naturwissenschaften* **37**, 491–492.

Wallenfels, K., and von Pechmann, E. [1951]. *Angew. Chem.* **63**, 44–45.

Webster, H. L. [1953]. *Nature* **172**, 453–454.

Weil, H., and Williams, T. I. [1950]. *Nature* **166**, 1000–1001.

Weil, H., and Williams, T. I. [1951]. *Nature* **167**, 906–907.

Weil, H. [1953a]. *Kolloid-Z.* **132**, 149–162; from [1954] *Chem. Abstr.* **48**, 74.

Weil, H., and Williams, T. I. [1953b]. *Naturwissenschaften* **40**, 1–7.

Weil-Malherbe, H., and Bone, A. D. [1954]. *Biochem. J.* **58**, 132–141.

Weiss, A., and Fallab, S. [1954]. *Helv. Chim. Acta* **37**, 1253–1256.

Weissmann, B., Bromberg, P. A., and Gutman, A. B. [1954]. *Proc. Soc. Exptl. Biol. Med.* **87**, 257–260.

Weller, L. E., Wittwer, S. H., and Sell, H. M. [1954]. *J. Am. Chem. Soc.* **76**, 629–630.

Wellington, E. F. [1951]. *Biochim. et Biophys. Acta* **7**, 238–243.

Wellington, E. F. [1952]. *Can. J. Chem.* **30**, 581–591.

Wellington, E. F. [1953]. *Can. J. Chem.* **31**, 484–487.

Wender, S. H., and Gage, T. B. [1949]. *Science* **109**, 287–289.

West, C. D., Reich, H., and Samuels, L. T. [1951]. *J. Biol. Chem.* **193**, 219–226.

Westall, R. G. [1953]. *Biochem. J.* **55**, 244–248.

Westmann, A. E. R., and Scott, A. E. [1951]. *Nature* **168**, 740.

Westmann, A. E. R., Scott, A. E., and Pedley, J. T. [1952]. *Chem. in Can.* **4**, 35–40; from [1953] *Chem. Abstr.* **47**, 12111.

Weurman, C., and Swain, T. [1953]. *Nature* **172**, 678.

Weygand, F., and Hofmann, H. [1950]. *Chem. Ber.* **83**, 405–413.

Weygand, F., Junk, R., and Leber, D. [1952]. *Z. physiol. Chem.* **291**, 191–196.

Whistler, R. L., and Hickson, J. L. [1955]. *Anal. Chem.* **27**, 1514–1517.

White, A. A., and Hess, W. C. [1956]. *Arch. Biochem. Biophys.* **64**, 57–66.

White, L. M., and Secor, G. E. [1953]. *Arch. Biochem. Biophys.* **43**, 60–66.

White, T., Kirby, K. S., and Knowles, E. [1952]. *J. Soc. Leather Trades' Chemists* **36**, 148.

Whiting, G. C. [1951]. *Nature* **168**, 833–834.

Whittaker, V. P., and Wijesundera, S. [1952]. *Biochem. J.* **51**, 348–351; **52**, 475–479.

Wichtl, M. [1956]. *Naturwissenschaften* **43**, 158.

Wiegand, O. F., and Schrank, A. R. [1956]. *Anal. Chem.* **48**, 259.

Wieland, O. P., Hutchings, B. L., and Williams, J. H. [1952]. *Arch. Biochem. Biophys.* **40**, 205–217.

Wieland, T., and Fischer, E. [1948]. *Naturwissenschaften* **35**, 29–30.

Wieland, T., and Fischer, E. [1949]. *Naturwissenschaften* **36**, 219.

Wieland, T., and Bauer, L. [1951a]. *Angew. Chem.* **63**, 511–513.

Wieland, T., and Wirth, L. [1951b]. *Angew. Chem.* **63**, 171–172.

Wiggins, L. F., and Williams, J. H. [1952]. *Nature* **170**, 279–280.

Wilkinson, J. H. [1956]. *Biochem. J.* **63**, 601–605.

Williams, A. H. [1955]. *Chem. & Ind. (London)* pp. 120–121.

Williams, B. L., and Wender, S. H. [1953]. *Arch. Biochem. Biophys.* **43**, 319–323.

Williams, K. T., and Bevenue, A. [1951]. *Science* **113**, 582.

Williams, K. T., Potter, E. F., and Bevenue, A. [1952]. *J. Assoc. Offic. Agr. Chemists* **35**, 483–486.

Williams, K. T., and Bevenue, A. [1953]. *J. Assoc. Offic. Agr. Chemists* **36**, 969–979.

Williams, K. T., and Bevenue, A. [1955]. *Anal. Chem.* **27**, 331.

Williams, R. J., and Kirby, H. [1948]. *Science* **107**, 481–483.

Williams, R. J. [1951]. *Texas Univ. Publ.* **4**, No. **5109**, pp. 205.

Williams, R. J. P. [1954]. *Brit. Med. J.* **10**, 165–169.

Williams, T. I., and Weil, H. [1952]. *Nature* **170**, 503.

Williamson, M. B., and Passmann, J. M. [1952]. *J. Biol. Chem.* **199**, 121–126.

Windsor, E. [1951]. *J. Biol. Chem.* **192**, 595–606.

Winegard, H. M., Toennies, G., and Block, R. J. [1948]. *Science* **108**, 506–507.

Wingo, W. J. [1953]. *Anal. Chem.* **25**, 1939–1940.

Wingo, W. J. [1954]. *Anal. Chem.* **26**, 1527–1528.

Winslow, E. H., and Liebhafsky, H. A. [1949]. *Anal. Chem.* **21**, 1338–1342.

Winsten, W. A., and Spark, A. H. [1947]. *Science* **106**, 192–193.

Winsten, W. A., and Eigen, E. [1948a]. *Proc. Soc. Exptl. Biol. Med.* **67**, 513–517.

Winsten, W. A., and Eigen, E. [1948b]. *J. Am. Chem. Soc.* **70**, 3333–3339.

Winsten, W. A., and Eigen, E. [1949]. *J. Biol. Chem.* **177**, 989–990.

Winsten, W. A., Jarowski, C. I., Murphy, F. X., and Lazier, W. A. [1950]. *J. Am. Chem. Soc.* **72**, 3969–3972.

Winteringham, F. P. W., Harrison, A., and Bridges, R. G. [1950]. *Nature* **166**, 999.

Winteringham, F. P. W. [1952a]. *Science* **116**, 452–453.

Winteringham, F. P. W., Harrison, A., and Bridges, R. G. [1952b]. *Analyst* **77**, 19–28.

Winteringham, F. P. W., Harrison, A., and Bridges, R. G. [1952c]. *Nucleonics* **10**(3), 52–57.

Winteringham, F. P. W. [1953]. *Nature* **172**, 727–728.

Winteringham, F. P. W., Bridges, P. M., and Hellyer, P. C. [1955]. *Biochem. J.* **59**, 13–21.

Wise, C. S., Dimler, R. J., Davis, H. A., and Rist, C. E. [1955]. *Anal. Chem.* **27**, 33–36.

Wohnlich, H. [1956]. *Z. anal. Chem.* **150**, 2–7.

Woiwod, A. J. [1949a]. *Biochem. J.* **45**, 412–417.

Woiwod, A. J. [1949b]. *J. Gen. Microbiol.* **3**, 312–318.

Wolf, G. [1956]. *Naturwissenschaften* **43**, 422.

Wolfrom, M. L., and Miller, J. B. [1956]. *Anal. Chem.* **28**, 1037.

Wolfson, W. Q., Cohn, C., and Devaney, W. A. [1949]. *Science* **109**, 541–543.

Wollish, E. G., Schmall, M., and Shafer, E. G. E. [1949]. *Anal. Chem.* **23**, 768–771.

Wood, S. E., and Strain, H. H. [1954]. *Anal. Chem.* **26**, 260–264.

Wood, T. [1955]. *Nature* **176**, 175–176.

Wood, T. [1956]. *Biochem. J.* **62**, 611–613.

Woodhouse, D. L. [1954]. *Biochem. J.* **56**, 349–352.

Woodruff, H. B., and Foster, J. C. [1950]. *J. Biol. Chem.* **183**, 569–576.

Woodward, C. C., and Rabideau, G. S. [1954]. *Anal. Chem.* **26**, 248.

Woolf, L. I. [1953]. *Nature* **171**, 841.

Woolley, D. W., Schaffner, G., and Braun, A. C. [1952]. *J. Biol. Chem.* **198**, 807–813.

Work, E. [1949]. *Biochim. et Biophys Acta* **3**, 400–411.

Work, E. [1950]. *Nature* **165**, 74–75.

Work, E. [1951]. *Biochem. J.* **49**, 17–23.

Wright, L. D., Cresson, E. L., and Driscoll, C. A. [1954]. *Proc. Soc. Exptl. Biol. Med.* **86**, 480–483.

Wunderly, C. [1954]. *Nature* **173**, 267–268.
Wyatt, G. R. [1950]. *Nature* **166**, 237–238.
Wyatt, G. R. [1951]. *Biochem. J.* **48**, 584.
Wyatt, G. R., and Cohen, S. S. [1952]. *Nature* **170**, 1072–1073.
Wykes, G. R. [1953]. *Biochem. J.* **53**, 294–296.
Wynn, V. [1949]. *Nature* **164**, 445.
Yagi, K. [1950a]. *Seikagaka* **22**, 162.
Yagi, K., and Ishiguro, I. [1950b]. *J. Japan. Biochem. Soc.* **22**, 163–164; from [1952] *Chem. Abstr.* **46**, 2118.
Yagi, K., and Ishiguro, I. [1950c]. *Vitamins (Japan)* **3**, 29–32; from [1951] *Chem. Abstr.* **45**, 1639.
Yagi, K. [1951]. *J. Biochem. (Japan)* **38**, 161–169; from [1951] *Chem. Abstr.* **45**, 9097.
Yagi, K. [1952]. *Igaku to Seibutsugaku* **25**, 266–268; from [1953] *Chem. Abstr.* **47**, 11307.
Yagi, Y., Michel, R., and Roche, J. [1953]. *Ann. pharm. franc.* **11**, 30–37; from [1954] *Chem. Abstr.* **48**, 2005.
Yamafuji, K., and Eto, M. [1953]. *Enzymolgia* **16**, 247–255.
Yamagishi, M., and Yoshida, T. [1953]. *J. Pharm. Soc. Japan* **73**, 675–676; from [1953] *Chem. Abstr.* **47**, 10410.
Yamaguchi, M., and Howard, F. D. [1955]. *Anal. Chem.* **27**, 332–333.
Yamaki, T. [1950]. *Misc. Repts. Research Inst. Nat. Resources* **17–18**, 180–188; from [1953] *Chem. Abstr.* **47**, 676.
Yamaki, T., and Nakamura, K. [1952]. *Sci. Papers Coll. Gen. Educ. Univ. Tokyo* **2**, 81–98.
Yanari, S. [1956]. *J. Biol. Chem.* **220**, 683–689.
Yoda, A. [1952]. *J. Chem. Soc. Japan* **73**, 18–19; from [1953] *Chem. Abstr.* **47**, 3185.
Zacharius, R. M., Thompson, J. F., and Steward, F. C. [1952]. *J. Am. Chem. Soc.* **74**, 2949.
Zaffaroni, A., Burton, R. B., and Keutmann, E. H. [1949]. *J. Biol. Chem.* **177**, 109–116.
Zaffaroni, A. [1950]. *J. Am. Chem. Soc.* **72**, 3828.
Zaffaroni, A., and Burton, R. B. [1951]. *J. Biol. Chem.* **193**, 749–767.
Zahn, H., and Rauchle, A. [1953]. *Z. anal. Chem.* **138**, 357–359; from [1953] *Chem. Abstr.* **47**, 9216.
Zahn, H., and Rexroth, E. [1955]. *Z. anal. Chem.* **148**, 181–186.
Zahradnik, R., and Kobrle, V. [1956]. *Chem. listy* **50**, 1649–1651; from [1957] *Chem. Abstr.* **51**, 1368.
Zakrzewski, S. F., and Nichol, C. A. [1953]. *J. Biol. Chem.* **205**, 361–368.
Zamenhof, S., Brawerman, G., and Chargaff, E. [1952]. *Biochim. et Biophys. Acta* **9**, 402–405.
Zatman, L. J., Kaplan, N. O., and Colowick, S. P. [1953]. *J. Biol. Chem.* **200**, 197–212.
Ženišek, A., and Král, J. A. [1953]. *Biochim. et Biophys. Acta* **12**, 479–480.
Zilliacus, H., and Roos, B. E. [1951]. *Acta Endocrinol.* **6**, 285–288; from [1953] *Chem. Abstr.* **47**, 12470.
Zimmerman, P. W. [1953]. *In* "Encyclopedia of Chemical Technology" (R. E. Kirk and D. F. Othmer, eds.), Vol. 10, pp. 723–736. Interscience, New York.
Zimmermann, G., and Nehring, K. [1951]. *Angew. Chem.* **63**, 556.

Zimmermann, G. [1953a]. *Z. anal. Chem.* **138,** 321–332; from [1953] *Chem. Abstr.* **47,** 9205.

Zimmermann, G., and Kludas, K. H. [1953b]. *Chem. Tech. (Berlin)* **5,** 203–206; from [1953] *Chem. Abstr.* **47,** 10048.

Zinzadze, C. [1935]. *Ind. Eng. Chem.* **7,** 227–230.

Zweig, G. [1956]. *Anal. Chem.* **28,** 428.

Zweig, G., and Hood, S. L. [1957]. *Anal. Chem.* **29,** 438–441.

Part II
PAPER ELECTROPHORESIS

INTRODUCTION

It may surprise some to realize that paper electrophoresis or ionophoresis[1] antedates the modern work on paper chromatography, which can be considered to have started with the work of Martin and Synge in 1944 (44-1).[2]

The first report on the use of paper electrophoresis appears to be that of König (37-1), which appeared in Portuguese in 1937. It is interesting to note that in it the use of ultraviolet light was suggested for locating separated substances, a technique later much used in paper chromatography. In 1939 another paper appeared by König in collaboration with von Klobusitzky (39-2), in which paper electrophoresis was used for separation of a yellow pigment from a snake venom, its first use for protein mixtures. This work attracted little attention, however. It is interesting to note that Tiselius (37-2) published his classical description of the moving boundary method in 1937.[3] McDonald (55-190) recently has called attention to the early work of Berraz (43-1) who separated inorganic ions on paper in 1943. In any case, it seems certain that the subsequent "rediscovery" of the method was influenced to a large extent by experience with paper chromatography, as well as with the silica gel ionophoresis of Consden, Gordon, and Martin (46-1). From 1947 to 1949 a number of laboratories independently developed methods of electrophoresis on paper which are still employed without significant modification. (Haugaard, (48-5); Wieland, (48-12); Durrum, (49-6); Garrison, (49-10).

Attention to the quantitative aspects of the method can be considered to have begun in 1948 with the application of the ingenious "retention analysis" principle to the quantitative determination of amino acids separated by paper electrophoresis by Wieland (48-13). In 1948, Block (48-3) and Bull (49-4) successfully applied photoelectric scanning to paper chromatograms, directly measuring the optical density of the ninhydrin amino acid spots. Cremer (50-7) and Turba (50-36) made paper electrophoresis quantitative for proteins by dye elution techniques. Also in 1950 Grassmann (50-17) described direct photoelectric scanning of dyed paper electrophoresis patterns of serum. Subsequently many scanners have been described, and this method appears to be the most promising for routine

[1] Martin and Synge (45-2) have used the terms ionophoresis to define "processes concerned with the movement in an electrical field of relatively small ions, electrophoresis for movement of large molecules and particles, and electrodialysis for the removal of smaller ions from larger molecules and particles."

[2] The Bibliography for Part II begins on page 580.

[3] In 1939 Strain (39-5) reported the combination of ionophoresis with chromatographic adsorption in the conventional Tswett column filled with cotton, and Coolidge (39-1) separated proteins in a column packed with ground glass wool across which an electrical potential was applied.

use where sufficient numbers of patterns are to be studied to warrant the fairly elaborate equipment required.

With one important exception, the subsequent direction of work on paper electrophoresis has been predictable and analogous to developments in paper chromatography, being concerned principally with improved details of technique and application to an ever-widening number of types of mixtures. The important exception is the independent development by Haugaard (48-6), Grassmann (49-10A; 50-16), and Svensson (49-24), of the continuous electrophoresis principle which until recently had no counterpart in chromatography.[4]

At the present writing more than two thousand papers dealing with the subject of zone electrophoresis have appeared. Over 90% of these have dealt with paper electrophoresis. A bewildering array of equipment, varying principally in minor details, confronts the inexperienced worker. Fortunately, all these types of apparatus fall into three basic categories. An understanding of the principal differences in these types is fundamental to the intelligent choice of equipment for any given practical problem. It is the purpose of this section of this book to acquaint the average laboratory worker with the different basic types of equipment available, to instruct him in their practical use, and to guide him in their appropirate application.

In addition, any of the basic types of operation may be carried out as a unidimensional strip, or as a two-dimensional sheet, or as a continuous curtain operation, and these variations will be discussed. As in the treatment of paper chromatography in this volume, theoretical considerations will not be emphasized except where a knowledge of them is required to obtain satisfactory results and help in their interpretation.

Since the first edition of this manual was published several significant developments in electrophoresis have made their appearance. These are the starch gel technique of Smithies (55-281), the pH and ionic strength gradient techniques of Kolin (55-151), and the density gradient stabilization of liquid columns employed by Svensson (55-289); also the high voltage or "hoch Spannung" techniques of Michl (51-45), Kickhofen and Westphal (52-95) and others. Since these techniques are not strictly paper techniques, they will not be emphasized in this manual, although a discussion of high voltage methods is included.

---

[4] Svensson (55-291) has recently described a continuous chromatographic apparatus based on a series of matched chromatographic columns disposed in a circular manner. Solms (55-282A) has described a continuous paper chromatographic apparatus in which a paper curtain with a serrated lower edge is disposed as a cylinder. (See Page 47.)

Chapter XV

GENERAL THEORY

The factors governing the migration of any ion in solution in an electrical field may be considered to fall into three separate classes:

1. Those characteristics related to the ion itself, namely, its charge (sign and magnitude), size, shape, tendency to dissociate, and amphoteric behavior, if any.

2. Those factors related to the environment in which the ion is being studied, such as the electrolyte concentration, ionic strength, dielectric properties, chemical properties, pH, temperature, viscosity, and the presence of non-polar molecules which may influence viscosity or dielectric properties of the electrolyte or which may interact to form charged complexes (for example, carbohydrates in the presence of borate buffers).

3. The character of the applied field, its intensity, purity (presence of alternating-current components), and distribution along the migration path. It is obvious that secondary interactions between factors 1 and 2, either electrostatic or by van der Waals' forces, may further influence the experimental situation.

A comprehensive study of all these factors and interactions is beyond the scope of this book; hence consideration is limited to those elements of recognized importance in the practical application of paper electrophoresis.

For a particle to migrate in an electrical field it is necessary that it possess a charge—that is, an excess or a deficiency of electrons resulting in a net electrostatic charge.[1] The important consideration is the net charge, not the absolute values of the individual charges. The unit charge is 4.80×10^{-10} e.s.u., and ions carry this charge or some integral multiple of it. This is not to say that fractional net charges cannot exist, since, although the charge at any instant is one integral or multiple unit, the time taken for measurement is generally long in comparison to the length of time this state exists, and thus we are dealing with a statistical time average which may be a fractional value (Q).

Several charging processes are known, including those resulting from electrolytic dissociation and those resulting from reaction of acids or bases with which we are practically always concerned in paper electrophoresis. Electrolytic dissociation in the electrolyte systems which are most com-

---

[1] Uncharged molecules or amphoteric materials in the isoelectric state may passively migrate in an electric field as a result of endosmosis with an apparent mobility. This is the most practical method so far introduced for measuring endosmosis in paper electrophoresis, where it is an important consideration. (See p. 502.)

monly used depends on the high dielectric constant of water which permits the ions to exist in solution in the dissociated state.

Other charging processes which are recognized include polarization, ion pair formation, specific chemical reactions, and hydrogen bonding. For a discussion of these the reader is referred to texts such as Abramson (42-1).

In salt-free very dilute systems the force, F, exerted on a particle by an applied electrical field is equal to the product of the field strength, X, and the net charge, Q.

$$F = XQ. \tag{1}$$

A particle moving in a constant field (constant force) in a viscous medium, however, attains a constant velocity because the viscous retarding force, F', opposing the motion increases linearly with acceleration (otherwise the particle would continuously accelerate). This viscous retarding force depends on the geometry of the particle but for a sphere is given by Stokes' law as

$$\frac{F'}{V} = 6\pi r\eta, \tag{2}$$

where V equals the electrophoretic velocity, η equals the viscosity of the medium, and r equals the radius of the particle. Thus for an isolated spherical particle obeying Stokes' law in the steady state the electrical forces and the viscous forces are equal ($F = F'$), and we have, from equations 1 and 2,

$$XQ = 6\pi r\eta V \tag{3}$$

The electrophoretic mobility, u, is the velocity, V, measured under standard conditions; that is, per unit field, X, expressed as volts per centimeter, or,

$$u = \frac{V}{X} \tag{4}$$

or

$$u = \frac{Q}{6\pi r\eta}. \tag{5}$$

Practically speaking, in paper electrophoresis we are not confronted with this idealized situation. Buffers or other salts are nearly always present in appreciable concentration, and the electrical interactions between charged ions can no longer be ignored as is permissible at infinite dilution.

The electrical forces exerted between ions in aqueous solution, as, for example, Na^+ and Cl^-, are of the same order as thermal forces and appreciably influence the distribution of other ions present. This results in a change in the net force that is applied by the electrical field. This is considered to be the principle cause of decreased mobility with increasing ionic strength. The force applied remains XQ, but a new retarding force is added, owing to the fact that ions of opposite charge group about the migrating ions, resulting in what is considered to be a local ionic atmosphere of a charge opposite to that of the migrating ion. As a consequence the fluid surrounding the migrating particle moves in a direction opposite to that of a migrating particle with an attendant decrease in mobility.

The degree of effectiveness of various electrolyte ions in creating this retarding effect depends on their concentration, c, and charge. It does not depend on the specific chemical nature of the ion but primarily on its valence. Lewis (21-1) derived the ionic strength function to describe quantitatively this effect:

$$\text{Ionic strength} = \frac{\Gamma}{2} = \frac{1}{2} \sum_1^s c_i Z_i^2 \tag{6}$$

for a strong electrolyte containing s ion types where c_i equals concentration of each type of ion (in moles per liter) and Z_i is its valence. Thus a KCl solution would have one-third the ionic strength of a $CaCl_2$ solution of the same molarity.

We have seen that the velocity, V, with which an ion migrates in an electrical field is proportional to the electrical force acting per unit charge. This force in turn is proportional to the field strength. The field strength, X, is expressed as the potential in volts divided by the distance between the electrodes in centimeters. In practice, geometrical considerations often make it impracticable to measure this distance directly. A simple Ohm's law transformation permits the field strength, X, at any cross section, s, between the electrodes to be calculated from the equation

$$X_s = \frac{i}{q_s \kappa_s}, \tag{7}$$

where i equals current in amperes, q_s equals the area at cross section s under consideration in square centimeters, and κ_s equals specific conductivity in mhos per centimeter at cross section s.

In order to carry out any type of electrophoretic separation, it is necessary that convection be controlled so that resulting mixing does not obscure or destroy any resolution attained. In the classical moving boundary method of Tiselius, the control of convection is effected by proper regulation of temperature gradients. In paper electrophoresis, which is one type of what Tiselius has called zone electrophoresis,[2] convection is prevented by

[2] The term zone electrophoresis, which was introduced by Tiselius (51-70) to dis-

the paper itself, provided that the paper is not overloaded with electrolyte (see p. 510).

A consideration of the moving boundary or free electrophoresis situation is informative because much of the fundamental theory can be applied to paper electrophoresis.

As a consequence of the passage of current through the solution, heat is developed. This heat is dissipated by conduction radially from the axis of the electrophoretic column through the glass walls of the cell and to the thermostatic medium. Thus the center of the column in the steady state is at a higher temperature than the solution at the walls of the electrophoresis vessel. This would be expected to give rise to thermal convection owing to the central warmer and thus less dense portion of the column rising and the concentric cooler lamellae descending.

However, at temperatures (about 4°C.) near the maximum density of water in water or dilute aqueous solutions there is little change of density with temperature. With a thermostat bath near 0°C. and with current flow maintained at a sufficiently low level so that heat can be dissipated at the proper rate and the column maintained near the temperature of maximum density for the solution in question, convection can be effectively prevented.[3]

Heat, H, expressed as watts per cubic centimeter, is generated by the passage of the current, i, in a cell of cross section q, as expressed by the following equation:

$$H = \frac{i^2}{q^2 \kappa}. \tag{8}$$

tinguish electrophoresis carried out in the presence of anticonvection agents from moving boundary electrophoresis, is coming into wide use. This is perhaps an unfortunate term because it emphasizes a non-essential criterion of the general method. Theoretically, one could carry out a zone-type separation in the moving boundary situation, and, conversely, one could carry out a moving boundary-type separation in the presence of an anticonvection medium. In this author's opinion the term anticonvection media or simply anticonvectant electrophoresis would meet the need for an accurate and practical general term to emphasize the distinction. The more specific terms such as paper electrophoresis or agar gel electrophoresis appear to be well established and are sufficiently precise for the more specific cases.

It is noted that there has been a recent tendency to ignore the distinction between electrophoresis and ionophoresis which according to the usage of Martin and Synge (45-2) are distinguished from each other on the basis of particle size. This distinction, however, is not fundamental, since ions of practically all ranges and size can be separated in either free or moving boundary systems or in systems employing anticonvection agents. For further discussion, see Smith (54-460).

[3] As pointed out by Longsworth (39-3), the key to the success of the Tiselius system rests on the recognition of the above-mentioned considerations. Also see this reference for a more detailed account of this phenomenon.

The limit of field intensity that may be applied for free solution or moving boundary electrophoresis is largely dictated by this equation, since convection must be prevented.   Alberty (48-1) gives the limit of permissible current flow for the usual moving boundary separations in the conventional Tiselius cells as about 25 ma.   Currents of this order generate the maximum amount of heat which can be dissipated in the usual systems without a temperature rise sufficient to introduce mixing by thermal convection.

On the other hand, when convection is prevented by anticonvectants, this consideration may be neglected.   Often the maximum (but usually not the optimal current) which may be employed is that just short of giving rise to physical disruption of the closed column by boiling, or by drying out of open paper strips, and of course by the thermal stability of the solution being separated and the thermal stability of the anticonvectant.   (For example, gelatin columns may sometimes be melted at room temperatures by the resultant heat from currents otherwise low enough to cause no damage to serum proteins being separated.)

It should be remembered, however, in cases where high current is used that even though thermal convection is controlled by the anticonvection medium the mobility of the ions in the center of the column will be higher than at the periphery, since ion mobilities are proportional to absolute temperature with a parabolic distribution of the migrating front.   For paper strip electrophoresis technique, the distribution of the electrolyte in a thin cross section has a marked advantage favoring dissipation of heat in a manner analogous to that achieved in a thin, flat, Tiselius type electrophoresis cell.   Also free diffusion increases with temperature, so for certain situations temperature control and low field strengths are often in order even when anticonvection media are employed.

It is obvious that the greater the difference in mobilities of any two ions, A and B, the more easily and quickly they may be separated; thus if u_A and u_B are mobilities of components A and B which migrate distances d_A and d_B , and if X is the field strength and t represents time, the separation of the zones is represented by the equation

$$d_A - d_B = (u_A - u_B)Xt. \tag{9}$$

For weak electrolytes and amphoteric substances which are of considerable importance in biological systems, the degree of separation depends on the degree of dissociation.   A guide for the selection of systems favorable for separations of this type has been given by Consden, Gordon, and Martin (46-1).   The following is their treatment developed in connection with their pioneering work on ionophoresis of amino acids in silica gel slabs.

Consider two acids, HA and HB, with dissociation constants, K_a and K_b , and ion mobilities, u_a and u_b .   Then the net mobility of HA, i.e., the mobility as determined from the movement of a zone of the acid in an ionophoretic apparatus, will be

$$U_a = \frac{u_a[\text{A}^-]}{[\text{HA}] + [\text{A}^-]} = \frac{u_a K_a}{[\text{H}^+] + K_a}. \tag{10}$$

For separability we are interested in the difference in net mobilities:

$$U_a - U_b = \frac{u_a K_a}{[\text{H}^+] + K_a} - \frac{u_b K_b}{[\text{H}^+] + K_b}. \tag{11}$$

It can be shown that the difference in net mobility is a maximum when

$$[\text{H}^+] = (\sqrt{(K_a K_b)})\left(\frac{\sqrt{\dfrac{u_a}{u_b}} - \sqrt{\dfrac{K_a}{K_b}}}{1 - \sqrt{\dfrac{u_a K_a}{u_b K_b}}}\right) \tag{12}$$

or

$$\text{pH} = \frac{\text{p}K_a + \text{p}K_b}{2} - \log\left(\frac{\sqrt{\dfrac{u_a}{u_b}} - \sqrt{\dfrac{K_a}{K_b}}}{1 - \sqrt{\dfrac{u_a K_a}{u_b K_b}}}\right) \tag{13}$$

When $K_a > K_b$ (i.e., $\text{p}K_a < \text{p}K_b$) and except when K_a/K_b lies between the values of u_a/u_b and u_b/u_a, and if the optimum pH is used, the maximum difference in net mobility can be shown to be

$$(U_a - U_b) = \frac{u_b\left(\sqrt{\dfrac{u_a K_a}{u_b K_b}} - 1\right)^2}{K_a/K_b - 1}. \tag{14}$$

Figure 1 shows $(U_a - U_b)/u_b$ plotted against $\text{p}K_b - \text{p}K_a$ for various values of u_a/u_b, and the intersecting family of lines shows the pH which must be employed. The equation for pH lines is

$$\frac{U_a - U_b}{u_b} = \frac{(K_a/K_b) - 1}{(1 + [\text{H}^+]/K_b)^2}. \tag{15}$$

It is not important that these pH values should be exactly followed; 0.1 pH unit makes little difference to $U_a - U_b$. Further, in Fig. 1, where pH $= \text{p}K_b + \infty$ is shown, there is little advantage in going beyond pH $= \text{p}K_b + 2$. This applies also to the left of this line where the separation depends only on the difference in ion mobility. It is also possible in the case of substances in which u_a/u_b is low, by working at a high pH, to separate them in the opposite direction to that shown in Fig. 1, using only the ion mobility difference.

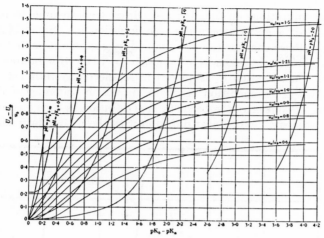

FIG. 1. Chart showing difference in net mobilities of two acids, for a difference in pK and given ion mobility ratio, when separating at the optimum pH, the value of which is given by the intersecting family of lines (Consden, Gordon, and Martin, 46-1).

The sign convention adopted in Fig. 1 is suitable for the separation of anions; i.e., the acid with the greater pK must be called HB. For the separation of cations, the base with the greater pK must be called A, and to determine the optimum pH, the sign of the addition to pK_b must be reversed. This rule holds also for ampholytes. Thus, in separating glycine and serine in alkaline solution, the ions are anions and pK_b must be greater than pK_a, even though the separation depends on differences in the dissociation constants of the amino groups.

Figures for mobilities of most amino acids are not available. An estimate may be made, however, by assuming them to be the same as the corresponding hydroxy (or fatty) acid; an extensive table of such values is given in the International Critical Tables. A correction must be made for the reduced mobility in the relatively strong solution of electrolyte. It is assumed that

$$u_a = \frac{\Lambda_{0\ acid} - \Lambda_{0\ H\ ion}}{96,500} \cdot \frac{\Lambda_{c\ electrolyte}}{\Lambda_{0\ electrolyte}};$$
(16)

i.e., the assumption is made that the ratio of the mobilities (of the substances to be separated) at infinite dilution and in the electrolyte actually used is the same as the ratio of the equivalent conductances of the electrolyte at infinite dilution and at the concentration used.

During the course of any electrophoretic separation, free diffusion occurs as a function of time, concentration, and temperature. Diffusion sometimes places limitations on the choice of field strength-time relationships chosen to effect a given separation (see equation 9). Some idea of the magnitude of these changes can be obtained by consideration of Fig. 2 and the following treatment taken from Peniston (51-51). If a sample initially at constant concentration C_0 is placed in an electrophoretic column in a band of width 2_b, a condition is created in which widening of the band and decrease of concentration occur by free diffusion as time passes (and as migration proceeds). For linear diffusion with these boundary conditions,

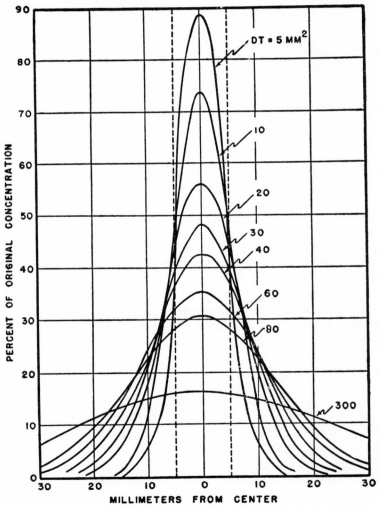

FIG. 2. Free diffusion from 1-cm. sample section (Peniston, 51-51).

integration of Fick's law (Byerly, 93-1) leads to the expression

$$\frac{C}{C_0} = \frac{1}{\sqrt{\pi}} \int_{-(b+x)/(2\sqrt{D \cdot t})}^{(b-x)/(2\sqrt{D \cdot t})} l^{-\beta^2} \cdot d\beta, \tag{17}$$

which can be expressed as the difference between two integrals:

$$\frac{C}{C_0} = \frac{1}{2}\left[\frac{2}{\sqrt{\pi}} \int_0^{(b-x/2\sqrt{D \cdot t})} l^{-\beta^2} \cdot d\beta - \frac{2}{\sqrt{\pi}} \int_0^{-(b+x/2\sqrt{D \cdot t})} l^{-\beta^2} \cdot d\beta \right]. \tag{18}$$

The solution can be constructed from probability integral tables. Figure 2 shows the calculation for free diffusion from the initial sample section of 10-mm. width in terms of reciprocal parameters D (square millimeters per day) and t (days). The rate of dispersion is roughly inversely proportional to the square of the initial width of the sample section and can be shown to impose limits on the extent to which the width of the sample section may be reduced in order to achieve equivalent separation of components with shorter migration distances; that is, by shorter migration times or lower voltage gradients.

The calculated curves can be considered to represent minimal dispersion because the actual experimental measurements made by the above authors showed greater dispersion of concentration distribution during migration than was to be expected from the above considerations. These deviations were considered to be due to temperature effects and initial boundary imperfections.

Thus far in this chapter discussion has been limited to considerations which apply to the migration of particles or ions in an electrical field in general. In the remainder of the chapter, theoretical considerations particularly related to the presence of the anticonvection medium (paper) will be taken up. Various special theoretical considerations will be taken up later in connection with applications with which they are specifically associated.

ENDOSMOSIS

A consideration of the electrokinetic properties of the solid-liquid interface has bearing on the migration of large particles (for example, colloidal solutions of proteins) as well as on the phenomenon of electroosmosis, both of which are of considerable practical importance in paper electrophoresis.

If an electrolyte solution is forced by pressure through a porous plug, an electrical potential can easily be shown to be developed across electrodes placed on either side of the plug. This potential is called the streaming potential.

Conversely, if an electrical potential is applied across such a pair of electrodes, a flow of electrolyte through the plugs can be demonstrated. This phenomenon is known as electroosmosis. It was discovered by Reuss in 1808 and is one of the first electrochemical effects ever observed. These phenomena can be demonstrated for single capillaries or for porous plugs which can be considered to be multiple capillaries.

To explain the above phenomena, the concept of the electrical double layer at the solid-liquid interface was first developed by Helmholtz (79-1). He considered that at the surface of a capillary the solid wall had one charge and the liquid in the capillary bore the opposite charge. The charge on the wall was assumed to be fixed while the other charge could move with the fluid. An external electrical potential would cause the charges in the liquid to migrate, which would carry the liquid along. This motion, however, would be opposed by frictional forces which are proportional to the viscosity of the liquid and the area of the surface over which the liquid flows and the velocity gradients in the liquid.

The electrical interface between the solid and the liquid can also be regarded as a condenser with parallel plates which are separated by d cm., each carrying a charge σ per square centimeter. Then according to electrostatic theory

$$\text{Zeta potential} = \zeta = \frac{4\pi\sigma d}{D}, \tag{19}$$

where ζ is the difference of potential between the plates and D is the dielectric constant. This is the so-called electrokinetic or zeta potential. This equation is of fundamental importance.

The modern conception of the double layer proposed by Gouy (10-1) considers this double layer to be diffuse, and thus on the liquid side of the double layer the interface has appreciable thickness extending some distance into the liquid phase. In this region, thermal forces cause movement of ions present but the distribution of positive and negative ions is not uniform, since it is influenced by the electrostatic field developed from the charge on the solid wall. This results in preferential attraction of particles of opposite sign. This picture is analogous to that of Debye (24-1) of oppositely charged ion atmospheres surrounding a given ion, as mentioned previously (p. 493).

It can be shown that a consideration of the diffuse double layer leads also to equation 19. It also can be shown (MacInnes, 39-4) that electroosmotic mobility, U_0, is related to the zeta potential and dielectric constant by the equation

$$U_0 = \frac{\zeta D}{4\pi\eta}, \tag{20}$$

and this is identical with the classical Helmholtz equation for electrophoresis of colloidal particles:

$$U_e = \frac{\zeta D}{4\pi\eta} \, . \tag{21}$$

In free or moving boundary electrophoresis the area of the cell walls compared to the volume of the column of fluid is so small that generally speaking electroosmosis is negligible, and it is not necessary therefore to make corrections for this in calculating mobilities. In most experiments with anti-convection media the surface area exposed is very large in relation to the volume of the electrolyte column, and endosmosis is pronounced. This must be considered in interpreting mobility measurements.

With supporting media such as filter paper and starch, the surfaces carry a negative charge at most pH's, and the flow of electrolyte is toward the cathode, being more marked at high pH. As discussed before, high ionic strengths tend to diminish this flow.

ELECTROPHORETIC MOBILITIES ON PAPER

From the previous discussion it is evident that any free or moving boundary mobility value must be defined in terms of pH, ionic strength and buffer ion species. This situation is even more complicated if one chooses to define "mobility" of ions on filter paper, or in the presence of other anticonvectants. In the latter case many additional conditions must be specified (see Svensson, 56-65A). The situation is complicated even in closed-strip systems (where the added complication of evaporation need not be considered and in which one can achieve a steady state). In systems where evaporation is permitted, a steady state is never achieved, and so-called "mobility" values (in the sense of the classical moving boundary mobilities) are largely suspect. In fact Svensson (56-65A) has stated that he feels that the measurement of mobilities in instruments in which evaporation is is permitted is "not only hopeless but also meaningless."

Probably the most careful work yet reported relating to mobility measurements on paper is that of Kunkel (51-32). It was shown that very acceptable mobility values can be obtained in the closed strip paper electrophoresis technique, if corrections are made for electroosmosis and for increased migration path length.

There now exists substantial agreement that the net migration rate in anticonvection media[4] is always less than in free electrophoresis, even

---

[4] Some workers have maintained that migration on filter paper occurs principally on the surface, not in the body of the paper, basing this assumption on the fact that patterns obtained showed a denser pattern on the upper surface to which the test sample had been applied. However, it can be easily shown that this phenomenon is an artifact arising during drying due to a shift of the pattern toward that surface of the paper which is dried most rapidly. Presumably if it were possible to apply heat perfectly uniformly to both sides of the paper simultaneously, both surfaces of

when corrections are made for endosmosis (which may be additive or subtractive, depending on the charge of the ionic species under consideration). This has been explained by Kunkel (51-32) by considering that an ion in this situation cannot follow the straight-line distance between two points but must deviate around the particles, fibers, or molecules of the anticonvection agent so that there results a net increase in length of path traversed (see Fig. 5). The increased path length factor is a property of the individual anticonvection medium.

Grassmann (56-18A) has pointed out that the increased (and unequal) path lengths traversed by migrating ions lead to "statistical scattering" that causes a widening and blurring of migrating zones. This loss of definition is superposed on that due to thermal diffusion as a function of distance traversed, and often is a factor limiting resolution.

Correction for endosmosis. As an electroosmosis indicator the large polysaccharide molecule, dextran, is used, which has a very low mobility ($\mu = -0.16 \times 10^{-5}$) in free electrophoresis in barbital buffers at pH 8.8 (see Fig. 3), and which can be detected by the dye bromophenol blue. Three per cent dextran solution (0.005 ml.) is applied at the origin in line with the sample being studied to form a reference spot which passively migrates to permit calculation of the mobilities of the proteins. Kunkel's treatment is as follows.

If d_{alb} is the distance that the albumin travels on the paper measured from the origin, and d_{dex} is the distance that the dextran travels in the opposite direction, the total distance that the albumin travels is $d_{\mathrm{alb}} + d_{\mathrm{dex}}$. The mobility, $-u_{\mathrm{alb}}$, is expressed by the formula

$$-u_{\mathrm{alb}} = \frac{d_{\mathrm{alb}} + d_{\mathrm{dex}}}{Xt}, \tag{22}$$

in which X is the field strength and t is the time. In the same way, the mobility of the electroosmotic flow may be expressed by the formula

$$u_{\mathrm{el}} = \frac{d_{\mathrm{dex}}}{Xt}. \tag{23}$$

Combining the two formulas,

$$\frac{d_{\mathrm{dex}}}{d_{\mathrm{alb}} + d_{\mathrm{dex}}} = \frac{u_{\mathrm{el}}}{-u_{\mathrm{alb}}}. \tag{24}$$

The relationship $u_{\mathrm{el}}/-u_{\mathrm{alb}}$ is constant regardless of distance, time, or field strength, and therefore $d_{\mathrm{dex}}/(d_{\mathrm{alb}} + d_{\mathrm{dex}})$ is a constant. The relationship

---

the paper would be identical. Practically speaking, it is difficult to achieve this. Therefore in scanning systems based upon reflection instead of transmission this fact should be taken into consideration.

$d_{\text{dex}}/d_{\text{alb}}$ is therefore also a constant, and once this is determined for any type of paper it is possible to calculate the distance of electroosmotic flow and then the total distance that any ion migrates. Kunkel (51–32) found that for Munktell No. 20, 150-g. paper, $d_{\text{dex}}/d_{\text{alb}}$ was 0.35 at 3°C. and pH 8.8 and that this factor could subsequently be used without further need of measurements with dextran. For a thick soft paper $d_{\text{dex}}/d_{\text{alb}}$ was 1.6, with the dextran showing greater movement to the cathode than albumin to the anode.

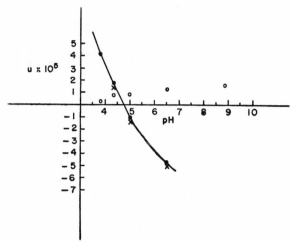

FIG. 3. Mobility values plotted against pH for human serum albumin on filter paper (●) and in free solution (×). The individual points (○) represent dextran mobilities (Kunkel 51-32).

The above results were all obtained with barbital buffers at pH 8.8. At lower pH levels the dextran shows a positive mobility which gradually decreases until it approaches zero at approximately pH 3.

Figure 3 shows dextran mobilities at various pH levels used in the determination of the isoelectric point of human albumin on Munktell No. 20 paper.

Employing $d_{\text{dex}} + d_{\text{alb}}$ as the distance of migration of albumin, an attempt was made to calculate the mobility of this protein on filter paper. Figure 4 shows the distance of migration of albumin, made visible with bromophenol blue, plotted as a function of time. A straight line was always obtained when the current was kept constant.[5]

Correction for Added Migration Path Length. The determination of mo-

[5] For a discussion of constant current versus constant voltage operations, see p. 520.

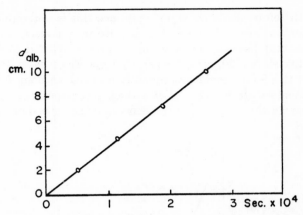

FIG. 4. The distance of migration of purified human albumin plotted as a function of time (Kunkel, 51-32).

bilities on paper involves several new considerations because the formulas used in free solution,

$$u = \frac{dl}{iV} \tag{25}$$

and

$$u = \frac{dq\kappa}{ti}, \tag{26}$$

in which V is the voltage, l the length of the channel, q the cross-sectional area, κ the conductivity, and i the current, are not applicable to liquid in a highly porous supporting medium. It may be shown that the expressions for field strength, V/l and $i/q_a\kappa$, are not equal. This is due to the fact that l does not represent the true distance of voltage drop through the paper. This can best be seen from a consideration of Fig. 5, in which a tortuous channel is envisioned in the paper (l'). This, of course, represents a great simplification of the intricate channeling of liquid that actually exists in the paper. In accordance with the diagram the protein particle takes the tortuous path d' which follows l' and is a fraction thereof and not the observed distance d. Since

$$l' = l\left(\frac{l'}{l}\right), \tag{27}$$

therefore

$$d' = d\left(\frac{l'}{l}\right). \tag{28}$$

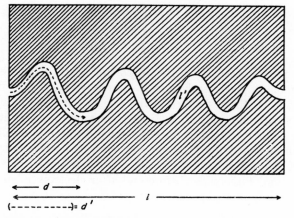

FIG. 5. Schematic drawing illustrating a theoretical path of ionic migration through filter paper (Kunkel, 51-32).

In free solution the protein particle migrates through a distance

$$d = ut \frac{V}{l} . \tag{29}$$

But in the paper the distance is

$$d' = ut \frac{V}{l'} . \tag{30}$$

Substituting equations 27 and 28,

$$d \left(\frac{l'}{l} \right) = \frac{utV}{l \left(\frac{l'}{l} \right)} \tag{31}$$

and

$$d = ut \frac{V}{l} \left(\frac{l}{l'} \right)^2 . \tag{32}$$

Trautman and Kunkel (56-67A) have pointed out that $(l'/l)^2$ has been termed "tortuosity" by petroleum geologists (49-21A). It is the geometrical correction for the shape of the electrophoresis cell represented by the fluid space of the porous supporting medium. When it is divided by the porosity, p, the volume fraction of fluid, it is identical with the "formation factor" of non-swelling porous rocks and sands (53-51A). Theoretical and experimental researches on the formation factor date back to Clerk Maxwell (53-326A). With insulating, non-swelling, media in at least 0.1 M KCl the determination of the tortuosity $(l'/l)^2$ is made by what amounts to a conductivity cell measurement according to:

$$(l'/l)^2 = \frac{R}{R_0'}, \quad p = \frac{R}{R_0''} \tag{33}$$

Here R is the (a.c.) resistance of the supporting media of length, l, wet with the high conductivity electrolyte to a volume fraction, p, of fluid to total volume v'/v; R_0' is the resistance of the electrolyte alone occupying a cell of the same total volume v; and R_0'' is the resistance of the electrolyte alone of a volume v' equal to that in the supporting medium in a cell of length l. This R_0'' can be calculated from the free solution conductivity κ, and the volume v' of the test electrolyte in the paper determined by weighing the (glass plates and) filter paper before and after electrolyte has entered the paper and dividing by its specific gravity:

$$R_0'' = \frac{1}{\kappa} \, l^2/v' \tag{34}$$

ADSORPTION

In the foregoing statements the tacit assumption has been made that there exists no adsorption between the solutes being separated and the anticonvection medium. In some of the early contributions, the lack of apparent adsorption led to the supposition that in paper electrophoresis of serum proteins and amino acids the role of adsorption was a relatively minor one, and indeed it remains rather remarkable that many individual components of such a complicated mixture as the serum proteins are adsorbed to such a small degree. Nonetheless, recent work has tended to emphasize that in almost all experimental situations some degree of adsorption, reversible or irreversible, does exist, and therefore it can be fairly stated that there exists an adsorptive chromatographic factor in practically all zone electrophoresis separations. In a mixture where components having lower mobilities are more strongly adsorbed on a given medium than components having higher mobilities it is obvious that this chromatographic effect will aid in the electrophoretic separation. On the other hand, the converse situation where the more rapidly migrating components are more strongly adsorbed will tend to make the separations more difficult.

Weber (53-302) has analyzed mathematically the role of reversible adsorption related to migration on porous surfaces including filter paper. He has shown that this would be expected to give rise to comet-shaped migration zones as have been frequently observed for certain substances. His analysis was extended also to continuous electrophoresis, and he was able to show theoretically that reversible adsorption does not interfere with resolution in this latter situation. The latter had been demonstrated experimentally (Durrum, 51-9).

Partition Chromatography

The theory of partition chromatography as treated elsewhere in this volume has so far not been applied to zone electrophoresis, because ordinarily the latter type of separation is carried out in completely miscible polar solvents. However, recent work utilizing non-polar additives, such as glycerol (Durrum, 51-9), and the demonstration that separations can be effected in completely non-aqueous systems (Paul, 52-157) suggests that the theory of partition chromatography will have to be taken into consideration in explaining electrokinetic phenomena in these special zone electrophoresis situations.

Membrane Polarization

Kunkel (54-275) has called attention to membrane polarization as a factor altering pH. He states that this can cause significant pH changes at the paper-liquid junction. Although in this author's experience no difficulties have been encountered which could be attributed to this phenomenon, a proper evaluation of its importance awaits further study.

The above remarks all apply to zone electrophoresis experiments in which evaporation is prevented and in which a steady state exists, and in which the migration is carried out in a path which is uniform with respect to the applied electrical field, with respect to its ionic composition, with respect to its anticonvection medium composition, and, finally, with respect to temperature as in the closed paper strip method. However, in another very important type of experimental technique none of the above conditions is present and a steady state never is achieved (except in the open continuous curtain technique). These fundamental differences in the two types of operation dictate largely the fields of applicability for which each major type is suited. Briefly, the closed strip technique should be used whenever one is interested in calculating mobility or isoelectric points. On the other hand, in general, the more convenient open strip technique affords a high degree of resolution and reproducibility with minimum attention where analysis of a mixture is the ultimate object.

Chapter XVI

METHODS

Since 1948 more than two thousand papers have appeared on the subject of paper electrophoresis. Many of these papers have described various types of paper electrophoresis apparatus. However, all the apparatus thus far described falls into a relatively small number of basic types. Familiarity with the characteristics of these basic types will permit the novice to choose the appropriate type of apparatus for his particular need. Table I lists a convenient classification of the fundamental types. Each type will be described in some detail, and further specific theoretical considerations applying to the various types will be considered in connection with each.

GENERAL CONSIDERATIONS

Figure 1 illustrates the first paper electrophoresis apparatus assembled in the author's laboratory. It consisted simply of two glass vessels between which a strip of filter paper was suspended with the ends dipping into a dilute acetic acid solution. A potential of a few volts direct current was applied to the two vessels from a dry battery through the medium of carbon rod electrodes. Even with this primitive apparatus, it was possible to demonstrate that separations of various amino acids could be effected. A discussion of the shortcomings of this apparatus will perhaps be informative.

In this arrangement it was difficult to prevent a slight sagging of the wet filter paper strips because of the poor wet strength of the filter paper used. As a result of this, electrolyte continuously "siphoned" from the vessels and collected at the lowest level of the catenary suspension of the paper. Furthermore, since the strip was open to the air, evaporation took place at a rapid rate and it was difficult to run any two experiments reproducibly.

To avoid the difficulties mentioned, an apparatus such as is shown in Fig. 2 was constructed. Sagging of the paper between the vessels was prevented by supporting the paper on a plate glass strip. Most of the evaporation from the strip was eliminated by applying a second glass strip on top of the first. Pressure was applied to the strip either by tubing clamps, as illustrated, or by applying an appropriate weight to the uppermost glass strip, with the lower glass strip being supported mechanically. This apparatus was found to overcome the above-mentioned difficulties but still had certain shortcomings. Owing to capillarity, electrolyte tended to run laterally from the filter paper between the glass strips at the edges of the paper with attendant uncertainties as to uniformity of the field. This apparatus can be considered to be a simple example of the closed strip type.

TABLE I

Basic Paper Electrophoresis Techniques

I. Closed strip (evaporation prevented)
    A. Solid support—glass (Figs. 2 and 5)
                  plastic
    B. Non-polar liquid—chlorobenzene
                      carbon tetrachloride
                      heptane (Fig. 7)
II. Semi-closed (evaporation permitted)
    Solid support—one side (Fig. 3)
III. Open strip (evaporation permitted) Minimal area of support
    A. Horizontal types (Figs. 1 and 11)
    B. Hanging strip types (Figs. 4 and 14)

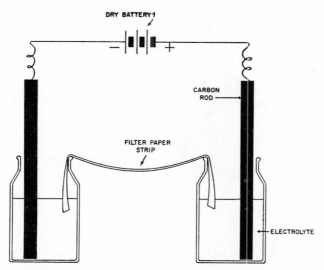

Fig. 1. Primitive open strip paper electrophoresis apparatus (Durrum, unpublished work).

Because it was considered desirable to maintain temperature control, experiments were carried out with a semi-closed system in which the paper was supported on one side in contact with a cooled glass surface. This type of apparatus is illustrated in Fig. 3. It soon became evident, however, that this type of apparatus gave much poorer resolution than the simpler apparatus illustrated in Fig. 4 (Durrum, 49-6, 50-9), in which the strip hangs free supported on rods in the same configuration.

The foregoing remarks illustrate what is probably the most common reason for poor resolution and poor reproducibility in paper electrophoresis.

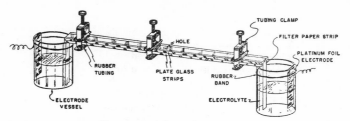

FIG. 2.   Closed strip paper electrophoresis apparatus (Durrum, unpublished work).

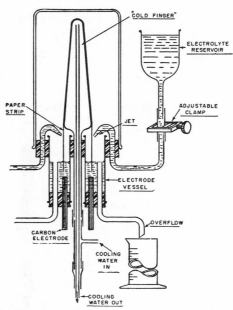

FIG. 3.   Semi-closed cooled paper electrophoresis apparatus (Durrum, unpublished work).

Evidently there is still widespread lack of realization that filter paper is capable of supporting more fluid electrolyte than it can control effectively from the standpoint of preventing convection.   This tendency is most marked in semi-closed strip and non-polar liquid sealed apparatuses because pressure cannot conveniently be applied to squeeze out this excess of electrolyte.   It is a common design defect in the horizontal open strip type of apparatus to have the level of the horizontal segment of the filter paper too close to the fluid level in the electrolyte vessels.   In the hanging strip type of apparatus gravity conveniently drains this excess fluid from the paper.   In the closed strip type of apparatus (Figs. 2 and 5), pressure can be applied to squeeze out this fluid excess.

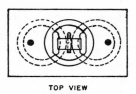

TOP VIEW

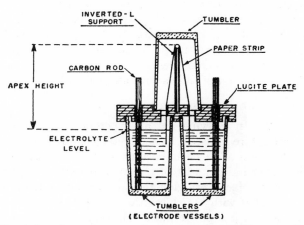

FIG. 4. Simple hanging strip paper electrophoresis cell (Durrum, 49-6).

FIG. 5. Pressure-regulating device for closed strip technique (Kunkel, 54-275).

In none of the apparatuses so far considered has any consideration been given to prevention of pH changes in the paper owing to electrolyte products being permitted to enter the paper strip ends.   If the volume of electrolyte in the electrode vessels is sufficient, electrode products may be so diluted as to offer no serious difficulty; however, recent practice has been to interpose baffle systems (see Figs. 7 and 11), agar-salt bridges, or intermediate wick arrangements, so designed that no electrode products reach the paper during the course of separation.   Another method to prevent electrode products from reaching the ends of the paper is illustrated in Fig. 3 where a continuous counterflow of buffer down the ends of the strip backwashes the electrode products.   The latter principle is particularly useful and easily adapted to continuous electrophoresis.

A detailed consideration of the various methods follows.

Closed Strip Method—Solid Support

Consider Fig. 2.   In carrying out an experiment with this apparatus, the following procedure is used.   Electrolyte is poured to the same level in each electrode vessel.   This is important to prevent hydrodynamic flows of fluid in the paper independent of electrical potential.[1]   The lower siliconed glass strip[2] is placed bridging the two vessels, and the filter paper strip is then saturated with buffer solution and placed on the lower glass strip; the top glass strip is put in place.   Upon application of pressure by the tubing clamps, buffer solution runs out laterally in the space between the glass plates.   Most of this will run down the edge of the strip to the ends if it is held vertically for a few minutes.   The electrical potential is applied across the platinum electrodes[3] for a few minutes prior to the ap-

---

[1] In some cases, differences in level can be utilized to compensate partially for endosmotic and hydrodynamic flows in a manner analogous to compensation in moving boundary electrophoresis.   In many recent types of apparatus a small channel connecting the electrode vessels has been provided which may be used for initial equilibration of fluid levels and clamped off during the run.   See Fig. 7.   In some recent apparatus designs (McDonald, 53-183; Williams, 55-328), a small channel between electrode vessels is permitted to remain open during the experiment.   The small portion of current flowing in this channel in properly designed cells is usually of the order of 10% of the total current flow and offers no practical disadvantage except that buffer life is somewhat diminished.

[2] All glass surfaces should be silicone-treated.   This can be done with the usual silicone stopcock grease found in most laboratories followed by polishing with a clean dry cloth or soft paper, but the author prefers to use a preparation such as General Electric "Dri film."

[3] In recent years platinum electrodes have completely replaced carbon electrodes in the author's laboratory because from day to day many different buffer solutions are utilized, and platinum electrodes are very easily cleaned.   On the other hand, it is difficult to remove traces of buffer salts from carbon electrodes.   However, the inexpensive carbon electrodes are perfectly satisfactory for routine use where the same buffer is always used.

plication of the sample.   Any excess fluid lateral to the strips still remaining will be seen to disappear gradually.   When no excess fluid is evident at the lateral edges of the paper strip between the glass strips, the sample to be separated is applied as a tiny drop through the hole in the upper glass strip. It is desirable to wait until the sample has absorbed into the paper strip before application of the potential again.   At the end of the experiment the circuit is broken, the strip assembly picked up horizontally, and the ends of the filter paper extending beyond the ends of the glass strip torn off flush with the ends of the glass strips *before* the pressure is released on the clamps.   This prevents reflux of excess electrolyte from the relatively wet ends of the filter paper toward the center.   Provisions should be taken to prevent this reflux in all types of paper electrophoresis; otherwise unnecessary smearing with attendant loss of resolution will occur.   The filter paper strip may now be stripped from the bottom of the glass plate with minimal disruption of the pattern.   It is easily dried (preferably horizontally) (compare p. 524) at this stage prior to staining or application of other detection techniques.   (See p. 525 for a consideration of proper drying practice.)

Figure 5 shows an apparatus developed by Kunkel (54-275) for carrying out closed strip paper electrophoresis.   This apparatus is provided with a calibrated pressure scale so that pressure can be reproducibly applied from experiment to experiment.   It was found that pressures in the range from 1 to 1.4 pounds per square inch are optimal for Whatman 3MM filter paper. To avoid bending of the plates, caused by this degree of pressure, it was necessary to use thick plate glass (2.5 × 25 × 23 cm.).

Experiments are carried out with this apparatus in the following manner: The sheet of filter paper to be used in the experiment is cut so that it is a few millimeters narrower than the siliconed glass plates but about 10 cm. longer than their long axis.   A pencil line is marked across the center of the resulting sheet.   The sheet is dipped in buffer solution and then placed between thick sheets of blotting paper under pressure for 1 minute to remove excess electrolyte.   The sheet is placed on top of the bottom glass plate, and samples of materials to be separated are either spotted or streaked along the central pencil mark.   The top glass plate is applied, and the pressure is adjusted to the proper value.   Silicone grease is applied to the edges of the plates to effect a seal.   The resulting assembly is then placed between electrode vessels in such a manner that the ends of the sheet dip into the electrolyte and the fluid level in the vessel is almost to the top surface of the lower plate.   Under these circumstances, electrolyte runs in from both the electrode vessels toward the center of the sheet.   This flow of fluid toward the center tends to sharpen the initial application zones. After about one-half hour equilibrium is established.   Then an electrical potential is applied for an appropriate length of time.   At the end of the experiment, the ends of the filter paper sheet extending beyond the glass

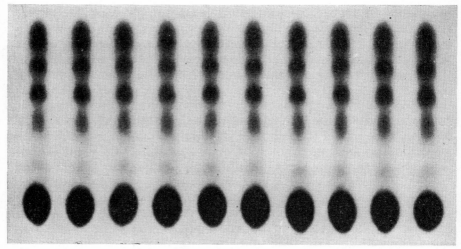

FIG. 6. Bromophenol blue-stained serum patterns prepared in closed strip paper electrophoresis apparatus (courtesy of H. G. Kunkel).

plates are removed *before* the pressure is released.   Under these conditions, minimal shifting of the pattern occurs, and the sheet can be removed for subsequent dyeing or other treatment.   It has also been shown that a "sandwich" comprising alternate layers of filter paper and thin plastic sheet (polyethylene) can be used to increase the capacity of the apparatus. In this type of operation as many as three sheets of filter paper can be utilized simultaneously and independently.

Figure 6 shows the excellent reproducibility that was attained with this method when ten samples of the same serum were run simultaneously in a closed strip apparatus and the above precautions taken.   In this experiment, the samples were spotted on the paper, but streaking can also be employed and presumably one could directly scan the streaked patterns. Scanning cannot be carried out on spotted patterns, because the simple scanners available cannot evaluate area and optical density functions simultaneously.   However, for quantitative purposes these strips can be cut up and eluted.

CLOSED STRIP METHOD—NON-POLAR IMMISCIBLE LIQUID SEAL

Cremer (50-7) first used a non-polar immiscible liquid, chlorobenzene, in order to seal the edges of the paper between the edges of the glass plate and electrode vessels and to help dissipate the heat that developed.   Other workers have used immiscible liquids for sealing completely unsupported strips.   Sealing agents heavier than the aqueous buffer solutions, such as carbon tetrachloride (Consden, 52-31), require different apparatus designs from those using lighter agents. Figure 7 shows an apparatus of the latter type in which heptane is used as a sealing and heat conduction medium. Heptane has also been used to seal the curtain in continuous electrophoresis (Durrum, 51-9), but the advantages do not appear to warrant the inconvenience involved.

The advantages of non-polar sealing agents are that they can be used to effect a perfect seal about the paper and act as an intermediate heat conductor both by convection and conduction to a thermostatic bath. The disadvantages are the general inconvenience incidental to their use as well as the following: they may be flammable (heptane); they may selectively extract more soluble buffer components resulting in pH changes; they may extract or denature substances being separated (lipids and lipoproteins); partition chromatographic effects may be observed (Durrum,

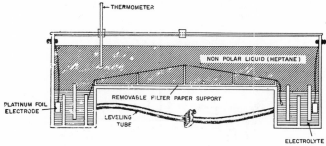

FIG. 7. Closed strip apparatus, heptane seal (Durrum, unpublished).

51-9); and finally any impurities in the sealing agent may contaminate the strips.

In view of the above, although separations with easily resolvable mixtures can be attained by these techniques, usually the resolution is poorer than that available with other more convenient types of apparatus because it is difficult to remove the excess electrolyte which is not protected against convection. (However, in the apparatus shown in Fig. 7 gravity does help to some extent in draining excess electrolyte.) Therefore, these systems generally are not recommended except for high voltage electrophoresis (see page 528) and as an adjunct to the closed strip technique between glass plates where it is desirable to effect a perfect seal and to help achieve precise temperature control.

Open Strip Techniques—General Considerations

The first paper electrophoresis experiment reported by König (37-1) is an example of the horizontal open strip method. In this technique, the strip hangs free in the surrounding saturated gaseous phase enclosed in a chamber (Feuchtkammer). Paper has been arranged in this chamber in almost every conceivable configuration, but it is usually either pulled horizontally taut[4] or allowed to hang free from a central support at the apex. In the latter, most commonly the highest point is at the center, although unequal limbs have also been utilized (Gordon, 52-63). Vertical disposition of the paper has also been reported (Michl, 51-45). Both the horizontal and

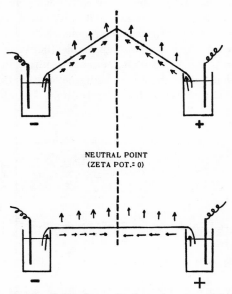

NEUTRAL POINT
(ZETA POT.= 0)

FIG. 8. Diagram showing hydrodynamic flows in open strip technique. (Durrum, unpublished). In most experimental situations the zeta potential is not zero and the neutral point is shifted usually toward the cathode.

the hanging strip methods are capable of giving excellent resolution, but the latter appears to afford superior reproducibility.

Figure 8 diagrammatically shows the situation existing in open strip techniques. Current flow in the strip results in heat being generated in the strip. This in turn results in evaporation from the surface of the strip into the surrounding vapor space. No true equilibrium is established, since in general the evaporated molecules do not return to the paper and

[4] On p. 508 the disadvantages of the catenary suspension have been mentioned and most workers have gone from that type of suspension to a taut suspension (McDonald, 50-30; 51-43) or to the hanging strip technique. Although Schneider (53-258) appears to favor the catenary suspension, the hemoglobin patterns shown by this worker are not impressive with respect to resolution.

the paper is not uniform along its length with respect to concentration, etc. The average temperature of the strip may be only slightly above that of the surroundings, since the heat absorbed by the evaporative process may partially compensate for heat generated by passage of the current (according to equation 8, Chapter XV) making the net rise in temperature somewhat less than would be anticipated were this factor not present.[5] Electrolyte is continuously flowing toward the center of the strip from the two electrode vessels to replace the portion of electrolyte which has been evaporated and thus maintain capillary saturation, but equilibrium is never achieved. Each succeeding increment of filter paper beyond the buffer vessel receives less volume of electrolyte by that amount which has been evaporated in the preceding increment. Since the actual cross section of the paper is constant, a flow rate gradient results in the fluid flow along the length of the filter paper strip from each buffer vessel decreasing as the center of the paper is approached. If the zeta potential were zero, the neutral point at which no dynamic fluid flow exists would correspond to the geometrical center of the horizontal open strip or the apex of the hanging strip technique. In most practical situations the zeta potential results in an endosmotic flow toward the cathode so that the true dynamic neutral position is displaced toward the cathode (see Fig. 8),[6] which indicates the situation where the zeta potential is zero.

Then, depending on the position where ions are applied, they must "swim" upstream against the current that is constantly increasing in swiftness as the electrode vessels are approached (if they are applied in the center), or along with the stream that is diminishing in swiftness (if applied toward one side of the center). If an ion happens to have a mobility falling within the gradient range so defined, it will come to a position of equilibrium independent of its position of application (Durrum, 51-8), where its tendency to flow against the hydrodynamic current, as a consequence of its charge in the electrical field, is exactly counterbalanced by the countercurrent flow of electrolyte. After a given ion has migrated to its

[5] In this connection it has been noted in continuous electrophoresis that the temperature within the chamber adjacent to the curtain may be from 1 to 2°C. lower than ambient temperature with certain cell designs where the ratio of chamber volume to curtain area is larger or where "flues" are incorporated in the cell to encourage evaporation. Also Macheboeuf (53-175) in the hanging strip method deliberately encouraged evaporative processes to promote migration or reactants toward each other in carrying out antigen-antibody experiments.

[6] This true dynamic neutral point should be the true origin in measuring mobilities as seen previously (p. 502) for the closed strip technique. It may be found experimentally for any given paper electrolyte system by use of a passively migrating uncharged substance, e.g., dextran. It assumes paramount importance in determination of isoelectric points.

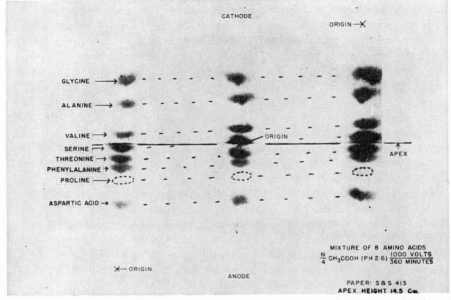

CATHODE

ORIGIN —X

GLYCINE ⟶

ALANINE ⟶

VALINE ⟶

ORIGIN

SERINE ⟶

THREONINE ⟶

APEX

PHENYLALANINE ⟩

PROLINE ⟶

ASPARTIC ACID →

MIXTURE OF 8 AMINO ACIDS

$\frac{N}{4}$ CH₃COOH (PH 2.6) $\frac{1000 \text{ VOLTS}}{360 \text{ MINUTES}}$

X— ORIGIN

ANODE

PAPER: S & S 413
APEX HEIGHT 14.5 Cm.

FIG. 9. Paper pattern illustrating the phenomenon of mobility equilibrium (Durrum, 51–8).

position of equilibrium, and if a steady state is maintained, the only process tending to move it is diffusion. Then if it should diffuse to a position on one side of the equilibrium line it would be driven back by the electrolyte flow, and if it happened to diffuse to the other side it would be pulled back by its migration tendency. It is a consequence of these equilibria that there results relatively even disposition of materials as bands at right angles to the axis of migration which is favorable for direct optical scanning.

This phenomenon which has been called mobility equilibrium can be best demonstrated where volatile weakly dissociated electrolytes (e.g., acetic acid) are employed, because in this case, the ionic strength does not tend to build up to a large degree owing to deposition of salts on the paper.[7] Figure 9 is a photograph showing an example of the attainment of mobility equilibrium for an experiment in which an amino acid mixture was applied

[7] Some workers have postulated the existence of an "ionic strength barrier," that is, a zone of increasing concentration due to evaporation of electrolyte at the ends of the strips near the electrode vessels. This is difficult to imagine, since the fluid flow from the electrode vessels toward the center of the strip would tend to build up the concentration of salts in such a manner as to make the most concentrated area develop at the center of the strip. Then this gradient would be expected to partially compensate for the mobility decrease as the electrode vessels are approached, which has been described above.

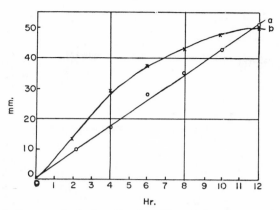

Fig. 10. Relative speed of migration for albumin in serum: a, 10°C.; b, at room temperature (25°C.). Ordinate, distance from albumin peak to the gamma globulin peak in millimeters (Grassmann, 52-66).

at positions as far as 20 cm. apart, yet after 6 hours had aligned themselves parallel.

Practical considerations sometimes dictate the use of relatively high field strengths with relatively high currents, and with some systems, for example, in serum protein separations, this tendency toward mobility equilibrium can be demonstrated for both the hanging strip and the horizontal open strip techniques, as discussed below. Also this can be inferred from the non-linear time-mobility curves of Fig. 10, which applies to horizontal open strip separations, and of Fig. 12, which applies to hanging strip separations (see Durrum, 49-6; 50-9). It is obvious that the conditions cited above are dependent entirely on the rate of evaporation from the paper, and this in turn is dependent primarily on the current flow, since the heat developed is a function of the square of the current. Any experimental condition which permits current flow to be held to the minimum will reduce evaporation and permit the migration path environment to approach the uniformity necessary for mobility measurements or isoelectric point determinations. Three methods are available to accomplish this. In the first, the cell may be refrigerated.[8] Figure 10 from Grassmann (52-66) shows that, when migration distances for serum albumin were measured as a function of time (in the cell shown in Fig. 11) at 25°C., a non-linear mobility curve was attained. On the other hand, when the cell was run at

[8] McDonald (51-43) utilized hydrogen (explosion hazard) or helium, which have higher heat conductivity than air, to promote cooling of the paper strips by conduction. How practical the use of these gases is for routine processes is not clear; however, the use of an inert gas appears to be attractive in situations where it is necessary to avoid oxidation of sensitive substances to be separated.

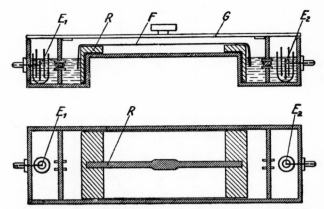

FIG. 11. Horizontal open strip paper electrophoresis apparatus: E_1 and E_2, electrodes; F, filter paper strip; G, lid; R, plastic frame; (Grassmann, 52–66).

10°C. a linear migration distance-time relationship was attained. The principle limitation to the use of refrigeration is that ambient temperatures appreciably below 0°C. may result in freezing of the electrolyte, and this type of cooling is not very efficient for open strip techniques.

A second method available is the use of electrolytes of low ionic strength ($u = 0.001–0.01$) extensively employed by McDonald (51-42). Because of their low conductance, high field strengths may be employed without generation of much heat. With 0.1 M acetic acid, linear mobility-time relationships were reported for leucine. The limitations of this method are the low buffering capacity and the fact that some substances, for example many proteins, will precipitate or dissociate at these high dilutions.

The third method available is to employ low field strengths with low currents for longer periods to time. Figure 12 shows the results of some experiments carried out in the author's laboratory with a hanging strip apparatus (Fig. 14) under varying conditions. It is evident that substantially linear time-migration distance relationships can be obtained by this method also. The limitation of this method is diffusion (see p. 497), which may obliterate the resolution of substances with very similar mobilities. Obviously, combinations of these methods may be applied as well.

It has been shown that with either horizontal or hanging strip techniques approximately linear time-mobility relationships can be achieved, if low currents[9] are employed. Nonetheless, the closed strip method is probably

[9] Modern electronic developments make available conveniently the choice of constant voltage or constant current power supplies. All moving boundary work is carried out at constant current. For some purposes constant voltage operation is convenient, for example, when strips are being removed serially. On the other hand, measurements (Durrum, unpublished) comparing total migration in two matched

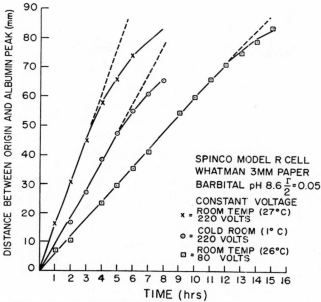

Fig. 12. Time-migration distance relationships at constant voltage for albumin in serum (Durrum, unpublished work).

the method of choice when mobilities or isoelectric determinations are the prime consideration. On the other hand, the convenience of the open strip techniques makes them the method of choice where one is interested in resolving substances for either qualitative or quantitative purposes.

HORIZONTAL OPEN STRIP METHOD

Several horizontal open strip apparatuses have been described since König (37-1), by Wieland (48-12), McDonald (51-43), and Grassmann (52-66). Figure 11 shows the cell described by Grassmann, which is more or less representative, featuring baffling means and a removable rack for supporting the paper strips which are held taut and this condition preserved during the experiment by capillary action of the wet paper surface on the plastic frame, R.

cells at constant current, one maintained at 4°C. and one maintained in a thermostatic chamber at 30°C., have shown serum component migration distances which differed by less than 6% for an ambient temperature change of 26°C. From Fig. 12 it can be seen that for an ambient temperature change of 27°C. at constant voltage the 6½-hour pattern showed difference in migration of about 25%. It is therefore concluded that for routine work and for day-to-day reproducibility that constant current operation is to be preferred.

In this variation, paper is held in one horizontal plane; therefore leveling is critical. All such cells incorporate some method such as a sliding device or end rollers which enable the wet paper strip to be carefully pulled taut without tearing. In one commercial apparatus (L. K. B.) the paper is supported in the horizontal plane on raised pointed projections stamped in a polystyrene rack. The strips are usually applied wet after drainage of most of the buffer or after blotting. In the first case, they are put in place, pulled taut, and the excess electrolyte allowed to drain off. Sheen, which represents excess electrolyte, has been used as a guide in judging the proper degree of wetness (McDonald, 52-130). In our experience, samples should not be applied until this "sheen" has disappeared. If the paper is blotted and the sample applied at any other position than the center, shifts will occur in the pattern, owing to streaming of the buffer from the electrode vessels toward the center. This can be used advantageously to sharpen the starting band as described on p. 513 for the closed strip system.[10]

If the sample is applied elsewhere, shifts will occur independent of electrical flow. It is evident that an ion can come to a position of mobility equilibrium only if its mobility happens to fall within the gradient range defined by the experimental conditions. On the other hand, if the ion has a mobility greater than that set by the range limits it will migrate through the gradient (but not at a uniform rate) into the electrode vessel. For example, under the experimental conditions defined by Fig. 9, the amino acid arginine when applied on the anode side of the center will migrate through the gradient range into the cathode vessel. Practically speaking, we do not often reach such a complete equilibrium as is illustrated in Fig. 9, except when very high currents are employed with attendant rapid evaporation from the strip.

The above factors should be kept in mind in choosing the most advantageous position for application of the sample being studied. Frequently, in order to have available the whole length of the strip for resolution, it is desirable to apply the sample well to one side of the center (if all the components are expected to migrate in the same direction).

[10] The assertion made by some that endosmosis is not important in horizontal strip method probably has its genesis in the observation that gamma globulin apparently does not migrate cathode-wise in the horizontal strip method (pH 8.6) when the sample is applied well toward the cathode side of the strip. Under these conditions the entire pattern is shifted as a result of the hydrodynamic flow from the cathode side toward the center, obscuring the apparent cathode-wise gamma globulin migration due to endosmosis. This has the effect of causing all serum components to migrate on top of the albumin tail. If the serum is applied at the center, the gamma globulin peak is not superimposed on the albumin tail, and the usual cathode-wise gamma globulin displacement is observed.

HANGING STRIP METHOD

A number of hanging strip apparatuses have been described, including those of Durrum (49-6, 50-9, 51-8), of Flynn (51-13), of Macheboeuf (51-37), of Wunderly (51-82), of Gordon (52-63) and of Williams (55-328). All the considerations which have been discussed in connection with the horizontal open strip method also are applicable to the hanging strip method. The purpose of elevating the center of the strip in this technique is primarily one of convenience in that it affords a simple, rapid, and reproducible method for establishing uniform drainage and maintenance of the hydrodynamic equilibrium on the strip before application of the sample and during the separation by the electrical potential. Apparently, a misconception exists that the elevation of the center in the hanging strip apparatus introduces "gravitational effects"[11] which prevent linear mobility-time relationships from being attained (McDonald, 52-130). This is not in accord with the experimental evidence, as has been demonstrated (Fig. 12). It is evident that this non-linearity is due to operation at high currents, not to gravity.

Figure 4 illustrates this type of apparatus in a simple form which consists merely of two electrode vessels containing electrolyte at the same level and a Lucite plate provided with slots bridging and sealing them. Mounted on this plate is a support (bent glass rod) for the apex of the strip. The strip is hung over the center support, the ends passing through the slots into the electrolyte, and the strip is isolated from the atmosphere by an inverted tumbler which fits into a groove in the Lucite plate. An electrical potential is applied through carbon electrodes which pass through the Lucite plate into the electrode vessels. In this simple apparatus no baffling is necessary, owing to the large ratio of electrolyte volume to paper strip area. Thus pH changes are controlled by dilution. This simple apparatus has been demonstrated to be capable of giving good resolution for many types of biological substances (Durrum, 49-6, 50-9).

The sample of the substance to be separated is applied either at the apex or at some position on either side of the apex. If the sample is to be applied to dry paper at the apex, after it is applied as a tiny drop (e.g., 0.005

[11] If one places a sample of the dye or other colored substance at any elevated position appreciably above the electrolyte level (in the latter position excess fluid is, of course, present) on a hanging strip apparatus which has come to hydrodynamic equilibrium without application of the electrical field, the dye spot will spread by diffusion as far in the upward direction from the point of application as in the downward direction. Gravity has no measurable effect in pulling the spot downward. This is the consequence of the fact that gravitational forces are very minor compared to the strong capillary forces which bind the liquid and which are instrumental in the prevention of convection.

ml.) electrolyte is brought up carefully on either side of the apex with the aid of a medicine dropper in such a manner that ascending buffer fronts coalesce at the apex, and, on standing, a visible sharpening of the band of the applied material can be observed (if it is colored). If the sample is to be applied at the apex of a wet strip, a tiny drop can be put on the electrolyte-saturated hanging strip, after the excess fluid has drained completely away (as evidenced by loss of sheen on the paper). If the sample is to be applied at some point other than the center, it is first put on a small strip or circle (diameter about 5 mm.) of paper which is then affixed by capillarity, after drainage as above, at the desired site on the strip. In this manner, smearing of the initial starting zone is avoided. At the end of the experiment, the current is turned off, and the strip is removed and dried prior to the application of some detection technique. A considerably more elaborate cell provided with a removable rack and intended for two-dimensional work has been described (Durrum, 51-8) (illustrated in Fig. 1, Chapter XVII). The purpose of the rack is to permit the strips to be immediately placed in the oven without disturbing them. It was found, however, that pattern shifts occurred incidental to drying in the oven, owing to the dependent drop of the electrolyte acting as a reservoir and feeding electrolyte continuously toward the apex of the paper which tends to dry first. Part A of Fig. 13 (Williams, 55-328) shows how, under these circumstances, a zone represented by *A* might be shifted back to the position of *A'* during drying.

Furthermore, the vertical temperature gradients found in most ovens tend to give uneven drying which causes pattern shifts of lesser magnitude. Shifts occurring in patterns during drying have been noted by others (Kun-

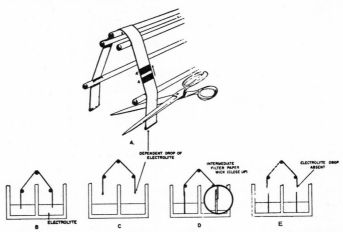

Fig. 13. Methods of removing dependent drops of electrolyte in hanging strip paper electrophoresis (Williams, 55-328).

kel, 51-32), and efforts have been made to avoid these by placing the strips directly in the dye-coagulation bath without prior oven drying. This latter procedure is not entirely satisfactory, because it is difficult to achieve uniform dyeing of protein patterns unless they are thoroughly denatured on the paper prior to staining. For example, in contrast to serum albumin, undenatured serum globulins will not bind bromophenol blue at all.

In the author's experience much more uniform results for quantitative purposes can be attained if the protein strips are thoroughly denatured in the oven by heat prior to dyeing. This is achieved routinely by heating them for at least 30 minutes in an oven at 120°C. (Whatman 3MM filter paper). Figure 3 of Chapter XIX shows a comparison of results obtained when matched strips are dyed in baths of equal dye concentrations with and without heat treatment. The apparent division of the albumin peak in the pattern on the right is an artifact because the central dense albumin area did not take up the dye uniformly. These considerations led to the development of the improved rack arrangement and cell shown in Fig. 13 (Williams, 55-328), in which pattern shifts incident to drying are completely avoided and thus resolution preserved. Figure 13 shows the basic principle of this arrangement. As a rack in a cell (as in B) is removed, a dependent drop of electrolyte develops (situation C). This can be avoided by cutting off the wet part of the bottom of the strip with a pair of scissors as is shown. This is not a convenient procedure. Special racks were developed which were designed to facilitate blotting of the ends of the paper prior to placing them in the oven, but it was found difficult always to blot several strips uniformly. Therefore, the use of an intermediate feed wick was adopted which gave the same effect as though the strip end had been cut off. The secondary shifts[12] due to vertical temperature gradients in the oven were circumvented by the use of the folding, removable rack section so that the strips could be pulled horizontally and dried without the pattern area being in contact with any element which would cast a shadow or give local cooling due to conduction or heat capacity effects.

Figure 14 is an exploded view of the hanging strip paper electrophoresis cell developed by Williams (55-328). The cell comprises a base section, A, divided into two electrode compartments by partition B.

In each electrode compartment a baffle system, C, prevents electrode products from reaching the intermediate feed wick, D, placed on a removable wick support, which is the outermost baffle. These electrode products develop medially at the platinum wire electrodes (not shown). The latter run the length of the cell and are mounted on each side of the central parti-

---

[12] Shifts will occur toward one surface or the other of the strips (see p. 501), although this causes no difficulty when elution or direct transmission scanning is used for quantitation.

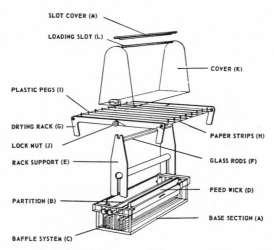

FIG. 14. Hanging strip paper electrophoresis cell with removable drying rack (Williams, 55-328).

tion, *B*.   The drying rack support, *E*, carries three siliconed glass rods, *F*, disposed so as to support the apices of the paper strips in a gentle arc to prevent breaking the paper fibers (this avoids creases which may appear as artifacts on scanning).   The removable folding drying rack, *G*, supports the filter paper strips, *H*, suspended freely between rubber pegs, *I*, mounted on a stainless steel rod (not shown).   A knurled lock nut, *J*, permits the rack to be locked in the horizontal or in the folded position.   The cover, *K*, is provided with a loading slot, *L*.   *M* is the cover for the loading slot.

In carrying out an electrophoretic separation in this cell, the following procedure is observed: The four removable medial plastic baffles are placed in the medial slots.   The heavy filter paper (Schleicher and Schuell 470) feed wicks, *D*, are placed in the brackets of the wick support.   The wick supports are then placed in the outermost slots with the filter paper wick facing outward.

With the drying rack extended, eight previously labeled filter paper strips, *H*, are suspended from the rubber pegs, *I*.   Then with the rack support, *E*, lowered into position in the cell centered by the plastic guides (not shown), the extended drying rack, *G*, is lowered onto the rack support, *E*, so that the medial pegs (not visible) of the lock nut assembly, *J*, are suspended in the slots in the top of *E*.   The knurled nuts, *J*, are loosened, and the rack is folded in such a manner that the apices of the strips are supported by the rods, *F*, and the ends make contact with the feed wick, *D*. The geometry is such that in this position the filter paper ends are pulled away from the stainless steel rod.   In this position, the knurled nut is

tightened.   One liter of the appropriate buffer is measured out, and about
two-thirds of this is poured into one end of the base section, about equally
divided between electrode compartments.   Cover, K, is put in place.   The
remaining buffer is carefully poured over the strips along their apices,
utilizing a short stemmed funnel which is inserted through the loading slot,
L, and which is passed back and forth along the slot.   If any of the strips
hang loosely, adjustment is readily made with a glass rod so that they hang
uniformly taut, and contact by capillarity is uniform with wick, D.   The
electrolyte levels in the two electrode compartments are equalized by
briefly raising one end of the cell off the table, whence the electrolyte in
the two compartments communicates through a hole in the central partition.   When the cell is again returned to the horizontal, this hole lies above
the electrolyte level so that no short circuit results.   The strips are permitted to drain for at least 15 minutes.   After this interval, the serum
sample is applied through the loading slot, L, by means of a pipette

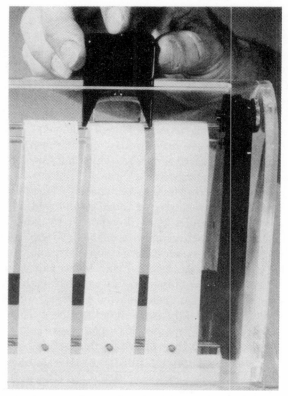

FIG. 15.   Showing how applicator described in text is used with a hanging strip
cell.   (Courtesy Spinco Division, Beckman Instruments, Inc.)

(streaked) or by means of a special applicator. Such an applicator is shown in Fig. 15. The applicator comprises a stainless steel bow which carries two closely spaced, tightly stretched parallel stainless steel wires. A measured sample is applied between the wires directly from a micro-pipette where it is held by surface forces until brought against a mois-tened strip of filter paper (de Wael, 56-7A; and Svensson, 55-5, 56-7A), have described other types of sample applicators.

After an appropriate electrical potential has been applied for the proper duration of the experiment, the cell is disconnected, the cover is removed, the lock nut is loosened, and the drying rack is extended. The lock nut is tightened, and the drying rack is transferred to the oven for drying. When drying is completed, the filter paper strips are transferred to the staining rack shown in Fig. 2, Chapter XIX, and the appropriate staining procedure carried out. The stained and rinsed strips are carefully removed from the staining rack, blotted, and returned to the extended drying rack for final drying.

High Voltage Electrophoresis

Kickhöfen (56-31A) has defined high voltage paper electrophoresis as that variation employed when potential gradients exceed 20 volts per cm. The principal problem in applying high potentials is the dissipation of heat produced incidental to the passage of current. Michl (51-45), who first reported working with high potentials, solved this problem by immersing the paper strip in a non-polar organic solvent (toluene). The more recent tendency is to remove excess heat by having the paper strip in intimate contact with a cooling plate of some sort which may be cooled by circula-tion of tap water or even refrigerant.

High voltage electrophoresis in general is usually carried out with paper which is comparatively dry compared to that employed in ordinary paper electrophoresis. For example, in work reported by Kickhöfen (56-31A) the moisture content is only about 110 % of the dry strip weight. One can imagine that under these circumstances there exists no "interstitial pud-dles" of liquid between fibers in which convection can occur, and it may be that this feature is most important in permitting the relatively high degree of resolution which has been reported by many workers for various substances studied. In the apparatus described by Werner and Westphal (55-322) the paper is soaked in buffer, then passed through a rubber clothes wringer type apparatus, and then placed on the cooling plate. In order to prevent further fluid from running into the relatively dry paper from the electrode vessels, cellophane barriers separate the ends of it from the elec-trolyte in the electrode vessels.

So far the technique has been applied principally to smaller molecules, particularly peptides and non-protein nitrogen constituents of serum, urine, and other biological materials. Unfortunately, it does not appear to be applicable to the separation of proteins, perhaps because of the relative dryness of the paper employed.

SUMMARY

In the foregoing sections of this chapter the various types of paper electrophoresis equipment which are available have been discussed and in a general way an attempt has been made to point out their appropriate application. In the following section, it will be assumed that a given type of cell has been chosen, and these remarks are intended to be rough guides for the selection of the other experimental variables. It is obvious from the multiplicity of factors involved in paper electrophoresis that no hard and fast rules can be set forth and that there is no substitute for a background of diversified experience. Nevertheless, for many common types of separations, optimal experimental conditions have been worked out in detail so that often a search of the literature will define these, and they can then serve as a guide in selecting the experimental variables applicable to new situations.

Papers. Many types of filter paper are available from various manufacturers. These papers vary considerably in texture, thickness, optical homogeneity, and the presence of foreign materials. In general, thick coarse papers give less sharp resolution than papers of fine texture, probably because the former are less efficient anticonvectants. The paper as it is received from the manufacturer often contains impurities which can be removed simply by washing with distilled water. In some cases, washing with dilute hydrochloric acid (0.1 M) or ethylenediaminetetraacetic acid (Versene, 0.01 M) is necessary to remove trace impurities which tend to adsorb certain substances. For chromatographic purposes, Connel (55-59) has described a washing technique for filter paper utilizing lithium hydroxide which is carried out over a period of about 40 days which removes many ultraviolet absorbing components leaving substantially pure alpha cellulose. Presumably this treatment could be applied to advantage in paper electrophetic applications.

Modified Papers. A considerable amount of work has been done in efforts to modify the paper surface in order to decrease adsorption and electroosmosis. For example, the author (unpublished work) has mildly acetylated the paper in an effort to modify its surface. These results were unsuccessful in reducing adsorption of proteins. Similarly, Porath (unpublished work, quoted by Tiselius, (53-294) esterified paper with diazomethane and by this means diminished, but did not completely suppress the adsorption of the basic protein, salmine. Flodin (quoted by Tiselius,

53-294) esterified paper with 2-aminoethylsulfuric acid which gave it ion exchange properties; he reported that certain proteins, which are strongly adsorbed oñ ordinary paper, could be treated without detectable adsorption at pH values lower than their isoelectric points.   Jermyn (53-134) soaked paper in periodic acid to form dialdehyde groups which were then coupled with hydrazine derivatives to provide basic surfaces for similar purposes.

Impregnation.   Kallee (52-90) treated paper with 0.1–0.2 % gelatin, serum albumin, and serum globulin in studying iodinated insulin and reported that adsorption of this substance could be prevented by this treatment. Michl (52-133) impregnated paper with $BaSO_4$, $SrSO_4$, ZnO, $Fe(OH)_3$, MgO, and TiO_2 but found them to be without effect in altering electro-osmosis when sucrose was used as an electroosmotic flow indicator.

Dyes.   Jetton (unpublished) studied alteration of serum protein patterns and endosmosis in barbiturate buffers on filter paper strips which had been previously dyed with strongly bound dyes including Evans Blue, Congo Red, Brilliant Purpurin R, Trypan Red, Erie Garnet B, Phyloxin, Eosine 4, Neutral Acriflavin, Neutral Red, Bismark Brown, Oil Red O, Methyl Violet, Toluidine Blue O, Basic Fuchsin, Brilliant Cresyl Blue, Nigrosin, Biebrich Scarlet, hematoxylin, and fluorescein, and found that the serum protein patterns were not altered appreciably by this treatment except with Congo Red, Brilliant Purpurin R, and Erie Garnet B.   Furthermore, only these three were observed to alter electroosmotic relationships.   Wunderly (52-212, 53-321) studied migration of serum on paper impregnated with butter yellow and other carcinogenic compounds.

Other Surfaces.   It should also be pointed out that "paper electrophoresis" can be carried out on many other types of media; for example, silk has been employed by Geldmacher-Mallinckrodt (53-84) for the separation of glycogen and galactogen, as well as glass paper (Strain, 52-195), glass cloth (tape), quartz cloth, and synthetic fiber cloths (nylon, orlon, and rayon). Also cotton string has been used in an analogous manner and can be used for ultramicroseparations (Durrum, unpublished).

The current which will be carried at any given potential by a strip of paper holding electrolyte is directly proportional to the amount of electrolyte which it holds.   Thus, for a given electrolyte, thick papers carry more current than thin papers and coarse porous papers carry more current than denser fine grained papers.   In this connection, it should be remembered that, if a strip of paper is twice as long as another strip, in order to have an equal field, twice the potential will be required (where evaporation is prevented).   If evaporation is permitted, these relationships may not be linear except at low current (see above; see also footnote 9, p. 520, for a discussion of constant current versus constant voltage operation).

Electrolytes.   The most commonly employed electrolytes are the ordinary

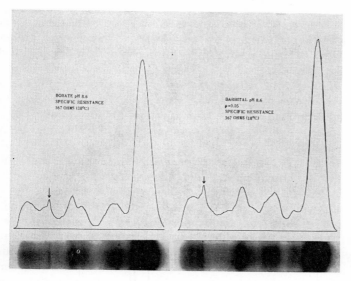

Fig. 16. Comparison of borate and barbiturate buffers for normal human serum (Durrum, unpublished work).

buffer solutions, and practically all the common ones have been used. Weakly dissociated acids and bases have found widespread application as well. In general, the strong electrolytes have been less popular, principally because of their high conductivity. Special types of buffers such as the borates can be used with normally uncharged molecules by virtue of their ability to form charged complexes, which can then be separated (Consden, 52-32; Jaenicke, 52-86; Michl, 52-134; Micheel, 52-132; Hashimoto, 52-75; Foster, 52-54, 53-75).

Borates also alter the familiar pattern in sera that is produced in barbiturate buffers. Figure 16 shows normal serum protein patterns obtained in borate and barbiturate buffers of identical pH and conductivity. It will be seen that in the borate pattern the alpha$_1$ globulin is not resolved. On the other hand, there is better resolution of the beta globulin into beta$_1$ and beta$_2$ fractions.

Zilversmit (53-328) studied migration of yttrium 91 and found that, although this substance existed in immobile forms in barbital buffers, when plasma was used as a buffer fractionation could be effected.

The choice of appropriate buffer will depend on the materials being separated and other factors. In general, it is desirable to utilize buffers of the lowest ionic strength compatible with maintaining pH, stability and solubility, since higher field strengths can be employed and separations effected in shorter times, so that diffusion will not interfere, as discussed previously (see Lederer, 52-118).   Tiselius (53-294) recommends pH values above the isoelectric point of proteins because negatively charged proteins are generally less strongly adsorbed on filter paper than are positively charged ones.

Buffer Additives.   Many substances have been added to buffers in an effort to prevent adsorption.   This was based on the hypothesis that these substances might compete with the serum proteins for adsorption sites.

PROTEINS.   These additives include serum (Kallee, 52-90) and serum albumin (Roth, 53-243).

DYES.   Roth (53-243) studied migration of albumin in buffers containing Amidoschwarz 10B or bromophenol blue.   Michl (52-133) studied methyl violet in buffers but did not observe any effect on electroosmosis.

SURFACE ACTIVE AGENTS.   Michl (52-133) studied zephirol but found it ineffective in modifying endosmosis.   Durrum (51-9) used propylene glycol and glycerol as viscosity-increasing and vapor pressure-decreasing agents in buffers in continuous electrophoresis, and recently Jencks (unpublished) has observed decreased adsorption of serum lipid components in the presence of 20 % glycerol.   Quastel (52-164) used Tween 80 in combined electrophoresis and chromatographic experiments on blood proteins. Flodin (quoted by Tiselius, 53-294) studied Tween 20 and sodium cetylsulfonate; it was reported that the latter eliminated adsorption of serum albumin and lens proteins but that its use was limited, owing to possible formation of irreversible complexes.   Jencks (unpublished) examined a large number of commercially available non-ionic detergents as possible agents for preventing the adsorption of lipoproteins on filter paper.   Evidence was obtained that, although they diminish adsorption of serum albumin, they all appear to obscure the lipid-lipoprotein relationships in serum.   Conclusions drawn from experiments in which detergents are employed must be viewed with considerable caution.

Chapter XVII

TWO-DIMENSIONAL TECHNIQUE

The analogy between two-dimensional[1] paper electrophoresis and two-dimensional chromatography is fairly obvious and has been described by Kunkel (51-32) and by Strain (52-195A) for the closed sheet method, and by Durrum (51-8) for the hanging sheet method. The two-dimensional techniques so far described have not received the attention afforded other methods. This is perhaps due to the fact that the somewhat simpler two-dimensional chromatographic techniques are very satisfactory for amino acid separations and the two-dimensional technique so far has proved disappointing for two-dimensional application to proteins (except for special purposes such as the study of adsorption), owing largely to the relatively limited pH and ionic strength ranges in which most proteins can be treated. Markham (56-39) has described a two-dimensional electrophoretic separation of serum muco-proteins in one dimension at pH 4.4 and in the other dimension at pH 8.6 in a closed strip apparatus.

Perhaps more important than "pure" two-dimensional electrophoresis is the combination of electrophoresis in one direction with chromatography in the other, in which case a new set of parameters is available in one dimension, which sometimes permits separations to be effected which cannot be carried out by either technique alone.

CLOSED SHEET TWO-DIMENSIONAL ELECTROPHORESIS

Kunkel (51-32), using a closed system (see Chapter XVI), studied patterns obtained in barbital buffer at pH 8.6, when human serum samples were applied at the corner of a square paper sheet between glass plates. An electric potential was applied across opposite sides of the sheet. Then the sheet was turned 90° and the potential was applied across the other two opposite sides for a period of similar duration. It was found that the serum components arranged themselves in a diagonal distribution. These experiments pointed out what is probably the greatest value of the method in connection with protein studies: that is, the detection of any trailing or adsorption. In the author's laboratory, the hanging sheet variation followed by staining with lipid dyes and counterstaining with protein dyes was found to be useful for studying adsorption of lipoproteins.

[1] In this chapter, we are using the term two-dimensional in the sense used in paper chromatography. Continuous electrophoresis used "discontinuously," as discussed in Chapter XVIII, is, strictly speaking, also a two-dimensional technique, but since the equipment is basically different it will be discussed separately.

533

Strain (52-195A) also carried out two-dimensional separations in a closed sheet system and in some experiments added a "third-dimension" by further separation of unresolved spots which were cut out and applied in a third step.   His work was largely concerned with the separation of inorganic ions, and very remarkable separations of various mixtures were reported.   Much of his work was done in the presence of complexing agents which modify the migration properties of some of the components being separated.

HANGING SHEET METHOD

Two-dimensional electrophoresis can be effected in the cell in Fig. 14, Chapter XVI.   Figure 1 represents a rack used to suspend a wide sheet of

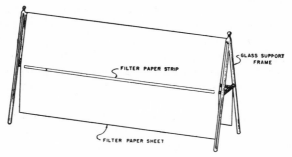

FIG. 1. Rack for two-dimensional hanging sheet technique showing how filter paper strips may be applied in the strip transfer variation (Durrum, 51-8).

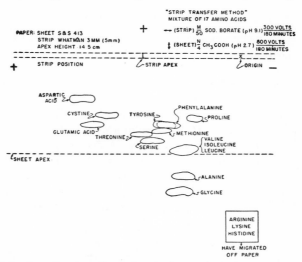

FIG. 2. Strip transfer two-dimensional electrophoresis pattern of amino acid mixture (Durrum, 51-8).

paper for two-dimensional electrophoresis according to the hanging sheet method (Durrum, 51-8).   The material to be separated is applied at some appropriate position along the center line of the sheet, and after the run is completed, the sheet is removed, dried, turned at 90°, and different buffer carefully brought up on either side of the apex (as described on p. 524) to keep the components separated in the first dimension in their position along the apex.   The potential is applied in the second dimension, and the resulting sheet dried and handled in the ordinary manner.   In carrying out separations, it is usually desirable to employ a volatile electrolyte in the

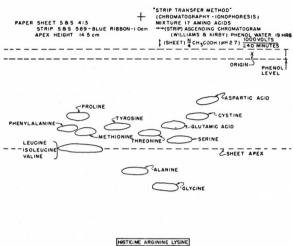

Fig. 3. Two-dimensional pattern of the same amino acid mixture shown in Fig. 2 but first dimension prepared by ascending chromatography (Durrum, 51-8).

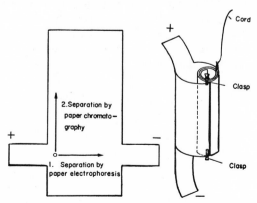

Fig. 4. Method for carrying out paper electrophoresis followed by ascending chromatography (Kickhöfen, 52-96).

first dimension; otherwise, residual buffer salts may cause considerable difficulties during the second dimensional separation. In order to circumvent this, the so-called strip transfer technique was developed. In this situation, the separation of the first dimension was carried out on a relatively narrow paper strip. This may be carried out in the presence of non-volatile buffers, and during the second dimension the strip is placed parallel with the apical support, where it adheres by capillary attraction (see Fig. 1) so that residual buffer salts migrate either before or behind the components as a separate band and do not interfere as they would if they were dispersed throughout the entire sheet.

COMBINATION OF ELECTROPHORESIS AND CHROMATOGRAPHY

Figure 2 represents a two-dimensional electrophoresis separation carried out according to this system. Application of this variation to the combination with chromatography is obvious, a unidimensional chromatogram being substituted for the narrow strip electrophoresis pattern.

Figure 3 is a two-dimensional pattern of a similar mixture in which the strip was prepared by ascending chromatography. It is evident that entirely different distribution of the amino acid spots is attained compared with that shown in Fig. 2.

Quastel (52-164) has used paper chromatography in the first dimension followed by electrophoresis in the second dimension in studies on serum proteins.

Kickhöfen (52-96) has described the combination of paper electrophoresis as a first dimension followed by ascending chromatography in the second dimension for the separation of amino acids, as shown in Fig. 4. The filter paper sheet (Whatman No. 1) was cut with tabs as shown, the sheet rolled up and potential applied across the tabs, after which the sheet was unrolled the tabs cut off, and ascending chromatography carried out.

Gerlaxhe (54-166) has described separation of most of the common amino acids by electrophoresis at either pH 2.4 or 11.6 in one dimension followed by chromatography in the other dimension in a butyl alcohol formic acid solvent (cf. Chapter V). Ingram (56-27) has used a similar system.

Chapter XVIII

CONTINUOUS ELECTROPHORESIS

Although Philpot (40-2) described a gravity-stabilized continuous electrophoresis apparatus in 1940 it appears that the first investigators to grasp the principle of continuous electrophoresis in anticonvection media were Haugaard and Kroner (48-6) who applied for a U. S. patent on the process in 1948. In 1949 and 1950, almost simultaneously and independently, Grassmann (49-10A, 50-16) and Svensson (49-24) published papers embodying the same principle. This method is basic and is undoubtedly one of the most important new methods that has been described in many years. Its present limitations with respect to the relatively small quantities of material which can be conveniently handled are in no way fundamental, and its application on an industrial scale only awaits appropriate engineering developments.

Continuous electrophoresis on paper and other anticonvection media differs from batch-type anticonvection electrophoresis in one important and fundamental respect, which does not appear to be generally appreciated: that difference is that the more slowly migrating components are not required to migrate over a path which has been previously traversed (and perhaps contaminated by adsorption) by the more rapidly migrating components; as a result, absolute separations can often be effected, as has been demonstrated by Sato (52-172) in radioactive tracer studies. This is of considerable importance in certain types of work where rapidly migrating components (for example, serum albumin) leave a tail on top of which the substances of slower mobility must migrate in the strip technique. In radioactive tracer studies particularly, this effect can be very troublesome and can often be avoided in the continuous method.

Figure 1 illustrates the basic principle of the method. A filter paper sheet is shown hanging from the edge of an electrolyte reservoir. The sheet is cut in such a manner that its lower edge affords tabs which dip into the electrode vessels. Between the electrode tabs, the edge is serrated to afford "drip points." At some position at the top of the filter paper curtain, a small tab is formed by making two parallel vertical cuts and one horizontal cut and by bending the portion of filter paper between these cuts forward. The mixture to be separated is continuously fed to this tab by means of a filter paper wick. Background electrolyte continuously "siphons" into the paper from the electrolyte reservoir and passes down the paper. Along with it passes the mixture being separated as a narrow band in the absence of an applied electrical potential. If an electrical potential is applied

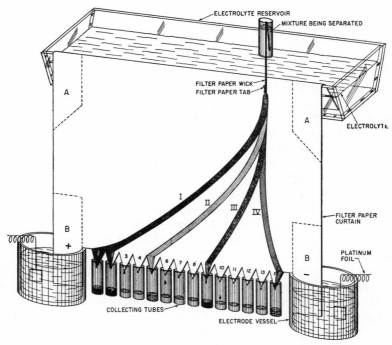

FIG. 1. Diagram showing principle of continuous paper electrophoresis (Durrum, 51-9).

across the filter paper curtain, the various mobility species are deviated toward the anode or the cathode, as the case may be, in accordance with their inherent mobility relationships under the given experimental conditions.

Figure 1 shows the separation of a hypothetical mixture comprising four distinct mobility species designated I, II, III, and IV. It is evident that the experimental arrangement shown permits collection of the separated materials from the various drip points. Of course, in order to obtain optimum results with this method, it is necessary to maintain a steady state; that is, it is important to feed the background electrolyte and the mixture being separated at constant rates, to maintain the electrical field intensity constant, and to maintain the temperature reasonably constant. To achieve this, it is necessary to add to the basic principle illustrated in Fig. 1 certain refinements which are described later in this chapter.

Continuous paper electrophoresis is not employed exclusively for preparative purposes. Frequently much useful information can be obtained from a study of the curtain itself, to provide information as to which collecting tubes are likely to contain the separated substances sought, as well as to the presence of minor quantities of impurities. For this reason, at the end of the run the paper curtain is usually carefully dried as quickly as possible and treated with some appropriate reagent to show the migration paths of the separated substances. Also, it is frequently useful to examine the paper curtain in ultraviolet light prior to any chemical treatment, as this may reveal the presence of bands which may be undetected by more specific chemical detection techniques.

All continuous methods have in common the superposition of an electrical field at some angle to the flow of background electrolyte. Ordinarily, this is achieved by passing the electrolyte by gravity vertically down the anticonvection medium.[1]

Some workers have attempted to prevent evaporation from the curtains by clamping them between glass plates (Strain, 51-65; Brattsten, 51-3), and good separations have been reported utilizing this method. Relatively elaborate closed curtain apparatuses have been built provided with circulating water to cool the curtain. The advantages of this procedure except for special situations[2] are often outweighed by manipulative difficulties. For many purposes the more convenient free-hanging curtain type apparatus may be substituted.

It is obvious that in the absence of adsorption, in the presence of uniform and constant electrical field distribution, and with prevention of evaporation, the separations obtainable are dependent purely on the vector relationships defined by the length of time the particles are subjected to the field (the length of time it takes a substance to pass from the entrance wick to the top level of the curtain serrations) and the applied electrical field (see B and D in Fig. 2 from Strain, (51-65). Frequently, however,

[1] Strain (51-65) has described discontinuous operation in this manner, utilizing capillary ascent to drive the fluid at right angles to the electrical field. This method, although feasible for discontinuous operation, does not seem promising for continuous operation because there appears to be no convenient method to continuously withdraw samples separated under these conditions. The discontinuous method, of course, can be used with gravity flow also. Durrum (unpublished work) demonstrated that separations could be effected on paper supported on one surface either horizontally or at relatively low angles, but the equipment offered no particular advantage over the more conveniently manipulated vertical sheet apparatus.

[2] These cases are situations where it is desirable to carry out separation in the absence of air or where cooling is necessary to prevent denaturation of sensitive materials. However, it is not necessary to run continuous paper electrophoresis equipment in a closed system in order to achieve cooling. Evaporative cooling from the free hanging sheet in properly designed cells can be shown to maintain low temperatures effectively so that it is sometimes possible to demonstrate that the temperature inside a cell of the type shown in Fig. 3 is as much as 2°C. lower than ambient temperature.

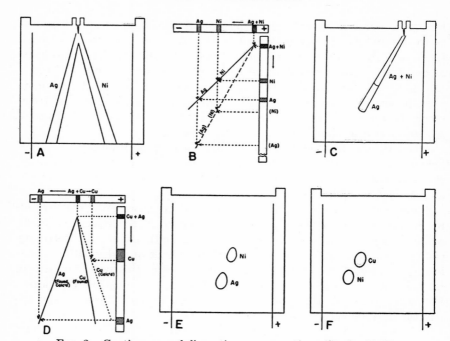

Fig. 2.   Continuous and discontinuous separations (Strain, 51-65).

A, silver and nickel nitrates, each 0.005 M in WL, 0.005 M Versene in 4 M NH₄OH; R, diphenylthiocarbazone and dithio-oxalic acid plus HCl; 160 volts, 95 ma.

B, silver and nickel separated by electrochromatography (upper paper strip) and by chromatography (paper strip at right); each ion 0.005 M in electrolyte and WL, 4 M NH₄OH; R, dithio-oxamide and diphenylthiocarbazone; solid vector, calculated path of silver and nickel in electrographic cell; dashed vector, calculated path of silver and nickel with low electrical current and rapid flow of WL.

C, relative migration rates of silver and nickel nitrates, each 0.005 M in WL, 4 M NH₄OH; 160 volts, ca. 60 ma., ca. 18 minutes.

D, silver and copper separated by electromigration (upper paper strip) and by chromatography (paper strip at right); each ion 0.005 M in WL, 0.01 M Versene in 4 M NH₄OH; R, dithio-oxamide and diphenylthiocarbazone; solid lines, observed paths in electrographic cell.

E, silver and nickel nitrates, each 0.005 M (0.01 ml.); WL, 4 M NH₄OH (60 ml.); arrow, point of addition; R, dithio-oxamide and diphenylthiocarbazone; 160 volts, ca. 40 ma., 20 minutes.

F, copper and nickel nitrates, each 0.005 M (0.01 ml); WL, 0.01 M ammonium acetate in 15 M NH₄OH (60 ml.); R, dithio-oxamide; 200 volts, ca. 35 ma., 20 minutes.

differential adsorption[3] will affect the "dwell-time" of the substance on the paper in such a manner as to modify profoundly relationships which would

[3] Strain (51-65) has pointed out that in the discontinuous procedure adsorption can lead to separation that would not be detected in the continuous method.

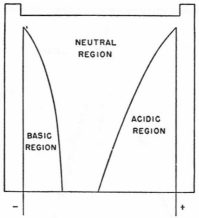

F IG. 3. Acidic and basic regions formed in a cell with electrodes up the side when a background electrolyte of 0.1 M ammonium acetate was employed as background electrolyte. 300 volts at 50 ma. (Strain 51-65).

hold in the absence of this factor, as in batch-type electrophoresis discussed previously. Differential adsorption may either hinder or help the situation, depending on the relationship of adsorption to mobility.[4]

In the free hanging curtain system, where evaporation is permitted, many factors modify the situation so that linear vector relationships no longer hold; these factors include (1) a non-homogeneous field distribution as a result of curtain geometry, (2) concentration gradients resulting from evaporation, and (3) unequal temperature distribution. These complicated equilibria are dependent on the geometry of any particular cell design and have not been worked out to date. Fortunately, this in no way detracts from the practical application of the method on an empirical basis.

Most workers in utilizing continuous electrophoresis have felt that it is important to maintain a relatively uniform field of potential distribution on the paper or other anticonvectant. This in general has been achieved by introducing electrodes along the edges of the paper. This

[4] A special situation in which differential adsorption can be utilized to good advantage in continuous paper electrophoresis is that where an impurity is present in a system in relatively small concentration but exhibits a relatively strong adsorption— for example, as was illustrated (Durrum, 51-9) for the separation of a minor impurity in a batch of the dye, acridine orange. In this situation, the minor component gradually "saturates" its path along the paper until a steady state is reached, and it begins to leave the paper at the same rate at which it is fed to the paper. In this special situation, a large reservoir of impurity may be built up upon the paper which may then be collected subsequently by cutting out this section of the paper and elution with appropriate solvents.

FIG. 4a.   A three-paired side-tab curtain according to DiCastro (55-70).

arrangement introduces a serious complication: it requires that special adaptations be incorporated in the apparatus to prevent electrode products from entering the main body of the curtain.   Figure 3 (Strain 51-65) shows how serious this effect can be in a practical case.   DiCastro and San Marco (54-109) and DiCastro (55-70) have utilized a cell designed to accept a curtain with three paired side tabs to afford a more uniform field (see Figs. 4a and 4b.).   Peeters (56-50A) has described a "cascade" electrode which is said to give uniform field distribution while at the same time reducing the introduction of electrode products to the curtain.

Svensson (49-24) and Brattsten (52-21) have given theoretical treatments for separations in systems without evaporation and with uniformly distributed electrical fields.

With regard to selecting the optimum field intensities for a given separation, several points must be taken into consideration.   In general, for a given flow rate down the paper curtain, the higher the field intensities, the better will be the resolution attainable, for a given set of experimental conditions.   However, since heating is incidental to the passage of current, when separating labile substances (for example, protein mixtures) it may

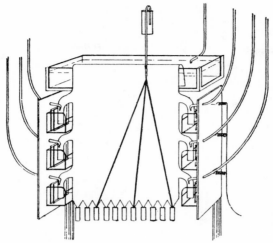

Fig. 4b. Continuous flow paper electrophoresis apparatus utilizing paired side-tab curtains according to DiCastro (54-109).

be desirable to employ low currents in order to permit separations to be effected at low temperature at some sacrifice of resolution.

These heating effects mentioned above may be particularly troublesome where non-volatile background electrolytes are employed. When currents are too high, evaporation may become too rapid and the water from the electrolyte may be evaporated so rapidly that the downward rate of flow is not sufficient to "wash the paper free" of the resulting concentrated electrolyte, and in extreme cases electrolyte solids may be deposited, thus destroying the necessary steady state. Nevertheless, under certain circumstances, it may be desirable to operate at currents just short of those causing deposition of solids since more concentrated fractions are thereby delivered from the drip points. In other words, if materials being separated are stable, the maximum permissible current is that value which is just short of that resulting in deposition of solids and which does not cause components to deviate too far laterally into the electrode vessels. Under these conditions, it is possible to maintain a steady state, and useful separations can be effected.

In cases of separations where volatile background electrolytes are employed, generally higher currents may be tolerated, provided that components of the mixture being separated do not deposit as solids, and of course are stable.

The current which flows for a given electrolyte is related to the applied voltage. However, this may not be a linear function in view of the factors considered above. Recent experience (Durrum, unpublished) has

FIG. 5. Free hanging curtain continuous electrophoresis cells (Durrum, 1951, unpublished work).

shown that the advantages of constant current operation[5] mentioned on p. 520 for open strip cells are also applicable to continuous operation to compensate partially for ambient temperature changes.

Since electrolytes of low ionic strength permit higher intensity electrical fields to be applied with relatively low current flow, it is often desirable to operate at minimum permissible electrolyte concentrations (as indicated by other factors such as prevention of the precipitation of proteins, required pH, etc.). For the same reason it is desirable to avoid attempting to separate mixtures which are too concentrated. For example, although in uni-dimensional separations or two-dimensional separations on paper it is not necessary to dialyze serum proteins, better resolution of protein mixtures usually is attained in the present method when the mixture being separated is dialyzed against the relatively dilute barbiturate buffer prior to separation. As a general rule, in applying the continuous method, the conductivity of the substances being separated should not be much greater than and preferably should be less than that of the background electrolyte.

Several methods are available for regulating rate of flow down the paper. Many types of filter paper are available in various degrees of porosity and thickness, and, in general, thick coarse papers afford more rapid flow (and poorer resolution) than thinner, more compact papers. However, flow of

[5] Consden (46-1) has pointed out the desirability of utilizing well-filtered full-wave rectified alternating current because it permits a greater field strength with less heating than a half-wave rectified potential source.

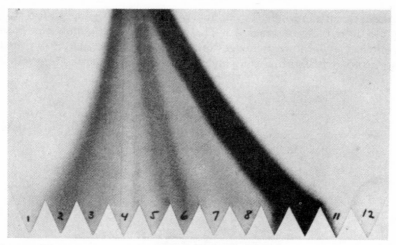

Fig. 6. Photograph of bromophenol blue-stained curtain (Whatman 3MM paper) used in the cell shown at the left in Fig. 5, for separation of human serum. Note faint band migrating in front of albumin (Durrum, unpublished).

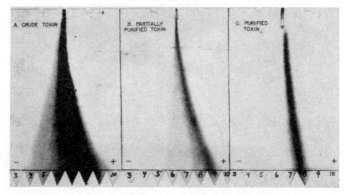

Fig. 7. Curtains showing purification of plague (*Pasteurella pestis*) toxin in a cell of the type shown in Fig. 5 (Ajl, 54-5).

background electrolyte down the paper may be controlled to some degree by adjusting the fluid level in the electrolyte reservoir with respect to the height of the upper edge of the sheet. Also, when it is desired to feed electrolyte to the paper at a rate less than the maximum for a given paper, it is possible to serrate the upper edge dipping into the electrolyte reservoir so that the flow is regulated by the depth to which the tips are immersed in the electrolyte. Sometimes a useful modification for locally controlling the flow rate down the paper is to apply added thicknesses of filter paper to the paper curtain where they adhere by capillary forces, as shown in Fig. 1 by the dotted lines in areas A. This permits greater volume and rate of flow of electrolyte down the edges of the paper curtain than in the center. Thus, a rapidly migrating component which might otherwise migrate into

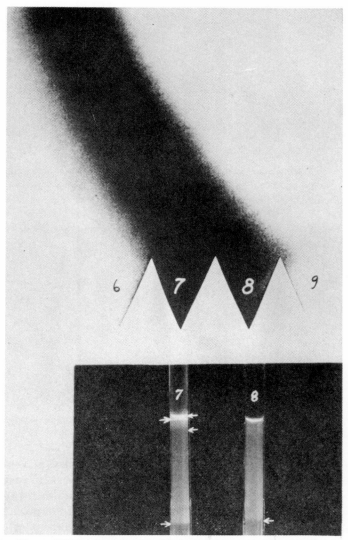

FIG. 8. Photograph of bromophenol blue-stained curtain and tubes prepared by the gel diffusion antigen-antibody detection technique (Oudin), indicating four antigens present in the albumin fraction collected from drip point 7 and only one from material from drip point 8 (see arrows) (Larson, 54-282).

one of the electrode compartments would be caused to deviate into one of the lateral drip points. Also, this modification may permit higher currents to be employed, since the local resistance at the electrode tabs is reduced. The cross section of highest electrical resistance in the system is, of course, at that part of the paper between the fluid level in the electrolyte vessels and the base of the sheet. The lower dotted lines in Fig. 1 encompass these areas (B) in which it is sometimes desirable to add an extra thickness of filter paper when high currents are caused to flow, since the local heating of top segments can thus be reduced. In a commercial apparatus to be described subsequently, this principle is extended and by the use of very heavy wicks (2″ × 1″ in cross section) up the edge, a relatively uniform field distribution is obtained.

Another experimental variable which has been utilized to advantage is the addition of an inert material to the background electrolyte in order to increase its viscosity, for the dual purpose of reducing flow rate down the paper curtain and of augmenting the anticonvection properties of the

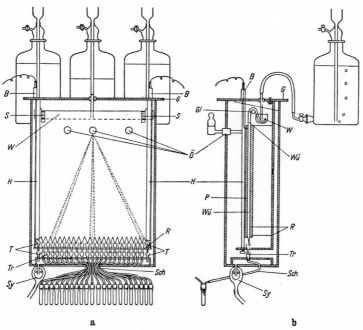

a   b

FIG. 9. Continuous electrophoresis apparatus according to Grassmann, (53-93): a, front view; b, cross section; R, supporting frame; W, buffer reservoir; S, bracket; H, support; P, platinum electrode; Wü, paper curtain; Sch, rubber tubing; B, electrode carriers; Gl, glass rod; T, collecting funnels for electrode rinsing; Tr, collecting funnels for separated components; Sy, overflow syphon; G, glass lid; Ö, sample applicator openings.

filter paper curtain. For example, both glycerol and propylene glycol have been successfully utilized in protein separations to reduce the flow rate down the paper curtain (Durrum, 51-9). These two substances have been found to be practically without effect upon the pH of many electrolyte systems in concentrations of order of 10–20%.

Another advantage when utilizing these substances is that the vapor pressure of the electrolyte is reduced, and, therefore, a given current results in less evaporation from the filter paper curtain.

Factors which are more directly concerned with the amount of material which may be separated under a given set of circumstances in a given interval include the feed rate, which is conveniently controlled by altering the width of the filter paper wick. The maximum permissible rate depends on the degree of resolution sought and the thickness of the paper as well as the dimensions of the apparatus.

Figure 5 is a photograph of two free hanging curtain continuous electrophoresis cells. The cell on the left is a two-curtain model (Durrum, 51-9). The cell on the right is a twelve-sheet apparatus (Durrum, unpublished) with a common electrolyte reservoir and common collecting chambers. In the latter cell as much as 50 ml. of serum can be passed through the cell in 24 hours with high resolution.

Fig. 10. Closed curtain continuous electrophoresis apparatus (Sato, 52-172).

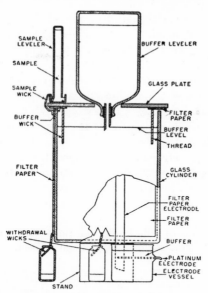

FIG. 11. Continuous flow paper electrophoresis apparatus according to Saroff (55-260).

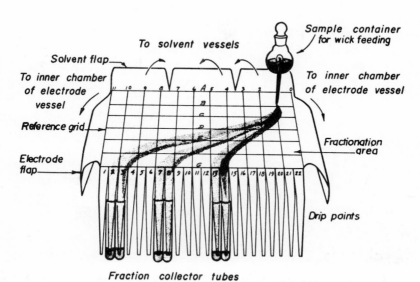

FIG. 12. Disposition of filter paper curtain in tilted sheet continuous flow paper electrophoresis apparatus according to Karler (55-144A).

Figure 6 (Durrum, unpublished) is a photograph of a stained curtain from a cell of the type shown in Fig. 5. The degree of resolution attainable in cells of this type is also illustrated by the stained curtains shown in Fig. 7 (Ajl, 54-5) and Fig. 8 (Larson, 54-282).

Figure 9 illustrates the apparatus of Grassmann (53-93). Figure 10 is a closed curtain apparatus which incorporates a pressure indicator and regulating device (Sato, 52-172). Figure 2 (A, C, E, and F) are diagrams of patterns obtained in an apparatus of this type (Strain, 51-65).

Karler (54-256) has described a continuous flow freehanging curtain apparatus built into a refrigerator with forced draft for cooling. Saroff (55-260) has described a continuous flow paper electrophoresis apparatus in which the curtain is diposed in a cylindical form which he reports has been successfully used for the fractionation of amino acid mixtures (Figure 11).

Since the first edition of this book was published, two continuous flow paper electrophoresis apparatuses have been offered commercially in the

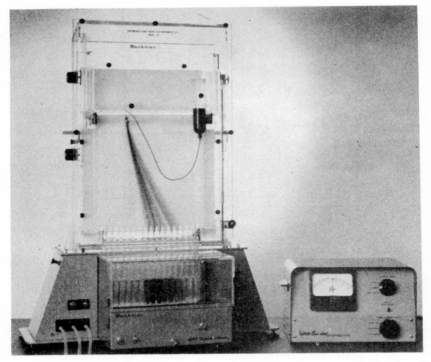

FIG. 13. Commercial (Spinco, Model CP) continuous flow paper electrophoresis apparatus with automatic fraction collector. (Courtesy Spinco Division, Beckman Instruments, Inc.)

FIG. 14. Commercial (Elphor) version continuous electrophoresis apparatus according to Grassmann, 1953. (Courtesy Professor W. Grassmann.)

United States. They are both licensed under the Haugaard and Kroner U. S. Patent (48-6). The first of these to become available is that designed by Karler.[6] In this apparatus the curtain is supported on a plastic screen or on elevated plastic points. The top of the curtain dips directly into the background electrolyte reservoir, and the rate at which the electrolyte passes down the curtain is controlled by adjusting the angle of the plane of the curtain. This, of course, is essentially a method of adjusting "head." The edges of the curtain bent at 90° to the plane of the curtain dip directly into electrode vessels. The capacity is stated to be up to 5 ml. of liquid sample per 24 hours (see Fig. 12).

The second apparatus to be offered commercially is that designed by Pickels and Durrum (56-11A).[7] This apparatus Fig. 13 provides a curtain 14″ × 12″ with 32 drip points. The usual curtain is a rather heavy paper such as S. & S. grade 470. Background electrolyte fluid is controlled by changing the fluid level in an upper reservoir which carries an intermediate drip curtain. Rates from maximal (flushing) to virtually zero are available by setting an indexed overflow weir tube by means of an

[6] Available from Micro-Chemical Specialties Company, Berkeley, California.
[7] Available from Beckman Instruments, Spinco Division, Palo Alto, California.

outside control knob.   To control the poor field distribution inherent in curtain apparatuses with simple bottom tabs, heavy filter paper wicks contact the sides of the curtain, and by this means a relatively uniform field is obtained.   These wicks are supplied with electrolyte from adjustable capillaries so that the flow down the wicks can be balanced to the principal background electrolyte flow to the curtain.   This arrangement permits the position of the pattern on the curtain to be controlled to a considerable degree.

For example, increasing the flow on the positive capillary and reducing the flow on the negative capillary tends to cause a shift of the pattern in a clockwise direction.   This unit is capable of treating fluid samples at rates up to 10 ml. per hour, depending upon the difficulty of resolution.

The apparatus has a small diaphragm-type pump incorporated in one base which pumps electrolyte from an electrolyte storage bottle placed on the floor to the adjustable upper reservoir.   In the other base, a variable speed clock mechanism driven by a synchronous motor slowly raises a rod to which are attached the sample tubes.   The speed at which this rod ascends, coupled with the sample tube of appropriate diameter, affords

Fig. 15. Commercial (Elphor Va) version continuous paper electrophoresis apparatus according to Grassmann (Courtesy Professor W. Grassmann.)

a range of sample flow rate up to 10 ml. per hour. That is the rate at which sample is fed to the curtain is regulated by the speed at which the sample vessel is raised. Figures 14 and 15 are photographs of commercial versions of the Grassmann apparatus which is commercially available in Europe.[8]

[8] Available from Bender and Hobein, Munich, Germany.

Chapter XIX

SOME QUANTITATIVE CONSIDERATIONS

The purpose of carrying out paper electrophoresis, as has been discussed in previous chapters, is primarily analytical (although even strip techniques can also be considered micro preparative). Many detection techniques based on color reactions, radioisotope tracers, and ultraviolet absorption and fluoresence which were developed for paper chromatography (examples of which have been discussed in other sections of this book) are applicable to paper electrophoresis as well.

Perhaps the only techniques which need to be discussed here are the staining methods which have been developed, particularly for the quantitative determination of proteins. The most commonly used dyes for protein studies are bromophenol blue (Durrum, 49-6), Azocarmine B (Turba, 50-36), and Amidoschwartz 10B (Grassmann, 51-20); light green S. F. (Dangerfield, 55-67; Rideout, 55-248) for lipid detection in sera Sudan black (Swahn, 52-197), Sudan III (Fasoli, 52-51), and Oil Red O (Durrum, 52-43); for glycoproteins a periodic acid Schiff reaction (Köiw, 52-100; Raynaud, 53-228).

The first attention to the quantitative aspects of dye binding for serum proteins on paper was that of Cremer (50-7), who developed an elution technique based on the dye bromophenol blue and reported results which gave good agreement with the moving boundary method. Agreement was found to be best for normal sera.

At this point, a fundamental difference in the two systems should be emphasized which has been ignored in several studies comparing paper electrophoresis with the classical moving boundary method. In the moving boundary method the Schlieren pattern is derived from the refractive index gradient as a function of the cell level. This is to say that any refractile component makes its contribution in a non-specific manner so that the areas under the curves represent the total of all refractile components, regardless of their chemical nature. On the other hand, the dyes commonly used in paper electrophoresis can be considered for practical purposes to be mutually exclusive, so that the areas under elution or directly scanned curves represent only the protein moiety for protein dyes and the lipid moeity for the lipophilic dyes. This, of course, is one of the advantages which paper electrophoresis has over the moving boundary method—it permits one to obtain evidence of the relative distribution of components of different chemical properties. As a consequence, it should *not* be anticipated that paper electrophoresis and moving boundary electrophoresis would give exactly similar analytical data, since in the latter case the results are expressed in terms of refractive index, whereas in the former they are usually expressed as dye binding capacity, which in the case of acid dyes is largely an expression of the number of basic groups (see below). This difference is exaggerated with pathological sera, where refractile lipids may contribute to the refractive index pattern to a greater degree than to the dye binding pattern, as noted by a number of workers.

We are then confronted with the necessity of establishing some absolute standard by which to judge quantitatively the results attained by various electrophoresis methods. Theoretically, some standard derived directly from the physical properties of the substances being separated would be ideal. For example, the possibility of measuring the ultraviolet absorption of separated proteins on paper without intermediate chemical steps is very attractive, but practically it has been disappointing because of the relatively low absorption compared to background (Durrum, unpublished). However, recent reports of direct scanning of unstained serum patterns in the ultraviolet by Harders (53-109) are encouraging. Perhaps the most suitable standard would be nitrogen values.

Jencks (55-137) has suggested the use of nitrogen values in order to avoid the variables associated with all dyeing procedures. In this case a nitrogen-free dye such as bromophenol blue is employed simply to locate the coagulated components on the paper strip. These are then cut up, and Kjeldahl nitrogen determinations made upon each. Under these conditions, of course, the electrophoresis should be performed with nitrogen-free buffers (not barbital) or else considerable precautions used to rinse the strips free from barbital buffer components. Unfortunately this whole procedure is rather tedious for routine use in the clinical laboratory.

Table I, Jencks (55-137) shows the relationship of nitrogen values to dye binding and refractive index for various protein constituents of serum. It should be emphasized that the values determined are probably strictly applicable only to those samples studied. It is unlikely that "dye binding factors" applicable to all sera exist.

It should be remembered that electrophoresis is a sorting process in which the parameter employed is the so-called mobility, a rather arbitrarily defined concept which depends upon pH, ionic strength, and buffer species. We must remember that the bands almost always represent mixtures of various molecular species which happen to have similar mobilities. Thus when they are sorted according to some other property, e.g., sedimentation (see Fig. 1), it is usually easy to show that they are in fact mixtures and further that the composition of the mixtures varies from sample to sample.

Unless we are dealing with a single molecular species or at least a mixture

TABLE I

RELATIONSHIP OF DYE BINDING TO BIURET, NITROGEN, AND REFRACTIVE
INDEX VALUES FOR DIFFERENT SERUM PROTEINS (JENCKS, 55-137)

	"Curtain" fractions g. dye/g. protein	Purified proteins g. dye/g. protein	Serum on strips[a] g. dye/g. nitrogen	Normal serum % total dye	"Factor" for re- fractive index
Albumin	—	0.38	—	70.8	1.0
	0.53	—	3.1	—	—
α_1-Globulin	—	—	—	2.7	2.6
α_2-Globulin	0.32	—	1.3	5.7	1.9
β-Globulin	0.34	—	2.1	8.3	2.1
γ-Globulin	0.31	0.28	1.3	12.6	1.1
Bovine albumin	—	0.39	—	—	—

[a] Abnormal serum.

of fixed composition, it is impossible to correlate strictly the amount of
dye bound (which it has been pointed out is largely a measure of the basic
groups present) with other characteristics (e.g., nitrogen content) *except for
a single sample.*

The foregoing remarks have considerable bearing on the problem of
agreement on some universally acceptable standard for dye techniques so
that numerical results from different laboratories can be compared. Unfortunately, no agreement yet exists. Three practical possibilities are:
(1) a standard protein or pool of a large number of individual sera, or
(2) a standard direct scanning densitometer, or finally, (3) a standard dye.

Concerning the first possibility, a "standard protein" such as crystalline
bovine or human serum albumin or a pooled serum sample could be used.
However the exact chemistry of the proteins has yet to be elucidated. It
is well known that bovine serum albumin differs from human albumin in
the number of basic groups it carries, and it is quite possible that even
more subtle differences exist even between comparable proteins of a single
species which affect dye binding. Pooled samples of serum suffer the
disadvantage that even in large pools, sampling differences may arise
through factors as yet unknown.

With regard to the use of values provided by some standard densitometer,
the second possibility, unless the dye used can be eluted easily, it must then
be evaluated by direct scanning of the strip. It is necessary, if the values
obtained by scanning are to provide a scale of reference, to include in the
standard a complete description of the spectral, optical, mechanical, and
even the electrical characteristics of the scanner. This procedure would
seem to be excessively arbitrary and presumably would not have universal
applicability.

On the other hand, with regard to the third possibility, certain dyes afford considerable advantages when employed as standards. It is an obvious corollary for any direct dyeing technique that the dye itself must be measured and equally obvious that the scale used to evaluate the dye by appropriate. Undoubtedly the most convenient and practical method to measure dye is by color. Many of the problems of direct densitometry of stained protein patterns on filter paper can be avoided by simple elution techniques using universally available standard colorimeters. Thus the importance that the dye selected be easily eluted. Suitable dyes of high purity and precisely defined chemical structure are available. A dye standard requires no assumptions to be made except that the dyeing technique employed is one in which the dye is bound stoichiometrically and reproducibly.

The scanning of filter paper strips by direct densitometry has come into wide use, and because of its convenience and rapidity will undoubtedly continue to be used more and more. However, in view of the above it is preferable to calibrate direct scanners in such a way that they give numerical values which agree with the values which would be obtained if the strip were actually cut up and eluted.

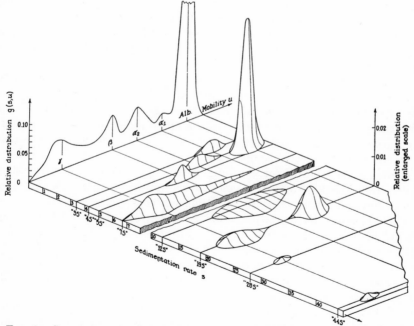

FIG. 1. Separation of a normal serum sample according to the parameters electrophoretic mobility and sedimentation rate. (Courtesy of Drs. R. Trautman and H. G. Kunkel.)

In dyeing of proteins, the assumption is made that a stoichiometric relationship exists between the denatured proteins and the dye. Unfortunately, this has not been rigorously established for many of the dye-protein systems which have been used for this purpose.

Cremer (50-7) noted that albumin had a greater affinity for bromopheno blue than did the globulin fractions (1.6 times as much dye per unit of nitrogen under their staining conditions). However, Griffiths (53-99) under different conditions found little difference in bromophenol blue uptake. Under the dyeing conditions shown in the diagram on page 559, this ratio is 1.3 for equivalent amounts of albumin and gamma globulin (biuret) (Jencks, 55-137). This may be compared to the value 1.42, the ratio of free basic groups in these proteins as determined from their amino acid composition (Brand, 45-1, 47-1). Grönwall (52-71) reported that each globulin fraction takes up a characteristic amount of dye which is different for each, and pathological globulins might take up still different amounts. These discrepancies are evidently largely dependent on details of dyeing and rinsing procedures, particularly on the thoroughness of denaturation in the oven prior to dyeing (see Fig. 3), and should be determined for any new procedure before results are compared with those from other laboratories or with the moving boundary method. It has been claimed that the dye Amidoschwartz 10B (Grassmann, 51-20) stains all the various serum components to a similar degree, but Sommerfelt (53-270) states that a factor (1.3) is necessary for globulins with this dye also when elution is used.

A difficulty in elution techniques is the arbitrary method in which strips must be cut up to define the separated zones, except in cases where complete resolution is attained such as with certain amino acids and lipoproteins. This can be minimized by direct scanning of the strips, utilizing the resulting pattern as a guide for cutting them up into the proper divisions corresponding to the protein components.

Quantitation from direct scanning techniques is more attractive than elution from the point of view of convenience, but it requires fairly elaborate equipment and is subject to the limitations discussed later.

Table II shows the steps in preparing serum patterns using the dye bromophenol blue for quantitative evaluation (Jencks, 55-137). A discussion of these steps will serve to point out some of the factors which must be considered in all quantitative dye processes.

As the strips come from the cell, the drying rack is extended (see Fig. 14, Chapter XVI), and the strips are dried horizontally for 30 minutes at 110–120°C. Elution studies have shown that unless the strips are subjected to this degree of heat for this duration, a stoichiometric relationship between dye uptake and protein concentration is not obtained. The pur-

TABLE II

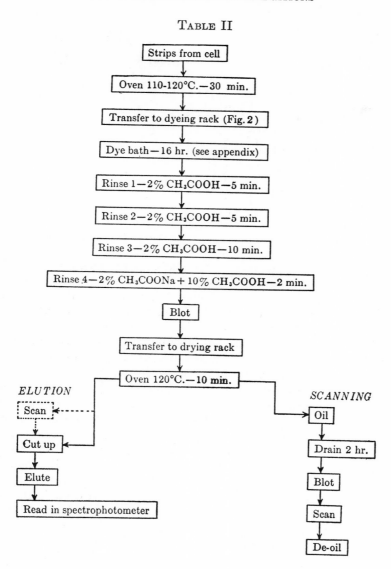

pose of drying the strips horizontally has been discussed, and it has been pointed out that during drying a shift in the pattern occurs toward that surface which receives the most heat, the bottom surface in most ovens. This does not result in detectable loss of resolution, however.

After the strips are removed from the oven, they are placed in a stainless steel dyeing rack of the type shown in Fig. 2. In order to obtain re-

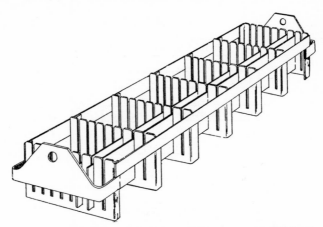

Fig. 2.   Stainless steel dyeing rack (Durrum, unpublished).

producibility it has been found essential that the strips be processed in some sort of rack which permits all surfaces of the strip to be readily accessible to dye or rinsing medium.   Careful studies have shown that when bromophenol blue is used in the dye bath indicated in the Appendix, 16 hours is necessary for the albumin to take up its stoichiometric equivalent of dye. A more dilute dye solution than that described previously (Durrum, 49–6) is used, because rinsing the background dye from the strip is much easier, and the 16-hour time is convenient for overnight dyeing.[1]   It will be noted that the dye bath as used currently contains no mercuric chloride, and ethanol has been replaced by water.   The importance of dyeing and fixing conditions is demonstrated in Fig. 3.   This shows scans of three matched serum strips dyed for 16 hours under different conditions in baths containing 0.01 % bromophenol blue and rinsed according to the schedule shown in Table II.   It is evident that both the oven pretreatment and the character of the dye bath have a profound influence on the degree of dye uptake.

The rinsing process is critical also and must be carried out with equal attention to detail.   The introduction of acidified rinses by Kunkel (51–32) marked a distinct advance over the use of tap water, affording much sharper differentiation of dye pattern compared to background.   It has been customary to follow the acetic acid rinses with a rinse containing 0.5 % sodium acetate plus 2 % acetic acid (Durrum, 52–43) in order to make certain that the bromophenol blue is all in the blue form after the strips are dried and to obviate the necessity of subjecting the strips to ammonia vapor in

[1] F. G. Williams (personal communication) has described a rapid bromophenol blue technique utilizing an alcoholic solution of the dye which is described in the Appendix.

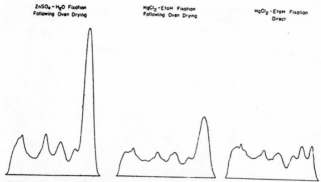

ZnSO₄ - H₂O Fixation
Following Oven Drying

HgCl₂ - EtoH Fixation
Following Oven Drying

HgCl₂ - EtoH Fixation
Direct

FIG. 3.   Effect of dye bath and heat fixation on dye uptake in serum patterns.
The dye baths all contain 0.01% bromophenol blue (Durrum, unpublished).

order to change their color from a yellowish green to a bright blue.   The
2% acetic acid rinse normally used has a pH of about 2.6; however, the
introduction of 0.5% sodium acetate raises the pH to about 3.6.   This increase of one pH unit is sufficient to cause a loss of dye in one 10-minute
rinse greater than that observed in the three previous rinses together.
Therefore recent practice, as indicated in Table II, is to substitute a shorter
final rinse in a more concentrated sodium acetate-acetic acid solution, which
causes negligible pattern dye loss.   After rinsing, the strips are blotted,
suspended on the drying rack, and dried for about 10 minutes at 110°C.

If the patterns are to be scanned directly, in an uncalibrated densitometer[2] they are next made translucent.   A number of agents have been
employed for this purpose, including a mixture of mineral oil and α-bromo-
naphthalene (Grassmann, 50–17), adjusted to $n_d = 1.51$ to match the
refractive index of the cellulose fibers, or methyl salicylate (Latner, 52–110).
Ordinary liquid petrolatum is used routinely in many laboratories and
appears to be as practical as the more carefully balanced agent of Grassmann.   In the Grassmann procedure dyed strips are floated under oil
onto glass plates and a second glass plate is placed on top of the strip in a
manner to prevent entrapment of air bubbles.   This "sandwich" is then

[2] When an instrument calibrated in optical density units is employed to scan paper
strips, it is necessary that Beer's law be followed as closely as possible.   Under these
circumstances it is an advantage to oil the strips and thus reduce the range of density
units covered to a sufficiently small value so that departures from Beer's law are
not great.   (See Fig. 10, which shows how serious this error can be.)

However with a calibrated densitometer, that is an instrument in which response
is empirically related to dye concentration, it is not necessary to oil the strips,
since departures from Beer's law are compensated by calibration.   By this latter
method the inconvenience of oiling and the possible introduction of additional
variables are eliminated.

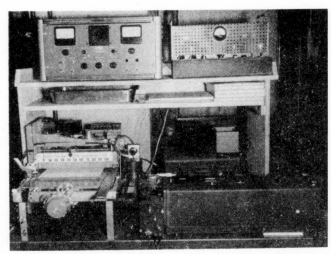

Fig. 4. Recording and integrating photoelectric scanner (Durrum, (55-78). Lower left, photomultiplier element (1P28 or 931 A) and housing, strip carriage coupled directly to chart paper table. The latter has been mounted beneath a Brown potentiometric recorder which is mounted on its face. A lead screw drives the chart under the recorder pen and simultaneously advances the paper strip through the slits. Lower right, Beckman Model DU monochromator. Upper right, logarithmic amplifier and integrating circuits. Upper left, El-Tronics radioactivity rate meter.

subjected to direct transmission scanning. In the scanner shown in Fig. 4, however, the strips are clamped by their edges and no glass comes in contact with the oiled surface. It is necessary, as has been pointed out by Latner (52–110), to displace any air bubbles trapped in the paper strip by the "clearing" agent. Latner subjected the strips to a vacuum in order to remove air bubbles prior to scanning. We have found it sufficient merely to let the strips hang for about 2 hours so that excess oil may drain from them prior to scanning. Just before scanning, they are blotted to remove any residual excess oil. After scanning, they may be "de-oiled" by treatment with ether or other fat solvent and filed for future reference.

If quantitative data are to be obtained by elution, the strips may be cut up and the bromophenol blue eluted with 0.01 N NaOH. The dye values should be read in the spectrophotometer (590 mμ) within an hour. Although bromophenol blue is not completely stable in the presence of alkali, there is no significant dye loss under these conditions.

A number of scanners have been described, including reflection and transmission types (Block, 48-3; Bull, 49-4; Grassmann, 50-17; Latner, 52-110; 54-285). At the present time, there is no agreement as to the best system. Most scanners have been built on the assumption that Beer's law is valid for treatment of dyed protein zones on paper. This assumption has been challenged recently by Crook (52-34, 54-91), who states that the light absorption of dyes on paper is approximated by a hyperbolic function and also concludes that only the transmission type of scanner is suitable.

Since the first edition of this book appeared, it has become generally agreed that Beer's law is not valid for colored material on filter paper even when scanners employ monochromatic light. At lower optical densities, especially those resulting in strips which have been made translucent, the deviations may be slight. However, almost invariably the densities obtained in the albumin area result in considerable error. That is the albumin value compared with elution (where the dye is properly measured in a colorimeter) is invariably too low (see Fig. 8).

Thus a correction is required to make values obtained from direct scanning agree with the amount of dye present (determined by elution). Since it is not practical to employ monochromatic light in the average scanner, a second correction for this is required. These two corrections can be combined into a single calibration as is done in one commercial servo-type scanner by incorporation of an appropriately designed cam (see Fig. 11).

Figure 4 shows a scanner (Durrum, 55-78) which was designed to obtain data on the direct scanning process. It is provided with positive chart and paper strip alignment and is calibrated with neutral density filters to plot linear optical density directly. Figure 5 shows how this scanner plots the transmission data. The strip is scanned first to plot the density curve, followed by a second scan which plots in superposition the integral of this curve.[3] The integral curve is then divided into segments corresponding to the density curve below. The area under the density curve can be determined simply by measuring the corresponding segment on the integral ordinate. This integral curve is of considerable utility when large numbers of strips are to be calculated, since it avoids tedious planimetry.

A Beckman Model DU monochromator may be used as a source of monochromatic light in the visible or ultraviolet region. The slits are designed for either optical or radioactive scanning, and the latter can be done simply by replacing the photomultiplier tube with an interchangeable shielded Geiger tube and a rate meter to actuate the recorder. Figure 6 is an example of a scan obtained when a mixture of amino acids containing carbon-14-labeled glycine was separated on a paper strip, treated with ninhydrin, and scanned first at 575 mμ, and then with the Geiger tube and rate meter.

Experience has shown that a closer approximation to Beer's law holds if monochromatic light from the Beckman DU is used rather than even the relatively narrow bands available with modern interference filters. So far,

[3] In an apparatus recently developed by the Bureau of Standards (S. R. Gilford), these two curves are plotted simultaneously on a dual pen recorder.

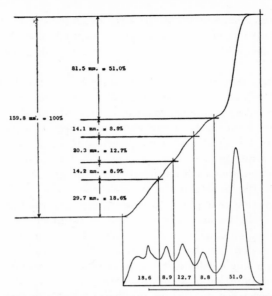

FIG. 5. Plot of protein curve produced by the scanner shown in Fig. 4 illustrating how areas are calculated (Durrum 55-78).

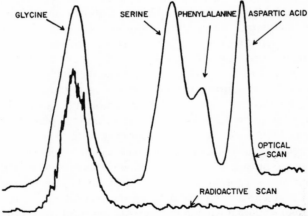

FIG. 6. Radioactive and optical scan for amino acid mixture separated by electrophoresis and scanned in the scanner shown in Fig. 4 (Durrum, 55-78).

little attention has been given to the influence of spectral purity in paper electrophoresis scanning, and many scanners are equipped with relatively broad band filters. Interference filters are distinctly superior, and the monochromator is even better. Some scanners utilize unfiltered (white) light. Figure 7 shows the same pattern scanned with light at a number of

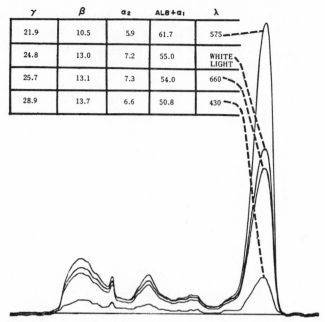

γ	β	α_2	ALB+α_1	λ
21.9	10.5	5.9	61.7	575
24.8	13.0	7.2	55.0	WHITE LIGHT
25.7	13.1	7.3	54.0	660
28.9	13.7	6.6	50.8	430

FIG. 7.   Influence of wavelength on relative protein percentages for bromophenol-blue stained strip (Durrum, unpublished).

different wavelengths and also shows how the calculated areas vary with the wavelength employed.

Figure 9 is an absorption curve for the dye bromophenol blue in solution (pH 8.6), alone, and in the presence of albumin and of gamma globulin. Studies have shown that when the dye is associated with any serum protein on paper a shift in the absorption maximum occurs from 591 to about 604 mμ.   Aniline red exhibits a similar behavior.

In order to get maximum contrast, one would anticipate that it would be most desirable to scan a strip at a wavelength close to the absorption maximum of the dye being measured.   However, in order to work at lower optical densities it may sometimes be desirable to use a narrow band at some other wavelength.

Inasmuch as the quantitative results obtained by paper electrophoresis are usually expressed in terms of the number of milligrams of dye associated with the various mobility species, it is desirable that results obtained by direct scanning be comparable to values obtained by elution.   This problem is more difficult than it would appear to be.   F. G. Williams, (personal communication) has shown that the details of the spectral absorbance curves for bromophenol blue bound to different proteins are sufficiently different to prevent agreement with elution. A scanner which "sees" the same amount of dye bound to different mobility species as different densities will not give the same results as obtained by elution where the dye is all the same color. This problem has recently been solved in the case of

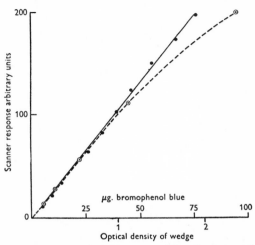

FIG. 8. Scanner response to a calibrated optical wedge, ●—●, and to increasing amounts of bromophenol blue streaked on paper, ◉—◉. The wedge was calibrated on a Macbeth-Ansco densitometer with the red filter. Dye concentration was measured by elution (Jencks, 55-137).

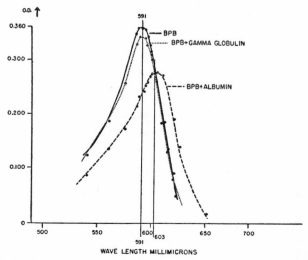

FIG. 9. Absorption curve for bromophenol blue in buffered solution (pH 8.6) in the presence of albumin and gamma globulin (Durrum, unpublished).

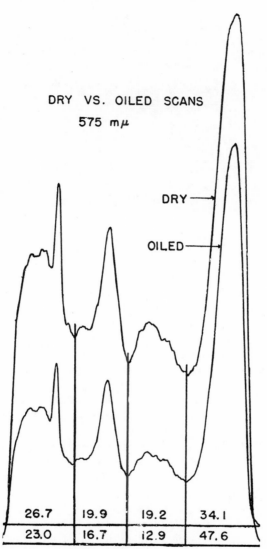

DRY VS. OILED SCANS

575 mμ

DRY →

OILED →

| 26.7 | 19.9 | 19.2 | 34.1 |
| 23.0 | 16.7 | 12.9 | 47.6 |

FIG. 10. Influence of dry versus translucent scans on relative protein percentages for bromophenol blue-stained strip (Durrum, unpublished).

the Spinco Analytrol (F. G. Williams, personal communication) by scanning with interference filters transmitting near the isobestic wave length for that dye (495 mμ).[4]

[4] In the early Spinco Analytrol models, the distribution of area beneath components was obtained after specifically calibrating with bromophenol blue-stained

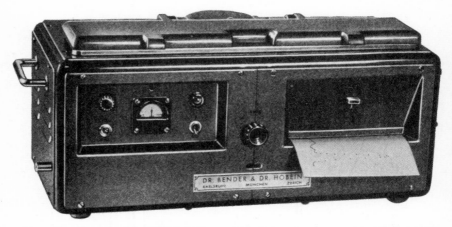

FIG. 11. Commercial (Elphor-Integraph). Servo type paper strip scanner and integrator. (Courtesy, Brinkmann Instruments, Inc.

Figure 10 illustrates scans of the same stained strip dry and after being made translucent with mineral oil in a scanner calibrated in optical density units (see Figs. 4 and 8). It is evident that a profound alteration in the apparent protein distribution is obtained. Elution studies have shown that the correct value is closer to that obtained from the oiled pattern.

Figure 11 illustrates an automatic recording densiometer with a built-in integrating device for measuring the areas under the curves.

Figure 11A shows a commercial integrating scanner which is based on a servo system. In this type scanner, the area under the density curves (Fig. 12) is shown by a corresponding series of pips, every tenth pip being longer than the rest. Perpendiculars are dropped from the density curve, and the number of corresponding pips is directly proportional to the area under this curve. This scanner may be provided with an optical density cam for other applications where Beer's law holds. Special cams can be calibrated to plot percent concentration directly for any standardized dyeing procedure. Scanners of this type make the question of validity of Beer's law applied to direct paper scanning largely of academic interest, since correction for the optical difficulties involved in measuring dye on paper can be incorporated empirically into the cam.

An error inherent in direct scanning is the lack of homogeneity of paper

albumin. The phrase "albumin equivalents" was coined to express this measurement. Such an artificial definition is not required with the more recent modifications of this instrument, since with the particular interference filters employed the area beneath components corresponds to the amount of bromophenol blue present. Under these conditions the scanner response is relatively independent of color changes in the dye associated with binding to different proteins.

FIG. 11A. Commercial (Spinco Analytrol) Servo type paper strip scanner and integrator. (Courtesy Spinco Division, Beckman Instruments, Inc.)

which is manifest in either reflectance or transmission-type scanning. When scans are carried out at a wavelength near the maximum absorption for the dye in question, the background errors often are negligible. On the other hand, these errors may be appreciable when contrast is less strong owing to scanning at some wavelength other than the maximum, using broad band filters, or studying substances in low concentration. Then, inhomogeneity of the paper may represent a serious limitation to precision and reproducibility.

Figure 13 is intended to illustrate the magnitude of this error. It shows three scan curves of the same strip of Whatman No. 2 filter paper which was marked with two crossed pencil lines for registration. The patterns were prepared with the scanner illustrated in Fig. 4, with a 1.0 × 23-mm. slit, and a Bausch and Lomb 577-mμ interference filter. Curve A was prepared from the untreated strip. B is the same strip after it was washed in distilled water and dried in an oven at 120°C. for 30 minutes. It is seen that, owing to shrinkage, the reference lines are closer together. For the distance they were separated (153.2 mm.) this amounts to about 1% shrinkage. This same blank strip was then run through the dyeing process shown in Table II and then scanned again (C). It is seen that no further shrinkage occurred and that this scan is practically indistinguishable from scan B. The significance of this figure is that it proves that it is feasible to prescan a paper strip to obtain a base line showing the optical inhomogeneity of the paper. This can subsequently be subtracted after a substance has been run, dyed, and scanned, to correct the resulting pattern. The curve shown is typical, and it can be seen that the ordinates at any point fall within limits that are of the order of 4 mm. apart.

A fundamental problem in paper electrophoresis is the albumin tail, (Kunkel, 51–32; Merklen, 52–131). alluded to on p. 506. These studies have shown that, independent of the absolute amount of albumin applied at the origin, a tail of irreversibly adsorbed albumin remains. It is as

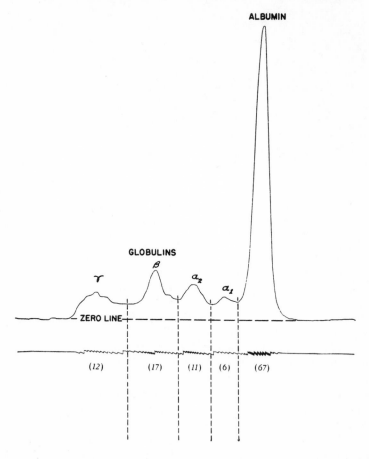

FIG. 12. Showing how data is presented in the Analytrol. (Courtesy Spinco Division, Beckman Instruments, Inc.)

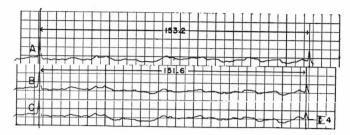

FIG. 13. Effect of staining procedures on blank strip of Whatman No. 2 filter paper (Durrum, unpublished).

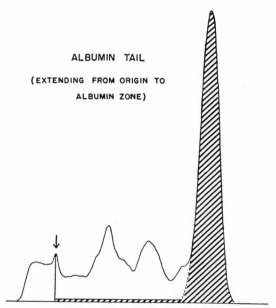

FIG. 14. Pattern illustrating position and magnitude of albumin tail.

though a carpet were unrolled in front of the subsequently migrating components upon which they were superposed. There is some evidence (see p. 532) that the saturation of the paper with this albumin tail cuts down the adsorption that might have been anticipated were the more slowly migrating components required to "saturate their own paths."

Figure 14 shows the relationship of the albumin tail to the total serum pattern. The tailing error shown amounts to 4 % of the albumin. This quantity was established for the conditions shown (Whatman 3MM filter paper, 30 mm. wide when 0.01 ml. of serum is employed and when the albumin migrates 80 mm.) by serial dilution and elution studies.   Thinner papers have been observed to give lesser degrees of tailing.   Therefore for utmost precision the albumin tail area (which is characteristic for each type of paper and of electrolyte) should be subtracted from the areas of the globulins (except gamma globulin (see footnote 10, p. 522) and this area added to the albumin peak.

In view of the multiplicity of factors that have been discussed, it might be imagined that paper electrophoresis is of little practical use for quantitative study of serum proteins.   Although the author has attempted to

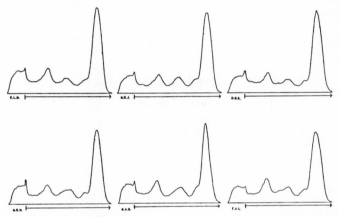

FIG. 15.   Bromophenol blue-stained scan patterns from six healthy individuals (Durrum, unpublished).

emphasize potential errors, he believes that with standardized dyeing and scanning techniques useful information can be found about clinical conditions even without making corrections for the albumin tail or the differential dyeing affinities of various proteins for bromophenol blue and other dyes.   Figures 15 and 16 illustrate this viewpoint.

Figure 15 shows six sera from presumably healthy individuals working in one laboratory.   These patterns were prepared by utilizing the staining technique shown in Table II and were scanned at 600 mμ after being made translucent.

Figure 15–16 shows a comparable series of patterns obtained from individuals who were sick enough to be hospitalized.   The pronounced variations in these patterns are of undoubted significance, although except perhaps in the case of the pattern associated with nephrosis they cannot be considered to be pathognomonic.

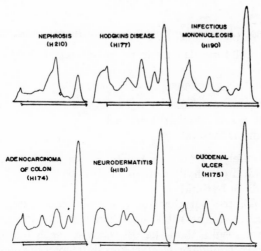

Fig. 16.   Bromophenol blue-stained scan patterns from six individuals ill enough to be hospitalized (Durrum, unpublished).

APPENDIX

Electrolytes Commonly Employed In Paper Electrophoresis

(All formulas are to be made up to 1 liter)

For Serum Protein Separations

Barbiturate buffer, pH 8.6, $\mu = 0.05$
1.84 g. barbital (diethylbarbituric acid)
10.30 g. sodium barbital

Barbiturate buffer, pH 8.6, $\mu = 0.075$
2.76 g. barbital (diethylbarbituric acid)
15.45 g. sodium barbital

It has been pointed out that for relatively short experiments (6 to 8 hours at moderate currents) 0.05 ionic strength barbital buffers, pH 8.6, give much better results than the 0.1 ionic strength buffers usually employed in moving boundary electrophoresis (Durrum, 49–6). This was confirmed by Flynn (51–13). It was suggested that this was due to an increase in the actual buffer concentration on the paper due to evaporation. Recent experience has shown that for long experiments (16 hours) at low currents, in which little evaporation occurs, somewhat better resolution is obtained, particularly in the forepart of the pattern (albumin-alpha globulin area) when buffers of somewhat higher ionic strength are employed. For example, in the hanging strip cell shown in Fig. 14, Chapter XVI, barbital buffer, pH 8.6 $\mu = 0.075$ gives excellent results in 16-hour runs with Whatman 3MM paper at 8 ma (see Williams, 55–328). Rundles (personal communication) has independently made similar observations.

Borate buffer, pH 8.6
8.80 g. sodium borate
4.65 g. boric acid
Borate buffer, pH 9.0
7.63 g. sodium borate
0.62 g. boric acid
Phosphate buffer, pH 7.4
0.6 g. monosodium phosphate monohydrate
2.2 g. disodium phosphate, anhydrous

Laurell and Laurell (55–166) have reported routine resolution of the beta-globulin band into sub fractions with fresh sera if a barbital buffer of ionic strength between 0.1–0.05 which contains 1.25 millimols of calcium ion (as calcium lactate) is used.

For fibrinogen separations in plasma Berkes (53–21) recommends phosphate buffer at pH 9.2.

For Basic Proteins

The adsorption of basic proteins on the filter paper is reduced by washing the paper (Whatman 3 MM) with 1% w/v Octab (octadecyldimethyl benzyl ammonium chloride, Fairchild Laboratories, Inc., 417 Cleveland Ave., Plainfield, N. J.). The paper is soaked in the detergent for 5–10 minutes and then thoroughly washed with water and dried.

For Milk Proteins

Milk proteins have been separated using a barbital buffer of pH 7.9 into 7 zones (K. E. Schulte and F. Müller; *Milchwissensch.* 1955, **10,** 90–97.)

For Muscle Proteins

pH 7.4 buffer: 26.45 g. Na 5,5-diethylbarbiturate
14.04 g. Na acetate 3H$_2$O
22.37 g. KCl
60.0 ml. of N acetic acid plus H$_2$O to 6 liters

(L. Kotter; W. Lenz and O. Prandl; *Zentr. Vetinärmed.* 1955, **2,** 495–506.)

For Amino Acid Separations

Phthalate buffer, pH 5.9
5.10 g. potassium acid phthalate
0.86 g. sodium hydroxide

This buffer is useful in amino acid work because it permits separation of aspartic acid, glutamic acid, the monoamino monocarboxylic acids (as a single group), histidine, arginine, and lysine (Durrum, 49–6). Acetic acid solutions from $N/4$ to $5 N$ are very useful for amino acid and peptide separations. Other weak acids such as lactic acid have been employed by Strain (51–65), particularly in connection with inorganic separations.

For DNP-Amino Acids

Veronal buffer (pH 8.3) at 200 v. for 2 hours (H. J. McDonald and M. C. Urbin, *Federation Proc.* 1953, **12,** 243–244) or 0.02 M Na borate (pH 8.8), 500 v for 45 hours. P. S. F. Newton, and E. P. Abraham, *Biochem. J.* 1953, **53,** 604–613.

For Sugar Derivatives

Foster (52–54) recommends Clark's borate buffer, pH 10, for separating sugar derivatives.

Paper Electrophoresis of Hemoglobins

(a) Preparation of hemoglobin sample (procedure based on that of (Drabkin, 46–21).

Take a convenient volume (1–10 ml.) of blood which has been treated with an anticoagulant (or passed over an ion-exchange resin, such as Dowex 50, to remove calcium) and centrifuge to separate the red cells (broken up clot can be used but is less convenient). Wash the cells 4 times with 0.9 % sodium chloride solution. Add an equal volume of distilled water to the packed, washed red cells and agitate to cause hemolysis. Add 0.4 volumes of toluene and shake 5–10 minutes to remove lipids. Centrifuge 20 minutes (3000 rpm); then remove the top two layers by aspiration. The resulting hemoglobin solution may be filtered through cotton, or a second centrifugation at 10,000–15,000 rpm may be applied (Larson, 53–153), although this latter step is not always necessary. The concentration of hemoglobin should be determined and then the solution diluted to about 3 % for optimal results, although concentrations from 1–10 % can be employed. Hemoglobin solutions may be stored frozen up to three months; for longer storage the hemoglobin should be converted to the carbon monoxide derivative which has essentially the same mobility (Larson, 53–153). This is easily accomplished by bubbling CO through the solution for 10 minutes and following the characteristic color change.

(b) Electrophoretic separation

To a strip of Whatman 3MM filter paper 30 mm. wide, which has been saturated with 0.05 ionic strength barbital buffer, pH 8.6 ± 0.1 (pH critical!) 0.01 ml. of 3 % hemoglobin solution is applied. Satisfactory resolution is obtained in the cell shown in Fig. 14, Chapter XVI, when a constant current of 22 ma (for 8 strips) is maintained for four hours. (In another hanging strip cell Motulsky (54–339) obtained satisfactory separations in 3–5 hours at constant voltage.)

(c) Quantitation

The relative proportions of the various hemoglobins present can be determined by direct transmission scanning of the dry, undyed strips at 520 mμ or by dyeing with bromophenol blue, as described in Chapter XIX, followed by elution (Motulsky, 54–339).

Dyeing Procedures

Protein

Bromophenol blue staining solution (for 1 l.) (See Table 2 Chapter XIX, for procedure)

0.1 g. bromophenol blue

50 g. zinc sulfate

50 ml. glacial acetic acid

Rapid bromophenol blue procedure (According to F. G. Williams, Personal Communication)

This technique is similar to that described above, except that prior to staining, the strips are rinsed in methanol for 6 minutes and then placed for 30 minutes in a dye bath of methanolic bromophenol blue 0.1% followed by three rinses in 5% acetic acid of six minutes duration (for Schleicher & Schuell 2043A paper). Elution may be carried out with $\frac{1}{2}$% sodium carbonate and optical density determined at 590 mμ. If the strips are to be scanned, they are exposed to concentrated ammonium hydroxide vapor and scanned at 495 mμ with a scanner which is calibrated to be linear with dye concentration.

Amidoschwartz 10B (Grassmann, 50–17)

Saturated solution in methyl alcohol with 10% acetic acid.

Dye 10 minutes.

Wash in methyl alcohol with 10% acetic acid until background is pale blue.

Air dry.

Elute if desired with 3–5% phenol in 10% acetic acid.

N.b.: Naphthalene Blue Black 12B.200 (ICI), Pontacyl Blue Black SX (DuPont) and Buffalo Black NBR (National Aniline) are sold as equivalent English and American dyes.

Azocarmine G (Turba 50–36)

Saturated solution in 50% methyl alcohol with 10% acetic acid.

Dye 10 minutes.

Wash 5 minutes in methyl alcohol, 5 minutes in 10% acetic acid.

Light Green S. F. (Rideout 55–248)

1% solution of Light Green S. F. dissolved in 1% acetic acid.

5–8 minute dyeing period, followed by three washes in 1% acetic acid, one minute each, with a final wash of 5–8 minutes.

Serum Proteins

The undyed chromatograms are dipped into glycerol and scanned at 250 mμ (K. H. Kimbel, *Naturwissenschaften* 1953, **40,** 200–201; Ch. Wunderly, *Plasma* 1954, **2,** 143–156).

Lipid

Oil Red O (National Aniline) (Durrum, 52–43)

60% alcohol saturated with dye for 16 hours at room temperature and filtered.

Stain overnight; rinse briefly in water to remove some background. Air dry.

Oil Blue N (National Aniline) can be used similarly but with a 4-hour staining period.

Sudan Black (National Aniline) (Swahn, 52–197)

60 % alcohol saturated with dye at boiling point, cooled, and filtered twice.

Stain 3 hours; rinse in 100 ml. 50 % alcohol for 15 minutes three times.

Sudan III (National Aniline) (Fasoli, 52–51) and other fat stains have also been used.

McDonald (56–40C) has described a staining technique for lipoproteins in serum in which acetylated Sudan Black B in alcohol is added to the serum sample prior to electrophoresis.

Carbohydrate (glucoproteins)

Carbohydrate stain: *Method 1* (Köiw, 52–100):

Periodic acid: 1.2 g. periodic acid dissolved in 30 ml. distilled water, add 15 ml. $M/5$ sodium acetate and 100 ml. ethyl alcohol. May be used several days if kept in dark.

Reducing solution: 5 g. potassium iodide, 5 g. sodium thiosulfate in 100 ml. distilled water, with stirring add 150 ml. ethyl alcohol and 2.5 ml. 2 N hydrochloric acid. Use at once.

Fuchsin sulfite: 2 g. basic fuchsin dissolved in 400 ml. boiling water, cooled to 50°C. and filtered. To filtrate add 10 ml. 2 N hydrochloric acid and 4 g. potassium metabisulfite. Stopper and let stand in cool, dark place overnight. Add 1 g. decolorizing charcoal and filter. Add 10 ml. or more 2 N hydrochloric acid in small amounts till a sample does not turn red when dried on glass slide. Keep in dark, well stoppered and cold. Discard when turns pink.

Sulfite rinse: 100 ml. distilled water, 1 ml. concentrated hydrochloric acid; 0.4 g. potassium metabisulfite.

Procedure:

Fix strip in ethanol.

5 minutes in periodic acid solution.

Rinse 70 % alcohol.

5–8 minutes in reducing solution.

Flood with 70 % alcohol.

25–45 minutes fuchsin sulfite solution.

Three rinses in sulfite rinse water.

Dehydrate in ethanol.

Dry on glass plate.

Violet red bands on pale background result.

Method 2 Sohar (E. Sohar; E. T. Bossak, and Adlersberg, D; *Proc. Soc. Exptl. Biol. Med.* 1955, **90**, 305–308) has modified the Schiff test as follows:
1. Replace 10 ml. of 2 N HCl with 15–20 ml. of concentrated HCl.
2. Immerse strips in fuchsin solution for 10–15 minutes under constant agitation.
3. Scan while still damp.

Method 3 (Drevon, B. and Donikan, R.; *Bull. soc. chem. biol.* 1955, **37**, 1321–1325).

Dry paper and extract with acetone.   Then carry out the following:
1. Place in boiling 1 % diphenylamine in glacial acetic for 5 minutes.
2. Air dry
3. Place in 37 % formaldehyde for 2 minutes.
4. Dry in the dark.

Glucoproteins show as red bands.

Enzyme Detection

Hanson (53–105) has described a method for localizing serum peptidases in paper electrophoresis by cutting up the patterns and placing them in a substrate solution contained in 0.05 M barbiturate buffer (pH 7.8) maintained at 38°C. for as long as 48 hours followed by separation of the split products (see Part I. Chapter V).

Carbohydrase Detection

Wetter (L. R. Wetter and J. J. Corrigal, *Nature* 1954, **174**, 695) has used the following procedures for carbohydrases after separation by paper electrophoresis:

Sprays:
1. 2 % maltose + 0.5 % notatin (glucose oxidase) for maltose.
2. 2 % sucrose + 0.5 % notatin for invertase.
3. 2 % dextrin + 0.5 % notatin for dextrinase.

After spraying the chromatogram, it is incubated at 30° for 30 minutes. The areas are then visualized by spraying with 0.06 % bromocresol purple in 95 % ethanol.   This procedure can be used when the enzyme liberates glucose as one of its end-products.

Bibliography for Part II

The bibliography for Section II is based upon a punch-card system which has been kept by the author for a number of years. It is fairly complete up to the end of 1955. It has been cross-checked with a number of other bibliographies including those of Lederer (55-170), McDonald (55-190), Wunderly (54-534), and other reviews.

The bibliography includes more than 1,700 papers on paper electrophoresis and closely related topics. The numbers designating the papers comprise two parts, the first indicating the year and the second the numerical sequence of the paper which has been arranged alphabetically according to senior author by year. English translations are provided for the article titles, and the language of origin is indicated. Although the classification of the bibliography based on the author's punch-cards must inevitably express to some degree his own particular interests, it is hoped that this will be useful to other workers.

The author would appreciate receiving reports of any errors or omissions noted in the bibliography or classification.

79-1.   Helmholtz, H.   Studies concerning electrical boundary layers (in German). *Wied. Ann.* [1879] **7**, 337.

86-1.   Lodge, O.   On the migration of ions and an experimental determination of absolute ionic velocity. *Brit. Assoc. Advance. Sci. Rept.* [1886] **56**, 389.

93-1.   Byerly, W. E.   "Fourier Series and Spherical Harmonics," 83 pp. Ginn, Boston, Massachusetts. [1893]

10-1.   Gouy, A.   The constitution of the electrical charge on the surface of an electrolyte (in French). *J. phys.* [1910] [4] **9**, 457–467.

21-1.   Lewis, G. N., and Randall, M.   The activity coefficient of strong electrolytes. *J. Am. Chem. Soc.* [1921] **43**, 1112.

23-1.   Kendall, J., and Crittenden, E. D.   The separation of isotopes. *Proc. Natl. Acad. Sci. U. S.* [1923] **9**, 75.

24-1.   Debye, P., and Huckel, E.   Remarks related to a thesis concerning the cataphoretic mobility of suspended particles (in German). *Physik. Z.* [1924] **25**, 49.

24-2.   Kendall, J., and White, J. T.   The separation of isotopes by the ionic migration method. *Proc. Natl. Acad. Sci. U. S.* [1924] **10**, 458.

25-1.   Kendall, J., and Clarke, B. L.   The separation of rare earths by the ionic migration method. *Proc. Natl. Acad. Sci. U. S.* [1925] **11**, 393.

26-1.   Kendall, J., and West, W.   An attempted separation of hafnium and zirconium by the ionic migration method. *J. Am. Chem. Soc.* [1926] **48**, 2619.

26-2.   Kendall, J., Jette, E. R., and West, W.   The separation of radium and mesothorium I from radium by the ionic migration method. *J. Am. Chem. Soc.* [1926] **48**, 3114.

28-1.   Kendall, J.   Separations by the ionic migration method. *Science* [1928] **67**, 163

BIBLIOGRAPHY FOR PART II 581

37-1. König, P. Employment of electrophoresis in chemical experiments with small quantities. *Actas e trabalhos do Terceiro Congresso Sud-Americano de Chimica, Rio de Janeiro e Sao Paulo* [1937] **2**, 334 (in part).

37-2. Tiselius, A. A new apparatus for electrophoretic analysis of colloidal mixtures. *Trans. Faraday Soc.* [1937] **33**, 524–531.

39-1. Coolidge, T. B. A simple cataphoresis apparatus. *J. Biol. Chem.* [1939] **127**, 551–553.

39-2. von Klobusitzky, D., and König, P. Biochemical study on the poison of the snake venon *Bothrops*. VI (in German). *Arch. exptl. Pathol. Pharmakol. Naunyn-Schmiedeberg's* [1939]. **192**, 271–275.

39-3. Longsworth, L. G., and MacInnes, D. A. Electrophoresis of proteins by the Tiselius method. *Chem. Revs.* [1939]. **24**, 271–287.

39-4. MacInnes, D. A. "The Principles of Electrochemistry," 478 pp. Reinhold, New York. [1939]

39-5. Strain, H. H. On the combination of electrophoretic and chromatographic adsorption methods. *J. Am. Chem. Soc.* [1939] **61**, 1292–1293.

40-1. Flood, H. On the production and use of ion exchange paper in inorganic chromatography (in German). *Z. anal. Chem.* [1940] **120**, 327.

40-2. Philpot, J. St. L. The use of thin layers in electrophoretic separation. *Trans. Faraday Soc.* [1940] **31**, 39.

42-1. Abramson, H. A., Moyer, L. S., and Gorin, M. H. "Electrophoresis of Proteins and the Chemistry of Cell Surfaces". Reinhold, New York. [1942].

43-1. Berraz, G. Electrocapillary analysis. *Anales asoc. quim. argent.* [1943] **31**, 96–97.

43-2. Berraz, G. Electrocapillary analysis. *Anal. inst. invest. cient. y tecnol., Univ. nac. litoral Santa Fé, Arg.* [1943] **1213**, 67–79.

44-1. Consden, R., Gordon, A. H., and Martin, A. J. P. Qualitative analysis of proteins: A partition chromatographic method using paper. *Biochem. J.* [1944] **38**, 224.

45-1. Brand, E., Saidel, L. J., Goldwater, W. H., Kassell, B., and Ryan, F. J. The empirical formula of beta-lactoglobulin. *J. Am. Chem. Soc.* [1945] **67**, 1524–1532.

45-2. Martin, A. J. P., and Synge, R. L. M. Analytical chemistry of the proteins. *Advances in Protein Chem.* [1945] **2**, 31–38.

45-3. Synge, R. L. M. The hydroxyamino component of gramicidin hydrolysates. *Biochem. J.* [1945] **39**, 355.

46-1. Consden, R., Gordon, A. H., and Martin, A. J. P. Ionophoresis in silica jelly. *Biochem. J.* [1946] **40**, 33–41.

46-2. Drabkin, D. L. Spectrophotometric studies. XIV. The crystallographic and optical properties of the hemoglobin of man in comparison with those of other species. *J. Biol. Chem.* [1946] **164**, 703.

46-3. Goodall, R., and Levi, A. A microchromatographic method of the detection and approximate determination of the different penicillins in a mixture. *Nature* [1946] **158**, 675.

46-4. Nielsen, L. E., and Kirkwood, J. G. The fractionation of proteins by electrophoresis convection. *J. Am. Chem. Soc.* [1946] **68**, 181.

47-1. Brand, E. Amino acid composition of simple proteins. *Ann. N. Y. Acad. Sci.* [1947] **47**, 187–288.

47-2. Butler, J. A. V., and Stephen, J. M. L. An apparatus for preparative electrophoresis. *Nature* [1947] **160**, 469.

47-3.   Consden, R., Gordon, A. H., Martin, A. J. P., and Synge, R. L. M.   The identification of lower peptides in complex mixtures. *Biochem. J.* [1947] **41**, 596–602.

47-4.   Polson, A., Mosley, V. M., and Wychoff, R. W. G.   The quantitative chromatography of silk hydrolysates. *Science* [1947] **105**, 603.

48-1.   Alberty, R. A.   An introduction to electrophoresis. I. Methods and calculations. *J. Chem. Educ.* [1948] **25**, 426–433.

48-2.   Alberty, R. A.   An introduction to electrophoresis. II. Analysis and theory. *J. Chem. Educ.* [1948] **25**, 619–625.

48-3.   Block, R. J.   Quantitative estimation of amino acids on paper chromatograms. *Science* [1948] **108**, 608–609.

48-4.   Forsyth, W.   Colour reagents for the paper chromatography of sugars. *Nature* [1948] **161**, 239.

48-5.   Haugaard, G., and Kroner, T. D.   Partition chromatography of amino acids with applied voltage. *J. Am. Chem. Soc.* [1948] **70**, 2135.

48-6.   Haugaard, G., and Kroner, T. D.   Chromatographic process and apparatus. U. S. Patent No. 2,555,487 filed Feb. 27, 1948.

48-7.   Martin, A. J. P., and Mittelmann, R.   Quantitative micro-analysis of amino-acid mixtures on paper partition chromatograms. *Biochem. J.* [1948] **43**, 353.

48-8.   Moore, S., and Stein, W. H.   Photometric ninhydrin method for use in the chromatography of amino acids. *J. Biol. Chem.* [1948] **176**, 367.

48-9.   Partridge, S. M.   Filter-paper partition chromatography of sugars. (Parts 1 and 2). *Biochem. J.* [1948] **42**, 238.

48-10.   Pratt, J. J., and Auclair, J. L.   Sensitivity of the ninhydrin reaction in paper partition chromatography. *Science* [1948] **108**, 213.

48-11.   Vischer, E., and Chargaff, E.   The separation and quantitative estimation of purines and pyrimidines in minute amounts. *J. Biol. Chem.* [1948] **176**, 703.

48-12.   Wieland, T., and Fischer, E.   Electrophoresis on filter paper (in German). *Naturwissenschaften* [1948] **35**, 29–30.

48-13.   Wieland, T.   Retention analysis and its usefulness for quantitative evaluation of paper chromatograms and paper ionophoretic patterns of artificial amino-acid mixtures (in German). *Angew. Chem.* [1948] **60**, 313.

48-14.   Williams, R. J., and Kirby, H.   Paper chromatography using capillary ascent. *Science* [1948] **107**, 481.

48-15.   Winegard, H. M., Toennies, G., and Block, R. J.   Detection of sulfur-containing amino acids on paper chromatograms. *Science* [1948] **108**, 506.

49-1.   Abramson, H. A.   Simplified preparative electrophoresis at room temperature. *Science* [1949] **110**, 716.

49-2.   Albanese, A. A., and Lein, M.   The chromatographic estimation of lysine and some applications of the method. *Science* [1949] **110**, 163.

49-3.   Aronoff, S.   Separation of the ionic species of lysine by means of partition chromatography. *Science* [1949] **110**, 590.

49-4.   Bull, H. B., Hahn, J. W., and Baptist, V. H.   Filter paper chromatography. *J. Am. Chem. Soc.* [1949] **71**, 550.

49-5.   Durrum, E. L.   A microelectrophoretic and microinophoretic technique. *Chem. & Eng. News* [1949] **27**, 601.

49-6.   Durrum, E. L.   A microelectrophoretic and microioinophoretic technique. Report Medical Dept. Field Research Lab., Fort Knox, Ky. Project No. 6-64-12-06 [1949].

49-7.   Durrum, E. L. Microelectrophoretic and microionophoretic technique. *Abstr. 115th Ann. Meeting, Am. Chem. Soc.* San Francisco [1949] p. 22c.

49-8.   Flood, H. Inorganic capillary analyses. *Discussions Faraday Soc.* [1949] **7**, 190.

49-9.   Fosdick, L. S., and Blackwell, R. Q. Scanning instrument for quantitative one-dimensional paper partition chromatography. *Science* [1949] **109**, 314.

49-10.   Garrison, W. M., Haymond, H. R., and Maxwell, R. D. A rapid electrical method of separating carrier-free radioactivities. *J. Chem. Phys.* [1949] **17**, 665.

49-10A. Grassmann, W. Process and apparatus for separating mixtures by means of cataphoresis. German Patent No. 805, 399, [1949] filed May 25.

49-11.   Hanes, C. A. and Isherwood, F. A. Separation of the phosphoric esters on the filter paper chromatogram. *Nature* [1949] **164**, 1107.

49-12.   Jermyn, M., and Isherwood, F. Improved separation of sugars on the paper partition chromatogram. *Biochem. J.* [1949] **44**, 402.

49-13.   Landua, A. J. and Awapara, J. Use of modified ninhydrin reagent in quantitative determinations of amino acids by paper chromatography. *Science* [1949] **109**, 385.

49-14.   Lederer, M. The paper chromatography of inorganic anions. *Australian J. Sci.* [1949] **11**, 174–175.

49-15.   Lederer, M. The paper partition chromatography of organic anions. *Australian. J. Sci.* [1949] **11**, 208.

49-16.   Lederer, M. Paper chromatography of some metals. *Australian J. Sci.* [1949] **12**, 78.

49-17.   Longenecker, W. H. Simplified partition chromatographic procedures. *Anal. Chem.* [1949] **21**, 1402.

49-18.   Partridge, S. M. Aniline hydrogen phthalate as a spraying reagent for chromatography of sugars. *Nature* [1949] **164**, 443.

49-19.   Patton, A. R., Foreman, E. M., and Wilson, P. C. Do amino acids fluoresce on papergrams? *Science* [1949] **110**, 593.

49-20.   Patton, A. R., and Foreman, E. M. Glycine reagent for paper chromatograms. *Science* [1949] **109**, 339.

49-21.   Roberts, E., and Frankel, S. Free amino acids in normal and neoplastic tissues of mice as studied by paper chromatography. *Cancer Research* [1949] **9**, 645–648.

49-21A. Rose, W. D., and Bruce, W. A. Evaluation of capillary character in petroleum reservoir rock. *Trans. Am. Inst. Mining Met. Engrs.* [1949] **186**, 127.

49-22.   Schneider, G. Blood serum in experimental amyloidosis. *Arch. pathol.* (in German). *Anat. u. Physiol. Virchow's* [1949] **317**, 26.

49-23.   Sease, J. W. Location of colorless chromatographic zones with an ultraviolet-sensitive multiplier phototube. *Anal. Chem.* [1949] **21**, 1430.

49-24.   Svensson, H., and Brattsten, I. An apparatus for continuous electrophoretic separation in flowing liquids. *Arkiv Kemi* [1949] **1**, 401–411.

49-25.   Synge, R. L. M., and Tiselius, A. Some adsorption experiments with aminoacids and peptides, especially compounds of tryptophan. *Acta Chem. Scand.* [1949] **3**, 231.

49-26.   Wender, S. H., and Gage, T. B. Paper chromatography of flavonoid pigments. *Science* [1949] **109**, 287.

49-27.   Wieland, T., Schmeiser, K., Fischer, E., and Maier-Leibritz, H. Quantitative determinations of alpha amino acids in paper chromatograms and ionophoretic patterns utilizing radioactive cooper (in German). *Naturwissenschaften* [1949] **36**, 280–281.

50-1. Beerstecher, E., Jr. Micromethod for estimation of potassium by paper chromatography. *Anal. Chem.* [1950] **22**, 1200.

50-2. Biserte, G., and Osteux, R. Separation of amino acids and polypeptides to the state of dinitrophenyl derivatives (in French). *Compt. rend.* [1950] **230**, 1404.

50-3. Biserte, G. Disposition of electrophoresis on paper (in French). *Biochim. et Biophys. Acta* [1950] **4**, 416.

50-4. Boursnell, J. C. A radioactivity scanning device for paper chromatograms using phosphorus-32. *Nature* [1950] **165**, 399.

50-5. Clegg, D. L. Paper chromatography. *Anal. Chem.* [1950] **22**, 48.

50-6. Consden, R., and Gordon, A. H. A study of the peptides of cystine in partial hydrolysates of wool. *Biochem. J.* [1950] **46**, 8–20.

50-7. Cremer, H. D., and Tiselius, A. Electrophoresis of serum on filter paper (in German). *Biochem. Z.* [1950] **320**, 273.

50-8. Drake, B. The use of polarography for automatic recording in the chromatography of proteins. *Acta Chem. Scand.* [1950] **4**, 554.

50-9. Durrum, E. L. A microelectrophoretic and microionophoretic technique. *J. Am. Chem. Soc.* [1950] **72**, 2943–2948.

50-10. Ewerbeck, H. The electrophoretic pattern of normal cerebrospinal fluid (in German). *Klin. Wochschr.* [1950] **28**, 692–693.

50-11. Franklin, A. E., and Quastel, J. H. Paper chromatography of protein mixtures and blood plasmas. *Proc. Soc. Exptl. Biol. Med.* [1950] **74**, 803.

50-12. Gal, E. M. Fluorescence of amino acids. *Science* [1950] **111**, 677.

50-13. Gardell, S., Gordon, A. H., and Aqvist, S. Electrophoresis of mucopolysaccharides in a slab of Hyflo-Super-Cel. *Acta Chem. Scand.* [1950] **4**, 907.

50-14. Goeller, J. P., and Sherry, S. Ultraviolet photography of paper chromatograms in the study of nucleic acids. *Proc. Soc. Exptl. Biol. Med.* [1950] **74**, 381.

50-15. Gordon, A. H., Keil, B., Šebesta, K., Knessl, O., and Šorm, F. Electrophoresis of proteins in agar jelly. *Collection Czechoslov. Chem. Communs.* [1950] **15**, 1.

50-16. Grassmann, W., and Hannig, K. A simple process for continuous separation of mixtures by filter paper electrophoresis (in German). *Naturwissenschaften* [1950] **37**, 397.

50-17. Grassmann, W., and Hannig, K. A simple process for the analysis of serum protein and other proteins mixtures (in German). *Naturwissenschaften* [1950] **37**, 496–497.

50-18. Grassmann, W. A process for separating substances by cataphoresis (in German). *Ber. ges. Physiol. u. exptl. Pharmakol.* [1950] **139**, 220.

50-19. Grassmann, W. A process for separating substances by cataphoresis (in German). *Z. Angew. Chem.* [1950] **62**, 170.

50-20. Gross, J., Leblong, C. P., Franklin, A. E., and Quastel, J. H. Presence of iodinated amino acids in unhydrolyzed thyroid and plasma. *Science* [1950] **111**, 605.

50-21. Hagland, H., and Tiselius, A. Zone electrophoresis in a glass powder column. *Acta Chem. Scand.* [1950] **4**, 957.

50-22. Hartmann, F., and Schumacher, G. Investigations on the systematic and biological variations in electrophoretic determinations of serum proteins. *Z. Naturforsch.* [1950] **5b**, 361.

50-23. Harvalik, Z. V. An electronic image converter and its use in chromatography. *Anal. Chem.* [1950] **22**, 1149.

50-24. Heftmann, E. Identification of estrogens by paper chromatography. *Science* [1950] **111**, 571.

50-25. Hoxter, G., and Mungioli, R. Electrophoretic changes in the serums of horses immunized against snake venom. *Intern. Congr. Microbiol. Abstr. Papers, 5th Congr. Rio de Janeiro* [1950] p. 202.

50-26. Körver, G. Electrophoresis on filter paper, a simple process for determination of serum proteins (in German). *Klin. Wochschr.* [1950] **28**, 693.

50-27. Kraus, K. A., and Smith, G. W. Electromigration on filter paper. *J. Am. Chem. Soc* [1950] **72**, 4329.

50-28. Magasanik, B., Vischer, E., Doniger, R., Elson, D. and Chargaff, E. The separation and estimation of ribonucleotides in minute quantities. *J. Biol. Chem.* [1950] **186**, 37.

50-29. Marshall, L. M., and DaCosta, W. A. Cumulative frequency distribution in manual chromatography. *Science* [1950] **111**, 155.

50-30. McDonald, H. J., Urbin, M. C., and Williamson, M. B. Measurement of ion migration of paper in an electric field. Transference numbers of nickel and copper sulphates. *Science* [1950] **112**, 227–229.

50-31. Miller, G. L., and Golder, R. H. Buffers of pH 2–12 for use in electrophoresis. *Arch. Biochem.* [1950] **29**, 420–423.

50-32. Rao, N. R., Shah, K. H., and Venkataraman, K. Chromatographic separation of dyes. *Curr. Sci.* [1950] **19**, 149.

50-33. Rockland, L. B., and Dunn, M. S. Partogrid, proportional divider for use in paper chromatography (partography). *Science* [1950] **111**, 332.

50-34. Tiselius, A. Electrophoresis and absorption analysis as a means for study of high molecular substances and their decomposition products. (in German). *Naturwissenschaften* [1950] **37**, 25–33.

50-35. Tiselius, A. Electrophoresis and chromatography in the chemistry of proteins (in French). *Rend. ist. super. sanità* [1950] **13**, 916.

50-36. Turba, F., and Enenkel, H. J. Electrophoresis of proteins on filter paper (in German). *Naturwissenschaften* [1950] **37**, 93.

50-37. Wender, S. H., Gage, T. B., and Douglas, C. D. Identification of flavinoid compounds by filter paper chromatography. *Handout Am. Chem. Soc. Meeting Chicago* [1950] Sept. 7th.

50-38. Wieland, T. and Wirth, L. Retention analysis of paper electropherograms. *Angew. Chem.* [1950] **62**, 473.

50-39. Zaffaroni, A., Burton, R. B., and Keutmann, E. H. Adrenal cortical hormones: Analysis by paper partition chromatography and occurrence in the urine of normal persons. *Science* [1950] **111**, 6.

51-1. Berkes, I. Electrophoresis as a tool in medicine and pharmacology (in Yugoslav with English summary). *Farm. Glasnik* [1951] **7**, 257–269.

51-2. Blackburn, S., and Lowther, A. G. The separation of N-2:4-Dinitrophenyl amino acids on paper chromatograms. *Biochem. J.* [1951] **48**, 126.

51-3. Brattsten, I., and Nilsson, A. A study in continuous zone electrophoresis in filter paper. *Arkiv Kemi* [1951] **3**, 337.

51-4. Ceccarini, F., and Zuccarini, N. Protein of blood in skin diseases (in Italian). *Ann. ital. dermatol. e sifilogr.* [1951] **8**, 337–344.

51-5. Davis, W. W., Parke, T. V., and Gamewell, R. Electrophoresis of proteins and small molecule electrolytes in agar-filled glass capillaries. *Abstr. 12th Intern. Congr. Pure and Appl. Chem.* [1951] p. 65.

51-6.   Dimmling, T., and Lutz, R.   Experimental bacteriological investigations on the effectiveness of hydroxyl ionophoresis (in German). *Deut. Zahnärztl. Z.* [1951 & 1952] **6**, 264 & 409.

51-7.   Durrum, E. L.   Paper ionophoresis. *Science* [1951] **113**, 66–68.

51-8.   Durrum, E. L.   Two dimensional electrophoresis and ionophoresis. *J. Colloid Sci.* [1951] **6**, 274–290.

51-9.   Durrum, E. L.   Continuous electrophoresis and ionophoresis on filter paper. *J. Am. Chem. Soc.* [1951] **73**, 4875–4880.

51-10. Eisenreich, F., and Eder, M.   A new method for the evaluation of paper electrophero-, ionophero-, and chromatograms (in German). *Klin. Wochschr.* [1951] **29**, 60.

51-11. English, A. C.   Separation of organic and inorganic compounds. *Science* [1951] **113**, 367.

51-12. Esser, H., Heinzler, Fr., Kazmeier, F., and Scholtan, W.   Quantitative serum fractionation by paper electrophoresis (in German). *Münch. med. Wochschr.* [1951] **93**, 985.

51-13. Flynn, F. V., and de Mayo, P.   Micro-electrophoresis of protein on filter-paper. *Lancet* [1951] **261**, 235–239.

51-14. Franklin, A. E., Quastel, J. H., and Van Straten, S. F.   Two dimensional chromatography of proteins. *Nature* [1951] **168**, 687.

51-15. Frierson, W., and Jones, J.   Radioactive tracers in paper partition chromatography of inorganic ions. *Anal. Chem.* [1951] **23**, 1447.

51-16. Fujisawa, Y.   Resolution of racemic amino acids on paper chromatograms. *Osaka City Med. J.* [1951] **1**, 7–13.

51-17. Goa, J.   A simplified method for the separation and quantitative determination of serum proteins by paper electrophoresis. *Scand. J. Clin. & Lab. Invest.* [1951] **3**, 236–240.

51-18. Gordon, A. H., and Reichard, P.   An electrophoretic investigation of the mixture of oligonucleotides formed by enzymic degradation of deoxyribonucleic acid by deoxyribonuclease. *Biochem. J.* [1951] **48**, 569.

51-19. Grassmann, W.   A new process for electrophoresis in the protein field (in German). *Naturwissenschaften* [1951] **38**, 200.

51-20. Grassmann, W., Hannig, K., and Knedel, M.   A process for electrophoretic determination of serum proteins on filter paper (in German). *Deut. med. Wochschr.* [1951] **76**, 333.

51-21. Gray, W.   Electrophoresis. *Sci. Am.* [1951] **185** (6), 45–53.

51-22. Hosoya, S., Soeda, M., Komutsu, N., Hara, N., Sonoda, Y., and Arai, R.   Antibiotics produced by a streptomyces, H-277 strain. *J. Antibiotics* (Japan) [1951] **4**, 313–316.

51-23. Hugentobler, F., Wunderly, C., and Schneider, G.   A preparative potentiality of paper electrophoresis: The structural analysis of protein fractions (in German). *Klin. Wochschr.* [1951] **29**, 705.

51-24. James, A. T., and Synge, R. L. M.   Non-peptide linkages in gramicidin. *Biochem. J.* [1951] **50**, 109.

51-25. Johnston, J. P., Ogston, A. G. and Stanier, J. E.   Modification of the Elson and Morgan Method for the estimation of glucosamine. *Analyst* [1951] **76**, 88.

51-26. Kanngiesser, W.   Paper electrophoresis of nucleic acids (in German). *Naturwissenschaften* [1951] **38**, 503.

51-27. Kashiwagi, T.   Electrophoresis of the Donaggio positive urine on filter paper. *Igaku to Seibutsugaku* [1951] **18**, 21–22; *Chem. Abstr.* **45**, 4768.

51-28. Köiw, E., Wallenius, G., and Gronwall, A.   Clinical use of electrophoresis on filter paper: Comparison with electrophoresis in a U-tube according to Tiselius method. *Bull. soc. chim. biol.* [1951] **33**, 1940–1950.

51-29. Körver, G.   The cause and significance of reduced gamma-globulin levels in blood serum in nursing infants (in German). *Monatsscher. Kinderheilk* [1951] **100**, 230.

51-30. Körver, G.   The serum pattern in acute rheumatic endocarditis of children (in German). *Z. Rheumaforsch.* [1951] **10**, 184.

51-31. Kritchevsky, T. H., and Tiselius, A.   Reversed phase partition chromatography of steroids on silicone-treated paper. *Science* [1951] **114**, 299.

51-32. Kunkel, H. G., and Tiselius, A.   Electrophoresis of proteins on filter paper. *J. Gen. Physiol.* [1951] **35**, 89.

51-33. Lederer, M., and Ward, F. L.   Micro-ionophoresis of inorganic ions. *Australian J. Sci.* [1951] **13**, 114.

51-34. Lederer, M.   Inorganic analysis by paper ionophoresis. *Nature* [1951] **167**, 864.

51-35. Lederer, M.   Filter paper electrophoresis. *Research* [1951] **4**, 371.

51-36. Lederer, M., and Cook, I.   Inorganic analysis by ionophoresis inside agar jelly. *Australian J. Sci.* [1951] **14**, 56.

51-37. Macheboeuf, M., Rebeyrotte, P., and Brunerie, M.   Applications to pathological serums, urines, and to ascites liquids by the method of paper microelectrophoresis (in French). *Bull. soc. chim. biol.* [1951] **33**, 1543–1551.

51-38. Markham, R., and Smith, J. D.   Structure of ribonucleic acid. *Nature* [1951] **168**, 406.

51-39. Markham, R., and Smith, J. D.   Chromatographic studies of nucleic acids. *Biochem. J.* [1951] **49**, 401.

51-40. Maurer, W., and Schild, K. T.   Paper electrophoresis of phosphorus-containing serum constituents studied with phosphorus[32] (in German). *Klin. Wochschr.* [1951] **29**, 514–515.

51-41. McDonald, H. J., Urbin, M. C., Marbach, E. P., and Williamson, M. B.   Isoelectric points of amino acids and proteins by ionography. *Federation Proc.* [1951] **10**, 218.

51-42. McDonald, H. J., Urbin, M. and Williamson, M. B.   Relation of movement to time in ionography. *J. Am. Chem. Soc.* [1951] **73**, 1893–1894.

51-43. McDonald, H. J., Urbin, M. C., and Williamson, M. B.   Ionography—some aspects of ion migration on paper in an electric field. *J. Colloid Sci.* [1951] **6**, 236–244.

51-44. McDonald, H. J., Urbin, M. C., and Williamson, M. B.   Ionography in the study of amino acids and proteins. *Abstr. 12th Intern. Congr. Pure and Appl. Chem.* [1951] pp. 67–68.

51-45. Michl, H.   Paper electrophoresis at field strengths of 50 volt/cm (in German). *Monatsh. Chem.* [1951] **82**, 489–493.

51-46. Michl, H., Riedl, K., and Wessely, F.   A chorionic gonadotropin (in German). *Monatsh. Chem.* [1951] **82**, 539.

51-47. Michl, H.   The quantitative evaluation of paper electrophoresis patterns (in German). *Monatsh. Chem.* [1951] **82**, 944.

51-48. Mills, G. T., and Smith, E. E. B.   The electrophoresis of enzymes of filter paper. *Biochem. J.* [1951] **49**, vi.

51-49. Nakamura, N.   The resolution of D,L-amino acids by means of paper chromatography. *Kagaku no Ryôiki* [1951] **5**, 457–461.

51-50. Pechar, J., and Hrabane, J.   Electrophoretic analysis of proteins precipitated from serum by acetone in the cold (in Czech). *Časopis lékáru čes-kých.* [1951] **90**, 225–227.

51-51.   Peniston, Q. P., Agar, H. and McCarthy, J. L.   Ionophoretic analyses in agar gels. *Anal. Chem.* [1951] **23**, 994–999.

51-52.   Perosa, L., and Raccuglia, G.   Applications of microelectrophoresis on paper (in Italian). *Boll. soc. ital. biol. sper.* [1951] **27**, 1590–1593.

51-53.   Pluckthun, H., and Gotting, H.   Contribution to the method of electrophoretic examinations of serum proteins on filter paper (in German). *Klin. Wochschr.* [1951] **29**, 415–418.

51-54.   Pollard, F. H. and McOmie, J. F. W.   The analysis of inorganic compounds by paper chromatography. *Endeavour* [1951] **10**, 213.

51-55.   Porath, J., and Flodin, P.   A new method for the detection of amino acids, peptides, proteins and other buffering substances on paper. *Nature* [1951] **168**, 202.

51-56.   Quagliariello, G., Guerritore, D., and Porcellati. G.   Chromatographic distribution on paper of nicotinic acid nicotinamide (in Italian). *Boll. soc. ital. biol. sper.* [1951] **27**, 1688–1691.

51-57.   Robinson, D., Smith, J. N., and Williams, R. T.   Studies in detoxication. 40: The metabolism of nitrobenzene in the rabbit. *o-*, *m-* and *p-*Nitrophenols, *o-*, *m-* and *p-*aminophenols and 4-nitrocatechol as metabolites of nitrobenzene. *Biochem. J.* [1951] **50**, 228–235.

51-58.   Schild, K., and Maurer, W.   Paper electrophoresis of hemolyzate from human erythrocytes with radioactive tracers (in German). *Naturwissenschaften* [1951] **38**, 303.

51-59.   Sato, J. R., Norris, W. P., and Strain, H. H.   Apparatus for the Continuous Resolution of Mixtures by Electromigration Plus Chromatography (Continuous Electro-Chromatography). Argonne National Laboratory. Publ. ANL-4724 Univ. Chicago Press, [1951] Chicago, Illinois.

51-60.   Schneider, G., and Wallenius, G.   Electrophoretic studies on cerebrospinal fluid proteins. *Scand. J. Clin. & Lab. Invest.* [1951] **3**, 145.

51-61.   Schneider, G.   Use of paper electrophoresis for serum proteins (in German). *Acta Chem. Scand.* [1951] **5**, 1020.

51-62.   Schwartz, V.   Micro-electrophoresis on filter paper. *Nature* [1951] **167**, 404.

51-63.   Smellie, R. M. S., and Davidson, J. N.   The separation of nucleotides by ionophoresis. *Biochem. J.* [1951] **49**, xv.

51-64.   Spiegler, K. S., and Coryell, C. D.   Electromigration in a cation exchange resin. *Science* [1951] **113**, 546.

51-65.   Strain, H. H., and Sullivan, J. C.   Analysis by electromigration plus chromatography. *Anal. Chem.* [1951] **23**, 816.

51-66.   Suzuki, T., and Maekawa, Y.   Microelectrophoresis and microionophoresis of amino acids and biogenic amines with filter paper (in Japanese). *Yakugaku Zasshi* [1951] **71**, 1298–1300.

51-67.   Swank, R. L., Franklin, A. E., and Quastel, J. H.   Paper chromatography of blood plasma in multiple sclerosis. *Proc. Soc. Exptl. Biol. Med.* [1951] **76**, 183.

51-68.   Synge, R. L. M.   Methods for isolating ω-amino-acids: γ-aminobutyric acid from rye grass. *Biochem. J.* [1951] **48**, 429.

51-69.   Synge, R. L. M.   Non-protein nitrogenous constituents of rye grass: Ionophoretic fractionation and isolation of a "bound amino-acid" fraction. *Biochem. J.* [1951] **49**, 642–650.

51-70. Tiselius, A. Recent developments of zone electrophoresis methods. *Abstr. 12th Intern. Congr. Pure and Appl. Chem.* [1951] pp. 67.

51-71. Tiselius, A. Electrophoresis methods in biochemistry. *Scientia* [1951] (*Milan*) **86,** 163.

51-72. Toennies, G., and Kolb, J. J. Techniques and reagents for paper chromatography. *Anal. Chem.* [1951] **23,** 823.

51-73. Turba, F., and Enenkel, H. J. Separation of derivatives of ATP by ionophoresis (in German). *Naturwissenschaften* [1951] **38,** 189.

51-74. Turba, F., and Turba, M. Separation of derivatives of the adenosintriphosphoric acid (ATP) by distribution chromatography in filter paper (in German). *Naturwissenschaften* [1951] **38,** 188.

51-75. Wallenfels, K., and Pechmann, E. V. Separation of enzyme mixtures by electrophoresis on filter paper (in German). *Angew. Chem.* [1951] **63,** 44.

51-76. Wallenius, G. A note on serum iron transportation. *Scand. J. Clin. & Lab. Invest.* [1951] **4,** 24.

51-77. Weber, R. Technique and application of paper ionophoresis (in German). *Helv. Chim. Acta* [1951] **34,** 2031–2042.

51-78. Wieland, T. and Bauer, L. Further attempts to separate purines and amino acids by paper chromatography and ionophoresis (in German). *Angew. Chem.* [1951] **63,** 511.

51-79. Wieland, T., and Feld, U. Paper chromatography and ionophoresis of oxycarbon acids and their quantitative determination (on retention analysis) (in German). *Angew. Chem.* [1951] **63,** 258.

51-80. Williams, R. R., and Smith, R. E. A continuously recording scanning device for radio-chromatographic analysis of labelled antigen-antibody reactions. *Proc. Soc. Exptl. Biol. Med.* [1951] **77,** 169.

51-81. Witmer, R. Electrophoresis of pathological human aqueous humor (in German). *Experientia* [1951] **7,** 347.

51-82. Wunderly, C., Schneider, G., and Hugentobler, F. The paper electrophoretic method and first experiences (in German). *Compt. rend. 3° congr. soc. intern. europ. hematol. (Rome)* [1951] p. 240.

51-83. Yajima, B., Matsume, H. and Kihibana, H. The migration of ions on an ion-exchange column through the influence of an electric current. *Japan. Chem. J.* [1951] **62,** 234.

51-84. Zittle, C. A. Reaction of borate with substances of biological interest. *Advances in Enzymol.* [1951] **12,** 493–527.

52-1. Acher, R., and Crocker, C. Specific color reactions for arginine and tyrosine after chromatography. *Biochim. et Biophys. Acta* [1952] **9,** 704–705.

52-2. Albon, N., and Gross, D. A uniform-temperature drying oven for quantitative chromatography. *Analyst* [1952] **77,** 406.

52-3. Anderson, A. B. The direct determination of nitrogen in protein fractions separated by electrophoresis in filter paper. *Biochem. J.* [1952] **52,** x.

52-4. Anderson, J. R. A., and Lederer, M. Quantitative analysis by electrochromatography on paper. I. Separation and gravimetric determination of copper. *Anal. Chim. Acta* [1952] **6,** 472–475.

52-5. Angela, G. C., and Ambrosini, C. The electrophoresis pattern in experimental q fever. *Giorn. mal. infettive e parassit.* [1952] **4,** 187–188.

52-6. Anonymous. Bibliograghy of paper chromatography (in German). No. 2. Carl Schleicher and Schull, Dassel/Kr. Einbeck. [1952].

52-7. Antonini, F. M., and Piva, G. Electrophoresis of the liquid of vesicles caused by Cantharides (in Italian). *Boll. soc. ital. biol. sper.* [1952] **28**, 761.

52-8. Antonini, F. M., and Piva, G. Paper electrophoresis (in Italian). *Boll. soc. ital. biol. sper.* [1952] **28**, 764.

52-9. Antonini, F. M., and Piva, G. Electrophoretic fractionation of serum of certain animals. *Boll. soc. ital. biol. sper.* [1952] **28**, 1887–1889.

52-10. Antonini, F. M., and Piva, G. Improved technique for electrophoresis on paper. *Boll. soc. ital. biol. sper.* [1952] **28**, 1885–1886.

52-11. Ardry, R. A clinical survey of serum proteins, electrophoresis, non-specific reactions and selective dosages. *Ann. biol. clin. (Paris)* [1952] **10**, 575.

52-12. Balston, J. N., and Talbot, B. E. "A Guide to Filter Paper and Cellulose Powder-Chromatography." H. Reeve Angel, London. [1952].

52-13. Barbagallo-Sangiorgi, G. Correspondence of the results of electrophoresis on paper with those obtained by the classical Nernst electrophoresis (in Italian). *Boll. soc. ital. biol. sper.* [1952] **28**, 1956.

52-14. Barbagallo-Sangiorgi, G., and Cajozzo, A. The behavior of the lipoprotein complexes of the serum in human arteriosclerosis. *Boll. soc. ital. biol. sper.* [1952] **28**, 1523–1525.

52-15. Barbagallo-Sangiorgi, G. The modification produced by delipidization on the electrophoretic diagram of the serum proteins in a subject with hyper-γ-globulinemia. *Boll. soc. ital. biol. sper.* [1952] **28**, 1522–1523.

52-16. Bennhold, H., Kallee, E., and Roth, E. Paper electrophoretic separation of proteins (in German). *Z. Naturforsch.* [1952] **7b**, 324.

52-17. Berkes, I. and Karas, V. Paper electrophoresis. I. The influence of the conductivity of the buffer on the degree of separation of the component of a mixture of proteins (in Czech). *Arkiv Kemi* [1952] **24**, 73.

52-18. Bockemuller, W., and Rebling, R. Apparatus for preparative electrophoresis (in German). *Chem.-Ing.-Tech.* [1952] **24**, 617.

52-19. Boussemart, E., and Marchand, M. Application of electrophoresis on paper to the examination of nursing infants' serum (in French). *Bull. soc. pharm. Bordeaux* [1952] **90**, 206.

52-20. Brante, G. Paper electrophoresis in the diagnostics of liver and bile duct diseases. *Scand. J. Clin. & Lab. Invest.* [1952] **4**, 293.

52-21. Brattsten, I. Continuous zone electrophoresis by crossed velocity fields in a glass powder column. The arrangement of a constant liquid flow and description of a single pump apparatus. *Arkiv Kemi* [1952] **4**, 503–522.

52-22. Bruggemann, J., and Drepper, K. Determination of amino acids on paper chromatograms (in German). *Naturwissenschaften* [1952] **39**, 301.

52-23. Bucher, T., Matzelt, D., and Pette, D. Paper electrophoresis of cerebrospinal fluid (in German). *Klin. Wochschr.* [1952] **30**, 325.

52-24. Bucher, T., Matzelt, D., and Pette, D. Paper electrophoretic patterns of the proteins of cerebrospinal fluid (in German). *Naturwissenschaften* **39**, 114.

52-25. Caspani, R. Paper electrophoresis. *Progr. Med.* [1952] **7**, 494–499.

52-26. Caspani, R., and Sticca, C. Electrophoretic analysis of the proteins of cerebrospinal fluid of acute non-purulent meningococcal meningitis (in Italian). *Minerva med.* [1952] II, 749–750.

52-27. Caspani, R., and Bernasconi, A. Advantages and limitations of paper electrophoresis compared to classical electrophoresis (in Italian). *Minerva med.* [1952] II, 1289.

52-28. Caspani, R. The application of electrophoresis to the study of normal cerebrospinal fluid (in Italian). *Minerva med.* [1952] II, 1346.

52-29. Cassidy, H. G. Investigation of paper chromatography: Flow of fluid in
filter paper. *Anal. Chem.* [1952] **24,** 1415.

52-30. Choisy, A., Derrien, Y., and Jayle, G. Paper electrophoretic comparison of
the proteins of the human and beef crystalline lens. *Compt. rend.* [1952]
234, 1918–1920.

52-31. Consden, R., and Stanier, W. M. A simple paper electrophoresis apparatus.
Nature [1952] **170,** 1069–1070.

52-32. Consden, R., and Stanier, W. M. Ionophoresis of sugars on paper and some
applications to the analysis of protein polysaccharide complexes. *Nature*
[1952] **169,** 783.

52-33. Coursaget, J., Gros, P., and Macheboeuf, M. Variations of the rate of degradation of serum γ-globulins with the duration of their presence in the
organism (in French). *Bull. soc. chim. biol.* [1952] **34,** 1078.

52-34. Crook, E. M., Harris, M., and Warren, F. L. Continuous direct photometry
of proteins separated by electrophoresis in filter paper. *Biochem. J.*
[1952] **51,** xxvi–xxvii.

52-35. Davidson, J. N., and Smellie, R. M. S. Phosphorus compounds in the cell.
II. Separation by ionophoresis on paper of the constituent nucleotides
of ribonucleic acid. *Biochem. J.* [1952] **52,** 594–599.

52-36. Deimel, M., and Maurer, W. Paper electrophoretic separation of ribonucleic
acid and desoxyribonucleic acid (in German). *Naturwissenschaften* **39,**
489.

52-37. Deiss, W. P., Albright, E. C., and Larson, F. C. A study of the nature of
the circulating thyroid hormone in euthyroid and hyperthyroid subjects
by use of paper electrophoresis. *J. Clin. Invest.* [1952] **31,** 1000.

52-38. Deiss, W. P., Albright, W. C., and Larson, F. C. A study of the nature of
the circulating thyroid hormone in euthyroid and hyperthyroid subjects
by use of paper electrophoresis. *J. Lab. Clin. Med.* [1952] **40,** 791.

52-39. Denffer, D., Behrens, M., and Fischer, A. Paper electrophoretic separation
of indole derivatives from plant extracts. (in German) *Naturwissenschaften* [1952] **39,** 258–259.

52-40. Denffer, D., Behrens, M., and Fischer, A. Paper-chromatographic and paper-electrophoretic detection of beta-indoleacetonitrile and of beta-
indolecarboxaldehyde in extracts from cabbage leaves (in German).
Naturwissenschaften. [1952] **39,** 550.

52-41. Dimroth, K., Jaenicke, L., and Vollbrechtshausen, I. Paper electrophoretic
differentiation of end products of nucleic acids (in German). *Z. physiol.
Chem.* [1952] **289,** 71–77.

52-42. Douste-Blazy, L., Polonovski, J., and Valdiguie, P. Fractionation of lipids
by countercurrent partition chromatography on paper (in French).
Compt. rend. [1952] **235,** 1643–1645.

52-43. Durrum, E. L., Paul, M. H., and Smith, E. R. B. Lipid detection in paper
electrophoresis. *Science* [1952] **116,** 428–430.

52-44. Ericson, L. E., Banhidi, Z. G., and Gasparetto, G. Separation of growth
factors for *Lactobacillus lactis, Lactobacillus leichmannii,* and *Leuconostoc
citrovorum* by means of ionophoresis on paper. *Acta Chem. Scand.* [1952]
6, 1130–1132.

52-45. Esser, H., Heinzler, F., Kazmeier, F., and Scholtan, W. A comparative study of the separation of serum protein fractions by means of paper electrophoresis and the moving boundary method of Tiselius (in German). *Arztl. Forsch.* [1952] **6**(1), 156.

52-46. Esser, H., Heinzler, F., and Wild, H.   A simple process for the concentration of cerebrospinal fluid for the determination of protein fractions by means of filter paper electrophoresis (in German). *Klin. Wochschr.* [1952] **30**, 228.

52-47. Esser, H., and Heinzler, F.   A method for concentrating cerebrospinal fluid and other dilute protein solutions for paper electrophoresis by filtration under pressure (in German). *Klin. Wochschr.* [1952] **30**, 600.

52-48. Esser, H. and Heinzler, F.   Electrophoretic protein analyses in cerebrospinal fluid (in German). *Deut. med. Wochschr.* [1952] **77**, 1329–1330.

52-49. Esser, H.   Electrophoretic analysis of cerebrospinal fluid proteins and its clinical significance (in German). *Münch. med. Wochschr.* [1952] **94**, 2313-2318.

52-50. Evans, E. E., and Walls, K. W.   The separation of biological stains by filter paper electrophoresis. *J. Bacteriol.* [1952] **63**, 422–423.

52-51. Fasoli, A.   Electrophoresis of serum lipoproteins on filter-paper. *Lancet* [1952] **262**, 106.

52-52. Fasoli, A.   Electrophoresis on paper and in microcell of serum protein: Comparison of the results of both methods (in Italian). *Bull. soc. ital. biol. sper.* [1952] **28**, 601.

52-53. Fischer, A., and Behrens, M.   Preparative paper chromatography and electrophoresis (in German). *Z. physiol. Chem.* [1952] **291**, 14–15.

52-54. Foster, A. B.   Separation of the dimethyl-L-rhamnopyranoses by ionophoresis. *Chem. & Ind. (London)* [1952] pp. 828–829.

52-55. Foster, A. B.   A simplified apparatus for filter paper ionophoresis. *Chem. & Ind. (London)* [1952] p. 1050.

52-56. Frunder, H., and Bornig, H.   Paper electrophoresis of lipid-free human serum (in German). *Z. ges. inn. Med. u. ihre Grenzgebiete* [1952] **7**, 855.

52-57. Frunder, M. A., and Frunder, H.   The electrophoretic pattern of retroplacental serum (in German). *Z. ges. inn. Med. u. ihre Grenzgebiete* [1952] **7**, 318–321.

52-58. Ganzin, M., Macheboeuf, M., and Rebeyrotte, P.   Comparison by paper microelectrophoresis of the proteins of blood serum from various species of mammals (in French). *Bull. soc. chim. biol.* [1952] **34**, 26.

52-59. Ganzin, M., and Macheboeuf, M.   Application of paper microelectrophoresis to the isolation of undenatured and homogeneous serum protein fractions of very small volume (in French). *Bull. soc. chim. biol.* [1952] **34**, 32.

52-60. Geschwind, I. I., and Li, C. H.   The reaction of bromphenol blue with amino acids and peptides. *J. Am. Chem. Soc.* [1952] **74**, 834–835.

52-61. Gillespie, J. M., Jermyn, M. A., and Woods, E. F.   Multiple nature of the enzymes of *Aspergillus oryzae* and of horse-radish. *Nature* [1952] **169**, 487–488.

52-62. Goa, J.   Discussion. *Scand. J. Clin. & Lab. Invest.* [1952] **4**, 310–312.

52-63. Gordon, A. H., Gross, J., O'Connor, D., and Pitt-Rivers, R.   Nature of the circulating thyroid hormone-plasma protein complex. *Nature* [1952] **169**, 19-20.

52-64. Gras, J.   Paper electrophoresis of normal and pathological serum proteins (in Spanish). *Rev. españ. fisiol.* [1952] **8**, 59.

52-65. Gräsbeck, R.   Serum protein changes following upon mycoardial infarction studied by means of paper electrophoresis (in Swedish with English summary). *Finska Läksällsk. Handlingar* [1952] **95,** 187.

52-66. Grassmann, W., and Hannig, K. A quantitative technique for analysis of serum proteins by means of paper electrophoresis (in German). *Z. physiol. Chem.* [1952] **290,** 1–27.

52-67. Not assigned.

52-68. Gray, R. A. Chromatography and electrophoresis of plant viruses on filter paper. *Arch. Biochem. Biophys.* [1952] **38,** 305.

52-69. Gregoire, J., and Derrien, Y. Distribution of cholinesterase activity in the protein fractions of human serum and horse serum as separated by electrophoresis on paper (in French). *Compt. rend. soc. biol.* [1952] **146,** 1491.

52-70. Griffiths, L. L. A direct scanning apparatus for reading electrophoretic paper strips. *J. Clin. Pathol.* [1952] **5,** 294.

52-71. Gronwall, A. On paper electrophoresis in the clinical laboratory. *Scand. J. Clin. & Lab. Invest.* [1952] **4,** 270–280.

52-72. Gros, P., Dubert, J. M., Sung, S. S., Coursaget, J., and Macheboeuf, M. Study of the rapidity of renewal of immune bodies and other protein fractions of blood serum by valine tagged with carbon[13] in its isopropyl grouping (in French). *Bull. soc. chim. biol.* [1952] **34,** 37.

52-73. Hanson, H., and Wenzel, M. Paper chromatographic detection of serum peptidases (in German). *Naturwissenschaften* [1952] **39,** 403.

52-74. Hartmann, F., and Muller, H. J. Preparative paper electrophoresis (in German). *Naturwissenschaften* [1952] **39,** 282.

52-75. Hasimoto, Y., Mori, I., and Kimura, M. Paper electromigration of flavonoids and sugars using a high constant-voltage current. *Nature* [1952] **170,** 975.

52-76. Hashimoto, Y., and Mori, I. High frequency papyrography: An apparatus for detecting substances on a filter paper by means of high frequency oscillators (in Japanese). *J. Pharm. Soc. Japan* [1952] **72,** 1532.

52-77. Henning, N., and Kinzlmeier, H. Electrophoretic examination of human gastric juice (in German). *Deut. med. Wochschr.* [1952] **77,** 998.

52-78. Hensley, W. J., and Blackburn, C. R. B. Electrophoretic identification of. serum haemochromogens on filter paper. *Australian J. Sci.* [1952] **15,** 66

52-79. Hohne, G., Jaster, R., and Kunkel, H. A. Electrophoretic measurements on the serum of roentgen-irradiated rats (in German). *Klin. Wochschr.* [1952] **30,** 952.

52-80. von Holt, C., Voight, K. D., and Gaede, K. Paper electrophoresis of proteins at increased voltages (in German). *Biochem. Z.* [1952] **323,** 345.

52-81. Homolka, J. Polarographic examination of blood proteins combined with electrophoresis. *Radiometer Polarographics* [1952] **1,** 110.

52-82. Hradec, J. Microelectrophoresis (in Czech, English summary). *Časopis lékárů českých* [1952] **91,** 1062.

52-83. Hubener, H. J., Bode, F, Mollat, H. J., and Wehner, M. Determination of urea on paper chromatograms (in German). *Z. physiol. Chem.* [1952] **290,** 136–138.

52-84. Imperato, C. Serum proteins in the nursling in normal and pathological conditions determined electrophoretically (in Italian). *Boll. soc. ital. biol. sper.* [1952] **28,** 875.

52-85. Jaenicke, L. The paper electrophoresis of sugars and sugar derivatives (in German). *Naturwissenschaften* [1952] **39,** 86.

52-86. Jaenicke, L., and Vollbrechtshausen, I. The paper electrophoretic separation of ribosides as borate complexes (in German). *Naturwissenschaften* [1952] **39**, 86–87.

52-87. Not assigned.

52-88. Jayle, M. F., Boussier, G., and Badin, J.   The electrophoresis of haptoglobin and its complex with hemoglobin (in French). *Congr. intern. biochim.*, *2ᵉ Congr., Paris* [1952] Résumés des communs. p. 183.

52-89. Jermyn, M. A.   Horse-radish peroxidase. *Nature* [1952] **169**, 488–489.

52-90. Kallee, E.   Insulin marked with iodine[131]. I. Detection (in German). *Z. Naturforsch.* [1952] **7b**, 661–663.

52-91. Karas, V. and Berkes, I.   The paper electrophoresis of the blood serum and the proteins in urine as a method for differential diagnosis in nephrosis. *Acta Pharma. Jugoslavica* [1952] **8**, 103.

52-92. Karsner, W. T., and Sanford, A. H.   Different methods for paper electrophoresis. *Year Book Pathol. and Clin. Pathol.* [1952] p. 298.

52-93. Kautzsch, E., Oswald, A., and Hofmann, G.   Paper electrophoresis in the clinic (in German). *Münch. med. Wochschr.* [1952] **94**, 921.

52-94. Kehl, R., and Stich, W.   Analysis of porphyrins and some bile pigments by paper chromatography. II. (in German). *Z. physiol. Chem.* [1952] **290**, 151.

52-95. Kickhöfen, B., and Westphal, O.   Paper electrophoresis at high potentials for separation of peptides (in German). *Z. Naturforsch.* [1952] **7b**, 655–659.

52-96. Kickhöfen, B., and Westphal, O.   A simple combination of paper electrophoresis and paper chromatography (in German). *Z. Naturforsch.* [1952] **7b**, 659–660.

52-97. Kirk, P. L., and Duggan, E. L.   Biochemical analysis. *Anal. Chem.* [1952] **24**, 124.

52-98. Knedel, M.   The clinical significance of paper electrophoresis for drug research (in German). *Arzneimittel-Forsch.* [1952] **2**, 182.

52-99. Köiw, E., Wallenius, G., and Gronwall, A.   Paper electrophoresis in clinical chemistry. *Scand. J. Clin. & Lab. Invest.* [1952] **4**, 47.

52-100. Köiw, E., and Gronwall, A.   Staining of protein-bound carbohydrates after electrophoresis of serum on filter paper. *Scand. J. Clin. & Lab. Invest.* [1952] **4**, 244–246.

52-101. Köiw, E.   Paper electrophoresis (in Swedish). *Sartryck ur Nordisk Med.* [1952] **47**, 736.

52-102. Kritchevsky, D., and Kirk, M.   Paper chromatography of steroids. *J. Am. Chem. Soc.* [1952] **74**, 4484.

52-103. Kruh, J., Dreyfus, J. C., and Schapira, G.   Biochemistry of hemoglobin studies with the aid of radioactive iron. III. Fractionation of the hemoglobins of the adult rabbit by paper chromatography (in French). *Bull. soc. chim. biol.* [1952] **34**, 773–777.

52-104. Kunkel, H. G., and Slater, R. J.   Lipoprotein patterns of serum obtained by zone electrophoresis. *J. Clin. Invest.* [1952] **31**, 677–684.

52-105. Kunkel, H. G., and Slater, R. J.   Zone electrophoresis in a starch supporting medium. *Proc. Soc. Exptl. Biol. Med.* [1952] **80**, 42.

52-106. Kutzim, H.   Blood proteins and antibiotics in paper electrophoresis (in German). *Klin. Wochschr.* [1952] **39**, 852.

52-107. Kutzim, H.   On the behavior of blood proteins toward the sulfanilamides in paper electrophoresis (in German). *Naturwissenschaften* [1952] **39**, 135.

52-108. Larson, F., Deiss, W. P., and Albright, E. C. Localization of protein bound radioactive iodine by filter paper electrophoresis. *Science* [1952] **115**, 626.

52-109. Laskowski, D. E., and Putscher, R. E. Dielectric indicator for column chromatography. *Anal. Chem.* [1952] **24**, 965.

52-110. Latner, A. L., Braithwaite, F., and Nunn, R. A. A photoelectric scanning device for electrophoresis on filter paper. *Biochem. J.* [1952] **51**, 10.

52-111. Latner, A. L. An apparatus for electrophoresis on filter paper. *Biochem. J.* [1952] **51**, 12.

52-112. Latner, A. L., and Richardson, M. W. A visual matching technique for paper electrophoresis of serum proteins. *Biochem. J.* [1952] **51**, xxxi.

52-113. Latner, A. L. A quantitative study in relation to electrophoresis of the staining of serum proteins on filter paper with naphthalene black. *Biochem. J.* [1952] **52**, xxix–xxx.

52-114. Latner, A. L., Raine, L., Ross, G. I. M., and Ungley, C. C. A preparative paper electrophoresis technique and its application to vitamin B_{12} binding in serum. *Biochem. J.* [1952] **52**, xxxiii.

52-115. Lederer, M. Paper chromatography of acridines. *Anal. Chim. Acta* [1952] **6**, 267–269.

52-116. Lederer, M. "Progrès récents de la chromatographie" 2e partie (Chimie minérale). Hermann, Paris. [1952]

52-117. Lederer, M., and Ward, F. L. Paper electrochromatography of inorganic substances. *Anal. Chim. Acta* [1952] **6**, 355.

52-118. Lederer, M. Electrochromatography inside filter paper. II. Diffusion and its effect on electrophoretic separations. *Anal. Chim. Acta* [1952] **6**, 521.

52-119. Levin, B., and Oberholzen, V. G. Paper electrophoresis of serum proteins. *Nature* [1952] **170**, 123.

52-120. Li, C. H. Preparation and properties of a highly active adrenocorticotropic hormone preparation. *J. Am. Chem. Soc.* [1952] **74**, 2124–2125.

52-121. Loos, R. Electrophoresis and ionophoresis on paper (in Dutch). *Mededel. Vlaam. Chem. Ver.* [1952] **14**, 135.

52-122. Macheboeuf, M., and Rebeyrotte, P. Several advantages of the microelectrophoresis of proteins (in French). *Rev. hématol.* [1952] **7**, 400–406.

52-123. Malmros, A. H., and Swahn, B. Lipoprotein studies (in Swedish with English summary). *Nord. Med.* [1952] **48**, 1028.

52-124. Manecke, G. Separation of ions in ion exchange columns by ionophoresis (in German). *Naturwissenschaften* [1952] **39**, 62.

52-125. Mariani, A. Perfecting microelectrophoresis techniques on paper (in Italian). *Rend. ist. super. sanità* [1952] **15**, 337–343.

52-126. Maurer, H. J. Autoradiography in paper electrophoretic and chromatographic experiments with radioactive isotopes (in German). *Röntgen Bl.* [1952] **5**, 185.

52-127. Maurer, W. The transport function of individual serum protein fractions for phosphatides (in German). *Klin. Wochschr.* [1952] **30**, 323.

52-128. Maurer, W., and Reichenbach, L. The binding of organic iodine in serum to the individual serum protein fractions (in German). *Naturwissenschaften* [1952] **39**, 261.

52-129. McDonald, H. J., and Marbach, E. P. Fractionation of an ACTH preparation by ionography. *J. Am. Chem. Soc.* [1952] **74**, 1619.

52-130. McDonald, H. J. Ionography: A new frontier in electrophoresis. *J. Chem. Educ.* [1952] **29**, 428–437.

52-131. Merklen, F. P., and Masseyeff, R. Adsorption of albumin as a cause of error in the quantitative estimation of serum proteins by electrophoresis on filter paper (in French). *Compt. rend. soc. biol.* [1952] **146**, 1905–1908.

52-132. Micheel, F., and van der Kamp, F. P. Separation of sugar mixtures by combined electrophoresis and paper chromatography (in German). *Angew. Chem.* [1952] **64**, 607–608.

52-133. Michl, H. Quantitative evaluation of filter paper electrophoresis patterns (in German). *Monatsh. Chem.* [1952] **83**, 210–220.

52-134. Michl, H. Paper ionophoresis at field strengths of 50 volts/cm. (in German). *Monatsh. Chem.* [1952] **83**, 737.

52-135. Miller, J. M., and Rockland, L. B. Determination of cysteine and glutathione in citrus juices by filter paper chromatography. *Arch. Biochem. Biophys.* [1952] **40**, 416.

52-136. Mould, D. L., and Asynge, R. L. M. Electrokinetic ultrafiltration analysis of polysaccharides: A new approach to the chromatography of large molecules. *Analyst* [1952] **77**, 964–970.

52-137. Muller, A., Bersin, T., and Schwarz, H. Studies concerning iron-3-saccharate: A new rapid method for paper chromatographic sugar detection (in German). *Schweiz. med. Wochschr.* [1952] **82**, 765.

52-138. Muller, D. C. Instrumental approaches to paper chromatography. *Analyst* [1952] **77**, 933.

52-139. Munich, W. Paper electrophoretic investigation of the proteins in the chamber fluid of the rabbit (in German). *Klin. Wochschr.* [1952] **30**, 849–850.

52-140. Neher, R., and Wettstein, A. Paper chromatography of weakly polar steroids (in German). *Helv. Chim. Acta* [1952] **35**, 276.

52-141. Heumann, W., and Habermann, E. Paper electrophoretic fractionation of animal poisons (in German). *Naturwissenschaften* [1952] **39**, 286.

52-142. Niedermeier, S. Quantitative fractionation of proteins of the aqueous humor. I. (in German). *Klin. Monatshbl. Augenheilk.* [1952] **120**, 644–645.

52-143. Nikkilä, E., Ekholm, K., and Silvola, H. Paper electrophoresis of enzymes: Amylase and trypsin. *Acta Chem. Scand.* [1952] **6**, 617.

52-144. Nikkilä, E. Distribution of lipids in serum protein fractions separated by electrophoresis in filter paper. *Ann. Med. Exptl. et Biol. Fenniae (Helsinki)* [1952] **30**, 331.

52-145. Nikkilä, E. A. The effect of heparin on serum lipoproteins. *Scand. J. Clin. & Lab. Invest.* [1952] **4**, 369.

52-146. Niklas, A., and Maurer, W. The rate of incorporation of S^{35}-L-methionine after oral administration in individually separated serum protein fractions (in German). *Naturwissenschaften* [1952] **39**, 260.

52-147. Norpoth, L., Cloesges, J., Finger, M., and Schulze, M. Electrophoretic studies on human gastric juice (in German). *Deut. med. Wochschr.* [1952] **77**, 563–564.

52-148. Noverraz, M. Determination of serum proteins by electrophoresis on filter paper (in French). *Schweiz. med. Wochschr.* [1952] **82**, 880.

52-149. Nowotny, A. The application of electrophoresis on filter paper (in German). *Acta Physiol. Acad. Sci. Hung.* [1952] **3**, 469.

52-150. Ortega, M. Electrophoresis on filter paper. I. Addition compounds of butyl bromide with 4-vinylpyridine-styrene copolymers (in French). *Anales real acad. farm.* [1952] **18**, 449–458.

52-151. Ott, H., Huber, H., and Korver, G. A comparison of electrophoresis according to the methods of Tiselius, Antweiller, and Turba (in German). *Klin. Wochschr.* [1952] **30**, 34.

52-152. Paladini, A. C., and Leloir, L. F. Detection of ultraviolet absorbing substances on paper chromatograms. *Anal. Chem.* [1952] **24**, 1024.

52-153. Paléus, S. Cytochrome c with the aid of paper electrophoresis. *Acta Chem. Scand.* [1952] **6**, 969.

52-154. Papastomatis, S. C., and Kensch, J. E. Ionophoretic separation of porphyrin pigments. *Nature* [1952] **170**, 33–34.

52-155. Parke, T. V., and Davis, W. W. Automatic spectrophotometry of paper strip chromatograms. *Anal. Chem.* [1952] **24**, 2019.

52-156. Pasternak, C., and Kent, P. Paper electrophoresis of chondroitin sulfates and other acidic carbohydrates. *Research* [1952] **5**, 486.

52-157. Paul, M. H., and Durrum, E. L. Ionophoresis in non-aqueous solvent systems. *J. Am. Chem. Soc.* [1952] **74**, 4721–4722.

52-158. Peter, H., Hanser, A., and Amelung, D. The influence of a "pure" immunizing procedure on the electrophoretic pattern of serum protein (in German). *Z. Immunitätsforsch.* [1952] **109**, 383–394.

52-159. Pezold, F. A. The solution of carcinogenic hydrocarbons in blood serum (in German). *Naturwissenschaften* [1952] **21**, 493.

52-160. Pittoni, A., and Trivellato, E. Electrophoresis of serous proteins in the presence of hemoglobin (in Italian). *Atti ist. veneto sci. lettere ed arti, Classe sci. mat. nat.* [1952–53] **111**, 69–76.

52-161. Ponder, E. Separation and assay of lysins and lysin-inhibitor complexes in blood and tissues. *J. Gen. Physiol.* [1952] **35**, 361.

52-162. Ponder, E., and Nesmith, J. Hemolsyins in spontaneous mouse breast tumors as compared to those in normal mouse tissue. *Cancer Research* [1952] **12**, 104.

52-163. Poulik, M. D. Filter paper electrophoresis of purified diphtheria toxoid. *Can. J. Med. Sci.* [1952] **30**, 417.

52-164. Quastel, J. H., and Van Straten, S. F. Protein separations and interactions on filter paper. *Proc. Soc. Exptl. Biol. Med.* [1952] **81**, 6.

52-165. Rafsky, H. A., Brill, A. A., Stern, K. G., and Corey, H. Electrophoretic studies on the serum of "normal" aged individuals. *Am. J. Clin. Sci.* [1952] **224**, 522.

52-166. Raynaud, R., d'Eshougues, J., Bourgarel, R., Cruck, S., and Karoubi, E. α-Globulin in febrile heart diseases (in French). *Arch. maladies coeur et vaisseaux* [1952] **45**, 880.

52-167. Robbins, J., and Rall, J. E. Zone electrophoresis in filter paper of serum I[131] after radioiodide administration. *Proc. Soc. Exptl. Biol. Med.* [1952] **81**, 530.

52-168. Rockland, L. B., Lieberman, J., and Dunn, M. S. Automatic determination of radioactivity on filter paper chromatograms. *J. Anal. Chem.* [1952] **24**, 778.

52-169. Rosenberg, I. N. Serum lipids studied by electrophoresis on paper. *Proc. Soc. Exptl. Biol. Med.* [1952] **80**, 751.

52-170. Röttger, H. A new dyeing technique for serum protein fractions in paper electrophoresis (in German). *Naturwissenschaften* [1952] **39**, 451.

52-171. Rydon, H. N., and Smith, P. W. G. A new method for the detection of peptides and similar compounds on paper chromatograms. *Nature* [1952] **169**, 922.

52-172. Sato, T. R., Norris, W. P., and Strain, H. H.   Apparatus for continuous electrochromatography. *Anal. Chem.* [1952] **24**, 776–778.

52-173. Sato, T. R., Diamond, H., Norris, W. P., and Strain, H. H.   Electrochromatographic separations of rare earths. *J. Am. Chem. Soc.* [1952] **74**, 6154.

52-174. Sattler, L., and Zerban, F. W.   New spray reagents for paper chromatography of reducing sugars. *Anal. Chem.* [1952] **24**, 1862.

52-175. Scheiffarth, F., and Berg, G.   Protein determination in rats and rabbits by paper electrophoresis (in German). *Z. ges. exptl. Med.* [1952] **119**, 550.

52-176. Schild, K. T., and Maurer, W.   Paper electrophoretic studies of the phosphorous metabolism of erythrocytes: Studies with radioactive phosphorous (in German). *Biochem. Z.* [1952] **323**, 235.

52-177. Schneider, G., and Wunderly, C.   Paper electrophoresis as a rapid method for clinical chemical laboratories (in German). *Schweiz. med. Wochschr.* [1952] **82**, 445.

52-178. Schneider, G., Lottenbach, K., and Wuhrmann, F.   Dysproteinemia and myocarditis (in German). *Z. ges. exptl. Med.* [1952] **118**, 377.

52-179. Scholtan, W., Schmengler, F. E., Esser, H., Heinzler, F., Kazmeier, E., Hinsberg, K., and Jahnke, K.   A comparative study for evaluation of the newer methods of protein determination in serum and plasma (in German). *Ärztl. Forsch.* [1952] **6**, 145–146.

52-180. Schwietzer, C. H., and Witterm, A.   The separation of vitamin B_{12} from liver extracts by paper electrophoresis (in German). *Arzneimittel-Forsch.* [1952] **2**, 185.

52-181. Schwyzer, R.   Detection, separation and identification of aliphatic amines by paper chromatography. *Acta Chem. Scand.* [1952] **6**, 219–222.

52-182. Shull, G. M., Sardina, J. L., and Nubel, R. C.   Paper chromatography of steroid compounds. *Arch. Biochem. Biophys.* [1952] **37**, 186–198.

52-183. Simonart, P., and Chow, K. Y.   Separation of pepsin from rennet by microelectrophoresis and by paper chromatography (in French with summaries in English and Dutch). *Neth. Milk Dairy J.* [1952] **6**, 206–213.

52-184. Sjövall, J.   Bile acids and steroids. III. Separation of bile acids by paper chromatography. *Acta Chem. Scand.* [1952] **6**, 1552.

52-185. Skarica, N.   Paper electrophoresis of serum proteins. I. A supplement to the methods of paper electrophoresis (English summary). *Arkiv Kemi* [1952] **24**, 85–102.

52-186. Slater, W. L., and Van Winkle, Q.   An electrophoretic study of the protein in skim milk. *J. Dairy Sci.* [1952] **35**, 1083.

52-187. Smith, J. D., and Markham, R.   The enzymatic breakdown of desoxyribosenucleic acids. *Biochim. Biophys. Acta* [1952] **8**, 350.

52-188. Soloway, Sidney, Rennie, F. J., and Stetten, D., Jr.   An automatic scanner for paper radiochromatograms. *Nucleonics* [1952] **10**(4), 52.

52-189. Sommerfelt, S. C.   Reproducibility with paper electrophoresis of serum proteins. *Scand. J. Clin. & Lab. Invest.* [1952] **4**, 307.

52-190. Sonnet, J., and Rodhain, J.   The study of serum proteins by electrophoresis on paper. I. Technique and normal results (in French). *Rev. belge pathol. et med. exptl.* [1952] **22**, 226–240.

52-191. Spiegler, K. S., and Coryell, C. D.   Electromigration in a cation exchange resin. II. Detailed analysis of two-component systems. *J. Phys. Chem.* [1952] **56**, 106–113.

52-192. Springer, G. F.   Method to indicate sugars on chromatograms. Personal communication. [1952]

52-193. Sternberg, J., Boucher, R., and Proulx, A.   A new method of clinical diagnosis: Electropherography of proteins (in French). *Union méd. Canada* [1952] **81**, 1.

52-194. Sternberg, J., and Tasse, J.   Électropherography of proteins. A semiautomatic apparatus. *Cong. intern. biochim. 2ᵉ Congr.*, Paris Résumés des communs., [1952] p. 193.

52-195. Strain, H. H., and Murphy, G. W.   Chromatography and analogous differential migration methods. *Anal. Chem.* [1952] **24**, 50.

52-195A. Strain, H. H.   Qualitative separations by two-way and three-way electrochromatography. *Anal. Chem.* [1952] **24**, 356–360.

52-196. Svenson, S.   Albumin and lipids in the serum of newborn infants. *Acta Paediat.* [1952] **41**, 613.

52-197. Swahn, B.   A method for localization and determination of serum lipids after electrophoretic separation on filter paper. *Scand. J. Clin. & Lab. Invest.* [1952] **4**, 98–103.

52-198. Takeda, K., Otsuka, H., and Kimura, T.   Recognition of proteins by simplified electrophoresis (in Japanese). *Yakugaku Zasshi* [1952] **72**, 1055.

52-199. Tauber, H., and Petit, E. L.   Two-dimensional paper chromatography of Proteins. *J. Am. Chem. Soc.* [1952] **74**, 2865.

52-200. Thomsen, G.   The binding by mercury of different pure serum proteins separated by paper electrophoresis (in German). *Naturwissenschaften* [1952] **39**, 451.

52-201. Tiselius, A.   Zone electrophoresis in filter paper and other media. Manuscript given at a meeting on the general discussion on the physical chemistry of the proteins. Faraday Soc. Cambridge, England [1952] Aug. 8, 5963.

52-202. Vishmyakor, A. P., Dobrovolskii, D. S., Ermakou, N. V., and Tukachinskii, S. E.   Electrophoretic determination of protein fractions on paper (in Russian). *Doklady Akad. Nauk S.S.S.R.* [1952] **87**, 1035–1038.

52-203. Vitte, G., Blanquet, P., and Boussemart, E.   Application of microelectrophoresis on paper to the study of cancerous serums (in French). *Bull. soc. pharm. Bordeaux* [1952] **90**, 205.

52-204. Walaszek, E. J., Kelsey, F. E., and Geiling, E. M. K.   Biosynthesis and isolation of radioactive colchicine. *Science* [1952] **116**, 225.

52-205. Wallenius, G.   Electrophoretic patterns of cerebrospinal fluid and serum compared in normal and pathological conditions. *Acta Soc. Med. Upsaliensis* [1952] **57**, 138–146.

52-206. Westphal, U. F., Stets, J. F., and Priest, S. G.   Influence of fatty acids and related anions on the azorubin-binding capacity of serum albumin. *Army Med. Research Lab. Report* [1952] No. **85**, 1–19.

52-207. Woodin, A. M.   The corneal mucopolysaccharide. *Biochem. J.* [1952] **51**, 319–330.

52-208. Wuhrmann, F.   Some recent clinical problems concerning serum globulins (in German). *Schweiz. med. Wochschr.* [1952] **82**, 937.

52-209. Wunderly, C. and DePoorter, D. A.   Paper electrophoresis: A valuable method for protein determination in serum and other fluids (in Dutch). *Belg. Tijdschr. Geneesk.* [1952] **8**, 481–497.

52-210. Wunderly, C., and Hassig, A.   The serological identification of albumin preparations, blood serum, and urinary proteins (in German). *Naturwissenschaften* [1952] **39**, 260.

52-211. Wunderly, C. Lyophilic properties of isolated serum-protein fractions. *Nature* [1952] **169**, 932.

52-212. Wunderly, C., and Pezold, F. A. Solution of carcinogenic hydrocarbons in blood serum (in German). *Naturwissenschaften* [1952] **39**, 493–494.

52-213. Wunderly, C., and Cagianut, B. Electrophoresis of pathological aqueous humor (in French). *Ann. oculist. (Paris)* [1952] **185**, 414.

52-214. Wunderly, C., and Reynaud, J. Electrophoretic analysis on paper and its application to the study of bilirubinemia (in French). *Rev. hématol.* [1952] **7**, 347.

53-1. Adachi, S. Paper chromatography of urea (in Japanese). *Kagaku (Tokyo)* [1953] **23**, 582–583.

53-2. Albright, E. C., Deiss, W. P., and Larson, F. C. Radiochromatographic identification of thyroxin in an alpha-globulin fraction of serum separated by starch zone electrophoresis. *Proc. Central Soc. Clin. Research* [1953].

53-3. Anonymous. Filter paper electrophoresis. *Seminar, Sharp and Dohme* [1953] p. 20.

53-4. Not assigned

53-5. Antónini, F. M., and Piva, G. Quantitative determination of fibrinogen by paper electrophoresis (in Italian). *Sperimentale* [1953] **103**, 324–330.

53-6. Antonini, F. M., and Piva, G. Electrophoresis on paper (in Italian). *Rec. progr. med.* [1953] **14**, 243–257.

53-7. Antonini, F. M., and Piva, G. Clinical applications of electrophoresis on paper (in Italian). *Rec. progr. med.* [1953] **14**, 258–282.

53-8. Antonini, F. M., and Salvini, L. Protein and lipoprotein fractions in experimental hypercholesteremia of rabbits (in Italian). *Giorn. gerontol.* [1953] **1**, 91.

53-9. Antonini, F. M., and Salvini, L. Application of paper electrophoresis to the study of protein and lipoprotein metabolism in human atherosclerosis (in Italian). *Giorn. gerontol.* [1953] **1**, 207.

53-10. Antonini, F. M., and Piva, G. Effect of heparin and of protamine sulphate on lipoprotein of human plasma *in vivo* (in Italian). *Giorn. gerontol.* [1953] **1**, 229.

53-11. Armitage, J. B., Cannon, J. R., Johnson, A. W., Parker, L. F., Smith, E. L., Stafford, W. H., and Todd, A. R. Chemistry of the vitamin B_{12} Group. III. The course of hydrolytic degradations. *J. Chem. Soc.* [1953] pp. 3849–3864.

53-12. Axelrod, L. R. The quantitative separation of estrogens by paper partition chromatography. *J. Biol. Chem.* [1953] **201**, 59–69.

53-13. Bamann, E., and Tietz, N. On the electrophoretic behavior of purified lipase-preparations of seeds. 5. Communication: On the lipase of higher plants (in German). *Biochem. Z.* [1953] **324**, 502.

53-14. Barnett, A. J. G., Lees, H., and Smith, D. K. The qualitative determination of higher fatty acids by means of string electrophoresis. *Biochem. J.* [1953] **53**, xxxiii.

53-15. Baudouin, A., Lowin, J., and Hilion, P. Electrophoresis on paper of the proteins of cerebrospinal fluid: Study of the lipoproteins (in French). *Compt. rend. soc. biol.* [1953] **147**, 1036–1040.

53-16. Bauer, H. The significance of paper electrophoresis of cerebrospinal fluid in clinical investigation (in German). *Deut. Z. Nervenheilk.* [1953] **170**, 381–401.

53-17. Bealing, F. J. Mold "glucosaccharase": A fructosidase. *Biochem. J.* [1953] **55**, 93–101.

53-18. Benhamou, E., Amouch, P., and Chemla, E. Diagnostic value of α_2-globulin and its practical interest (in French). *Presse méd.* [1953] **61**, 1725–1727.

53-19. Bergamini, C. Filter paper electrophoresis of the vitamins of the B complex (in Italian). *Sperimentale, Sez. chim. biol.* [1953] **4**, 85–92.

53-20. Berkes, I. Electromigration (electrophoresis and ionophoresis) on paper (in Jugoslav). *Kem. i ind.* (*Zagreb*) [1953] **2**, 62–64, 98–101.

53-21. Berkes, I., and Karas, V. Fibrinogen determination by paper electrophoresis (in German). *Biochem. Z.* [1953] **324**, 499–501.

53-22. Not assigned

53-23. Berlingozzi, S., Rapi, G., and Dettori, M. Paper chromatography of proteins. I. Serum proteins (in Italian). *Sperimentale, Sez. chim. biol.* [1953] **4**, 69–74.

53-24. Blackburn, S., and Robson, A. Radiochemical method for the microestimation of alpha-amino acids separated on paper partition chromatograms. *Biochem. J.* [1953] **53**, 295–299.

53-25. Blasius, R., Nowy, H., and Seitz, W. Electrophoretic investigations of cardiac muscle proteins (in German). *Klin. Wochschr.* [1953] **31**, 478.

53-26. Blass, J., Macheboeuf, M., and Rebeyrotte, P. Application of electrorheophoresis to the identification of various biological amines in mixtures of amino acids (in French). *Bull. soc. chim. biol.* [1953] **35**, 953.

53-27. Block, R. J., Bolling, D., Weiss, K. W., and Zweig, G. Bovine whey proteins. I. Preparation of the ferric derivatives of whey proteins. *Arch. Biochem. Biophys.* [1953] **47**, 88.

53-28. Bogdanowicz, G., Osinski, P., and Stein, F. Paper electrophoresis of serum proteins in diabetes mellitus and its complications (in French). *Acta Clin. Belg.* [1953] **8**, 585–617.

53-29. Boguth, W. Paper electrophoretic analysis of dog serum (in German). *Naturwissenschaften* [1953] **40**, 22.

53-30. Boguth, W. Paper electrophoretic examinations of serums of domestic animals (in German). *Zentr. Veterinärmed.* [1953] **1**, 168–187.

53-31. Bompiani, A. Paper electrophoresis of estrone, estriol and 17-beta-estradiol (in Italian). *Boll. soc. ital. biol. sper.* [1953] **26**, 1320–1322.

53-32. Bowen, T. J. Filter paper electrophoresis of proteins. *Lab. Practice* [1953] **2**, 413–418.

53-33. Bracco, M., Magistretti, M., and Rubino, G. Direct determination by ultraviolet rays of protein fractions subjected to electrophoresis (in Italian). *Plasma* (*Milan*) [1953] **1**, 201–207.

53-34. Braunsteiner, H., and Reinhardt, F. Nature of paramyloid in plasmacytoma (in German). *Klin. Wochschr.* [1953] **31**, 710–712.

53-35. Brohult, A. Protein chemistry of leukemia in childhood. *Acta Paediat.* [1953] **42**, 391.

53-36. Brown, J. A. Determination of vitamins A and E by paper chromatography. *Anal. Chem.* [1953] **25**, 774–777.

53-37. Brown, J. A., and Marsh, M. M. Automatic measurement of light absorption and fluorescence on paper chromatography. *Anal. Chem.* [1953] **25**, 1865.

53-38. Burgio, G. R., and Giacalone, O. Electrophoretic data in dystrophia in the nursling (in Italian). *Boll. soc. ital. biol. sper.* [1953] **29**, 695.

53-39. Burma, D. P. Separation of the purines and pyrimidines by ionophoresis on filter paper. *Science* [1953] **118**, 694.

53-40. Burma, D. P. Electrochromatography on paper. *Anal. Chim. Acta* [1953] **9**, 518–524.

53-41. Cann, J. R., and Frisell, W. R. A fractionation of D-amino acid oxidase by electrophoresis convection. *J. Am. Chem. Soc.* [1953] **75**, 2425.

53-42. Careddu, P. Variations in serum proteins effected by lipids (in Italian). *Boll. soc. ital. biol. sper.* [1953] **29**, 258–261.

53-43. Caspani, R., Masera, N., and Ballerini, G. Protein of blood in tuberculous patients subjected to lung exeresis (in Italian). *Minerva Chir.* [1953] **8**, 827–836.

53-44. Cheftel, R. I., Munier, R., and Macheboeuf, M. Paper microchromatography of hydrosoluble and non-volatile aliphatic acids. IV. Detection technique of dicarboxylic acids (in French). *Bull. soc. chim. biol.* [1953] **35**, 1091–1093.

53-45. Chiesura, P. Electrophoretic studies of the variation of proteinemia in the course of nephrotic syndrome (in Italian). *Minerva Med.* [1953] **1**, 1–23.

53-46. Chiesura, P. Electrophoretic investigations of urinary proteins (in Italian). *Minerva Med.* [1953] **1**, 835.

54-47. Christman, J. F., and Werner, H. J. Chromatography and biological stains. IV. Preparation of a suitable fat stain from commercial Sudan III. *Stain Technol.* [1953] **28**, 259.

53-48. Christomanos, A. A. Electrophotometric paper chromatography of amino acids (in German with English summary). *Enzymologia* [1953] **16**, 87–90.

53-49. Common, R. H., McKinley, W. P., and Maw, W. A. Filter paper electrophoresis of avian serum proteins. *Science* [1953] **118**, 86.

53-50. Confortini, P., and Dagradi, A. Gamma-globulins. I. Correlation between the Kunkel reaction and paper electrophoresis (in Italian). *Biol. Latina* [1953] **6**, 464–471.

53-51. Confortini, P., and Dagradi. A. Gamma-globulins. II. Correlation between the reaction of de la Huerga and Popper and paper electrophoress. *Biol. Latina* [1953] **6**, 472–477.

53-51A. Cornell, D., and Katz, D. L. Flow of gases through consolidated porous media. *Ind. Eng. Chem.* [1953] **45**, 2145.

53-52. Deiss, W. P., Albright, E. C., and Larson, F. C. Comparison of *in vitro* serum protein binding of thyroxine and triiodothyronine. *Proc. Soc. Expt. Biol. Med.* [1953] **84**, 513–516.

53-53. Delcourt, A., and Delcourt, R. Separation and localization of enzymes of biological fluids by electrophoresis on paper (in French). *Compt. rend. soc. biol.* [1953] **147**, 1104–1107.

53-54. Deltour, G. H., and Bekaert, J. Electrophoresis on paper and radioautography of labeled thyroglobulin from normal rats and rats treated with various agents that modify thyroid activity (in French). *Compt. rend. soc. biol.* [1953] **147**, 388–391.

53-55. Demling, L., Kinzlmeier, H., and Henning, N. Electrophoretic examination of structural elements of the cell (in German). *Klin. Wochschr.* [1953] **31**, 1103–1104.

53-56. van Dommelen, C. K. V., and Schulte, M. J. Clinical significance of the determinations of blood proteins by means of paper electrophoresis (in Dutch). *Pharm. Weekblad* [1953] **88**, 669–672.

53-57. Drevon, B. So-called mobilities and positions of proteins during electrophoresis on paper. A graphic interpretation of electrophoretic diagrams (in French). *Compt. rend. soc. biol.* [1953] **147**, 1416–1417.

53-58. Dubert, J. M., Slizewicz, P., Rebeyrotte, P., and Macheboeuf, M. New method of separation of serum proteins by methanol. Application to rabbit and horse serums (in French). *Ann. inst. Pasteur* [1953] **84**, 370.

53-59. Durant, J. A., and Abbott, A. L. Routine methods in paper partition chromatography and electrophoresis. *J. Med. Lab. Tech.* [1953] **2**, 164.

53-60. Durrum, E. L. The separation of serum proteins by zone electrophoresis. Paper presented at 124th annual meeting of the American Chemical Society, Chicago [1953]

53-61. Dustin, J. P. Paper electrophoresis with controlled evaporation (in French). *Electrophoresis.* 1st Colloquium of the Laboratory of the Saint-Jean à Bruges Hospital (Belgium). [1953]

53-62. Eaton, J. C., and Gardner, M. D. Separation of cerebrospinal fluid proteins by paper electrophoresis. *Biochem. J.* [1953] **56**, xxv.

53-63. Ebel, K. H. Paper electrophoretical investigations on the composition of the plasma proteins of dogs, cows, and calves (in German with English summary). *Zentr. Veterinärmed.* [1953] **1**, 70–76.

53-64. Emrich, R. Determination of serum proteins by filter paper electrophoresis (in German). *Schweiz. med. Wochschr.* [1953] **83**, 77.

53-65. Enríquez de Salamanca, F., Zuazo de León, C., González Alvarez, J., and Otero de la Gándara, J. Paper electrophoresis. III. Investigation of the protein fraction in biological fluids by the concentration method (in Spanish with English summary). *Arch. med. exptl. (Madrid)* [1953] **16**, 359–362.

53-66. Eymer, K. P. Paper electrophoretic studies of experimental liver damage in the rat. *Z. klin. Med.* [1953] **152**, 137, *Excerpta Med.* [1954]. *Sect. II* **7**, 1287.

53-67. Falconer, J. S., Jenden, D. J., and Taylor, D. B. The application of solubility measurements to the study of complex protein solutions and to the isolation of individual proteins. *Discussions Faraday Soc.* [1953] **13**, 40.

53-68. Figueroa, E. S., and Seibert, F. B. Chromatography of alpha, epsilon-diamino-pimelic acid on starch columns. *Proc. Soc. Exptl. Biol. Med.* [1953] **83**, 535–537; *Chem. Abstr.* [1953]. **47**, 12434.

53-69. Fiser-Herman, M., and Davorin, P. Paper electrophoresis of hematin albumins (in German). *Biochem. Z.* [1953] **324**, 96.

53-70. Fiser-Herman, M., and Berkes, S. Examination of the content of a cyst (In Jugoslav with German summary). *Acta Pharm. Jugoslav.* [1953] **3**, 119.

53-71. Fisher, B. Recent contributions of electrophoresis to clinical pathology. *Am. J. Clin. Pathol.* [1953] **23**, 246.

53-72. Fletcher, E., and Malpress, F. H. Paper chromatography of phosphate esters. *Nature* [1953] **171**, 838–839.

53-73. Flodin, P., Consden, R., and Durrum, E. L. General discussion. *Discussions Faraday Soc.* [1953] **13**, 46.

53-74. Forell, M. M., and Koller, F. The evaluation of liver function by determination of factor V, factor VII, and prothrombin. Effect of synkavite and vitamin K_1 (in German). *Münch. Med. Wochschr.* [1953] **95**, 433–47; *Chem. Abstr.* [1953]. **47**, 7081.

53-75. Foster, A. B., and Stacey, M. Ionophoresis of some carbohydrate derivatives. *J. Appl. Chem. (London).* [1953] **3**, 19–21.

53-76. Foster, A. B. Ionophoresis of some disaccharides. *J. Chem. Soc.* [1953] pp. 982–986.

53-77. Foster, A. B., Martlew, E. F., and Stacey, M. Correlation of the rates of deamination of glucosaminides with configuration at the glycosidic center. *Chem. & Ind. (London)* [1953] p. 825.

53-78. Foster, A. B., and Stacey, M. Structure of (+)-bornesitol. *Chem. & Ind. (London)* [1953] p. 279.

53-79. Foster, A. B. Structure of sequoyitol. *Chem. & Ind. (London)* p. 591.

53-80. Foster, M. C., and Ashton, G. C. Paper electrophoresis of streptomycins. *Nature* [1953] **172,** 958–959.

53-81. Galletti, F., Gelli, G., and Loli-Piccolimini, M. Study on the serum glycoproteins in pulmonary tuberculosis (in Italian). *Arch. patol. e clin. med.* [1953] **31,** 307.

53-82. Gallico, E., Chierego, F., and Rabotti, G. C. Electrophoretic study on proteins of pathological fluids (in Italian). *Tumori* [1953] **39,** 281–288.

53-83. Geldmacher-Mallinckrodt, M., and May, F. Electrophoresis of galactogen and glycogen in presence of other carbohydrates (in German). *Z. physiol. Chem.* [1953] **293,** 256.

53-84. Geldmacher-Mallinckrodt, M., and Weinland, H. Separation of glycogen and galactogen by electrophoresis on silk. *Z. physiol. Chem.* [1953] **292,** 65–72.

53-85. Chiglione, C., and Bozzi-Tichadou, M. A technique for fixation and intensification of chromatograms of reducing sugars (in French). *Bull. soc. chim. biol.* [1953] **35,** 1441–1442.

53-86. Ghosh, A. R., and Burma, D. P. Paper chromatography and paper ionophoresis in the identification of yeast nucleic acid. *Sci. and Culture (Calcutta)* [1953] **19,** 103.

53-87. Giri, K. V., Krishnaswamy, P. R., Kalyankar, G. D., and Rao, P. L. N. Separation and identification of the degradation products of purines and nucleic acids on acid hydrolysis by circular paper chromatography. *Experientia* [1953] **9,** 296–297.

53-88. Gleason, T. L., and Friedberg, F. Filter paper electrophoresis of serum proteins from small animals. *Physiol. Zool.* [1953] **26,** 95.

53-89. González Alvarez, J., Otero de la Gándara, J., Enríquez de Salamanca, F., and Zuazo de León, C. Paper electrophoresis. I. Mean values for the protein fractions of normal serums. (in Spanish with English summary). *Arch. med. exptl. (Madrid)* [1953] **16,** 283–289.

53-90. Gornall, A. G., and MacDonald, M. P. Quantitative determination of the steroid hormones with 2,4-dinitrophenylhydrazine. *J. Biol. Chem.* [1953] **201,** 279–297.

53-91. Grabar, P., and Williams, C. A. Method permitting the simultaneous study of electrophoretic and immunochemical properties of a mixture of proteins. Application to blood serum (in French.) *Biochim. et Biophys. Acta* [1953] **10,** 193–194.

53-92. Graf, E., and List, P. H. A reversal effect in paper electrophoresis of blood serums (in German). *Naturwissenschaften* [1953] **40,** 273.

53-93. Grassmann, W., and Hannig, K. Separation of mixtures of filter paper by migration in an electrical field (in German). *Z. physiol. Chem.* [1953] **292,** 32–50.

53-94. Grassmann, W., and Hubner, L. Electrophoretic process for detection of loose addition compounds (in German). *Naturwissenschaften* [1953] **40,** 272–273; *Chem. Abstr.* [1954]. **48,** 424

53-95. Grassmann, W., and Deffner, G. Distributive chromatographic behavior of proteins and peptides in solutions containing phenol (in German). *Z. Physiol. Chem.* [1953] **293**, 89.

53-96. Greenway, R. M., Kent, P. W., and Whitehouse, M. W. Detection of non-reducing carbohydrates in paper electrophoresis and chromatography. *Research (London)* [1953] **6**, Suppl. No. 1, 6S.

53-97. Gries, G., Aly, F. W., and von Oldershausen, H. F. Method of paper electrophoresis of cerebrospinal fluid (in German). *Klin. Wochschr.* [1953] **31**, 644.

53-98. Griffiths, L. L., and Gilchrist, L. Cryoglobulinaemia in alcoholic cirrhosis. *Lancet* [1953] p. 882.

53-99. Griffiths, L. L. The electrophoresis of serum and other body fluids in filter paper. *J. Lab. Clin. Med.* [1953] **41**, 188–198.

53-100. Griffiths, L. L., and Brews, V. A. L. The electrophoretic pattern in multiple myelomatosis. *J. Clin. Pathol.* [1953] **6**, 187.

53-101. Gross, D. Paper electrophoresis of sugars at high potential gradients. *Nature* [1953] **172**, 908.

53-102. Groulade, P., and Groulade, J. Microelectrophoresis on paper of serum from normal and pathologic dogs (in French). *Ann. inst. Pasteur* [1953] **85**, 508.

53-103. Guassardo, G., Comirato-Sandrucci, M., and Angelino, P. F. Protein of blood and electrophoretic protein picture in congenital heart disease; before and after operation (in Italian). *Minerva cardioangiol.* [1953] **1** 36–41.

53-104. Hanser, W. Electrophoresis of serum and urinary protein in acute lupus erythematosus. *Ärztl. Wochschr.* [1953] **8**, 840.

53-105. Hanson, H., and Wenzel, M. Localization of serum peptidases in the serum protein fractions (in German). *Klin. Wochschr.* [1953] **31**, 24–25.

53-106. Harasawa, S., and Sakamoto, T. Electro-paper chromatography: I. Separation of alkali metals and magnesium. *Nippon Kagaku Zasshi* [1953] **74**, 862–864.

53-107. Harboe, N., and D'Ermo, F. Moving-boundary and filter-paper electrophoresis (in Italian with English summary). *Policlinico (Rome) Sez. med.* [1953] **60**, 292.

53-108. Harders, C. L., and van Mulken, J. M. Paper electrophoresis of proteins (method) (in Dutch). *Pharm. Weekblad* [1953] **88**, 673–683.

53-109. Harders, C. L. A review of some clinical experiences with paper electrophoresis (in Dutch). *Chem. Weekblad* [1953] **49**, 246–247.

53-110. Hartman, R. S., and Nungester, W. J. An electrophoretic method for titration of antisera and its application to anti-tumor sera. *Proc. Soc. Exptl. Biol. Med.* [1953] **84**, 710–713.

53-111. Hashimoto, Y. Microchemical determination of triterpenoids by paper electrophoresis. *Experientia* [1953] **9**, 194.

53-112. Heinrich, W. Paper electrophoresis of pepsin (in German). *Biochem. Z.* [1953] **323**, 469.

53-113. Hellstrom, N. Apparatus for chromatography. *Acta Chem. Scand.* [1953] **7**, 329–334.

53-114. Henning, N., Kinzlmeier, H., and Demling, L. The electrophoretically demonstrable proteins of normal and pathological gastric juice (in German). *Münch. med. Wochschr.* [1953] **95**, 423.

53-115. Herman, G., and Oberhausen, E. Evaluation of paper electrophoresis (in German). *Naturwissenschaften* [1953] **40**, 412.

53-116. Hill, H., and Schumann, G.   High-voltage paper electrophoretic studies of hog serum. *Tierärztl. Umschau* [1953] **8**, 355–356; *Chem. Abstr.* [1954]. **48**, 4072.

53-117. Hiller, E., and Bischof, H.   Protein and amino-acid content of human gastric juices as determined by paper electrophoresis and paper chromatography. *Die Medizinische* [1953] pp. 1541–1545; *Chem. Abstr.* [1954]. **48**, 2851.

53-118. Hohne, G., Jaster, R., and Kunkel, H. A.   The influence of cysteine on the alterations in serum proteins of the rat induced by radiation (in German). *Klin. Wochschr.* [1953] **31**, 910.

53-119. Holdsworth, E. S.   Differentiation of vitamin B12-active compounds by ionophoresis and microbiological assay. Ionophoresis. *Nature* [1953] **171**, 148–149, *Chem. Abstr.* [1953]. **47**, 8847.

53-120. Holdsworth, E. S.   Continuous electrophoresis on paper. *Biochem. J.* [1953] **55**, xiv.

53-121. Homolka, J.   Detection of proteins during paper electrophoresis (in Czech). *Chem. listy.* [1953] **47**, 287.

53-122. Horst, W., and Rosler, H.   The transport of hormone iodine in human serum examined by paper electrophoresis and radioactive iodine (in German). *Klin. Wochschr.* [1953] **31**, 13.

53-123. Horst, W., and Schafer, K. H.   Iron binding in serum and other biological fluids examined by paper electrophoresis and radioactive iron (in German). *Klin. Wochschr.* [1953] **31**, 940.

53-124. Horstebrock, R., Schlepper, M., and Schummelfeder, N.   Detection and separation of hemosiderin and hemoglobin by paper electrophoresis (in German). *Naturwissenschaften* [1953] **40**, 141.

53-125. Hradec, J.   Electrophoretic studies in patients with lung diseases with special reference to the diagnosis of carcinoma (in Czech with English summary). *Časopis lékáru českých* [1953] **32**, 867.

53-126. Humoller, F. L., and Zimmerman, H. J.   Electrophoretic separation of serum proteins obtained from a drop of blood. *Abstr. 124th Ann. Meeting Am. Chem. Soc., Chicago* [1953] p. 40c.

53-127. Inzerillo, R., and Azzena, D.   Electrophoretic studies on experimental exudates (in Italian). *Arch. "E. Maragliano" patol. e clin.* [1953] **8**, 1487–1504.

53-128. Irvin, J. L., and Irvin, E. M.   Filter paper electrophoresis of nucleo-proteins and nucleic acids. *Federation Proc.* [1953] **12**, 223.

53-129. Jacobsson, K.   Electrophoretic demonstration of two trypsin inhibitors in human blood serum. *Scand. J. Clin. & Lab. Invest.* [1953] **5**, 97–98; *Chem. Abstr.* [1953]. **47**, 7621.

53-130. Jankovic, B. D., and Krijnen, H. W.   Serological activity of globulin fractions of anti-D serums separated by paper electrophoresis. *Nature* [1953] **171**, 982–983; *Chem. Abstr.* [1953]. **47**, 12588.

53-131. Jasinski, B., Stiefel, G. E., Marki, H., and Wuhrmann, F.   The lupus erythematosus phenomenon and similar cell picture in cantharidin blisters and their relationship to the gamma-globulins (in German). *Klin. Wochschr.* [1953] **31**, 252.

53-132. Jasinski, B., and Wuhrmann, F.   Investigation of serum proteins and serum iron with radioactive iron (in German). *Verhandl. deut. Ges. inn. Med.* [1953] **59**, 326.

53-133. Jerchel, D., and Scheurer, H.   The action of invert soaps on proteins as studied by means of paper electrophoresis (in German). *Z. Naturforsch.* [1953] **8b**, 541-547.

53-134. Jermyn, M. A., and Thomas, R. Reduction of liquid flow in paper electrophoresis. *Nature* [1953] **172**, 728–729.

53-135. Kallee, E., and Roth, E. The paper electrophoretic proof of dye binding capacity (in German). *Z. Naturforsch.* [1953] **8b**, 34.

53-136. Kanngiesser, W. Paper electrophoresis of phosphatides of healthy and virus-infected plants in pyridine-acetic acid-chloroform (in German). *Biochem. Z.* [1953] **325**, 12–15; *Chem. Abstr.* [1954] **48**, 4644.

53-137. Karte, H. Electrophoresis of blood-serum proteins in infancy (in German). *Z. Kinderheilk.* [1953] **73**, 467–486; *Chem. Abstr.* [1954] **48**, 861.

53-138. Kariyone, T., Hashimoto, Y., Mori, I., and Kimura, M. Microchemical study of plant components. IXa. Paper chromatography of alcohols by the potassium xanthate method (in Japanese). *Yakugaku Zasshi* [1953] **73**, 1095.

53-139. Kawai, Koichiro. Paper chromatography of bilirubin (in Japanese). *Igaku Kenkyuu* [1953] **23**, 572–581.

53-140. Kimbel, K. H. Protein detection on electrophoresis strips by ultraviolet absorption (in German). *Naturwissenschaften* [1953] **40**, 200–201.

53-141. Kinersly, T. Preliminary paper electrophoretic study of saliva. *Yale J. Biol. and Med.* [1953] **26**, 211.

53-142. King, N. K., and Doery, H. M. Applications of electrophoresis in studying new antibiotics. *Nature* [1953] **171**, 878.

53-143. Klein, Erich. Iodine content of individual blood proteins (in German). *Z. ges. exptl. Med.* [1953] **121**, 44–55.

53-144. Klingenberg, H. G., Schauenstein, E., and Zima, H. Electrophoretic detection of two protein components in fibrinogen (in German). *Z. Naturforsch.* [1953] **8b**, 483.

53-145. Knedel, M. Electrophoretic protein fractionation on filter paper (in Italian). *Plasma (Milan)* [1953] **1**, 87–100.

53-146. Köiw, E. A photometric scanning device for paper electrophoresis. *Scan. J. Clin. & Lab. Invest.* [1953] **5**, 99–101.

53-147. Komar, J. A new method of electrophoresis on filter paper. *Bull. Sci. Conseil Acad. RPF Yugoslav.* [1953] **1**, 14; *Chem. Abstr.* [1954] **48**, 1771.

53-148. Kravchenko, N. A., Samarina, O. P., and Kritsman, M. G. Modification of the method of the electrophoretic separation of proteins on filter paper (in Russian). *Biokhimiya* [1953] **18**, 34–36.

53-149. Kunkel, H. G., Taylor, S. P., and du Vigneaud, V. Electrophoretic properties of oxytocin. *J. Biol. Chem.* [1953] **200**, 559–564.

53-150. Kunkel, H. G. · Zone electrophoresis in a starch supporting medium. *Abstr. 124th Ann. Meeting Am. Chem. Soc. Chicago* [1953] p. 43c.

53-151. Kutacek, M., and Kolousek, J. Electrophoresis on filter paper in agricultural biochemistry. I. Separation and evaluation of the serum proteins of domestic animals (in Czech with summary in English). *Sbornik Ceskoslov. akad. zemědělských věd*, [1953] *Rada A* **26**, 575–586.

53-152. Labrosse, E. H. Paper chromatography of adrenocortical steroids. Project No. 21-4001-0002, *U.S.A.F. School of Aviation Med.* [1953] *Rept.* **1**, 1–5.

53-153. Larson, D. L., and Ranney, H. M. Filter paper electrophoresis of human hemoglobin. *J. Clin. Invest.* [1953] **32**, 1070–1076.

53-154. Latner, A. L., Ungley, C. C., Cox, E. V., and Raine, L. Electrophoresis of human gastric juice in relation to Castle's intrinsic factor. *Brit. Med. J.* [1953] **1,** 467.

53-155. La Torretta, G., and Magri, E.   Behavior of serum protein during hemorrhagic shock in puerperas (in Italian). *Arch. ostet. e ginecol.* [1953] **58,** 499–507.

53-156. Lautsch, W., Manecke, G., and Broser, W.   Preparation and use of ion-exchange papers (in German). *Z. Naturforsch.* [1953] **8b,** 232–236; *Chem. Abstr.* [1953] **47,** 10394.

53-157. Lederer, M. M.   Paper electrochromatography of lanthanides and of lanthane (in French). *Compt. rend.* [1953] **236,** 200–201.

53-158. Lederer, M. M.   Paper chromatography of inorganic ions. VI. Separation of the per-compounds of titanium, vanadium and molybdenun. *Anal. Chim. Acta* [1953] **8,** 259.

53-159. Leloir, L. F., and Cabib, E.   The enzymic synthesis of trehalose phosphate. *J. Am Chem. Soc.* [1953] **75,** 5445–5446.

53-160. Letterer, E., and Schneider, G.   The importance of serum proteins in amyloidosis (in German with English summary). *Plasma (Milan)* [1953] **1,** 263; *Excerpta Med.* [1954] *Sect. V.* **7,** 452.

53-161. Lever, W. F.   Determination of lipoprotein in the plasma of patients with various skin diseases (in German). *Hautarzt* [1953] **4,** 426.

53-162. Levin, B., and Oberholzer, V. G.   Paper electrophoresis of serum proteins. *Am. J. Clin. Pathol.* [1953] **23,** 205.

53-163. Levy, R. S., and Mazia, D.   Partial purification of renal alkaline phosphatase by electrophoresis on paper. *Arch. Biochem. Biophys.* [1953] **44,** 280–283.

53-164. Lindqvist, B.   Electrophoresis as an aid in cheese investigations (in Swedish). *Svenska Mejeritidn.* [1953] **45,** 169–172.

53-165. Livingston, C. H., Payne, M. G., Fults, J. L., and Blouch, R. M.   Chromatogram spotting apparatus. *Science* [1953] **118,** 56.

53-166. Loomeijer, F. J., and Witter, A.   Paper electrophoresis of ACTH. *Acta Endocrinol.* [1953] **12,** 167.

53-167. Loos, R.   Paper electrophoresis of saponins (in Dutch). *Pharm. Tijdschr. België* [1953] **30,** 201–206.

53-168. Loos, R.   A review of methods employed in paper electrophoresis (in Dutch). *Electrophoresis. 1st Colloquium of the Laboratory of the Saint-Jean à Bruges Hospital (Belgium)* [1953].

53-169. Loos, R.   Electrophoresis of saponins on paper (in Dutch). *J. pharm Belg.* [1953] **8,** 292-293; *Chem. Abstr.* [1954] **48,** 951.

53-170, Loos, R.   Two dimensional methods in paper electrophoresis (in Dutch). *Electrophoresis. 1st Colloquium of the Laboratory of the Saint-Jean à Bruges Hospital (Belgium)* [1953].

53-171. Loos, R.   Applications of the paper electrophoresis (in Dutch). *Pharm. Tijdschr.* [1953] **30,** 128–134; *Chem. Abstr.* [1954] **48,** 953.

53-172. Lucas, F., and Schmager, A.   Clinical experiences and paper electrophoretic investigations of the blood proteins in tuberculosis under vitamin T therapy (in German) *Ärztl. Wochschr.* [1953] **8,** 359–362; *Chem. Abstr.* [1953] **47,** 7613.

53-173. Ludford, C. G., and Lederer, M.   The antibiotics of *Escherichia coli. Australian. J. Exptl. Biol. Med. Sci.* [1953] **31,** 553–560.

53-174. Mach, W., and Geffert, R.   A new method of quick electrophoresis with the aid of impulses of medium and high frequencies (in German). *Arzneimittel-Forsch.* [1953] **3,** 534–535.

53-175. Macheboeuf, M., Rebeyrotte, P., Dubert, J., and Brunerie, M.   Paper micro-electrophoresis with continuous evaporation of the solvent (electrorheo-phoresis) (in French). *Bull. soc. chim. biol.* [1953] **35**, 334–345.

53-176. Macheboeuf, M., Dubert, J. M., and Rebeyrotte, P.   Microelectrophoresis on paper with continuous evaporation of the solvent. II. Theoretical study in the application to the measurement of electrophoretic mobilities (in French). *Bull. soc. chim. biol.* [1953] **35**, 346–364.

53-177. Macheboeuf, M. A.   Microelectrophoresis on paper with continuous evapor-ation of the solvent (electrorheophoresis) (in German). *chem. Weekblad* [1953] **49**, 237–241; *Chem. Abstr.* [1953] **47**, 7856.

53-178. Mariani, Aurelio, and Toschi, G.   Paper electrophoresis of muscle proteins (in Italian). *Atti accad. nazl. Lincei Rend. sci. fis. mat. e nat.* [1953] **14**, 285–289; *Rend. ist. super. sanità* [1953] **16**, 148–153.

53-179. Martini, V., and Riva, G.   Comparative research on Tiselius' and paper electrophoresis methods (in Italian). *Giorn. biochim.* [1953] **2**, 166–179.

53-180. Maurer, W., and Muller, E. R.   Investigation of transport function of single serum proteins for phospholipids done by a new paper electrophoretic method (in German). *Biochem. Z.* [1953] **324**, 255–265.

53-181. Maurer, W.   Rate of new formation of serum protein fractions after admin-istration of S^{35}-methionine and transport function of serum protein fractions for phosphatides and the organic iodine compounds of the serum. Paper electrophoresis with serum protein labeled with Sulfur-35, Phosphorus-32, and Iodine-131 (in German). *Arch. exptl. Path. u. Phar-makol. Naunyn-Schmiedeberg's* [1953] **218**, 3–16.

53-182. McCarthy, E. F.   The effect of cortisone administration on the electrophor-etic pattern of the plasma proteins in certain pathological conditions. *Irish J. Med. Sci.* [6] [1953] **327**, 102–107.

53-183. McDonald, H. S., Marbach E. P., Urbin, M. C., Lappe, R. J., and Spitzer, R. H.   Electromigration in stabilized electrolytes. Parts I, II, and III. Development of technique; factors influencing mobility; applications of the technique. *Clin. Chem.* [1953] **5**, 17, 35, and 51–59.

53-184. McDonald, H. J., and Urbin, M. C.   Behavior of amino acids and some de-rivatives in simultaneous crossed-current ionography. *Federation Proc.* [1953] **12**, 243–244.

53-185. McDonald, H. J., and Marbach, E. P.   An ionographic enrichment of an adrenocorticotropic hormone (ACTH) preparation. *J. Biochem. (Tokyo)* (1953) **40**, 111.

53-186. McDonald, H. J., and Spitzer, R. H.   Polyvinylpyrrolidone: The electro-migration characteristics of the blood plasma expander. Circulation Research [1953] **1**, 396.

53-187. McKinley, W. P., Oliver, W. F., Maw, W. A., and Common, R. H.   Filter paper electrophoresis of serum proteins of the domestic fowl. *Proc. Soc. Exptl. Biol. Med.* [1953] **84**, 346–351.

53-188. Menighini, C. L., Levi, L., and Pozzo, G.   Lipoprotein metabolism in pso-riasis. IV. Serum lipoproteins by the method of electrophoresis on paper (in Italian). *Giorn. ital. dermatol. e sifilol.* [1953] **94**, 326–332; *Chem. Abstr.* [1954]. **48**, 7760.

53-189. Michalec, C., and Hais, I. M.   Paper ionophoresis and electrophoresis. *Chem. listy* (1953) **47**, 284–319.

53-190. Michl, H.   The determination of purine derivatives on filter paper (in Ger-man). *Naturwissenschaften* [1953] **40**, 390.

53-191. Mies, H. J.   The concentrating of cerebrospinal fluid as a preparative method for paper electrophoresis (in German). *Klin. Wochschr.* [1953] **31**, 159–166.

53-192. Miettinen, J. K., and Moisio, T.   A self-recording strip photometer for paper electrophoresis and paper chromatography. *Acta Chem. Scand.* [1953] **7**, 1225–1238.

53-193. Miettinen, J. K.   Quantitative paper chromatography and paper electrophoresis. *Suomen Kemistilehti* [1953] **26**, 49–63; *Chem. Abstr.* [1954] **48**, 9255.

53-194. Milletti, M., and Adembri, G.   Paper chromatographic separation of some alkaloids in form of their reineckates (in Italian). *Sperimentale, Sez. chim biol.* [1953] **4**, 99–104.

53-195. Moore, A. M., and Boylen, J. B.   A simple method for making transfers in paper chromatography. *Science* [1953] **118**, 19.

53-196. Mori, I.   Filter-paper chromatography. IV. High-frequency papyrography, a new analytical technique using high frequency for paper chromatograms (in Japanese with English summary). *Yakugaku Zasshi* [1953] **73**, 958–961.

53-197. Muller, H. K., and Kleifeld, O.   The paper electrophoretic investigation of phosphate metabolism of the lenses of younger and older animals with radioactive phosphorus (in German). *Arch. Ophthalmol. Graefe's* [1953] **154**, 165–176.

53-198. Muller, R.   The quantitative determination of indoleacetic acid by means of paper chromatography and paper electrophoresis (in German). *Beitr. Biol. Pflanz.* [1953] **30**, 1.

53-199. Neish, W. J. P.   On the separation of α-keto acid dinitrophenylhydrazones by ionophoresis and their polarographic estimation (in French). *Rec. trav. chim.* [1953] **72**, 105.

53-200. Newcombe, A. G., and Reid, S. G.   Chromatographic separation using chemically treated papers of aldehydes and ketones on the basis of their reactivity. *Nature* [1953] **172**, 455–456.

53-201. Newton, G. G. F., and Abraham, E. P.   Observations on the nature of bacitracin A. *Biochem. J.* [1953] **53**, 604–613.

53-202. Nikkilä, E. A.   Studies on the lipids protein relationships in normal and pathological sera and the effect of heparin on serum lipoproteins. *Scand. J. Clin. & Lab. Invest.* [1953] *Suppl.* **8**, 1–101.

53-203. Nikkilä, E. A., Haahti, E., and Pesola, R.   The technique of preparative electrophoresis of proteins in supporting medium (starch). *Acta Chem. Scand.* [1953] **7**, 1222–1223.

53-204. Norpoth, L., Surmann, T., and Clösges, J.   Location of gastric enzymes in the electrophoresis diagram (in German). *Klin. Wochschr.* [1953] **31**, 1005–1006.

53-205. Novelli, A., and Guerrero, I. T.   Examination by paper chromatography of the alkaloids related to opium (in Italian). *Publs. inst. invest. microquim. Univ. nacl. litoral (Rosario, Arg.)* [1953] **17**, 205–210.

53-206. van Os, G. A. J.   A critical review of the quantitative determination of protein fractions with paper electrophoresis (in Dutch). *Chem. Weekblad* [1953] **49**, 242–246.

53-207. van Os, G. A. J., and Smets, W.   Analysis of serum protein by means of electrophoresis on paper (in Dutch). *Ned. Tijdschr. Geneesk* [1953] **97**, 479.

53-208. Ott, H. Binding of colloidal particles to plasma proteins (in German). *Z. ges. exptl. Med.* [1953] **122**, 346–355.

53-209. Pende, G., and Giordano, G. Electrophoretic picture (of blood proteins) in hyperfolliculism (in Italian). *Arch. "E. Maragliano" patol. e clin.* [1953] **8**, 1351–1360.

53-210. Pernis, B. Amino acid composition of human serum proteins (in Italian with English summary). *Plasma (Milan)* [1953] **1**, 365.

53-211. Pernis, B., and Wunderly, C. Quantitative determination of amino acids on filter paper. Staining in two stages. *Biochim. et Biophys. Acta* [1953] **11**, 209.

53-212. Peters, H. J. Paper electrophoresis of cerebrospinal fluid (in Dutch). *Chem. Weekblad* [1953] **49**, 248–249.

53-213. Peterson, J. E., Chaney, A. L., and Hsu, F. Paper electrophoresis of serum lipoprotein. *Med. Arts & Sci.* [1953] **7** (4), 91

53-214. Pezold, F. A. On the binding of disodium phenoltetrabromophthalein sulfonate to human serum with special reference to the "bromosulphalein tests" (in German). *Z. ges. exptl. Med.* [1953] **121**, 600–613.

53-215. Pezold, F. A., and Peiser, U. Affinity of serum protein fractions, separated by paper electrophoresis and denatured, toward the protein dyes amido black, azocarmine, and bromphenol blue (in German). *Klin. Wochschr.* [1953] **31**, 982–985.

53-216. Plough, I. E., Teschan, P. E., and Seligson, D. The toxic effects of modified human globin. *J. Lab. Clin. Med.* [1953] **42**, 224–231.

53-217. Pluckthun, H., and Matthes, A. Paper electrophoretic studies on spinal fluid proteins (in German). *Z. Kinderheilk.* [1953] **72**, 521–531.

53-218. Poli, E., Caspani, R., Jucker, S., and Villa, A. M. Contribution to the analysis of the alterations of the serum electrophoretic tracing in hepatopathies (in Italian). *Minerva Med.* [1953] **14**, 1414–1421.

53-219. Poli, E., Bevacqua, V., and Curletto, R. Electrophoretic analysis of bone marrow serum: Demonstration of a proteopoietic activity of the marrow (in French). *Plasma (Milan)* [1953] **1**, 101–107.

53-220. Poli, E., Bevacqua, V., Rabagliati, U., and Villa, A. M. Analysis of proteinemia and proteinuria in a nephrotic group in relation to the pathogenesis of the nephrotic syndrome (in Italian, summary in English). *Plasma (Milan)* [1953] **1**, 299–328.

53-221. Poli, E. The plasmocytomas (in Italian). *Boll. oncologia* [1953] **27**, 3–37.

53-222. Ponder, E. Hemolysins obtained from tissues. Their separation by paper electrophoresis and electroconvection (in French with English summary). *Rev. hématol.* [1953] **8**, 119–131.

53-223. Poulik, M. D. Purification of diphtheria toxoid by continuous electrophoresis on filter paper. *Can. J. Med. Sci.* [1953] **31**, 485–492; *Chem. Abstr.* [1954] **48**, 2231.

53-224. Pučar, Z. Paper electrophoresis in moist chamber (in German). *Arkiv Kemi* [1953] **25**, 205–217.

53-225. Ranney, H. M., Larson, D. L., and McCormack, G. H. Some clinical, biochemical and genetic observations on hemoglobin C. *J. Clin. Invest.* [1953] **32**, 1277.

53-226. Rao, S. S. Apparatus for paper electrophoresis. *Current Sci. (India)* [1953] **22**, 274–275.

53-227. Raymond, S. Channel area in electroconvection apparatus. *Science* [1953] **118**, 388.

53-228. Raynaud, R., d'Eshougues, J. R., Pasquet, P., and Di Giovanni, S. Serum glucoproteins and paper electrophoresis (in French). *Algérie méd.* [1953] **57,** 721.

53-229. Raynaud, R., d'Eshougues, J. R., Pasquet, P., and Di Giovanni, S. Clinical interest in serum lipoproteins in the syndrome chronic thrombo arteriosis of the limbs (in French). *Algérie méd.* [1953] **57,** 685–707.

53-230. Raynaud, R., d'Eshougues, J. R., Vargues, R., and Pasquet, P. Comparative investigation of serum proteins by electrophoresis and the reticulo-endothelial response (in French). *Algérie méd.* [1953] **57,** 709–719.

53-231. Raynaud, R., d'Eshougues, J. R., Pasquet, P., and Di Giovanni, S. Study of lipoproteins in atherosclerosis by paper electrophoresis (in French). *Bull. mém. soc. méd. hôp. Paris* [4] **69,** (13/14), 394.

53-232. Raynaud, R., d'Eshougues, J. R., Pasquet, P., and Di Giovanni, S. Technique of study of serum lipoproteins by paper electrophoresis (in French). *Ann. biol. clin. (Paris)* [1953] **11,** 377.

53-233. Reindel, F., and Hoppe, W. A new staining method for detection of amino acids, peptides, and proteins on paper chromatograms and electropherograms (in German). *Naturwissenschaften* [1953] **40,** 221.

53-234. Reynaud, J. Differentiation of human hemoglobins of the adult, fetal, and sickle-cell anemia types by electrophoresis on paper (in French). *Compt. rend. soc. biol.* [1953] **147,** 838–841.

53-235. Rienits, K. G. Electrophoresis of acid mucopolysaccharides on filter paper. *Biochem. J.* [1953] **53,** 79–85.

53-236. Riva, G., and Martini, V. Clinical and laboratory experiences with paper electrophoresis (in German). *Schweiz. med. Wochschr.* [1953] **83,** 73.

53-237. Robert, L., and Penaranda, F. S. Interaction of aldehydes, reductones, and amino acids and proteins. II. Kinetics of the interaction of amino acids and acetaldehyde, followed by chromatography and ionophoresis on paper (in French). *Bull. soc. chim. biol.* [1953] **35,** 791–799; *Chem. Abstr.* [1954] **48,** 2157.

53-238. Roberts, S., and Brunish, R. Hepatic and extra-hepatic regulation of serum protein metabolism. *Federation Proc.* [1953] **12,** 259.

53-239. Roche, J., and Bouchilloux, S. Purification of intestinal alkaline phosphatase and its electrophoresis on paper (in French). *Bull. soc. chim. biol.* [1953] **35,** 567–573.

53-240. Roche, J., and Bouchilloux, S. Purification of alkaline phosphatase and its fractionation after paper electrophoresis (in French). *Compt. rend. soc. biol.* [1953] **147,** 464.

53-241. Rondelet, J., and Lontie, R. Some remarks on continuous electrophoresis (in French). *Electrophoresis. 1st Colloquium of the Laboratory of the Saint-Jean à Bruges Hospital (Belgium)* [1953]

53-242. Rossi-Fanelli, A., Mondovi, B., and Boffi, V. Separation of the phosphoric esters of thiamine by paper electrophoresis. I. (in Italian). *Boll. soc. ital. biol. sper.* [1953] **29,** 1330–1333.

53-243. Roth, E., and Kallee, E. Paper electrophoretic studies on the binding of dyestuffs. II. (in German). *Z. Naturforsch.* [1953] **8b,** 614–615.

53-244. Röttger, H. Comparative measurements of paper electrophoresis strips with four different optical instruments (in German). *Experientia* [1953] **9,** 150.

53-245. Röttger, H. New photoelectric instrument for evaluation of paper electrophoresis strips (in German). *Klin. Wochschr.* [1953] **31**, 85; *Chem. Abstr.* [1953] **47**, 4143.

53-246. Ruzdic, E., and Pucar, Z. Comparative determinations of single fractions of serum proteins by precipitation methods and electrophoresis on filter paper (in Jugoslav with English summary). *Acta Pharm. Jugoslav.* [1953] **3**, 130–142.

53-247. Salt, H. B. Microanalytical methods for proteins in blood plasma. *Analyst* [1953] **78**, 4–14.

53-248. Sanger, F., and Thompson, E. O. P. The amino-acid sequence in the glycyl chain of insulin. I. The identification of lower peptides from partial hydrolysates. *Biochem. J.* [1953] **53**, 353.

53-249. Sanger, F., and Thompson, E. O. P. The amino-acid sequence in the glycyl chains of insulin. II. The investigation of peptides from enzymic hydrolysates. *Biochem. J.* [1953] **53**, 366.

53-250. Sansoni, B., and Klement, R. Separation of phosphates by means of paper electrophoresis. *Angew. Chem.* [1953] **65**, 422–423.

53-251. Sato, T., Kisieleski, W., Norris, W. P., and Strain, H. H. Electrochromatographic separations of calcium and phosphate ions. *Anal. Chem.* [1953] **25**, 438.

53-252. Savard, K. Paper partition chromatography of C_{19} and C_{21}-ketosteroids. *J. Biol. Chem.* [1953] **202**, 457–477.

53-253. Scheidegger, J. J. Relation between sodium salicylate and the serum proteins studied by paper electrophoresis (in French). *Schweiz. med. Wochschr.* [1953] **83**, 406–407; *Chem. Abstr.* [1954] **48**, 3558.

53-254. Schild, K. T., and Bottenbruch, L. Paper electrophoretic separation of P^{32}-labelled hexose phosphate esters (in German). *Z. physiol. Chem.* [1953] **292**, 1–6.

53-255. Schilling, R. F., and Deiss, W. P. Intrinsic factor studies. I. Paper electrophoresis of mixture of gastric juice and radioactive vitamin B_{12}. *Proc. Soc. Exptl. Biol. Med.* [1953] **83**, 506.

53-256. Schmeiser, K., and Jerchel, D. Determination of phosphorus by neutron activation in paper electropherograms (in German). *Angew. Chem.* [1953] **65**, 490–491.

53-257. Schmidt, G. W. The behavior of serum-protein fractions in dehydrated infants during parenteral liquid administration (in German). *Z. Kinderheilk.* [1953] **73**, 621–631; *Chem. Abstr.* [1954] **48**, 4117.

53-258. Schneider, R. G. Paper electrophoresis of hemoglobin as a practical method of differentiating various types of sickle cell disease and of hemoglobin "C" trait. *Texas Repts. Biol. Med.* [1953] **11**, 352–365.

53-259. Scholz, E., and Hagedorn, P. Investigation of medicinal mixtures with paper electrophoresis. III. Paper chromatography of galenic tinctures (in German). *Deut. Apotheker Ztg.* [1953] **93**, 81–82; *Chem. Abstr.* [1953] **47**, 4044.

53-260. Schulz, J., Jamison, W., and Shay, H. Filter paper chromatography of hydrolysates of rat serum proteins fractionated by filter paper electrophoresis. *Federation Proc.* [1953] **12**, 128–129.

53-261. Schwarze, P. The protein complex of the potato tuber by paper electrophoresis (in German). *Naturwissenschaften* [1953] **40**, 21–22; *Chem. Abstr.* [1953] **47**, 11357.

53-262. Shul'man, M. S. The electrochemistry of starch: III. Electrical conductivity of starch solution in different conditions of gelatin-ization and ageing (in Russian). *Colloid J.* (*U.S.S.R.*) [1953] **15**, 221–222.

53-263. Simonart, P., and Crevier, M. Formation of alpha-ketoglutaric acid by *Rhizopus nigricans* (in French). *Intern. Congr. Microbiol., 6th Congr. Rome* [1953] **6**, 720.

53-264. Slavik, K., and Matoulkova, V. Metabolism of folic acid. I. Formation of formyl derivative in liver homogenates (in Czech). *Chem. listy* [1953] **47**, 1516–1521.

53-265. Slater, R. J., and Kunkel, H. G. Filter paper electrophoresis with special reference to urinary proteins. *J. Lab. Clin. Med.* [1953] **41**, 619.

53-266. von Slotta, K. Chemistry of snake poisons (in German). *Experientia* [1953] **9**, 81.

53-267. Smith, E. W., and Conley, C. L. Filter paper electrophoresis of human hemoglobin with special reference to the incidence and clinical significance of hemoglobin C. *Bull. Johns Hopkins Hosp.* [1953] **93**, 94–106.

53-268. Smith, E. R. B., Crawford, T. M., Jetton, M. R., and Durrum, E. L. Study of lipoprotein fractions by paper electrophoresis. *Federation Proc.* [1953] **12**, 269.

53-269. Smith, L. L., and States, S. J. Isolation of cholesterol from tissue extracts by paper chromatography. Project No. 21-1601-0007, *U.S.A.F. School of Aviation Med.* [1953] *Rept.* **3**, 1–4.

53-270. Sommerfelt, S. Comments regarding the evaluation of paper electrophoresis of proteins. *Scand. J. Clin. & Lab. Invest.* [1953] **5**, 105–106.

53-271. Sommerfelt, S. Paper electrophoresis of isolated plasma protein fractions. *Scand. J. Clin. & Lab. Invest.* [1953] **5**, 299.

53-272. Sonnet, J. A study of serum proteins by paper electrophoresis. The reproducibility of results (in French). *Electrophoresis. 1st Colloquium of the Laboratory of the Saint-Jean à Bruges Hospital (Belgium).* [1953]

53-273. Sonnet, J., and Sibille, A. Importance of electrophoresis of the blood proteins in myocardial infarction. *Acta Cardiol.* (*Brussels*) [1953] **8**, 479.

53-274. Soulier, J. P., and Alagille, D. Lipoproteins in human and experimental atherosclerosis by electrophoresis and protein aspecific reactions. *Plasma* (*Milan*) [1953] **1**, 439.

53-275. Soulier, J. P., and Alagille, D. Study of lipoproteins in human and experimental atherosclerosis, by electrophoresis and the non-specific reactions of proteins. The effect of heparin (in French). *Semaine Hôp.* [1953] **29**, 1–11.

53-276. Spaet, T. Identification of abnormal hemoglobins by means of paper electrophoresis. *J. Lab. Clin. Med.* [1953] **41**, 161.

53-277. Spaet, T. Practical application of paper electrophoresis (in clinical chemistry). *Calif. Med.* [1953] **79**, 271–273.

53-278. Spaet, R. H., and Kinsell, B. G. Studies on the normal serum panagglutinin active against trypsinated human erythrocytes. II. Relationship to cold agglutination. *J. Lab. Clin. Med.* [1953] **42**, 205–211.

53-279. Steger, J. Electrophoretic studies of cerebrospinal fluid (in German). *Deut. Z. Nervenheilk.* [1953] **171**, 1–19; *Chem. Abstr.* [1954] **48**, 6567.

53-280. Sternberg, J. Paper electrophoresis of proteins in clinical diagnosis. *Can. Med. Assoc. J.* [1953] **68**, 284–285.

53-281. Stockl, W., and Zacherl, M. K. Paper electrophoretic studies of bovine and horse serum (in German). *Z. physiol. Chem.* [1953] **293**, 278.

53-282. Stran, H. M., and Seegar-Jones, G. E. The filter paper electrophoretic identification of urinary chorionic gonadotrophin. *Bull. Johns Hopkins Hosp.* [1953] **93**, 51–53.

53-283. Strange, R. E., and Harkness, N. Paper electrophoresis of polyglutamyl peptide. *Nature* [1953] **171**, 77–78.

53-284. Sturmer, K., and Warkalla, H. J. Can the time of ovulation be determined with the aid of variations in the total serum proteins? (in German). *Geburtshilfe u. Frauenheilk.* [1953] **13**, 460.

53-285. Suenderhauf, H., and Wunderly, C. Recent examination of the protein partition in urine in the late toxemias of pregnancy (in German). *Gynaecologia* [1953] **135**, 101.

53-286. Taylor, S. P. Jr., du Vigneaud, V., and Kunkel, H. G. Electrophoretic studies of oxytocin and vasopressin. *J. Biol. Chem.* [1953] **205**, 45–53.

53-287. Taylor, S. P., du Vigneaud, V., and Kunkel, H. G. Electrophoretic properties of oxytocin and vasopressin. *Federation Proc.* [1953] **12**, 924.

53-288. Tegethoff, B. The identification of ascorbic acid in plant tissues by paper chromatography (in German). *Z. Naturforsch.* [1953] **8b**, 374–376.

53-289. Tepe, H. J., and Firzlaff, H. U. Paper electrophoretic studies in the treatment of pulmonary tuberculosis with isoniazid (in German). *Tuberkulosearzt* [1953] **7**, 574–583; *Chem. Abstr.* [1954] **48**, 8405.

53-290. Thing, E., Birch-Anderson, A., and Ravn, H. Melanophore reaction and adrenocorticotrophic hormone. V. On the migration of melanophore and adrenocorticotrophic activity during paper electrophoresis. *Acta Endocrinol.* [1953] **14**, 113–122.

53-291. Tigaud, J. Comparative study of electrophoretic techniques. Cell and paper electrophoresis. *J. méd. Lyon* [1953] **34**, 999–1004; *Chem. Abstr.* [1954] **48**, 7175.

53-292. Timasheff, S. N., Shumaker, J. B., Jr., and Kirkwood, J. G. Semicontinuous electrophoresis convection. *Arch. Biochem. Biophys.* [1953] **47**, 455–464.

53-293. Tiselius, A. I. Experimental techniques. Zone electrophoresis in filter paper and other media. *Discussions Faraday Soc.* [1953] **13**, 29.

53-294. Tiselius, A., and Flodin, P. Zone electrophoresis. *Advances in Protein Chemistry* [1953] **8**, 461–486.

53-295. Togni, G., and Meier, O. On the behavior of serum cholinesterase of the horse in paper electrophoresis (in German). *Experientia* [1953] **9**, 106.

53-296. Tomašević-Berkeš, P. Electrophoresis of serum proteins on filter paper (in Yugoslav). *Poseban Otisak iz Vojnosanitetskog Pregleda* [1953] **7–8**, 1–5.

53-297. Valle López, M., and Martínez Llinares, V. Paper electrophoresis. A simple apparatus with added devices to stabilize the experiments. (in Spanish with English summary). *Arch. med. exptl. (Madrid)* [1953] **16**, 363–370.

53-298. Vandegaer, J. E., and Miettinen, J. K. A paper electrophoretic investigation of milk-serum proteins. *Acta Chem. Scand.* [1953] **7**, 1239–1242; *Chem. Abstr.* [1954] **48**, 12830.

53-299. Van Middlesworth, L., Tuttle, A. H., and Threlkeld, A. Iodinated protein in milk. *Science* [1953] **118**, 749.

53-300. Voight, K. D., and Beckmann, I. Paper electrophoresis of steroids. *Acta Endocrinol.* [1953] **13**, 19–23.

53-301. de Wael, J. Technique and theory of paper electrophoresis (in Dutch) *Chem. Weekblad* [1953] **49**, 229–236.

53-302. Weber, R.　The theory of the electrophoretic separation in porous media (in German). *Helv. Chim. Acta* [1953] **36**, 424–434.

53-303. Webster, H. L.　Direct deamination of adenosine diphosphate by washed myofibrils. *Nature* [1953] **172**, 453.

53-304. Weicker, H.　The routine application of paper electrophoresis and the direct plotting of curves by means of ECG photo equipment (in German). *Klin. Wochschr.* [1953] **31**, 161–164.

53-305. Weicker, H., and Bohlinger, F.　Comparison of various electrophoresis methods with direct recording by means of ECG photo equipment (in German). *Klin. Wochschr.* [1953] **31**, 1114–1116.

53-306. Wenzel, M., and Hanson, H.　The photoelectric determination of blood proteins on paper (in German). *Z. physiol. Chem.* [1953] **292**, 137.

53-307. Werkheiser, W. C., and Winzler, R. J.　Separation and determination of ribonucleotides and related compounds by ionophoresis on filter paper. *J. Biol. Chem.* [1953] **204**, 971–981; [1954]. *Chem. Abstr.* **48**, 791.

53-308. Wetter, L. R.　Proteolytic enzymes of microorganisms. VI. The separation of proteases from *Mortierella renispora* by zone electrophoresis. *Can. J. Biochem. and Physiol.* [1953] **32**, 20–26; [1954]. *Chem. Abstr.* **48**, 5288.

53-309. White, W. F., and Giffee, J. W.　Paper electrophoresis of the pituitary hormones. *Abstr. 124th Ann. Meeting Am. Chem. Soc., Chicago* [1953] p. 43c.

53-310. Wiedermann, D., and Nesvadba, M.　Note on the filter-paper electrophoresis of proteins (in Czech). *Chem. listy* [1953] **47**, 1525–1527.

53-311. Wiedermann, D.　Paper electrophoresis of urine (in Czech). *Lékařské listy* [1953] **8**, 468–472; *Chem. Abstr.* [1954] **48**, 5265.

53-312. Wiedermann, D.　The subfractions of serum globulins by paper electrophoresis (in German). *Schweiz. med. Wochschr.* [1953] **83**, 1208–1209.

53-313. Wieland, T., Goldmann, H., Kern, W., Schultze, H. E., and Matheka, H. D. Fractionation of protein mixtures with polyacrylic acid (in German). *Makromol. Chem.* [1953] **10**, 136–146.

53-314. Wieme, R. J.　The movement of hemoglobin added to human serum in paper electrophoresis (in French). *Experientia* [1953] **9**, 380–381; *Chem. Abstr.* [1954] **48**, 5320.

53-315. Wieme, R. J.　A note on the migration of bilirubin and hemoglobin with paper electrophoresis at pH 8.5 (in French). *Electrophoresis. 1st Colloquium of the Laboratory of the Saint-Jean à Bruges Hospital (Belgium)* [1953].

53-316. Wikberg, E.　Isolation of a mixed disulfide of glutathione and cysteinyl-glycine from a partial hydrolysate of glutathione. *Nature* [1953] **172**, 398.

53-317. Woods, E. F., and Gillespie, J. M.　A critical study of the use of paper electrophoresis for separating proteins and measuring their isoelectric points. *Australian J. Biol. Sci.* [1953] **6**, 130–141.

53-318. Wuhrmann, F., and Jasinski, B.　Investigations on the linkage of iron to the serum beta-globulin by means of radioactive iron (Fe^{59}) and its clinical significance (in German). *Schweiz. med. Wochschr.* [1953] **83**, 661–672.

53-319. Wunderly, C.　Paper electrophoresis. Methods and results (in German). *Chimia (Switz.)* [1953] **7**, 145.

53-320. Wunderly, C., and Gloor, H.　An investigation and characterization of the normal blood proteins of larvae and of lethal genotypes by means of paper electrophoresis (in German). *Protoplasma* [1953] **42**, 273–282.

53-321. Wunderly, C.   The solubilization of 4-dimethylaminoazobenzene (butter yellow) in serum. *Science* [1953] **117**, 248–249.

53-322. Wunderly, C., and Pezold, F.   The binding of lipid dyes to the individual serum protein fractions (in German). *Z. ges. exptl. Med.* [1953] **120**, 613.

53-323. Wunderly, C., Gloor, E., and Hassig, A.   An immuno-chemical study of isolated serum protein fractions. *Brit. J. Exptl. Pathol.* [1953] **34**, 81.

53-324. Wunderly, C., and Wuhrmann, F.   Permeability of the capillaries and the blood proteins (in German with English summary). *Plasma (Milan)* [1953] **1**, 27.

53-325. Wunderly, C., Hassig, A., and Lottenbach, F.   The differentiation of serum albumin from the albumins of spinal fluid, pleural effusions and edema fluid (in German). *Klin. Wochschr.* [1953] **31**, 49.

53-326. Wunsche, H. W.   The protein of cantharides induced blisters in healthy persons and in patients with pulmonary tuberculosis (in German). *Klin. Wochschr.* [1953] **31**, 170.

53-326A. Wyllie, M. R. J., and Gregory, A. R.   Formation factors of unconsolidated porous media: Influence of particle shape and effect cementation. *Trans. Am. Inst. Mining Met. Engrs.* [1953] **198**, [in *J. Petroleum Technol.* **5**(4), 103].

53-327. Zettel, H., and Endress, M.   Serum proteins in carcinoma. *Chirug* [1953] **24**, 498.

53-328. Zilversmit, D. B., and Hood, S. L.   Effect of buffer on paper electrophoretic studies on state of yttrium in blood. *Proc. Soc. Exptl. Biol. Med.* [1953] **84**, 573–576.

53-329. Zimmermann, G., and Kludas, K. H.   Paper chromatography of serum proteins (in German). *Chem. Tech. (Berlin)* [1953] **5**, 203.

53-330. Zweig, G., and Block, R. J.   Paper electrophoresis of alpha, beta and gamma caseins. *Federation Proc.* [1953] **12**, 296.

54-1.   Ackerman, P. G., Toro, G., and Kountz, W. B.   Zone electrophoresis in the study of serum lipoproteins. I. Methods and preliminary results. *J. Lab. Clin. Med.* [1954] **44**, 517–530.

54-2.   Adjutantis, G.   Electrophoretic separation on filter paper of the soluble liver-cell proteins of the rat using borate buffer. *Nature* [1954] **173**, 539–540.

54-3.   Aggeler, P. M., Spaet, T. H., and Emery, B. E.   Purification of plasma thromboplastin factor B (plasma thromboplastin component) and its identification as a beta 2 globulin. *Science* [1954] **119**, 806.

54-4.   Aimi, R., and Murakami, T.   Phosphorylase protein in paper electrophoresis. *Kagaku (Tokyo)* [1954] **24**, 632.

54-5.   Ajl, S. J., Reedal, J., Durrum, E. L., and Warren, J.   Studies on plague. I. Purification and properties of the endotoxin of *Pasteurella pestis*. *Federation Proc.* [1954] **13**, 485.

54-6.   Akerfeldt, S.   A spot area method for quantitative determination of amino acids on two dimensional paper chromatograms. *Acta Chem. Scand.* [1954] **8**, 521–522.

54-7.   Albano, A.   Rapid components formed by minimal amounts of polysaccharide acids added to serum (in Italian). *Plasma (Milan)* [1954] **2**, 607.

54-8.   Anonymous.   "Column Electrophoresis Apparatus". *Sci. Tools* [1954] **1**, 19.

54-9.   Antonini, F. M., and Piva, G.   Some aspects of protein, lipoprotein and glycoprotein metabolism in tuberculosis (in Italian). *Giorn. mal. infettive e parassit.* [1954] **6**, 249.

54-10. Arbouys, S., Fine, J., and Eyquem, A.   Electrophoretic study of the serum of rodents (in French). *Ann. inst. Pasteur* [1954] **87**, 169.

54-11. Ardry, R.   The use of interpretive diagrams of electrophoretic mobilities (in French). *Ann. biol. clin. (Paris)* [1954] **12**, 171–176.

54-12. Ardry, R.   Interaction of proteins with surface-active agents. II. Limited action of the detergents on human serum (in French). *Bull. soc. chim. biol.* [1954] **36**, 603.

54-13. Arends, T., Coonrad, E. V., and Rundles, R. W.   Serum proteins in Hodgkin's disease and malignant lymphoma. *Am. J. Med.* [1954] **16**, 833–841.

54-14. Armstrong, S. H., Jr., McLeod, K., Wolter, J., and Kukral, J.   The persistence in the blood of the radioactive label of albumin, gamma globulins, globulins of intermediate mobility studied with S^{35} and paper electrophoresis methods and preliminary results. *J. Lab. Clin. Med.* [1954] **43**, 918–937.

54-15. Baar, S.   Estimation of glucose by paper partition chromatography. *Biochem. J.* [1954] **58**, 175.

54-16. Babin, R., Mesnard, P., and Delman, G.   The electrophoretic sign of some enzymes (in French). *Bull. soc. pharm. Bordeaux* [1954] **92**, 85-88.

54-17. Bajusz, E., and Kovary, L.   Determination of dehydrogenase activity of serum protein fractions separated by paper electrophoresis (in Italian). *Plasma (Milan)* [1954] **2**, 615–619.

54-18. Baker, R. W. R., and Pellegrino, C.   The separation and detection of serum enzymes by paper electrophoresis. *Scand. J. Clin. & Lab. Invest.* [1954] **6**, 94.

54-19. Barnett, A. J. G., and Smith, D. K.   Electrophoretic movement of higher fatty acids on filter paper. *Nature* [1954] **174**, 659–660.

54-20. Bassir, O.   A continuous-scanning device for paper electrophoresis and strip chromatography. *Chem. & Ind. (London)* [1954] p. 709–710; *Chem. Abstr.* [1954] **48**, 11850.

54-21. Berbalk, H.   Electrophoresis. I. Difficulties with apparatus and sources of error in paper electrophoresis (in German). *Monatsh. Chem.* [1954] **85**, 1314–1319.

54-22. Berg, G., and Scheiffarth, F.   Relative position of various protein fractions on the basis of mobility measurements with paper electrophoresis. The possible characterization of species specificity of serums (in German). *Klin. Wochschr.* [1954] **32**, 472–474.

54-23. Bergamini, C. and Versorese, W.   Relation between concentration and total optical density in radial inorganic paper chromatography. *Anal. Chim. Acta* [1954] **10**, 328–334.

54-24. Berger, J. A.   The phenol reaction of Kunkel and Ahrens. Its application in clinical biochemistry. *Trav. soc. pharm. Montpellier* [1954] **14**, 156.

54-25. Bergren, W. R.   Separation of abnormal hemoglobins by paper electrophoresis. *Abstr. 125th Ann. Meeting Am. Chem. Soc. Kansas City, Missouri* [1954].

54-26. Bergren, W. R., Sturgeon, P., and Itano, H. A.   Zone electrophoresis of abnormal hemoglobins. *Am. J. Clin. Pathol.* [1954] **25**, 160.

54-27. Berkes, I., and Briski, B.   Paper electrophoresis of the protamines of the *Mugil* and *Pagrus* fish. (In Yugoslav with English summary). *Kemi ind. (Zagreb)* [1954] **6**, 177–180.

54-28. Berkes, I., Devic-Mikac, D., and Karas, V.   Paper electrophoretic investigation of the internal effusions classified by the Rivalta reaction (in German). *Z. physiol. Chem.* [1954] **294,** 142.

54-29. Berinozzi, A. Recent acquisition in paper chromatography and electrophoretic method (in Italian). *Sperimentale, Sez. chim. biol.* [1954] **5,** 33.

54-30. Biserte, G., Boulanger, P., and Dantrevaux, M. Partial peptic hydrolysis of cryoalbumin (in French). *Bull. soc. chim. biol.* [1954] **36,** 127–140.

54-31. Biserte, G., Charbonnier, A., and Guerin, F. The development of the proteinogram and of the lipoproteinogram of human sera kept in a 37° incubator (in French) *Compt. rend.* [1954] **239,** 127.

54-32. Blass, J., Lecomte, O., and Polonovski, J. A technique of electrophoresis associated with paper chromatography; chromato-ionophoresis applied to amino acids and amine bases (in French). *Bull. soc. chim. biol.* [1954] **36,** 627–640.

54-33. Blöch, J., and Graf, E. Lipid electrophoresis. I. Communication: Determinations in patients with diabetes mellitus (in German). *Wien. Klin. Wochschr.* [1954] **66,** 652.

54-34. Bode, F., and Ludwig, U. M. A simple and accurate method for the determination of urea in the clinical laboratory (in German). *Schweiz. med. Wochschr.* [1954] **84,** 629.

54-35. Boguth, W. Paper-electrophoretic serum examination of domestic mammals. II. (in German). *Zentr. Veterinärmed.* [1954] **1,** 311–329; *Chem. Abstr.* [1954] **48,** 8397.

54-36. Boi, G. Electrophoretic blood protein behavior in tuberculous meningitis. *Ann. ital. pediat.* [1954] **7,** 460–474. (in Italian with English summary)

54-37. Bollinger, R. E., Grady, H. J., and Slinker, B. J. The effect of injected heparin on the electrophoresis of the lipoproteins in patients with hypercholesterol. *Am. J. Med. Sci.* [1954] **227,** 193–200.

54-38. Bon, W. F. A new method for the detection of proteins on paper electropherograms. Preliminary report (in Dutch). *Chem. Weekblad* [1954] **50,** 131–132.

54-39. Bonetti, E., and Dent, C. E. Determination of the optical configuration of naturally occurring amino acids using specific enzymes and paper chromatography. *Biochem. J.* [1954] **57,** 77–81.

54-40. Boser, H. Detection of adenine on paper chromatograms of nucleo-protein hydrolyzates (in German). *Z. physiol. Chem.* [1954] **298,** 145.

54-41. Bossak, E. T., Wang, C. I., and Adlersberg, D. Comparative studies of serum (serum lipoproteins) in various species by paper electrophoresis. *Proc. soc. exptl. biol. med.* [1954] **87,** 637–643.

54-42. Bosticco, A., and Ubertalle, A. Milk analysis by paper electrophoresis. I. Electrophoretic picture of mammal milk in relation to its species. II. Electrophoretic picture of heat-treated cow milk (in Italian with English summary). *Atti soc. ital. sci. vet.* [1954] **8,** 326–329, 329–332.

54-43. Boyd, G. S. The estimation of serum lipoproteins: A micromethod based on zone electrophoresis and cholesterol estimation. *Biochem. J.* [1954] **58,** 680.

54-44. Bradish, C. J., and Smart, N. V. Fractionation of serum proteins by zone electrophoresis in glass powder. *Nature* [1954] **174,** 272–273.

54-45. Bradley, J. E. S. Automatic recording scanner for isotope-bearing chromatograms. *Biochem. J.* [1954] **56,** 48.

54-46. Brattsten, I. Continuous fractionation of serum by zone electrophoresis. *Acta Chem. Scand.* [1954] **8,** 1947.

54-47. Bräuniger, H., and Raudonat, H. W. Paper electrophoretic studies of solutions of beta-piperidino-ethyl p-propoxyphenyl ketone (Falicaine) (in German). *Pharm. Zentralhalle* [1954] **93**, 136–138.

54-48. Braunsteiner, H., Falkner, R., Neumayer, A., and Pakesch, F. Macromolecular cryoglobulinemia (in German). *Klin. Wochschr.* [1954] **32**, 722–726.

54-49. Broicher, H., and Odenthal, H. Relations between electrophoretic changes in serum proteins and pathologic-anatomical observations by laparoscopy and biopsy in chronic liver diseases (in German). *Klin. Wochschr.* [1954] **32**, 592–597.

54-50. Brown, T. Electrophoretic analysis of serum proteins in pregnancy. Preliminary report. *J. Obstet. Gynaecol. Brit. Empire* [1954] **61**, 781.

54-51. Bruscha, W. Changes in blood cell sedimentation rate and electrophoretic protein fractions in megaphen-treated patients (in German). *Klin. Wochschr.* [1954] **32**, 669–671.

54-52. Burke, D. C. Ionophoresis of some nucleosides and their derived bases. *Chem. & Ind. (London)* [1954] p. 1510.

54-53. Burma, D. P. Paper ionophoresis of alkaloids (in English.) *Naturwissenschaften* [1954] **41**, 19.

54-54. Bussard, M. A. The use of agar as a substitute for paper in routine zone electrophoresis of proteins (in French). *Compt. rend.* [1954] **239**, 1702–1704.

54-55. Bussard, A., and Cote, R. The constitution of cobra (*Naja naja*) venom. *Compt. rend.* [1954] **239**, 915.

54-56. Burtin, P., Grabar, P., Boussier, G., and Jayle, M. F. Immunochemical study of haptoglobin. *Bull. soc. chim. biol.* [1954] **36**, 1029–1035.

54-57. Cabib, E., and Leloir, L. F. Guanosine diphosphate mannose. *J. Biol. Chem.* [1954] **206**, 779–790; *Chem. Abstr.* **48**, 5246.

54-58. Cagli, V., and Scuro, L. A. Comparative study of the working of the specific agglutinins and of the electrophoretic picture of serum proteins in a typhoid infection of the rabbit; Influence of treatment with chloroamphenicol (in Italian). *Boll. soc. ital. biol. sper.* [1954] **30**, 144.

54-59. Cagli, V., and Mancia, M. The electrophoretic pattern of normal rabbit serum and that infected with *Salmonella typhosa* (in Italian with English summary.) *Boll. ist. sieroterap. (Milan)* [1954] **33**, 366.

54-60. Cagli, V. Study of serum protein fractions of the rat by electrophoresis on paper (in Italian). *Boll. soc. ital. biol. sper.* [1954] **30**, 273.

54-61. Camba, R., and Carta, R. Electrophoretic studies on human seminal plasma (in Italian). *Arch. "De Vecchi" Anat. patol. e med. clin.* [1954] **22**, 565.

54-62. Camba, R. Electrophoresis on paper of aqueous extracts of human seminal plasma dried on cloth (in Italian). *Ateneo parmense* [1954] **25**, 393.

54-63. Cannon, J. R., and Gilson, A. R. A simple apparatus and technique for preparative paper electrophoresis. *Chem. & Ind. (London)* [1954] p. 120–121; *Chem. Abstr.* [1954] **48**, 4886.

54-64. Caputo, A. Electrophoretic behavior of hyaluronidase. *Nature* [1954] **173**, 358–359.

54-65. Carlson, L. A., and Olhagen, B. The electrophoretic mobility of chylomicrons in a case of essential hyperlipemia. *Scand. J. Clin. & Lab. Invest.* [1954] **6**, 70–73.

54-66. Carlson, L. A. Electrophoretic studies of serum lipoproteins. I. A description of apparatus and technique for their separation in starch. *Acta Chem. Scand.* [1954] **8**, 510-520.

54-67. Carta, R., and Cambra, R. Electrophoresis of various biological liquids (in Italian). *Rassegna med. sarda* [n.s.] [1954] **5-6**, 1–8.

54-68. Caselli, P., and Schumacher, H. The direction of lysozyme in tears by means of microelectrophoresis (in German). *Klin. Monatsbl. Augenheilkd.* [1954] **124**, 148–154.

54-69. Caselli, P. Paper electrophoresis of heparin, alone and in the presence of serum proteins (in Italian). *Giorn. biochim.* [1954] **3**, 76.

54-70. Caselli, P., and Schumacher, H. Micro-electrophoretic studies on serum-lysozyme (in German). *Z. ges. exptl. Med.* [1954] **124**, 65.

54-71. Caspani, R., and Magistretti, M. New method of staining electrophoretic tracings on filter paper (in Italian with English summary). *Plasma (Milan)* [1954] **1**, 1.

54-72. Casselman, W. G. B. Acetylated Sudan Black B as a reagent for lipids *Biochim. et Biophys. Acta* [1954] **14**, 450.

54-73. Ceccaldi, P. F., Wegmann, R., and Biez-Charreton, J. Chromatography of lipids on paper (in French). *Bull. soc. chim. biol.* [1954] **36**, 415–424.

54-74. Cerf, N. Photoelectric densitometer for electrophoresis on paper (in French). *Chim. anal.* [1954] **36**, 268.

54-75. Chernoff, A. I., and Minnich, V. Hemoglobin E, A hereditary abnormality of human hemoglobin. *Science* [1954] **120**, 605–606.

54-76. Chiesura, P. Variations of serum proteins in acute and chronic glomerulonephritis (in Italian). *Minerva nefrol.* [1954] **1**, 75.

54-77. Choremis, K. W., Kyriakidou, W., Malliopoulou, T., Zoumboulakis, D., and Tolis, A. Comparative ionogram studies in dystrophy and toxicosis (in German). *Z. Kinderheilk.* [1954] **74**, 333–352.

54-78. Cifonelli, J. A., and Smith, F. Detection of glycosides and other carbohydrate compounds on paper chromatograms. *Anal. Chem.* [1954] **26**, 1132–1134.

54-79. Clouet, D. H., Ball, C. O. T., Meneely, G. R., and Hahn, P. F. Electrophoresis of plasma proteins and ascitic fluid of dogs with radiation cirrhosis. *Proc. Soc. Exptl. Biol. Med.* [1954] **87**, 362.

54-80. Conn, H. O., and Klatskin, G. Filter paper electrophoretic patterns of serum in multiple myelome. *Am. J. Med.* [1954] **16**, 822–832.

54-81. Cooper, G. R., and Mandel, E. E. Paper electrophoresis in clinical diagnosis. *Program Sci. Assembly 103rd Ann. Meeting Am. Med. Assoc. (San Francisco)* [1954] June 21–25.

54-82. Cooper, G. R., Mandel, E. E., Owings, R. H., and Fetner, J. Paper electrophoresis with automatic scanning and recording. *J. Lab. Clin. Med.* [1954] **44**, 636.

54-83. Corda, R. Blood protein in acute and subacute glomerulo-nephritis of children. (in Italian with English summary). *Ann. ital. pediat.* [1954] **7**, 495.

54-84. Corradetti, A., Verolini, F., and Toschi, G. Pathological and immunological host-parasite relationships between albino rat and *Plasmodium berghei. Indian J. Malariology* [1954] **8**, 391.

54-85. Corradetti, A., Toschi, G., and Verolini, G. Serum proteins during the primary attack in rats infected with *Plasmodium berghei* (in Italian). *Riv. parassitol.* [1954] **15**, 141.

54-86. Corsini, F.   Protein of cerebrospinal fluid (CSF) shown by paper electrophoresis. *Clin. Pediat.* [1954] **36**, 33–46.

54-87. Corticelli, B.   A simple graphic method for the identification of electrophoretic fractions of blood serum (in Italian). *Boll. soc. ital. biol. sper.* [1954] **30**, 1238.

54-88. Corwin, L. M., and Orten, J. M.   Simplified procedure for separating porphyrins from urine by paper chromatography. *Anal. Chem.* [1954] **26**, 608–609.

54-89. Crestfield, A. M., and Allen, F. W.   Studies of the mobility of ribonuclease by zone electrophoresis. *J. Biol. Chem.* [1954] **211**, 363.

54-90. Crevier, M., and Belanger, L. F.   Demonstration by electrophoresis and autoradiography of a sulfomucoprotein containing radiosulfate synthesized by the gastric glands of the rat (in French). *Compt. rend. soc. biol.* [1954] **148**, 1530.

54-91. Crook, E. M., Harris, H., Hassan, F., and Warren, F. L.   Continuous direct photometry of dyed materials in filter paper with special reference to the estimation of proteins separated by electrophoresis. *Biochem. J.* [1954] **56**, 434–444.

54-92. Crosbie, G. W., Hutchinson, W. C., McIndoe, W. M., Childs, M., and Davison, J. N.   Protein-bound components of liver and brain. *Biochim. et Biophys. Acta* [1954] **14**, 580–581.

54-93. Cserey-Penchany, E., and Molnar, B.   The vitamin B_{12} content of liver extracts as determined by electrophoretic and microbiologic methods (in Hungarian). *Acta Microbiol. Acad. Sci. Hung.* [1954] **1**, 115.

54-94. Culvier, R., Berger, J. A., Tronche, P., and Chagnaud, J.   A study of the proteins of cerebrospinal fluid (CSF) by microelectrophoresis on paper. The spinal-proteinogram (in French). *Ann. biol. clin. (Paris)* [1954] **12**, 389.

54-95. Curletto, R., and Terzi, G. F.   Plasmoreticulum and electrophoretic behavior of serum of rabbits treated by heterologous blood; Changes from ethylurethan (in Italian). *Plasma (Milan)* [1954] **2**, 157–177.

54-96. Cutroneo, A.   Serum protein in normal and tuberculous children (in Italian). *Riv. pediat. Siciliana* [1954] **9**, 401.

54-97. Cutroneo, A.   Modification of a method for concentrating protein of cerebrospinal fluid (CSF) for electrophoretic investigation (in Italian with English summary). *Aggiron. pediat.* [1954] **5**, 627.

54-98. Dagradi, A., and Bertolin, G.   Electrophoretical fractions of protein of the hydrocele fluid (in Italian). *Chir. e patol. sper.* [1954] **2**, 477.

54-99. Deimel, M.   Separation of ribonucleic acid and desoxyribonucleic acid by electrophoresis (in German). *Biochem. Z.* [1954] **325**, 358.

54-100. Delanne, R., Steens, A., and van Meerbeck, J.   Note on the electrophoretic variations of protein balance on flocculation tests after intensive muscular activity (in Dutch). *Bruxelles-Méd.* [1954] **34**, 2364.

54-101. Della Porta, V.   The serum protein pattern in the so-called thrombosis of the retinal vein (in Italian). *Ann. ottalmol. e clin. oculist.* [1954] **80**, 319.

54-102. Delmon, G., Banquet, P., and Babin, R.   Paper microelectrophoresis on cancerous subjects (in French). *Ann. biol. clin. (Paris)* [1954] **12**, 46.

54-103. De Marco, C., and Mondovi, B.   Serum-protein fractions before and after radium treatment (in Italian with English summary). *Minerva ginecol.* [1954] **6**, 725.

54-104. De Marco, C., and Stirpe, F.   Electrophoretic analysis of proteins present in amniotic fluid (in Italian with English summary). *Giorn. biochim.* [1954] **3**, 291.

54-105. De Martiis, M., and Ricci, G. A method for the study of lipoproteins by means of paper electrophoresis (in Italian). *Boll. soc. ital. biol. sper.* [1954] **30**, 1343.

54-106. Dettker, A., and Anduren, H. A time-saving apparatus for paper electrophoresis. *Scand. J. Clin. & Lab. Invest.* [1954] **6**, 74–75.

54-107. Di Castro, G. Two dimensional electrophoresis on paper. *J. Polymer. Sci.* [1954] **12**, 445–448.

54-108. Di Castro, G. Some remarks on two-dimensional paper electrophoresis. *Experientia* [1954] **10**, 27–28.

54-109. Di Castro, G., and San Marco, M. Continuous electrophoresis on paper. *J. Chem. Soc.* [1954] p. 4157.

54-110. Di Domizio, G. The composition of skeletal muscle protein in febrile animals with spontaneous disease (in Italian with English summary). *Arch. vet. ital.* [1954] **5**, 289–291.

54-111. Di Domizio, G. Contribution to the study of muscle proteins of the cow and the horse (in Italian with English summary). *Arch vet. ital.* [1954] **5**, 97–99.

54-112. Diemair, W., Janecke, H., and Ott, D. Effect of ultraviolet irradiation on the proteins of milk (in German). *Z. anal. Chem.* [1954] **143**, 244.

54-113. Discombe, G., Jones, R. F., and Winstanley, D. P. Estimation of gamma-globulin. *J. Clin. Pathol.* [1954] **7**, 106–109.

54-114. Dobson, H. L., and Stribling, S. H. Heparin effect on serum lipoproteins as studies by free and filter paper electrophoresis. *Proc. 27th Ann. Meeting, Central Soc. Clin. Research.* [1954]

54-115. Donzelot, E., and Kaufmann, H. Electrophoresis in myocardial infarction (in Italian). *Minerva med.* [1954] **1**, 1508–1510.

54-116. Drevon, B. Improvement on the paper electrophoresis of serum proteins: Decolorization of the strips by extraction in the Kumagawa apparatus (in French). *Bull. soc. chim. biol.* [1954] **36**, 921.

54-117. Drilhon, A. Study of the serum lipoproteins in some fish by means of paper electrophoresis (in French). *Compt. rend.* [1954] **238**, 940–942; *Chem. Abstr.* **48**, 7212.

54-118. Drilhon, A. Electrophoretic study of the proteins of the hemolymph of *Bombyx mori* during its life cycle (in French). *Compt. rend.* [1954] **238**, 2452–2454.

54-119. Drilhon, A. Biological study of serum proteins of blood of several fishes by electrophoresis on paper (in French). *Compt. rend. soc. biol.* [1954] **148**, 1218.

54-120. Durrum, E. L., Smith, E. R. B., and Jetton, M. R. Simple multiple-sample dialyzer. *Science* [1954] **120**, 956.

54-121. Ehrmantraut, H. C., and Weinstock, A. Method of applying the Beckman spectrophotometer to the measurement of paper chromatograms. *Biochim. et Biophys. Acta* [1954] **15**, 589.

54-122. Eisfeld, G., and Koch, E. The behavior of alkaline and acid serum phosphatases of man on paper electrophoresis (in German). *Z. ges. inn. Med. u. ihre Grenzgebiete* [1954] **9**, 514.

54-123. Eisfeld, G., and Seefeldt, H. Paper electrophoretic behavior of paraaminosalicylic acid (PAS) and isonicotinic acid hyrazide (INH) in presence of serum albumin (in German). *Naturwissenschaften* [1954] **41**, 305.

54-124. Engelke, J. L., Strain, H. H., and Wood, S. E.   Electro-osmosis in paper. Electrochromatography with electrode vessels. *Anal. Chem.* [1954] **26,** 1864–1868.

54-125. Engelke, J. L., and Strain, H. H.   Electrical mobility of phosphate ions in paper electrochromatography. *Anal. Chem.* [1954] **26,** 1872–1874.

54-126. Enselme, J., Tigaud, J., Lambert, R., and Cottet, J.   Electrophoretic study of the proteins of rat serum. A statistical study of the results (in French). *Bull. soc. chim. biol.* [1954] **36,** 1599.

54-127. Enselme, J., and Tigaud, J.   Controlled denaturation of plasma proteins. I. Preparation and composition of an electrophoretically pure protein extracted from plasma treated with formaldehyde and heat (in French). *Bull. soc. chim. biol.* [1954] **36,** 815–820; see also Parts II and III. *Ibid.* pp. 821–825, 1087–1091.

54-128. Esser, H., Heinzler, F., and Pau, H.   Electrophoretic separation of protein fractions in the human aqueous humor (in German). *Arch. Ophthalmol. Graefe's* [1954] **155,** 11-16; *Chem. Abstr.* [1954] **48,** 8375.

54-129. Farina, L., Galletti, F., Giungi, F., and Loli-Piccolomini, M.   Serum glycoproteins in obstetrics and gynecology. I. Protein, polysaccharide, mucoprotein, and protein fractions in normal terminal pregnancy (in Italian). *Riv. ital. ginecol.* [1954] **37,** 257.

54-130. Farina, L., Galletti, F., and Loli-Piccolomini, M.   Serum glycoproteins in obstetrics and gynecology. II. Protein, polysaccharide, mucoprotein fractions in fetal blood (in Italian). *Riv. ital. ginecol.* [1954] **37,** 473.

54-131. Fasano, E., and Galletti, F.   Significance of the protein picture in tuberculosis of the lungs (in Italian). *Bull. sci. med.* [1954] **126,** 12–24.

54-132. Fasoli, A., Magid, E. B., Glassman, M. D., and Foa, P. P.   Serum lipoproteins in experimental diabetes. I. Serum lipoprotein pattern of normal and depancreatized dogs. *Proc. Soc. Exptl. Biol. Med.* [1954] **85,** 609–613.

54-133. Fasoli, A., Glassman, M. D., Magid, E B., and Foa, P. P.   Serum lipoproteins in experimental diabetes. II. Action of heparin in vivo on lipoproteins of depancreatized dogs. *Proc. Soc. Exptl. Biol. Med.* [1954] **86,** 298–301.

54-134. Fasoli, A., Magid, E. B., Glassman, M. D., and Foa, P. P.   Serum lipoproteins in experimental diabetes. III. Effect of anterior pituitary growth hormone. *Proc. Soc. Exptl. Biol. Med.* [1954] **87,** 167–169.

54-135. Fasoli, A.   Paper electrophoresis of the lipoproteins of the serum (in Italian). *Boll. soc. ital. biol. sper.* [1954] **28,** 603.

54-136. Felder, O.   What is the value of running observations on the serum-protein composition in tuberculosis? (in German). *Münch. med. Wochschr.* [1954] **96,** 879–883.

54-137. Feruglio, F., and Rimini, R.   Flocculation tests and electrophoretic patterns of exudates and transudates (in Italian with English summary). *Studi sassaresi* [1954] **32,** 28.

54-138. Feruglio, F. S., and Rimini, R.   Electrophoretic studies on proteinurias (in Italian). *Minerva nefrol.* (1954) **1,** 155.

54-139. Fine, J. M., Vincon-Alrig, M., and Groulade, J.   Electrophoretic serum studies in diseases of the blood and of hematopoietic organs (in French). *Presse méd.* [1954] **62,** 1043.

54-140. Fischer, A.   Separation of indole derivatives by chromatography on paper and electrophoresis on paper (in German). *Planta* [1954] **43,** 288–314.

54-141. Fischer, F. G., and Neumann, W. P. Snake venoms. II. The electrophoretic analysis of the venoms of *Naja haje* and *Naja nigricollis*. III. The electrophoretic analysis of the venoms of *Bitis arietans* and *Echis carinatus* (in German). *Z. physiol. Chem.* [1954] **297**, 92–99, 100–103.

54-142. Fischer, H., Kreuzer, L., and Argenton, H. The importance of lower molecular albumin components for shock and the prevention of blood coagulation (in German with English summary). *Rept. 1st Intern. Congr. Thrombosis and Emboli* [1954] p. 136.

54-143. Fischer, H., and Wagner, L. Effect of low molecular proteins (basic) on cells and organisms (in German). *Naturwissenschaften* [1954] **41**, 533.

54-144. Flodin, P., and Porath, J. Column electrophoresis apparatus. *Sci. Tools* [1954] **1**, 19.

54-145. Flodin, P., and Porath, J. Zone electrophoresis in starch columns. *Biochim. et Biophys. Acta* [1954] **13**, 175–182.

54-146. Florio, I., and Guagliano, G. Serum electrophoresis patterns of animals subjected to skin homografts (in Italian). *Boll. soc. med. chir. Pavia* [1954] **68**, 705–713.

54-147. Flynn, F. V. The serum proteins, electrophoretic patterns of serum protein in health and disease. *Proc. Roy. Soc. Med.* [1954] **47**, 827.

54-148. Fonss-Bech, P., and Li, C. H. Zone electrophoresis of hypophyseal growth hormone (somatotropin) on starch. *J. Biol. Chem.* [1954] **207**, 175–180.

54-149. Fox, C. E. Apparatus for chromatographic and electrophoretic analysis. *Chem. Products* [1954] **17**, 260–266.

54-150. Francescon, M., and Butto, M. Unusual terminal blood protein picture in a case of disseminated acute lupus erythematosus (in Italian). *Riforma med.* [1954] **68**, 66.

54-151. Francke, C., Harders, C. L., van Mulken, J. M., and Robert, W. N. Iron metabolism in multiple myeloma investigated by means of radioactive iron (in Dutch with English summary). *Ned. Tijdschr. Geneesk.* [1954] **98**, 3377.

54-152. François, J., Wieme, R. J., Rabaey, M., and Neetens, A. Paper electrophoresis of water-soluble proteins from the lenses of various mammals (in French). *Experientia* [1954] **10**, 79–80; *Chem. Abstr.* **48**, 8904.

54-153. Franglen, G. T., and Martin, N. H. The interaction of dyes with proteins on paper with special reference to paper electrophoresis. *Biochem. J.* [1954] **57**, 626–630.

54-154. Franglen, G. T., and Martin, N. H. The use and limitations of filter-paper electrophoresis. *J. Clin. Pathol.* [1954] **6**, 87.

54-155. Fraux, J. Electrophoretic study of plasma proteins in eczema of nursling infants (in French). *Trav. soc. pharm. Montpellier* [1954] **14**, 163.

54-156. Freislederer, W., and Stoeber, E. The clinical use of serum in rheumatism during childhood (in German). *Z. Kinderheilk.* [1954] **75**, 532.

54-157. Frentz, R. Paper electrophoresis of serum proteins of *Carcinus maenas* (in French). *Compt. rend.* [1954] **239**, 1867.

54-158. Freytag, H. Application of the Hanau ultraviolet lamp in qualitative analysis. III. Detection of barbituric acid, 2-thiobarbituric acid, and pyridine (in German). *Z. anal. Chem.* [1954] **142**, 12–15.

54-159. Gabrieli, E. R., Goulian, D., Jr., Kinersly, T., and Collet, R. Zone paper electrophoresis studies on radio-iodinated human serum albumin. *J. Clin. Invest.* [1954] **33**, 136–141.

54-160. Gaisinskaya, O. M., L'vova, V. V., and Uspenskaya, V. D.   Electrophoretic studies of the proteins of blood serum of the dog (in Russian). *Biokhimiya* [1954] **19**, 319–331.

54-161. Galos, B., and Ostrowski, W.   Electrophoretic separation of sugars and their derivatives. *Bull. acad. polon. sci. Classe II* [1954] **2**, 61.

54-162. Gatto, I., and La Grutta, A.   A study of human hemoglobin by paper electrophoresis (in Italian). *Boll. soc. ital. biol. sper.* [1954] **30**, 1369.

54-163. Gaudiano, A., and Cingolani, E.   Chromatography and electrophoresis on paper of riboflavin and its phosphoric esters (in Italian). *Boll. soc. ital. biol. sper.* [1954] **30**, 637.

54-164. Gaudiano, A., Toffoli, F., and Boccacci, N.   Chemical determination of synthetic co-carboxylase (in Italian). *Rend. inst. super. sanità* [1954] **17**, 498.

54-165. Geinitz, W.   Serum proteins of animals frequently used for experiments or serum production (in German). *Klin. Wochschr.* [1954] **32**, 1108.

54-166. Gerlaxhe, S., and Renard, M.   Chromato-electrorheophoresis of amino acids (in French). *Compt. rend. 27ᵉ congr. intern. chim. indust.*

54-167. Ghosh, A. R.   Horizontal and vertical methods of migration in paper ionophoresis (in German). *Naturwissenschaften* [1954] **41**, 257.

54-168. Gibert-Queralto, J., Balaguer-Vintro, I., and Grau-Codina, L.   The lipogram of arteriosclerosis and its changes by heparin (in Spanish). *Med. españ.* [1954] **32**, 58.

54-169. Gigante, D., Rossi-Espagnet, A., Capone, M., and Marinoni, F.   Serum protein in malignant blood diseases. I. Serum protein picture in chronic leukemic lymphadenosis. II. Serum protein picture in malignant lymphogranuloma. III. Serum protein picture in lymphosarcoma and reticulosarcoma (in Italian). *Progr. med.* [1954] **10**, 545–552, 641–650, 705–710.

54-170. Gigante, D., Capone, M., Marinoni, G., and Rossi-Espagnet, A.   Electrophoretic research on rat liver and spleen proteins (in Italian). *Riv. infortuni e mal. profess.* [1954] **41**, 210.

54-171. Giordano, G.   Modifications of the electrophoretic pattern in rats bearing benzopyrene tumors (in Italian). *Boll. soc. ital. biol. sper.* [1954] **30**, 612–614.

54-172. Godin, P.   A new spray reagent for paper chromatography of polyols and cetoses. *Nature* [1954] **174**, 134.

54-173. Not Assigned

54-174. González Alvarez, J., and Enríquez de Salamanca, F.   Paper electrophoresis. IV. The variations of protein fractions in the post-operative course. (in Spanish with summary in English). *Arch. med. exptl.* (Madrid) **17**, 555.

54-175. van Gool, J.   The azocarmine B color-binding capacity of albumin and gamma-globulin (in Dutch). *Chem. Weekblad* [1954] **50**, 705.

54-176. Gordon, A. H., and McFarlane, A. S.   Zone electrophoresis of pathological sera labelled with I¹³¹. *Biochem. J.* [1954] **58**, 1.

54-177. Gordon, S., and Nardi, G. L.   Paper chromatography of free amino acids in blood plasma. *J. Lab. Clin. Med.* [1954] **43**, 827–830.

54-178. Gottfried, S. P., Pope, R. H., Friedman, N. H., and Di Mauro, S.   Simple method for the determination of alpha and beta lipoproteins in serum by paper electrophoresis. *J. Lab. Clin. Med.* [1954] **44**, 651–654.

54-179. Grabar, P.   Protein studies with the help of immunological methods (in French). *Bull. soc. chim. biol.* [1954] **36**, 65–77.

54-180. Graf, E., and List, D. P. H.   Paper electrophoresis. Paper electrophoretic determination of morphine and chelidonine in natural mixtures (in German). *Arzneimittel-Forsch.* [1954] **4**, 450–453.

54-181. Granick, S.   Enzymatic conversion of delta-amino levulinic acid to porphobilinogen. *Science* [1954] **120**, 105–106.

54-182. Gras, J., and Salazar, M.   Serum protein fractionation by sodium thiosulfate and paper electrophoresis (in Italian). *Plasma (Milan)* [1954] **2**, 1–18.

54-183. Gras, J., Torras, V., and Salazar, M.   A study of the correlation between albumin and gamma-globulin in human sera (in Italian). *Plasma (Milan)* [1954]**2**, 297.

54-184. Grassmann, W., and Hannig, K.   Additions to the technique of serum analysis by paper electrophoresis (in German). *Klin. Wochschr.* [1954] **32**, 838–846.

54-185. Grassmann, W., Endres, H., and Steber, A.   Esterified linkages in the procollagen (in German). *Z. Naturforsch.* [1954] **9b**, 513.

54-186. Grassmann, W., and Stadler, P.   Electrophoretic investigation on natural and synthetic tanning materials (in German). *Leder* [1954] **5**, 206–211.

54-187. Grassmann, W., and Hannig, K.   Electrophoretic investigations of snake and insect toxins (in German). *Z. physiol. Chem.* [1954] **296**, 30.

54-188. Gross, D.   Paper electrophoresis of the oligosaccharides synthesized from sucrose by yeast invertase. *Nature* [1954] **173**, 487–489.

54-189. Gross, P. R.   Alterations in the proteins of sea-urchin egg homogenates treated with calcium. *Biol. Bull.* [1954] **107**, 364.

54-190. Gross, P., and Weicker, H.   The importance of lipid electrophoresis (in German). *Klin. Wochshr.* [1954] **32**, 509–514.

54-191. Groulade, J., Tizzani, R. J., and Drufovka, B.   Quantitative paper microelectrophoretic study of serum proteins in liver disease (in French). *Presse méd.* [1954] **62**, 1349.

54-192. Groulade, J., Drieux, H., Groulade, P., and Drufovka, B.   Paper microelectrophoresis of serum from dogs affected by *Miyagawanella psittaci* (in French). *Rev. pathol. gén. et comparée.* [1954] **54**, 1453.

54-193. Grune, A.   Paper chromatography with special consideration of the qualities of paper (in Italian). *Arzneimittel-Forsch.* [1954] **4**, 347–354.

54-194. Gruttner, R.   Evaluation of paper electrophoresis and paper chromatograms by measurement of reflected radiation (in German). *Klin. Wochschr.* [1954] **32**, 263–264.

54-195. Hagihara, F., Suzuki, T., and Takagi, Y.   Snake venom. I. Paper electrophoresis of snake venoms and their enzyme activities (in Japanese with English summary). *Yakugaku Zasshi* [1954] **74**, 167–171.

54-196. Hagihara, F.   Paper microionophoresis. I. Paper microionophoresis of volatile biogenic amines (in Japanese with English summary). *Yakugaku Zasshi* [1954] **74**, 486–487.

54-197. Hagihara, F.   Paper microionophoresis. II. Paper microionophoresis of Jaffe reaction-positive substances (in Japanese with English summary). *Yakugaku Zasshi* [1954] **74**, 488.

54-198. Hagihara, F.   Paper microionophoresis. III. Paper microionophoresis of diazo-positive substances (in Japanese with English summary). *Yaku-gaku Zasshi* [1954] **74**, 490.

54-199. Hagihara, F.   Paper microionophoresis. IV. Antigen-antibody reaction on filter paper (in Japanese with English summary). *Yakugaku Zasshi* [1954] **74**, 999.

54-200. Hais, I. M., and Macek, K.   "Paper chromatography" (in Czech), Czechoslovak Academy of Science, Prague [1954] p. 724.

54-201. Halasz, N. A., and Krehl, W. A.   An application of the paper electrophoresis technique to serum changes in arteriosclerosis. *Yale J. Biol. and Med.* [1954] **27**, 119–134.

54-202. Hanst, C.   Review and bibliography of paper electrophoresis (in Dutch). *Mededel. Vlaam. Chem. Ver.* [1954] **16**, 170.

54-203. Harasawa, S., and Sakamoto, T.   Electro-paper chromatography (in Japanese). *Nippon Kagaku Zasshi* [1954] **75**, 229–231.

54-204. Hardwicke, J.   The estimation of serum proteins by electrophoresis on filter paper. *Biochem. J.* [1954] **57**, 166–171.

54-205. Hardwicke, J.   Serum and urinary protein changes in the nephrotic syndrome. *Proc. Roy. Soc. Med.* [1954] **47**, 832.

54-206. Harris, H., and Warren, F. L.   Separations of basic amino acids of ionophoresis in filter paper. *Biochem. J.* [1954] **57**, xxxii–xxxiii.

54-207. Hartung, J.   Paper electrophoresis of the blood serum of normal and leukemic cattle (in German). *Deut. tierärztl. Wochschr.* [1954] **61**, 300.

54-208. Hayles, A. B., Stickler, G. B., and McKenzie, B.   Decrease in serum gamma-globulin (Agammaglobulinemia): Report of three cases. *Pediatrics* [1954] **14**, 449–454.

54-209. Heilmeyer, L., Clotten, R., Sano, I. Sturm, A., Jr., and Lipp, A.   Analysis of non-protein nitrogen by means of the high voltage pherogram. A new analytical method (in German). *Klin. Wochschr.* [1954] **32**, 831–837.

54-210. Heim, W. G., and Schechtman, A. M.   Electrophoretic analysis of the serum of the chicken during development. *J. Biol. Chem.* [1954] **209**, 241–247.

54-211. Heinen, W., Czaja, J., Loosen, H., and Zwelett, G.   Electrophoretic investigations after controlled physical exercise (in German). *Ärztl. Wochschr.* [1954] **9**, 968.

54-212. Hennemann, H. H., and Gillert, K.-E.   Tests of serum lability and electrophoretic studies in patients with positive Coombs test (in German). *Deut. Arch. klin. Med.* [1954] **201**, 158.

54-213. Herbst, F. S. M., and Hurley, N. A.   Effects of heparin on alimentary hyperlipemia. An electrophoretic study. *J. Clin. Invest.* [1954] **33**, 907–911.

54-214. Hirtz, J. and Comand, R.   The behavior of three types of foot-and-mouth disease virus in the course of electrophoresis in starch (in French). *J. Immunol.* [1954] **18**, 206–213; *Chem. Abstr.* [1954] **48**, 10206.

54–215. Hoch, H., and Chanutin, A.   An electrophoretic study of human plasma stored at room temperature. *J. Biol. Chem.* [1954] **209**, 661–669.

54-216. Hoch-Ligeti, C., and Irvine, K.   Effects of hormone administration on serum protein patterns. *Proc. Soc. Exptl. Biol. Med.* [1954] **87**, 324–328.

54-217. Hohne, H. and Kunkel, H. A.   Electrophoretic investigations on extracts from tumor tissues (in German). *Klin. Wochschr.* [1954] **32**, 748.

54-218. Homolka, J.   Paper electrophoretic-polarographic studies on changes in blood proteins (in German with English Summary). *Ann. paediat.* [1954] **183**, 96.

54-219. Hooft, C., and Clara, R. Study of serum in infants with lipid nephrosis by means of paper microelectrophoresis. *Acta paediat.* [1954] **43**, 136.

54-220. Hooghwinkel, G. J. M., Smits, G., and Kroon, D. B. Mucopolysaccharides bound to thyroglobulin. Histo-chemical and paper electrophoretic investigation. *Biochim. et Biophys. Acta* [1954] **15**, 78–86; *Chem. Abstr.* [1954] **48**, 13761.

54-221. Horejši, J. The applicability of paper electrophoretic separation of blood proteins in the clinical laboratory (in Czech). *Časopis lékáru českých* [1954] **93**, 1107.

54-222. Horst, W., and Schumacher, H. H. Paper electrophoretic investigations of thyroid extracts and serum after in vitro addition of radioiodide, radiomanganese, and radiocobalt as well as after an in vivo dose of radioiodide (in German). *Klin. Wochschr.* [1954] **32**, 361–364.

54-223. Horst, W. Transport and binding in serum as investigated by paper electrophoresis and radioactive indicators. ($Fe^{55/59}$, Cu^{64}, $Co^{56/57}$, Mn^{52}, Ga^{67}, S^{35}, I^{131},) (in German). *Klin. Wochschr.* [1954] **32**, 961.

54-224. Hradec, J., and Lemez, L. The blood of chick embryos. III. Development of blood serum proteins from the eighth day of incubation (in Czech with English summary). *Českoslov. morfol.* [1954] **2**, 260.

54-225. Hradec, J., Dusek, Z., and Dlouha, O. Blood proteins in cancer (in Czech with English summary). *Českoslov. onkol.* [1954] **1**, 275.

54-226. Hradec, J. A new apparatus for serial microelectrophoretic protein analysis on filter paper (in Czech with English summary) .*Časopis lékáru českých* [1954] **93**, 877–883.

54-227. Hunt, T. E., and Trew, J. A. Zone electrophoretic studies of plasma proteins in rheumatoid arthritis and ankylosing spondylitis. *Ann. Rheumatic Diseases* [1954] **13**, 201.

54-228. Imperato, C. Disproteinemia in infant pathology (in Italian). *23rd Congr. Ital. Soc. Pediatrics, Bologna* [1954] p. 268.

54-229. Inagami, K. Proteins of the body fluid in the silkworm. III. The electrophoretic components of the body fluid proteins. *Nippon Sanshigaku Zasshi* [1954] **23**, 304.

54-230. Introna, F. Electrophoresis of serum proteins in electrotrauma (in Italian). *Minerva medicolegale e arch. antropol. criminale* [1954] **74**, 94.

54-231. Irisawa, H., and Irisawa, A. F. Blood serum protein of the marine elasmobranchii. *Science* [1954] **120**, 849–852.

54-232. Irisawa, H., and Irisawa, A. F. Fractionation of lymph by paper electrophoresis (in Japanese). *Nisshin Igaku* [1954] **41**, 662.

54-233. Isherwood, F. A., and Cruickshank, D. H. A new method for the colorimetric estimation of amino acids on paper chromatograms. *Nature* [1954] **174**, 123.

54-234. Itano, H. A., Bergren, W. R., and Sturgeon, P. Identification of a fourth abnormal human hemoglobin. *J. Am. Chem. Soc.* [1954] **76**, 2278.

54-235. Iyer, G. Y. N. Human serum amino acids. I. Separation and identification by paper chromatography. *Indian J. Med. Research* [1954] **42**, 225–229.

54-236. Jasinski, B. Changes of the EKG-curve in portal hypertension especially in liver cirrhosis (in German). *Helv. Med. Acta* [1954] **21**, 530.

54-237. Jayle, M. G., Lagrue, G., and Boussier, G. Plasma protein disturbances in nephropathies (in French). *Presse méd.* [1954] **62**, 1246.

54-238. Jensen, C. E., and Vilstrup, T. Protein studies of endolymph and perilymph of the inner ear. *Acta Chem. Scand.* [1954] **8**, 399.

54-239. Jerchel, D., Becker, H., and Schmeiser, K.   Paper electrophoretic studies of the action of carbon[14]-labeled invert soap, dodecyltrimethylammonium bromide, on serum albumin (in German). *Z. Naturforsch.* [1954] **9b**, 169–172.

54-240. Jermyn, M. A., and Thomas, R.   Multiple components in horse-radish peroxidases. *Biochem. J.* [1954] **56**, 631.

54-241. Not assigned.

54-242. Jimenez, J. M.   Distribution of protein components of human serum in Costa Rica (in Spanish with English summary). *Rev. biol. trop. Univ. Costa Rica* [1954] **2**, 59.

54-243. Jirgensons, B., and Sirotzky, S.   Optical rotation and viscosity of native and denatured proteins. IV. Fractions of serum albumin and gamma-globulin from various sources. *Arch. Biochem. Biophys.* [1954] **52**, 400.

54-244. Johnson, R., Albert, S., and Pinkus, H.   Serum proteins in mice bearing induced and spontaneous mammary gland carcinomas. *Cancer Research* [1954] **14**, 830.

54-245. Jollès, P., and de Repentigny, J.   Paper electrophoresis and purification of metmyoglobins by chromatography with Amberlite XE-64. *Biochim. et Biophys. Acta* [1954] **15**, 161.

54-246. Jorke, D., and Heuchel, G.   Hypoglobulinemia and its clinical meaning (in Italian). *Plasma (Milan)* [1954] **2**, 597.

54-247. Kainrath, W., and Stockl, W.   Paper-electrophoretic determination of swine serum under physiologic conditions and following inoculation with erysipelas antigens (in German). *Wien. Tierärztl. Monatsschr.* [1954] **41**, 140–151; *Chem. Abstr.* [1954] **48**, 6564.

54-248. Kakimoto, S.   Protein fractions in serum in infectious diseases (in Japanese). *Igaku Kenkyu* [1954] **24**, 2069.

54-249. Kallee, E., and Seybold, G.   On insulin labeled with Iodine[131]. III. (in German). *Z. Naturforsch.* [1954] **9b**, 307–319.

54-250. Kallee, E.   On insulin labeled with Iodine[131]. II (in German). *Klin. Wochschr.* [1954] **32**, 508–509.

54-251. Kallee, E.   Detection of trace proteins. *Radioisotope Conf., Oxford, Eng. I, Med. and Physiol. Applications* [1954] p. 330.

54-252. Kaminski, M.   Immunochemical and electrophoretic studies of the globulins of egg white. *Biochim. et Biophys. Acta* [1954] **13**, 216–223.

54-253. Kaminski, M., and Durieux, J.   An immunological and electrophoretic study of the protein constituents of the different biological fluids of hens' eggs during incubation (in French). *Bull. soc. chim. biol.* [1954] **36**, 1037.

54-254. Kanagami, H.   On the electrophoretic analysis of serum protein of pulmonary tuberculosis. II. Relation between the qualitative classification of pulmonary tuberculosis and serum protein components (in Japanese). *Sci. Repts. Research Insts. Tôhoku Univ.* [1954] **C5**, 415–423.

54-255. Kaps, G.   Electrophoretic studies on brain tissue, particularly in the vicinity of tumors. The pathogenesis of brain swelling and edema (in German). *Arch. psychiat. Nervenkrankh.* [1954] **192**, 115–129.

54-256. Karler, A.   An improved apparatus for continuous-flow paper electrophoresis with preliminary applications. *Abstr. 125th Ann. Meeting Am. Chem. Soc., Kansas City, Missouri* [1954] p. 16c.

54-257. Kasavina, B. S., and Gorkin, V. Z.   Electrophoretic studies of protein fractions in the blood serum of animals suffering from bone fractures (in Russian). *Byull. Eksptl. Biol. Med.* [1954] **38**, 38.

54-258. Kaufman, H., and Majerus, N. Electrophoretic results in myocardial infarct (in French). *Ann. biol. clin. (Paris)* [1954] **12**, 153–167.

54-259. Kawerau, E. Electrophoresis of serum and urine proteins on filter-paper strips and agar jelly with the bridge unit. *Analyst* [1954] **79**, 681.

54-260. Kazmeier, F., and Gassen, A. Paper chromatography of human serum protein (in German). *Klin. Wochschr.* [1954] **32**, 81–85.

54-261. Keiding, N. R. Levels of serum protein fractions in diabetic patients with retinitis proliferans. *Proc. Soc. Exptl. Biol. Med.* [1954] **86**, 390–394.

54-262. Keil, A. W. Paper electrophoretic studies on the soluble proteins of ox obturator nerve (in German). *Arch. ges. Physiol. Pflüger's* [1954] **259**, 146–151.

54-263. Keller, C. Clinical chemistry of exudates of the pleural cavity. I. Electrophoresis. Nitrogen fractions. Test for lability (in German). *Deut. Arch. klin. Med.* [1954] **201**, 136.

54-264. Kellner, W., and Heindl, K. Investigation of total protein and electrophoresis of serum of blood donors (in German). *Ärztl. Wochschr.* [1954] **9**, 155–157.

54-265. Kemula, W., and Bartosiewicz, W. Electrophoretic separation of proteins on paper and their automatic photometric evaluation (in Polish with English summary). *Roczniki Chem.* [1954] **28**, 100–108.

54-266. Ketterer, B., and Kirk, R. L. Studies on the pituitary melanophore-expanding hormone with reference to its identity with adrenocorticotropic hormone. III. The application of filter paper electrophoresis of four melanophore-expanding extracts. *J. Endocrinol.* [1954] **11**, 19–25; *Chem. Abstr* [1954] **48**, 11601.

54-267. Kettker, A., and Anduren, H. A new time-saving apparatus for paper electrophoresis. *Scand. J. Clin. & Lab. Invest.* [1954] **6**, 74–75.

54-268. Keuning, F. J. Quantitative determination of serum protein fractions obtained by paper electrophoresis (in Dutch). *Chem. Weekblad* [1954] **50**, 702.

54-269. Klement, R., and Frieser, H. Separation of monophosphate, phosphite, hypophosphite, and hypodiphosphate by means of paper electrophoresis (in German). *Angew. Chem.* [1954] **66**, 138; *Chem. Abstr.* [1954] **48**, 5676.

54-270. Kolin, A. Centripetal and centrifugal electromagnetophoresis. *J. Appl. Phys.* [1954] **25**, 1065–1066.

54-271. Krebs, K. G., and Wankmuller, A. Electrophoresis of pharmaceuticals (in German). *Deut. Apotheker Ztg.* [1954] **94**, 171, 192, 234.

54-272. Kuhns, W. J. Immunochemical studies of antitoxin produced in normal and allergic individuals hyperimmunized with diphtheria toxoid. V. Peculiar electrophoretic configuration of serum proteins and protein-bound polysaccharides in certain antitoxic sera. Demonstration of serum changes in certain severe manifestations of allergy. *J. Exptl. Med.* [1954] **100**, 485.

54-273. Kuhns, W. J. Immunochemical studies of antitoxin produced in normal and allergic individuals hyperimmunized with diphtheria toxoid. IV. Differences between human precipitating and nonprecipitating skin-sensitizing diphtheria antitoxin as shown by electrophoresis. *J. Exptl. Med.* [1954] **99**, 577–588; *Chem. Abstr.* [1954] **48**, 13029.

54-274. Kunkel, H. G., and Bearn, A. G. Phospholipid studies of different serum lipoproteins employing phosphorous[32]. *Proc. Soc. Exptl. Biol. Med.* [1954] **86**, 887.

54-275. Kunkel, H. G.   Zone electrophoresis. In "Methods of Biochemical Analysis" (D. Glick, ed.), Vol. 1, pp. 141-170. Interscience, New York [1954].

54-276. Kushner, D. S., Herzog, E., Dubin, A., and Popper, H.   Serum mucoprotein and paper electrophoretic patterns in myeloma. *Proc. 27th Ann. Meeting, Central Soc. Clin. Research.* [1954]

54-277. Kutacek, M., and Kratochvil, L.   Paper electrophoresis in agricultural biochemistry. II. Separation and qualitative estimation of fractions of casein prepared according to Hammarsten (in Czech). *Sbornik Ceskoslov. Akad. Zemedel. Ved.* [1954] **27**, 355.

54-278. Kutzim, H.   Electrophoresis of fluids poor in protein after ultrafiltration through collodion thimbles (in German). *Deut. med. Wochschr.* [1954] **79**, 168-170.

54-279. Labus, J., and Cermak, M.   The dynamics of serum protein fractions in tuberculosis. *Bratislav. lekárske listy* [1954] **34**, 1410-1422.

54-280. Lagrue, G., Mazziconacci, P., and Vialatte, J.   Electrophoresis of blood and urine in lipid nephrosis (in French). *Ann. méd. (Paris)* [1954] **55**, 196-237.

54-281. Lang, N., Schettler, G., and Wildhack, R.   On a case of "agammaglobulinemia" and on the behavior of radioactive gammaglobulin in the serum given by injection (in German). *Klin. Wochschr.* [1954] **32**, 856.

54-282. Larson, D. L., and Feinberg, R.   Fractionation of human serum albumin using continuous filter-paper electrophoresis. *Science* [1954] **120**, 426-427.

54-283. Larson, F. C., Deiss, W. P., and Albright, E. C.   Radiochromatographic identification of thyroxin in an alpha globulin fraction of serum separated by starch electrophoresis. *J. Clin. Invest.* [1954] **33**, 230.

54-284. Laszlo, Z.   Electroosmosis in an alternating field. V (in German). *Kolloid-Z.* [1954] **137**, 34-36.

54-285. Latner, A. L., Molyneux, L., and Rose, J. D.   A semiautomatic recording densitometer for use after paper strip electrophoresis. *J. Lab. Clin. Med.* [1954] **43**, 157-164.

54-286. Laurence, D. J. R.   A fully automatic recording densitometer for scanning paper electrophoresis patterns. *J. Sci. Instr.* [1954] **31**, 137-138.

54-287. Lederer, M.   The separation of lanthanum and actinium by continuous paper electrophoresis. *Anal. Chim. Acta* [1954] **11**, 145-148.

54-288. Lederer, M.   Paper electrophoresis of inorganic substances. VII. Separation of acids in dilute hydrochloric acid as electrolyte. *Chem. & Ind. (London)* [1954], p. 1481.

54-289. Lehmann, H., and Edington, G. M.   Haemoglobin G: A new haemoglobin found in a West African. *Lancet* [1954] **2**, 173-174.

54-290. Lehmann, H., and Edington, G. M.   Haemoglobin S and haemoglobin C—A case with sickle cell haemoglobin C disease. *J. Clin. Pathol.* [1954] **7**, 171.

54-291. Lehmann, H., and Edington, G. M.   A case of sickle cell haemoglobin C disease and a survey of haemoglobin C incidence in West Africa. *Trans. Roy. Soc. Trop. Med. & Hyg.* [1954] **48**, 332-335.

54-292. Lehmann, H., and Smith, E. B.   Separation of different haemoglobins by paper electrophoresis. *Trans. Roy. Soc. Trop. Med. & Hyg.* [1954] **48**, 12.

54-293. Lehmann, H.   Distribution of the sickle cell gene. *Eugenics Rev.* [1954] **46**, 3-23.

54-294. Lemieux, R. U., and Bauer, H. F.   Spray reagent for the detection of carbohydrates. *Anal. Chem.* [1954] **26**, 920.

54-295. Lerch, P., and Neukomm, S.   Measurement of the radioactivity of substances separated by chromatography and electrophoresis (in French). *Schweiz. med. Wochschr.* [1954] **84**, 515–518.

54-296. Levy, A. L.   A paper chromatographic method for the estimation of amino acids. *Nature* [1954] **174**, 126.

54-297. Li, C. H., Geschwind, I. I., Levy, A. L., Harris, J. I., Dixon, J. S., Pon, N. G., and Porath, J. O.   Isolation and properties of alpha-corticotropin from sheep pituitary glands. *Nature* [1954] **173**, 251–253.

54-298. Lindqvist, B., and Storgards, T.   Research on the ripening process in cheese. II. Assay of the "soluble nitrogen" in cheese by combined ethanol fractionation and electrophoresis in paper (in German with English Summary). *Milchwissenschaft* [1954] **9**, 322–330.

54-299. Lindqvist, B., Storgards, T., and Goransson, M.-B.   Electrophoresis in paper as a means of studying the ripening process in cheese. *Intern. Dairy Congr., Proc. 13th Congr., The Hague* [1954] **3**, 1261.

54-300. Lissitzky, S., Garcia, I., and Roche, J.   The characterization of guanidine derivatives of biological origin by combined electrophoresis and chromatography on paper (in French). *Experientia* [1954] **10**, 379–381; *Chem. Abstr.* [1955] **49**, 1126.

54-301. Lissitzky, S.   Separation of iodothyronines of biological interest by paper electrophoresis (in French). *Compt. rend.* [1954] **238**, 1167–1168; *Chem. Abstr.* [1954] **48**, 8309.

54-302. Lissitzky, S., Cesaire, G., and Massonet, R.   A simple technique for extraction of free amino acids from biological fluids and extracts preparatory to their chromatographic separation (in French). *Bull. soc. chim. biol.* [1954] **36**, 655.

54-303. List, P. H.   Determination of alkaloids in pherograms (in German). *Naturwissenschaften* [1954] **41**, 454.

54-304. Lorenzini, R.   Importance of the electrophoretic lipidogram of serum for identifying a dyslipemic state (in Italian). *Boll. soc. med.-chir. Modena* [1954] **54**, 353.

54-305. Lorenzini, R.   Technique of serum lipid investigation by paper electrophoresis (in Italian). *Plasma (Milan)* [1954] **2**, 561.

54-306. Lupant-Andre, F.   Characterization of alkaloids by paper electrophoresis (in French). *Ann. soc. roy. sci. med. et nat.* Bruxelles [1954] **7**, 129

54-307. Lux, E., Sibilly, A., Mandel, P., and Fontaine, R.   Electrophoretic changes of the serum during venous and arterial thrombosis and their sequels (in French). *Presse méd.* [1954] **62**, 1160.

54-308. Macek, K., Queisnerova, M., and Hacaperkova, J.   Paper electrophoresis of some pituitary hormones (in Czech). *Chem. listy* [1954] **48**, 627–629.

54-309. Macek, K.   An investigation of the developing process in the paper chromatography of proteins (in Russian). *Collection Czechoslov. Chem. Communs.* [1954] **19**, 1302; (in Czech). *Chem. listy* [1954] **48**, 1181–1188.

54-310. Macheboeuf, M., Rebeyrotte, P., Dubert, J.-M., and Brunerie, M.   "Microelectrophoresis" (in French). Editions de l'Expansion Scientifique, Paris. [1954].

54-311. Mackay, I. R., Volwiler, W., Goldsworthy, P. D., Eriksen, N., and Wood, P. A.   Paper electrophoresis of serum proteins: Photometric quantitation and comparison with free electrophoresis. *J. Clin. Invest.* [1954] **33**, 855–866.

54-312. Maki, Masafumi. Inorganic electrochromatography (in Japanese). *Bunseki Kagaku* [1954] **3**, 39–40.

54-313. Maki, Masafumi. Electrochromatography. II. Effect of time, potential gradient, temperature, concentration, and volume of solution (in Japanese). *Bunseki Kagaku* [1954] **3**, 311.

54-314. Makino, K., and Matsuzaki, K. Detection of nucleic acid components on paper chromatogram (in Japanese). *J. Biochem.* (Tokyo) [1954] **41**, 457–462.

54-315. Marini-Bettolo, G. B., and Lederer, M. Paper electrophoresis of *Strychnos* alkaloids. *Nature* [1954] **174**, 133–134.

54-316. Martin, E., Scheidegger, J. J., Grabar, P., and Williams, C. A. Immuno-electrophoretic analysis of blood serum (in German). *Bull. schweiz. Akad. med. Wiss.* [1954] **10**, 193.

54-317. Martinette, Sister M. Filter paper electrophoresis. *J. Chem. Educ.* [1954] **31**, 18–19.

54-318. Martínez Llinares, V., Valle López, M., Castiñeira, M., and Roldán, D. T. Electrophoresis on paper: Simplification of the technique and comparison with the classical electrophoresis (in Spanish). *Rev. asoc. bioquím. arg.* [1954] **19**, 125.

54-319. Mauze, J., and Arnaud, G. Electrophoresis of the serum from lepers (in French, abstract in English). *Intern. J. Leprosy* [1954] **22**, 55.

54-320. McBay, A. J., and Algeri, E. J. Application of densitometry to paper chromatography of barbiturates. *Am. J. Clin. Patho.* [1954] **24**, 1139.

54-321. McCready, R. M., and McComb, E. A. Quantitative determination of sugars on paper chromatograms by a reflectance method. *Anal. Chem.* [1954] **26**, 1645–1647.

54-322. McEwen, W. K., and Kimura, S. J. Electrophoretic studies of tears. *Program. Sci. Assembly, 103rd Ann. Meeting Am. Med. Assoc.*, New York [1954].

54-323. McKinley, W. P., Maw, W. A., Oliver, W. F., and Common, R. H. The determination of serum protein fractions on filter paper electropherograms by the biuret reaction, and some observations on the serum proteins of the estrogenized immature pullet. *Can. J. Biochem. Physiol.* [1954] **32**, 189–199.

54-324. Mechura, B. Paper-electrophoretic technique (in Czech). *Chem. listy* [1954] **48**, 463.

54-325. Meguro, H., and Morikawa, K. An electrophoretic study of serums in tuberculous rabbits. *Japan. J. Tuberc.* [1954] **2**, 229.

54-326. Micheel, F., and Albers, P. Chromatographic analysis with paper made from butyrylbenzoyl- and phthaloycellulose (in German). *Mikrochim. Acta* [1954] p. 489.

54-327. Michl, H. The poison of the *Bothrops jararaca* (in German). *Monatsh. Chem.* [1954] **85**, 1240.

54-328. Michl, H. Electrophoretic and enzymic study of *jararaca* toxin (in German). *Naturwissenschaften* [1954] **41**, 403.

54-329. Michl, H., and Haberler, F. Determination of purines in caffeine containing drugs (in German). *Monatsh. Chem.* [1954] **85**, 779.

54-330. Miescher, P., and Fauconnet, M. The absorption of the lupus erythematosus factor by isolated cell nuclei (in French with English summary). *Experientia* [1954] **10**, 252–254.

54-331. Miglior, M. and Pirodda, A.   Electrophoretic investigations of changes of protein composition in the normal human crystalline lens in relation to age (in Italian, with English summary). *Giorn. gerontol.* [1954] **2**, 516.

54-332. Miglior, M., and Pirodda, A.   Determination of the proteins in human tears by electrophoresis (in German). *Giorn. ital. oftal.* [1954] **7**, 429.

54-333. Miller, L. L., Bly, C. G., and Bale, W. F.   Plasma and tissue proteins produced by non-hepatic rat organs as studied with lysine-ϵ-C^{14}; gamma globulins, the chief plasma protein fraction produced by non-hepatic tissues. *J. Exptl. Med.* [1954] **99**, 133–153.

54-334. Mitchell, L. C.   The utility of silver nitrate as chromogenic agent to locate anions on paper chromatograms. *J. Assoc. Offic. Agr. Chemists* [1954] **37**, 1021.

54-335. Mondovi, B., and Navazio, F.   Paper electrophoresis of some keto acid phenylhydrazones of some biological importance (in Italian with English summary). *Giorn. biochim.* [1954] **3**, 259.

54-336. Mori, I., and Kimura, M.   Filter paper chromatographic analysis. VIII. Conditions for paper electrophoresis (in Japanese). *Yakugaku Zasshi* [1954] **74**, 179–181; *Chem. Abstr.* [1954] **48**, 5709.

54-337. Mori, I.   Filter paper chromatographic analysis. IX. Conditions for paper electrophoresis (in Japanese). *Yakugaku Zasshi* [1954] **74**, 181–184; *Chem. Abstr.* [1954] **48**, 5709.

54-338. Morita, M.   Paper chromatography with high-frequency apparatus (in Japanese). *Japan* 5050 ('54), Aug. 12.

54-339. Motulsky, A. G., Paul, M. H., and Durrum, E. L.   Paper electrophoresis of abnormal hemoglobins and its clinical applications: A simple semiquantitative method for the study of hereditary hemoglobinopathies. *Blood* [1954] **9**, 897–910.

54-340. Mould, D. L., and Synge, R. L.   Separations of polysaccharides related to starch by electrokinetic ultrafiltration in collodion membranes. *Biochem. J.* [1954] **58**, 571.

54-341. Mould, D. L., and Synge, R. L. M.   The electrophoretic mobility and fractionation of complexes of hydrolysis products of amylose with iodine and potassium iodide. *Biochem. J.* [1954] **58**, 585.

54-342. Mouriquand, J., and Haour, P.   Electrophoretic study of extracts of urine of normal women (in French). *Compt rend. soc. biol.* [1954] **148**, 1840–1843.

54-343. Murata, A.   Quantitative chromatography on treated filter paper. I. Preparation of the paper (in Japanese). *Nippon Kagaku Zasshi* [1954] **75**, 827.

54-344. Musso, A., and Lanzo, A.   Plasma proteins in post-operative disease (in Italian). *Plasma (Milan)* [1954] **2**, 553.

54-345. Neumann, W., and Habermann, E.   Active substances in bee venom (in German). *Arch. exptl. Pathol. Pharmakol. Naunyn-Schmiedeberg's* [1954] **222**, 367–387.

54-346. Nikkilä, E. A. and Grasbeck, R.   Heparin in lipid nephrosis. Effects on edema, proteinuria, serum proteins, lipids, and lipoproteins. *Acta Med. Scand.* [1954] **150**, 39.

54-347. Nishimura, S., and Kono, M.   Serum protein components of murine leprosy (in Japanese). *Med. J. Osaka Univ.* [1954] **5**, 645.

54-348. Noller, H. G.   Thread electrophoresis: A method for the electrophoretic separation of minute amounts of protein (in German). *Klin. Wochschr.* [1954] **32**, 988.

54-349. Nordmann, R., Gauchery, O., Du Ruisseau, J. P., Thomas, Y., and Nordmann, J.   Identification of the organic acids of urine by paper chromatography (in French). *Compt. rend.* [1954] **238,** 2459–2461.

54-350. Obe, G., and Hermann, G.   Paper electrophoretic determinations of seminal plasma, ejaculate and prostatic fluid (in German). *Z. Urol.* [1954] **47,** 26.

54-351. Obladen, H. B.   The electrophoretic blood protein picture as prognostic criterion in pulmonary tuberculosis (in German). *Beitr. Klin. Tuberk.* [1954] **112,** 495.

54-352. Oeff, K.   Paper electrophoretic investigation on the linkage of radioactive biliselectan to serum albumin (in German). *Arch. exptl. Pathol. Pharmakol. Naunyn-Schmiedeberg's* [1954] **222,** 523–528.

54-353. Oeff, K., Rust, S., Schwarz, E., and Weise, H. J.   Paper electrophoretic study on the bond between penicillin and proteins (in German). *Naturwissenschaften* [1954] **41,** 500.

54-354. Oeff, K.   Detection of extravascular portions of radioactive plasma protein fractions by exchange transfusion (in German). *Klin. Wochschr.* [1954] **32,** 747–748; *Chem. Abstr.* [1954] **48,** 12974.

54-355. Oosterhuis, H. K.   Studies on paper electrophoresis (of plasma proteins). Comparison with the chemical method as an aid in clinical diagnosis. *J. Lab. Clin. Med.* [1954] **44,** 280–291.

54-356. Opplt, J., and Marcan, K.   Scanning method for paper electrophoretic analysis (in Czech). *Časopis lékáru českých* [1954] **93,** 934–935.

54-357. Osserman, E. F., and Lawlor, D. P.   Preliminary observations on difference in carbohydrate binding between abnormal serum and urine proteins of multiple myeloma. *Science* [1954] **120,** 715.

54-358. Ostrowski, E., Skarzynski, B., and Zak, Z.   Vitamin B_{12} in the protein fractions of human blood serum (in Polish). *Bull. acad. polon. sci. Classe II* [1954] **2,** 9–13.

54-359. Ott, H., and Roth, E.   Fat staining of serum lipoproteins on filter paper (in German). *Klin. Wochschr.* [1954] **32,** 1099–1100.

54-360. Owen, C. A., Jr., and McKenzie, B. F.   Application of paper electrophoresis to separation of blood-clotting factors. *J. Appl. Phys.* [1954] **6,** 696–700.

54-361. Paiva, A. C. M., Bandiera, T., and Prado, J. L.   Nonidentity between pepsitensin and hypertensin revealed by paper electrophoresis. *Science* [1954] **120,** 611–612.

54-362. Palomba, R., and Romini, R.   Protein metabolism in operated patients. I. Changes of the serum protein fractions (in Italian). *Giorn. ital. chir.* [1954] **10,** 673.

54-363. Paton, J. B., Robertson, G. K., and Wellby, M. L.   The separation of proteins and biological fluids by paper electrophoresis. *Med. J. Australia* [1954] **1,** 108–113.

54-364. Pechar, J., and Havlova, M.   Electrophoresis of proteins on paper (in Czech with English summary). *Sborník pathofysiol. travéní výživy.* [1954] **8,** 165–171.

54-365. Picora, L., Piccoli, P., and Calabro, F.   Electrophoretic analysis of blood serum in experimental lead poisoning (in Italian). *Folia med. (Naples)* [1954] **37,** 309.

54-366. Pellegrino, C., and Martelli, A.   Application of electrophoresis on paper to the separation of soluble proteins of organs (in Italian). *Boll. soc. ital. biol. sper.* [1954] **30,** 591.

53-367. Pernis, B., Wuhrmann, F., and Wunderly, C.   Aminoacid composition of macroglobulins in four cases of macroglobulinemia (in German). *Acta haematol.* [1954] **11**, 309–315.

54-368. Perosa, L., and Bini, L. Alkali-resistant Cooley's anemia hemoglobin is different from alkali resistant fetal hemoglobin. *Experientia* [1954] **10**, 469.

54-369. Peters, J. H., and Gutmann, H. R. The identification of derivatives of fluorene and biphenyl by filter-paper electrophoresis. *J. Am. Chem. Soc.* [1954] **76**, 2267–2268.

54-370. Pezold, F. A., and Kofes, A. Photometry of stained filter paper strips by the transparency method (in German). *Klin. Wochschr.* [1954] **32**, 504–507.

54-371. Pezold, F. A., Kessel, M., and Koertge, P. On the behavior of the serum proteins in rabbits under experimental chronic intoxication with allylformate (in German). *Arch. exptl. Pathol. Pharmakol. Naunyn-Schmiedeberg's* [1954] **221**, 123–134.

54-372. Pfau, P. Serum proteins of fetus, newborn and postmature infants (in German). *Arch. Gynäkol.* [1954] **185**, 208.

54-373. Pfeil, E., and Kanngiesser, W. On preparative electrophoresis using the Elphor-V-Apparatus (in German). *Z. physiol. Chem.* [1954] **29**, 79.

54-374. Pieper, J., and Molinski, H. Methodology of paper electrophoresis according to Grassmann and Hannig (in German). *Klin. Wochschr.* [1954] **32**, 985.

54-375. Pieper, J. Special protein fractions of cerebrospinal fluid (in German). *Klin. Wochschr.* [1954] **32**, 597–600; *Chem. Abstr.* [1954] **48**, 10875.

54-376. Pinna, P. Electrophoretic blood protein behavior in favism. (in Italian with English summary). *Ann. ital. pediat.* [1954] **7**, 486.

54-377. Pinteric, L., and Poulik, M. D. An apparatus for demonstration and evaluation of biological protein materials. *Can. J. Public Health* [1954] **44**, 163.

54-378. Podroužek, V., and Měchura, B. The photometry of paper electropherograms (in Czech). *Časopis lékáru českých* [1954] **93**, 661.

54-379. Porath, J. Purification of bacitracin polypeptides by charcoal chromatography and zone electrophoresis. *Acta Chem. Scand.* [1954] **8**, 1813.

54-380. Porter, W. L., and Hoban, N. Ultramicrotechnique for enzymatic hydrolysis of sugars prior to chromatogram analysis. *Anal. Chem.* [1954] **26**, 1846–1848.

54-381. Portier, A., Cabannes, R., and Massonnat, J. Evolution of the hemoglobinograms in a case of hemoglobinosis C (homozygotous) trait by splenectomy (in French). *Compt. rend. soc. biol.* [1954] **148**, 1779.

54-382. Prankerd, T. A. J., Altman, K. I., and Anderson, J. R. Electrophoresis of human red cell stroma. *Nature* [1954] **174**, 1146.

54-383. Pučar, Z. Contributions to paper electrophoresis in a wet chamber. II. Electrical measurements (in German). *Arhiv. kem.* [1954] **26**, 29.

54-384. Pučar, Z. Contributions to paper electrophoresis in a wet chamber. III. On the use of the H-curves (in German). *Arhiv. kem.* [1954] **26**, 41.

54-385. Pučar, Z. Determinations of the protein fractions of serum by electrophoresis on filter paper in a wet chamber (in German). *Acta Pharm. Jugoslav.* [1954] **4**, 10.

54-386. Raacke-Fels, I. D., and Li, C. H. Electrophoretic inhomogeneity of crystalline ribonuclease. *Biochim. et Biophys. Acta* [1954] **14**, 290–291.

54-387. Raacke-Fels, I. D., Li, C. H., and Lostroh, A. Zone electrophoresis on starch of human chorionic gonadotrophin and its separation into two active components. *Acta Endocrinol.* [1954] **17**, 366.

54-388. Ramshorn, K. Paper electrophoresis of serum (in German). *Pharmazie* [1954] **9**, 181.

54-389. Raymond, S. Constant current or constant voltage? *Science* [1954] **120**, 677–678.

54-390. Raynaud, R., d'Eshougues, J. R., Pasquet, P., and Pasquet, V. Serum glycoproteins in acute rheumatic rheumatism. Clinical value of electrophoretic fractionation (in French). *Ann. méd. (Paris)* [1954] **55**, 58–68.

54-391. Raynaud, R., d'Eshougues, J. R., and Pasquet, P. Serum proteins in recent myocardial infarctions (in French). *Arch. maladies coeur et vaisseaux* [1954] **47**, 71–74.

54-392. Raynaud, R., d'Eshougues, J. R., and Pasquet, P. Study of twenty cases of nephrotic syndrome by paper electrophoresis. *Bull. acad. nat. méd. (Paris)* [1954] **118**, 111.

54-393. Renyi-Vamos, F., Szendroi, Z., Magasi, P. The protein fraction of lymph (in Hungarian). *Acta Physiol. Acad. Sci. Hung.* [1954] **6**, 409.

54-394. Rebeyrotte, P. Application of electrorheophoresis to the study of acid precipitable lipoprotein synapses (in French). *Bull. soc. chim. biol.* [1954] **36**, 1617.

54-395. Rhodes, J. M., and Sorkin, E. Paper electrophoretic separation of tuberculin constituents. *Experientia* [1954] **10**, 427.

54-396. Ribeiro, L. P. Paper electrophoresis and its clinical application (in Portuguese). *Hospital (Rio de Janeiro)* [1954] **46**, 147.

54-397. Rice, W. G., and Yamaoka, M. The occurrence of a p-amino-salicylic acid-positive protein fraction in paper electrophoresis of serum in myelomatosis (multiple myeloma). *J. Lab. clin. Med.* [1954] **44**, 544.

54-398. Rizzi, F., Rossetti, V., and Salvetti, V. Etiopathogenesis of atherosclerosis: Modifications of serum lipoprotein complexes (chylomicrons) caused by heparin (in Italian). *Folia Cardiol. Suppl. Atti soc. ital. cardiol. 15° Congr.* [1954] **12**, 288.

54-399. Robertson, G. K. Paper chromatography of urine in galactosemia. *Med. J. Australia* [1954] pp. 698–700.

54-400. Roboz, E., Hess, W. C., Forster, F. M., and Temple, D. M. Paper electrophoretic studies in multiple sclerosis. *Neurology* [1954] **4**, 811–817.

54-401. Roboz, E., Hess, W. C., and Temple, D. M. Paper electrophoretic estimation of proteins in cerebrospinal fluid. *J. Lab. Clin. Med.* [1954] **43**, 785–790.

54-402. Roboz, E., Hess, W. C., Forster, F. M., and Temple, D. M. *A.M.A.* Serum lipid studies in multiple sclerosis. *Arch. Neurol. Psychiat.* [1954] **72**, 154–159.

54-403. Rodrigues, E., and Ribeiro, L. P. Simple methods for paper electrophoresis for use in clinical laboratories (in Portuguese). *Hospital (Rio de Janeiro)* [1954] **46**, 611.

54-404. Roland, J. F., and Gross, A. M. Quantitative determination of amino acids using monodimensional paper chromatography. *Anal. Chem.* [1954] **26**, 502.

54-405. Romani, J. D. A new method for locating amino sugars in connection with electrophoresis on paper (in Italian). *Compt. rend. soc. biol.* [1954] **148**, 1069–1071.

54-406. Romani, J. D. Parallel study of changes in blood glycoproteins and alpha-, and α-globulins in relation to the histological structure of a turpentine inflammation granuloma in the rat (in Italian). *Compt. rend. soc. biol.* [1954] **148**, 1970.

54-407. Romani, J. D.   Evaluation of serum glycoproteins by paper electrophoresis (in French). *Presse méd.* [1954] **62**, 1578.

54-408. Rondinini, B., and Malossi, M.   Electrophoretic investigation of serum and cerebrospinal fluid protein in Heine-Medin disease (in Italian). *Clin. pediat.* [1954] **36**, 821.

54-409. van Ros, G., and van Sande, M.   Paper electrophoresis and its application to the study of the proteinogram in various pathological states. *Ann. soc. roy. méd. et nat. Bruxelles* [1954] **7**, 153.

54-410. Rosenberg, I. N., Young, E., and Proger, S.   Serum lipoproteins of normal and athersclerotic persons studied by paper electrophoresis. *Am. J. Med.* [1954] **16**, 818–821.

54-411. Rossi, A., Paper electrophoresis in the study of lipoprotein in the serum of aged people (in Italian). *Giorn. gerontol.* [1954] **2**, 262.

54-412. Rossi-Fanelli, A., and Mondovi, B.   Separation of the phosphoric esters of thiamine by paper electrophoresis. II (in Italian). *Boll. soc. ital. biol. sper.* [1954] **30**, 1008–1011.

54-413. Roy, A. B.   Sulfatase of ox liver. III. Further observations of sulfatase B and an investigation of the origin of fractions A and B. *Biochem. J.* [1954] **57**, 465–470; *Chem. Abstr.* [1954] **48**, 10824.

54-414. Rundles, R. W., Coonrad, E. V., and Arends, T.   Serum proteins in leukemia. *Am. J. Med.* [1954] **16**, 842–853.

54-415. Not assigned.

54-416. Russ, E. M., Eder, H. A., and Barr, D. P.   Protein-lipid relationships in human plasma. III. In pregnancy and the newborn. *J. Clin. Invest.* [1954] **33**, 1662.

54-417. Sachs, B. A., Cady, P., and Ross, G.   Abnormal lipid-like material and carbohydrate in the sera of patients with multiple myeloma. *Am. J. Med.* [1954] **17**, 662.

54-418. Saifer, A., and Oreskes, I.   Circular paper chromatography. II. Isatin as a color reagent for amino acid. *Science* [1954] **119**, 124.

54-419. Sakal, E. H., and Merrill, E. J.   Ultraviolet spectrophotometric determination of reserpine. *J. Am. Pharm. Assoc. Sci. Ed.* [1954] **43**, 709.

54-420. Salvetti, V., Rossetti, V., and Rizzi, F.   Etiopathogenesis of atherosclerosis: Modifications of serum lipoproteins caused by heparin, studied by paper electrophoresis (in Italian). *Folia cardiol. suppl. atti soc. ital. cardiol. 15° Congr.* [1954] **12**, 293.

54-421. Sandor, G.   A physiological finding of remarkable constancy: The standard diagram of the solubility of serum proteins as influenced by pH (in French). *Compt. rend. soc. biol.* [1954] **148**, 477–481.

54-422. Sandor, G., and Sabetay, Y.   The sparingly soluble globulin system of blood serum. II. Isolation of three euglobulins in almost electrophoretically homogeneous states. Their relation to gamma-globulins and lipides (in French). *Bull. soc. chim. biol.* [1954] **36**, 613.

54-423. Sansoni, B., and Klement, R.   Continuous paper electrophoresis of condensed phosphates. *Angew. Chem.* [1954] **66**, 598.

54-424. Santamaria, R., Vergine, A., and Sorrentino, F.   Aggregation of the proteins of the serum and the plasma in nephrosis (in Italian). *Boll. soc. ital. biol. sper.* [1954] **30**, 610.

54-425. Santamaria, R., Vergine, A., and Di Jeso, F.   The protective action of mono-iodoacetate on the aggregation of serum proteins (in Italian). *Boll. soc. ital. biol. sper.* [1954] **30**, 606.

54-426. Santarato, R.   Electrophoretic behavior of plasma of rabbits long-treated with antibiotics. I. Dihydrostreptomycin. *Arch. intern. pharmacodynamie* [1954] **98**, 394.

54-427. Sato, R. R., Norris, W. P., and Strain, H. H.   Electrochromatographic sequences. *Anal. Chem.* [1954] **26**, 267–271.

54-428. Satoskar, R. S., and Lewis, R. A.   Plasma protein pattern of Indian students. *Indian J. Med. Sci.* [1954] **8**, 663.

54-429. Scanu, A., and Schiano, S.   A new method of continuous ether extraction in the cold for serum lipids. Application to study of the lipoprotein complexes. I. Normal human serum (in Italian with summary in English). *Riv. ist. sieroterap. ital.* [1954] **29**, 276.

54-430. Scanu, A.   The fractionation curve for serum proteins with sodium thiosulfate. II. Human pathological serum. III. Comparison with electrophoresis (in Italian). *Riv. ist. sieroterap. ital.* [1954] **29**, 59, 171.

54-431. Scardi, V.   A new migration chamber for electrophoresis on paper (in Italian). *Boll. soc. ital. biol. sper.* [1954] **30**, 533.

54-432. Scheiffarth, F., and Berg, G.   Serum protein determination in rats and rabbits with paper electrophoresis. II. Effect of the mode of sensitization with the same antigen on the behavior of the serum proteins (in German). *Z. ges. exptl. Med.* [1954] **123**, 201–209.

54-433. Scheinberg, I. H., Harris, R. S., and Spitzer, J. L.   Differential titration by means of paper electrophoresis and the structure of human hemoglobin. *Proc. Natl. Acad. Sci. U. S.* [1954] **40**, 777.

54-434. Schenck, G., and Hartel, J.   On piperazin as a reagent for the differentiation of aromatic endoles on paper chromatograms (in German). *Naturwissenschaften* [1954] **41**, 18–19.

54-435. Scheurlen, P. G.   Temporary and qualitative dynamics of experimental dysproteinemias (electrophoretic research). I and II (in German with English summary). *Plasma (Milan)* [1954] **2**, 209.

54-436. Schleyer, F. L.   Paper electrophoresis of proteins in serums from corpses (in German). *Arch. exptl. Pathol. Pharmakol. Naunyn-Schmiedeberg's* [1954] **221**, 306–311.

54-437. Schleyer, F. L.   Investigations of blood-group antibodies in serum protein fractions by paper electrophoresis (in German). *Klin. Wochschr.* [1954] **32**, 730–732.

54-438. Schmid, O. J., and Voigt, K. D.   Solubility and electrophoretic behavior of steroid-detergent mixtures in aqueous buffers. *Nature* [1954] **174**, 129.

54-439. Schneider, R. G.   Incidence of hemoglobin C trait in 505 normal negroes. A family with homozygous hemoglobin C and sickle-cell trait union. *J. Lab. Clin. Med.* [1954] **44**, 133–144.

54-440. Schneider, W., Nowakowski, H., and Voigt, K. D.   Paper electrophoresis of human sperm plasma. I. Method and nature of the fractions (in German). *Klin. Wochschr.* [1954] **32**, 863–867.

54-441. Schulte, K. E., and Muller, F.   Electrophoretic studies on milk proteins. The electrophoretic separation of the proteins of human milk (in German with English summary). *Milchwissenschaft* [1954] **9**, 375.

54-442. Schulte, M. J.   The reproducibility of the determination of blood proteins by paper electrophoresis (in Dutch). *Pharm. Weekblad* [1954] **89**, 849.

54-443. Schulz, D. M., Dryer, R. L., and Holdcraft, M. A. A spectrophotometer adapter for reading paper strips. *Am. J. Clin. Pathol.* [1954] **24**, 1110.

54-444. Schummelfeder, N., and Heyer, W. Paper electrophoretic investigations in nucleic acids (in German). *Naturwissenschaften* [1954] **41**, 164–165.

54-445. Schwartzkopff, W., and Hubner, E. Critical evaluation of paper electrophoresis and neutral salt precipitation in the determination of plasma protein fractions (in German). *Ärztl. Wochschr.* [1954] **9**, 1129.

54-446. Segovia, F. Electrophoresis apparatus. *Laboratorio (Granada, Spain)* [1954] **9**, 205.

54-447. Sevela, M. Remarks concerning proteinurias studied by electrophoresis (in Czech). *Časopis lékáru českých* [1954] **93**, 626–629.

54-448. Shall, S. The plasma protein electrophoretic patterns in a female baboon with primary amyloidosis. *S. African J. Med. Sci.* [1954] **19**, 112.

54-449. Siliprandi, D., and Siliprandi, N. Separation and quantitative determination of thiamine and thiamine phosphoric esters and their preparation in pure form. *Biochim. et Biophys. Acta* [1954] **14**, 52–61.

54-450. Siliprandi, N., and Siliprandi, D. Separation and determination of phosphate esters of thiamine by paper electrophoresis. *Riv. ist. sieroterap. ital.* [1954] **29**, 361–365.

54-451. Siliprandi, N., Siliprandi, D., and Lis, H. Separation and determination of vitamin B_6 group (pyridoxine, pyridoxal, pyridoxamine, pyridoxal phosphate and pyridoxamine phosphate): Separation by paper electrophoresis of riboflavin (riboflavin, FMN and FAD) and of nicotinamide (nicotinamide, DPN and TPN) groups. *Biochim. et Biophys. Acta* [1954] **14**, 212–218.

54-452. Simmonds, D. H. Improved electrolytic desalter. *Anal. Chem.* [1954] **26**, 1253.

54-453. Simon, N. Radioactive gold in filter paper electrophoresis patterns of plasma. *Science* [1954] **119**, 95.

54-454. Singer, K., Chapman, Goldberg, S. R., Rubinstein, H. M., and Rosenbloom, S. A. Studies on a normal hemoglobins. IX. Pure (homozygous) hemoglobin C disease. X. A new syndrome: Hemoglobin C-thalassemie disease. *Blood* [1954] **9**, 1023, 1032.

54-455. Singher, H., and Tyler, E. T. Clinical features and chemical morphology of semen and some of its variations. *Program Sci. Assembly 103rd Ann. Meeting Am. Med. Assoc., New York* [1954].

54-456. Slizewicz, P. Action of heat on horse serum (in French). *Ann. inst. Pasteur* [1954] **86**, 458–464.

54-457. Slizewicz, P. Study by ultracentrifugation of horse serum (in French). *Ann. inst. Pasteur* [1954] **86**, 189.

54-458. Slotta, K., and Borchert, P. The hemolytic factor of snake venom. *Mem. inst. Butantan (São Paulo)* [1954] **26**, 297–309.

54-459. Slotta, K. H., and Borchert, P. Histamine and protein toxins in bee venom. *Mem. inst. Butantan (São Paulo)* [1954] **26**, 279–295.

54-460. Smith, E. R. B., and Durrum, E. L. Anticonvectant electrophoresis nomenclature. *Chem. Eng. News* [1954] **32**, 2174.

54-461. Smolarek, W., and Dlugosch, G. Paper electrophoretic separation of tuberculostatics, *p*-aminosalicylic acid and isonicotinoyl hydrazide (in German). *Naturwissenschaften* [1954] **41**, 18.

54-462. Sober, H. A., and Peterson, E. A. Chromatography of proteins on cellulose ion-exchanges. *J. Am. Chem. Soc.* [1954] **76**, 1711.

54-463. Sokol, A., Milar, A., Rosocha, J., Spenik, M., and Mikla, D. Electrophoretic

investigations of the serum proteins in rabbits during hyperimmuniza-
tion against swine erysipelas (in Czech). *Vet. časopis* [1954] **3**, 121.

54-464. Solarino, G., and Tripodo, C.   The electrophoretic picture of the blood proteins of animals immunized and exposed to prolonged treatment with
azoiprite (in Italian with English summary). *Boll. soc. ital. biol. sper.*
[1954] **30**, 737.

54-465. Solarino, G., and Tripodo, C.   II. Behavior of the picture of protein electrophoresis (in Italian). *Boll. soc. ital. biol. sper.* [1954] **30**, 741.

54-466. Solarino, G., and Tripodo, C.   Experimental plasmocytosis from DDT and
immunobiologic reaction. I. Behavior of serum and antibodies and complement. II. Behavior of the electrophoretic pattern of proteins (in Italian with English summary). *Boll. ist. sieroterap. Milan.* [1954] **33**, 401, 482.

54-467. Spier, H. W., Rockl, H., and Pascher, G.   Studies of the soluble proteins in
human skin by paper electrophoresis. *Klin. Wochschr.* [1954] **32**, 795–798.

54-468. Sporer, A. H., Freed, S., and Sancier, K. M.   Paper chromatography of
chlorophylls. *Science* [1954] **119**, 68.

54-469. Stahl, R., and Dlugosch, G.   Investigations by paper electrophoresis and
determinations of serum protein in blood donors (in German). *Bluttrans-
fusion* [1954] **3**, 15–17.

54-470. Stauber, L. A.   Parasitological reviews. Application of electrophoretic techniques in the field of parasitic diseases. *Exptl. Parasitol.* [1954] **3**, 544.

54-471. Steel, A. E.   Separation and identification of alkali metals on paper chromatograms. *Nature* [1954] **173**, 315–316.

54-472. Steger, J.   Investigations of body fluids low in protein (cerebrospinal fluid
and urine) by electrophoresis (in German). *Münch. med. Wochschr.* [1954]
96, 747–750.

54-473. Stickler, G. B., Burke, E. C., and McKenzie, B. F.   Electrophoretic studies
of nephrotic syndrome in children: Preliminary report. *Proc. Staff Meet-
ings Mayo Clinic* [1954] **29**, 555.

54-474. Stowe, B. B., and Thimann, K. V.   The paper chromatography of indole
compounds and some indole-containing auxins of plant tissues. *Arch.
Biochem. Biophys.* [1954] **51**, 499–516.

54-475. Strain, H. H., Sato, T. R., and Engelke, J.   Chromatography and analogous
differential migration methods. *Anal. Chem.* [1954] **26**, 90.

54-476. Stran, H. M., and Jones, G. E. S.   Some properties of human urinary gonado-
tropins as elaborated by filter-paper electrophoresis. *Bull. Johns Hopkins
Hosp.* [1954] **95**, 162–169.

54-477. Svensson, H.   A new column electrochromatography apparatus. *IVA* **25**,
[1954] (5), 252.

54-478. Svensson, H., and Belfanti, S.   Paper electrophoresis of serum. Reproducibility and comparison with U-tube electrophoresis. *Plasma (Milan)* [1954]
2, 503–511.

54-479. Svensson, H., and Olhagen, B.   Electrophoresis of serum and plasma in free
solution without preceding dialysis. *Sci. Tools* [1954] **1**, 9–10.

54-480. Swahn, B.   Studies on blood lipids. *Scand. J. Clin. & Lab. Invest.* [1954]
Suppl. No. **9**, 1–114.

54-481. Szirmai, E.   Plasma protein in radium treated gynecologic carcinomas (in
Italian). *Plasma (Milan)* [1954] **2**, 533.

54-482. Takata, M., Hatashita, T., and Mashiko, T.   Heterogeneity of gamma-
globulin of human serum. *Plasma (Milan)* [1954] **2**, 403.

54-483. Talafant, E.   Nature of direct and indirect bilirubin (in Czech). *Biochim. et Biophys. Acta* [1954] **13**, 159.

54-484. Tempestine, E., and Messina, G.   Proteins and the protein metabolism of dental pulp. I. Paper-electrophoresis studies (in Italian). *Boll. soc. ital. biol. sper.* [1954] **30**, 895.

54-485. Terry, D. W., Motulsky, A. G., and Rath, C. E.   Homozygous hemoglobin C. A new hereditary hemolytic disease. *New England J. Med.* [1954] **251**, 365–373.

54-486. Tiselius, A.   Some applications of the separation of large molecules and colloidal particles. *J. Chem. Soc.* [1954] pp. 2650–2657.

54-487. Topp, D. C.   Paper electrophoretic separation. *Am. J. Med. Technol.* [1954] **20**, 116.

54-488. Toschi, G., and Boccacci, M.   Localization of some enzymes of the chromatogram of muscle extracts fractionated by means of paper electrophoresis. I. Phosphorylase (in Italian). *Boll. soc. ital. biol. sper.* [1954] **30**, 563.

54-489. Toschi, G., and Boccacci, M.   Localization of some enzymes of the chromatograms of muscle extracts fractionated by means of paper electrophoresis. II. Aldolase with triphosphatase dehydrogenase (in Italian). *Boll. soc. ital. biol. sper.* [1954] **30**, 563.

54-490. Toschi, G., and Boccacci, M.   Localization of some enzymes of the chromatograms of muscle extracts fractionated by means of paper electrophoresis. III. Adenosine triphosphorylase (in Italian). *Boll. soc. ital. biol. sper.* [1954] **30**, 567.

54-491. Toschi, G., and Mariani, A.   Paper electrophoresis of muscle proteins. *Atti accad. nazl. Lincei Rend. Classe sci. fis. mat. e nat.* [1954] **16**, 365–368.

54-492. Toschi, G., and Mariani, A.   Paper electrophoresis of muscle proteins (in Italian). *Rend. ist. super. sanità* [1954] **17**, 780–785.

54-493. Tripodo, C., and Capaldo, A.   Researches on the biology of phenylbutazone (in Italian with English summary). *Riv. biol. (Perugia)* [1954] **46**, 501.

54-494. Tsao, M. U.   A power source for filter paper electrophoresis. *Scand. J. Clin. & Lab. Invest.* [1954] **6**, 76–77.

54-495. Tumulty, P. A.   The clinical course of systemic lupus erythematosus. *J. Am. Med. Assoc.* [1954] **156**, 947–953.

54-496. Ulrich, F., Li, C. H., and Tarver, H.   Electrophoresis of rat plasma. III. Preparation of S-labeled albumin. *Arch. Biochem. Biophys.* [1954] **50**, 421–426.

54-497. Urra, J. A., Caso, I. V., Fontan, J. R., and Zoffman, A.   Plasma protein in leptospirosis. *Plasma (Milan)* [1954] **2**, 529.

54-498. Uzman, L. L., and Rosen, H.   Partition of neuraminic acid among human serum proteins. *Science* [1954] **120**, 1031–1032.

54-499. Vadasz, J., and Horvath, L.   Evaluation of serum fractions of rats deprived of spleen in several generations by means of an elphograph (densitometer) (in Hungarian). *Acta. Biol. Acad. Sci. Hung.* [1954] **5**, 131.

54-500. Valle López, M., and Martínez Llinares, V.   Construction of a plantilla patron by the identification of the protein fractions (in Spanish). *Arch. med. exptl. (Madrid)* [1954] **17**, 223.

54-501. Valle López, M.   Simplification of electrophoretic techniques. Reading and evaluation of proteins on filter paper (in Spanish). *Laboratorio (Granda, Spain)* [1954] **9**, 401–405.

54-502. Valle López, M. Comparative study of classical and paper electrophoresis (in Spanish). *Anales inst. farmacol. españ.* (Madrid) [1954] **3**, 295.

54-503. Valmet, E., and Svensson, H. Problems inherent in paper electrophoresis. The LKB paper electrophoresis apparatus. *Sci. Tools* [1954] **1**, 3–7.

54-504. Vandenbelt, J. M., Childs, C. E., Lundquest, D., and Saladonis, J. A constituent of human perspiration with intense ultraviolet absorption *Science* [1954] **119**, 514.

54-505. Verga, V., and Giordano, G. Effect of irradiation of the proteins of the serum of rats bearing benzopyrene tumors (in Italian). *Boll. soc. ital. biol. sper.* [1954] **30**, 614.

54-506. Verschure, J. C. M. Gamma-globulinemia. (in Dutch with English summary). *Ned. Tijdsch . Geneesk.* [1954] **98**, 2805.

54-507. Verschure, J. C. M., and Hoefsmit, M. I. A quick clinical method of paper electrophoresis. (in Dutch with English summary). *Ned. Tijdsch . Geneesk.* (1954] **98**, 3410.

54-508. Verschure, J. C. M., and Boom, J. A. Clinical application of paper electrophoresis (in Dutch). *Ned. Tijdsch . Geneesk.* [1954] **98**, 2607–2613.

54-509. Vesselinovitch, S. D., and Funnell, H. S. A rapid method for filter paper electrophoresis. *Can. J. Biochem. and Physiol.* [1954] **32**, 567–570.

54-510. Vilstrup, T., and Jensen, C. E. Three reports on the chemical composition of the fluids of the labyrinth. I. Determination of hyaluronic acid in the endolymph. *Ann. Otol. Rhinol. & Laryngol.* [1954] **63**, 151.

54-511. Vilstrup, T., Vilstrup, G., Kornerup, V., and Jensen, C. E. Three reports of the chemical composition of the fluids of the labyrinth. III. Fractionation of the proteins of the labyrinth fluids and of the vitreous body. *Ann. Otal. Rhinol. & Laryngol.* [1954] **53**, 151–156.

54-512. Voigt, K. D., and Beckmann, I. Paper electrophoresis of steroids. II. Fractionation of neutral urinary steroids in normal and pathological conditions. *Acta Endocrinol.* [1954] **15**, 251–264.

54-513. Voigt, K. D., and Schrader, E. A. Paper electrophoretic and arteriographic examinations in arteriosclerotic and endangiitic obliterations of blood vessels (in German). *Z. Kreislaufforsch.* [1954] **43**, 2.

54-514. Volk, B. W., Saifer, A., Rabiner, A. M., and Oreskes, I. The protein profile in multiple sclerosis. *Program Sci. Assembly, 103rd Ann. Meeting Am. Med. Assoc., New York* [1954].

54-515. de Vries, G. Conductometric detection of ions in paper chromatograms. *Nature* [1954] **173**, 735–736.

54-516. de Vries, G., and van Dalen, E. Amperometric method of ions in paper chromatography (in German). *Rec. trav. chim.* [1954] **73**, 1028.

54-517. Wade, H. E., and Morgan, D. M. Analysis of adenosine triphosphate (ATP) and adenosine diphosphate (ADP) preparations by paper ionophoresis. *Biochem. J.* [1954] **56**, 41–43.

54-518. Wadman, W. H., Thomas, G. J., and Pardee, A. B. Quantitative method using paper chromatography for estimation of reducing oligosaccharides. *Anal. Chem.* [1954] **26**, 1192–1195.

54-519. de Wael, J., and Diaz-Cadavieco, R. Separation of amino acids by monodimensional, ascending chromatography and their determination on paper by direct photometry (in French). *Rec. trav. chim.* [1954] **73**, 333–346.

54-520. Wagenhofer, E., and Zucha, J. Paper electrophoresis of the cerebrospinal fluid. *Bratislav. Lakárské Listy* [1954] **34**, 713–727; *Chem. Abstr.* [1954] **48**, 13942.

54-521. Wagner, G. Microanalysis of marfanil preparations (in German). *Pharmazie* [1954] **9**, 975.

54-522. Wagner, G. Paper ionophoresis of sulfonamides (in German). *Pharmazie* [1954] **9**, 385.

54-523. Wagner, G. Paper electrophoretic determination of *p*-aminobenzoic acid (PABA) in procaine and of *m*-aminophenol in *p*-aminosalicylic acid (PASA) (in German). *Pharmazie* [1954] **9**, 556.

54-524. Wagner, G. A contribution to the microanalysis of aromatic oxycarbon-acids (in German). *Pharmazie* [1954] **9**, 741.

54-525. Waldhof, Z. Paper for chromatography. Brit. Patent 709,620, [1954] May 26.

54-526. Weimer, H. E., Redlich-Moshin, J., Boak, R. A., and Carpenter, C. M. Serum protein studies in experimental tuberculosis of the guinea pig. *Am. Rev. Tuberc.* [1954] **70**, 344.

54-527. Westphal, O., and Luderitz, O. Chemical examination of lipopolysaccharides of gram negative bacteria (in German). *Angew. Chem.* [1954] **66**, 407.

54-528. Wetter, L. R., and Corrigal, J. J. Detection of carbohydrate in paper electrophoresis. *Nature* [1954] **174**, 695.

54-529. Wieland, T., and Dose, K. Changes in the protein partitioning in blood serum in *Amanita* poisoning (in German). *Biochem. Z.* [1954] **325**, 439–447.

54-530. Wolff, R., and Magnin, P. The use of amidoschwarz 10B for revealing the protein fractions obtained by electrophoresis on paper (in French). *Bull. soc. chim. biol.* [1954] **36**, 925.

54-531. Wollenberger, A. Zone electrophoresis of muscle extracts: Separation of phosphocreatine, creatine, β-alanine peptides, and nucleotides. *Nature* [1954] **173**, 205–207.

54-532. Wood, S. E., and Strain, H. H. Electro-osmosis in paper. Electrochromatography with electrodes on paper. *Anal. Chem.* [1954] **26**, 1869–1872.

54-533. Wunderly, C., and Piller, S. The staining of the proteins, lipids and carbohydrates of the blood serum after paper electrophoresis. A chemical triad (in German). *Klin. Wochschr.* [1954] **32**, 425–432.

54-534. Wunderly, C. "Die Papierelektrophorese" (in German; Italian, French and Spanish editions also available). H. R. Sauerländer, Aarau and Frankfurt am Main. [1954].

54-535. Wunderly, C., Steiger, R., and Bohringer, H. R. Investigations of the aqueous humor of the human eye. *Experientia* [1954] **10**, 432.

54-536. Wunderly, C. Improvement of paper electrophoresis (in Italian). *Plasma (Milan)* [1954] **2**, 143–156.

54-537. Yamashina, I. Enterokinase, I. The purification and general properties (in German). *Arkiv Kemi* [1954] **7**, 539.

54-538. Yasunaga, S., and Shimomura, O. Inorganic chromatography. IV. Fundamental studies on paper electrochromatography (in Japanese). *Yakugaku Zasshi* [1954] **74**, 62–66.

54-539. Yasunaga, S. and Shimomura, O. Inorganic chromatography. V. Fundamental studies on paper chromatography (in Japanese). *Yakugaku Zasshi* [1954] **74**, 66–68.

54-540. Yasunaga, S., and Shimomura, O. Inorganic chromatography. VI Apparatus for paper electrochromatography (in Japanese). *Yakugaku Zasshi* [1954] **74**, 778.

54-541. Yasunaga, S., and Shimomura, O. Effect of electro-osmosis on paper electrophoresis (in Japanese). *Yakugaku Zasshi* [1954] **74**, 988.

54-542. Zacutti, A. Testosterone action on the plasma protein picture in normal pregnancy (in Italian). *Minerva ginecol.* [1954] **6**, 117.

54-543. Zittle, C. A., Dellamonica, E. S., and Custer, J. H. Purification of human red cell acetylcholinesterase. *Arch. Biochem. Biophys.* [1954] **48**, 43–49.

54-544. Zweig, G., and Block, R. J. Bovine whey proteins. III. The preparation of crystalline alpha-lactalbumin and beta-lactoglobulin from ferrilactin. *Arch. Biochem. Biophys.* [1954] **51**, 200–207.

55-1. Not assigned

55-2. Ajl, S. J., Reedal, J. S., Durrum, E. L., and Warren, J. Studies on plague. I. Purification and properties of the toxin of *Pasteurella pestis. J. Bacteriol.* [1955] **70**, 158–169.

55-3. Adlersberg, D., Bossak, E. T., Sher, I. H., and Sobotka, H. Electrophoresis and monomolecular layer studies with serum lipoproteins. *Clin. Chem.* [1955] **1**, 18–33.

55-4. Andersch, M. A., and Barbusca, F. A graphic method for the conversion of transmission curves to a corrected density curve for the calculation of proteins separated by paper electrophoresis. *J. Lab. Clin. Med.* [1955] **45**, 958.

55-5. Anonymous. Sample applicator-paper electrophoresis accessories. *Sci. Tools* [1955] **2**, 34.

55-6. Arbouys, S., Fine, J., and Eyquem, A. Electrophoretic studies of the serum of *Cynocephalus* monkeys (in French). *Ann. inst. Pasteur* [1955] **88**, 671.

55-7. Bachelet, M., Claude, R., and Lederer, M. Electrophoresis of some uranyl salts (in French). *Compt. rend.* [1955] **240**, 419.

55-8. Banerjee, R. P., Hausler, H. F., and Sen Gupta, P. C. Paper electrophoresis of kala-azar serum. *Bull. Calcutta School Trop. Med.* [1955] **3**, 57–58.

55-9. Bansi, H. W., Gronow, R. T., and Redetzki, H. On the clinical value of lipid electrophoresis, its relationship to the serum lipids and how they are influenced by oral fat applications (in German). *Klin. Wochschr.* [1955] **33**, 101.

55-10. Barbanti, A. Electrophoretic estimations on serum and plasma in women at the end of pregnancy (in Italian). *Minerva ginecol.* [1955] **7**, 26–32.

55-11. Barnett, A. J. G., and Smith, D. K. Movement of higher fatty acids under electrophoresis on filter-paper strips. *J. Sci. Food Agr.* [1955] **6**, 53; *Nature* [1954] **174**, 569–660.

55-12. Baron, J. B., Guillon, S., Peyrau, M. Results of electrophoresis of serum in cataract, glaucoma, detachment of the retina, iridocyclitis, and retrolental fibroplasia (in French). *Ann. biol. clin. (Paris)* [1955] **13**, 104–107.

55-13. Barrollier, J. Change of paper chromatograms and electropherograms to transparent dry film (in German). *Naturwissenschaften* [1955] **42**, 126.

55-14. Bell, D. J., and Northcote, D. H. Qualitative differentiation between certain O-methyl derivatives of D-fructose by using borate-paper electrophoresis and urea-hydrochloric acid spray. *Chem. & Ind. (London)* [1955] p. 1328.

55-15. Beltz, J. H. Paper electrophoresis. A procedure for serum proteins. *Bull. Natl. Assoc. Clin. Labs.* [1955] **6**, 143–151.

55-16. Berbalk, H., and Schier, O. Electrophoresis. II. The paper electrophoresis of organic acids and phenols (in German). *Monatsh. Chem.* [1955] **85**, 146.

55-17. Berg, G., Gotz, H., and Scheiffarth, F. The reduction of separation times in paper electrophoresis by the use of increased voltage (in German). *Klin. Wochschr.* [1955] **33**, 447–448.

55-18. Berg, G., Frenger, W., and Scheiffarth, F. The electrophoresis of agglutins (in German). *Klin. Wochschr.* [1955] **33**, 767.

55-19. Berg, G., Kimbel, K. G., Scheiffarth, F. Variation width of serum protein fractions of normal experimental rats (in German). *Naturwissenschaften* [1955] **42**, 51.

55-20. Berlingozzi, S., and Rapi, G. Radial electrophoresis and electrophoresis on paper disks. I. Principle and apparatus (in Italian with English summary). *Chim. e ind. (Milan)* [1955] **37**, 351.

55-21. Berry, E. R., and Chanutin, A. Detailed electrophoretic analyses of sera of healthy young men. *J. Clin. Invest.* [1955] **34**, 1513–1519.

55-22. Biondo, G. Electrophoretic studies on the blood serum of goats immunized against alpha-epizoatic (in Italian). *Boll. soc. ital. biol. sper.* [1955] **31**, 307–308.

55-23. Biserte, G. Apparatus for electrophoresis in starch (in French). *Ann. biol. clin.* (Paris) [1955] **13**, 254–263.

55-24. Bjornesjo, K. B. Staining of protein-bound serum polysaccharides in electrophoresis strips. *Scand. J. Clin. & Lab. Invest.* [1955] **7**, 153–159.

55-25. Blass, J. A simple technique for paper chromatography of urinary amino acids for routine clinical use (in French). *Ann. biol. clin. (Paris)* [1955] **13**, 56.

55-26. Block, R. J., Durrum, E. L., and Zweig, G. "A Manual of Paper Chromatography and Paper Electrophoresis." Academic Press, New York. [1955].

55-27. Block, S. S., Stephens, R. L., Barreto, A., and Murrill, W. A. Chemical identification of the *Amanita* toxin in mushrooms. *Science* [1955] **121**, 505.

55-28. Block, W. D., Rukavina, J. G., and Curtis, A. C. An atypical electrophoretic peak in serum of patients with familial primary systemic amyloidosis. *Proc. Soc. Exptl. Biol. Med.* [1955] **89**, 175.

55-29. van Bochove, C., and Roebersen, H. G. Macromolecular membranes for electrodialysis. Dutch Patent 77,406, Feb. 15, [1955].

55-30. Bodanszky, A., and Kollonitsch, J. Color reagent for paper chromatography of steroids. *Nature* [1955] **175**, 729.

55-31. Bon, W. F. On the difference of alpha-crystalline prepared from the periphery and from the center of the bovine eye-lens (in Dutch). *Koninkl. Ned. Akad. Wetenschap. Proc.* [1955] **C58**, 344.

55-32. Bossak, E. T., Wang, C., and Adlersberg, D. Effect of cortisone on plasma globulins in the dog. Studies by paper electrophoresis. *Proc. Soc. Exptl. Biol. Med.* [1955] **88**, 634–640.

55-33. Bozzetti, E. Electrophoretic behavior of serum during therapy with electric shock (in Italian). *Boll. soc. ital. biol. sper.* [1955] **31**, 241–243.

55-34. Brattsten, I. Continuous zone electrophoresis by crossed velocity fields in a supporting medium. Fractionation of protein mixtures and description of the cuvette. *Arkiv Kemi* [1955] **8**, 40 227.

55-35. Brattsten, I. Continuous zone electrophoresis by crossed velocity fields in a supporting medium. The electric control of the fractionation process. *Arkiv Kemi* [1955] **8**, 205.

55-36. Brattsten, I., Kolldahl, H., and Laurell, A. H. F. Distribution of reagins in the serum protein fractions obtained by continuous zone electrophoresis. *Acta Allergol.* [1955] **8**, 339–348.

55-37. Brattsten, I. Continuous zone electrophoresis by crossed velocity fields in a supporting medium. Analysis of protein fractions obtained from normal human serum. *Arkiv Kemi* [1955] **8**, 437.

55-38. Brown, H., Sanger, F., and Kitai, R. The structure of pig and sheep insulins. *Biochem. J.* [1955] **60**, 556.

55-39. Brusa, P., and Quinte, V. Effect of amino acids on serum proteins of dystrophic infants (in Italian). *Minerva pediat.* [1955] **7**, 281–285.

55-40. Buras, E. M., Jr., and Hobart, S. R. Partial acetylation of paper for chromatography. *Anal. Chem.* [1955] **27**, 1507.

55-41. Burke, D. C., and Foster, A. B. Ionophoresis of the adenosine phosphates. *Chem. & Ind. (London)* [1955] p. 94.

55-42. Burstein, M., and Samaille, J. Delipidation of serum by calcium oxalate (in French). *Compt. rend.* [1955] **240**, 2022.

55-43. Burtin, P., Hartmann, L., Fauvert, R., and Grabar, P. Identification of the Bence-Jones protein. The value of the immunochemical method (in French). *Compt. rend.* [1955] **241**, 339–341.

55-44. Cabannes, R., and Serain, D. Heterogeneity of bovine hemoglobin: Electrophoretic identification of two hemoglobins (in French). *Compt. rend. soc. biol.* [1955] **149**, 7.

55-45. Cabannes, R., Sendra, L., and Dalaut. New human hereditary hemoglobin with a more rapid migration than normal hemoglobin (in French). *Compt. rend. soc. biol.* [1955] **149**, 914.

55-45. Cabannes, R., and Serain, C. Study of the hemoglobin of the North African dromedary (in French). *Compt. rend. soc. biol.* [1955] **149**, 1103.

55-47. Cabannes, R., and Serain, C. Electrophoretic study of the hemoglobins of the domesticated mammals of Africa (in French). *Compt. rend. soc. biol.* [1955] **149**, 1193.

55-48. Cabannes, R., and Portier, A. Application of paper electrophoresis to the study of human hemoglobins (in French). *Pédiatrie* [1955] **10**, 1–6.

55-49. Carson, W. N., Jr., Michelson, C. E., and Koyama, K. Salt bridges of porous glass and ion exchange membranes. *Anal. Chem.* [1955] **27**, 472–474.

55-50. Cerletti, P., and Siliprandi, N. Electrophoretic separation and determination of flavins. *Biochem. J.* [1955] **61**, 324–328.

55-51. Cetingil, A. I. Myeloma. *Bull. fac. méd. Istanbul* [1955] **18**, 134.

55-52. Cetini, G. Electrochromatography of inorganic ions on starch (in Italian). *Ann. chim. (Rome)* [1955] **45**, 216.

55-53. Christiansen, H. V. L. Electrophoresis of plasma proteins. *Lancet* [1955] **268**, 1227.

55-54. Chu, T. C., and Chu, E. J.-H. Paper chromatography of iron complexes of porphyrins. *J. Biol. Chem.* [1955] **212**, 1–7.

55-55. Cifonelli, J. A., and Smith, F. Detection amino acids on paper chromatograms. *Anal. Chem.* [1955] **27**, 1501–1502.

55-56. Clegg, R. E., Heim, R. E., Suelter, C. H., and McFarland, R. H. The distribution of radioactive phosphorous in the electrophoretic components of egg-yolk proteins. *Poultry Sci.* [1955] **34**, 210.

55-57. Cohen, S. Variations in plasma protein mass during the menstrual cycle of *Papio ursinus*. *J. Endocrinol.* [1955] **12**, 196.

55-58. Comfort, A. Effect of large doses of heparin. Clearing factor on lipoprotein migration in the rabbit. *J. Physiol. (London)* [1955] **127**, 225.

55-59. Connell, G., Dixon, G. H., and Hanes, C. S. Quantitative chromatographic methods of enzymic trans-peptidation reactions. *Can. J. Biochem. and Physiol.* [1955] **33**, 416.

55-60. Consden, R., and Powell, M. N. The use of borate buffer in paper electrophoresis of serum. *J. Clin. Pathol.* [1955] **8**, 150.

55-61. Courtice, F. C., and Morris, B. The exchange of lipids between plasma and lymph of animals. *Quart. J. Exptl. Physiol.* [1955] **40**, 138.

55-62. Cresseri, A. Observations on a vitamin B_{12} binding factor from hog gastric mucosa (in Italian). *Experientia* [1955] **11**, 111.

55-63. Crestfield, A. M., and Allen, F. W. Improved apparatus for zone electrophoresis. *Anal. Chem.* [1955] **27**, 422–423.

55-64. Crestfield, A. M., and Allen, F. W. Resolution of ribonucleotides by zone electrophoresis. *Anal. Chem.* [1955] **27**, 424–425.

55-65. Cummings, A. J., and Flynn, F. V. Amino-acid composition of serum proteins in health and disease. *J. Clin. Pathol.* [1955] **8**, 153.

55-66. Cutroneo, A., and Lombardo, G. The fragmentation of erythrocytes and the electrophoretic behavior of hemoglobin in some anemias of infancy (in Italian). *Boll. soc. ital. biol. sper.* [1955] **31**, 211.

55-67. Dangerfield, W. G., and Smith, E. B. An investigation of serum lipids and lipoproteins by paper electrophoresis. *J. Clin. Pathol.* [1955] **8**, 132.

55-68. De Franchis, M., and Marsala, F. Postoperative changes of blood protein fractions. *Fracastoro* [1955] **48**, 39.

55-69. De Franchis, M. Blood protein picture of surgical patients with ulcers (in Italian). *Arch. ital. mal. app. dig.* [1955] **21**, 45.

55-70. Dicastro, G. Continuous electrophoresis on paper. *Giorn. biochim.* [1955] **25**, 464.

55-71. Di Domizio, G. Protein composition of heart muscle, determined by paper electrophoresis (in Italian with English summary). *Arch. vet. ital.* [1955] **6**, 19–23.

55-72. Dobbie, H., Kermack, W. O., and Lees, H. Complex-formation between polypeptides and metals. I. Applications of various experimental methods to the glycine-copper system. II. The reaction between cupric ions and some dipeptides. III. The reaction between cupric ions and diglycylglycine. *Biochem. J.* [1955] **59**, 240.

55-73. Drabkin, D. L., and Marsh, J. B. Metabolic channeling in experimental nephrosis. I. Protein and carbohydrate metabolism. *J. Biol. Chem.* [1955] **212**, 623–631.

55-74. Drevon, B., Cier, A., and Lemarchands, H. Electrophoretic study of the serum proteins of the hepatectomized dog (in French). *Compt. rend. soc. biol.* [1955] **149**, 124.

55-75. Drilhon, A., and Vago, C. Distinction between two etiologic types of flaccidity in the silkworm, *Bombyx mori*. Differential diagnosis by electrophoresis. *Compt. rend. soc. biol.* [1955] **149**, 39.

55-76. Dubost, P., and Pascal, S. Serum proteins by differential electrophoresis in patients treated with chlorpromazine in a psychiatric clinic (in French). *Rec. trav. chim.* [1955] **74**, 586.

55-77. Dumazert, C., Ghiglione, C., and Bozzi-Tichadou, M. Electrophoresis of proteins in a column (in French). *Bull. soc. chim. biol.* [1955] **37**, 123.

55-78. Durrum, E. L., and Gilford, S. R. Recording integration photoelectric and radioactive scanner for paper electrophoresis and chromatography. *Rev. Sci. Instr.* [1955] **26**, 51–56.

55-79. Eder, H. A., Russ, E. M., Pritchett, R. A. R., Wilber, M. M., and Barr, D. P. Protein-lipid relationships in human plasma: In biliary cirrhosis, obstructive jaundice, and acute hepatitis. *J. Clin. Invest.* [1955] **34**, 1147.

55-80. Eggstein, M., and Hundeshagen, H. Method of paper electrophoresis (in German). *Klin. Wochschr.* [1955] **33**, 14.

55-81. Eiber, H. B., Goldbloom, A. A., Deutschberger, O., Chapman, I., and Loewe, W. R. An outline of the newer methods of study of atherosclerotics. With emphasis on the 80–100 year group. *Geriatrics* [1955] **10**, 213.

55-82. Enselme, J., and Dreyfus, J. C. Séméiologie électrophorétique des protéines du plasma sanguin [suivi de séméiologie électrophorétique des protéines] de l'hémoglobine (in French). Camugli, Lyon. [1955].

55-83. Ericson, A. T., Clegg, R. E., and Hein, R. E. Influence of calcium on mobility of the electrophoretic components of chicken blood serum. *Science* [1955] **122**, 199.

55-84. Erluison, G., and Gallinelli, R. Electrophoretic observation on plasma proteins in normal pregnancy and in toxicosis before and after delivery (in Italian with English summary). *Monit. ostet.-ginecol.* [1955] **26**, 26.

55-85. Feruglio, F. S., and Rimini, R. Determination of gluco- and lipoprotein of serum by means of paper electrophoresis. I. The dye technique (in Italian). *Boll. soc. ital. biol. sper.* [1955] **31**, 99.

55-86. Feruglio, F. S., and Rimini, R. Determination of gluco- and lipoprotein of serum by means of paper electrophoresis. II. Literature and results in normal persons (in Italian). *Boll. soc. ital. biol. sper.* [1955] **31**, 101.

55–87. Fischer, M. A., Magee, M. Z., and Coulter, E. P. The serum protein of the X-irradiated rat. *Arch. Biochem Biophys.* [1955] **56**, 66.

55-88. Fletcher, K., and Stanley, P. G. Detection of iodine-containing compounds on paper chromatograms. *Nature* [1955] **175**, 730.

55-89. Franglen, G. T. Chromatography and paper electrophoresis of sulfonphthalein dyes. *Nature* [1955] **175**, 134.

55-90. Franglen, G. T., Martin, N. H., and Treherne, J. D. An apparatus for paper electrophoresis. *J. Clin. Pathol.* [1955] **8**, 144.

55-91. Franken, F. H., and Klein, E. The interpretation of the paper electrophoretic lipograms for the determination of liver diseases (in German). *Deut. med. Wochschr.* [1955] **80**, 1074.

55-92. Franken, F. H., and Kommerell, B. A new transparency procedure for photoelectric evaluation of paper electrophoresis strips (in German). *Deut. med. Wochschr.* [1955] **80**, 1817.

55-93. von Frijtag-Drabbe, C. A. J., and Reinhold, J. G. Application of zone electrophoresis to analysis of serum proteins. *Anal. Chem.* [1955] **27**, 1090–1095.

55-94. Galansino, G., Fasoli, A., Magill, A. M., and Foa, P. P. Serum lipoproteins in experimental diabetes. IV. Effect of prolactin. *Proc. Soc. Exptl. Biol. Med.* [1955] **88**, 477.

55-95. Galli, G., and Nieri, I. Blood protein picture in human and experimental mycosis. *Minerva pediat.* [1955] **7**, 32.

55-96. Gamp, A. Investigation of the behavior of protein-bound carbohydrates in rheumatoid arthritis. I. Glucosamine content of serum (in German with English summary). *Z. Rheumaforsch.* [1955] **14**, 167.

55-97. Gatto, I., and La Grutta, A. Researches with paper electrophoresis on the Hb of the umbilical cord of the newborn and suckling (in Italian with English summary). *Pediatria (Naples)* [1955] **63**, 1–13.

55-98. Gatto, I., and La Grutta, A. Paper electrophoresis of Hb in thalassemia, drepanocytosis and thalassodrepanocytosis (in Italian with English summary). *Minerva pediat.* [1955] **7**, 1–19.

55-99. Gelli, G., and Poli, L. Serum lipoprotein and protein in newborn and premature infants (in Italian with English summary). *Acta Paediat. Latina* [1955] **8**, 251–274.

55-100. Gemolotto, G. Electrophoretic analysis of the protein content of the blood serum in some eye infections. II. Glaucoma (in Italian). *Ann. ottalmol. e clin. oculist.* [1955] **81**, 35.

55-101. Ghosh, B. N., and Ghosh, S. Evaluation of true zeta potential of the particles of cellulose and gelatin forming diaphragms. *J. Indian Chem. Soc.* [1955] **31**, 649.

55-102. Giglietti, A., and Tiecco, G. Paper electrophoresis of serums of pigs treated by *teschen* virus (in Italian with English summary). *Arch. vet. ital.* [1955] **6**, 25–32.

55-103. Giri, K. V. A simple paper chromatographic method for the study of serum protein patterns in health and disease. *Experientia* [1955] **11**, 165.

55-104. Goldbloom, A. A. Newer clinical and laboratory studies in the aged. V. Lipidogram by paper electrophoresis in aged normal patients 80–100 years of age. *Am. J. Digest. Disease* [1955] **22**, 51.

55-104a. Goldbloom, A. A., Eiber, H. B., Chapman, I., Deutschberger, O., and Loewe, W. R. Newer clinical and laboratory studies in the aged. IV. Atherosclerosis in normal patients 80 to 100 years of age. *Geriatrics* [1955] **10**, 213–220.

55-105. González Alvarez, J., and Otero de la Gándara, J. Proteins of blood and urine in the nephrosis syndrome studied by means of paper electrophoresis. *Rec. trav. chim.* [1955] **74**, 591.

55-106. Gottfried, S. P., Pope, R. H., Friedman, N. H., Akerson, I. B., and Di Mauro, S. Serum beta-lipoproteins of normal, atherosclerotic, and lipemic individuals. Changes in concentration, stability, and mobility upon incubation at 6.5° and 37.5°, as determined by paper electrophoresis. *Clin. Chem.* [1955] **1**, 253.

55-107. Gottfried, S. P., Pope, R. H., Friedman, N. H., Akerson, I. B., and Di Mauro, S. Lipoprotein studies in atherosclerotic and lipemic individuals by means of paper electrophoresis. *Am. J. Med. Sci.* [1955] **229**, 34–40.

55-108. Grabar, P., and Williams, C. A., Jr. Immuno-electrophoretic analysis of 6mixtures of antigenic substances. *Biochim. et Biophys. Acta* [1955] **17**, 7.

55-109. Grabar, P. Study of the metalaffine beta-globulin in human serum by the immuno-electrophoretic method (in French). *Ann. Acad. Sci. Fennicae Ser. A. II.* [1955] **60**, 401.

55-110. Grabar, P., Fauvert, R., Burtin, P., and Hartmann, L. Immuno-electrophoretic analysis of the serum of myelomas (in French). *Compt. rend.* [1955] **241**, 262.

55-111. Gräsbeck, R., and Lamberg, B. A. Electrophoretic lipoprotein pattern in disorders of thyroid function. *Acta Endocrinol.* [1955] **19**, 82.

55-112. Grasset, E., and Schwartz, D. E. Fractionation by electrophoresis on paper of the venom of *Vipera vissellii*. Properties and dosage of coagulating and anti-coagulating factors of this venom (in French). *Ann. inst. Pasteur* [1955] **88**, 271.

55-113. Grassmann, W., and Kuhn, K. Degradation of collagen and pro-collagen by sodium periodate and phenyl iodosoacetate (in German with English summary). *Z. physiol. Chem.* [1955] **301**, 1–16.

55-114. Grassmann, W., Hannig, K., and Plocke, M. A method for the quantitative determination of the content of amino acids in protein hydrolysated by combining of electrophoresis and chromatography (in German). *Z. physiol. Chem.* [1955] **299**, 258.

55-115. Gregory, G. F.   A method for rapidly transferring a substance on paper to the origin of a chromatogram. *Science* [1955] **121**, 169.

55-116. Gross, D.   Paper electrophoresis of amino acids and oligopeptides at very high potential gradients. *Nature* [1955] **176**, 72–73.

55-117. Gross, D.   Paper electrophoresis of polyhydric alcohols. *Nature* [1955] **176**, 362–363.

55-118. Groulade, J., and Jacqueline, F.   Quantitative study of fibrinogen by paper electrophoresis in chronic inflammatory rheumatism. Correlation of serum proteins, glycoproteins, and lipoproteins (in French). *Semaine hôpit.* [1955] **31**, 1–7.

55-119. Hais, I. M.   Paper ionophoresis of 4-hydrozycoumatin derivatives (in Czech). *Chem. listy* [1955] **49**, 709.

55-120. Hais, I. M., Macek, K., and Francova, V.   Paper chromatography and electrophoresis of chloramphenicol and related substances (in Czech). *Cs. farmecie* [1955] **4**, 127–129.

55-121. Hamerman, D.   Staining methods in chromatography of acidic and neutral mucopolysaccharides. *Science* [1955] **121**, 924.

55-122. Hartman, R. J. S.   Electrophoretic method for titration of antiserum and its application to antitumor serum. Univ. Microfilms (Ann Arbor, Michigan) Publ. No. 11290, [1955] pp. 1–133.

55-123. Hassall, C. H., and Reyle, K.   Hyloglycin A and B, two biologically active polypeptides from *Blighia sapida*. *Biochem. J.* [1955] **60**, 334–338.

55-124. Herdan, G.   A new statistical method for the comparison of electrophoretic analyses of normal and pathological sera. *Klin. Wochschr.* [1955] **33**, 538; *Acta genet. et Statist. Med.* [1955] **5**, 105–115.

55-125. Hirsch, A.   Dependence of serum electrophoretic behavior on the pH of buffer solutions (in Italian with English summary). *Giorn. biochim.* [1955] **4**, 71.

55-126. Hobart, M. H., and Rose, C. F. M.   A simple method for the continuous electrophoresis of serum proteins. *J. Clin. Pathol.* [1955] **8**, 338.

55-127. Hoch, H., and Barr, G. H.   Paper electrophoresis with superimposed pH gradient. *Science* [1955] **122**, 243–244.

55-128. Hohne, G., Kunkel, H. A., and Anger, R.   The serum proteins of the rat after whole-body irradiation with 3000 r (in German). *Klin. Wochschr.* [1955] **33**, 284.

55-129. Holdsworth, E. S.   An apparatus for continuous electrophoresis on paper. *Biochem. J.* [1955] **59**, 340–345.

55-130. Homolka, J., and Mydlil, V.   The blood protein picture in diarrhea of infants in comparison with other diseases (in German). *Ann. Paediat.* [1955] **185**, 142.

55-131. Homolka, J., and Mydlil, V.   Blood proteins in infants from a quantitative and qualitative point of view (in German). *Ann. Paediat.* [1955] **185**, 129.

55-132. Hořejší, J.   The importance of blood-plasma analysis for clinical diagnosis (in Czech). *časopis lékáru českých* [1955] **94**, 1021.

55-133. Huisman, T. H. J., van der Schaaf, P. C., and van der Sar, A.   Investigation on the abnormal haemoglobin in sicklaemia and sicklecell trait. *Documenta Med. Geograph. et Trop.* [1955] **7**, 285.

55-134. Huisman, T. H. J., van der Schaaf, P. C., and van der Sar, A.   Some characteristic properties of hemoglobin C. *Blood* [1955] **10**, 1079.

55-135. Hunter, F. M.   Description of a B_1 lipoprotein found in chylomicron layer *obtained* by ultracentrifugation of (human) serum. *Proc. Soc. Exptl. Biol. Med.* [1955] **88,** 538.

55-136. Jacobsson, K. Trypsin and plasmin inhibitors in human serum. *Scand. J. Clin. & Lab. Invest.* [1955] *Suppl.* **14,** 55.

55-137. Jencks, W. P., Jetton, M. R., and Durrum, E. L. Paper electrophoresis as a quantitative method. *Biochem. J.* [1955] **60,** 205.

55-138. Jencks, W. P., and Durrum, E. L. Paper electrophoresis as a quantitative method: The staining of serum lipoproteins. *J. Clin. Invest.* [1955] **34,** 1437–1448.

55-139. Jirgensons, B. Optical rotation and other physicochemical properties of serum albumin of cancer patients. *Cancer* [1955] **8,** 809.

55-140. Jirgensons, B. The intrinsic viscosity of serum albumin. *Makromol. Chem* [1955] **16,** 192.

55-141. Jirgensons, B. Characterization of human serum albumin by means of optical rotation. *J. Am. Chem. Soc.* [1955] **77,** 2289.

55-142. Johnson, V. L., and Dunlap, J. S. Electrophoretic separation of hemoglobins from the chicken. *Science* [1955] **122,** 1186.

55-143. Not assigned.

55-144. van Kampen, E. J., and Zondag, H. G. Quantitative paper electrophoresis of serum proteins (in Dutch). *Chem. Weekblad* [1955] **51,** 535–543.

55-144A. Karler, A. Instructions for electrochromatography apparatus. Brochure No. EC 310 (June) [1955] Microchemical Specialties Co., Berkeley, Calif.

55-145. Kember, N. F., and Wells, R. A. Ion-exchange separations on chemically modified cellulose. *Nature* [1955] **175,** 512.

55-146. Keys, A., Anderson, J. T., Fidanza, F., Keys, M. H., and Swahn, B. Effects of diet on blood lipids in man particularly cholesterol and lipoproteins. *Clin. Chem.* [1955] **1,** 34–52.

55-147. Kimbel, K. H., and Bünte, H. Determination of total (serum) protein from paper electropherograms (in German). *Klin. Wochschr.* [1955] **33,** 187.

55-148. Klein, E., and Franken, F. H. The electrophoretic lipoprotein spectrum of serum after treatment with heparin and in hepatic disorders (in German). *Deut. med. Wochschr.* [1955] **80,** 44.

55-149. Kleinsorg, H., Krüskemper, H. L., and Lopez-Calleja, C. Serum protein changes in experimental hypothyroidism after administration of iodine-131 (in German with English summary). *Acta Endocrinol.* [1955] **19,** 157.

55-150. Knedel, M., and Bube, F. W. Model experiments on the chemical reactions of serum lability tests (in German). *Klin. Wochschr.* [1955] **33,** 64.

55-151. Kolin, A. Isoelectric spectra and mobility spectra: A new approach to electrophoretic separation. *Proc. Natl. Acad. Sci. U. S.* [1955] **41,** 101.

55-152. Kolin, A. Electrophoretic "line spectra". *J. Chem. Phys.* [1955] **23,** 407.

55-153. Kolin, A. Magnification of resolution of electrophoretic sorting patterns (in English). *Naturwissenschaften* [1955] **42,** 367.

55-154. Kotter, L., Lenz, W., and Prandl, O. A method of separating globular muscle proteins by paper electrophoresis (in German with English summary). *Zentr. Veterinärmed.* [1955] **2,** 495–506.

55-155. Köttgen, U., Braun, E., and Friedberg, V. Preserving human milk by freeze-drying (in German). *Deut. med. Wochschr.* [1955] **80,** 923.

55-156. Kuhns, W. J. Abnormal protein patterns in disease. *Am. Practitioner and Dig. Treatment* [1955] **6,** 1157.

55-157. Kukowka, A. Serum protein fractions and blood pH in rheumatics. *Z. Rheumaforsch.* [1955] **14,** 24.

55-158. Kummel, J. Electrophoretic studies in experimental rabbit syphilis (in German). *Ärztl. Wochschr.* [1955] **10**, 58.

55-159. Lamberg, B.-A., and Grasbeck, R. The serum protein pattern in disorders of thyroid function. *Acta Endocrinol.* [1955] **19**, 91.

55-160. Langan, T. A., Durrum, E. L., and Jencks, W. P. Paper electrophoresis as a quantitative method: Measurement of alpha and beta lipoprotein cholesterol. *J. Clin. Invest.* [1955] **34**, 1427–1436.

55-161. Largier, J. F. Purification of tetanus toxin by multimembrane electro-decantation. *Biochim. et Biophys. Acta* [1955] **16**, 291.

55-162. Lass, A., Tepe, H. J., and Wunderlich, K. Binding of isoniazid to serum proteins (in German). *Klin. Wochschr.* [1955] **33**, 315.

55-163. Latner, A. L. Correction of paper strip serum electrophoresis diagrams (to true total protein values). *J. Lab. Clin. Med.* [1955] **45**, 147–148.

55-164. Laudahn, G. (Lack of) correlation between iron and copper in serum and beta-globulin, determined electrophoretically, in liver disease (in German). *Klin. Wochschr.* [1955] **33**, 511.

55-165. Laurell, A. B. On antibodies separated by paper electrophoresis with special reference to the Wassermann reagins. *Acta Pathol. Microbiol. Scand. Suppl.* [1955] **103**, 1–92.

55-166. Laurell, C. B., and Laurell, S. Electrophoresis of plasma proteins. *Lancet* [1955] **269**, 40.

55-167. Laurell, S. Effect of free fatty acids on the migration rates of lipoproteins in paper electrophoresis. *Scand. J. Clin. & Lab. Invest.* [1955] **6**, 28.

55-168. Lecoq, R. Inversion of blood level of adenine and protein in advanced forms of chronic alcoholism (in French). *Thérapie* [1955] **10**, 810–818.

55-169. Lederer, M. "An Introduction to Paper Electrophoresis and Related Methods," p. 145. Elsevier, Amsterdam. [1955].

55-170. Lederer, M. "An Introduction to Paper Electrophoresis and Related Methods." Elsevier, Amsterdam. [1955].

55-171. Lederer, M. Chromatography on paper impregnated with ion-exchange resins. Preliminary report. *Anal. Chim. Acta* [1955] **12**, 142.

55-172. Lemaire, A., and Cottet, J. The biochemistry of animal atherosclerosis (in French). *Presse méd.* [1955] **63**, 1339–1341.

55-173. Leone, A. Total serum protein and its fractions in premature and immature children. *Ann. ital. pediat.* [1955] **8**, 1–10.

55-174. Leonti, F. Electrophoretic studies on the proteins of the sap of forage plants (in Italian). *Boll. soc. ital. biol. sper.* [1955] **31**, 308.

55-175. Leupold, H., and Thiele, H. Serum protein changes in panmyelopathies (in German). *Folia Haematol.* [1955] **73**, 106.

55-176. Levy, D. Practical note on paper electrophoresis. *Ann. biol. clin. (Paris)* [1955] **13**, 292–294.

55-177. Lorenzini, R. Observations on the electrophoretic patterns of serum lipoproteins (in Italian with English summary). *Fegato (Rome)* [1955] **1**, 401.

55-178. Lorenzini, R., Innocenti, E., Morini, C., and Mucci, A. Electrophoretic lipidogram of serum in normal adults: Influence of age (in Italian). *Boll. soc. med.-chir. Modena* [1955] **55**, 115.

55-179. Lorenzini, R., Innocenti, E., and Mucci, A. Electrophoretic pattern of serum lipoproteins in clinical practice. Critical review of the proteinogram and lipogram of the normal adult male (in Italian with English summary). *Acta Gerontol.* [1955] **5**, 1–18.

55-180. Lundquist, F., Thorsteinsson, T., and Buus, O. Purification and properties of some enzymes in human seminal plasma. *Biochem. J.* [1955] **59**, 69.

55-181. von Lutterotti, M. Electrophoretic variations in the composition of proteins in cardiac insufficiency (in German). *Arch. Kreislaufforsch.* [1955] **22**, 170–206.

55-182. Macek, K., and Přibil, R. Use of complexons in chemical analysis. XLV. Contribution to the paper electrophoresis of some metals (in Czech). *Chem. listy* [1955] **49**, 367.

55-183. Malchiodi, C., and Zinicola, N. Electrophoretic serum proteins in chronic obliternas arteriopathies of joints (in Italian). *Ateneo parmense* [1955] **26**, 83.

55-184. Marini-Bettolo, G. B., and Lederer, M. In "An Introduction to Paper Electrophoresis and Related Methods" by M. Lederer, p. 60. Elsevier, Amsterdam. [1955].

55-185. Marini-Bettolo, G. B., and Lederer, M. In "An Introduction to Paper Electrophoresis and Related Methods" by M. Lederer, p. 44. Elsevier, Amsterdam. [1955].

55-186. Markham, R. L. Paper electrophoresis of serum mucoproteins. *Ann. Rheumatic Diseases* [1955] **14**, 212.

55-187. McConnell, K. P., and Van Loon, E. J. Distribution of selenium[75] in serum proteins as determined by paper electrophoresis. *J. Biol. Chem.* [1955] **212**, 747.

55-188. McDaniel, R. A., and Grossman, M. I. Paper electrophoretic study of carbon-14 fat emulsion cleared from post-heparin rat plasma. *Proc. Soc. Exptl. Biol. Med.* [1955] **89**, 442–443.

55-189. McDonald, H. J., and Raymond, S. Prevention of evaporation in horizontal strip ionography. *Science* [1955] **121**, 403.

55-190. McDonald, H. J. Ionography: Electrophoresis in stabilized media. Year Book, Chicago, Illinois. [1955].

55-191. McDonald, H. J., and Bermes, E. W. New procedure for staining lipoprotein in ionographic separations. *Biochim. et Biophys. Acta* [1955] **17**, 290.

55-192. McDonald, H. J., Bermes, E. W., Jr., and Spitzer, R. H. Chemical significance of ionography. *Federation Proc.* [1955] **14**, 733–745.

55-193. McEwen, W. K., and Kimura, S. J. Filter paper electrophoresis of tears. I. Lysozyme and its correlation with keratoconjunctivitis sicca. *Am. J. Ophthalmol.* [1955] **39**, 200.

55-194. McGarry, E., Schon, A. H., and Rose, B. The isolation and electrophoretic characterization of the proteins in the urine of normal subjects. *J. Clin. Invest.* [1955] **34**, 832.

55-195. McKinley, W. P. Paper electrophoresis of steroid derivatives. *Science* [1955] **121**, 139–140.

55-196. Mead, T. H. Apparatus and technique for two-dimensional paper ionophoresis. *Biochem. J.* [1955] **59**, 534–543.

55-197. Melcher, L. R., Steinfeld, J. L., and Reed, R. Studies on iodine-131 tagged red blood cell antibodies. *Proc. Soc. Exptl. Biol. Med.* [1955] **88**, 649.

55-198. Merlevede, E., Pottiez, F., and Verhelle, O. Free amino acids in gastric juice. A comparison of normal and pathological states (in French with English summary). *Arch. intern. pharmacodynamie* [1955] **100**, 265.

55-199. Meulemans, O. Relative migration velocities of serum protein fractions (in Dutch). *Maandschr. Kindergeneesk.* [1955] **23**, 488–494.

55-200. Meyniel, G., and de Mende, S. Electrophoretic study of serum proteins of irradiated animals (in French). *Bull. soc. chim. biol.* [1955] **37**, 127.

55-201. Miller, R. D. Neglected aspects of electro-osmosis in porous bodies. *Science* [1955] **122**, 373.

55-202. Mininni, G., Contro, S., and Checchia, C. Effects of ovariectomy on experimental atherosclerosis in rabbits. *Circulation Research* [1955] **3**, 191.

55-203. Mitidieri, E., Ribeiro, L. P., Affonso, O. R., and Villela, G. G. Localization of xanthine dehydrogenase (XD) in rat serum by paper electrophoresis. *Biochim. et Biophys. Acta* [1955] **17**, 587.

55-204. Moggi, P., Rapi, G., and Francalancia, L. Researches in myopathies. II. Electrophoretic determination of protein, lipoprotein and glycoprotein (in Italian with English summary). *Riv. clin. pediat.* [1955] **55**, 18–26.

55-205. Moggi, P., Francalancia, L., and Rapi, F. Electrophoretic determination of serum protein, lipoprotein, and glycoprotein in myopathies (in Italian). *Minerva pediat.* [1955] **7**, 439.

55-206. Møller, K. M. Phosphamidase activity of human seminal phosphatase. *Biochim. et Biophys. Acta* [1955] **16**, 162.

55-207. Mondovi, B., Antonini, E., and Modiano, G. On the presence of some artifacts in the paper chromatography and electrophoresis of keto-acids phenylydrazones extracted from biological fluids (in Italian with English summary). *Ricerca sci.* [1955] **25**, 2343.

55-208. Mondovi, B., and Antonini, E. Continuous paper electrophoresis apparatus (in Italian). *Ricerca sci.* [1955] **25**, 2631.

55-209. Mondovi, B., Modiano, G., and De Marco, C. Electrophoresis on paper of some sulphur compounds of biological interest (in Italian with English summary). *Giorn. biochim.* [1955] **4**, 324.

55-210. Montella, G. Electrophoretic study of protein in patients with gastroduodenal ulcers (in Italian). *Arch. ital. mal. app. diger.* [1955] **21**, 151.

55-211. Morris, B., and Courtice, F. C. Lipide exchange between plasma and lymph in experimental lipemia. *Quart. J. Exptl. Physiol.* [1955] **40**, 149.

55-212. Morris, B., and Courtice, F. C. The protein and lipid composition of the plasma of different animal species determined by zone electrophoresis and chemical analysis. *Quart. J. Exptl. Physiol.* [1955] **40**, 127.

55-213. Muendel, C. H., and Selke, W. A. Continuous ion exchange with an endless belt of phosphorylated cotton. *Ind. Eng. Chem.* [1955] **47**, 374.

55-214. Muić, N., and Piantanida, M. Venom of the sand viper. Electrophoretic and chemical characterization of the main fractions (in German with English summary). *Z. physiol. Chem.* [1955] **299**, 6.

55-215. Muić, N., and Meniga, A. Phosphatidase A activity of *Ammodytes* viper venom. *Arkiv kem.* [1955] **27**, 131–136.

55-216. Munier, R. Electrophoresis in zones on an inert support (in French). *Chim. anal.* [1955] **37**, 253.

55-217. Munier, R. Electrophoresis in zones on an inert support. II (in French). *Chim. anal* [1955] **37**, 283.

55-218. Neale, F. C. The demonstration of the iron-binding globulin (transferrin) in serum and urine proteins by use of ⁵⁹Fe combined with paper electrophoresis. *J. Clin. Pathol.* [1955] **8**, 334.

55-219. Neely, R. A., and Neill, D. W. Accuracy and reproducibility of paper protein electrophoresis. *Nature* [1955] **176**, 33.

55-220. O'Brien, D., and Sharp, B. B. Agammaglobulinemia. *Proc. Roy. Soc. Med.* [1955] **48**, 336.

55-221. Oeff, K., Rust, S., Schwarz, E., and Weise, H. J. The binding of penicillin to serum proteins (in German). *Klin. Wochschr.* [1955] **33**, 419.

55-222. Oliver, M. F., and Boyd, G. S. Plasma lipid and serum lipoprotein patterns during pregnancy and puerperium. *Clin. Sci.* [1955] **14**, 15.

55-223. Osserman, E. F., and Lawlor, D. P. Abnormal serum and urine in thirty-five cases of multiple myeloma, as studied by paper electrophoresis. *Am. J. Med.* [1955] **18**, 462.

55-224. Ostrowski, W. Paper electrophoresis (in Polish). Wiadomošci *Chemi.* [1955] **9**, 21–35.

55-225. Paget, M. Anomalous protein in serum and urine in myeloma patients. *Ann. biol. clin. (Paris)* [1955] **13**, 156.

55-226. Paléus, S. Purification of cytochrome c. *Congr. intern. biochim.*, Résumés communs., *2ᵉ Congr., Paris, 1952*, p. 282; [1955]. Cytochrome c. *Svensk Kem. Tidskr.* [1955] **67**, 275.

55-227. Parfentjev, I. A., and Johnson, M. L. Plasma-protein pattern and its significance in geriatrics and cancer diagnosis. *Geriatrics* [1955] **10**, 232.

55-228. Parker, L. F. J. Zone electrophoresis on filter paper. *Analyst* [1955] **80**, 638.

55-229. Patti, F. Effect of X-rays on dilute solutions of sodium eosinate. *J. Chim. phys.* [1955] **52**, 77.

55-230. Pechar, J., and Havlova, M. Electrophoresis of proteins on paper (in Czech). *Československ. gastroenterol. výživa* [1955] **9**, 205.

55-231. Perasalo, O., and Louhimo, I. The electrophoretic protein analysis in amyloid degeneration (in German). *Medizinische* [1955] p. 1030.

55-232. Not assigned.

55-233. Piez, K. A., and Eagle, H. Systematic effect of C^{14}-labeling on ion exchange chromatography of amino acids. *Science* [1955] **122**, 968.

55-234. Pitney, W. R., Beard, M. F., and Van Loon, E. J. The vitamin B_{12} content of electrophoretic fractions of liver homogenates. *J. Biol. Chem.* [1955] **212**, 47.

55-235. Porath, J., Roos, P., Landgrebe, F. W., and Mitchell, G. M. Isolation of melanophore-stimulating peptide from pig pituitary gland. *Biochim. et Biophys Acta* [1955] **17**, 598.

55-236. Porter, R. R. Fractionation of rabbit gamma-globulin by partition chromatography. *Biochem. J.* [1955] **59**, 405.

55-237. Preece, I. A., and Hobkirk, R. Paper electrophoresis of polysaccharides. *Chem. & Ind.* [1955] pp. 257–258.

55-238. Přibil, R., and Cihalik, J. Paper ionophoresis of inorganic compounds (in Czech). *Collection Czechoslov. Chem. Communs.* [1955] **20**, 715–716.

55-239. Putnam, F. W. Abnormal human serum globulins. *Science* [1955] **122**, 275.

55-240. Raacke-Fels, I. D., and Li, C. H. Corticotropins. (ACTH). VI. Isoelectric point of alpha-corticotropin as determined by zone electrophoresis on starch. *J. Biol. Chem.* [1955] **215**, 277.

55-241. Rao, S. S., Kulkarni, M. E., Cooper, S. N., and Radhakrishnan, M. R. Analysis of proteins of bovine lens, vitreous, and aqueous humor by electrophoresis and by Oudin's gel diffusion technique. *Brit. J. Ophthalmol.* [1955] **39**, 163.

55-242. Raynaud, R. What a cardiologist may expect from electrophoresis (in French). *Semaine hôp.* [1955] **31**, 787.

55-243. Ressler, N., and Jacobson, S. D. Electrophoresis of serum proteins in a viscous film. *Science* [1955] **122**, 1088–1089.

55-244. Revelli, E., Barbanti, A., and Fanzago, G. Experimental venous thrombosis.

Electrophoretic evaluation coupled with histological study and hemocoagulation (in Italian with English summary). *Minerva med.* [1955] **1,** 1209.

55-245. Ribeiro, L. P., Mitidieri, E., Affonso, O. R., and Villela, G. G. Localization of xanthine dehydrogenase in rat serum by paper electrophoresis. *Biochim. et Biophys. Acta* [1955] **17,** 587.

55-246. Ribeiro, L. P., Mitidieri, E., Villela, G. G. Paper electrophoretic and enzymatic studies on blood serum, venom, and liver of "Bothrops jararaca". *Mem. inst. Oswaldo Cruz* [1955] **53,** 487.

55-247. Ribeiro, L. P. Paper electrophoresis and its clinical application (in Portuguese). *Hospital (Rio de Janeiro)* [1955] **47,** 169.

55-248. Rideout, L. A., and Prichard, R. W. Inexpensive stain for paper electrophoresis. *Science* [1955] **121,** 374.

55-249. Robbins, J., Petermann, M. L., and Rall, J. E. Electrophoresis of the thyroxine-binding protein of serum at pH 4.5. *J. Biol. Chem.* [1955] **212,** 403.

55-250. Robbins, J., and Rall, J. E. Effects of triiodothyronine and other thyroxine analogs on thyroxine-binding in human serum. *J. Clin. Invest.* [1955] **34,** 1331.

55-251. Robbins, J., and Rall, J. E. Thyroxine binding capacity of serum in normal man. *J. Clin. Invest.* [1955] **34,** 1324.

55-252. Romani, J. D. Clinical interest of electrophoresis of glycoproteins in pleural fluids (in French). *Gaz. hôpitaux (Paris)* [1955] **19,** 717.

55-253. de Rosnay, C. D., Martin-Dupont, C., and Labadie, P. Middlebrook-Dubos test, electrophoresis, and Vernes reaction in tuberculosis (in French). *J. méd. Bordeaux et Sud-Ouest* [1955] **132,** 673.

55-254. Rossi-Espagnet, A., and Capone, M. Syndrome of low gamma-globulin in the blood (in Italian). *Policlinico (Rome) Sez. prat.* [1955] **62,** 766.

55-255. Ryle, A. P., Sanger, F., Smith, L. F., and Kitai, R. The disulphide bonds of insulin. *Biochem. J.* [1955] **60,** 541.

55-256. Sandor, G. Activity coefficient of an isoelectric protein (in French). *Compt. rend. soc. biol.* [1955] **149,** 2119.

55-257. Sandor, G. The reticuloendothelial response in multiple myeloma (in French). *Bull. acad. nat. méd.* [3] No. 23 & 24, 396 [1955].

55-258. Sanger, F., Thompson, E. O. P., and Kitai, R. The amide groups of insulin. *Biochem. J.* [1955] **59,** 509.

55-259. Sansoni, B. Separation of phosphates by paper electrophoresis. IV. Condensation of phosphate anions under simple conditions in aqueous solution (in German). *Angew. Chem.* [1955] **67,** 327.

55-260. Saroff, H. A. Easily assembled continuous electrophoresis apparatus. *Nature* [1955] **175,** 896.

55-261. Sato, T. R., Norris, W. P., and Strain, H. H. Effect of concentration and sorption upon migration of cations in paper electrochromatography. *Anal. Chem.* [1955] **27,** 521–525.

55-262. Scheiffarth, F., Berg, G., and Gotz, H. Plasma electrophoresis on filter paper (in German with English summary). *Z. physiol. Chem.* [1955] **302,** 126.

55-263. Scheiffarth, F., Berg, G., and Gotz, H. Possible separations of subfractions of serum proteins (in German). *Ärtzl. Wochschr.* [1955] **10,** 853.

55-264. Scheiffarth, F., Kimbel, K. H., and Berg, G. Variation of serum protein fractions of normal test rabbits (in German). *Naturwissenschaften* [1955] **42,** 214–215.

55-265. Scheurlen, P. G. On the common clinical importance of serum protein changes especially the alpha 1- and alpha 2-globulins (in German). *Z. klin. Med.* [1955] **152**, 500.

55-266. Scheurlen, P. G. Serum protein alterations in diabetes mellitus (in German). *Klin. Wochschr.* [1955] **33**, 198.

55-267. Schilling, J. A., Milch, L. E., Joseph, B., Criscuolo, D., Cheatham, M. P., Cyr, A., Hill, C. L., Robinson, L. C., Gerard, W. A., and Groye, B. L. Fractional analysis of experimental wound fluid. *Proc. Soc. Exptl. Biol. Med.* [1955] **89**, 189.

55-268. Schroeder, W., and Voigt, K. D. The possibility for the separation of steroids by means of paper electrophoresis and inverse current diffusion (in German). *Rec. trav. chim.* [1955] **74**, 603.

55-269. Schulte, K. E., and Müller, F. Electrophoretic studies on milk proteins. I. Separation of albumins of cow's milk and whey (in German with English summary). *Milchwissenschaft* [1955] **10**, 90–97.

55-270. Schulte, K. E., and Müller, F. Electrophoretic studies on milk proteins. II Examination of the whey proteins at the beginning of lactation (in German with English summary). *Milchwissenschaft* [1955] **10**, 130.

55-271. Schulte, K. E. and Müller, F. Electrophoretic studies on milk proteins. III. Milk proteins of goat's and ewe's milk (in German with English Summary). *Milchwissenschaft* [1955] **10**, 228.

55-272. Schulte, K. E., and Müller, F. Electrophoretic studies on milk proteins. V. Pasteurized milk and products (in German with English summary). *Milchwissenschaft* [1955] **10**, 270.

55-273. Schultz, J., Grannis, G., Kimmel, H., and Shay, H. Characterization of the electrophoretic components of the sera of dog, rat and man in terms of six amino acids. *Arch. Biochem. Biophys.* [1955] **57**, 174.

55-274. Schultz, O. E., and Strauss, D. Paper chromatographic determination of alkaloids (in German). *Arzneimittel-Forsch.* [1955] **5**, 342.

55-275. Schulze, G., Winne, D., and Zurmöhle, W. Lipids, proteins, and enzyme activity in experimental kidney damage by uranyl nitrate (in German). *Arch. exptl. Pathol. Pharmakol. Naunyn-Schmiedeberg's* [1955] **226**, 114.

55-276. Segovia, F. Determination of proteinemia by paper electrophoresis (in Spanish). *Rev. Seguro de enfermedad* [1955] **3**, 18.

55-277. Sehon, A. H., Kaye, M., McGarry, E., and Rose, B. Localization of an insulin-neutralizing factor by zone electrophoresis in a serum of an insulin-resistant patient. *J. Lab. Clin. Med.* [1955] **45**, 765.

55-278. Shimomura, O. Paper electrophoresis. I. Paper electrophoresis of aniline and phenol derivatives. II. pH-Mobility curves of various substances. *Nippon Kagaku Zasshi* [1955] **76**, 277, 562.

55-279. Skeggs, L. T., Jr., Marsh, W. H., Kahn, J. R., and Shumway, N. P. Aminoacid composition and electrophoretic properties of hypertension I. *J. Exptl. Med.* [1955] **102**, 435.

55-280. Slater, R. J., Ward, S. M., and Kunkel, H. G. Immunological relationships among the myeloma proteins. *J. Exptl. Med.* [1955] **101**, 85.

55-281. Smithies, O. Zone electrophoresis in starch gels: Group variations in the serum proteins of normal human adults. *Biochem. J.* [1955] **61**, 629–641.

55-282. Smithies, O. Grouped variations in the occurrence of new protein components in normal human serum. *Nature* [1955] **175**, 307.

55-282A. Solms, J. Continuous paper chromatography (in German). *Helv. Chim. Acta* [1955] **38**, 1127.

55-283. Sorof, S., Ott, M. G., and Young, E. M. Zonal electrophoresis in a density gradient of sucrose solution by use of the Schlieren optical system. *Arch. Biochem. Biophys.* [1955] **57**, 140.

55-284. Spackman, D. H., Smith, E. L., and Brown, D. M. Leucine aminopeptidase. IV. Isolation and properties of the enzyme from swine kidney. *J. Biol. Biol. Chem.* [1955] **212**, 255.

55-285. Stefanelli, S. Protein of blood after gynecologic operations. *Monit. ostet.-ginecol.* [1955] **25**, 519.

55-286. Stiefel, G. E., and Jasinski, B. Colloidal iron and its transport in the blood (in French). *Semaine hôp.* [1955] **31**, 1–3.

55-287. Ströle, U. The use of carboxyl paper in paper chromatography (in German). *Z. anal. Chem.* [1955] **144**, 256.

55-288. Svartz, N., and Schlossmann, K. Cold precipitable haemagglutinating factor in serum from patients with rheumatoid arthritis. *Ann. Rheumatic Diseases* [1955] **14**, 191–194.

55-289. Svensson, H., and Valmet, E. Density gradient electrophoresis. A new method of separating electrically charged compounds. *Sci. Tools* [1955] **2**, 11.

55-290. Svennson, H. On the possible interference of electrode reaction products in electrophoresis. *Acta Chem. Scand.* [1955] **9**, 1689–1699.

55-291. Svensson, H., Agrell, C.-E., Dehlen, S.-O., and Hagdahl, L. An apparatus for continuous chromatographic separation. *Sci. Tools* [1955] **2**, 17.

55-292. Syllaba, J., Opplt, J. J., and Fiserova, B. The role of dysproteinemia in the diagnosis and prognosis of liver diseases (in Czech). *Časopis lékáru českých* [1955] **94**, 699.

55-293. Tangheroni, W., and Gelli, G. Comparative study of protein, lipoprotein, and urinary protein in the nephrotic syndrome (in Italian). *Minerva med.* [1955] **1**, 292.

55-294. Tauber, H. Separation of alpha-keto-acid dinitrophenylhydrazones by paper electrophoresis and their colorimetric determination. *Anal. Chem.* [1955] **27**, 287–289.

55-295. Tayeau, F., and Nivet, R. Esterification of serum cholesterol and lipoprotein associations (in French). *Compt. rend.* [1955] **240**, 567.

55-296. Tekman, S., and Ugur, A. Paper electrophoresis of a purified specific antibody. *Nature* [1955] **175**, 594.

55-297. Tekman, S., and Ugur, A. An electrophoretic study of the pure antibodies formed against anthranyl-azo-globulin antigens. *Forum Med.* [1955] **1**, 152–156.

55-298. Thatcher, F. S., Matheson, B. H., and Simon, W. R. Studies with staphylococcal toxins. III. The application of paper ionophoresis to the resolution of components of toxic concentrates. *Can. J. Microbiol.* [1955] **1**, 372.

55-299. Tiselius, A. Electrophoresis and chromatography of proteins and polypeptides (in German). *Angew. Chem.* [1955] **67**, 245.

55-300. Tizzani, R. J. Microelectrophoresis on paper of adult normal serum. (Proteins, glyco- and lipoproteins). A statistical study. Thesis [1955] pp. 1–77.

55-301. Tropeano, L. Paper electrophoresis of serum glyco- and lipoproteins in myeloma (in Italian). *Progr. med.* [1955] **11**, 65.

55-302. Tuttle, A. H. Serum pigment in newborn infants. I. Erythroblastosis fetalis. *Am. J. Diseases Children* [1955] **89**, 544.

55-303. Tuttle, A. H.   Demonstration of hemoglobin reactive substance in human serum. *Science* [1955] **121**, 701.

55-304. Uriel, J., and Scheidegger, J. J.   Electrophoresis in agar gel and staining of the component fractions (in French). *Bull. soc. chim. biol.* [1955] **37**, 165.

55-305. Vargues, R., Darmon, J., and Kaziz, Y.   Isolation of beta-lipo-euglobin from blood serum (in French). *Compt. rend.* [1955] **240**, 1583.

55-306. Villela, G. G., Mitidieri, E., and Ribeiro, L. P.   Flavoproteins in the blood serum of the Brazilian snake *Bothrops jararaca. Arch. Biochem. Biophys.* [1955] **56**, 270.

55-307. Villela, G. G., Affonso, O. R., Ribeiro, L. P., and Mitidieri, E.   Distribution of xanthine oxidase in the liver and the serum of the rat (in Spanish with English summary). *Mem. inst. Oswaldo Cruz* [1955] **53**, 563.

55-308. Villela, G. G., and Ribeiro, L. P.   Hemoglobins of the worm *Tetrameres confusa. Rev. brasil. biol.* [1955] **15**, 383.

55-309. Villela, G. G., and Ribeiro, L. P.   Hemoglobins of a parasitic nematode of the hen (in Portuguese). *Anais acad. brasil cienc.* [1955] **27**, 87.

55-310. Voigt, K. D., and Schrader, E. A.   Lipo- and glycoprotein relations in arteriographically confirmed arteriosclerosis (in German). *Klin. Wochschr.* [1955] **33**, 465.

55-311. Voigt, K. D., Schroeder, W., and Bedkmann, I.   Chromatographic and electrophoretic determinations of corticosteroids. *Acta Endocrinol.* [1955] **18**, 325.

55-312. Wade, H. E., and Morgan, D. M.   Fractionation of phosphates by paper ionophoresis and chromatography. *Biochem. J.* [1955] **60**, 264–270.

55-313. Wagner, G.   Paper ionophoretic and paper chromatographic experiments separating some of the sympathicomimetic amines (in German). *Sci. Pharm.* [1955] **23**, 148.

55-314. Wagner, G.   On paper chromatography and paper ionophoresis of some analgetica related to morphine (in German). *Pharmazie* [1955] **10**, 470.

55-315. Wallner, A.   Normal values and errors of method in paper electrophoresis (in German). *Med. Monatsschr.* [1955] **9**, 520.

55-316. Walsh, J. R., Humoller, F. L., Zimmerman, H. J.   Hepatic function in multiple myeloma. *J. Lab. Clin. Med.* [1955] **45**, 253–259.

55-317. Walz, L., and Rasbach, K.   Electrophoretic serum protein changes in active pulmonary tuberculosis with and without chemotherapy (in German). *Medizinische* [1955] p. 421.

55-318. Wehmeyer, P.   Anomaly in electrophoresis of some virus-containing solutions. *Acta Pathol. Microbiol. Scand.* [1955] **36**, 66.

55-319. Weichert, R.   Paper-chromatographic resolutions of D,L-histidine. *Acta Chem. Scand.* [1955] **9**, 547.

55-320. Weicker, H.   The behavior of serum lipoproteins during damage to the liver parenchyma and their significance to the various forms of icterus (in German). *Ärztl. Wochschr.* [1955] **10**, 1057–1064.

55-321. Weir, J. H., Tsuji, F. I., and Chase, A. M.   The isoelectric point of *Cypridina* Luciferase. *Arch. Biochem. Biophys.* [1955] **56**, 235.

55-322. Werner, G., and Westphal, O.   Separations of substances by high voltage electrophoresis (in German). *Angew. Chem.* [1955] **67**, 251–256.

55-323. Werner, G.   An apparatus for high-tension paper electrophoresis (in German). *Rec. trav. chim.* [1955] **74**, 613.

55-324. Westphal, U., Firschein, H. E., and Pearce, E. M.   Binding of hydrocortisone-4-C^{14} and progesterone-4-C^{14} to serum albumin, demonstrated by paper electrophoresis. *Science* [1955] **121**, 601.

55-325. Wieland, T., and Pfleiderer, G. Analytical and micropreparative carrier electrophoresis with high voltages (in German). *Angew. Chem.* [1955] **67**, 257–260.

55-326. Williams, C. A., Jr., and Grabar, P. Immunoelectrophoretic studies on serum proteins. I. The antigens of human serum. *J. Immunol.* [1955] **74**, 158.

55-327. Williams, C. A., Jr., and Grabar, P. Immunoelectrophoretic studies on serum proteins. II. Immune sera: Antibody distribution. III. Human gamma-globulin. *J. Immunol.* [1955] **74**, 397–403, 404–410.

55-328. Williams, F. G., Jr., Pickels, E. G., and Durrum, E. L. Improved hanging-strip paper electrophoresis technique. *Science* [1955] **121**, 829.

55-329. Winkler, C., and Schellert, P. Electrophoretic investigations of serum proteins in rats with Walker carcinoma (in German). *Klin. Wochschr.* [1955] **33**, 678.

55-330. Wolff, H. P., Lang, N., and Knedel, M. Investigations of the binding of copper to serum proteins with copper-64 (in German). *Z. ges. exptl. Med.* [1955] **125**, 358–368.

55-331. Wolvius, D., and Verschure, J. C. M. The reliability of the determination of urinary proteins by electrophoresis of filter paper (in French). *Rec. trav. chim.* [1955] **74**, 596.

55-332. Wood, H. W. Paper electrophoresis of reducing agents. *Nature* [1955] **175**, 1084.

55-333. Wood, H. W. Bisulphite as oxidizing agent. *Chem. & Ind.* [1955] (*London*). p. 1119.

55-334. Wood, T. A reagent for the detection of chloride and of certain purines and pyrimidines on paper chromatograms. *Nature* [1955] **176**, 175.

55-335. Yamane, H. The interaction of nucleic acid and serum albumin. *J. Physiol. Soc. Japan* [1955] **17**, 549.

55-336. Zentner, H. A modified method of filter paper electrophoresis. *Nature* [1955] **175**, 953.

55-337. Zettel, H., Knedel, M., Endress, M., and Endress, H. Electrophoretic investigations on the behavior of the serum proteins in pulmonary diseases (in German). *Z. klin. Med.* [1955] **153**, 134.

55-338. Zittle, C. A., Della Monica, E. S., Custer, J. H., and Krikorian, R. Purification of human red cell acetylcholinesterase by electrophoresis, ultracentrifugation, and gradient extraction. *Arch. Biochem. Biophys.* [1955] **56**, 469.

56-0. Abdel-Wahab, E. M., Rees, V. H., and Laurence, D. J. R. Evaluation of the albumin-globulin ratio of blood plasma or serum by paper electrophoresis. *Ciba Foundation Symposium Paper Electrophoresis*. [1956] 30–42.

56-1. Andreani, D. V., and Gray, C. H. Serum polysaccharides in diabetes mellitus (in Italian). *Clin. Chim. Acta* [1956] **1**, 7.

56-2. Arends, T. The importance of abnormal hemoglobins in pediatrics (in Spanish). *Arch. venezolanos puericultura y pediat.* [1956] **19**, 67–80.

56-3. Baumann, F., and Blaedel, W. J. Application of high frequency methods to detection of bands in partition chromatography. *Anal. Chem.* [1956] **28**, 2–4.

56-4. Briggs, D. R., Garner, E. F., and Smith, F. Separation of carbohydrates by electrophoresis on glass filter paper. *Nature* [1956] **178**, 154–155.

56-5. Burtin, P., Hartman, L., Fauvert, R., and Grabar, P. Studies on the proteins in myeloma. I. Critical study of the techniques of identification of Bence-Jones protein and of their diagnostic value (in French with English summary). *Rev. franç. études clin. et biol.* [1956] **1**, 17.

56-6. Caputo, A., and Dose, K. Primary action of X-rays on lysozyme. *Nature* [1956] **178**, 209.

56-7. Chapin, M. A. The distribution of lipid and phospholipid in paper electrophoresis of normal serum lipoproteins. *J. Lab. Clin. Med.* [1956] **47**, 386.

56-7A. *Ciba Foundation Symposium on Paper Electrophoresis.*

56-8. Cox, F. M., Lanchantin, G. F., and Ware, A. G. Chromatographic purification of human serum accelerator globulin. *J. Clin. Invest.* [1956] **35**, 106–113.

56-9. Cresseri, A. Various individual and isolated components present in a mucin preparation of gastric mucosa of the hog: Their chemical, physical and biological properties (in Italian with English summary). *Pubbl. chim. biol. med.* [1956] **2**, 235.

56-9A. Crook, E. M. Analysis of separated materials. I. *Ciba Foundation Symposium Paper Electrophoresis.* [1956] 132–148.

56-10. Crowle, A. J. A simplified agar electrophoretic method for use in antigen separation and serologic analysis. *J. Lab. Clin. Med.* [1956] **48**, 642–648.

56-11. Dittmer, A. "Papierelektrophorese. Grundlagen—Methodik—Klinische Betrachtungen" (in German). *G. Fischer, Jena.* [1956].

56-11A. Durrum, E. L. Some design problems in continuous flow electrophoresis. *Abstr. 130th Ann. Meeting Am. Chem. Soc. Atlantic City*, [1956].

56-11B. Durrum, E. L. The future of the technique in its application to clinical research and routine analysis. *Ciba Foundation Symposium Paper Electrophoresis.* [1956] 197–205.

56-12. Evans, J. V., King, J. W. B., Cohen, B. L., Harris, H., and Warren, F. L. Genetics of haemoglobin and blood potassium differences in sheep. *Nature* [1956] **178**, 849–850.

56-13. Ferri, R. G., Mendes, E., Cardoso, T. J. B., and Tutiya, T. Electrophoresis of serum protein in asthma. Preliminary report. *J. Allergy* [1956] **27**, 494–503.

56-14. Franglen, G. T. Protein-dye interactions considered in relation to the estimation of protein in paper electrophoresis. *Ciba Foundation Symposium Paper Electrophoresis.* [1956] 172–182.

56-15. Giri, K. V. Agar electrophoresis of serum proteins on cellophane and polyester films. *J. Lab. Clin. Med.* [1956] **48**, 775–778.

56-16. Gleye, M., and Sandor, G. Study of the humoral effects of adrenaline (in French). *Compt. rend.* [1956] **242**, 948–950.

56-17. Grabar, P., Fauvert, R., Burtin, P., and Hartman, L. Study of the proteins in myeloma. II. Immuno-electrophoretic analysis of the serums of 30 patients with myeloma (in French with English summary). *Rev. franç. études clin. et biol.* [1956] **1**, 175.

56-18. Grabar, P., Nowinski, W. W., and Genereaux, B. D. Use of pectin in gel electrophoresis. *Nature* [1956] **178**, 430.

56-18A. Grassmann, W. General methods of paper electrophoresis with examples of its use in medical and biochemical problems. *Ciba Foundation Symposium Paper Electrophoresis.* [1956] 2–21.

56-19. Gross, D. High-voltage paper electrophoresis of non-volatile organic acids and their mixtures with amino-acids. *Nature* [1956] **178**, 29.

56-20. Gross, W., and Snell, R. S. The serum gamma-globulin-level in malignant disease. *Nature* [1956] **178**, 855.

56-21. Hack, M. H. Some properties of human serum lipoproteins. *Proc. Soc. Exptl. Biol. Med.* [1956] **91**, 92-95.

56-22. Hakim, A. A. Enzyme-substrate complex formation: A first stage in ribonuclease activity. *Nature* [1956] **178**, 1293–1295.

56-23. Halbrecht, I., and Klibanski, C. Identification of a new normal embryonic haemoblobin. *Nature* [1956] **178**, 794–795.

56-24. Herbst, F. S. M., Lever, W. F., and Waddell, W. R. Effects of intravenously administered fat on the serum lipoproteins. *Science* [1956] **123**, 843.

56-25. Hooft, C., Vandenberghen, C., and van Belle, M. The lipoproteins in lipoid nephrosis of the child (in French with English summary). *Acta Med. Belg.* [1956] **25**, 155-166.

56-26. Hooft, C., Vandenberghen, C., and van Belle, M. The lipidogram of lipoid nephrosis during measles infection (in French with English summary). *Acta Med. Belg.* [1956] **25**, 167–171.

56-27. Ingram, V. M. A specific chemical difference between the globins of normal human and sickle-cell anaemia haemoglobin. *Nature* [1956] **178**, 792-794.

56-28. Itano, H. A., Bergren, W. R., and Sturgeon, P. The abnormal human hemoglobins. *Medicine* [1956] **35**, 121–159.

56-28A. Jencks, W. P., Hyatt, M. R., Jetton, M. R., Mattingly, T. W., and Durrum, E. L. A study of serum lipoproteins in normal and atherosclerotic patients by paper electrophoretic techniques. *J. Clin. Invest.* [1956] **35**, 980–990.

56-28B. Jencks, W. P., Smith, E. R. B., and Durrum, E. L. The clinical significance of the analysis of serum protein distribution by filter paper electrophoresis. *Am. J. Med.* [1956] **21**, 387–405.

56-29. Jirgensons, B. Optical rotation and viscosity of native and denatured proteins. VII. Human serum albumin in alkaline solutions. *Makromol. Chem.* [1956] **18/19**, 48–61.

56-30. Jonxis, J. H. P., Huisman, T. H. J., van der Schaaf, P. C., and Prins, H. K. Amino-acid composition of haemoglobin E. *Nature* [1956] **177**, 627–628.

56-30A. Kaminski, M., and Durieux, J. Comparative studies of the serum of the hen, rooster, young chick, embryo, and egg-white (in French). *Exptl. Cell Research* [1956] **10**, 590–618.

56-31. Kaminski, M. Gobulins in the chicken egg-white. *Nature* [1956] **178**, 981.

56-31A. Kickhöfen, B. High voltage paper electrophoresis. *Ciba Foundation Symposium Paper Electrophoresis.* [1956] 206–212.

56-32. Kitahara, S. Separation of *o*- and *p*-chloraniline by paper electrophoresis. Personal communication. [1956]

56-33. Klatskin, G., Reinmuth, O. M., and Barnes, W. A study of the densitometric method of analyzing filter paper. Electrophoretic patterns of serum. *J. Lab. Clin. Med.* [1956] **48**, 476.

56-33A. Köiw, E. Paper electrophoresis. *Ciba Foundation Symposium Paper Electrophoresis.* [1956] 79–85.

56-34. Kulick, C. G. Continuous electrophoresis on paper. *Med. Technicians Bull.* [1956] **7**, 53.

56-35. Larin, N. M. Detection by paper electrophoresis of the protein denaturation in heat-inactivated serum for the complement fixation reaction. *Nature* [1956] **178**, 1243.

56-35A. Laurell, H. A paper electrophoretic study of the effect of ACTH and cortisone on the protein-bound serum polysaccharides in some patients with rheumatoid arthritis, ulcerative colitis, etc. *Ciba Foundation Symposium Paper Electrophoresis.* [1956] 58–78.

56-36. Lemaire, A., Enselme, J., Cottet, J., Casassus, P., and Tigaud. The lipoproteins of serum. Their study by paper electrophoresis (in French). *Ann. méd. (Paris)* [1956] **57** (1).

56-37. Lemaire, A., Cottet, J., and Ledermann, S. The biochemistry of human atheroscleroris (in French). *Presse méd.* [1956] **64,** 1129–1132.

56-38. Levin, B., and Davies, G. Separation of steroid conjugates by paper electrophoresis. *Nature* [1956] **178,** 918.

56-39. Markham, R. L. A modified method of two-dimensional zone electrophoresis applied to mucoproteins in serum and urine. *Nature* [1956] **177,** 125.

56-40. Markham, R. L., Jacobs, J. H., and Fletcher, E. T. D. Zone electrophoresis of serum and urine at pH 4.5 and its application to the isolation and investigation of mucoproteins. *J. Lab. Clin. Med.* [1956] **48,** 559–570.

50-40A. Martin, N. H. Analysis of separated materials. *Ciba Foundation Symposium Paper Electrophoresis.* [1956] 160–171.

56-40B. McDonald, H. J. Area under peaks: Dropping perpendiculars versus extending curves to baseline. *Ciba Foundation Symposium Paper Electrophoresis.* [1956] 149–150.

56-40C. McDonald, H. J. A new approach to the staining of lipoproteins. *Ciba Foundation Symposium Paper Electrophoresis.* [1956] 183–186.

56-41. Miller, G. L., and Blum, R. Resolution of fungal cellulase by zone electrophoresis. *J. Biol. Chem.* [1956] **218,** 131.

56-42. Mitidieri, E., Affonso, O. R., Ribeiro, L. P., and Villela, G. G. Detection of xanthine dehydrogenase activity in soluble proteins of rat liver separated by paper electrophoresis. *Nature* [1956] **178,** 492–493.

56-43. Morris, C. J. O. R. Recent advances in electrophoretic separation methods for biologically important substances. *Phys. in Med. & Biol.* [1956] **1,** 3–17.

56-44. Muić, N. Immunochemical and biochemical properties of ammodytes viper venom (*Vipéra ammodytes* L.). *Bull. Sci. Conseil acad. RPF Yougoslavie* [1956] **2,**105.

56-45. Muić, N., Stanić, M., and Meniga, A. Contribution to the knowledge of spider venom of *Latrodectus tredecimguttatus* Rossi (in German with English summary). *Z. physiol. Chem.* [1956] **305,** 70–74.

56-46. Not assigned

56-47. Murray, I. M. Interaction of gelatin-stabilized radiogold colloid and plasma proteins. *Proc. Soc. Exptl. Biol. Med.* [1956] **91,** 252–255.

56-48. Owen, J. A. Determination of Serum-protein fractions by zone electrophoresis on paper and direct reflection photometry. *Analyst* [1956] **81,** 26–37.

56-49. Paigen, K. Convenient starch electrophoresis apparatus. *Anal. Chem.* [1956] **28,** 284.

56-50. Paronetto, F., Wang, C. I., and Adlersberg, D. Comparative studies of lipoproteins by starch and paper electrophoresis. *Science* [1956] **124,** 1148.

56-50A. Peeters, H., Vuylsteke, P., and Noe, R. Cascade electrodes in continuous electrophoresis (in Dutch with English summary). *4th Colloquium, St. Jans Hospitaal, Bruges, Belgium.* [1956]

56-51. Pezold, F. A. Isolation of alpha-lipoproteins from human serum in the ultracentrifuge and their identification by paper electrophoresis (in German). *Naturwissenschaften* [1956] **43**, 280.

56-52. Prins, H. K., and Huisman, T. H. J.   Chromatographic behaviour of haemoglobin E. *Nature* [1956] **177**, 840–841.

56-52A. Pučar, Z.   Studies on paper electrophoresis in a damp room. IV. Continuous electrophoresis and two-dimensional electrochromatography (in German). *Croat. Chem. Acta* [1956] **28**, 195–209.

56-53. Ribeiro, L. P., and Villela, G. G.   Paper electrophoretic studies of hemoglobins from the worm *Tetrameres confusa*. A comparison with hen hemoglobins. *Rev. brasil. biol.* [1956] **16**, 145–147.

56-54. Ribeiro, L. P., Abreu, R. R., and Villela, G. G.   The use of paper electrophoresis and paper chromatography for the separation of flavins. *Rev. brasil. biol.* [1956] **16**, 71–76.

56-55. Roberts, H. R., and Carleton, F. J.   Determination of specific activity of carbon-14-labeled sugars on paper chromatograms using an automatic scanning device. *Anal. Chem.* [1956] **28**, 11.

56-56. Not assigned

56-57. Russ, E. M., Raymunt, J., and Barr, D. P.   Lipoproteins in primary biliary cirrhosis. *J. Clin. Invest.* [1956] **35**, 133–144.

56-58. Sandor, G., and Slizewicz, P.   Euglobulin III, an alpha-lipoeuglobulin which is homogeneous electrophoretically and ultracentrifugally and its immunological significance (in French). *Compt. rend.* [1956] **242**, 1377–1380.

56-59. Schaffner, F., Scherbel, A. L., and Lytle, R. I.   Electrophoretic serum glycoproteins in acute viral hepatitis. *J. Lab. Clin. Med.* [1956] **48**, 551–558.

56-60. Scheidegger, J. J.   Immunoelectrophoresis (in French). *Semaine hôp.* [1956] **32**(37).

56-61. Schier, O.   Detection and determination of alkalies by paper electrophoresis (in German). *Angew. Chem.* [1956] **68**, 63–66.

56-62. von Schrader-Beielstein, H. W., and Seeliger, H. P. R.   Electrophoretic examination of mushroom sera (in German). *Z. Immunitätsforsch.* [1956] **113**, 328.

56-63. Snell, R. S., and Gross, W.   Electrophoretic evaluation of the serum proteins in malignant disease. *Nature* [1956] **178**, 1238.

56-64. Sohar, E., Bossak, E. T., Wang, C. I., and Adlersberg, D.   Serum components in the newborn. *Science* [1956] **123**, 461.

56-64A. Sommerfelt, S. C.   Some practical points regarding the reading of the paper electrophoretic strip. *Ciba Foundation Symposium Paper Electrophoresis.* [1956] 151–159.

56-65. Stickler, G. B., McKenzie, B. F., Wakim, K. G., and Burke, E. C.   The effect of plasma transfusion and treatment with corticotropin on the electrophoretic patterns in serum and urine of children with the nephrotic syndrome. *J. Lab. Clin. Med.* [1956] **47**, 392–402.

56-65A. Svensson, H.   Physicochemical aspects and their relationship to the design of apparatus. *Ciba Foundation Symposium Paper Electrophoresis.* [1956] 86–104.

56-66. Thorup, O. A., Itano, H. A., Wheby, M., and Levall, B. S.   Hemoglobin J. *Science* [1956] 123, 889.

56-67. Thulin, K. E.   The reaction of streptococcal agglutination relative to the RAS factor in rheumatoid arthritis. I and II. *Acta Rheum. Scand.* [1956] **1**, 24.

56-67A. Trautman, R., and Kunkel, H. G.   Geometrical factors in the determination of mobility and diffusion spreading for zone electrophoresis in supporting media. *Abstr. 130th Ann. Meeting Am. Chem. Soc., Atlantic City.* [1956]

56-68. Tuft, H. S.   Blood protein abnormalities in asthmatic children. *J. Allergy* [1956] **27,** 487–493.

56-69. Tuttle, A. H.   Letter to the editor. *Science* [1956] **123,** 461.

56-70. Verschure, J. C. M.   Electro-chromograms of human bile. *Clin. Chim. Acta* [1956] **1,** 38.

56-70A. de Wael, J.   Application of paper electrophoresis to the differential diagnosis of canine diseases. *Ciba Foundation Symposium Paper Electrophoresis.* [1956] 22–29.

56-70B. de Wael, J.   The combined influence of evaporation and diffusion on the separation of serum proteins by paper electrophoresis. *Ciba Foundation Symposium Paper Electrophoresis.* [1956] 105–118.

56-71. Waldmann-Meyer, H., and Schilling, K.   Protein adsorption on filter paper. *Science* [1956] **124,** 1028.

56-71A. White, J. C., Beaven, G. H., and Ellis, M.   Analysis of human haemoglobins by paper electrophoresis. *Ciba Foundation Symposium Paper Electrophoresis.* [1956] 43–57.

56-71B. Wieme, R. J., and Rabaey, M.   Crystallin proteins and their relationship to the cataract (in French). *2nd Colloquium, St. Jans Hospitaal, Bruges, Belgium.* [1954]

56-72. Wieme, R. J.   Hemoglobin-reactive substance in human serum. *Science* [1956] **123,** 461.

56-73. Wunderly, C.   Control of the staining procedure after paper electrophoresis. *Nature* [1956] **177,** 586.

56-74. Wunderly, C.   Advances in paper electrophoresis (in German). *Chimia (Switz.)* [1956] **10,** 1–26.

Subject Classification for Bibliography, Part II

52—38
55—111, 159
Thalassemia
55—98
Typhoid (rabbit)
54—58
Tuberculosis (meningitis)
54—36
Tuberculosis (pulmonary)
53—43, 81, 326
54—96, 131, 136, 254, 325
55—337
Venous thrombosis, experimental
55—244
Virus diseases
55—102

MISCELLANEOUS SUBSTANCE STUDIES

Alkaloids
52—204
53—194, 205
54—53, 180, 303
55—274, 314
Amino acids
45—3
48—5, 6, 7, 8, 12, 13, 15
49—2, 3, 6, 7, 21, 25, 27
50—2, 3, 9
51—8, 10, 23, 41, 43, 44, 45, 66, 77, 78, 82
52—1, 22, 31, 32, 60, 72, 95, 96, 121, 133, 135, 146
53—24, 26, 34, 41, 48, 52, 117, 118, 164, 184, 210, 211, 238, 248, 249, 260, 316
54—6, 27, 32, 39, 119, 123, 166, 174, 181, 195, 198, 206, 209, 233, 235, 296, 302, 317, 333, 367, 404, 405, 418, 519
55—38, 39, 65, 113, 114, 116, 196, 198, 207, 250, 255, 258, 273, 279, 284, 323
56—6, 45, 70
Antibiotics
45—3
46—3
48—7
49—17, 25
51—24
52—106, 107

53—80, 142, 201
54—58, 123, 145, 223, 353, 359, 426, 461, 521, 522
55—22
Bases (organic)
39—5
45—3
51—66, 77
52—31, 106
53—26
54—27, 32, 47, 166
55—313
56—32
Carbohydrates
51—75
52—31, 32, 54, 75, 85, 86, 100, 121, 134, 137, 156, 174
53—72, 75, 84, 85, 96, 101, 228, 254
54—15, 69, 78, 172, 188, 272, 294, 391, 399, 405
55—14, 101, 117, 121, 237, 322, 323
Diazopositive substances
54—198
Drugs (miscellaneous)
54—51, 58, 123, 133, 134, 168, 213, 216, 371, 461, 493, 498, 542
55—74, 94, 148, 221
56—24
Dyes
51—77
52—60, 157, 206, 211, 212
53—47, 135, 215, 243, 321
54—175, 259, 268, 269, 378
55—89, 191
Enzymes and coenzymes
50—36
51—18, 48, 58, 73
52—69, 73, 143, 149, 153, 161, 176, 183, 198
53—41, 53, 105, 112, 133, 141, 159, 163, 204, 239, 240, 249, 255, 303, 313
54—4, 18, 39, 64, 68, 89, 122, 163, 181, 188, 195, 240, 332, 380, 386, 488, 489, 490, 528, 537
55—180, 193, 203, 206, 214, 215, 226, 245, 246, 284, 306, 307, 321, 338
56—6, 41, 42
Fibrinogen
53—5
55—118

Index to R_f Values

A

Acacetin, 331
Acetaldehyde, 342
Acetamide, 347
Acetic acid, 219
  aceto-, 239
  α-aminophenyl-, 148
  butoxy-, 219
  α-bromo-, 219
  2,4-DNP-hydrazide of, 227
  ethoxy-, 219
  guanido, 129
  hydroxamate of, 224
  methoxy, 219
  phenyl, 308
  phenyl, hydroxy derivatives of, 307
  propoxy, 219
Acetoguaiacone, dye derivative, 311
Acetone, 239, 342
Acetovanillone, 342
Acetyl phosphate hydroxamate, 224
Acids, aromatic, 307–309
Aconitic acid, 233
Acriflavine, 381
Acrolein, 34
Acrylic acid, [imidazolyl-4(5)], 352
Actinium, 434
Adansoniaflavonoside, 333
Adansoniagenine, 330
Adenine, 296, 299
  deoxyriboside, 296, 299
Adenosine, 285, 296, 298
Adenosine diphosphate, 291, 297, 298
Adenosine diphosphoribose, 298
  2-phospho-, 298
Adenosine monophosphate, 291, 298
Adenosine triphosphate, 291, 297, 298
Adenylic acid,
  -5, 297, 298
  "a", 296, 298
  "b", 296, 298
  deoxy, 299
Adipic acid, 233
  hydroxamate of, 224
ADP, see Adenosine diphosphate
Adrenaline, 164, 371
  methyl-, 371

Aesculetin, 378
Aesculin, 378
Aglycones, 282
  flavonoid, 330–333
Agmatine, 164, 346, 347
Ajmaline, 365
Alanine, 12, 101, 148
  DNP-, 157
  guanido-, 129
  trimethyl-, 150
Alaninol, 161
Alcohols, amino, 161
  polyhydric, 205
Aldehydes, 342
  derivatives, 342
Aldrin, 388
Alectoronic acid, 376
Alizarin, 382
Alkali metals, 441
Alkaline earths, 441
Alkaloids, 363–365
Alkoxy acids, 219
Allethrin, 388
Allethrolone, 388
Allopregnanedione-3, 20, 275
Allothreonine, 148
Allyl alcohol, derivatives, 339
Allylamine, 164
Aluminum, 414, 418, 433, 435
Amines, 164
Amino alcohols, 161
Ammonium chloride, 352
Ammonium ion, 438
Ammonium thiocyanate, 347
AMP, see Adenosine monophosphate
n-Amylamine, 164
Anabasine, N-methyl, 364
1,4-Androstadiene-3,17-dione, 268
4,9(11)-Androstadiene-3,17-dione, 268
  derivatives, 268
Androstane-3,17-dione, 268
  5α-, 268
Androstanedione-3,17, 275
  Δ⁴-, 275
Androstanol-17α-one-3, 275
Androstanone-3, 275
  -17, 275

675

E

Elaidic acid, 245
Eldoral, 374
β-Eleostearic acid, 245
Ellagic acid, 303
Emicymarin, 282
Emodin, 382
  aloe-, 382
Enanthic acid, 245
Endocrocin, 382
Endrin, 388
Ephedrin, 164, 363
Epinine, 371
EPN Insecticide, 388
Equilenin, 274, 275
Equilin, 274, 275
Equisporol, 330
Equisporonol, 330
Equisporonoside, 333
Erbium, 434
Ergothionine, 352
Erucic acid, 245
Erythritol, 205
Esculetin, 333
Eserine, 363
Estradiol, 269, 276
  -17α, 269, 275
  -17β, 269, 275
4-Estrene-3,17-dione, 269
  derivatives, 269
4-Estren-3-one, 269
  derivatives, 269
Estriol, 274, 275
Estrone, 269, 275, 276
Ethane,
  1,2-diamino-, 164
Ethanolamine, 149, 161, 164, 352
  m-hydroxyphenyl-, 371
  phosphate, 149
Ethionine, 135
Ethyl alcohol, 339
  derivatives, 339
Ethylamine, 357
  derivatives, 164, 357
Ethylene diamine, 357
  derivatives, 357
Ethylene glycol, 205
Etiocholanedione-3,17, 275
Etiocholanol-3α-one-17, 275
Etioporphyrin, 325

Eugenol,
  dehydro-, dye derivatives, 311
  derivatives, 311
"Eukadol", 363
Europium, 434
Evernic acid, 376
Everninic acid, 376

F

Fatty acids, 219
  2,4-DNP-hydrazides of, 227
FDC Dyes, 381
Felinine, 135
Ferricyanide anion, 415
Ferrocyanide anion, 415
Ferulic acid, 378
Flavanone, 7-hydroxy-, 332
Flavellagic acid, 303
Flavin,
  adenine-, dinucleotide, 403
  mononucleotide, 403
Flavone,
  3,3',4',5,7-pentahydroxy-, 331
Flavonoid aglycones, 330–333
Flavonoid pigments, 330–333
Flavonol, 330
Fluorescein, 380
  derivatives, 380
Fluoride anion, 415
Formaldehyde, 342
Formic acid, 219
  hydroxamate of, 224
Fraxetin, 378
Fraxin, 378
Fructose, 189
Fucose, 189
Fucoside, methyl-γ-, 208
Fumaric acid, 233
Furfural, 342
  5-methyl-2, 342

G

Gadolinium, 434
Galactone-γ-lactone, 208
Galactose, 189
  2-deoxy-, 296
Galactosides, methyl, 208
Galacturonic acid, 189, 208
Galaheptulose, 190
Galangin, 330
Gallic acid, 308

Subject Index

A

For R_f values, see preceding index.

Allopregnane-3β,17α,21-trial-20-one, 265
Alloxan, 182
  as reagent, 126
Aluminon reagent, 423, 425, 428, 435
Aluminum, 412, 417, 423
  alloys, 419
  color reagents for, 424, 425, 426, 433, 435
  quantitation of, 428
  solvents for, 431, 433, 435
Aluminum chloride reagent, 328, 329
Amethopterin, 406
Amido Schwartz 10B, dye preparation, 577
Amine(s), 163–165
  aliphatic, 353
  aromatic, determination, 354
    use in sugar detection, 178
  DNP-, 165–166
  esters, 165
p-Aminoacetophenone reagent, 403
Amino acids, 110–163
  acetylated, 3, 10–11
  α-, 140
  basic, 52
  calibration curves for, 92, 97
  camphor sulfonates, 123
  chromatography, theory of, 116
  chromatopile separation of, 44
  circular chromatography of, 39, 42, 145
  copper derivatives, 108–109, 128
  D-, enzymatic detection, 141
  desalting of, 119–123
  detectable quantities, 110
  dimethyl derivatives, 159
  dinitrophenyl derivatives (DNP), 154–155
  dipping of chromatograms, 63
  extraction from urine, 119
  filter paper for, 110–112
  free, removal from tissues, 119
  hydantoin derivatives, 160
  hydrazide derivatives, 160
  isomer resolution, 141
  from α-keto acid dinitrophenylhydrazones, 236
  large-scale separation, 139–140
  liquid-liquid extraction, 7
  multiple development, 37
  multiple spot phenomenon, 113
  ninhydrin reagent for, 123–126
  oxidation, 145

paper electrophoresis of,
  buffers for, 575
  combined with chromatography, 94, 536
  DNP-, buffers for, 575
  fractionation by continuous, 550
  mobilities of, 497, 518–519
  scanning, 564
  two-dimensional technique, 534, 535
"pipsyl derivatives", 73
polychromic reagent for, 64
quantitative determination, 87–109, 141–147
radioactive, separation of, 145
radiodetection, 73
reagents for, 123–139
R_f of, related to structure, 14
R_f reversal, 17
R_f:solvent relationship, 114–116
solvents for, 151–154
standard solutions, 96, 99
thiohydantoin derivatives, 160
two-dimensional chromatography of, 36, 114, 115, 116, 117, 118
uncommon, 162–163
Amino alcohols, 161–162
p-Aminobenzaldehyde reagent, 210
p-Aminobenzoic acid reagent, 367, 403
2-Amino biphenyl reagent, 179, 183
D-Amino oxidase, 141
p-Aminophenol reagent, 182
p-Aminophenolacetate reagent, 401
Amino sugars, 207–210
Ammonium hydroxide, chromatogram treatment, 100
Ammonium ion, 46, 437, 438
Ammonium molybdate-ammonium chloride reagent, 181, 247, 427, 439
Ammonium sulfate, in protein separation, 169
Ammonium vanadate reagent, 231
AMP, see Adenosine monophosphate
Amylase, 166, 167
Amyl nitrite, 133
Amyloses, 192, 194
Anabasine, 360
"Analytrol", 569, 570
Analysis, gradient elution, 48
Analysis, structural, 17–18
Androstane-3,11,17-trione, 265
Δ^4-Androstene-3,11,17-trione, 265

Androsterone, 258
Aniline,
 chloro-, 354
 sugar photometry using, 187
Aniline diphenylamine phosphate reagent, 194
Aniline oxalate reagent, 181, 193, 207
Aniline phthalate reagent, 179, 181, 194, 201, 210, 212, 214
Aniline-xylose reagent, 231
Anions,
 detection, 427–428
 theory of separation of, 497
Anisaldehyde, 344
 reagent for steroids, 262, 282
p-Anisidine reagent, 133, 179, 182, 203–204, 210, 212
Anisidine, tetra-azotized di-o-, reagent, 306
Anthocyanins, 327–336
Anthracene reagent, 244
Anthranilic acid, 320
Anthranol reagent, 244
Anthraquinone pigments, 381
Anthrone reagent, 179, 184
Antibiotics, 68, 391–409
Antimony, 424, 427
Antimony pentachloride chromogenic spray, 260, 262
Antimony trichloride reagent, 262, 278, 399
Apparatus,
 desalting, 53, 121
 paper electrophoresis, 509
Apples, polyphenoloxidase from, 375
Applicator, for paper electrophoresis, 527–528
Apricot,
 pigment isolation from, 327
 quercitin isolation from, 329
Aquaria, chromatographic chambers from, 29
Arabinose, 181, 183, 188
Arbutin, 306
Arcaine, 348
Arginine, 98, 101, 103, 105, 111, 128–130, 346, 347
Aromatic acids, 301–320
Arsenic, 412, 413, 417, 423
 color reagents for, 122, 424, 426, 434

quantitation, 440, 441
 solvent for, 434, 444
Arsenite ion, 428
Arsenomolybdate reagent, 262
Ascending chromatography, 28–33
Ascending-descending chromatography, 33–35
Ascorbic acid, 144, 173–174, 206–207, 407–409
Asparagine, 111
Aspartic acid, 98, 100, 111
Aspergillus oryzae,
 separation of enzymes in, 167
Atomizers, 64–65
ATP, see Adenosine triphosphate
Atropine, 360
Auramine, 49, 361
Aureomycin, 397–398
Autoradiography, 69–71
Avena coleoptiles,
 use in indole detection, 320
Azetidine-2-carboxylic acid, 162
Azocarmine G, 577

B

Bacillus subtilis,
 test organism for antibiotics, 393, 395
Bacterial polysaccharides, 190
Barbiturate(s),
 buffers, 531, 574, 575
 determination of, 373
 fluorescent visualization with, 66
Barium, 412, 415, 419, 437
 color reagents for, 422, 424, 426, 427, 432, 435, 436
 solvents for, 432, 435, 436
Barium hydroxide,
 hydrolyzing agent, 119
 removal of proteins by, 172
Barriers, for chromatography, 49
Beer's Law,
 validity in photoelectric scanning, 563
Benedict's solution, 328, 329
Benzaldehyde(s), 341, 344
 hydroxy-, 340, 341, 343, 345
Benzene(s),
 halogenated, 306
 hexachlorides, 384
 purification of, 146

For R_f values, see preceding index.

Catechins, 375
Cations,
  high frequency detection of, 67
  gradient elution analysis of, 48
  interference by, in chromatography, 53
  theory of electrophoretic separation, 497
Cellulases, 167
Cellulose,
  acetate, supporting media, 18
  effect on R_f, 115
  hydrolysis of, 191
Centrifugal chromatography, 49
Cephalins, 246
Ceric sulfate:arsenious acid reagent, 138
Cerium, 423
  color reagents for, 425, 433
  solvent for, 433
Cesium, 412, 423, 425, 438
Chambers, paper chromatography, 23–38
  critical solvent volume of, 61, 147
  glass aquaria as, 95, 99
  saturation with solvent, 60
  spraying, 65
Chebulagic acid, 375
Chebulic acid, 375
Chebulinic acid, 375
Chloramine-T, 145
Chloranil:tetrachlorobenzoquinone, 165
p-Chloraniline reagent, 134
Chlorate ion, 417
Chlorella, autoradiographic analysis, 69, 70
Chlorides, continuous chromatography of, 47
Chlorine, 412, 413, 417, 427, 437, 439
  color reagent for, 427
Chlormycetin, 396–397
Chloroaniline, 355
Chlorobenzene, seal in paper electrophoresis, 514
Chlorogenic acid, 305, 306, 311, 375, 377
  isolation from plants, 302, 374
  solvent for, 303
Chlorophenol red, 231
Chlorophyll pigments, 321, 323
  isolation, 322
  reagent, 244
Chloroplast pigments, 321, 323
Cholanic acid,
  3,9-epoxy-11-, 265

Cholesterol, 258
  7-dehydro-, 258
Cholic acid, 276, 277, 279
  chenodeoxy-, 278
Choline, 351–353, 402
  esters, 351–353
  lipids, 248–249
  solvent for, 246
Cholinesterase,
  use in pesticide determination, 387
Cholylhydroxamic acid, 277, 278
Chondroitinsulfate, 194
Chondrosamine, 208, 209
Chromate ion, 417, 423
"Chromatoblock," 46
"Chromatobox," 33
Chromatogram(s),
  circular, 41
  detection,
    enzymatic, 68
    microbiological, 68
  "differential charring" of, 66
  dipping of, 63–64
  drying, 61–62
  elution techniques for, 82–83
  evaluation, 81
  fluorescent visualization, 66–67
  high-frequency detection, 67–68
  infrared detection, 67
  preservation of, 84, 125–126
  translucency improvers for, 94, 147
  neutron activation, 75
  spot transfer, 83
  spraying techniques, 64–66
  ultraviolet absorption, 66–67
  visual comparison of, 85–87
Chromatography, adsorption, 3, 6
  paper treatment for, 253–254
Chromatography, column,
  column factors in, 7
  compared to paper chromatography, 107
Chromatography, paper,
  ascending, 28–33
  ascending-descending, 33–35
  capillary action in, 4
  centrifugal, 49
  chambers for, see Chambers
  circular, 18–19, 37–43
  column-disk, 48–49

For R_f values, see preceding index.

For R_f values, see preceding index.

For R_f values, see preceding index.

For R_f values, see preceding index.

For R_f values, see preceding index.

Paper, filter,
acetylated, 213, 241, 258, 529
adsorption by,
  in chromatography, 17
  in electrophoresis, 506
alumina-treated, 253–254, 256, 321, 323, 413
ammonia-treated, 253
bisulfite-treated, 340
buffered, 52, 112, 124, 142, 340, 359
1,3-butanediol treated, 253, 256
for butanol solvents, 112
butyryl-cellulose, 51
calcium chloride-treated, 253
carbonate-treated, 304
characteristics, 51
choice of, 50–51
for circular chromatography, 38–40
column, 44–45
cylinder, 30, 31–32, 36
for continuous electrophoresis, 544
dimethylformamide-treated, 341
dimethyl phthalate-treated, 359
dye-treated, 530
electrophoretic mobilities on, 501–506
esterified, 254, 529
ethylene glycol monophenyl ether-treated, 255, 267, 279
formamide-treated, 253, 254, 279, 359
"ghost" spots on, 216
heptanol-treated, 253, 255
4-hydroxybenzthiazole-treated, 412
ion exchange resin-containing, 18, 412
for large-scale separations, 112
lithium chloride-treated, 253
modified, 51–52, 110
octadecyloxymethyl-treated, 241
for paper electrophoresis, 529–530
paraffin oil-treated, 241
phenyl cellosolve-treated, 253
propylene glycol-treated, 253, 255, 267
protein-impregnated, 530
purification of, 199–200, 216
Quilon-treated, 256
reversed phase, 43, 240
rubber latex-treated, 240
salts-impregnated, 417
sewing of, 36, 37, 111
silicone-treated, 240, 254, 256, 359
sodium molybdate-treated, 200

sodium-p-toluene sulfonate-treated, 256
solvents for various, 60
starch-impregnated, 160
theoretical path of ionic migration on, 505
p-toluenesulfonate-treated, 253
translucent agents for, 561
for two-dimensional chromatography, 36
"Vaseline"-impregnated, 322
washing of, 215
zinc carbonate-impregnated, 304
Paper, glass, 321, 322
silicic acid-treated, 254, 257, 340
Papyrography, conductometric, 67–68
Paraffin oil:bromonaphthalene reagent, 147
Parathion, 386
Partition coefficient, 12, 13, 16–17
Pauly reagents, 132, 138
Peanut, protein isolation, 167
Penicillins, 391, 392–394
Pentacyanoamino ferrate reagent, 348
Pentanoic acids, amino, 112, 162
Pentanol solvents, 153
Pentoses, 184
hexosamines of, 209
Peptides,
buffer for separation of, 375
hydrazinolysis of C-terminal groups, 160
isolation from tissue, 119
R_f, related to structure of, 14
Peptidases, serum, 579
Peracetic acid, 132
Perchloric acid, 119
Perfluorooctanoic acid, 119
Periodate-Nessler reagent, 137
Periodic acid, paper treated with, 530
Permanganate ion, 423
Permanganate reagent, 127
Peroxidase, 167
Pesticides, 384–389
o-Phenanthroline ferrous reagent, 138
Phenol(s), 301–320
buffered solvent, 147
colored derivatives of, 302
extraction, 301–302
poly-, 373–377
purification of, 153–154

For R_f values, see preceding index.

Potassium, 412, 416, 423, 437
  color reagents for, 425, 435, 437, 438
  solvents for, 432, 435
Potassium bismuth iodide reagent, 164, 401
Potassium chromate reagent, 426
Potassium cyanate, 160
Potassium cyanide reagent, 293
Potassium ferricyanide reagent, 370, 400, 423
Potassium ferrocyanide reagent, 423, 424, 434, 435, 438
Potassium iodide reagent, 426
Potassium mercury thiocyanate reagent, 370
Potassium metaperiodate reagent, 212
Potassium naphthoquinone sulfonate, 372
Potassium periodate, 423
Potassium permanganate reagent, 179–180, 203, 260, 261, 423
Potato, chlorogenic acid isolation from, 374
Praseodymium, 423, 434, 438
Pregnane-17α,21-diol-3,11,20-trione, 265
4-Pregnene-3,20-dione, 266
Preparative chromatography, 43–48
Press, autoradiography, 69
Progesterone, 256
Proline, 98, 102, 105, 109, 111, 134, 135–137
  acetyl-, 11
  hydroxy-, 98, 102, 109, 111, 134, 135–137
Propylene glycol, 548
Proteinases, 167–168
Proteins,
  basic, separation of, 575
  as buffer additives, 532
  DNP-derivatives of, 154–155
  enzymatic determination, 166
  hydrolysis, 99, 116–117
  milk, buffer for, 575
  muscle, buffer for, 575
  paper electrophoresis of,
    curve for scanning, 564
    dyes for, 554, 576
    general directions, 525
    scanning of, 565, 567
  precipitants, 119
  separation, 166–169

serum, electrophoresis of, 514, 570, 572, 577
  buffers for, 574
  chromatography combined with, 536
  continuous 545, 546
  dyes for, 556, 558, 561
  quantitation, 558–566
  treatment with phenylisothiocyanate, 160
Protocatechuic aldehyde, 344
Protoporphyrin, 323, 324
Protoveratrine(s), 360
Pteridines, synthetic, 336
Pterins, 327–336
Pulvic acid, 374
Purines, 284–301
  determination by fluorescence, 80
  extraction from urine, 286
  riboside, 288
  solvents for, 288
Pyrethrins, 386–387, 389
Pyridine, 360, 362
  purification, 154
  as salt extractant, 171, 196
Pyridine carboxylic acids, 362, 366
Pyridoxine, 366, 367, 369, 405
Pyrimidines, 284–301
  "pipsyl" derivatives, 293
  solvents for, 288
Pyrocatechol reagent, 426
Pyrogallol reagent, 423
Pyrollidine, 360
Pyruvic acid, 234, 236, 237

Q

Quercitin, 327, 329, 335
  isolation from apricot, 329
  as reagent, 426
"Quilon," 254
Quinalizarin reagent, 423, 434
L-Quinic acid, 303, 304
Quinine reagent, 244
Quinol(s), 304, 306
Quinoline(s), 356, 362
Quinone reagent, 163
Quinoxalinol derivatives, keto acids, 238

R

R, definition, 7
Rack, chromatography, 31, 32, 95
  "two-way," 35

For R_f values, see preceding index.

For R_f values, see preceding index.

For R_f values, see preceding index.